GREAT BOOKS OF THE WESTERN WORLD

28. GILBERT
GALILEO
HARVEY

29. CERVANTES

30. FRANCIS BACON

31. DESCARTES
SPINOZA

32. MILTON

33. PASCAL

34. NEWTON
HUYGENS

35. LOCKE
BERKELEY
HUME

36. SWIFT
STERNE

37. FIELDING

38. MONTESQUIEU
ROUSSEAU

39. ADAM SMITH

40. GIBBON I

41. GIBBON II

42. KANT

43. AMERICAN STATE PAPERS
THE FEDERALIST
J. S. MILL

44. BOSWELL

45. LAVOISIER
FOURIER
FARADAY

46. HEGEL

47. GOETHE

48. MELVILLE

49. DARWIN

50. MARX
ENGELS

51. TOLSTOY

52. DOSTOEVSKY

53. WILLIAM JAMES

54. FREUD

GREAT BOOKS OF THE WESTERN WORLD

ROBERT MAYNARD HUTCHINS, *EDITOR IN CHIEF*

9.

ARISTOTLE: II

THE WORKS OF ARISTOTLE

VOLUME II

WILLIAM BENTON, *Publisher*

ENCYCLOPÆDIA BRITANNICA, INC.

CHICAGO · LONDON · TORONTO · GENEVA · SYDNEY · TOKYO · MANILA

The text and annotations of this edition are reprinted from *The Works of Aristotle,* translated into English under the editorship of W. D. Ross, by arrangement with Oxford University Press.

THE UNIVERSITY OF CHICAGO

The Great Books
is published with the editorial advice of the faculties
of The University of Chicago

Library of Congress Catalog Card Number: 55–10318

GENERAL CONTENTS, VOLUME II

BIOLOGICAL TREATISES

CONTENTS: HISTORY OF ANIMALS

BOOK I

BOOK II

BOOK III

BOOK IV

BOOK V

BOOK VI

HISTORY OF ANIMALS

BOOK I

I

486a Of the parts of animals some are simple: to wit, all such as divide into parts uniform with themselves, as flesh into flesh; others are composite, such as divide into parts not uniform with themselves, as, for instance, the hand does not divide into hands nor the face into faces.

And of such as these, some are called not parts merely, but limbs or members. Such are those parts that, while entire in themselves, have within themselves other diverse parts: as, for instance, the head, foot, hand, the arm as a whole, the chest; for these are all in themselves entire parts, and there are other diverse parts belonging to them.

All those parts that do not subdivide into parts uniform with themselves are composed of parts that do so subdivide, for instance, hand is composed of flesh, sinews, and bones. Of animals, some resemble one another in all their parts, while others have parts wherein they differ. Sometimes the parts are identical in form or species, as, for instance, one man's nose or eye resembles another man's nose or eye, flesh flesh, and bone bone; and in like manner with a horse, and with all other animals which we reckon to be of one and the same species: for as the whole is to the whole, so each to each are the parts severally. In other cases the parts are identical, save only for a difference in the way of excess or defect, as is the case in such animals as are of one and the same genus. By 'genus' I mean, for instance, Bird or Fish, for each of these is subject to difference in respect of its genus, and there are many species of fishes and of birds.

Within the limits of genera, most of the parts as a rule exhibit differences through con-**486b** trast of the property or accident, such as colour and shape, to which they are subject: in that some are more and some in a less degree the subject of the same property or accident; and also in the way of multitude or fewness, magnitude or parvitude, in short in the way of excess or defect. Thus in some the texture of the flesh is soft, in others firm; some have a long bill, others a short one; some have abundance of feathers, others have only a small quantity. It happens further that some have parts that others have not: for instance, some have spurs and others not, some have crests and others not; but as a general rule, most parts and those that go to make up the bulk of the body are either identical with one another, or differ from one another in the way of contrast and of excess and defect. For 'the more' and 'the less' may be represented as 'excess' or 'defect'.

Once again, we may have to do with animals whose parts are neither identical in form nor yet identical save for differences in the way of excess or defect: but they are the same only in the way of analogy, as, for instance, bone is only analogous to fish-bone, nail to hoof, hand to claw, and scale to feather; for what the feather is in a bird, the scale is in a fish.

The parts, then, which animals severally possess are diverse from, or identical with, one another in the fashion above described. And they are so furthermore in the way of local disposition: for many animals have identical organs that differ in position; for instance, some **487a** have teats in the breast, others close to the thighs.

Of the substances that are composed of parts uniform (or homogeneous) with themselves, some are soft and moist, others are dry and solid. The soft and moist are such either absolutely or so long as they are in their natural conditions, as, for instance, blood, serum, lard, suet, marrow, sperm, gall, milk in such as have it, flesh and the like; and also, in a different way, the superfluities, as phlegm and the excretions of the belly and the bladder. The dry and solid are such as sinew, skin, vein, hair, bone, gristle, nail, horn (a term which as applied to the part involves an ambiguity, since the whole also by virtue of its form is designated horn), and such parts as present an analogy to these.

Animals differ from one another in their

Note: The bold face numbers and letters are approximate indications of the pages and columns of the standard Berlin Greek text; the bracketed numbers, of the lines in the Greek text; they are here assigned as they are assigned in the Oxford translation.

modes of subsistence, in their actions, in their habits, and in their parts. Concerning these differences we shall first speak in broad and general terms, and subsequently we shall treat of the same with close reference to each particular genus.

Differences are manifested in modes of subsistence, in habits, in actions performed. For instance, some animals live in water and others on land. And of those that live in water some do so in one way, and some in another: that is to say, some live and feed in the water, take in and emit water, and cannot live if deprived of water, as is the case with the great majority of fishes; others get their food and spend their days in the water, but do not take in water but air, nor do they bring forth in the water. Many of these creatures are furnished with feet, as the otter, the beaver, and the crocodile; some are furnished with wings, as the diver and the grebe; some are destitute of feet, as the water-snake. Some creatures get their living in the water and cannot exist outside it: but for all that do not take in either air or water, as, for instance, the sea-nettle and the oyster. And of creatures that live in the water some live in the sea, some in rivers, some in lakes, and some in marshes, as the frog and the newt.

Of animals that live on dry land some take in air and emit it, which phenomena are termed 'inhalation' and 'exhalation'; as, for instance, man and all such land animals as are furnished with lungs. Others, again, do not inhale air, yet live and find their sustenance on dry land; as, for instance, the wasp, the bee, and all other insects. And by 'insects' I mean such creatures as have nicks or notches on their bodies, either on their bellies or on both backs and bellies.

487b And of land animals many, as has been said, derive their subsistence from the water; but of creatures that live in and inhale water not a single one derives its subsistence from dry land.

Some animals at first live in water, and by and by change their shape and live out of water, as is the case with river worms, for out of these the gadfly develops.

Furthermore, some animals are stationary, and some are erratic. Stationary animals are found in water, but no such creature is found on dry land. In the water are many creatures that live in close adhesion to an external object, as is the case with several kinds of oyster. And, by the way, the sponge appears to be endowed with a certain sensibility: as a proof of which it is alleged that the difficulty in detaching it from its moorings is increased if the movement to detach it be not covertly applied.

Other creatures adhere at one time to an object and detach themselves from it at other times, as is the case with a species of the so-called sea-nettle; for some of these creatures seek their food in the night-time loose and unattached.

Many creatures are unattached but motionless, as is the case with oysters and the so-called holothuria. Some can swim, as, for instance, fishes, molluscs, and crustaceans, such as the crawfish. But some of these last move by walking, as the crab, for it is the nature of the creature, though it lives in water, to move by walking.

Of land animals some are furnished with wings, such as birds and bees, and these are so furnished in different ways one from another; others are furnished with feet. Of the animals that are furnished with feet some walk, some creep, and some wriggle. But no creature is able only to move by flying, as the fish is able only to swim, for the animals with leathern wings can walk; the bat has feet and the seal has imperfect feet.

Some birds have feet of little power, and are therefore called *Apodes*. This little bird is powerful on the wing; and, as a rule, birds that resemble it are weak-footed and strong-winged, such as the swallow and the drepanis or (?) Alpine swift; for all these birds resemble one another in their habits and in their plumage, and may easily be mistaken one for another. (The apus is to be seen at all seasons, but the drepanis only after rainy weather in summer; for this is the time when it is seen and captured, though, as a general rule, it is a rare bird.)

Again, some animals move by walking on the ground as well as by swimming in water.

Furthermore, the following differences are manifest in their modes of living and in their actions. Some are gregarious, some are solitary, **488a** whether they be furnished with feet or wings or be fitted for a life in the water; and some partake of both characters, the solitary and the gregarious. And of the gregarious, some are disposed to combine for social purposes, others to live each for its own self.

Gregarious creatures are, among birds, such as the pigeon, the crane, and the swan; and, by the way, no bird furnished with crooked talons is gregarious. Of creatures that live in water many kinds of fishes are gregarious, such as the so-called migrants, the tunny, the pelamys, and the bonito.

Man, by the way, presents a mixture of the two characters, the gregarious and the solitary.

Social creatures are such as have some one common object in view; and this property is not common to all creatures that are gregarious. Such social creatures are man, the bee, the wasp, the ant, and the crane.

Again, of these social creatures some submit to a ruler, others are subject to no governance: as, for instance, the crane and the several sorts of bee submit to a ruler, whereas ants and numerous other creatures are every one his own master.

And again, both of gregarious and of solitary animals, some are attached to a fixed home and others are erratic or nomad.

Also, some are carnivorous, some graminivorous, some omnivorous: whilst some feed on a peculiar diet, as for instance the bees and the spiders, for the bee lives on honey and certain other sweets, and the spider lives by catching flies; and some creatures live on fish. Again, some creatures catch their food, others treasure it up; whereas others do not so.

Some creatures provide themselves with a dwelling, others go without one: of the former kind are the mole, the mouse, the ant, the bee; of the latter kind are many insects and quadrupeds. Further, in respect to locality of dwelling-place, some creatures dwell under ground, as the lizard and the snake; others live on the surface of the ground, as the horse and the dog. [Some make to themselves holes, others do not so.]

Some are nocturnal, as the owl and the bat; others live in the daylight.

Moreover, some creatures are tame and some are wild: some are at all times tame, as man and the mule; others are at all times savage, as the leopard and the wolf; and some creatures can be rapidly tamed, as the elephant.

Again, we may regard animals in another light. For, whenever a race of animals is found domesticated, the same is always to be found in a wild condition; as we find to be the case with horses, kine, swine, [men,] sheep, goats, and dogs.

Further, some animals emit sound while others are mute, and some are endowed with voice: of these latter some have articulate speech, while others are inarticulate; some are given to continual chirping and twittering, some are prone to silence; some are musical, and some unmusical; but all animals without
488b exception exercise their power of singing or chattering chiefly in connexion with the intercourse of the sexes.

Again, some creatures live in the fields, as the cushat; some on the mountains, as the hoopoe; some frequent the abodes of men, as the pigeon.

Some, again, are peculiarly salacious, as the partridge, the barn-door cock and their congeners; others are inclined to chastity, as the whole tribe of crows, for birds of this kind indulge but rarely in sexual intercourse.

Of marine animals, again, some live in the open seas, some near the shore, some on rocks.

Furthermore, some are combative under offence; others are provident for defence. Of the former kind are such as act as aggressors upon others or retaliate when subjected to ill usage, and of the latter kind are such as merely have some means of guarding themselves against attack.

Animals also differ from one another in regard to character in the following respects. Some are good-tempered, sluggish, and little prone to ferocity, as the ox; others are quick-tempered, ferocious and unteachable, as the wild boar; some are intelligent and timid, as the stag and the hare; others are mean and treacherous, as the snake; others are noble and courageous and high-bred, as the lion; others are thorough-bred and wild and treacherous, as the wolf: for, by the way, an animal is high-bred if it come from a noble stock, and an animal is thorough-bred if it does not deflect from its racial characteristics.

Further, some are crafty and mischievous, as the fox; some are spirited and affectionate and fawning, as the dog; others are easy-tempered and easily domesticated, as the elephant; others are cautious and watchful, as the goose; others are jealous and self-conceited, as the peacock. But of all animals man alone is capable of deliberation.

Many animals have memory, and are capable of instruction; but no other creature except man can recall the past at will.

With regard to the several genera of animals, particulars as to their habits of life and modes of existence will be discussed more fully by and by.

2

Common to all animals are the organs whereby they take food and the organs whereinto they take it; and these are either identical with one another, or are diverse in the ways above specified: to wit, either identical in form, or varying in respect of excess or defect, or resembling one another analogically, or differing in position.

Furthermore, the great majority of animals have other organs besides these in common, whereby they discharge the residuum of their food: I say, the great majority, for this state-
489a ment does not apply to all. And, by the way, the organ whereby food is taken in is called the mouth, and the organ whereinto it is taken, the belly; the remainder of the alimentary system has a great variety of names.

Now the residuum of food is twofold in kind, wet and dry, and such creatures as have organs receptive of wet residuum are invariably found with organs receptive of dry residuum; but such as have organs receptive of dry residuum need not possess organs receptive of wet residuum. In other words, an animal has a bowel or intestine if it have a bladder; but an animal may have a bowel and be without a bladder. And, by the way, I may here remark that the organ receptive of wet residuum is termed 'bladder', and the organ receptive of dry residuum 'intestine or bowel'.

3

Of animals otherwise, a great many have, besides the organs above-mentioned, an organ for excretion of the sperm: and of animals capable of generation one secretes into another, and the other into itself. The latter is termed 'female', and the former 'male'; but some animals have neither male nor female. Consequently, the organs connected with this function differ in form, for some animals have a womb and others an organ analogous thereto.

The above-mentioned organs, then, are the most indispensable parts of animals; and with some of them all animals without exception, and with others animals for the most part, must needs be provided.

One sense, and one alone, is common to all animals—the sense of touch. Consequently, there is no special name for the organ in which it has its seat; for in some groups of animals the organ is identical, in others it is only analogous.

4

Every animal is supplied with moisture, and, if the animal be deprived of the same by natural causes or artificial means, death ensues: further, every animal has another part in which the moisture is contained. These parts are blood and vein, and in other animals there is something to correspond; but in these latter the parts are imperfect, being merely fibre and serum or lymph.

Touch has its seat in a part uniform and homogeneous, as in the flesh or something of the kind, and generally, with animals supplied with blood, in the parts charged with blood. In other animals it has its seat in parts analogous to the parts charged with blood; but in all cases it is seated in parts that in their texture are homogeneous.

The active faculties, on the contrary, are seated in the parts that are heterogeneous: as, for instance, the business of preparing the food is seated in the mouth, and the office of locomotion in the feet, the wings, or in organs to correspond.

Again, some animals are supplied with blood, as man, the horse, and all such animals as are, when full-grown, either destitute of feet, or two-footed, or four-footed; other animals are bloodless, such as the bee and the wasp, and, of marine animals, the cuttle-fish, the crawfish, and all such animals as have more than four feet.

5

Again, some animals are viviparous, others oviparous, others vermiparous or 'grub-bearing'. Some are viviparous, such as man, the
489b horse, the seal, and all other animals that are hair-coated, and, of marine animals, the cetaceans, as the dolphin, and the so-called Selachia. (Of these latter animals, some have a tubular air-passage and no gills, as the dolphin and the whale: the dolphin with the air-passage going through its back, the whale with the air-passage in its forehead; others have uncovered gills, as the Selachia, the sharks and rays.)

What we term an egg is a certain completed result of conception out of which the animal that is to be develops, and in such a way that in respect to its primitive germ it comes from part only of the egg, while the rest serves for food as the germ develops. A 'grub' on the other hand is a thing out of which in its entirety the animal in its entirety develops, by differentiation and growth of the embryo.

Of viviparous animals, some hatch eggs in their own interior, as creatures of the shark kind; others engender in their interior a live foetus, as man and the horse. When the result of conception is perfected, with some animals a living creature is brought forth, with others an egg is brought to light, with others a grub. Of the eggs, some have egg-shells and are of two different colours within, such as birds' eggs; others are soft-skinned and of uniform colour, as the eggs of animals of the shark kind. Of the grubs, some are from the first capable of movement, others are motionless. However, with regard to these phenomena we shall speak precisely hereafter when we come to treat of Generation.

Furthermore, some animals have feet and some are destitute thereof. Of such as have feet, some animals have two, as is the case with men and birds, and with men and birds only; some have four, as the lizard and the dog; some have more, as the centipede and the bee; but allsoever that have feet have an even number of them.

Of swimming creatures that are destitute of feet, some have winglets or fins, as fishes: and of these some have four fins, two above on the back, two below on the belly, as the gilthead and the basse; some have two only,—to wit, such as are exceedingly long and smooth, as the eel and the conger; some have none at all, as the muraena, but use the sea just as snakes use dry ground—and by the way, snakes swim in water in just the same way. Of the shark-kind some have no fins, such as those that are flat and long-tailed, as the ray and the sting-ray, but these fishes swim actually by the undulatory motion of their flat bodies; the fishing frog, however, has fins, and so likewise have all such fishes as have not their flat surfaces thinned off to a sharp edge.

Of those swimming creatures that appear to have feet, as is the case with the molluscs, these creatures swim by the aid of their feet and their fins as well, and they swim most rapidly backwards in the direction of the trunk, as is the case with the cuttle-fish or sepia and the calamary; and, by the way, neither of these lat-
490a ter can walk as the poulpe or octopus can.

The hard-skinned or crustaceous animals, like the crawfish, swim by the instrumentality of their tail-parts; and they swim most rapidly tail foremost, by the aid of the fins developed upon that member. The newt swims by means of its feet and tail; and its tail resembles that of the sheatfish, to compare little with great.

Of animals that can fly some are furnished with feathered wings, as the eagle and the hawk; some are furnished with membranous wings, as the bee and the cockchafer; others are furnished with leathern wings, as the flying fox and the bat. All flying creatures possessed of blood have feathered wings or leathern wings; the bloodless creatures have membranous wings, as insects. The creatures that have feathered wings or leathern wings have either two feet or no feet at all: for there are said to be certain flying serpents in Ethiopia that are destitute of feet.

Creatures that have feathered wings are classed as a genus under the name of 'bird'; the other two genera, the leathern-winged and membrane-winged, are as yet without a generic title.

Of creatures that can fly and are bloodless some are coleopterous or sheath-winged, for they have their wings in a sheath or shard, like the cockchafer and the dungbeetle; others are sheathless, and of these latter some are dipterous and some tetrapterous: tetrapterous, such as are comparatively large or have their stings in the tail, dipterous, such as are comparatively small or have their stings in front. The coleoptera are, without exception, devoid of stings; the diptera have the sting in front, as the fly, the horsefly, the gadfly, and the gnat.

Bloodless animals as a general rule are inferior in point of size to blooded animals; though, by the way, there are found in the sea some few bloodless creatures of abnormal size, as in the case of certain molluscs. And of these bloodless genera, those are the largest that dwell in milder climates, and those that inhabit the sea are larger than those living on dry land or in fresh water.

All creatures that are capable of motion move with four or more points of motion; the blooded animals with four only: as, for instance, man with two hands and two feet, birds with two wings and two feet, quadrupeds and fishes severally with four feet and four fins. Creatures that have two winglets or fins, or that have none at all like serpents, move all the same with not less than four points of motion; for there are four bends in their bodies as they move, or two bends together with their fins. Bloodless and many-footed animals, whether furnished with wings or feet, move with more than four points of motion; as, for instance, the dayfly moves with
490b four feet and four wings: and, I may observe in passing, this creature is exceptional

not only in regard to the duration of its existence, whence it receives its name, but also because though a quadruped it has wings also.

All animals move alike, four-footed and many-footed; in other words, they all move cross-corner-wise. And animals in general have two feet in advance; the crab alone has four.

6

Very extensive genera of animals, into which other subdivisions fall, are the following: one, of birds; one, of fishes; and another, of cetaceans. Now all these creatures are blooded.

There is another genus of the hard-shell kind, which is called oyster; another of the soft-shell kind, not as yet designated by a single term, such as the spiny crawfish and the various kinds of crabs and lobsters; and another of molluscs, as the two kinds of calamary and the cuttle-fish; that of insects is different. All these latter creatures are bloodless, and such of them as have feet have a goodly number of them; and of the insects some have wings as well as feet.

Of the other animals the genera are not extensive. For in them one species does not comprehend many species; but in one case, as man, the species is simple, admitting of no differentiation, while other cases admit of differentiation, but the forms lack particular designations.

So, for instance, creatures that are quadrupedal and unprovided with wings are blooded without exception, but some of them are viviparous, and some oviparous. Such as are viviparous are hair-coated, and such as are oviparous are covered with a kind of tessellated hard substance; and the tessellated bits of this substance are, as it were, similar in regard to position to a scale.

An animal that is blooded and capable of movement on dry land, but is naturally unprovided with feet, belongs to the serpent genus; and animals of this genus are coated with the tessellated horny substance. Serpents in general are oviparous; the adder, an exceptional case, is viviparous: for not all viviparous animals are hair-coated, and some fishes also are viviparous.

All animals, however, that are hair-coated are viviparous. For, by the way, one must regard as a kind of hair such prickly hairs as hedgehogs and porcupines carry; for these spines perform the office of hair, and not of feet as is the case with similar parts of sea-urchins.

In the genus that combines all viviparous quadrupeds are many species, but under no common appellation. They are only named as it were one by one, as we say man, lion, stag, horse, dog, and so on; though, by the way, there is a sort of genus that embraces all creatures that have bushy manes and bushy tails, **491a** such as the horse, the ass, the mule, the jennet, and the animals that are called Hemioni in Syria,—from their externally resembling mules, though they are not strictly of the same species. And that they are not so is proved by the fact that they mate with and breed from one another.

For all these reasons, we must take animals species by species, and discuss their peculiarities severally.

These preceding statements, then, have been put forward thus in a general way, as a kind of foretaste of the number of subjects and of the properties that we have to consider in order that we may first get a clear notion of distinctive character and common properties. By and by we shall discuss these matters with greater minuteness.

After this we shall pass on to the discussion of causes. For to do this when the investigation of the details is complete is the proper and natural method, and that whereby the subjects and the premisses of our argument will afterwards be rendered plain.

In the first place we must look to the constituent parts of animals. For it is in a way relative to these parts, first and foremost, that animals in their entirety differ from one another: either in the fact that some have this or that, while they have not that or this; or by peculiarities of position or of arrangement; or by the differences that have been previously mentioned, depending upon diversity of form, or excess or defect in this or that particular, on analogy, or on contrasts of the accidental qualities.

To begin with, we must take into consideration the parts of Man. For, just as each nation is wont to reckon by that monetary standard with which it is most familiar, so must we do in other matters. And, of course, man is the animal with which we are all of us the most familiar.

Now the parts are obvious enough to physical perception. However, with the view of observing due order and sequence and of combining rational notions with physical perception, we shall proceed to enumerate the parts: firstly, the organic, and afterwards the simple or non-composite.

7

The chief parts into which the body as a whole is subdivided, are the head, the neck, the trunk (extending from the neck to the privy parts), which is called the thorax, two arms and two legs.

Of the parts of which the head is composed the hair-covered portion is called the 'skull'. The front portion of it is termed 'bregma' or 'sinciput', developed after birth—for it is the last of all the bones in the body to acquire solidity,—the hinder part is termed the 'occiput', and the part intervening between the sinciput and the occiput is the 'crown'. The brain lies underneath the sinciput; the occiput

491b is hollow. The skull consists entirely of thin bone, rounded in shape, and contained within a wrapper of fleshless skin.

The skull has sutures: one, of circular form, in the case of women; in the case of men, as a general rule, three meeting at a point. Instances have been known of a man's skull devoid of suture altogether. In the skull the middle line, where the hair parts, is called the crown or vertex. In some cases the parting is double; that is to say, some men are double-crowned, not in regard to the bony skull, but in consequence of the double fall or set of the hair.

8

The part that lies under the skull is called the 'face': but in the case of man only, for the term is not applied to a fish or to an ox. In the face the part below the sinciput and between the eyes is termed the forehead. When men have large foreheads, they are slow to move; when they have small ones, they are fickle; when they have broad ones, they are apt to be distraught; when they have foreheads rounded or bulging out, they are quick-tempered.

9

Underneath the forehead are two eyebrows. Straight eyebrows are a sign of softness of disposition; such as curve in towards the nose, of harshness; such as curve out towards the temples, of humour and dissimulation; such as are drawn in towards one another, of jealousy.

Under the eyebrows come the eyes. These are naturally two in number. Each of them has an upper and a lower eyelid, and the hairs on the edges of these are termed 'eyelashes'. The central part of the eye includes the moist part whereby vision is effected, termed the 'pupil', and the part surrounding it called the 'black'; the part outside this is the 'white'. A part common to the upper and lower eyelid is a pair of nicks or corners, one in the direction of the nose, and the other in the direction of the temples. When these are long they are a sign of bad disposition; if the side toward the nostril be fleshy and comb-like, they are a sign of dishonesty.

All animals, as a general rule, are provided with eyes, excepting the ostracoderms and other imperfect creatures; at all events, all viviparous animals have eyes, with the exception of the mole. And yet one might assert that, though the mole has not eyes in the full sense, yet it has eyes in a kind of a way. For in point of absolute fact it cannot see, and has no eyes visible externally; but when the outer skin is removed, it is found to have the place where eyes are usually situated, and the black parts of the eyes rightly situated, and all the place that is usually devoted on the outside to eyes: showing that the parts are stunted in development, and the skin allowed to grow over.

10

492a Of the eye the white is pretty much the same in all creatures; but what is called the black differs in various animals. Some have the rim black, some distinctly blue, some greyish-blue, some greenish; and this last colour is the sign of an excellent disposition, and is particularly well adapted for sharpness of vision. Man is the only, or nearly the only, creature, that has eyes of diverse colours. Animals, as a rule, have eyes of one colour only. Some horses have blue eyes.

Of eyes, some are large, some small, some medium-sized; of these, the medium-sized are the best. Moreover, eyes sometimes protrude, sometimes recede, sometimes are neither protruding nor receding. Of these, the receding eye is in all animals the most acute; but the last kind are the sign of the best disposition. Again, eyes are sometimes inclined to wink under observation, sometimes to remain open and staring, and sometimes are disposed neither to wink nor stare. The last kind are the sign of the best nature, and of the others, the latter kind indicates impudence, and the former indecision.

11

Furthermore, there is a portion of the head, whereby an animal hears, a part incapable of breathing, the 'ear'. I say 'incapable of breathing', for Alcmaeon is mistaken when he says that goats inspire through their ears. Of the ear one part is unnamed, the other part is called the 'lobe'; and it is entirely composed of gristle and flesh. The ear is constructed internally like the trumpet-shell, and the innermost bone is like the ear itself, and into it at the end the sound makes its way, as into the bottom of a jar. This receptacle does not communicate by any passage with the brain, but does so with the palate, and a vein extends from the brain towards it. The eyes also are connected with the brain, and each of them lies at the end of a little vein. Of animals possessed of ears man is the only one that cannot move this organ. Of creatures possessed of hearing, some have ears, whilst others have none, but merely have the passages for ears visible, as, for example, feathered animals or animals coated with horny tessellates.

Viviparous animals, with the exception of the seal, the dolphin, and those others which after a similar fashion to these are cetaceans, are all provided with ears; for, by the way, the shark-kind are also viviparous. Now, the seal has the passages visible whereby it hears; but the dolphin can hear, but has no ears, nor yet any passages visible. But man alone is unable to move his ears, and all other animals can move them. And the ears lie, with man, in the same horizontal plane with the eyes, and not in a plane above them as is the case with some quadrupeds. Of ears, some are fine, some are coarse, and some are of medium texture; the last kind are best for hearing, but they serve in no way to indicate character. Some ears are large, some small, some medium-sized; again, some stand out far, some lie in close and tight, **492b** and some take up a medium position; of these such as are of medium size and of medium position are indications of the best disposition, while the large and outstanding ones indicate a tendency to irrelevant talk or chattering. The part intercepted between the eye, the ear, and the crown is termed the 'temple'. Again, there is a part of the countenance that serves as a passage for the breath, the 'nose'. For a man inhales and exhales by this organ, and sneezing is effected by its means: which last is an outward rush of collected breath, and is the only mode of breath used as an omen and regarded as supernatural. Both inhalation and exhalation go right on from the nose towards the chest; and with the nostrils alone and separately it is impossible to inhale or exhale, owing to the fact that the inspiration and respiration take place from the chest along the windpipe, and not by any portion connected with the head; and indeed it is possible for a creature to live without using this process of nasal respiration.

Again, smelling takes place by means of the nose,—smelling, or the sensible discrimination of odour. And the nostril admits of easy motion, and is not, like the ear, intrinsically immovable. A part of it, composed of gristle, constitutes, a septum or partition, and part is an open passage; for the nostril consists of two separate channels. The nostril (or nose) of the elephant is long and strong, and the animal uses it like a hand; for by means of this organ it draws objects towards it, and takes hold of them, and introduces its food into its mouth, whether liquid or dry food, and it is the only living creature that does so.

Furthermore, there are two jaws; the front part of them constitutes the chin, and the hinder part the cheek. All animals move the lower jaw, with the exception of the river-crocodile; this creature moves the upper jaw only.

Next after the nose come two lips, composed of flesh, and facile of motion. The mouth lies inside the jaws and lips. Parts of the mouth are the roof or palate and the pharynx.

The part that is sensible of taste is the tongue. The sensation has its seat at the tip of the tongue; if the object to be tasted be placed on the flat surface of the organ, the taste is less sensibly experienced. The tongue is sensitive in all other ways wherein flesh in general is so: that is, it can appreciate hardness, or warmth and cold, in any part of it, just as it can appreciate taste. The tongue is sometimes broad, sometimes narrow, and sometimes of medium width; the last kind is the best and the clearest in its discrimination of taste. Moreover, the tongue is sometimes loosely hung, and sometimes fastened: as in the case of those who mumble and who lisp.

The tongue consists of flesh, soft and spongy, and the so-called 'epiglottis' is a part of this organ.

That part of the mouth that splits into two **493a** bits is called the 'tonsils'; that part that splits into many bits, the 'gums'. Both the tonsils and the gums are composed of flesh. In the gums are teeth, composed of bone.

Inside the mouth is another part, shaped like a bunch of grapes, a pillar streaked with veins. If this pillar gets relaxed and inflamed it is called 'uvula' or 'bunch of grapes', and it then has a tendency to bring about suffocation.

12

The neck is the part between the face and the trunk. Of this the front part is the larynx [and the back part the gullet]. The front part, composed of gristle, through which respiration and speech is effected, is termed the 'windpipe'; the part that is fleshy is the oesophagus, inside just in front of the chine. The part to the back of the neck is the epomis, or 'shoulder-point'.

These then are the parts to be met with before you come to the thorax.

To the trunk there is a front part and a back part. Next after the neck in the front part is the chest, with a pair of breasts. To each of the breasts is attached a teat or nipple, through which in the case of females the milk percolates; and the breast is of a spongy texture. Milk, by the way, is found at times in the male; but with the male the flesh of the breast is tough, with the female it is soft and porous.

13

Next after the thorax and in front comes the 'belly', and its root the 'navel'. Underneath this root the bilateral part is the 'flank': the undivided part below the navel, the 'abdomen', the extremity of which is the region of the 'pubes'; and above the navel the 'hypochondrium'; the cavity common to the hypochondrium and the flank is the gut-cavity.

Serving as a brace girdle to the hinder parts is the pelvis, and hence it gets its name (ὀσφὺς), for it is symmetrical (ἰσοφυές) in appearance; of the fundament the part for resting on is termed the 'rump', and the part whereon the thigh pivots is termed the 'socket' (or acetabulum).

The 'womb' is a part peculiar to the female; and the 'penis' is peculiar to the male. This latter organ is external and situated at the extremity of the trunk; it is composed of two separate parts: of which the extreme part is fleshy, does not alter in size, and is called the glans; and round about it is a skin devoid of any specific title, which integument if it be cut asunder never grows together again, any more than does the jaw or the eyelid. And the connexion between the latter and the glans is called the frenum. The remaining part of the penis is composed of gristle; it is easily susceptible of enlargement; and it protrudes and recedes in the reverse directions to what is observable in the identical organ in cats. Underneath the penis are two 'testicles', and the integument of these is a skin that is termed the 'scrotum'.

Testicles are not identical with flesh, and are not altogether diverse from it. But by and by
493b we shall treat in an exhaustive way regarding all such parts.

14

The privy part of the female is in character opposite to that of the male. In other words, the part under the pubes is hollow or receding, and not, like the male organ, protruding. Further, there is an 'urethra' outside the womb; (which organ serves as a passage for the sperm of the male, and as an outlet for liquid excretion to both sexes).

The part common to the neck and chest is the 'throat'; the 'armpit' is common to side, arm, and shoulder; and the 'groin' is common to thigh and abdomen. The part inside the thigh and buttocks is the 'perineum', and the part outside the thigh and buttocks is the 'hypoglutis'.

The front parts of the trunk have now been enumerated.

The part behind the chest is termed the 'back'.

15

Parts of the back are a pair of 'shoulder-blades', the 'back-bone', and, underneath on a level with the belly in the trunk, the 'loins'. Common to the upper and lower part of the trunk are the 'ribs', eight on either side, for as to the so-called seven-ribbed Ligyans we have not received any trustworthy evidence.

Man, then, has an upper and a lower part, a front and a back part, a right and a left side. Now the right and the left side are pretty well alike in their parts and identical throughout, except that the left side is the weaker of the two; but the back parts do not resemble the front ones, neither do the lower ones the upper: only that these upper and lower parts may be said to resemble one another thus far, that, if the face be plump or meagre, the abdomen is plump or meagre to correspond; and that the legs correspond to the arms, and where the upper arm is short the thigh is usually short also, and where the feet are small the hands are small correspondingly.

Of the limbs, one set, forming a pair, is 'arms'. To the arm belong the 'shoulder', 'upper-arm', 'elbow', 'fore-arm', and 'hand'. To the hand belong the 'palm', and the five 'fingers'. The part of the finger that bends is termed 'knuckle', the part that is inflexible is termed the 'phalanx'. The big finger or thumb is single-jointed, the other fingers are double-jointed. The bending both of the arm and of the finger takes place from without inwards in all cases; and the arm bends at the elbow. The inner part of the hand is termed the 'palm', and is fleshy and divided by joints or lines: in the case of long-lived people by one **494a** or two extending right across, in the case of the short-lived by two, not so extending. The joint between hand and arm is termed the 'wrist'. The outside or back of the hand is sinewy, and has no specific designation.

There is another duplicate limb, the 'leg'. Of this limb the double-knobbed part is termed the 'thigh-bone', the sliding part of the 'knee-cap', the double-boned part the 'leg'; the front part of this latter is termed the 'shin', and the part behind it the 'calf', wherein the flesh is sinewy and venous, in some cases drawn upwards towards the hollow behind the knee, as in the case of people with large hips, and in other cases drawn downwards. The lower extremity of the shin is the 'ankle', duplicate in either leg. The part of the limb that contains a multiplicity of bones is the 'foot'. The hinder part of the foot is the 'heel'; at the front of it the divided part consists of 'toes', five in number; the fleshy part underneath is the 'ball'; the upper part or back of the foot is sinewy and has no particular appellation; of the toe, one portion is the 'nail' and another the 'joint', and the nail is in all cases at the extremity; and toes are without exception single-jointed. Men that have the inside or sole of the foot clumsy and not arched, that is, that walk resting on the entire under-surface of their feet, are prone to roguery. The joint common to thigh and shin is the 'knee'.

These, then, are the parts common to the male and the female sex. The relative position of the parts as to up and down, or to front and back, or to right and left, all this as regards externals might safely be left to mere ordinary perception. But for all that, we must treat of them for the same reason as the one previously brought forward; that is to say, we must refer to them in order that a due and regular sequence may be observed in our exposition, and in order that by the enumeration of these obvious facts due attention may be subsequently given to those parts in men and other animals that are diverse in any way from one another.

In man, above all other animals, the terms 'upper' and 'lower' are used in harmony with their natural positions; for in him, upper and lower have the same meaning as when they are applied to the universe as a whole. In like manner the terms, 'in front', 'behind', 'right' and 'left', are used in accordance with their natural sense. But in regard to other animals, in some cases these distinctions do not exist, and in others they do so, but in a vague way. For instance, the head with all animals is up and above in respect to their bodies; but man alone, as has been said, has, in maturity, **494b** this part uppermost in respect to the material universe.

Next after the head comes the neck, and then the chest and the back: the one in front and the other behind. Next after these come the belly, the loins, the sexual parts, and the haunches; then the thigh and shin; and, lastly, the feet.

The legs bend frontwards, in the direction of actual progression, and frontwards also lies that part of the foot which is the most effective of motion, and the flexure of that part; but the heel lies at the back, and the ankle-bones lie laterally, earwise. The arms are situated to right and left, and bend inwards: so that the convexities formed by bent arms and legs are practically face to face with one another in the case of man.

As for the senses and for the organs of sensation, the eyes, the nostrils, and the tongue, all alike are situated frontwards; the sense of hearing, and the organ of hearing, the ear, is situated sideways, on the same horizontal plane with the eyes. The eyes in man are, in proportion to his size, nearer to one another than in any other animal.

Of the senses man has the sense of touch more refined than any animal, and so also, but in less degree, the sense of taste; in the development of the other senses he is surpassed by a great number of animals.

16

The parts, then, that are externally visible are arranged in the way above stated, and as a rule have their special designations, and from use and wont are known familiarly to all; but this is not the case with the inner parts. For the fact is that the inner parts of man are to a very great extent unknown, and the consequence is that we must have recourse to an examination of the inner parts of other animals whose nature in any way resembles that of man.

In the first place then, the brain lies in the front part of the head. And this holds alike with all animals possessed of a brain; and all blooded animals are possessed thereof, and, by the way, molluscs as well. But, taking size for size of animal, the largest brain, and the moistest, is that of man. Two membranes enclose it: the stronger one near the bone of the skull; the inner one, round the brain itself, is finer. The brain in all cases is bilateral. Behind this, right at the back, comes what is termed the 'cerebellum', differing in form from the brain as we may both feel and see.

The back of the head is with all animals **495a** empty and hollow, whatever be its size in the different animals. For some creatures have big heads while the face below is small in proportion, as is the case with round-faced animals; some have little heads and long jaws, as is the case, without exception, among animals of the mane-and-tail species.

The brain in all animals is bloodless, devoid of veins, and naturally cold to the touch; in the great majority of animals it has a small hollow in its centre. The brain-caul around it is reticulated with veins; and this brain-caul is that skin-like membrane which closely surrounds the brain. Above the brain is the thinnest and weakest bone of the head, which is termed 'bregma' or 'sinciput'.

From the eye there go three ducts to the brain: the largest and the medium-sized to the cerebellum, the least to the brain itself; and the least is the one situated nearest to the nostril. The two largest ones, then, run side by side and do not meet; the medium-sized ones meet—and this is particularly visible in fishes,—for they lie nearer than the large ones to the brain; the smallest pair are the most widely separate from one another, and do not meet.

Inside the neck is what is termed the 'oesophagus' (whose other name is derived from its length and narrowness), and the windpipe. The windpipe is situated in front of the oesophagus in all animals that have a windpipe, and all animals have one that are furnished with lungs. The windpipe is made up of gristle, is sparingly supplied with blood, and is streaked all round with numerous minute veins; it is situated, in its upper part, near the mouth, below the aperture formed by the nostrils into the mouth—an aperture through which, when men, in drinking, inhale any of the liquid, this liquid finds its way out through the nostrils. In betwixt the two openings comes the so-called epiglottis, an organ capable of being drawn over and covering the orifice of the windpipe communicating with the mouth; the end of the tongue is attached to the epiglottis. In the other direction the windpipe extends to the interval between the lungs, and hereupon bifurcates into each of the two divisions of the lung; for the lung in all animals possessed of the organ has a tendency to be double. In viviparous animals, **495b** however, the duplication is not so plainly discernible as in other species, and the duplication is least discernible in man. And in man the organ is not split into many parts, as is the case with some vivipara, neither is it smooth, but its surface is uneven.

In the case of the ovipara, such as birds and oviparous quadrupeds, the two parts of the organ are separated to a distance from one another, so that the creatures appear to be furnished with a pair of lungs; and from the windpipe, itself single, there branch off two separate parts extending to each of the two divisions of the lung. It is attached also to the great vein and to what is designated the 'aorta'. When the windpipe is charged with air, the air passes on to the hollow parts of the lung. These parts have divisions, composed of gristle, which meet at an acute angle; from the divisions run passages through the entire lung, giving off smaller and smaller ramifications. The heart also is attached to the windpipe, by connexions of fat, gristle, and sinew; and at the point of juncture there is a hollow. When the windpipe is charged with air, the entrance of the air into the heart, though imperceptible in some animals, is perceptible enough in the larger ones. Such are the properties of the windpipe, and it takes in and throws out air only, and takes in nothing else either dry or liquid, or else it causes you pain until you shall have coughed up whatever may have gone down.

The oesophagus communicates at the top with the mouth, close to the windpipe, and is attached to the backbone and the windpipe by membranous ligaments, and at last finds its way through the midriff into the belly.

It is composed of flesh-like substance, and is elastic both lengthways and breadthways.

The stomach of man resembles that of a dog; for it is not much bigger than the bowel, but is somewhat like a bowel of more than usual width; then comes the bowel, single, convoluted, moderately wide. The lower part of the gut is like that of a pig; for it is broad, and the part from it to the buttocks is thick and short. The caul, or great omentum, is attached to the middle of the stomach, and consists of a fatty membrane, as is the case with all other animals whose stomachs are single and which have teeth in both jaws.

The mesentery is over the bowels; this also is membranous and broad, and turns to fat. It is attached to the great vein and the aorta, and there run through it a number of veins closely **496a** packed together, extending towards the region of the bowels, beginning above and ending below.

So much for the properties of the oesophagus, the windpipe, and the stomach.

17

The heart has three cavities, and is situated above the lung at the division of the windpipe, and is provided with a fatty and thick membrane where it fastens on to the great vein and the aorta. It lies with its tapering portion upon the aorta, and this portion is similarly situated in relation to the chest in all animals that have a chest. In all animals alike, in those that have a chest and in those that have none, the apex of the heart points forwards, although this fact might possibly escape notice by a change of position under dissection. The rounded end of the heart is at the top. The apex is to a great extent fleshy and close in texture, and in the cavities of the heart are sinews. As a rule the heart is situated in the middle of the chest in animals that have a chest, and in man it is situated a little to the left-hand side, leaning a little way from the division of the breasts towards the left breast in the upper part of the chest.

The heart is not large, and in its general shape it is not elongated; in fact, it is somewhat round in form: only, be it remembered, it is sharp-pointed at the bottom. It has three cavities, as has been said: the right-hand one the largest of the three, the left-hand one the least, and the middle one intermediate in size. All these cavities, even the two small ones, are connected by passages with the lung, and this fact is rendered quite plain in one of the cavities. And below, at the point of attachment, in the largest cavity there is a connexion with the great vein [near which the mesentery lies]; and in the middle one there is a connexion with the aorta.

Canals lead from the heart into the lung, and branch off just as the windpipe does, running all over the lung parallel with the passages from the windpipe. The canals from the heart are uppermost; and there is no common passage, but the passages through their having a common wall receive the breath and pass it on to the heart; and one of the passages conveys it to the right cavity, and the other to the left.

With regard to the great vein and the aorta we shall, by and by, treat of them together in a discussion devoted to them and to them alone.

496b In all animals that are furnished with a lung, and that are both internally and externally viviparous, the lung is of all organs the most richly supplied with blood; for the lung is throughout spongy in texture, and along by every single pore in it go branches from the great vein. Those who imagine it to be empty are altogether mistaken; and they are led into their error by their observation of lungs removed from animals under dissection, out of which organs the blood had all escaped immediately after death.

Of the other internal organs the heart alone contains blood. And the lung has blood not in itself but in its veins, but the heart has blood in itself; for in each of its three cavities it has blood, but the thinnest blood is what it has in its central cavity.

Under the lung comes the thoracic diaphragm or midriff, attached to the ribs, the hypochondria and the backbone, with a thin membrane in the middle of it. It has veins running through it; and the diaphragm in the case of man is thicker in proportion to the size of his frame than in other animals.

Under the diaphragm on the right-hand side lies the 'liver', and on the left-hand side the 'spleen', alike in all animals that are provided with these organs in an ordinary and not preternatural way; for, be it observed, in some quadrupeds these organs have been found in a transposed position. These organs are connected with the stomach by the caul.

To outward view the spleen of man is narrow and long, resembling the self-same organ in the pig. The liver in the great majority of animals is not provided with a 'gall-bladder';

but the latter is present in some. The liver of a man is round-shaped, and resembles the same organ in the ox. And, by the way, the absence above referred to of a gall-bladder is at times met with in the practice of augury. For instance, in a certain district of the Chalcidic settlement in Euboea the sheep are devoid of gall-bladders; and in Naxos nearly all the quadrupeds have one so large that foreigners when they offer sacrifice with such victims are bewildered with fright, under the impression that the phenomenon is not due to natural causes, but bodes some mischief to the individual offerers of the sacrifice.

Again, the liver is attached to the great vein, but it has no communication with the aorta; for the vein that goes off from the great vein goes right through the liver, at a point where are the so-called 'portals' of the liver. The spleen also is connected only with the great vein, for a vein extends to the spleen off from it.

After these organs come the 'kidneys', and these are placed close to the backbone, and resemble in character the same organ in kine. In **497a** all animals that are provided with this organ, the right kidney is situated higher up than the other. It has also less fatty substance than the left-hand one and is less moist. And this phenomenon also is observable in all the other animals alike.

Furthermore, passages or ducts lead into the kidneys both from the great vein and from the aorta, only not into the cavity. For, by the way, there is a cavity in the middle of the kidney, bigger in some creatures and less in others; but there is none in the case of the seal. This latter animal has kidneys resembling in shape the identical organ in kine, but in its case the organs are more solid than in any other known creature. The ducts that lead into the kidneys lose themselves in the substance of the kidneys themselves; and the proof that they extend no farther rests on the fact that they contain no blood, nor is any clot found therein. The kidneys, however, have, as has been said, a small cavity. From this cavity in the kidney there lead two considerable ducts or ureters into the bladder; and others spring from the aorta, strong and continuous. And to the middle of each of the two kidneys is attached a hollow sinewy vein, stretching right along the spine through the narrows; by and by these veins are lost in either loin, and again become visible extending to the flank. And these off-branchings of the veins terminate in the bladder. For the bladder lies at the extremity, and is held in position by the ducts stretching from the kidneys, along the stalk that extends to the urethra; and pretty well all round it is fastened by fine sinewy membranes, that resemble to some extent the thoracic diaphragm. The bladder in man is, proportionately to his size, tolerably large.

To the stalk of the bladder the private part is attached, the external orifices coalescing; but a little lower down, one of the openings communicates with the testicles and the other with the bladder. The penis is gristly and sinewy in its texture. With it are connected the testicles in male animals, and the properties of these organs we shall discuss in our general account of the said organ.

All these organs are similar in the female; for there is no difference in regard to the internal organs, except in respect to the womb, and with reference to the appearance of this organ I must refer the reader to diagrams in my 'Anatomy'. The womb, however, is situated over the bowel, and the bladder lies over the womb. But we must treat by and by in our pages of the womb of all female animals viewed generally. For the wombs of all female animals are not identical, neither do their local dispositions coincide.

497b These are the organs, internal and external, of man, and such is their nature and such their local disposition.

BOOK II

1

With regard to animals in general, some parts or organs are common to all, as has been said, and some are common only to particular genera; the parts, moreover, are identical with or different from one another on the lines already repeatedly laid down. For as a general rule all animals that are generically distinct have the majority of their parts or organs different in form or species; and some of them they have only analogically similar and diverse in kind or genus, while they have others that are alike in kind but specifically diverse; and many parts or organs exist in some animals, but not in others.

For instance, viviparous quadrupeds have all a head and a neck, and all the parts or organs of the head, but they differ each from other in the shapes of the parts. The lion has its neck composed of one single bone instead of vertebrae; but, when dissected, the animal is found in all internal characters to resemble the dog.

The quadrupedal vivipara instead of arms have forelegs. This is true of all quadrupeds, but such of them as have toes have, practically speaking, organs analogous to hands; at all events, they use these fore-limbs for many purposes as hands. And they have the limbs on the left-hand side less distinct from those on the right than man.

The fore-limbs then serve more or less the purpose of hands in quadrupeds, with the exception of the elephant. This latter animal has its toes somewhat indistinctly defined, and its front legs are much bigger than its hinder ones; it is five-toed, and has short ankles to its hind feet. But it has a nose such in properties and such in size as to allow of its using the same for a hand. For it eats and drinks by lifting up its food with the aid of this organ into its mouth, and with the same organ it lifts up articles to the driver on its back; with this organ it can pluck up trees by the roots, and when walking through water it spouts the water up by means of it; and this organ is capable of being crooked or coiled at the tip, but not of flexing like a joint, for it is composed of gristle.

Of all animals man alone can learn to make equal use of both hands.

All animals have a part analogous to the chest in man, but not similar to his; for the chest in man is broad, but that of all other animals is narrow. Moreover, no other animal but man has breasts in front; the elephant, cer-
498a tainly, has two breasts, not however in the chest, but near it.

Moreover, also, animals have the flexions of their fore and hind limbs in directions opposite to one another, and in directions the reverse of those observed in the arms and legs of man; with the exception of the elephant. In other words, with the viviparous quadrupeds the front legs bend forwards and the hind ones backwards, and the concavities of the two pairs of limbs thus face one another.

The elephant does not sleep standing, as some were wont to assert, but it bends its legs and settles down; only that in consequence of its weight it cannot bend its leg on both sides simultaneously, but falls into a recumbent position on one side or the other, and in this position it goes to sleep. And it bends its hind legs just as a man bends his legs.

In the case of the ovipara, as the crocodile and the lizard and the like, both pairs of legs, fore and hind, bend forwards, with a slight swerve on one side. The flexion is similar in the case of the multipeds; only that the legs in between the extreme ends always move in a manner intermediate between that of those in front and those behind, and accordingly bend sideways rather than backwards or forwards. But man bends his arms and his legs towards the same point, and therefore in opposite ways: that is to say, he bends his arms backwards, with just a slight inclination inwards, and his legs frontwards. No animal bends both its fore-limbs and hind-limbs backwards; but in the case of all animals the flexion of the shoulders is in the opposite direction to that of the elbows or the joints of the forelegs, and the flexure in the hips to that of the knees of the hind-legs: so that since man differs from other animals in flexion, those animals that possess such parts as these move them contrariwise to man.

Birds have the flexions of their limbs like those of the quadrupeds; for, although bipeds, they bend their legs backwards, and instead of arms or front legs have wings which bend frontwards.

The seal is a kind of imperfect or crippled quadruped; for just behind the shoulder-blade its front feet are placed, resembling hands, like the front paws of the bear; for they are fur-
498b nished with five toes, and each of the toes has three flexions and a nail of inconsiderable size. The hind feet are also furnished with five toes; in their flexions and nails they resemble the front feet, and in shape they resemble a fish's tail.

The movements of animals, quadruped and multiped, are crosswise, or in diagonals, and their equilibrium in standing posture is maintained crosswise; and it is always the limb on the right-hand side that is the first to move. The lion, however, and the two species of camels, both the Bactrian and the Arabian, progress by an amble; and the action so called is when the animal never overpasses the right foot with the left, but always follows close upon it.

Whatever parts men have in front, these parts quadrupeds have below, in or on the belly; and whatever parts men have behind, these parts quadrupeds have above on their backs. Most quadrupeds have a tail; for even the seal has a tiny one resembling that of the stag. Regarding the tails of the pithecoids we must give their distinctive properties by and by.

All viviparous quadrupeds are hair-coated, whereas man has only a few short hairs excepting on the head, but, so far as the head is concerned, he is hairier than any other animal. Further, of hair-coated animals, the back is hairier than the belly, which latter is either comparatively void of hair or smooth and void of hair altogether. With man the reverse is the case.

Man also has upper and lower eyelashes, and hair under the armpits and on the pubes. No other animal has hair in either of these localities, or has an under eyelash; though in the case of some animals a few straggling hairs grow under the eyelid.

Of hair-coated quadrupeds some are hairy all over the body, as the pig, the bear, and the dog; others are especially hairy on the neck and all round about it, as is the case with animals that have a shaggy mane, such as the lion; others again are especially hairy on the upper surface of the neck from the head as far as the withers, namely, such as have a crested mane, as in the case with the horse, the mule, and, among the undomesticated horned animals, the bison.

The so-called hippelaphus also has a mane on its withers, and the animal called pardion, in either case a thin mane extending from the head to the withers; the hippelaphus has, ex-
499a ceptionally, a beard by the larynx. Both these animals have horns and are cloven-footed; the female, however, of the hippelaphus has no horns. This latter animal resembles the stag in size; it is found in the territory of the Arachotae, where the wild cattle also are found. Wild cattle differ from their domesticated congeners just as the wild boar differs from the domesticated one. That is to say they are black, strong looking, with a hook-nosed muzzle, and with horns lying more over the back. The horns of the hippelaphus resemble those of the gazelle.

The elephant, by the way, is the least hairy of all quadrupeds. With animals, as a general rule, the tail corresponds with the body as regards thickness or thinness of hair-coating; that is, with animals that have long tails, for some creatures have tails of altogether insignificant size.

Camels have an exceptional organ wherein they differ from all other animals, and that is the so-called 'hump' on their back. The Bactrian camel differs from the Arabian; for the former has two humps and the latter only one, though it has, by the way, a kind of a hump below like the one above, on which, when it kneels, the weight of the whole body rests. The camel has four teats like the cow, a tail like that of an ass, and the privy parts of the male are directed backwards. It has one knee in each leg, and the flexures of the limb are not manifold, as some say, although they appear to be so from the constricted shape of the region of the belly. It has a huckle-bone like that of kine, but meagre and small in proportion to its bulk. It is cloven-footed, and has not got teeth in both jaws; and it is cloven-footed in the following way: at the back there is a slight cleft extending as far up as the second joint of the toes; and in front there are small hooves on the tip of the first joint of the toes; and a sort of web passes across the cleft, as in geese. The foot is fleshy underneath, like that of the bear; so that, when the animal goes to war, they protect its feet, when they get sore, with sandals.

The legs of all quadrupeds are bony, sinewy, and fleshless; and in point of fact such is the case with all animals that are furnished with
499b feet, with the exception of man. They are also unfurnished with buttocks; and this last point is plain in an especial degree in birds. It is the reverse with man; for there is scarcely any part of the body in which man is so fleshy as in the buttock, the thigh, and the calf; for the part of the leg called gastrocnemia or 'calf' is fleshy.

Of blooded and viviparous quadrupeds some have the foot cloven into many parts, as is the case with the hands and feet of man (for some animals, by the way, are many-toed, as the lion, the dog, and the pard); others have feet cloven in twain, and instead of nails have hooves, as the sheep, the goat, the deer, and the hippopotamus; others are uncloven of foot, such for instance as the solid-hooved animals, the horse and the mule. Swine are either cloven-footed or uncloven-footed; for there are in Illyria and in Paeonia and elsewhere solid-hooved swine. The cloven-footed animals have two clefts behind; in the solid-hooved this part is continuous and undivided.

Furthermore, of animals some are horned, and some are not so. The great majority of the horned animals are cloven-footed, as the ox, the stag, the goat; and a solid-hooved animal with a pair of horns has never yet been met with. But a few animals are known to be singled-horned and single-hooved, as the Indian ass; and one, to wit the oryx, is single-horned and cloven-hooved.

Of all solid-hooved animals the Indian ass alone has an astragalus or huckle-bone; for the pig, as was said above, is either solid-hooved or cloven-footed, and consequently has no well-formed huckle-bone. Of the cloven-footed many are provided with a huckle-bone. Of the many-fingered or many-toed, no single one has been observed to have a huckle-bone, none of the others any more than man. The lynx, however, has something like a hemiastragal, and the lion something resembling the sculptor's 'labyrinth'. All the animals that have a huckle-bone have it in the hinder legs. They have also the bone placed straight up in the joint; the upper part, outside; the lower part, inside; the sides called Coa turned towards one another, the sides called Chia outside, and the keraiae or 'horns' on the top. This, then, is the position of the huckle-bone in the case of all animals provided with the part.

Some animals are, at one and the same time, furnished with a mane and furnished also with a pair of horns bent in towards one an- **500a** other, as is the bison (or aurochs), which is found in Paeonia and Maedica. But all animals that are horned are quadrupedal, except in cases where a creature is said metaphorically, or by a figure of speech, to have horns; just as the Egyptians describe the serpents found in the neighbourhood of Thebes, while in point of fact the creatures have merely protuberances on the head sufficiently large to suggest such an epithet.

Of horned animals the deer alone has a horn, or antler, hard and solid throughout. The horns of other animals are hollow for a certain distance, and solid towards the extremity. The hollow part is derived from the skin, but the core round which this is wrapped—the hard part—is derived from the bones; as is the case with the horns of oxen. The deer is the only animal that sheds its horns, and it does so annually, after reaching the age of two years, and again renews them. All other animals retain their horns permanently, unless the horns be damaged by accident.

Again, with regard to the breasts and the generative organs, animals differ widely from one another and from man. For instance, the breasts of some animals are situated in front, either in the chest or near to it, and there are in such cases two breasts and two teats, as is the case with man and the elephant, as previously stated. For the elephant has two breasts in the region of the axillae; and the female elephant has two breasts insignificant in size and in no way proportionate to the bulk of the entire frame, in fact, so insignificant as to be invisible in a sideways view; the males also have breasts, like the females, exceedingly small. The she-bear has four breasts. Some animals have two breasts, but situated near the thighs, and teats, likewise two in number, as the sheep; others have four teats, as the cow. Some have breasts neither in the chest nor at the thighs, but in the belly, as the dog and pig; and they have a considerable number of breasts or dugs, but not all of equal size. Thus the she-pard has four dugs in the belly, the lioness two, and others more. The she-camel, also, has two dugs and four teats, like the cow. Of solid-hooved animals the males have no dugs, excepting in the case of males that take after the mother, which phenomenon is observable in horses.

Of male animals the genitals of some are external, as is the case with man, the horse, and most other creatures; some are internal, as with **500b** the dolphin. With those that have the organ externally placed, the organ in some cases is situated in front, as in the cases already mentioned, and of these some have the organ detached, both penis and testicles, as man; others have penis and testicles closely attached to the belly, some more closely, some less; for this organ is not detached in the wild boar nor in the horse.

The penis of the elephant resembles that of the horse; compared with the size of the animal it is disproportionately small; the testicles are not visible, but are concealed inside in the vicinity of the kidneys; and for this reason the male speedily gives over in the act of intercourse. The genitals of the female are situated where the udder is in sheep; when she is in heat, she draws the organ back and exposes it externally, to facilitate the act of intercourse for the male; and the organ opens out to a considerable extent.

With most animals the genitals have the position above assigned; but some animals discharge their urine backwards, as the lynx, the lion, the camel, and the hare. Male animals differ from one another, as has been said, in this particular, but all female animals are retromingent: even the female elephant like other animals, though she has the privy part below the thighs.

In the male organ itself there is a great diversity. For in some cases the organ is composed of flesh and gristle, as in man; in such cases, the fleshy part does not become inflated, but the gristly part is subject to enlargement. In other cases, the organ is composed of fibrous tissue, as with the camel and the deer; in other cases it is bony, as with the fox, the wolf, the marten, and the weasel; for this organ in the weasel has a bone.

When man has arrived at maturity, his upper part is smaller than the lower one, but with all other blooded animals the reverse holds good. By the 'upper' part we mean all extending from the head down to the parts used for excretion of residuum, and by the 'lower' part all else. With animals that have feet the hind legs are to be rated as the lower part in our comparison of magnitudes, and with animals devoid of feet, the tail, and the like.

When animals arrive at maturity, their properties are as above stated; but they differ greatly from one another in their growth towards maturity. For instance, man, when young, has his upper part larger than the lower, but in **501a** course of growth he comes to reverse this condition; and it is owing to this circumstance that—an exceptional instance, by the way—he does not progress in early life as he does at maturity, but in infancy creeps on all fours; but some animals, in growth, retain the relative proportion of the parts, as the dog. Some animals at first have the upper part smaller and the lower part larger, and in course of growth the upper part gets to be the larger, as is the case with the bushy-tailed animals such as the horse; for in their case there is never, subsequently to birth, any increase in the part extending from the hoof to the haunch.

Again, in respect to the teeth, animals differ greatly both from one another and from man. All animals that are quadrupedal, blooded, and viviparous, are furnished with teeth; but, to begin with, some are double-toothed (or fully furnished with teeth in both jaws), and some are not. For instance, horned quadrupeds are not double-toothed; for they have not got the front teeth in the upper jaw; and some hornless animals, also, are not double-toothed, as the camel. Some animals have tusks, like the boar, and some have not. Further, some animals are saw-toothed, such as the lion, the pard, and the dog; and some have teeth that do not interlock but have flat opposing crowns, as the horse and the ox; and by 'saw-toothed' we mean such animals as interlock the sharp-pointed teeth in one jaw between the sharp-pointed ones in the other. No animal is there that possesses both tusks and horns, nor yet do either of these structures exist in any animal possessed of 'saw-teeth'. The front teeth are usually sharp, and the back ones blunt. The seal is saw-toothed throughout, inasmuch as he is a sort of link with the class of fishes; for fishes are almost all saw-toothed.

No animal of these genera is provided with double rows of teeth. There is, however, an animal of the sort, if we are to believe Ctesias. He assures us that the Indian wild beast called the 'martichoras' has a triple row of teeth in both upper and lower jaw; that it is as big as a lion and equally hairy, and that its feet resemble those of the lion; that it resembles man in its face and ears; that its eyes are blue, and its colour vermilion; that its tail is like that of the land-scorpion; that it has a sting in the tail, and has the faculty of shooting off arrow-wise the spines that are attached to the tail; that the sound of its voice is a something between the sound of a pan-pipe and that of a trumpet; that it can run as swiftly as **501b** a deer, and that it is savage and a man-eater.

Man sheds his teeth, and so do other animals, as the horse, the mule, and the ass. And man sheds his front teeth; but there is no instance of an animal that sheds its molars. The pig sheds none of its teeth at all.

2

With regard to dogs some doubts are entertained, as some contend that they shed no teeth whatever, and others that they shed the canines, but those alone; the fact being, that they do shed their teeth like man, but that the circumstance escapes observation, owing to the fact that they never shed them until equivalent teeth have grown within the gums to take the place of the shed ones. We shall be justified in supposing that the case is similar with wild beasts in general; for they are said to shed their canines only. Dogs can be distinguished from one another, the young from the old, by their teeth; for the teeth in young dogs are white and sharp-pointed; in old dogs, black and blunt.

3

In this particular, the horse differs entirely from animals in general: for, generally speaking, as animals grow older their teeth get blacker, but the horse's teeth grow whiter with age.

The so-called 'canines' come in between the sharp teeth and the broad or blunt ones, partaking of the form of both kinds; for they are broad at the base and sharp at the tip.

Males have more teeth than females in the case of men, sheep, goats, and swine; in the case of other animals observations have not yet been made: but the more teeth they have the more long-lived are they, as a rule, while those are short-lived in proportion that have teeth fewer in number and thinly set.

4

The last teeth to come in man are molars called 'wisdom-teeth', which come at the age of twenty years, in the case of both sexes. Cases have been known in women upwards of eighty years old where at the very close of life the wisdom-teeth have come up, causing great pain in their coming; and cases have been known of the like phenomenon in men too. This happens, when it does happen, in the case of people where the wisdom-teeth have not come up in early years.

5

The elephant has four teeth on either side, by which it munches its food, grinding it like so much barley-meal, and, quite apart from these, it has its great teeth, or tusks, two in number. In the male these tusks are comparatively large and curved upwards; in the female, they are comparatively small and point
502a in the opposite direction; that is, they look downwards towards the ground. The elephant is furnished with teeth at birth, but the tusks are not then visible.

6

The tongue of the elephant is exceedingly small, and situated far back in the mouth, so that it is difficult to get a sight of it.

7

Furthermore, animals differ from one another in the relative size of their mouths. In some animals the mouth opens wide, as is the case with the dog, the lion, and with all the saw-toothed animals; other animals have small mouths, as man; and others have mouths of medium capacity, as the pig and his congeners.

[The Egyptian hippopotamus has a mane like a horse, is cloven-footed like an ox, and is snub-nosed. It has a huckle-bone like cloven-footed animals, and tusks just visible; it has the tail of a pig, the neigh of a horse, and the dimensions of an ass. The hide is so thick that spears are made out of it. In its internal organs it resembles the horse and the ass.]

8

Some animals share the properties of man and the quadrupeds, as the ape, the monkey, and the baboon. The monkey is a tailed ape. The baboon resembles the ape in form, only that it is bigger and stronger, more like a dog in face, and is more savage in its habits, and its teeth are more dog-like and more powerful.

Apes are hairy on the back in keeping with their quadrupedal nature, and hairy on the belly in keeping with their human form—for, as was said above, this characteristic is reversed in man and the quadruped—only that the hair is coarse, so that the ape is thickly coated both on the belly and on the back. Its face resembles that of man in many respects; in other words, it has similar nostrils and ears, and teeth like those of man, both front teeth and molars. Further, whereas quadrupeds in general are not furnished with lashes on one of the two eyelids, this creature has them on both, only very thinly set, especially the under ones; in fact they are very insignificant indeed. And we must bear in mind that all other quadrupeds have no under eyelash at all.

The ape has also in its chest two teats upon poorly developed breasts. It has also arms like man, only covered with hair, and it bends
502b these legs like man, with the convexities of both limbs facing one another. In addition, it has hands and fingers and nails like man, only that all these parts are somewhat more beast-like in appearance. Its feet are exceptional in kind. That is, they are like large hands, and the toes are like fingers, with the middle one the longest of all, and the under part of the foot is like a hand except for its length, and stretches out towards the extremities like the palm of the hand; and this palm at the after end is unusually hard, and in a clumsy obscure kind of way resembles a heel. The creature uses its feet either as hands or feet, and doubles them up as one doubles a

fist. Its upper-arm and thigh are short in proportion to the forearm and the shin. It has no projecting navel, but only a hardness in the ordinary locality of the navel. Its upper part is much larger than its lower part, as is the case with quadrupeds; in fact, the proportion of the former to the latter is about as five to three. Owing to this circumstance and to the fact that its feet resemble hands and are composed in a manner of hand and of foot: of foot in the heel extremity, of the hand in all else—for even the toes have what is called a 'palm': —for these reasons the animal is oftener to be found on all fours than upright. It has neither hips, inasmuch as it is a quadruped, nor yet a tail, inasmuch as it is a biped, except by the way that it has a tail as small as small can be, just a sort of indication of a tail. The genitals of the female resemble those of the female in the human species; those of the male are more like those of a dog than are those of a man.

9

The monkey, as has been observed, is furnished with a tail. In all such creatures the internal organs are found under dissection to correspond to those of man.

So much then for the properties of the organs of such animals as bring forth their young into the world alive.

10

Oviparous and blooded quadrupeds—and, by the way, no terrestrial blooded animal is oviparous unless it is quadrupedal or is devoid of feet altogether—are furnished with a head, a neck, a back, upper and under parts, the front legs and hind legs, and the part analogous to the chest, all as in the case of viviparous quadrupeds, and with a tail, usually large, in exceptional cases small. And all these creatures are many-toed, and the several toes are cloven apart. Furthermore, they all have the ordinary organs of sensation, including a **503a** tongue, with the exception of the Egyptian crocodile.

This latter animal, by the way, resembles certain fishes. For, as a general rule, fishes have a prickly tongue, not free in its movements; though there are some fishes that present a smooth undifferentiated surface where the tongue should be, until you open their mouths wide and make a close inspection.

Again, oviparous blooded quadrupeds are unprovided with ears, but possess only the passage for hearing; neither have they breasts, nor a copulatory organ, nor external testicles, but internal ones only; neither are they hair-coated, but are in all cases covered with scaly plates. Moreover, they are without exception saw-toothed.

River crocodiles have pigs' eyes, large teeth and tusks, and strong nails, and an impenetrable skin composed of scaly plates. They see but poorly under water, but above the surface of it with remarkable acuteness. As a rule, they pass the day-time on land and the night-time in the water; for the temperature of the water is at night-time more genial than that of the open air.

11

The chameleon resembles the lizard in the general configuration of its body, but the ribs stretch downwards and meet together under the belly as is the case with fishes, and the spine sticks up as with the fish. Its face resembles that of the baboon. Its tail is exceedingly long, terminates in a sharp point, and is for the most part coiled up, like a strap of leather. It stands higher off the ground than the lizard, but the flexure of the legs is the same in both creatures. Each of its feet is divided into two parts, which bear the same relation to one another that the thumb and the rest of the hand bear to one another in man. Each of these parts is for a short distance divided after a fashion into toes; on the front feet the inside part is divided into three and the outside into two, on the hind feet the inside part into two and the outside into three; it has claws also on these parts resembling those of birds of prey. Its body is rough all over, like that of the crocodile. Its eyes are situated in a hollow recess, and are very large and round, and are enveloped in a skin resembling that which covers the entire body; and in the middle a slight aperture is left for vision, through which the animal sees, for it never covers up this aperture with the cutaneous envelope. It keeps twisting its eyes round **503b** and shifting its line of vision in every direction, and thus contrives to get a sight of any object that it wants to see. The change in its colour takes place when it is inflated with air; it is then black, not unlike the crocodile, or green like the lizard but black-spotted like the pard. This change of colour takes place over the whole body alike, for the eyes and the tail come alike under its influence. In its movements it is very sluggish, like the tortoise. It assumes a greenish hue in dying, and retains this hue after death. It resembles the lizard in the position of the oesophagus and the windpipe. It has no flesh anywhere except a few scraps of flesh on the head and on the jaws and near to the root of the tail. It has blood only round about the heart, the eyes, the region above the heart, and in all the veins extending from these parts; and in all these there is but little blood after all. The brain is situated a little above the eyes, but connected with them. When the outer skin is drawn aside from off the eye, a something is found surrounding the eye, that gleams through like a thin ring of copper. Membranes extend wellnigh over its entire frame, numerous and strong, and surpassing in respect of number and relative strength those found in any other animal. After being cut open along its entire length it continues to breathe for a considerable time; a very slight motion goes on in the region of the heart, and, while contraction is especially manifested in the neighbourhood of the ribs, a similar motion is more or less discernible over the whole body. It has no spleen visible. It hibernates, like the lizard.

12

Birds also in some parts resemble the above-mentioned animals; that is to say, they have in all cases a head, a neck, a back, a belly, and what is analogous to the chest. The bird is remarkable among animals as having two feet, like man; only, by the way, it bends them backwards as quadrupeds bend their hind legs, as was noticed previously.[1] It has neither hands nor front feet, but wings—an exceptional structure as compared with other animals. Its **504a** haunch-bone is long, like a thigh, and is attached to the body as far as the middle of the belly; so like to a thigh is it that when viewed separately it looks like a real one, while the real thigh is a separate structure betwixt it and the shin. Of all birds those that have crooked talons have the biggest thighs and the strongest breasts. All birds are furnished with many claws, and all have the toes separated more or less asunder; that is to say, in the greater part the toes are clearly distinct from one another, for even the swimming birds, although they are web-footed, have still their claws fully articulated and distinctly differentiated from one another. Birds that fly high in air are in all cases four-toed: that is, the greater part have three toes in front and one behind in place of a heel; some few have two in front and two behind, as the wryneck.

This latter bird is somewhat bigger than the chaffinch, and is mottled in appearance. It is peculiar in the arrangement of its toes, and resembles the snake in the structure of its tongue; for the creature can protrude its tongue to the extent of four finger-breadths, and then draw it back again. Moreover, it can twist its head backwards while keeping all the rest of its body still, like the serpent. It has big claws, somewhat resembling those of the woodpecker. Its note is a shrill chirp.

Birds are furnished with a mouth, but with an exceptional one, for they have neither lips nor teeth, but a beak. Neither have they ears nor a nose, but only passages for the sensations connected with these organs: that for the nostrils in the beak, and that for hearing in the head. Like all other animals they all have two eyes, and these are devoid of lashes. The heavy-bodied (or gallinaceous) birds close the eye by means of the lower lid, and all birds blink by means of a skin extending over the eye from the inner corner; the owl and its congeners also close the eye by means of the upper lid. The same phenomenon is observable in the animals that are protected by horny scutes, as in the lizard and its congeners; for they all without exception close the eye with the lower lid, but they do not blink like birds. Further, birds have neither scutes nor hair, but feathers; and the feathers are invariably furnished with quills. They have no tail, but a rump with tail-feathers, short in such as are long-legged and web-footed, large in others. These latter kinds of birds fly with their feet tucked up close to the belly; but the small-rumped or short-tailed birds fly with their legs stretched out at full length. All are furnished with a tongue, but the organ is variable, being **504b** long in some birds and broad in others. Certain species of birds above all other animals, and next after man, possess the faculty of uttering articulate sounds; and this faculty is chiefly developed in broad-tongued birds. No oviparous creature has an epiglottis over the windpipe, but these animals so manage the opening and shutting of the windpipe as not to allow any solid substance to get down into the lung.

Some species of birds are furnished additionally with spurs, but no bird with crooked talons is found so provided. The birds with talons are among those that fly well, but those that have spurs are among the heavy-bodied.

[1] I, 498a 28.

Again, some birds have a crest. As a general rule the crest sticks up, and is composed of feathers only; but the crest of the barn-door cock is exceptional in kind, for, whereas it is not just exactly flesh, at the same time it is not easy to say what else it is.

13

Of water animals the genus of fishes constitutes a single group apart from the rest, and including many diverse forms.

In the first place, the fish has a head, a back, a belly, in the neighbourhood of which last are placed the stomach and viscera; and behind it has a tail of continuous, undivided shape, but not, by the way, in all cases alike. No fish has a neck, or any limb, or testicles at all, within or without, or breasts. But, by the way, this absence of breasts may be predicated of all non-viviparous animals; and in point of fact viviparous animals are not in all cases provided with the organ, excepting such as are directly viviparous without being first oviparous. Thus the dolphin is directly viviparous, and accordingly we find it furnished with two breasts, not situated high up, but in the neighbourhood of the genitals. And this creature is not provided, like quadrupeds, with visible teats, but has two vents, one on each flank, from which the milk flows; and its young have to follow after it to get suckled, and this phenomenon has been actually witnessed.

Fishes, then, as has been observed, have no breasts and no passage for the genitals visible externally. But they have an exceptional organ in the gills, whereby, after taking the water in by the mouth, they discharge it again; and in the fins, of which the greater part have four, and the lanky ones two, as, for instance, the eel, and these two situated near to the gills. In like manner the grey mullet— as, for instance, the mullet found in the lake at Siphae —have only two fins; and the same is the case with the fish called Ribbon-fish. Some of the lanky fishes have no fins at all, such as the muraena, nor gills articulated like those of other fish.

And of those fish that are provided with gills, some have coverings for this organ, **505a** whereas all the selachians have the organ unprotected by a cover. And those fishes that have coverings or opercula for the gills have in all cases their gills placed sideways; whereas, among selachians, the broad ones have the gills down below on the belly, as the torpedo and the ray, while the lanky ones have the organ placed sideways, as is the case in all the dog-fish.

The fishing-frog has gills placed sideways, and covered not with a spiny operculum, as in all but the selachian fishes, but with one of skin.

Morever, with fishes furnished with gills, the gills in some cases are simple in others duplicate; and the last gill in the direction of the body is always simple. And, again, some fishes have few gills, and others have a great number; but all alike have the same number on both sides. Those that have the least number have one gill on either side, and this one duplicate, like the boar-fish; others have two on either side, one simple and the other duplicate, like the conger and the scarus; others have four on either side, simple, as the elops, the synagris, the muraena, and the eel; others have four, all, with the exception of the hindmost one, in double rows, as the wrasse, the perch, the sheat-fish, and the carp. The dog-fish have all their gills double, five on a side; and the sword-fish has eight double gills. So much for the number of gills as found in fishes.

Again, fishes differ from other animals in more ways than as regards the gills. For they are not covered with hairs as are viviparous land animals, nor, as is the case with certain oviparous quadrupeds, with tessellated scutes, nor, like birds, with feathers; but for the most part they are covered with scales. Some few are rough-skinned, while the smooth-skinned are very few indeed. Of the Selachia some are rough-skinned and some smooth-skinned; and among the smooth-skinned fishes are included the conger, the eel, and the tunny.

All fishes are saw-toothed excepting the scarus; and the teeth in all cases are sharp and set in many rows, and in some cases are placed on the tongue. The tongue is hard and spiny, and so firmly attached that fishes in many instances seem to be devoid of the organ altogether. The mouth in some cases is wide-stretched, as it is with some viviparous quadrupeds. . . .

With regard to organs of sense, all save eyes, fishes possess none of them, neither the organs nor their passages, neither ears nor nostrils; but all fishes are furnished with eyes, and the eyes devoid of lids, though the eyes are not hard; with regard to the organs connected with the other senses, hearing and smell, they are devoid alike of the organs themselves and of passages indicative of them.

505b Fishes without exception are supplied with blood. Some of them are oviparous, and some viviparous; scaly fish are invariably oviparous, but cartilaginous fishes are all viviparous, with the single exception of the fishing-frog.

14

Of blooded animals there now remains the serpent genus. This genus is common to both elements, for, while most species comprehended therein are land animals, a small minority, to wit the aquatic species, pass their lives in fresh water. There are also sea-serpents, in shape to a great extent resembling their congeners of the land, with this exception that the head in their case is somewhat like the head of the conger; and there are several kinds of sea-serpent, and the different kinds differ in colour; these animals are not found in very deep water. Serpents, like fish, are devoid of feet.

There are also sea-scolopendras, resembling in shape their land congeners, but somewhat less in regard to magnitude. These creatures are found in the neighbourhood of rocks; as compared with their land congeners they are redder in colour, are furnished with feet in greater numbers and with legs of more delicate structure. And the same remark applies to them as to the sea-serpents, that they are not found in very deep water.

Of fishes whose habitat is in the vicinity of rocks there is a tiny one, which some call the Echeneïs, or 'ship-holder', and which is by some people used as a charm to bring luck in affairs of law and love. The creature is unfit for eating. Some people assert that it has feet, but this is not the case: it appears, however, to be furnished with feet from the fact that its fins resemble those organs.

So much, then, for the external parts of blooded animals, as regards their numbers, their properties, and their relative diversities.

15

As for the properties of the internal organs, these we must first discuss in the case of the animals that are supplied with blood. For the principal genera differ from the rest of animals, in that the former are supplied with blood and the latter are not; and the former include man, viviparous and oviparous quadrupeds, birds, fishes, cetaceans, and all the others that come under no general designation by reason of their not forming genera, but groups of which simply the specific name is predicable, as when we say 'the serpent', 'the crocodile'.

All viviparous quadrupeds, then, are furnished with an oesophagus and a windpipe, situated as in man; the same statement is applicable to oviparous quadrupeds and to birds, only that the latter present diversities in the
506a shapes of these organs. As a general rule, all animals that take up air and breathe it in and out are furnished with a lung, a windpipe, and an oesophagus, with the windpipe and oesophagus not admitting of diversity in situation but admitting of diversity in properties, and with the lung admitting of diversity in both these respects. Further, all blooded animals have a heart and a diaphragm or midriff; but in small animals the existence of the latter organ is not so obvious owing to its delicacy and minute size.

In regard to the heart there is an exceptional phenomenon observable in oxen. In other words, there is one species of ox where, though not in all cases, a bone is found inside the heart. And, by the way, the horse's heart also has a bone inside it.

The genera referred to above are not in all cases furnished with a lung: for instance, the fish is devoid of the organ, as is also every animal furnished with gills. All blooded animals are furnished with a liver. As a general rule blooded animals are furnished with a spleen; but with the great majority of non-viviparous but oviparous animals the spleen is so small as all but to escape observation; and this is the case with almost all birds, as with the pigeon, the kite, the falcon, the owl: in point of fact, the aegocephalus is devoid of the organ altogether. With oviparous quadrupeds the case is much the same as with the viviparous; that is to say, they also have the spleen exceedingly minute, as the tortoise, the freshwater tortoise, the toad, the lizard, the crocodile, and the frog.

Some animals have a gall-bladder close to the liver, and others have not. Of viviparous quadrupeds the deer is without the organ, as also the roe, the horse, the mule, the ass, the seal, and some kinds of pigs. Of deer those that are called Achainae appear to have gall in their tail, but what is so called does resemble gall in colour, though it is not so completely fluid, and the organ internally resembles a spleen.

However, without any exception, stags are

found to have maggots living inside the head, and the habitat of these creatures is in the hollow underneath the root of the tongue and in the neighbourhood of the vertebra to which the head is attached. These creatures are as large as the largest grubs; they grow all together in a cluster, and they are usually about twenty in number.

Deer then, as has been observed, are without a gall-bladder; their gut, however, is so bitter that even hounds refuse to eat it unless the animal is exceptionally fat. With the elephant **506b** also the liver is unfurnished with a gall-bladder, but when the animal is cut in the region where the organ is found in animals furnished with it, there oozes out a fluid resembling gall, in greater or less quantities. Of animals that take in sea-water and are furnished with a lung, the dolphin is unprovided with a gall-bladder. Birds and fishes all have the organ, as also oviparous quadrupeds, all to a greater or a lesser extent. But of fishes some have the organ close to the liver, as the dog-fishes, the sheat-fish, the rhine or angel-fish, the smooth skate, the torpedo, and, of the lanky fishes, the eel, the pipe-fish, and the hammer-headed shark. The callionymus, also, has the gall-bladder close to the liver, and in no other fish does the organ attain so great a relative size. Other fishes have the organ close to the gut, attached to the liver by certain extremely fine ducts. The bonito has the gall-bladder stretched alongside the gut and equalling it in length, and often a double fold of it. Others have the organ in the region of the gut; in some cases far off, in others near; as the fishing-frog, the elops, the synagris, the muraena, and the sword-fish. Often animals of the same species show this diversity of position; as, for instance, some congers are found with the organ attached close to the liver, and others with it detached from and below it. The case is much the same with birds: that is, some have the gall-bladder close to the stomach, and others close to the gut, as the pigeon, the raven, the quail, the swallow, and the sparrow; some have it near at once to the liver and to the stomach as the aegocephalus; others have it near at once to the liver and the gut, as the falcon and the kite.

16

Again, all viviparous quadrupeds are furnished with kidneys and a bladder. Of the ovipara that are not quadrupedal there is no instance known of an animal, whether fish or bird, provided with these organs. Of the ovipara that are quadrupedal, the turtle alone is provided with these organs of a magnitude to correspond with the other organs of the animal. In the turtle the kidney resembles the same organ in the ox; that is to say, it looks like one single organ composed of a number of small ones. [The bison also resembles the ox in all its internal parts.]

17

With all animals that are furnished with these parts, the parts are similarly situated, and with the exception of man, the heart is in the middle; in man, however, as has been observed, **507a** the heart is placed a little to the left-hand side. In all animals the pointed end of the heart turns frontwards; only in fish it would at first sight seem otherwise, for the pointed end is turned not towards the breast, but towards the head and the mouth. And (in fish) the apex is attached to a tube just where the right and left gills meet together. There are other ducts extending from the heart to each of the gills, greater in the greater fish, lesser in the lesser; but in the large fishes the duct at the pointed end of the heart is a tube, white-coloured and exceedingly thick. Fishes in some few cases have an oesophagus, as the conger and the eel; and in these the organ is small.

In fishes that are furnished with an undivided liver, the organ lies entirely on the right side; where the liver is cloven from the root, the larger half of the organ is on the right side: for in some fishes the two parts are detached from one another, without any coalescence at the root, as is the case with the dog-fish. And there is also a species of hare in what is named the Fig district, near Lake Bolbe, and elsewhere, which animal might be taken to have two livers owing to the length of the connecting ducts, similar to the structure in the lung of birds.

The spleen in all cases, when normally placed, is on the left-hand side, and the kidneys also lie in the same position in all creatures that possess them. There have been known instances of quadrupeds under dissection, where the spleen was on the right hand and the liver on the left; but all such cases are regarded as supernatural.

In all animals the wind-pipe extends to the lung, and the manner how, we shall discuss hereafter; and the oesophagus, in all that have the organ, extends through the midriff into the stomach. For, by the way, as has been observed, most fishes have no oesophagus, but the stomach is united directly with the mouth, so that in some cases when big fish are pursuing little ones, the stomach tumbles forward into the mouth.

All the afore-mentioned animals have a stomach, and one similarly situated, that is to say, situated directly under the midriff; and they have a gut connected therewith and closing at the outlet of the residuum and at what is termed the 'rectum'. However, animals present diversities in the structure of their stomachs. In the first place, of the viviparous quadrupeds, such of the horned animals as are not equally furnished with teeth in both jaws are furnished with four such chambers. These animals, by the way, are those that are said to chew the cud. In these animals the oesophagus extends from the mouth downwards along the **507b** lung, from the midriff to the big stomach (or paunch); and this stomach is rough inside and semi-partitioned. And connected with it near to the entry of the oesophagus is what from its appearance is termed the 'reticulum' (or honeycomb bag); for outside it is like the stomach, but inside it resembles a netted cap; and the reticulum is a great deal smaller than the stomach. Connected with this is the 'echinus' (or many-plies), rough inside and laminated, and of about the same size as the reticulum. Next after this comes what is called the 'enystrum' (or abomasum), larger and longer than the echinus, furnished inside with numerous folds or ridges, large and smooth. After all this comes the gut.

Such is the stomach of those quadrupeds that are horned and have an unsymmetrical dentition; and these animals differ one from another in the shape and size of the parts, and in the fact of the oesophagus reaching the stomach centralwise in some cases and sideways in others. Animals that are furnished equally with teeth in both jaws have one stomach; as man, the pig, the dog, the bear, the lion, the wolf. [The Thos, by the by, has all its internal organs similar to the wolf's.]

All these, then have a single stomach, and after that the gut; but the stomach in some is comparatively large, as in the pig and bear, and the stomach of the pig has a few smooth folds or ridges; others have a much smaller stomach, not much bigger than the gut, as the lion, the dog, and man. In the other animals the shape of the stomach varies in the direction of one or other of those already mentioned; that is, the stomach in some animals resembles that of the pig; in others that of the dog, alike with the larger animals and the smaller ones. In all these animals diversities occur in regard to the size, the shape, the thickness or the thinness of the stomach, and also in regard to the place where the oesophagus opens into it.

There is also a difference in structure in the gut of the two groups of animals above mentioned (those with unsymmetrical and those with symmetrical dentition) in size, in thickness, and in foldings.

The intestines in those animals whose jaws are unequally furnished with teeth are in all cases the larger, for the animals themselves are larger than those in the other category; for very few of them are small, and no single one of the horned animals is very small. And some possess appendages (or caeca) to the gut, but no animal that has not incisors in both jaws has a straight gut.

The elephant has a gut constricted into chambers, so constructed that the animal appears to have four stomachs; in it the food is found, but there is no distinct and separate receptacle. Its viscera resemble those of the pig, **508a** only that the liver is four times the size of that of the ox, and the other viscera in like proportion, while the spleen is comparatively small.

Much the same may be predicated of the properties of the stomach and the gut in oviparous quadrupeds, as in the land tortoise, the turtle, the lizard, both crocodiles, and, in fact, in all animals of the like kind; that is to say, their stomach is one and simple, resembling in some cases that of the pig, and in other cases that of the dog.

The serpent genus is similar and in almost all respects furnished similarly to the saurians among oviparous land animals, if one could only imagine these saurians to be increased in length and to be devoid of legs. That is to say, the serpent is coated with tessellated scutes, and resembles the saurian in its back and belly; only, by the way, it has no testicles, but, like fishes, has two ducts converging into one, and an ovary long and bifurcate. The rest of its internal organs are identical with those of the saurians, except that, owing to the narrowness and length of the animal, the viscera are correspondingly narrow and elongated, so that they are apt to escape recognition from the similarities in shape. Thus, the windpipe of the creature is exceptionally long, and the oesophagus is longer still, and the windpipe commences so close to the mouth that the tongue appears to be underneath it; and the windpipe seems to project over the tongue, owing to the fact that the tongue draws back into a sheath and does not remain in its place as in other animals. The tongue, moreover, is thin and long and black, and can be protruded to a great distance. And both serpents and saurians have this altogether exceptional property in the tongue, that it is forked at the outer extremity, and this property is the more marked in the serpent, for the tips of his tongue are as thin as hairs. The seal, also, by the way, has a split tongue.

The stomach of the serpent is like a more spacious gut, resembling the stomach of the dog; then comes the gut, long, narrow, and single to the end. The heart is situated close to the pharynx, small and kidney-shaped; and for this reason the organ might in some cases appear not to have the pointed end turned towards the breast. Then comes the lung, single, and articulated with a membranous passage, very long, and quite detached from the heart. The liver is long and simple; the spleen is short and round: as is the case in both respects with the saurians. Its gall resembles that of the fish; the water-snakes have it beside **508b** the liver, and the other snakes have it usually beside the gut. These creatures are all saw-toothed. Their ribs are as numerous as the days of the month; in other words, they are thirty in number.

Some affirm that the same phenomenon is observable with serpents as with swallow-chicks; in other words, they say that if you prick out a serpent's eyes they will grow again. And further, the tails of saurians and of serpents, if they be cut off, will grow again.

With fishes the properties of the gut and stomach are similar; that is, they have a stomach single and simple, but variable in shape according to species. For in some cases the stomach is gut-shaped, as with the scarus, or parrot-fish; which fish, by the way, appears to be the only fish that chews the cud. And the whole length of the gut is simple, and if it have a reduplication or kink it loosens out again into a simple form.

An exceptional property in fishes and in birds for the most part is the being furnished with gut-appendages or caeca. Birds have them low down and few in number. Fishes have them high up about the stomach, and sometimes numerous, as in the goby, the galeos, the perch, the scorpaena, the citharus, the red mullet, and the sparus; the cestreus or grey mullet has several of them on one side of the belly, and on the other side only one. Some fish possess these appendages but only in small numbers, as the hepatus and the glaucus; and, by the way, they are few also in the dorado. These fishes differ also from one another within the same species, for in the dorado one individual has many and another few. Some fishes are entirely without the part, as the majority of the selachians. As for all the rest, some of them have a few and some a great many. And in all cases where the gut-appendages are found in fish, they are found close up to the stomach.

In regard to their internal parts birds differ from other animals and from one another. Some birds, for instance, have a crop in front of the stomach, as the barn-door cock, the cushat, the pigeon, and the partridge; and the crop consists of a large hollow skin, into which the food first enters and where it lies undigested. Just where the crop leaves the oesophagus it is somewhat narrow; by and by it broadens out, but where it communicates with the stomach it narrows down again. The stomach (or gizzard) in most birds is fleshy and hard, and inside is a strong skin which comes away from the fleshy part. Other birds have no crop, but instead of it an oesophagus wide and roomy, either all the way or in **509a** the part leading to the stomach, as with the daw, the raven, and the carrion-crow. The quail also has the oesophagus widened out at the lower extremity, and in the aegocephalus and the owl the organ is slightly broader at the bottom than at the top. The duck, the goose, the gull, the catarrhactes, and the great bustard have the oesophagus wide and roomy from one end to the other, and the same applies to a great many other birds. In some birds there is a portion of the stomach that resembles a crop, as in the kestrel. In the case of small birds like the swallow and the sparrow neither the oesophagus nor the crop is wide, but the stomach is long. Some few have neither a crop nor a dilated oesophagus, but the latter is exceedingly long, as in long-necked birds, such as the porphyrio, and, by the way, in the case of all these birds the excrement is unusually moist. The quail is exceptional in regard to these organs, as compared with other birds; in other words, it has a crop, and at the same time its oesophagus is wide and spacious in front of the stomach, and the crop is at some distance, relatively to its size, from the oesophagus at that part.

Further, in most birds, the gut is thin, and simple when loosened out. The gut-appendages or caeca in birds, as has been observed, are few in number, and are not situated high up, as in fishes, but low down towards the extremity of the gut. Birds, then, have caeca—not all, but the greater part of them, such as the barn-door cock, the partridge, the duck, the night-raven, [the localus,] the ascalaphus, the goose, the swan, the great bustard, and the owl. Some of the little birds also have these appendages; but the caeca in their case are exceedingly minute, as in the sparrow.

BOOK III

I

Now that we have stated the magnitudes, the properties, and the relative differences of the other internal organs, it remains for us to treat of the organs that contribute to generation. These organs in the female are in all cases internal; in the male they present numerous diversities.

In the blooded animals some males are altogether devoid of testicles, and some have the organ but situated internally; and of those males that have the organ internally situated, some have it close to the loin in the neighbourhood of the kidney and others close to the belly. Other males have the organ situated externally. In the case of these last, the penis is in some cases attached to the belly, whilst in oth-
509b ers it is loosely suspended, as is the case also with the testicles; and, in the cases where the penis is attached to the belly, the attachment varies accordingly as the animal is emprosthuretic or opisthuretic.

No fish is furnished with testicles, nor any other creature that has gills, nor any serpent whatever: nor, in short, any animal devoid of feet, save such only as are viviparous within themselves. Birds are furnished with testicles, but these are internally situated, close to the loin. The case is similar with oviparous quadrupeds, such as the lizard, the tortoise and the crocodile; and among the viviparous animals this peculiarity is found in the hedgehog. Others among those creatures that have the organ internally situated have it close to the belly, as is the case with the dolphin amongst animals devoid of feet, and with the elephant among viviparous quadrupeds. In other cases these organs are externally conspicuous.

We have already alluded to the diversities observed in the attachment of these organs to the belly and the adjacent region; in other words, we have stated that in some cases the testicles are tightly fastened back, as in the pig and its allies, and that in others they are freely suspended, as in man.

Fishes, then, are devoid of testicles, as has been stated, and serpents also. They are furnished, however, with two ducts connected with the midriff and running on to either side of the backbone, coalescing into a single duct above the outlet of the residuum, and by 'above' the outlet I mean the region near to the spine. These ducts in the rutting season get filled with the genital fluid, and, if the ducts be squeezed, the sperm oozes out white in colour. As to the differences observed in male fishes of diverse species, the reader should consult my treatise on Anatomy, and the subject will be hereafter more fully discussed when we describe the specific character in each case.[1]

The males of oviparous animals, whether biped or quadruped, are in all cases furnished with testicles close to the loin underneath the midriff. With some animals the organ is whitish, in others somewhat of a sallow hue; in all cases it is entirely enveloped with minute and delicate veins. From each of the two testicles extends a duct, and, as in the case of fishes, the two ducts coalesce into one above the outlet of the residuum. This constitutes the penis, which organ in the case of small ovipara is inconspicuous; but in the case of the larger ovipara, as in the goose and the like, the organ becomes quite visible just after copulation.

The ducts in the case of fishes and in biped and quadruped ovipara are attached to the loin under the stomach and the gut, in betwixt them and the great vein, from which ducts or blood-vessels extend, one to each of the two testicles. And just as with fishes the male sperm is found in the seminal ducts, and the
510a ducts become plainly visible at the rutting season and in some instances become invisible after the season is passed, so also is it with the testicles of birds; before the breeding

[1] v. 5.

season the organ is small in some birds and quite invisible in others, but during the season the organ in all cases is greatly enlarged. This phenomenon is remarkably illustrated in the ring-dove and the partridge, so much so that some people are actually of opinion that these birds are devoid of the organ in the winter-time.

Of male animals that have their testicles placed frontwards, some have them inside, close to the belly, as the dolphin; some have them outside, exposed to view, close to the lower extremity of the belly. These animals resemble one another thus far in respect to this organ; but they differ from one another in this fact, that some of them have their testicles situated separately by themselves, while others, which have the organ situated externally, have them enveloped in what is termed the scrotum.

Again, in all viviparous animals furnished with feet the following properties are observed in the testicles themselves. From the aorta there extend vein-like ducts to the head of each of the testicles, and another two from the kidneys; these two from the kidneys are supplied with blood, while the two from the aorta are devoid of it. From the head of the testicle alongside of the testicle itself is a duct, thicker and more sinewy than the other just alluded to—a duct that bends back again at the end of the testicle to its head; and from the head of each of the two testicles the two ducts extend until they coalesce in front at the penis. The duct that bends back again and that which is in contact with the testicle are enveloped in one and the same membrane, so that, until you draw aside the membrane, they present all the appearance of being a single undifferentiated duct. Further, the duct in contact with the testicle has its moist content qualified by blood, but to a comparatively less extent than in the case of the ducts higher up which are connected with the aorta; in the ducts that bend back towards the tube of the penis, the liquid is white-coloured. There also runs a duct from the bladder, opening into the upper part of the canal, around which lies, sheathwise, what is called the 'penis'.

All these descriptive particulars may be regarded by the light of the accompanying diagram; wherein the letter *A* marks the starting-point of the ducts that extend from the aorta; the letters *KK* mark the heads of the testicles and the ducts descending thereunto; the ducts extending from these along the testicles are marked ΩΩ; the ducts turning back, in which is the white fluid, are marked *BB;* the penis Δ; the bladder *E;* and the testicles ΨΨ.

[By the way, when the testicles are cut off or removed, the ducts draw upwards by contrac-

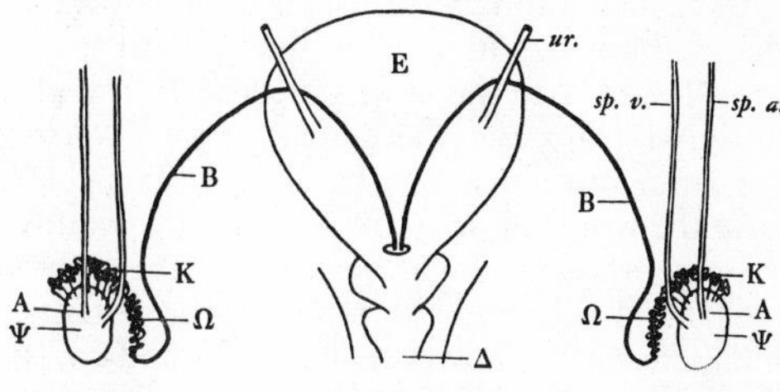

E κύστις. ΨΨ ὄρχεις. Δ αἰδοῖον.
AA τῶν πόρων ἀρχὴ τῶν ἀπὸ τῆς ἀορτῆς.
KK κεφαλαὶ τῶν ὄρχεων καὶ οἱ καθήκοντες πόροι.
ΩΩ οἱ πόροι οἱ ἀπὸ τούτων πρὸς τῷ ὄρχει καθήμενοι.
BB οἱ ἀνακάμπτοντες, ἐν οἷς ἡ ὑγρότης ἡ λευκή.
sp. v. sp. a. spermatic vein and artery:
ur. ureters.

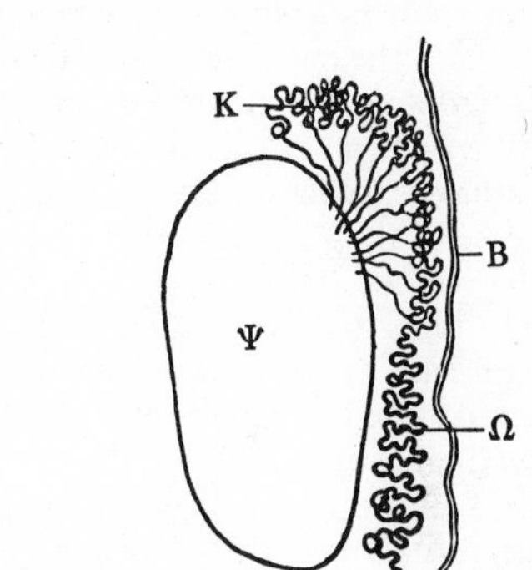

Ψ testis. K caput epididymis.
Ω corpus epididymis. B vas deferens.

Υ ὑστέρα ἡ δελφύς (uterus)
M μήτρα (orifice of the uterus).
KK κεράτια (uterine horns).
EE ἑλιγμοί (Fallopian tubes).

510b tion. Moreover, when male animals are young, their owner sometimes destroys the organ in them by attrition; sometimes they castrate them at a later period. And I may here add, that a bull has been known to serve a cow immediately after castration, and actually to impregnate her.]

So much then for the properties of testicles in male animals.

In female animals furnished with a womb, the womb is not in all cases the same in form or endowed with the same properties, but both in the vivipara and the ovipara great diversities present themselves. In all creatures that have the womb close to the genitals, the womb is two-horned, and one horn lies to the right-hand side and the other to the left; its commencement, however, is single, and so is the orifice, resembling in the case of the most numerous and largest animals a tube composed of much flesh and gristle. Of these parts one is termed the *hystera* or *delphys,* whence is derived the word ἀδελφός, and the other part, the tube or orfice, is termed *metra.* In all biped or quadruped vivipara the womb is in all cases below the midriff, as in man, the dog, the pig, the horse, and the ox; the same is the case also in all horned animals. At the extremity of the so-called *ceratia,* or horns, the wombs of most animals have a twist or convolution.

In the case of those ovipara that lay eggs externally, the wombs are not in all cases similarly situated. Thus the wombs of birds are close to the midriff, and the wombs of fishes down below, just like the wombs of biped and quadruped vivipara, only that, in the case of the fish, the wombs are delicately formed, membranous, and elongated; so much so that in extremely small fish, each of the two bifurcated parts looks like a single egg, and those fishes whose egg is described as crumbling would appear to have inside them a pair of eggs, whereas in reality each of the two sides consists not of one but of many eggs, and this accounts for their breaking up into so many particles.

The womb of birds has the lower and tubular portion fleshy and firm, and the part close to the midriff membranous and exceedingly thin and fine: so thin and fine that the eggs might seem to be outside the womb altogether. In the larger birds the membrane is more distinctly visible, and, if inflated through the tube, lifts and swells out; in the smaller birds all these parts are more indistinct.

The properties of the womb are similar in oviparous quadrupeds, as the tortoise, the lizard, the frog and the like; for the tube below **511a** is single and fleshy, and the cleft portion with the eggs is at the top close to the midriff. With animals devoid of feet that are internally oviparous and viviparous externally, as is the case with the dogfish and the other so-called Selachians (and by this title we designate such creatures destitute of feet and furnished with gills as are viviparous), with these animals the womb is bifurcate, and beginning down below it extends as far as the midriff, as in the case of birds. There is also a narrow part between the two horns running up as far as the midriff, and the eggs are engendered here and above at the origin of the midriff; afterwards they pass into the wider space and turn from eggs into young animals. However, the differences in respect to the wombs of these fishes as compared with others of their own species or with fishes in general, would be more satisfactorily studied in their various forms in specimens under dissection.

The members of the serpent genus also present divergencies either when compared with the above-mentioned creatures or with one another. Serpents as a rule are oviparous, the viper being the only viviparous member of the genus. The viper is, previously to external parturition, oviparous internally; and owing to this perculiarity the properties of the womb in the viper are similar to those of the womb in the selachians. The womb of the serpent is long, in keeping with the body, and starting below from a single duct extends continuously on both sides of the spine, so as to give the impression of thus being a separate duct on each side of the spine, until it reaches the midriff, where the eggs are engendered in a row; and these eggs are laid not one by one, but all strung together. [And all animals that are viviparous both internally and externally have the womb situated above the stomach, and all the ovipara underneath, near to the loin. Animals that are viviparous externally and internally oviparous present an intermediate arrangement; for the underneath portion of the womb, in which the eggs are, is placed near to the loin, but the part about the orifice is above the gut.]

Further, there is the following diversity observable in wombs as compared with one another: namely that the females of horned nonambidental animals are furnished with cotyledons in the womb when they are pregnant, and such is the case, among ambidentals, with the hare, the mouse, and the bat; whereas all other animals that are ambidental, viviparous, and furnished with feet, have the womb quite smooth, and in their case the attachment of the embryo is to the womb itself and not to any cotyledon inside it.

The parts, then, in animals that are not homogeneous with themselves and uniform in their texture, both parts external and parts internal, have the properties above assigned to them.

2

511b In sanguineous animals the homogeneous or uniform part most universally found is the blood, and its habitat the vein; next in degree of universality, their analogues, lymph and fibre, and, that which chiefly constitutes the frame of animals, flesh and whatsoever in the several parts is analogous to flesh; then bone, and parts that are analogous to bone, as fish-bone and gristle; and then, again, skin, membrane, sinew, hair, nails, and whatever corresponds to these; and, furthermore, fat, suet, and the excretions: and the excretions are dung, phlegm, yellow bile, and black bile.

Now, as the nature of blood and the nature of the veins have all the appearance of being primitive, we must discuss their properties first of all, and all the more as some previous writers have treated them very unsatisfactorily. And the cause of the ignorance thus manifested is the extreme difficulty experienced in the way of observation. For in the dead bodies of animals the nature of the chief veins is undiscoverable, owing to the fact that they collapse at once when the blood leaves them; for the blood pours out of them in a stream, like liquid out of a vessel, since there is no blood separately situated by itself, except a little in the heart, but it is all lodged in the veins. In *living* animals it is impossible to inspect these parts, for of their very nature they are situated inside the body and out of sight. For this reason anatomists who have carried on their investigations on dead bodies in the dissecting-room have failed to discover the chief roots of the veins, while those who have narrowly inspected bodies of living men reduced to extreme attenuation have arrived at conclusions regarding the origin of the veins from the manifestations visible externally. Of these investigators, Syennesis, the physician of Cyprus, writes as follows:—

'The big veins run thus[1]:—from the navel across the loins, along the back, past the lung, in under the breasts; one from right to left, and the other from left to right; that from the left, through the liver to the kidney and the testicle, that from the right, to the spleen and kidney and testicle, and from thence to the penis.'

Diogenes of Apollonia[2] writes thus:—

'The veins in man are as follows:—There are two veins pre-eminent in magnitude. These extend through the belly along the backbone, one to right, one to left; either one to the leg on its own side, and upwards to the head, past the collar bones, through the throat. From these, veins extend all over the body, from **512a** that on the right hand to the right side and from that on the left hand to the left side; the most important ones, two in number, to the heart in the region of the backbone; other two a little higher up through the chest in underneath the armpit, each to the hand on its own side: of these two, one being termed the vein *splenitis,* and the other the vein *hepatitis*. Each of the pair splits at its extremity; the one branches in the direction of the thumb and the other in the direction of the palm; and from these run off a number of minute veins branching off to the fingers and to all parts of the hand. Other veins, more minute, extend from the main veins; from that on the right towards the liver, from that on the left towards the spleen and the kidneys. The veins that run to the legs split at the juncture of the legs with the trunk and extend right down the thigh. The largest of these goes down the thigh at the back of it, and can be discerned and traced as a big one; the second one runs inside the thigh, not quite as big as the one just mentioned. After this they pass on along the knee to the shin and the foot (as the upper veins were described as passing towards the hands), and arrive at the sole of the foot, and from thence continue to the toes. Moreover, many delicate veins separate off from the great veins towards the stomach and towards the ribs.

'The veins that run through the throat to the head can be discerned and traced in the neck as large ones; and from each one of the two, where it terminates, there branch off a number of veins to the head; some from the right side towards the left, and some from the left side towards the right; and the two veins terminate near to each of the two ears. There is another pair of veins in the neck running along the big vein on either side, slightly less in size than the pair just spoken of, and

[1] Ps. Hippocr. *de Nat. Ossium*, ix. p. 174 (Littré); i. p. 507 (Kühn).

[2] Cf. Littré, i. p. 220, ix. p. 163. *Oeuvres complêts d'-Hippocrates*, edited by Littré.

with these the greater part of the veins in the head are connected. This other pair runs through the throat inside; and from either one of the two there extend veins in underneath the shoulder blade and towards the hands; and these appear alongside the veins splenitis and hepatitis as another pair of veins smaller in size. When there is a pain near the surface of the body, the physician lances these two latter veins; but when the pain is within and in the region of the stomach he lances the veins splenitis and hepatitis. And from these, other veins depart to run below the breasts.

512b 'There is also another pair running on each side through the spinal marrow to the testicles, thin and delicate. There is, further, a pair running a little underneath the cuticle through the flesh to the kidneys, and these with men terminate at the testicle, and with women at the womb. These veins are termed the spermatic veins. The veins that leave the stomach are comparatively broad just as they leave; but they become gradually thinner, until they change over from right to left and from left to right.

'Blood is thickest when it is imbibed by the fleshy parts; when it is transmitted to the organs above-mentioned, it becomes thin, warm, and frothy.'

3

Such are the accounts given by Syennesis and Diogenes. Polybus[1] writes to the following effect:—

'There are four pairs of veins. The first extends from the back of the head, through the neck on the outside, past the backbone on either side, until it reaches the loins and passes on to the legs, after which it goes on through the shins to the outer side of the ankles and on to the feet. And it is on this account that surgeons, for pains in the back and loin, bleed in the ham and in the outer side of the ankle. Another pair of veins runs from the head, past the ears, through the neck; which veins are termed the jugular veins. This pair goes on inside along the backbone, past the muscles of the loins, on to the testicles, and onwards to the thighs, and through the inside of the hams and through the shins down to the inside of the ankles and to the feet; and for this reason, surgeons, for pains in the muscles of the loins and in the testicles, bleed on the hams and the inner side of the ankles. The third pair extends from the temples, through the neck, in underneath the shoulder-blades, into the lung; those from right to left going in underneath the breast and on to the spleen and the kidney; those from left to right running from the lung in underneath the breast and into the liver and the kidney; and both terminate in the fundament. The fourth pair extend from the front part of the head and the eyes in

513a underneath the neck and the collar-bones; from thence they stretch on through the upper part of the upper arms to the elbows and then through the fore-arms on to the wrists and the jointings of the fingers, and also through the lower part of the upper-arms to the armpits, and so on, keeping above the ribs, until one of the pair reaches the spleen and the other reaches the liver; and after this they both pass over the stomach and terminate at the penis.'

The above quotations sum up pretty well the statements of all previous writers. Furthermore, there are some writers on Natural History who have not ventured to lay down the law in such precise terms as regards the veins, but who all alike agree in assigning the head and the brain as the starting-point of the veins. And in this opinion they are mistaken.

The investigation of such a subject, as has been remarked, is one fraught with difficulties; but, if any one be keenly interested in the matter, his best plan will be to allow his animals to starve to emaciation, then to strangle them on a sudden, and thereupon to prosecute his investigations.

We now proceed to give particulars regarding the properties and functions of the veins. There are two blood-vessels in the thorax by the backbone, and lying to its inner side; and of these two the larger one is situated to the front, and the lesser one is to the rear of it; and the larger is situated rather to the right-hand side of the body, and the lesser one to the left; and by some this vein is termed the 'aorta', from the fact that even in dead bodies part of it is observed to be full of air. These blood-vessels have their origins in the heart, for they traverse the other viscera, in whatever direction they happen to run, without in any way losing their distinctive characteristic as blood-vessels, whereas the heart is as it were a part of them (and that too more in respect to the frontward and larger one of the two), owing to the fact that these two veins are

[1] The following quotation appears in the treatise *de Nat. Hom.* (vi. p. 58 L, i. p. 364 K), which treatise is accordingly ascribed to Polybus (cf. K. i. p. cxlvii), and in the composite treatise *de Nat. Oss.* (ix. p. 174 L, i. p. 506 K), cf. Littré, ix. p. 162.

above and below, with the heart lying midway.

The heart in all animals has cavities inside it. In the case of the smaller animals even the largest of the chambers is scarcely discernible; the second larger is scarcely discernible in animals of medium size; but in the largest animals all three chambers are distinctly seen. In the heart then (with its pointed end directed frontwards, as has been observed) the largest of the three chambers is on the right-hand side and highest up; the least one is on the left-hand side; and the medium-sized one lies in betwixt the other two; and the largest one of the three chambers is a great deal larger than either of the two others. All three, however, are connected with passages leading in the direction of the lung, but all these communications are indistinctly discernible by reason of their minuteness, except one.

513b The great blood-vessel, then, is attached to the biggest of the three chambers, the one that lies uppermost and on the right-hand side; it then extends right through the chamber, coming out as blood-vessel again; just as though the cavity of the heart were a part of the vessel, in which the blood broadens its channel as a river that widens out in a lake. The aorta is attached to the middle chamber; only, by the way, it is connected with it by a much narrower pipe.

The great blood-vessel then passes through the heart [and runs from the heart into the aorta]. The great vessel looks as though made of membrane or skin, while the aorta is narrower than it, and is very sinewy; and as it stretches away to the head and to the lower parts it becomes exceedingly narrow and sinewy.

First of all, then, upwards from the heart there stretches a part of the great blood-vessel towards the lung and the attachment of the aorta, a part consisting of a large undivided vessel. But there split off from it two parts; one towards the lung and the other towards the backbone and the last vertebra of the neck.

The vessel, then, that extends to the lung, as the lung itself is duplicate, divides at first into two; and then extends along by every pipe and every perforation, greater along the greater ones, lesser along the less, so continuously that it is impossible to discern a single part wherein there is not perforation and vein; for the extremities are indistinguishable from their minuteness, and in point of fact the whole lung appears to be filled with blood. The branches of the blood-vessels lie above the tubes that extend from the windpipe. And that vessel which extends to the vertebra of the neck and the backbone, stretches back again along the backbone; as Homer represents in the lines[1] :—

⟨Antilochus, as Thoön turned him round⟩,
Transpierc'd his back with a dishonest wound;
The hollow vein that to the neck extends,
Along the chine, the eager javelin rends.

From this vessel there extend small blood-vessels past each rib and each vertebra; and at the vertebra above the kidneys the vessel bifurcates. And in the above way the parts branch off from the great blood-vessel.

But up above all these, from that part which is connected with the heart, the entire vein branches off in two directions. For its branches extend to the sides and to the collarbones, and then pass on, in men through the armpits to the arms, in quadrupeds to the fore-
514a legs, in birds to the wings, and in fishes to the upper or pectoral fins. The trunks of these veins, where they first branch off, are

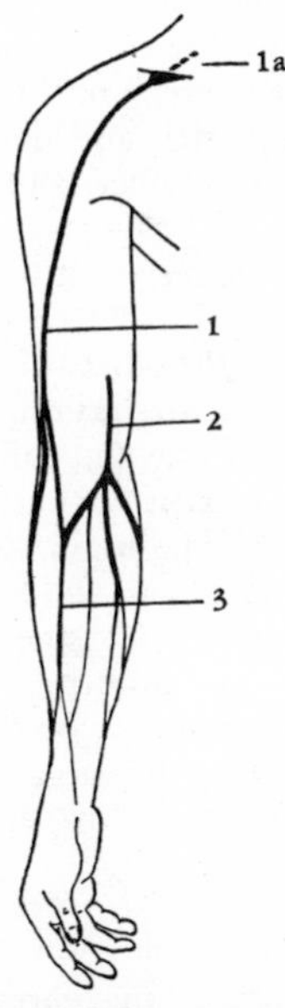

Superficial veins of the arm. 1. *Vena cephalica*, sometimes prolonged (1*a*) to enter the external jugular. 2. *Vena basilica s. hepatitis*, passing upwards to join the *venae cosmites brachiales*. 3. *Vena media superficialis*.

[1] *Iliad*, XIII. 546.

called the 'jugular' veins; and, where they branch off to the neck [from the great vein] they run alongside the windpipe; and, occasionally, if these veins are pressed externally,

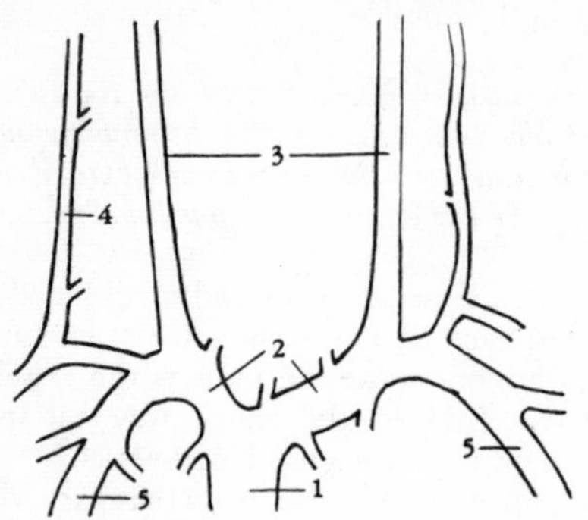

The Superior vena cava and its branches. 1. Sup. vena cava. 2. Innominate veins. 3. Int. jugular. 4. Ext. jugular. 5. Subclavian.

men, though not actually choked, become insensible, shut their eyes, and fall flat on the ground. Extending in the way described and keeping the windpipe in betwixt them, they pass on until they reach the ears at the junction of the lower jaw with the skull. Hence again they branch off into four veins, of which one bends back and descends through the neck and the shoulder, and meets the previous branching off of the vein at the bend of the arm, while the rest of it terminates at the hand and fingers.

Each vein of the other pair stretches from the region of the ear to the brain, and branches off in a number of fine and delicate veins into the so-called meninx, or membrane, which surrounds the brain. The brain itself in all animals is destitute of blood, and no vein, great or small, holds its course therein. But of the remaining veins that branch off from the last-mentioned vein some envelop the head, others close their courses in the organs of sense and at the roots of the teeth in veins exceedingly fine and minute.

4

And in like manner the parts of the lesser one of the two chief blood-vessels, designated the aorta, branch off, accompanying the branches from the big vein; only that, in regard to the aorta, the passages are less in size, and the branches very considerably less than are those of the great vein. So much for the veins as observed in the regions above the heart.

The part of the great vein that lies underneath the heart extends, freely suspended, right through the midriff, and is united both to the aorta and the backbone by slack membranous communications. From it one vein, short and wide, extends through the liver, and from it a number of minute veins branch off into the liver and disappear. From the vein that passes through the liver two branches separate off, of which one terminates in the diaphragm or so-called midriff, and the other
514b runs up again through the armpit into the right arm and unites with the other veins at the inside of the bend of the arm; and it is in consequence of this local connexion that, when the surgeon opens this vein in the forearm, the patient is relieved of certain pains in the liver; and from the left-hand side of it there extends a short but thick vein to the spleen and the little veins branching off it disappear in that organ. Another part branches off from the left-hand side of the great vein, and ascends, by a course similar to the course recently described, into the left arm; only that the ascending vein in the one case is the vein that traverses the liver, while in this case it is distinct from the vein that runs into the spleen. Again, other veins branch off from the big vein; one to the omentum, and another to the pancreas, from which vein run a number of veins through the mesentery. All these veins coalesce in a single large vein, along the entire gut and stomach to the oesophagus; about these parts there is a great ramification of branch veins.

As far as the kidneys, each of the two remaining undivided, the aorta and the big vein extend; and here they get more closely attached to the backbone, and branch off, each of the two, into a Λ shape, and the big vein gets to the rear of the aorta. But the chief attachment of the aorta to the backbone takes place in the region of the heart; and the attachment is effected by means of minute and sinewy vessels. The aorta, just as it draws off from the heart, is a tube of considerable volume, but, as it advances in its course, it gets narrower and more sinewy. And from the aorta there extend veins to the mesentery just like the veins that extend thither from the big vein, only that the branches in the case of the aorta are considerably less in magnitude; they are, indeed, narrow and fibrillar, and they end in delicate hollow fibre-like veinlets.

There is no vessel that runs from the aorta into the liver or the spleen.

From each of the two great blood-vessels there extend branches to each of the two flanks, and both branches fasten on to the bone. Vessels also extend to the kidneys from the big vein and the aorta; only that they do not open into the cavity of the organ, but their ramifications penetrate into its substance. From the aorta run two other ducts to the bladder, firm and continuous; and there are other ducts from the hollow of the kidneys, in no way communicating with the big vein. From the centre of each of the two kidneys springs a hollow sinewy vein, running along **515a** the backbone right through the loins; by and by each of the two veins first disappears in its own flank, and soon afterwards reappears stretching in the direction of the flank. The extremities of these attach to the bladder, and also in the male to the penis and in the female to the womb. From the big vein no vein extends to the womb, but the organ is connected with the aorta by veins numerous and closely packed.

Furthermore, from the aorta and the great vein at the points of divarication there branch off other veins. Some of these run to the groins —large hollow veins—and then pass on down through the legs and terminate in the feet and toes. And, again, another set run through the groins and the thighs cross-garter fashion, from right to left and from left to right, and unite in the hams with the other veins.

In the above description we have thrown light upon the course of the veins and their points of departure.

In all sanguineous animals the case stands as here set forth in regard to the points of departure and the courses of the chief veins. But the description does not hold equally good for the entire vein-system in all these animals. For, in point of fact, the organs are not identically situated in them all; and, what is more, some animals are furnished with organs of which other animals are destitute. At the same time, while the description so far holds good, the proof of its accuracy is not equally easy in all cases, but is easiest in the case of animals of considerable magnitude and supplied abundantly with blood. For in little animals and those scantily supplied with blood, either from natural and inherent causes or from a prevalence of fat in the body, thorough accuracy in investigation is not equally attainable; for in the latter of these creatures the passages get clogged, like water-channels choked with slush; and the others have a few minute fibres to serve instead of veins. But in all cases the big vein is plainly discernible, even in creatures of insignificant size.

5

The sinews of animals have the following properties. For these also the point of origin is the heart; for the heart has sinews within itself in the largest of its three chambers, and the aorta is a sinew-like vein; in fact, at its extremity it is actually a sinew, for it is there no longer hollow, and is stretched like the sinews where they terminate at the jointings of the bones. Be it remembered, however, that the sinews do not proceed in unbroken sequence from one point of origin, as do the blood-vessels.

For the veins have the shape of the entire body, like a sketch of a mannikin; in such a way that the whole frame seems to be filled up **515b** with little veins in attenuated subjects—for the space occupied by flesh in fat individuals is filled with little veins in thin ones—whereas the sinews are distributed about the joints and the flexures of the bones. Now, if the sinews were derived in unbroken sequence from a common point of departure, this continuity would be discernible in attenuated specimens.

In the ham, or the part of the frame brought into full play in the effort of leaping, is an important system of sinews; and another sinew, a double one, is that called 'the tendon', and others are those brought into play when a great effort of physical strength is required; that is to say, the epitonos or back-stay and the shoulder-sinews. Other sinews, devoid of specific designation, are situated in the region of the flexures of the bones; for all the bones that are attached to one another are bound together by sinews, and a great quantity of sinews are placed in the neighbourhood of all the bones. Only, by the way, in the head there is no sinew; but the head is held together by the sutures of the bones.

Sinew is fissile lengthwise, but crosswise it is not easily broken, but admits of a considerable amount of hard tension. In connexion with sinews a liquid mucus is developed, white and glutinous, and the organ, in fact, is sustained by it and appears to be substantially composed of it. Now, vein may be submitted to the actual cautery, but sinew, when submitted to such action, shrivels up altogether; and, if sinews be cut asunder, the severed parts will not again cohere. A feeling of numbness is incidental only to parts of the frame where sinew is situated.

There is a very extensive system of sinews connected severally with the feet, the hands, the ribs, the shoulder-blades, the neck, and the arms.

All animals supplied with blood are furnished with sinews; but in the case of animals that have no flexures to their limbs, but are, in fact, destitute of either feet or hands, the sinews are fine and inconspicuous; and so, as might have been anticipated, the sinews in the fish are chiefly discernible in connexion with the fin.

6

The *ines* (or fibrous connective tissue) are a something intermediate between sinew and vein. Some of them are supplied with fluid, the lymph; and they pass from sinew to vein and from vein to sinew. There is another kind of *ines* or fibre that is found in blood, but not in the blood of all animals alike. If this fibre be left in the blood, the blood will coagulate; if it be removed or extracted, the blood is found to be incapable of coagulation. While, however, this fibrous matter is found in the blood of the great majority of animals, it is not found in all. For instance, we fail to find it in the blood of the deer, the roe, the antelope, and some other animals; and, owing to this deficiency of the fibrous tissue, the blood of these animals does not coagulate to the extent observed in the blood of other animals. The **516a** blood of the deer coagulates to about the same extent as that of the hare: that is to say, the blood in either case coagulates, but not into a stiff or jelly-like substance, like the blood of ordinary animals, but only into a flaccid consistency like that of milk which is not subjected to the action of rennet. The blood of the antelope admits of a firmer consistency in coagulation; for in this respect it resembles, or only comes a little short of, the blood of sheep. Such are the properties of vein, sinew, and fibrous tissue.

7

The bones in animals are all connected with one single bone, and are interconnected, like the veins, in one unbroken sequence; and there is no instance of a bone standing apart by itself. In all animals furnished with bones, the spine or backbone is the point of origin for the entire osseous system. The spine is composed of vertebrae, and it extends from the head down to the loins. The vertebrae are all perforated, and, above, the bony portion of the head is connected with the topmost vertebrae, and is designated the 'skull'. And the serrated lines on the skull are termed 'sutures'.

The skull is not formed alike in all animals. In some animals the skull consists of one single undivided bone, as in the case of the dog; in others it is composite in structure, as in man; and in the human species the suture is circular in the female, while in the male it is made up of three separate sutures, uniting above in three-corner fashion; and instances have been known of a man's skull being devoid of suture altogether. The skull is composed not of four bones, but of six; two of these are in the region of the ears, small in comparison with the other four. From the skull extend the jaws, constituted of bone. [Animals in general move the lower jaw; the river-crocodile is the only animal that moves the upper one.] In the jaws is the tooth-system; and the teeth are constituted of bone, and are half-way perforated; and the bone in question is the only kind of bone which it is found impossible to grave with a graving tool.

On the upper part of the course of the backbone are the collar-bones and the ribs. The chest rests on ribs; and these ribs meet together, whereas the others do not; for no animal has bone in the region of the stomach. Then come the shoulder-bones, or blade-bones, and the arm-bones connected with these, and the bones in the hands connected with the bones of the arms. With animals that have forelegs, the osseous system of the foreleg resembles that of the arm in man.

Below the level of the backbone, after the haunch-bone, comes the hip-socket; then the leg-bones, those in the thighs and those in the shins, which are termed colenes or limb-bones, **516b** a part of which is the ankle, while a part of the same is the so-called 'plectrum' in those creatures that have an ankle; and connected with these bones are the bones in the feet.

Now, with all animals that are supplied with blood and furnished with feet, and are at the same time viviparous, the bones do not differ greatly one from another, but only in the way of relative hardness, softness, or magnitude. A further difference, by the way, is that in one and the same animal certain bones are supplied with marrow, while others are destitute of it. Some animals might on casual observation appear to have no marrow whatsoever in their bones: as is the case with the lion, owing to his having marrow only in small amount, poor and thin, and in very few bones; for marrow is found in his thigh and arm-bones. The bones of the lion are exceptionally hard; so hard, in fact, that if they are rubbed hard against one another they emit sparks like flint-stones. The dolphin has bones, and not fish-spine.

Of the other animals supplied with blood, some differ but little, as is the case with birds; others have systems analogous, as fishes; for viviparous fishes, such as the cartilaginous species, are gristle-spined, while the ovipara have a spine which corresponds to the backbone in quadrupeds. This exceptional property has been observed in fishes, that in some of them there are found delicate spines scattered here and there throughout the fleshy parts. The serpent is similarly constructed to the fish; in other words, his backbone is spinous. With oviparous quadrupeds, the skeleton of the larger ones is more or less osseous; of the smaller ones, more or less spinous. But all sanguineous animals have a backbone of either one kind or other: that is, composed either of bone or of spine.

The other portions of the skeleton are found in some animals and not found in others, but the presence or the absence of this and that part carries with it, as a matter of course, the presence or the absence of the bones or the spines corresponding to this or that part. For animals that are destitute of arms and legs cannot be furnished with limb-bones: and in like manner with animals that have the same parts, but yet have them unlike in form; for in these animals the corresponding bones differ from one another in the way of relative excess or relative defect, or in the way of analogy taking the place of identity. So much for the osseous or spinous systems in animals.

8

Gristle is of the same nature as bone, but differs from it in the way of relative excess or relative defect. And just like bone, cartilage also, if cut, does not grow again. In terrestrial viviparous sanguinea the gristle formations are unperforated, and there is no marrow in them as there is in bones; in the selachia, however—for, be it observed, they are gristle-spined **517a** —there is found [in the case of the flat species], in the region of the backbone, a gristle-like substance analogous to bone, and in this gristle-like substance there is a liquid resembling marrow. In viviparous animals furnished with feet, gristle formations are found in the region of the ears, in the nostrils, and around certain extremities of the bones.

9

Furthermore, there are parts of other kinds, neither identical with, nor altogether diverse from, the parts above enumerated: such as nails, hooves, claws, and horns; and also, by the way, beaks, such as birds are furnished with—all in the several animals that are furnished therewithal. All these parts are flexible and fissile; but bone is neither flexible nor fissile, but frangible.

And the colours of horns and nails and claw and hoof follow the colour of the skin and the hair. For according as the skin of an animal is black, or white, or of medium hue, so are the horns, the claws, or the hooves, as the case may be, of hue to match. And it is the same with nails. The teeth, however, follow after the bones. Thus in black men, such as the Aethiopians and the like, the teeth and bones are white, but the nails are black, like the whole of the skin.

Horns in general are hollow at their point of attachment to the bone which juts out from the head inside the horn, but they have a solid portion at the tip, and they are simple and undivided in structure. In the case of the stag alone of all animals the horns are solid throughout, and ramify into branches (or antlers). And, whereas no other animal is known to shed its horns, the deer sheds its horns annually, unless it has been castrated; and with regard to the effects of castration in animals we shall have much to say hereafter.[1] Horns attach rather to the skin than to the bone; which will account for the fact that there are found in Phrygia and elsewhere cattle that can move their horns as freely as their ears.

Of animals furnished with nails—and, by the way, all animals have nails that have toes, and toes that have feet, except the elephant; and the elephant has toes undivided and slightly articulated, but has no nails whatsoever—of animals furnished with nails, some are straight-nailed, like man; others are crooked-**517b** nailed, as the lion among animals that walk, and the eagle among animals that fly.

[1] ix. 50 (631b).

10

The following are the properties of hair and of parts analogous to hair, and of skin or hide. All viviparous animals furnished with feet have hair; all oviparous animals furnished with feet have horn-like tessellates; fishes, and fishes only, have scales—that is, such oviparous fishes as have the crumbling egg or roe. For of the lanky fishes, the conger has no such egg, nor the muraena, and the eel has no egg at all.

The hair differs in the way of thickness and fineness, and of length, according to the locality of the part in which it is found, and according to the quality of skin or hide on which it grows. For, as a general rule, the thicker the hide, the harder and the thicker is the hair; and the hair is inclined to grow in abundance and to a great length in localities of the bodies hollow and moist, if the localities be fitted for the growth of hair at all. The facts are similar in the case of animals whether coated with scales or with tessellates. With soft-haired animals the hair gets harder with good feeding, and with hard-haired or bristly animals it gets softer and scantier from the same cause. Hair differs in quality also according to the relative heat or warmth of the locality: just as the hair in man is hard in warm places and soft in cold ones. Again, straight hair is inclined to be soft, and curly hair to be bristly.

11

Hair is naturally fissile, and in this respect it differs in degree in diverse animals. In some animals the hair goes on gradually hardening into bristle until it no longer resembles hair but spine, as in the case of the hedgehog. And in like manner with the nails; for in some animals the nail differs as regards solidity in no way from bone.

Of all animals man has the most delicate skin: that is, if we take into consideration his relative size. In the skin or hide of all animals there is a mucous liquid, scanty in some animals and plentiful in others, as, for instance, in the hide of the ox; for men manufacture glue out of it. (And, by the way, in some cases glue is manufactured from fishes also.) The skin, when cut, is in itself devoid of sensation; and this is especially the case with the skin on the head, owing to there being no flesh between it and the skull. And wherever the skin **518a** is quite by itself, if it be cut asunder, it does not grow together again, as is seen in the thin part of the jaw, in the prepuce, and the eyelid. In all animals the skin is one of the parts that extends continuous and unbroken, and it comes to a stop only where the natural ducts pour out their contents, and at the mouth and nails.

All sanguineous animals, then, have skin; but not all such animals have hair, save only under the circumstances described above. The hair changes its colour as animals grow old, and in man it turns white or grey. With animals, in general, the change takes place, but not very obviously, or not so obviously as in the case of the horse. Hair turns grey from the point backwards to the roots. But, in the majority of cases, grey hairs are white from the beginning; and this is a proof that greyness of hair does not, as some believe to be the case, imply withering or decrepitude, for no part is brought into existence in a withered or decrepit condition.

In the eruptive malady called the white-sickness all the hairs get grey; and instances have been known where the hair became grey while the patients were ill of the malady, whereas the grey hairs shed off and black ones replaced them on their recovery. [Hair is more apt to turn grey when it is kept covered than when exposed to the action of the outer air.] In men, the hair over the temples is the first to turn grey, and the hair in the front grows grey sooner than the hair at the back; and the hair on the pubes is the last to change colour.

Some hairs are congenital, others grow after the maturity of the animal; but this occurs in man only. The congenital hairs are on the head, the eyelids, and the eyebrows; of the later growths the hairs on the pubes are the first to come, then those under the armpits, and, thirdly, those on the chin; for, singularly enough, the regions where congenital growths and the subsequent growths are found are equal in number. The hair on the head grows scanty and sheds out to a greater extent and sooner than all the rest. But this remark applies only to hair in front; for no man ever gets bald at the back of his head. Smoothness on the top of the head is termed 'baldness', but smoothness on the eyebrows is denoted by a special term which means 'forehead-baldness'; and neither of these conditions of baldness supervenes in a man until he shall have come under the influence of sexual passion. For no boy ever gets bald, no woman, and no castrated man. In fact, if a man be castrated before reaching puberty, the later growths of hair never come at all; and, if the operation take place subsequently, the after-growths, and these only, shed off; or, rather, two of the growths shed off, but not that on the pubes.

Women do not grow hairs on the chin; except that a scanty beard grows on some women after the monthly courses have stopped; and a similar phenomenon is observed at times in priestesses in Caria, but these cases are looked upon as portentous with regard to coming events. The other after-growths are **518b** found in women, but more scanty and sparse. Men and women are at times born constitutionally and congenitally incapable of the after-growths; and individuals that are destitute even of the growth upon the pubes are constitutionally impotent.

Hair as a rule grows more or less in length as the wearer grows in age; chiefly the hair on the head, then that in the beard, and fine hair grows longest of all. With some people as they grow old the eyebrows grow thicker, to such an extent that they have to be cut off; and this growth is owing to the fact that the eyebrows are situated at a conjuncture of bones, and these bones, as age comes on, draw apart and exude a gradual increase of moisture or rheum. The eyelashes do not grow in size, but they shed when the wearer comes first under the influence of sexual feelings, and shed all the quicker as this influence is the more powerful; and these are the last hairs to grow grey.

Hairs if plucked out before maturity grow again; but they do not grow again if plucked out afterwards. Every hair is supplied with a mucous moisture at its root, and immediately after being plucked out it can lift light articles if it touch them with this mucus.

Animals that admit of diversity of colour in the hair admit of a similar diversity to start with in the skin and in the cuticle of the tongue.

In some cases among men the upper lip and the chin is thickly covered with hair, and in other cases these parts are smooth and the cheeks are hairy; and, by the way, smooth-chinned men are less inclined than bearded men to baldness.

The hair is inclined to grow in certain diseases, especially in consumption, and in old age, and after death; and under these circumstances the hair hardens concomitantly with its growth, and the same duplicate phenomenon is observable in respect of the nails.

In the case of men of strong sexual passions the congenital hairs shed the sooner, while the hairs of the after-growths are the quicker to come. When men are afflicted with varicose veins they are less inclined to take on baldness; and if they be bald when they become thus afflicted, they have a tendency to get their hair again.

If a hair be cut, it does not grow at the point of section; but it gets longer by growing upward from below. In fishes the scales grow harder and thicker with age, and when the animal gets emaciated or is growing old the scales grow harder. In quadrupeds as they grow old the hair in some and the wool in others gets deeper but scantier in amount: and the hooves or claws get larger in size; and the same is the case with the beaks of birds. The claws also increase in size, as do also the nails.

12

519a With regard to winged animals, such as birds, no creature is liable to change of colour by reason of age, excepting the crane. The wings of this bird are ash-coloured at first, but as it grows old the wings get black. Again, owing to special climatic influences, as when unusual frost prevails, a change is sometimes observed to take place in birds whose plumage is of one uniform colour; thus, birds that have dusky or downright black plumage turn white or grey, as the raven, the sparrow, and the swallow; but no case has ever yet been known of a change of colour from white to black. [Further, most birds change the colour of their plumage at different seasons of the year, so much so that a man ignorant of their habits might be mistaken as to their identity.] Some animals change the colour of their hair with a change in their drinking-water, for in some countries the same species of animal is found white in one district and black in another. And in regard to the commerce of the sexes, water in many places is of such peculiar quality that rams, if they have intercourse with the female after drinking it, beget black lambs, as is the case with the water of the Psychrus (so-called from its coldness), a river in the district of Assyritis in the Chalcidic Peninsula, on the coast of Thrace; and in Antandria there are two rivers of which one makes the lambs white and the other black. The river Scamander also has the reputation of making lambs yellow, and that is the reason, they say, why Homer designates it the 'Yellow River'.[1] Animals as a general rule have no hair on their internal surfaces, and, in regard to their extremities, they have hair on the upper, but not on the lower side.

The hare, or dasypod, is the only animal known to have hair inside its mouth and underneath its feet. Further, the so-called mouse-whale instead of teeth has hairs in its mouth resembling pigs' bristles. Hairs after being cut grow at the bottom but not at the top; if feathers be cut off, they grow neither at top nor bottom, but shed and fall out. Further, the bee's wing will not grow again after being plucked off, nor will the wing of any creature that has undivided wings. Neither will the sting grow again if the bee lose it, but the creature will die of the loss.

13

In all sanguineous animals membranes are found. And membrane resembles a thin close-textured skin, but its qualities are different, as it admits neither of cleavage nor of extension. Membrane envelops each one of the bones and each one of the viscera, both in the larger and the smaller animals; though in the **519b** smaller animals the membranes are indiscernible from their extreme tenuity and minuteness. The largest of all the membranes are the two that surround the brain, and of these two the one that lines the bony skull is stronger and thicker than the one that envelops the brain; next in order of magnitude comes the membrane that encloses the heart. If membrane be bared and cut asunder it will not grow together again, and the bone thus stripped of its membrane mortifies.

14

The omentum or caul, by the way, is membrane. All sanguineous animals are furnished with this organ; but in some animals the organ is supplied with fat, and in others it is devoid of it. The omentum has both its starting-point and its attachment, with ambidental vivipara, in the centre of the stomach, where the stomach has a kind of suture; in non-ambidental vivipara it has its starting-point and attachment in the chief of the ruminating stomachs.

15

The bladder also is of the nature of membrane, but of membrane peculiar in kind, for it is extensile. The organ is not common to all animals, but, while it is found in all the vivipara, the tortoise is the only oviparous animal that is furnished therewithal. The bladder, like ordinary membrane, if cut asunder will not grow together again, unless the section be just at the commencement of the urethra: except indeed in very rare cases, for instances of healing have been known to occur. After death, the organ passes no liquid excretion; but in life, in addition to the normal liquid excretion, it passes at times dry excretion also, which turns into stones in the case of sufferers from that malady. Indeed, instances have been known of concretions in the bladder so shaped as closely to resemble cockle-shells.

Such are the properties, then, of vein, sinew and skin, of fibre and membrane, of hair, nail, claw and hoof, of horns, of teeth, of beak, of gristle, of bones, and of parts that are analogous to any of the parts here enumerated.

16

Flesh, and that which is by nature akin to it in sanguineous animals, is in all cases situated in between the skin and the bone, or the substance analogous to bone; for just as spine is a counterpart of bone, so is the flesh-like substance of animals that are constructed on a spinous system the counterpart of the flesh of animals constructed on an osseous one.

Flesh can be divided asunder in any direction, not lengthwise only as is the case with sinew and vein. When animals are subjected to emaciation the flesh disappears, and the creatures become a mass of veins and fibres; when they are over fed, fat takes the place of flesh. **520a** Where the flesh is abundant in an animal, its veins are somewhat small and the blood abnormally red; the viscera also and the stomach are diminutive; whereas with animals whose veins are large the blood is somewhat black, the viscera and the stomach are large, and the flesh is somewhat scanty. And animals with small stomachs are disposed to take on flesh.

17

Again, fat and suet differ from one another. Suet is frangible in all directions and congeals if subjected to extreme cold, whereas fat can melt but cannot freeze or congeal; and soups made of the flesh of animals supplied with fat do not congeal or coagulate, as is found with horse-flesh and pork; but soups made

[1] *Iliad*, xx. 74.

from the flesh of animals supplied with suet do coagulate, as is seen with mutton and goat's flesh. Further, fat and suet differ as to their localities: for fat is found between the skin and flesh, but suet is found only at the limit of the fleshy parts. Also, in animals supplied with fat the omentum or caul is supplied with fat, and it is supplied with suet in animals supplied with suet. Moreover, ambidental animals are supplied with fat, and non-ambidentals with suet.

Of the viscera the liver in some animals becomes fatty, as, among fishes, is the case with the selachia, by the melting of whose livers an oil is manufactured. These cartilaginous fish themselves have no free fat at all in connexion with the flesh or with the stomach. The suet in fish is fatty, and does not solidify or congeal. All animals are furnished with fat, either intermingled with their flesh, or apart. Such as have no free or separate fat are less fat than others in stomach and omentum, as the eel; for it has only a scanty supply of suet about the omentum. Most animals take on fat in the belly, especially such animals as are little in motion.

The brains of animals supplied with fat are oily, as in the pig; of animals supplied with suet, parched and dry. But it is about the kidneys more than any other viscera that animals are inclined to take on fat; and the right kidney is always less supplied with fat than the left kidney, and, be the two kidneys ever so fat, there is always a space devoid of fat in between the two. Animals supplied with suet are specially apt to have it about the kidneys, and especially the sheep; for this animal is apt to die from its kidneys being entirely enveloped. Fat or suet about the kidney is superinduced by overfeeding, as is found at Leontini
520b in Sicily; and consequently in this district they defer driving out sheep to pasture until the day is well on, with the view of limiting their food by curtailment of the hours of pasture.

18

The part around the pupil of the eye is fatty in all animals, and this part resembles suet in all animals that possess such a part and that are not furnished with hard eyes.

Fat animals, whether male or female, are more or less unfitted for breeding purposes. Animals are disposed to take on fat more when old than when young, and especially when they have attained their full breadth and their full length and are beginning to grow depthways.

19

And now to proceed to the consideration of the blood. In sanguineous animals blood is the most universal and the most indispensable part; and it is not an acquired or adventitious part, but it is a consubstantial part of all animals that are not corrupt or moribund. All blood is contained in a vascular system, to wit, the veins, and is found nowhere else, excepting in the heart. Blood is not sensitive to touch in any animal, any more than the excretions of the stomach; and the case is similar with the brain and the marrow. When flesh is lacerated, blood exudes, if the animal be alive and unless the flesh be gangrened. Blood in a healthy condition is naturally sweet to the taste, and red in colour, blood that deteriorates from natural decay or from disease more or less black. Blood at its best, before it undergoes deterioration from either natural decay or from disease, is neither very thick nor very thin. In the living animal it is always liquid and warm, but, on issuing from the body, it coagulates in all cases except in the case of the deer, the roe, and the like animals; for, as a general rule, blood coagulates unless the fibres be extracted. Bull's blood is the quickest to coagulate.

Animals that are internally and externally viviparous are more abundantly supplied with blood than the sanguineous ovipara. Animals that are in good condition, either from natural causes or from their health having been attended to, have the blood neither too abundant—as creatures just after drinking have the liquid inside them in abundance—nor again very scanty, as is the case with animals when exceedingly fat. For animals in this condition have pure blood, but very little of it, and the fatter an animal gets the less becomes its supply of blood; for whatsoever is fat is destitute of blood.
521a A fat substance is incorruptible, but blood and all things containing it corrupt rapidly, and this property characterizes especially all parts connected with the bones. Blood is finest and purest in man; and thickest and blackest in the bull and the ass, of all vivipara. In the lower and the higher parts of the body blood is thicker and blacker than in the central parts.

Blood beats or palpitates in the veins of all animals alike all over their bodies, and blood is the only liquid that permeates the entire frames of living animals, without exception and at all times, as long as life lasts. Blood is developed first of all in the heart of animals before the body is differentiated as a whole. If blood be removed or if it escape in any considerable quantity, animals fall into a faint or swoon; if it be removed or if it escape in an exceedingly large quantity they die. If the blood get exceedingly liquid, animals fall sick; for the blood then turns into something like ichor, or a liquid so thin that it at times has been known to exude through the pores like sweat. In some cases blood, when issuing from the veins, does not coagulate at all, or only here and there. Whilst animals are sleeping the blood is less abundantly supplied near the exterior surfaces, so that, if the sleeping creature be pricked with a pin, the blood does not issue as copiously as it would if the creature were awake. Blood is developed out of ichor by coction, and fat in like manner out of blood. If the blood get diseased, haemorrhoids may ensue in the nostril or at the anus, or the veins may become varicose. Blood, if it corrupt in the body, has a tendency to turn into pus, and pus may turn into a solid concretion.

Blood in the female differs from that in the male, for, supposing the male and female to be on a par as regards age and general health, the blood in the female is thicker and blacker than in the male; and with the female there is a comparative superabundance of it in the interior. Of all female animals the female in man is the most richly supplied with blood, and of all female animals the menstruous discharges are the most copious in woman. The blood of these discharges under disease turns into flux. Apart from the menstrual discharges, the female in the human species is less subject to diseases of the blood than the male.

Women are seldom afflicted with varicose veins, with haemorrhoids, or with bleeding at the nose, and, if any of these maladies supervene, the menses are imperfectly discharged.

Blood differs in quantity and appearance according to age; in very young animals it resembles ichor and is abundant, in the old it is thick and black and scarce, and in middle-aged animals its qualities are intermediate. In old
521b animals the blood coagulates rapidly, even blood at the surface of the body; but this is not the case with young animals. Ichor is, in fact, nothing else but unconcocted blood: either blood that has not yet been concocted, or that has become fluid again.

20

We now proceed to discuss the properties of marrow; for this is one of the liquids found in certain sanguineous animals. All the natural liquids of the body are contained in vessels: as blood in veins, marrow in bones [and other moistures in membranous structures of the skin or gut].

In young animals the marrow is exceedingly sanguineous, but, as animals grow old, it becomes fatty in animals supplied with fat, and suet-like in animals with suet. All bones, however, are not supplied with marrow, but only the hollow ones, and not all of these. For of the bones in the lion some contain no marrow at all, and some are only scantily supplied therewith; and that accounts, as was previously observed,[1] for the statement made by certain writers that the lion is marrowless. In the bones of pigs it is found in small quantities; and in the bones of certain animals of this species it is not found at all.

These liquids, then, are nearly always congenital in animals, but milk and sperm come at a later time. Of these latter, that which, whensoever it is present, is secreted in all cases ready-made, is the milk; sperm, on the other hand, is not secreted out in all cases, but in some only, as in the case of what are designated *thori* in fishes.

Whatever animals have milk, have it in their breasts. All animals have breasts that are internally and externally viviparous, as for instance all animals that have hair, as man and the horse; and the cetaceans, as the dolphin, the porpoise, and the whale—for these animals have breasts and are supplied with milk. Animals that are oviparous or only externally viviparous have neither breasts nor milk, as the fish and the bird.

All milk is composed of a watery serum called 'whey', and a consistent substance called curd (or cheese); and the thicker the milk, the more abundant the curd. The milk, then, of non-ambidentals coagulates, and that is why cheese is made of the milk of such animals under domestication; but the milk of ambidentals does not coagulate, nor their fat either, and the milk is thin and sweet. Now the camel's milk is the thinnest, and that of the human species next after it, and that of the ass next again, but cow's milk is the thickest.

[1] Cf. 516b 7.

Milk does not coagulate under the influence of **522a** cold, but rather runs to whey; but under the influence of heat it coagulates and thickens. As a general rule milk only comes to animals in pregnancy. When the animal is pregnant milk is found, but for a while it is unfit for use, and then after an interval of usefulness it becomes unfit for use again. In the case of female animals not pregnant a small quantity of milk has been procured by the employment of special food, and cases have been actually known where women advanced in years on being submitted to the process of milking have produced milk, and in some cases have produced it in sufficient quantities to enable them to suckle an infant.

The people that live on and about Mount Oeta take such she-goats as decline the male and rub their udders hard with nettles to cause an irritation amounting to pain; hereupon they milk the animals, procuring at first a liquid resembling blood, then a liquid mixed with purulent matter, and eventually milk, as freely as from females submitting to the male.

As a general rule, milk is not found in the male of man or of any other animal, though from time to time it has been found in a male; for instance, once in Lemnos a he-goat was milked by its dugs (for it has, by the way, two dugs close to the penis), and was milked to such effect that cheese was made of the produce, and the same phenomenon was repeated in a male of its own begetting. Such occurrences, however, are regarded as supernatural and fraught with omen as to futurity, and in point of fact when the Lemnian owner of the animal inquired of the oracle, the god informed him that the portent foreshadowed the acquisition of a fortune. With some men, after puberty, milk can be produced by squeezing the breasts; cases have been known where on their being subjected to a prolonged milking process a considerable quantity of milk has been educed.

In milk there is a fatty element, which in clotted milk gets to resemble oil. Goat's milk is mixed with sheep's milk in Sicily, and wherever sheep's milk is abundant. The best milk for clotting is not only that where the cheese is most abundant, but that also where the cheese is driest.

Now some animals produce not only enough milk to rear their young, but a superfluous amount for general use, for cheese-making and for storage. This is especially the case with the sheep and the goat, and next in degree with the cow. Mare's milk, by the way, and milk of the she-ass are mixed in with Phrygian cheese. And there is more cheese in cow's milk than in goat's milk; for graziers tell us that from nine gallons of goat's milk they can get nineteen cheeses at an obol apiece, and from the same amount of cow's milk, thirty. Other animals give only enough of milk to rear their young withal, and no superfluous amount and none fitted for cheese-making, as is the case with all animals that have more than **522b** two breasts or dugs; for with none of such animals is milk produced in superabundance or used for the manufacture of cheese.

The juice of the fig and rennet are employed to curdle milk. The fig-juice is first squeezed out into wool; the wool is then washed and rinsed, and the rinsing put into a little milk, and if this be mixed with other milk it curdles it. Rennet is a kind of milk, for it is found in the stomach of the animal while it is yet suckling.

21

Rennet then consists of milk with an admixture of fire, which comes from the natural heat of the animal, as the milk is concocted. All ruminating animals produce rennet, and, of ambidentals, the hare. Rennet improves in quality the longer it is kept; and cow's rennet, after being kept a good while, and also hare's rennet, is good for diarrhoea, and the best of all rennet is that of the young deer.

In milk-producing animals the comparative amount of the yield varies with the size of the animal and the diversities of pasturage. For instance, there are in Phasis small cattle that in all cases give a copious supply of milk, and the large cows in Epirus yield each one daily some nine gallons of milk, and half of this from each pair of teats, and the milker has to stand erect, stooping forward a little, as otherwise, if he were seated, he would be unable to reach up to the teats. But, with the exception of the ass, all the quadrupeds in Epirus are of large size, and relatively, the cattle and the dogs are the largest. Now large animals require abundant pasture, and this country supplies just such pasturage, and also supplies diverse pasture grounds to suit the diverse seasons of the year. The cattle are particularly large, and likewise the sheep of the so-called Pyrrhic breed, the name being given in honour of King Pyrrhus.

Some pasture quenches milk, as Median grass or lucerne, and that especially in ruminants; other feeding renders it copious, as cytisus and vetch; only, by the way, cytisus in flower is not recommended, as it has burning properties, and vetch is not good for pregnant kine, as it causes increased difficulty in parturition. However, beasts that have access to good feeding, as they are benefited thereby in regard to pregnancy, so also being well nourished produce milk in plenty. Some of the leguminous plants bring milk in abundance, as for instance, a large feed of beans with the ewe, the common she-goat, the cow, and the small **523a** she-goat; for this feeding makes them drop their udders. And, by the way, the pointing of the udder to the ground before parturition is a sign of there being plenty of milk a-coming.

Milk remains for a long time in the female, if she be kept from the male and be properly fed, and, of quadrupeds, this is especially true of the ewe; for the ewe can be milked for eight months. As a general rule, ruminating animals give milk in abundance, and milk fitted for cheese manufacture. In the neighbourhood of Torone cows run dry for a few days before calving, and have milk all the rest of the time. In women, milk of a livid colour is better than white for nursing purposes; and swarthy women give healthier milk than fair ones. Milk that is richest in cheese is the most nutritious, but milk with a scanty supply of cheese is the more wholesome for children.

22

All sanguineous animals eject sperm. As to what, and how, it contributes to generation, these questions will be discussed in another treatise. Taking the size of his body into account, man emits more sperm than any other animal. In hairy-coated animals the sperm is sticky, but in other animals it is not so. It is white in all cases, and Herodotus is under a misapprehension when he states that the Aethiopians eject black sperm.

Sperm issues from the body white and consistent, if it be healthy, and after quitting the body becomes thin and black. In frosty weather it does not coagulate, but gets exceedingly thin and watery both in colour and consistency; but it coagulates and thickens under the influence of heat. If it be long in the womb before issuing out, it comes more than usually thick; and sometimes it comes out dry and compact. Sperm capable of impregnating or of fructification sinks in water; sperm incapable of producing that result dissolves away. But there is no truth in what Ctesias has written about the sperm of the elephant.

BOOK IV

I

We have now treated, in regard to blooded animals of the parts they have in common and of the parts peculiar to this genus or that, and of the parts both composite and simple, **523b** whether without or within. We now proceed to treat of animals devoid of blood. These animals are divided into several genera.

One genus consists of so-called 'molluscs'; and by the term 'mollusc' we mean an animal that, being devoid of blood, has its flesh-like substance outside, and any hard structure it may happen to have, inside—in this respect resembling the red-blooded animals,—such as the genus of the cuttle-fish.

Another genus is that of the malacostraca. These are animals that have their hard structure outside, and their soft or flesh-like substance inside, and the hard substance belonging to them has to be crushed rather than shattered; and to this genus belongs the crawfish and the crab.

A third genus is that of the ostracoderms or 'testaceans'. These are animals that have their hard substance outside and their flesh-like substance within, and their hard substance can be shattered but not crushed; and to this genus belong the snail and the oyster.

The fourth genus is that of insects; and this genus comprehends numerous and dissimilar species. Insects are creatures that, as the name implies, have nicks either on the belly or on the back, or on both belly and back, and have no one part distinctly osseous and no one part distinctly fleshy, but are throughout a something intermediate between bone and flesh; that is to say, their body is hard all through, inside and outside. Some insects are wingless, such as the *iulus* and the centipede; some are winged, as the bee, the cockchafer, and the wasp; and the same kind is in some cases both winged and wingless, as the ant and the glow-worm.

In molluscs the external parts are as follows: in the first place, the so-called feet; secondly,

and attached to these, the head; thirdly, the mantle-sac, containing the internal parts, and incorrectly designated by some writers the head; and, fourthly, fins round about the sac. In all molluscs the head is found to be between the feet and the belly. All molluscs are furnished with eight feet, and in all cases these feet are severally furnished with a double row of suckers, with the exception of one single species of poulpe or octopus. The sepia, the small calamary and the large calamary have an exceptional organ in a pair of long arms or tentacles, having at their extremities a portion rendered rough by the presence of two rows of suckers; and with these arms or tentacles they apprehend their food and draw it into their mouths, and in stormy weather they cling by them to a rock and sway about in the rough water like ships lying at anchor. They
524a swim by the aid of the fins that they have about the sac. In all cases their feet are furnished with suckers.

The octopus, by the way, uses his feelers either as feet or hands; with the two which stand over his mouth he draws in food, and the last of his feelers he employs in the act of copulation; and this last one, by the way, is extremely sharp, is exceptional as being of a whitish colour, and at its extremity is bifurcate; that is to say, it has an additional something on the rachis, and by rachis is meant the smooth surface or edge of the arm on the far side from the suckers.

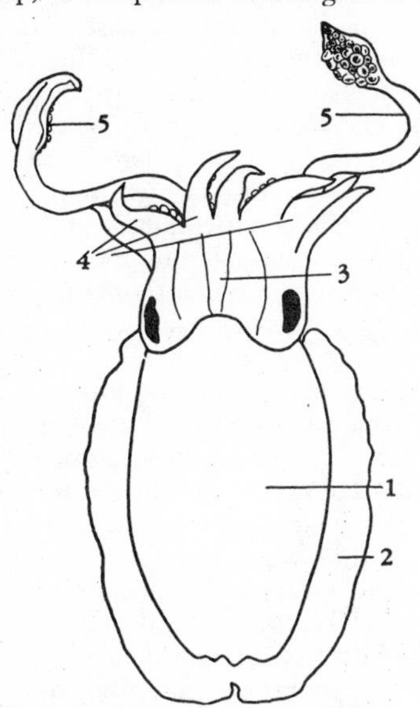

Sepia officinalis (σηπία)

1. Body or 'mantle-sac' (κύτος). 2 Fin (πτερύγιον). 3. Head (κεφαλή). 4. Arms (πόδες). 5. Tentacles (προβοσκίδες). 4, 5. (πλεκτάναι).

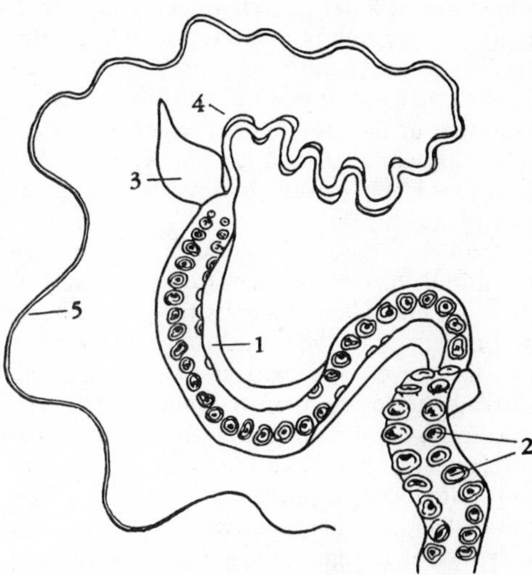

Hectocotylized arm of an Octopus (*Philonexis catenulatus* = *Ocythoe tuberculata*).

1. The arm (ῥάχις). 2. Suckers (κοτυληδόνες). 3. Sac of penis (τι (?) ἐπὶ τῇ ῥάχει). 4. (ἄκρον δικρόον). 5. 'Penis' (τὸ ὀξύ).

In front of the sac and over the feelers they have a hollow tube, by means of which they discharge any sea-water that they may have taken into the sac of the body in the act of receiving food by the mouth. They can shift the tube from side to side, and by means of it they discharge the black liquid peculiar to the animal.

Stretching out its feet, it swims obliquely in the direction of the so-called head, and by this mode of swimming it can see in front, for its eyes are at the top, and in this attitude it has its mouth at the rear. The 'head', while the creature is alive, is hard, and looks as though it were inflated. It apprehends and retains objects by means of the under-surface of its arms, and the membrane in between its feet is kept at full tension; if the animal get on to the sand it can no longer retain its hold.

There is a difference between the octopus and the other molluscs above mentioned: the body of the octopus is small, and his feet are long, whereas in the others the body is large and the feet short; so short, in fact, that they cannot walk on them. Compared with one another, the teuthis, or calamary, is long-shaped, and the sepia flat-shaped; and of the calamaries the so-called teuthus is much bigger than the teuthis; for teuthi have been found as much as five ells long. Some sepiae attain a length of two ells, and the feelers of the octopus are sometimes as long, or even longer. The species teuthus is not a numerous one; the teuthus differs from the teuthis in shape; that is, the sharp extremity of the teuthus is broader than that of the other, and, further, the encircling fin goes all round the trunk, whereas it is in part lacking in the teuthis; both animals are pelagic.

In all cases the head comes after the feet, in the middle of the feet that are called arms or
524b feelers. There is here situated a mouth, and two teeth in the mouth; and above these two large eyes, and betwixt the eyes a small cartilage enclosing a small brain; and within the mouth it has a minute organ of a fleshy nature, and this it uses as a tongue, for no other tongue does it possess. Next after this, on the outside, is what looks like a sac; the flesh of which it is made is divisible, not in long straight strips, but in annular flakes; and all molluscs have a cuticle around this flesh. Next after or at the back of the mouth comes a long and narrow oesophagus, and close after that a crop or craw, large and spherical, like that of a bird; then comes the stomach, like the

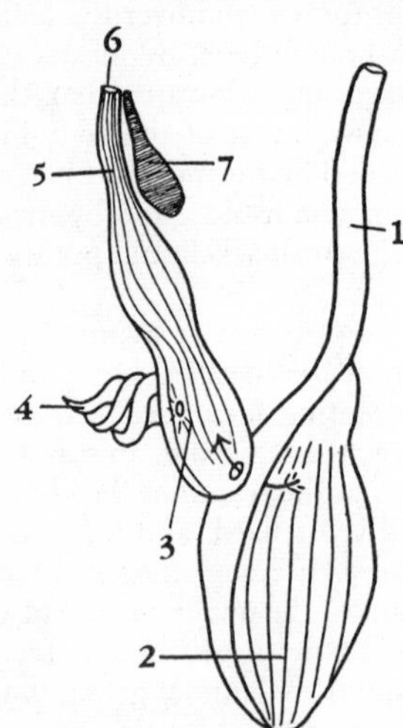

Alimentary canal of *Todarodes sagittatus* (? τεῦθος).

1. Oesophagus (στόμαχος). 2. Crop (πρόλοβος). 3. Stomach (κοιλία). 4. Caecum (τὸ ἔσχατον (?) τῆς κοιλίας, ὅμοιον τῇ ἐν τοῖς κήρυξιν ἑλίκῃ). 5. Intestine (ἔντερον). 6. Anus (ἔξοδος). 7. Ink-sac (θόλος ἐν χιτῶνι ὑμενώδει).

fourth stomach in ruminants; and the shape of it resembles the spiral convolution in the trumpet-shell; from the stomach there goes back again, in the direction of the mouth, a thin gut, and the gut is thicker than the oesophagus.

Molluscs have no viscera, but they have what is called a mytis, and on it a vessel containing a thick black juice; in the sepia or cuttle-fish this vessel is the largest, and this juice is most abundant. All molluscs, when frightened, discharge such a juice, but the discharge is most copious in the cuttle-fish. The mytis, then, is situated under the mouth, and the oesophagus runs through it; and down below at the point to which the gut extends is the vesicle of the black juice, and the animal has the vesicle and the gut enveloped in one and the same membrane, and by the same orifice discharges both the black juice and the residuum. The animals have also certain hair-like or furry growths in their bodies.

In the sepia, the teuthis, and the teuthus the hard parts are within, towards the back of the body; those parts are called in one the sepium, and in the other the 'sword'. They differ from one another, for the sepium in the cuttle-fish and teuthus is hard and flat, being a substance intermediate between bone and fishbone, with (in part) a crumbling, spongy texture, but in the teuthis the part is thin and somewhat gristly. These parts differ from one another in shape, as do also the bodies of the animals. The octopus has nothing hard of this kind in its interior, but it has a gristly substance round the head, which, if the animal grows old, becomes hard.

The females differ from the males. The males have a duct in under the oesophagus, extending from the mantle-cavity to the lower portion of the sac, and there is an organ to which it attaches, resembling a breast; in the
525a female there are two of these organs, situated higher up; with both sexes there are underneath these organs certain red formations. The egg of the octopus is single, uneven on its surface, and of large size; the fluid substance within is all uniform in colour, smooth, and in colour white; the size of the egg is so great as to fill a vessel larger than the creature's head. The sepia has two sacs, and inside them a number of eggs, like in appearance to white hailstones. For the disposition of these parts I must refer to my anatomical diagrams.

The males of all these animals differ from the females, and the difference between the sexes is most marked in the sepia; for the back of the trunk, which is blacker than the belly, is rougher in the male than in the female, and in the male the back is striped, and the rump is more sharply pointed.

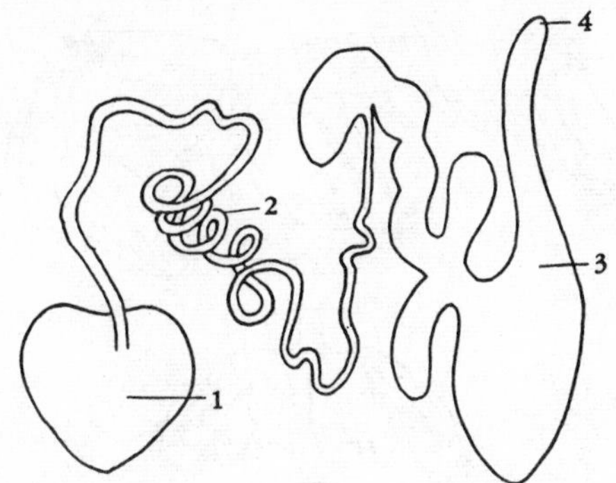

Male organs of *Sepia officinalis.*

1. Testis (ὅμοιον μαστῷ). 2. Vas deferens. 3. Spermatophoral reservoir (πόρος ὑπὸ τὸν στόμαχον κτλ.). 4. Genital aperture.

There are several species of the octopus. One keeps close to the surface, and is the largest of them all, and near the shore the size is larger than in deep water; and there are others, small, variegated in colour, which are not articles of food. There are two others, one called the *heledone,* which differs from its congeners in the length of its legs and in having one row of suckers—all the rest of the molluscs having

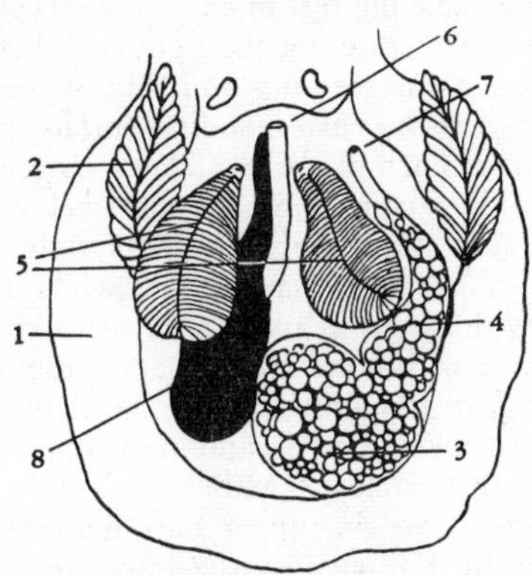

Dissection of female *Sepia officinalis* (σηπία).

1. The mantle (κέλυφος). 2. Gills (τὰ τριχώδη). 3. Ovary. 4. Oviduct (δύο κύτη, καὶ πολλὰ ᾠὰ ἐν αὐτοῖς). 5. Nidamental glands (δύο . . . ὅμοια μαστῷ). 6. Anus (ἔξοδος). 7. Genital aperture (ᾗ τὸν θορὸν ἀφίησι διὰ τοῦ πόρου). 8. Ink-sac (θόλος).

two,—and the other nicknamed variously the *bolitaina* or the 'onion,' and the *ozolis* or the 'stinkard'.

There are two others found in shells resembling those of the testaceans. One of them is nicknamed by some persons the *nautilus* or the *pontilus,* or by others the 'polypus' egg'; and the shell of this creature is something like a separate valve of a deep scallop-shell. This polypus lives very often near to the shore, and is apt to be thrown up high and dry on the beach; under these circumstances it is found with its shell detached, and dies by and by on dry land. These polypods are small, and are shaped, as regards the form of their bodies, like the *bolbidia.* There is another polypus that is placed within a shell like a snail; it never comes out of the shell, but lives inside the shell like the snail, and from time to time protrudes its feelers.

So much for molluscs.

2

With regard to the Malacostraca or crustaceans, one species is that of the crawfish, and a second, resembling the first, is that of the lobster; the lobster differing from the crawfish in having claws, and in a few other respects as well. Another species is that of the carid, and another is that of the crab, and there are many **525b** kinds both of carid and of crab.

Of carids there are the so-called *cyphae,* or 'hunch-backs', the *crangons,* or squillae, and the little kind, or shrimps, and the little kind do not develop into a larger kind.

Of the crab, the varieties are indefinite and incalculable. The largest of all crabs is one nicknamed *Maia,* a second variety is the *pagurus* and the crab of Heracleotis, and a third variety is the fresh-water crab; the other varieties are smaller in size and destitute of special designations. In the neighbourhood of Phoenice there are found on the beach certain crabs that are nicknamed the 'horsemen', from their running with such speed that it is difficult to overtake them; these crabs, when opened, are usually found empty, and this emptiness may be put down to insufficiency of nutriment. [There is another variety, small like the crab, but resembling in shape the lobster.]

All these animals, as has been stated, have their hard and shelly part outside, where the skin is in other animals, and the fleshy part inside; and the belly is more or less provided with lamellae, or little flaps, and the female here deposits her spawn.

The crawfishes have five feet on either side, including the claws at the end; and in like manner the crabs have ten feet in all, including the claws. Of the carids, the hunch-backed, or prawns, have five feet on either side, which are sharp-pointed—those towards the head; and five others on either side in the region of the belly, with their extremities flat; they are devoid of flaps on the under side such as the crawfish has, but on the back they resemble the crawfish. It is very different with the *crangon,*

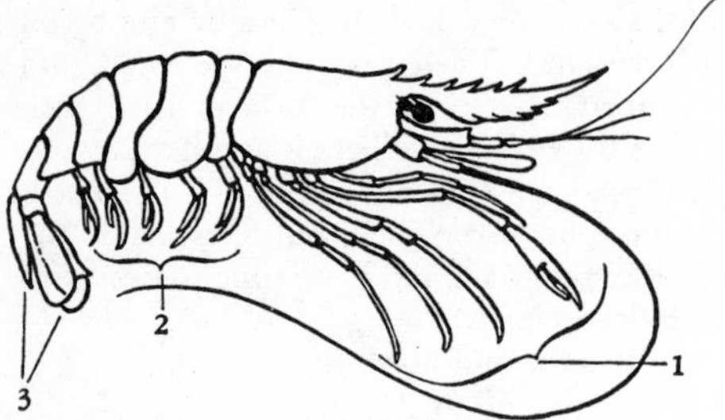

The Common Prawn, *Palaemon serratus* (καρὶς ἡ κυφή).

1. Five thoracic legs (πόδες ὀξεῖς πρὸς τῇ κεφαλῇ). 2. Five abdominal appendages (πόδες οἱ κατὰ τὴν γαστέρα, τὰ ἄκρα ἔχοντες πλατέα). 3. The 'telson' with the last pair of swimmerets (οὐρὰ καὶ πτερύγια τέτταρα).

or *squilla;* it has four front legs on either side, then three thin ones close behind on either side, and the rest of the body is for the most part devoid of feet. Of all these animals the feet bend out obliquely, as is the case with insects; and the claws, where claws are found, turn inwards. The crawfish has a tail, and five fins on it; and the round-backed carid has a tail and four fins; the squilla also has fins at the tail on either side. In the case of both the hump-backed carid and the squilla the middle part of the tail is spinous: only that in the squilla the part is flattened and in the carid it is sharp-pointed. Of all animals of this genus the crab is the only one devoid of a rump; and, while the body of the carid and the crawfish is elongated, that of the crab is rotund.

In the crawfish the male differs from the female: in the female the first foot is bifurcate,
526a in the male it is undivided; the belly-fins in the female are large and overlapping on the neck, while in the male they are smaller and do not overlap; and, further, on the last feet of the male there are spur-like projections, large and sharp, which projections in the female are small and smooth. Both male and female have two antennae in front of the eyes, large and rough, and other antennae underneath, small and smooth. The eyes of all these creatures are hard and beady, and can move either to the inner or to the outer side. The

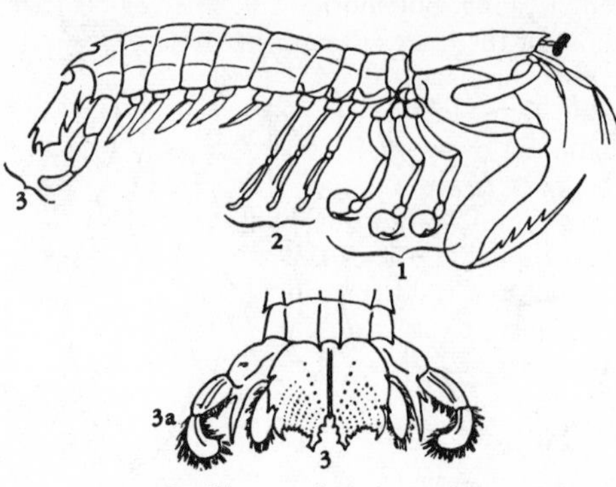

Squilla mantis (κραγγών).

1. The large claws and three following appendages (πόδες τέτταρες οἱ πρῶτοι). 2. The last three thoracic limbs (ἄλλοι τρεῖς λεπτοί). 3. The 'telson' and terminal swimmerets (οὐρὰ καὶ πτερύγια).

eyes of most crabs have a similar facility of movement, or rather, in the crab this facility is developed in a higher degree.

The lobster is all over grey-coloured, with a mottling of black. Its under or hinder feet, up to the big feet or claws, are eight in number; then come the big feet, far larger and flatter at the tips than the same organs in the crawfish; and these big feet or claws are exceptional in their structure, for the right claw has the extreme flat surface long and thin, while the left claw has the corresponding surface thick and round. Each of the two claws, divided at the end like a pair of jaws, has both below and above a set of teeth: only that in the right claw they are all small and saw-shaped, while in the left claw those at the apex are saw-shaped and those within are molar-shaped, these latter being, in the under part of the cleft claw, four teeth close together, and in the upper part three teeth, not close together. Both right and left claws have the upper part mobile, and bring it to bear against the lower one, and both are curved like bandy-legs, being thereby naturally adapted for apprehension and constriction. Above the two large claws come two others, covered with hair, a little underneath the mouth; and underneath these the gill-like formations in the region of the mouth, hairy and numerous. These organs the animal keeps in perpetual motion; and the two hairy feet it bends and draws in towards its mouth. The feet near the mouth are furnished also with delicate outgrowing appendages. Like the crawfish, the lobster has two teeth, or mandibles, and above these teeth are its antennae, long, but shorter and finer by far than those of the crawfish, and then four other antennae similar in shape, but shorter and finer **526b** than the others. Over these antennae come the eyes, small and short, not large like the eyes of the crawfish. Over the eyes is a peaky rough projection like a forehead, larger than the same part in the crawfish; in fact, the frontal part is more pointed and the thorax is much broader in the lobster than in the crawfish, and the body in general is smoother and more full of flesh. Of the eight feet, four are bifurcate at the extremities, and four are undivided. The region of the so-called neck is outwardly divided into five divisions, and sixthly comes the flattened portion at the end, and this portion has five flaps, or tail-fins; and the inner or under parts, into which the female drops her spawn, are four in number and hairy, and on each of the aforesaid parts is a spine turned outwards, short and straight. The body in general and the region of the thorax in particular are smooth, not rough as in the crawfish; but on the large claws the outer portion has larger spines. There is no apparent difference between the male and female, for they both have one claw, whichever it may be, larger than the other, and neither male nor female is ever found with both claws of the same size.

All crustaceans take in water close by the mouth. The crab discharges it, closing up, as it does so, a small portion of the same, and the crawfish discharges it by way of the gills; and, by the way, the gill-shaped organs in the crawfish are very numerous.

The following properties are common to all crustaceans: they have in all cases two teeth, or mandibles (for the front teeth in the crawfish are two in number), and in all cases there is in the mouth a small fleshy structure serving for a tongue; and the stomach is close to the mouth, only that the crawfish has a little oesophagus in front of the stomach, and there is a straight gut attached to it. This gut, in the crawfish and its congeners, and in the carids, extends in a straight line to the tail, and terminates where the animal discharges the residuum, and where the female deposits her spawn; in the crab it terminates where the flap is situated, and in the centre of the flap. [And, by the way, in all these animals the spawn is deposited outside.] Further, the female has the place for the spawn running along the gut. And, again, all these animals have, more or less, an organ termed the 'mytis', or 'poppy-juice'.

We must now proceed to review their several differentiae.

527a The crawfish then, as has been said, has two teeth, large and hollow, in which is contained a juice resembling the mytis, and in between the teeth is a fleshy substance, shaped like a tongue. After the mouth comes a short oesophagus, and then a membranous stomach attached to the oesophagus, and at the orifice of the stomach are three teeth, two facing one another and a third standing by itself underneath. Coming off at a bend from the stomach is a gut, simple and of equal thickness throughout the entire length of the body until it reaches the anal vent.

These are all common properties of the crawfish, the carid, and the crab; for the crab, be it remembered, has two teeth.

Again, the crawfish has a duct attached all the way from the chest to the anal vent; and this duct is connected with the ovary in the female, and with the seminal ducts in the male. This passage is attached to the concave surface of the flesh in such a way that the flesh is in betwixt the duct and the gut; for the gut is related to the convexity and this duct to the concavity, pretty much as is observed in quadrupeds. And the duct is identical in both the sexes; that is to say, the duct in both is thin and white, and charged with a sallow-coloured moisture, and is attached to the chest.

[The following are the properties of the egg and of the convolutes in the carid.]

The male, by the way, differs from the female in regard to its flesh, in having in connexion with the chest two separate and distinct white substances, resembling in colour and conformation the tentacles of the cuttle-fish, and they are convoluted like the 'poppy' or quasi-liver of the trumpet-shell. These organs have their starting-point in 'cotyledons' or papillae, which are situated under the hindmost feet; and hereabouts the flesh is red and blood-coloured, but is slippery to the touch and in so far unlike flesh. Off from the convolute organ at the chest branches off another coil about as thick as ordinary twine; and underneath there are two granular seminal bodies in juxta-position with the gut. These are the organs of the male. The female has red-coloured eggs, which are adjacent to the stomach and to each side of the gut all along to the fleshy parts, being enveloped in a thin membrane.

Such are the parts, internal and external, of the carid.

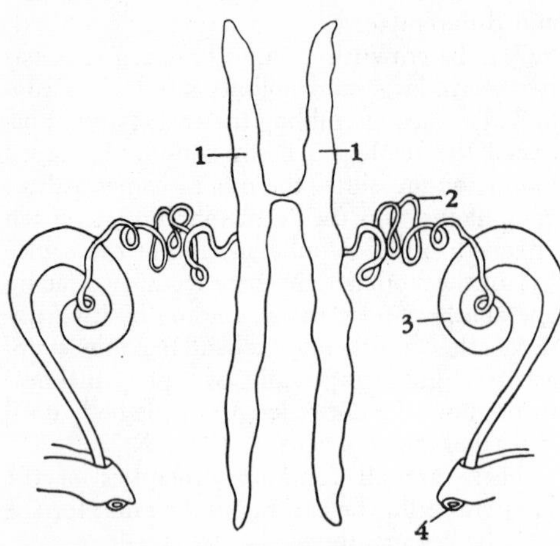

Male organs of Crawfish, *Palinurus vulgaris* (ἀστακός).

1. Testes(δύο ἄττα ψαθυρά, θορικά). 2. 'Vas deferens' (ἄλλος ἑλιγμός, ὥσπερ ἀρπεδόνη τὸ πάχος). 3. 'Ductus ejaculatorius' (δύο λεύκ' ἄττα καθ' αὑτά, ὅμοια τὸ χρῶμα καὶ τὴν σύστασιν ταῖς τῆς σηπίας προβοσκίσιν). 4. Orifice (κοτυληδών, ᾗ ἐστιν ὑποκάτω τῶν ἐσχάτων ποδῶν).

3

527b The inner organs of sanguineous animals happen to have specific designations; for these animals have in all cases the inner viscera, but this is not the case with the bloodless animals, but what they have in common with red-blooded animals is the stomach, the oesophagus, and the gut.

With regard to the crab, it has already been stated that it has claws and feet, and their position has been set forth; furthermore, for the most part they have the right claw bigger and stronger than the left. It has also been stated[1] that in general the eyes of the crab look sideways. Further, the trunk of the crab's body is single and undivided, including its head and any other part it may possess. Some crabs have eyes placed sideways on the upper part, immediately under the back, and standing a long way apart, and some have their eyes in the centre and close together, like the crabs of Heracleotis and the so-called 'grannies'. The mouth lies underneath the eyes, and inside it there are two teeth, as is the case with the crawfish, only that in the crab the teeth are not rounded but long; and over the teeth are two lids, and in betwixt them are structures such as the crawfish has besides its teeth. The crab takes in water near by the mouth, using the lids as a check to the inflow, and discharges the water by two passages above the mouth, closing by means of the lids the way by which it entered; and the two passage-ways are just underneath the eyes. When it has taken in water it closes its mouth by means of both lids, and ejects the water in the way above described. Next after the teeth comes the oesophagus, very short, so short in fact that the stomach seems to come straightway after the mouth. Next after the oesophagus comes the stomach, two-horned, to the centre of which is attached a simple and delicate gut; and the gut terminates outwards, at the operculum, as has been previously stated. [The crab has the parts in between the lids in the neighbourhood of the teeth similar to the same parts in the crawfish.] Inside the trunk is a sallow juice and some few little bodies, long and white, and others spotted red. The male differs from the female in size and breadth, and in respect of the ventral flap; for this is larger in the female than in the male, and stands out further from the trunk, and is more hairy [as is the case also with the female in the crawfish].

So much, then, for the organs of the malacostraca or crustacea.

4

With the ostracoderma, or testaceans, such **528a** as the land-snails and the sea-snails, and all the 'oysters' so-called, and also with the sea-urchin genus, the fleshy part, in such as have flesh, is similarly situated to the fleshy part in the crustaceans; in other words, it is inside the animal, and the shell is outside, and there is no hard substance in the interior. As compared with one another the testaceans present many diversities both in regard to their shells and to the flesh within. Some of them have no flesh at all, as the sea-urchin; others have flesh, but it is inside and wholly hidden, except the head, as in the land-snails, and the so-called *cocalia,* and, among pelagic animals, in the purple murex, the ceryx or trumpet-shell, the sea-snail, and the spiral-shaped testaceans in general. Of the rest, some are bivalved and some univalved; and by 'bivalves' I mean such as are enclosed within two shells, and by 'univalved' such as are enclosed within a single shell, and in these last the fleshy part is ex-

[1] IV. 2 (526a 9).

posed, as in the case of the limpet. Of the bivalves, some can open out, like the scallop and the mussel; for all such shells are grown together on one side and are separate on the other, so as to open and shut. Other bivalves are closed on both sides alike, like the solen or razor-fish. Some testaceans there are, that are entirely enveloped in shell and expose no portion of their flesh outside, as the tethya or ascidians.

Again, in regard to the shells themselves, the testaceans present differences when compared with one another. Some are smooth-shelled, like the solen, the mussel, and some clams, viz. those that are nicknamed 'milk-shells', while others are rough-shelled, such as the pool-oyster or edible oyster, the pinna, and certain species of cockles, and the trumpet-shells; and of these some are ribbed, such as the scallop and a certain kind of clam or cockle, and some are devoid of ribs, as the pinna and another species of clam. Testaceans also differ from one another in regard to the thickness or thinness of their shell, both as regards the shell in its entirety and as regards specific parts of the shell, for instance, the lips; for some have thin-lipped shells, like the mussel, and others have thick-lipped shells, like the oyster. A property common to the above mentioned, and, in fact, to all testaceans, is the smoothness of their shells inside. Some also are capable of motion, like the scallop, and indeed some aver that scallops can actually fly, owing to the circumstance that they often jump right out of the apparatus by means of which they are caught; others are incapable of motion and are attached fast to some external object, as is the case with the pinna. All the spiral-shaped testaceans can move and creep,
528b and even the limpet relaxes its hold to go in quest of food. In the case of the univalves and the bivalves, the fleshy substance adheres to the shell so tenaciously that it can only be removed by an effort; in the case of the stromboids, it is more loosely attached. And a peculiarity of all the stromboids is the spiral twist of the shell in the part farthest away from the head; they are also furnished from birth with an operculum. And, further, all stromboid testaceans have their shells on the right-hand side, and move not in the direction of the spire, but the opposite way. Such are the diversities observed in the external parts of these animals.

The internal structure is almost the same in all these creatures, and in the stromboids especially; for it is in size that these latter differ from one another, and in accidents of the nature of excess or defect. And there is not much difference between most of the univalves and bivalves; but, while those that open and shut differ from one another but slightly, they differ considerably from such as are incapable of motion. And this will be illustrated more satisfactorily hereafter.

The spiral-shaped testaceans are all similarly constructed, but differ from one another, as has been said, in the way of excess or defect (for the larger species have larger and more conspicuous organs, and the smaller have smaller and less conspicuous), and, furthermore, in relative hardness or softness, and in other such accidents or properties. All the stromboids, for instance, have the flesh that extrudes from the mouth of the shell, hard and stiff; some more, and some less. From the middle of this protrudes the head and two horns, and these horns are large in the large species, but exceedingly minute in the smaller ones. The head protrudes from them all in the same way; and, if the animal be alarmed, the head draws in again. Some of these creatures have a mouth and teeth, as the snail; teeth sharp, and small, and delicate. They have also a proboscis just like that of the fly; and the proboscis is tongue-shaped. The ceryx and the purple murex have this organ firm and solid; and just as the myops, or horse-fly, and the oestrus, or gadfly, can pierce the skin of a quadruped, so is that proboscis proportionately stronger in these testaceans; for they bore right through the shells of other shell-fish on
529a which they prey. The stomach follows close upon the mouth, and, by the way, this organ in the snail resembles a bird's crop. Underneath come two white firm formations, mastoid or papillary in form; and similar formations are found in the cuttle-fish also, only that they are of a firmer consistency in the cuttle-fish. After the stomach comes an oesophagus, simple and long, extending to the poppy or quasi-liver, which is in the innermost recess of the shell. All these statements may be verified in the case of the purple murex and the ceryx by observation within the whorl of the shell. What comes next to the oesophagus is the gut; in fact, the gut is continuous with the oesophagus, and runs its whole length uncomplicated to the outlet of the residuum. The gut has its point of origin in the region of the coil of the mecon, or so-called 'poppy', and is wider hereabouts [for, remember, the

mecon is for the most part a sort of excretion in all testaceans]; it then takes a bend and runs up again towards the fleshy part, and terminates by the side of the head, where the animal discharges its residuum; and this holds good in the case of all stromboid testaceans, whether terrestrial or marine. From the stomach there is drawn in a parallel direction with the oesophagus, in the larger snails, a long white duct enveloped in a membrane, resembling in colour the mastoid formations higher up; and in it are nicks or interruptions, as in the egg-mass of the crawfish, only, by the way, the duct of which we are treating is white and the egg-mass of the crawfish is red. This formation has no outlet nor duct, but is enveloped in a thin membrane with a narrow cavity in its interior. And from the gut downward extend black and rough formations, in close connexion, something like the formations in the tortoise, only not so black. Marine snails, also, have these formations, and the white ones, only that the formations are smaller in the smaller species.

The non-spiral univalves and bivalves are in some respect similar in construction, and in some respects dissimilar, to the spiral testaceans. They all have a head and horns, and a mouth, and the organ resembling a tongue; but these organs, in the smaller species, are indiscernible owing to the minuteness of these animals, and some are indiscernible even in the larger species when dead, or when at rest and motionless. They all have the mecon, or poppy, but not all in the same place, nor of equal size, nor similarly open to observation; thus, the limpets have this organ deep down in the bottom of the shell, and the bivalves at the hinge connecting the two valves. They also have in all cases the hairy growths or beards, in a circular form, as in the scallops. And, with **529b** regard to the so-called 'egg', in those that have it, when they have it, it is situated in one of the semi-circles of the periphery, as is the case with the white formation in the snail; for this white formation in the snail corresponds to the so-called egg of which we are speaking. But all these organs, as has been stated, are distinctly traceable in the larger species, while in the small ones they are in some cases almost, and in others altogether, indiscernible. Hence they are most plainly visible in the large scallops; and these are the bivalves that have one valve flat-shaped, like the lid of a pot. The outlet of the excretion is in all these animals (save for the exception to be afterwards related) on one side; for there is a passage whereby the excretion passes out. [And, remember, the mecon or poppy, as has been stated, is an excretion in all these animals —an excretion enveloped in a membrane.] The so-called egg has no outlet in any of these creatures, but is merely an excrescence in the fleshy mass; and it is not situated in the same region with the gut, but the 'egg' is situated on the right-hand side, and the gut on the left. Such are the relations of the anal vent in most of these animals; but in the case of the wild limpet (called by some the 'sea-ear'), the residuum issues beneath the shell, for the shell is perforated to give an outlet. In this particular limpet the stomach is seen coming after the mouth, and the egg-shaped formations are discernible. But for the relative positions of these parts you are referred to my Treatise on Anatomy.

The so-called *carcinium* or hermit crab is in a way intermediate between the crustaceans and the testaceans. In its nature it resembles the crawfish kind, and it is born simple of itself, but by its habit of introducing itself into a shell and living there it resembles the testaceans, and so appears to partake of the characters of both kinds. In shape, to give a simple illustration, it resembles a spider, only that the part below the head and thorax is larger in this creature than in the spider. It has two thin red horns, and underneath these horns two long eyes, not retreating inwards, nor turning sideways like the eyes of the crab, but protruding straight out; and underneath these eyes the mouth, and round about the mouth several hair-like growths, and next after these two bifurcate legs or claws, whereby it draws in objects towards itself, and two other legs on either side, and a third small one. All below the thorax is soft, and when **530a** opened in dissection is found to be sallow-coloured within. From the mouth there runs a single passage right on to the stomach, but the passage for the excretions is not discernible. The legs and the thorax are hard, but not so hard as the legs and the thorax of the crab. It does not adhere to its shell like the purple murex and the ceryx, but can easily slip out of it. It is longer when found in the shell of the stromboids than when found in the shell of the neritae.

And, by the way, the animal found in the shell of the neritae is a separate species, like to the other in most respects; but of its bifurcate feet or claws, the right-hand one is small and the left-hand one is large, and it progresses chiefly by the aid of this latter and larger one. [In the shells of these animals, and in certain others, there is found a parasite whose mode of attachment is similar. The particular one which we have just described is named the *cyllarus*.]

The nerites has a smooth large round shell, and resembles the ceryx in shape, only the poppy-juice is, in its case, not black but red. It clings with great force near the middle. In calm weather, then, they go free afield, but when the wind blows the carcinia take shelter against the rocks: the neritae themselves cling fast like limpets; and the same is the case with the haemorrhoid or aporrhaid and all others of the like kind. And, by the way, they cling to the rock, when they turn back their operculum, for this operculum seems like a lid; in fact this structure represents the one part, in the stromboids, of that which in the bivalves is a duplicate shell. The interior of the animal is fleshy, and the mouth is inside. And it is the same with the haemorrhoid, the purple murex, and all suchlike animals.

Such of the little crabs as have the left foot or claw the bigger of the two are found in the neritae, but not in the stromboids. [There are some snail-shells which have inside them creatures resembling those little crayfish that are also found in fresh water. These creatures, however, differ in having the part inside the shell soft.] But as to the characters, you are referred to my Treatise on Anatomy.

5

The urchins are devoid of flesh, and this is a character peculiar to them; and while they are in all cases empty and devoid of any flesh within, they are in all cases furnished with the black formations. There are several species of the urchin, and one of these is that which is **530b** made use of for food; this is the kind in which are found the so-called eggs, large and edible, in the larger and smaller specimens alike; for even when as yet very small they are provided with them. There are two other species, the *spatangus,* and the so-called *bryssus;* these animals are pelagic and scarce. Further, there are the *echinometrae,* or 'mother-urchins', the largest in size of all the species. In addition to these there is another species, small in size, but furnished with large hard spines; it lives in the sea at a depth of several fathoms; and is used by some people as a specific for cases of strangury. In the neighbourhood of Torone there are sea-urchins of a white colour, shells, spines, eggs and all, and that are longer than the ordinary sea-urchin. The spine in this species is not large nor strong, but rather limp; and the black formations in connexion with the mouth are more than usually numerous, and communicate with the external duct, but not with one another; in point of fact, the animal is in a manner divided up by them. The edible urchin moves with greatest freedom and most often; and this is indicated by the fact that these urchins have always something or other on their spines.

All urchins are supplied with eggs, but in some of the species the eggs are exceedingly small and unfit for food. Singularly enough, the urchin has what we may call its head and its mouth down below, and a place for the issue of the residuum up above; [and this same property is common to all stromboids and to limpets]. For the food on which the creature lives lies down below; consequently the mouth has a position well adapted for getting at the food, and the excretion is above, near to the back of the shell. The urchin has, also, five hollow teeth inside, and in the middle of these teeth a fleshy substance serving the office of a tongue. Next to this comes the oesophagus, and then the stomach, divided into five parts, and filled with excretion, all the five parts uniting at the anal vent, where the shell is perforated for an outlet. Underneath the stomach, in another membrane, are the so-called eggs, identical in number in all cases, and that number is always an odd number, to wit five. Up above, the black formations are attached to the starting-point of the teeth, and they are bitter to the taste, and unfit for food. A similar or at least an analogous formation is found in many animals; as, for instance, in the tortoise, the toad, the frog, the stromboids, **531a** and, generally, in the molluscs; but the formation varies here and there in colour, and in all cases is altogether uneatable, or more or less unpalatable. In reality the mouth-apparatus of the urchin is continuous from one end to the other, but to outward appearance it is not so, but looks like a horn lantern with the panes of horn left out. The urchin uses its spines as feet; for it rests its weight on these, and then moving shifts from place to place.

6

The so-called *tethyum* or ascidian has of all these animals the most remarkable characteristics. It is the only mollusc that has its entire body concealed within its shell, and the shell is a substance intermediate between hide and shell, so that it cuts like a piece of hard leather. It is attached to rocks by its shell, and is provided with two passages placed at a distance from one another, very minute and hard to see, whereby it admits and discharges the sea-water; for it has no visible excretion [whereas of shell fish in general some resemble the urchin in this matter of excretion, and others are provided with the so-called mecon, or poppy-juice]. If the animal be opened, it is found to have, in the first place, a tendinous membrane running round inside the shell-like substance, and within this membrane is the flesh-like substance of the ascidian, not resembling that in other molluscs; but this flesh, to which I now allude, is the same in all ascidia. And this substance is attached in two places to the membrane and the skin, obliquely; and at the point of attachment the space is narrowed from side to side, where the fleshy substance stretches towards the passages that lead outwards through the shell; and here it discharges and admits food and liquid matter, just as it would if one of the passages were a mouth and the other an anal vent; and one of the passages is somewhat wider than the other one. Inside it has a pair of cavities, one on either side, a small partition separating them; and one of these two cavities contains the liquid. The creature has no other organ whether motor or sensory, nor, as was said in the case of the others, is it furnished with any organ connected with excretion, as other shell-fish are. The colour of the ascidian is in some cases sallow, and in other cases red.

There is, furthermore, the genus of the sea-nettles, peculiar in its way. The sea-nettle, or sea-anemone, clings to rocks like certain of the testaceans, but at times relaxes its hold. It has
531b no shell, but its entire body is fleshy. It is sensitive to touch, and, if you put your hand to it, it will seize and cling to it, as the cuttle-fish would do with its feelers, and in such a way as to make the flesh of your hand swell up. Its mouth is in the centre of its body, and it lives adhering to the rock as an oyster to its shell. If any little fish come up against it it clings to it; in fact, just as I described it above as doing to your hand, so it does to anything edible that comes in its way; and it feeds upon sea-urchins and scallops. Another species of the sea-nettle roams freely abroad. The sea-nettle appears to be devoid altogether of excretion, and in this respect it resembles a plant.

Of sea-nettles there are two species, the lesser and more edible, and the large hard ones, such as are found in the neighbourhood of Chalcis. In winter time their flesh is firm, and accordingly they are sought after as articles of food, but in summer weather they are worthless, for they become thin and watery, and if you catch at them they break at once into bits, and cannot be taken off the rocks entire; and being oppressed by the heat they tend to slip back into the crevices of the rocks.

So much for the external and the internal organs of molluscs, crustaceans, and testaceans.

7

We now proceed to treat of insects in like manner. This genus comprises many species, and, though several kinds are clearly related to one another, these are not classified under one common designation, as in the case of the bee, the drone, the wasp, and all such insects, and again as in the case of those that have their wings in a sheath or shard, like the cockchafer, the carabus or stag-beetle, the cantharis or blister-beetle, and the like.

Insects have three parts common to them all; the head, the trunk containing the stomach, and a third part in betwixt these two, corresponding to what in other creatures embraces chest and back. In the majority of insects this intermediate part is single; but in the long and multipedal insects it has practically the same number of segments as of nicks.

All insects when cut in two continue to live, excepting such as are naturally cold by nature, or such as from their minute size chill rapidly; though, by the way, wasps notwithstanding their small size continue living after severance. In conjunction with the middle portion either the head or the stomach can live,
532a but the head cannot live by itself. Insects that are long in shape and many-footed can live for a long while after being cut in twain, and the severed portions can move in either direction, backwards or forwards; thus, the hinder portion, if cut off, can crawl either in the direction of the section or in the direction of the tail, as is observed in the scolopendra.

All insects have eyes, but no other organ of sense discernible, except that some insects have a kind of a tongue corresponding to a similar organ common to all testaceans; and by this organ such insects taste and imbibe their food. In some insects this organ is soft; in other insects it is firm; as it is, by the way, in the purple-fish, among testaceans. In the horsefly and the gadfly this organ is hard, and indeed it is hard in most insects. In point of fact, such insects as have no sting in the rear use this organ as a weapon, (and, by the way, such insects as are provided with this organ are unprovided with teeth, with the exception of a few insects); the fly by a touch can draw blood with this organ, and the gnat can prick or sting with it.

Certain insects are furnished with prickers or stings. Some insects have the sting inside, as the bee and the wasp, others outside, as the scorpion; and, by the way, this is the only insect furnished with a long tail. And, further, the scorpion is furnished with claws, as is also the creature resembling a scorpion found within the pages of books.

In addition to their other organs, flying insects are furnished with wings. Some insects are dipterous or double-winged, as the fly; others are tetrapterous or furnished with four wings, as the bee; and, by the way, no insect with only two wings has a sting in the rear. Again, some winged insects have a sheath or shard for their wings, as the cockchafer; whereas in others the wings are unsheathed, as in the bee. But in the case of all alike, flight is in no way modified by tail-steerage, and the wing is devoid of quill-structure or division of any kind.

Again, some insects have antennae in front of their eyes, as the butterfly and the horned-beetle. Such of them as have the power of jumping have the hinder legs the longer; and these long hind-legs whereby they jump bend backwards like the hind-legs of quadrupeds. All insects have the belly different from the back; as, in fact, is the case with all animals. The flesh of an insect's body is neither shell-like nor is it like the internal substance of shell-covered animals, nor is it like flesh in the ordinary sense of the term; but it is a something intermediate in quality. Wherefore they have nor spine, nor bone, nor sepia-bone, nor **532b** enveloping shell; but their body by its hardness is its own protection and requires no extraneous support. However, insects have a skin; but the skin is exceedingly thin. These and such-like are the external organs of insects.

Internally, next after the mouth, comes a gut, in the majority of cases straight and simple down to the outlet of the residuum: but in a few cases the gut is coiled. No insect is provided with any viscera, or is supplied with fat; and these statements apply to all animals devoid of blood. Some have a stomach also, and attached to this the rest of the gut, either simple or convoluted as in the case of the *acris* or grasshopper.

The *tettix* or cicada, alone of such creatures (and, in fact, alone of all creatures), is unprovided with a mouth, but it is provided with the tongue-like formation found in insects furnished with frontward stings; and this formation in the cicada is long, continuous, and devoid of any split; and by the aid of this the creature feeds on dew, and on dew only, and in its stomach no excretion is ever found. Of the cicada there are several kinds, and they differ from one another in relative magnitude, and in this respect that the *achetes* or chirper is provided with a cleft or aperture under the *hypozoma* and has in it a membrane quite discernible, whilst the membrane is indiscernible in the *tettigonia*.

Furthermore, there are some strange creatures to be found in the sea, which from their rarity we are unable to classify. Experienced fishermen affirm, some that they have at times seen in the sea animals like sticks, black, rounded, and of the same thickness throughout; others that they have seen creatures resembling shields, red in colour, and furnished with fins packed close together; and others that they have seen creatures resembling the male organ in shape and size, with a pair of fins in the place of the testicles, and they aver that on one occasion a creature of this description was brought up on the end of a nightline.

So much then for the parts, external and internal, exceptional and common, of all animals.

8

We now proceed to treat of the senses; for there are diversities in animals with regard to the senses, seeing that some animals have the use of all the senses, and others the use of a limited number of them. The total number of the senses (for we have no experience of any special sense not here included), is five: sight, hearing, smell, taste, and touch.

Man, then, and all vivipara that have feet, and, further, all red-blooded ovipara, appear to **533a** have the use of all the five senses, except where some isolated species has been subjected to multilation, as in the case of the mole. For this animal is deprived of sight; it has no eyes visible, but if the skin—a thick one, by the way—be stripped off the head, about the place in the exterior where eyes usually are, the eyes are found inside in a stunted condition, furnished with all the parts found in ordinary eyes; that is to say, we find there the black rim, and the fatty part surrounding it; but all these parts are smaller than the same parts in ordinary visible eyes. There is no external sign of the existence of these organs in the mole, owing to the thickness of the skin drawn over them, so that it would seem that the natural course of development were congenitally arrested; [for extending from the brain at its junction with the marrow are two strong sinewy ducts running past the sockets of the eyes, and terminating at the upper eye-teeth]. All the other animals of the kinds above mentioned have a perception of colour and of sound, and the senses of smell and taste; the fifth sense, that, namely, of touch, is common to all animals whatsoever.

In some animals the organs of sense are plainly discernible; and this is especially the case with the eyes. For animals have a special locality for the eyes, and also a special locality for hearing: that is to say, some animals have ears, while others have the passage for sound discernible. It is the same with the sense of smell; that is to say, some animals have nostrils, and others have only the passages for smell, such as birds. It is the same also with the organ of taste, the tongue. Of aquatic red-blooded animals, fishes possess the organ of taste, namely the tongue, but it is in an imperfect and amorphous form, in other words it is osseous and undetached. In some fish the palate is fleshy, as in the fresh-water carp, so that by an inattentive observer it might be mistaken for a tongue.

There is no doubt but that fishes have the sense of taste, for a great number of them delight in special flavours; and fishes freely take the hook if it be baited with a piece of flesh from a tunny or from any fat fish, obviously enjoying the taste and the eating of food of this kind. Fishes have no visible organs for
533b hearing or for smell; for what might appear to indicate an organ for smell in the region of the nostril has no communication with the brain. These indications, in fact, in some cases lead nowhere, like blind alleys, and in other cases lead only to the gills; but for all this fishes undoubtedly hear and smell. For they are observed to run away from any loud noise, such as would be made by the rowing of a galley, so as to become easy of capture in their holes; for, by the way, though a sound be very slight in the open air, it has a loud and alarming resonance to creatures that hear under water. And this is shown in the capture of the dolphin; for when the hunters have enclosed a shoal of these fishes with a ring of their canoes, they set up from inside the canoes a loud splashing in the water, and by so doing induce the creatures to run in a shoal high and dry up on the beach, and so capture them while stupefied with the noise. And yet, for all this, the dolphin has no organ of hearing discernible. Furthermore, when engaged in their craft, fishermen are particularly careful to make no noise with oar or net; and after they have spied a shoal, they let down their nets at a spot so far off that they count upon no noise being likely to reach the shoal, occasioned either by oar or by the surging of their boats through the water; and the crews are strictly enjoined to preserve silence until the shoal has been surrounded. And, at times, when they want the fish to crowd together, they adopt the stratagem of the dolphin-hunter; in other words they clatter stones together, that the fish may, in their fright, gather close into one spot, and so they envelop them within their nets. [Before surrounding them, then, they preserve silence, as was said; but, after hemming the shoal in, they call on every man to shout out aloud and make any kind of noise; for on hearing the noise and hubbub the fish are sure to tumble into the nets from sheer fright.] Further, when fishermen see a shoal of fish feeding at a distance, disporting themselves in calm bright weather on the surface of the water, if they are anxious to descry the size of the fish and to learn what kind of a fish it is, they may succeed in coming upon the shoal whilst yet basking at the surface if they sail up without the slightest noise, but if any man make a noise previously, the shoal will be seen to scurry away in alarm. Again, there is a
534a small river-fish called the *cottus* or bullhead; this creature burrows under a rock, and fishers catch it by clattering stones against the rock, and the fish, bewildered at the noise, darts out of its hiding-place. From these facts it is quite obvious that fishes can hear; and indeed some people, from living near the sea and frequently witnessing such phenomena, affirm that of all living creatures the fish is the quickest of hearing. And, by the way, of all fishes the quickest of hearing are the *cestreus* or mullet, the *chremps,* the *labrax* or basse, the *salpe* or saupe, the *chromis* or sciaena, and such like. Other fishes are less quick of hearing, and, as might be expected, are more

apt to be found living at the bottom of the sea.

The case is similar in regard to the sense of smell. Thus, as a rule, fishes will not touch a bait that is not fresh, neither are they all caught by one and the same bait, but they are severally caught by baits suited to their several likings, and these baits they distinguish by their sense of smell; and, by the way, some fishes are attracted by malodorous baits, as the saupe, for instance, is attracted by excrement. Again, a number of fishes live in caves; and accordingly fishermen, when they want to entice them out, smear the mouth of a cave with strong-smelling pickles, and the fish are soon attracted to the smell. And the eel is caught in a similar way; for the fisherman lays down an earthen pot that has held pickles, after inserting a 'weel' in the neck thereof. As a general rule, fishes are especially attracted by savoury smells. For this reason, fishermen roast the fleshy parts of the cuttle-fish and use it as bait on account of its smell, for fish are peculiarly attracted by it; they also bake the octopus and bait their fish-baskets or weels with it, entirely, as they say, on account of its smell. Furthermore, gregarious fishes, if fish-washings or bilge-water be thrown overboard, are observed to scud off to a distance, from apparent dislike of the smell. And it is asserted that they can at once detect by smell the pres-
534b ence of their own blood; and this faculty is manifested by their hurrying off to a great distance whenever fish-blood is spilt in the sea. And, as a general rule, if you bait your weel with a stinking bait, the fish refuse to enter the weel or even to draw near; but if you bait the weel with a fresh and savoury bait, they come at once from long distances and swim into it. ⌈And all this is particularly manifest in the dolphin; for, as was stated, it has no visible organ of hearing, and yet it is captured when stupefied with noise; and so, while it has no visible organ for smell, it has the sense of smell remarkably keen.] It is manifest, then, that the animals above mentioned are in possession of all the five senses.

All other animals may, with very few exceptions, be comprehended within four genera: to wit, molluscs, crustaceans, testaceans, and insects. Of these four genera, the mollusc, the crustacean, and the insect have all the senses: at all events, they have sight, smell, and taste. As for insects, both winged and wingless, they can detect the presence of scented objects afar off, as for instance bees and snipes detect the presence of honey at a distance; and they do so recognizing it by smell. Many insects are killed by the smell of brimstone; ants, if the apertures to their dwellings be smeared with powdered origanum and brimstone, quit their nests; and most insects may be banished with burnt hart's horn, or better still by the burning of the gum styrax. The cuttle-fish, the octopus, and the crawfish may be caught by bait. The octopus, in fact, clings so tightly to the rocks that it cannot be pulled off, but remains attached even when the knife is employed to sever it; and yet, if you apply fleabane to the creature, it drops off at the very smell of it. The facts are similar in re-
535a gard to taste. For the food that insects go in quest of is of diverse kinds, and they do not all delight in the same flavours: for instance, the bee never settles on a withered or wilted flower, but on fresh and sweet ones; and the conops or gnat settles only on acrid substances and not on sweet. The sense of touch, by the way, as has been remarked, is common to all animals. Testaceans have the senses of smell and taste. With regard to their possession of the sense of smell, that is proved by the use of baits, e.g. in the case of the purple-fish; for this creature is enticed by baits of rancid meat, which it perceives and is attracted to from a great distance. The proof that it possesses a sense of taste hangs by the proof of its sense of smell; for whenever an animal is attracted to a thing by perceiving its smell, it is sure to like the taste of it. Further, all animals furnished with a mouth derive pleasure or pain from the touch of sapid juices.

With regard to sight and hearing, we cannot make statements with thorough confidence or on irrefutable evidence. However, the solen or razor-fish, if you make a noise, appears to burrow in the sand, and to hide himself deeper when he hears the approach of the iron rod (for the animal, be it observed, juts a little out of its hole, while the greater part of the body remains within),—and scallops, if you present your finger near their open valves, close them tight again as though they could see what you were doing. Furthermore, when fishermen are laying bait for neritae, they always get to leeward of them, and never speak a word while so engaged, under the firm impression that the animal can smell and hear; and they assure us that, if any one speaks aloud, the creature makes efforts to escape. With regard to testaceans, of the walking or creeping species the urchin appears to have the least developed sense of smell; and, of the stationary species, the ascidian and the barnacle.

So much for the organs of sense in the general run of animals. We now proceed to treat of voice.

9

Voice and sound are different from one another; and language differs from voice and sound. The fact is that no animal can give utterance to voice except by the action of the pharynx, and consequently such animals as are devoid of lung have no voice; and language is the articulation of vocal sounds by the instrumentality of the tongue. Thus, the voice and larynx can emit vocal or vowel sounds; non-vocal or consonantal sounds are made by **535b** the tongue and the lips; and out of these vocal and non-vocal sounds language is composed. Consequently, animals that have no tongue at all or that have a tongue not freely detached, have neither voice nor language; although, by the way, they may be enabled to make noises or sounds by other organs than the tongue.

Insects, for instance, have no voice and no language, but they can emit sound by internal air or wind, though not by the emission of air or wind; for no insects are capable of respiration. But some of them make a humming noise, like the bee and the other winged insects; and others are said to sing, as the cicada. And all these latter insects make their special noises by means of the membrane that is underneath the 'hypozoma'—those insects, that is to say, whose body is thus divided; as for instance, one species of cicada, which makes the sound by means of the friction of the air. Flies and bees, and the like, produce their special noise by opening and shutting their wings in the act of flying; for the noise made is by the friction of air between the wings when in motion. The noise made by grasshoppers is produced by rubbing or reverberating with their long hind-legs.

No mollusc or crustacean can produce any natural voice or sound. Fishes can produce no voice, for they have no lungs, nor windpipe and pharynx; but they emit certain inarticulate sounds and squeaks, which is what is called their 'voice', as the *lyra* or gurnard, and the sciaena (for these fishes make a grunting kind of noise) and the *caprus* or boar-fish in the river Achelous, and the *chalcis* and the cuckoo-fish; for the chalcis makes a sort of piping sound, and the cuckoo-fish makes a sound greatly like the cry of the cuckoo, and is nicknamed from the circumstance. The apparent voice in all these fishes is a sound caused in some cases by a rubbing motion of their gills, which by the way are prickly, or in other cases by internal parts about their bellies; for they all have air or wind inside them, by rubbing and moving which they produce the sounds. Some cartilaginous fish seem to squeak.

But in these cases the term 'voice' is inappropriate; the more correct expression would be 'sound'. For the scallop, when it goes along supporting itself on the water, which is technically called 'flying', makes a whizzing sound; and so does the sea-swallow or flying-fish: for this fish flies in the air, clean out of the water, being furnished with fins broad and long. Just then as in the flight of birds the sound made by their wings is obviously not voice, so is it in the case of all these other creatures.

The dolphin, when taken out of the water, gives a squeak and moans in the air, but these **536a** noises do not resemble those above mentioned. For this creature has a voice ⟨and can therefore utter vocal or vowel sounds⟩, for it is furnished with a lung and a windpipe; but its tongue is not loose, nor has it lips, so as to give utterance to an articulate sound ⟨or a sound of vowel and consonant in combination.⟩

Of animals which are furnished with tongue and lung, the oviparous quadrupeds produce a voice, but a feeble one; in some cases, a shrill piping sound, like the serpent; in others, a thin faint cry; in others, a low hiss, like the tortoise. The formation of the tongue in the frog is exceptional. The front part of the tongue, which in other animals is detached, is tightly fixed in the frog as it is in all fishes; but the part towards the pharynx is freely detached, and may, so to speak, be spat outwards, and it is with this that it makes its peculiar croak. The croaking that goes on in the marsh is the call of the males to the females at rutting time; and, by the way, all animals have a special cry for the like end at the like season, as is observed in the case of goats, swine, and sheep. [The bull-frog makes its croaking noise by putting its under jaw on a level with the surface of the water and extending its upper jaw to its utmost capacity. The tension is so great that the upper jaw becomes transparent, and the animal's eyes shine through the jaw like lamps; for, by the way, the commerce of the sexes takes place usually in the night time.] Birds can utter vocal sounds; and such of them can articulate best as have the tongue moderately flat, and also such as have thin delicate tongues. In some cases, the male and the female utter the same note; in other cases, different notes. The smaller birds are more vocal and given to chirping than the larger ones; but in the pairing season every species of bird becomes particularly vocal. Some of them call when fighting, as the quail, others cry or crow when challenging to combat, as the partridge, or when victorious, as the barn-door cock. In some cases cock-birds and hens sing alike, as is observed in the nightingale, only that the hen stops singing when brooding or rearing her young; in other birds, the cocks sing more than the hens; in fact, with barn-door fowls and quails, the cock sings and the hen does not.

Viviparous quadrupeds utter vocal sounds of different kinds, but they have no power of
536b converse. In fact, this power, or language, is peculiar to man. For while the capability of talking implies the capability of uttering vocal sounds, the converse does not hold good. Men that are born deaf are in all cases also dumb; that is, they can make vocal sounds, but they cannot speak. Children, just as they have no control over other parts, so have no control, at first, over the tongue; but it is so far imperfect, and only frees and detaches itself by degrees, so that in the interval children for the most part lisp and stutter.

Vocal sounds and modes of language differ according to locality. Vocal sounds are characterized chiefly by their pitch, whether high or low, and the kinds of sound capable of being produced are identical within the limits of one and the same species; but articulate sound, that one might reasonably designate 'language', differs both in various animals, and also in the same species according to diversity of locality; as for instance, some partridges cackle, and some make a shrill twittering noise. Of little birds, some sing a different note from the parent birds, if they have been removed from the nest and have heard other birds singing; and a mother-nightingale has been observed to give lessons in singing to a young bird, from which spectacle we might obviously infer that the song of the bird was not equally congenital with mere voice, but was something capable of modification and of improvement. Men have the same voice or vocal sounds, but they differ from one another in speech or language.

The elephant makes a vocal sound of a windlike sort by the mouth alone, unaided by the trunk, just like the sound of a man panting or sighing; but, if it employ the trunk as well, the sound produced is like that of a hoarse trumpet.

10

With regard to the sleeping and waking of animals, all creatures that are red-blooded and provided with legs give sensible proof that they go to sleep and that they waken up from sleep; for, as a matter of fact, all animals that are furnished with eyelids shut them up when they go to sleep. Furthermore, it would appear that not only do men dream, but horses also, and dogs, and oxen; aye, and sheep, and goats, and all viviparous quadrupeds; and dogs show their dreaming by barking in their sleep. With regard to oviparous animals we cannot be sure that they dream, but most undoubtedly they sleep. And the same may be said of water animals, such as fishes, molluscs,
537a crustaceans, to wit crawfish and the like. These animals sleep without doubt, although their sleep is of very short duration. The proof of their sleeping cannot be got from the condition of their eyes—for none of these creatures are furnished with eyelids—but can be obtained only from their motionless repose.

Apart from the irritation caused by lice and what are nicknamed fleas, fish are met with in a state so motionless that one might easily catch them by hand; and, as a matter of fact, these little creatures, if the fish remain long in one position, will attack them in myriads and devour them. For these parasites are found in the depths of the sea, and are so numerous that they devour any bait made of fish's flesh if it be left long on the ground at the bottom; and fishermen often draw up a cluster of them, all clinging on to the bait.

But it is from the following facts that we may more reasonably infer that fishes sleep. Very often it is possible to take a fish off its guard so far as to catch hold of it or to give it a blow unawares; and all the while that you are preparing to catch or strike it, the fish is quite still but for a slight motion of the tail. And it is quite obvious that the animal is sleeping, from its movements if any disturbance be made during its repose; for it moves just as you would expect in a creature suddenly awakened. Further, owing to their being asleep, fish may be captured by torchlight. The watchmen in the tunny-fishery often take advantage of the fish being asleep to envelop them in a circle of nets; and it is quite obvious that they were thus sleeping by their lying still and allowing

the glistening under-parts of their bodies to become visible, while the capture is taking place. They sleep in the night-time more than during the day; and so soundly at night that you may cast the net without making them stir. Fish, as a general rule, sleep close to the ground, or to the sand or to a stone at the bottom, or after concealing themselves under a rock or the ground. Flat fish go to sleep in the sand; and they can be distinguished by the outlines of their shapes in the sand, and are caught in this position by being speared with pronged instruments. The basse, the chrysophrys or gilt-head, the mullet, and fish of the like sort are often caught in the daytime by the prong owing to their having been surprised when sleeping; for it is scarcely probable that such fish could be pronged while awake. Cartilaginous fish sleep at times so soundly that they may be caught by hand. The dolphin and the whale, and all such as are furnished with a
537b blow-hole, sleep with the blow-hole over the surface of the water, and breathe through the blow-hole while they keep up a quiet flapping of their fins; indeed, some mariners assure us that they have actually heard the dolphin snoring.

Molluscs sleep like fishes, and crustaceans also. It is plain also that insects sleep; for there can be no mistaking their condition of motionless repose. In the bee the fact of its being asleep is very obvious; for at night-time bees are at rest and cease to hum. But the fact that insects sleep may be very well seen in the case of common every-day creatures; for not only do they rest at night-time from dimness of vision (and, by the way, all hard-eyed creatures see but indistinctly), but even if a lighted candle be presented they continue sleeping quite as soundly.

Of all animals man is most given to dreaming. Children and infants do not dream, but in most cases dreaming comes on at the age of four or five years. Instances have been known of full-grown men and women that have never dreamed at all; in exceptional cases of this kind, it has been observed that when a dream occurs in advanced life it prognosticates either actual dissolution or a general break-up of the system.

So much then for sensation and for the phenomena of sleeping and of awakening.

11

With regard to sex, some animals are divided into male and female, but others are not so divided, but can only be said in a comparative way to bring forth young and to be pregnant. In animals that live confined to one spot there is no duality of sex; nor is there such, in fact, in any testaceans. In molluscs and in crustaceans we find male and female: and, indeed, in all animals furnished with feet, biped or quadruped; in short, in all such as by copulation engender either live young or egg or grub. In the several genera, with however certain exceptions, there either absolutely is or absolutely is not a duality of sex. Thus, in quadrupeds the duality is universal, while the absence of such duality is universal in testaceans, and of these creatures, as with plants, some individ-
538a uals are fruitful and some are not.

But among insects and fishes, some cases are found wholly devoid of this duality of sex. For instance, the eel is neither male nor female, and can engender nothing. In fact, those who assert that eels are at times found with hair-like or worm-like progeny attached, make only random assertions from not having carefully noticed the locality of such attachments. For no eel nor animal of this kind is ever viviparous unless previously oviparous; and no eel was ever yet seen with an egg. And animals that are viviparous have their young in the womb and closely attached, and not in the belly; for, if the embryo were kept in the belly, it would be subjected to the process of digestion like ordinary food. When people rest duality of sex in the eel on the assertion that the head of the male is bigger and longer, and the head of the female smaller and more snubbed, they are taking diversity of species for diversity of sex.

There are certain fish that are nicknamed the *epitragiae*, or capon-fish, and, by the way, fish of this description are found in fresh water, as the carp and the *balagrus*. This sort of fish never has either roe or milt; but they are hard and fat all over, and are furnished with a small gut; and these fish are regarded as of super-excellent quality.

Again, just as in testaceans and in plants there is what bears and engenders, but not what impregnates, so is it, among fishes, with the *psetta*, the *erythrinus*, and the *channe;* for these fish are in all cases found furnished with eggs.

As a general rule, in red-blooded animals furnished with feet and not oviparous, the male is larger and longer-lived than the female (except with the mule, where the female is longer-lived and bigger than the male);

whereas in oviparous and vermiparous creatures, as in fishes and in insects, the female is larger than the male; as, for instance, with the serpent, the *phalangium* or venom-spider, the gecko, and the frog. The same difference in size of the sexes is found in fishes, as, for instance, in the smaller cartilaginous fishes, in the greater part of the gregarious species, and in all that live in and about rocks. The fact that the female is longer-lived than the male is inferred from the fact that female fishes are 538b caught older than males. Furthermore, in all animals the upper and front parts are better, stronger, and more thoroughly equipped in the male than in the female, whereas in the female those parts are the better that may be termed hinder-parts or underparts. And this statement is applicable to man and to all vivipara that have feet. Again, the female is less muscular and less compactly jointed, and more thin and delicate in the hair—that is, where hair is found; and, where there is no hair, less strongly furnished in some analogous substance. And the female is more flaccid in texture of flesh, and more knock-kneed, and the shin-bones are thinner; and the feet are more arched and hollow in such animals as are furnished with feet. And with regard to voice, the female in all animals that are vocal has a thinner and sharper voice than the male; except, by the way, with kine, for the lowing and bellowing of the cow has a deeper note than that of the bull. With regard to organs of defence and offence, such as teeth, tusks, horns, spurs, and the like, these in some species the male possesses and the female does not; as, for instance, the hind has no horns, and where the cock-bird has a spur the hen is entirely destitute of the organ; and in like manner the sow is devoid of tusks. In other species such organs are found in both sexes, but are more perfectly developed in the male; as, for instance, the horn of the bull is more powerful than the horn of the cow.

BOOK V

I

As to the parts internal and external that all animals are furnished withal, and further as to the senses, to voice, and sleep, and the duality of sex, all these topics have now been 539a touched upon. It now remains for us to discuss, duly and in order, their several modes of propagation.

These modes are many and diverse, and in some respects are like, and in other respects are unlike to one another. As we carried on our previous discussion genus by genus, so we must attempt to follow the same divisions in our present argument; only that whereas in the former case we started with a consideration of the parts of man, in the present case it behoves us to treat of man last of all because he involves most discussion. We shall commence, then, with testaceans, and then proceed to crustaceans, and then to the other genera in due order; and these other genera are, severally, molluscs, and insects, then fishes viviparous and fishes oviparous, and next birds; and afterwards we shall treat of animals provided with feet, both such as are oviparous and such as are viviparous, and we may observe that some quadrupeds are viviparous, but that the only viviparous biped is man.

Now there is one property that animals are found to have in common with plants. For some plants are generated from the seed of plants, whilst other plants are self-generated through the formation of some elemental principle similar to a seed; and of these latter plants some derive their nutriment from the ground, whilst others grow inside other plants, as is mentioned, by the way, in my treatise on Botany. So with animals, some spring from parent animals according to their kind, whilst others grow spontaneously and not from kindred stock; and of these instances of spontaneous generation some come from putrefying earth or vegetable matter, as is the case with a number of insects, while others are spontaneously generated in the inside of animals out of the secretions of their several organs.

In animals where generation goes by heredity, wherever there is duality of sex generation is due to copulation. In the group of fishes, however, there are some that are neither male nor female, and these, while they are identical generically with other fish, differ from them specifically; but there are others that stand altogether isolated and apart by themselves. Other fishes there are that are always female and never male, and from them are conceived what correspond to the wind-eggs in birds. Such eggs, by the way, in birds are all unfruitful; but it is their nature to be independently capable of generation up to the egg-stage, un- 539b less indeed there be some other mode than the one familiar to us of intercourse with the male; but concerning these topics we shall treat more precisely later on.[1] In the case of certain fishes, however, after they have spontaneously generated eggs, these eggs develop into living animals; only that in certain of these cases development is spontaneous, and in others is not independent of the male; and the method of proceeding in regard to these matters will be set forth by and by, for the method is somewhat like to the method followed in the case of birds. But whensoever creatures are spontaneously generated, either in other animals, in the soil, or on plants, or in the parts of these, and when such are generated male and female, then from the copulation of such spontaneously generated males and females there is generated a something—a something never identical in shape with the parents, but a something imperfect. For instance, the issue of copulation in lice is nits; in flies, grubs; in fleas, grubs egg-like in shape; and from these issues the parent-species is never reproduced, nor is any animal produced at all, but the like nondescripts only.

First, then, we must proceed to treat of 'covering' in regard to such animals as cover and are covered; and then after this to treat in due order of other matters, both the exceptional and those of general occurrence.

2

Those animals, then, cover and are covered in which there is a duality of sex, and the modes of covering in such animals are not in all cases similar nor analogous. For the red-blooded animals that are viviparous and furnished with feet have in all cases organs adapted for procreation, but the sexes do not in all cases come together in like manner. Thus, opisthuretic animals copulate with a rearward presentment, as is the case with the lion, the hare, and the lynx; though, by the way, in the case of the hare, the female is often observed to cover the male.

The case is similar in most other such animals; that is to say, the majority of quadrupeds copulate as best they can, the male mounting the female; and this is the only method of copulating adopted by birds, though there are certain diversities of method observed even in birds. For in some cases the female squats on the ground and the male mounts on top of her, as is the case with the cock and hen bustard, and the barn-door cock and hen; in other cases, the male mounts without the female squatting, as with the male and female crane; for, with these birds, the male mounts on to the back of the female and covers her, and like the cock-sparrow consumes but very little time in the operation. Of quadrupeds, bears perform the operation lying prone on one another, in **540a** the same way as other quadrupeds do while standing up; that is to say, with the belly of the male pressed to the back of the female. Hedgehogs copulate erect, belly to belly.

With regard to large-sized vivipara, the hind only very rarely sustains the mounting of the stag to the full conclusion of the operation, and the same is the case with the cow as regards the bull, owing to the rigidity of the penis of the bull. In point of fact, the females of these animals elicit the sperm of the male in the act of withdrawing from underneath him; and, by the way, this phenomenon has been observed in the case of the stag and hind, domesticated, of course. Covering with the wolf is the same as with the dog. Cats do not copulate with a rearward presentment on the part of the female, but the male stands erect and the female puts herself underneath him; and, by the way, the female cat is peculiarly lecherous, and wheedles the male on to sexual commerce, and caterwauls during the operation. Camels copulate with the female in a sitting posture, and the male straddles over and covers her, not with the hinder presentment on the female's part but like the other quadrupeds mentioned above, and they pass the whole day long in the operation; when thus engaged they retire to lonely spots, and none but their keeper dare approach them. And, be it observed, the penis of the camel is so sinewy that bow-strings are manufactured out of it. Elephants, also, copulate in lonely places, and especially by river-sides in their usual haunts; the female squats down, and straddles with her legs, and the male mounts and covers her. The seal covers like all opisthuretic animals, and in this species the copulation extends over a lengthened time, as is the case with the dog and bitch; and the penis in the male seal is exceptionally large.

3

Oviparous quadrupeds cover one another in the same way. That is to say, in some cases the male mounts the female precisely as in the viviparous animals, as is observed in both the land and the sea tortoise. . . . And these creatures

[1] v. 5 (541a 26); vi. 2 (559b 20); *On the Generation of Animals*, iii. 6, &c.

have an organ in which the ducts converge, and with which they perform the act of copulation, as is also observed in the toad, the frog, and all other animals of the same group.

4

Long animals devoid of feet, like serpents and muraenae, intertwine in coition, belly to **540b** belly. And, in fact, serpents coil round one another so tightly as to present the appearance of a single serpent with a pair of heads. The same mode is followed by the saurians; that is to say, they coil round one another in the act of coition.

5

All fishes, with the exception of the flat selachians, lie down side by side, and copulate belly to belly. Fishes, however, that are flat and furnished with tails—as the ray, the trygon, and the like—copulate not only in this way, but also, where the tail from its thinness is no impediment, by mounting of the male upon the female, belly to back. But the rhina or angel-fish, and other like fishes where the tail is large, copulate only by rubbing against one another sideways, belly to belly. Some men assure us that they have seen some of the selachia copulating hindways, like dog and bitch. In all the cartilaginous species the female is larger than the male; and the same is the case with other fishes for the most part. And among cartilaginous fishes are included, besides those already named, the bos, the lamia, the aetos, the narce or torpedo, the fishing-frog, and all the galeodes or sharks and dogfish. Cartilaginous fishes, then, of all kinds, have in many instances been observed copulating in the way above mentioned; for, by the way, in viviparous animals the process of copulation is of longer duration than in the ovipara.

It is the same with the dolphin and with all cetaceans; that is to say, they come side by side, male and female, and copulate, and the act extends over a time which is neither short nor very long.

Again, in cartilaginous fishes the male, in some species, differs from the female in the fact that he is furnished with two appendages hanging down from about the exit of the residuum, and that the female is not so furnished; and this distinction between the sexes is observed in all the species of the sharks and dog-fish.

Now neither fishes nor any animals devoid of feet are furnished with testicles, but male serpents and male fishes have a pair of ducts which fill with milt or sperm at the rutting season, and discharge, in all cases, a milk-like juice. These ducts unite, as in birds; for birds, by the way, have their testicles in their **541a** interior, and so have all ovipara that are furnished with feet. And this union of the ducts is so far continued and of such extension as to enter the receptive organ in the female.

In viviparous animals furnished with feet there is outwardly one and the same duct for the sperm and the liquid residuum; but there are separate ducts internally, as has been observed in the differentiation of the organs. And with such animals as are not viviparous the same passage serves for the discharge also of the solid residuum; although, internally, there are two passages, separate but near to one another. And these remarks apply to both male and female; for these animals are unprovided with a bladder except in the case of the tortoise; and the she-tortoise, though furnished with a bladder, has only one passage; and tortoises, by the way, belong to the ovipara.

In the case of oviparous fishes the process of coition is less open to observation. In point of fact, some are led by the want of actual observation to surmise that the female becomes impregnated by swallowing the seminal fluid of the male. And there can be no doubt that this proceeding on the part of the female is often witnessed; for at the rutting season the females follow the males and perform this operation, and strike the males with their mouths under the belly, and the males are thereby induced to part with the sperm sooner and more plentifully. And, further, at the spawning season the males go in pursuit of the females, and, as the female spawns, the males swallow the eggs; and the species is continued in existence by the spawn that survives this process. On the coast of Phoenicia they take advantage of these instinctive propensities of the two sexes to catch both one and the other: that is to say, by using the male of the grey mullet as a decoy they collect and net the female, and by using the female, the male.

The repeated observation of this phenomenon has led to the notion that the process was equivalent to coition, but the fact is that a similar phenomenon is observable in quadrupeds. For at the rutting seasons both the males and the females take to running at their genitals, and the two sexes take to smelling each other at those parts.

[With partridges, by the way, if the female

gets to leeward of the male, she becomes thereby impregnated. And often when they happen to be in heat she is affected in this wise by the voice of the male, or by his breathing down on her as he flies overhead; and, by the way, both the male and the female partridge keep the mouth wide open and protrude the tongue in the process of coition.]

The actual process of copulation on the part of oviparous fishes is seldom accurately observed, owing to the fact that they very soon fall aside and slip asunder. But, for all that, the process has been observed to take place in the manner above described.

6

541b Molluscs, such as the octopus, the sepia, and the calamary, have sexual intercourse all in the same way; that is to say, they unite at the mouth, by an interlacing of their tentacles. When, then, the octopus rests its so-called head against the ground and spreads abroad its tentacles, the other sex fits into the outspreading of these tentacles, and the two sexes then bring their suckers into mutual connexion.

Some assert that the male has a kind of penis in one of his tentacles, the one in which are the [two] largest suckers; and they further assert that the organ is tendinous in character, growing attached right up to the middle of the tentacle, and that the latter enables it to enter the nostril or funnel of the female.

Now cuttle-fish and calamaries swim about closely intertwined, with mouths and tentacles facing one another and fitting closely together, and swim thus in opposite directions; and they fit their so-called nostrils into one another, and the one sex swims backwards and the other frontwards during the operation. And the female lays its spawn by the so-called 'blow-hole'; and, by the way, some declare that it is at this organ that the coition really takes place.

7

Crustaceans copulate, as the crawfish, the lobster, the carid and the like, just like the opisthuretic quadrupeds, when the one animal turns up its tail and the other puts his tail on the other's tail. Copulation takes place in the early spring, near to the shore; and, in fact, the process has often been observed in the case of all these animals. Sometimes it takes place about the time when the figs begin to ripen. Lobsters and carids copulate in like manner.

Crabs copulate at the front parts of one another, belly to belly, throwing their overlapping opercula to meet one another: first the smaller crab mounts the larger at the rear; after he has mounted, the larger one turns on one side. Now, the female differs in no respect from the male except in the circumstance that its operculum is larger, more elevated, and more hairy, and into this operculum it spawns its eggs and in the same neighbourhood is the outlet of the residuum. In the copulative process of these animals there is no protrusion of a member from one animal into the other.

8

Insects copulate at the hinder end, and the **542a** smaller individuals mount the larger; and the smaller individual is the male. The female pushes from underneath her sexual organ into the body of the male above, this being the reverse of the operation observed in other creatures; and this organ in the case of some insects appears to be disproportionately large when compared to the size of the body, and that too in very minute creatures; in some insects the disproportion is not so striking. This phenomenon may be witnessed if any one will pull asunder flies that are copulating; and, by the way, these creatures are, under the circumstances, averse to separation; for the intercourse of the sexes in their case is of long duration, as may be observed with common everyday insects, such as the fly and the cantharis. They all copulate in the manner above described, the fly, the cantharis, the sphondyle, [the phalangium spider] and any others of the kind that copulate at all. The phalangia—that is to say, such of the species as spin webs—perform the operation in the following way: the female takes hold of the suspended web at the middle and gives a pull, and the male gives a counter pull; this operation they repeat until they are drawn in together and interlaced at the hinder ends; for, by the way, this mode of copulation suits them in consequence of the rotundity of their stomachs.

So much for the modes of sexual intercourse in all animals; but, with regard to the same phenomenon, there are definite laws followed as regards the season of the year and the age of the animal.

Animals in general seem naturally disposed to this intercourse at about the same period of the year, and that is when winter is changing into summer. And this is the season of spring, in which almost all things that fly or walk or swim take to pairing. Some animals

pair and breed in autumn also and in winter, as is the case with certain aquatic animals and certain birds. Man pairs and breeds at all seasons, as is the case also with domesticated animals, owing to the shelter and good feeding they enjoy: that is to say, with those whose period of gestation is also comparatively brief, as the sow and the bitch, and with those birds that breed frequently. Many animals time the season of intercourse with a view to the right nurture subsequently of their young. In the human species, the male is more under sex-
542b ual excitement in winter, and the female in summer.

With birds the far greater part, as has been said, pair and breed during the spring and early summer, with the exception of the halcyon.

The halcyon breeds at the season of the winter solstice. Accordingly, when this season is marked with calm weather, the name of 'halcyon days' is given to the seven days preceding, and to as many following, the solstice; as Simonides the poet says:—

God lulls for fourteen days the winds to sleep
In winter; and this temperate interlude
Men call the Holy Season, when the deep
Cradles the mother Halcyon and her brood.

And these days are calm, when southerly winds prevail at the solstice, northerly ones having been the accompaniment of the Pleiads. The halcyon is said to take seven days for building her nest, and the other seven for laying and hatching her eggs. In our country there are not always halcyon days about the time of the winter solstice, but in the Sicilian seas this season of calm is almost periodical. The bird lays about five eggs.

9

[The aithyia, or diver, and the larus, or gull, lay their eggs on rocks bordering on the sea, two or three at a time; but the gull lays in the summer, and the diver at the beginning of spring, just after the winter solstice, and it broods over its eggs as birds do in general. And neither of these birds resorts to a hiding-place.]

The halcyon is the most rarely seen of all birds. It is seen only about the time of the setting of the Pleiads and the winter solstice. When ships are lying at anchor in the roads, it will hover about a vessel and then disappear in a moment, and Stesichorus in one of his poems alludes to this peculiarity. The nightingale also breeds at the beginning of summer, and lays five or six eggs; from autumn until spring it retires to a hiding-place.

Insects copulate and breed in winter also, that is when the weather is fine and south winds prevail; such, I mean, as do not hibernate, as the fly and the ant. The greater part of wild animals bring forth once and once only in the year, except in the case of animals like the hare, where the female can become superfoetally impregnated.

In like manner the great majority of fishes breed only once a year, like the shoal-fishes (or,
543a in other words, such as are caught in nets), the tunny, the pelamys, the grey mullet, the chalcis, the mackerel, the sciaena, the psetta and the like, with the exception of the labrax or basse; for this fish (alone amongst those mentioned) breeds twice a year, and the second brood is the weaker of the two. The trichias and the rock-fishes breed twice a year; the red mullet breeds thrice a year, and is exceptional in this respect. This conclusion in regard to the red mullet is inferred from the spawn; for the spawn of the fish may be seen in certain places at three different times of the year. The scorpaena breeds twice a year. The sargue breeds twice, in the spring and in the autumn. The saupe breeds once a year only, in the autumn. The female tunny breeds only once a year, but owing to the fact that the fish in some cases spawn early and in others late, it looks as though the fish bred twice over. The first spawning takes place in December before the solstice, and the latter spawning in the spring. The male tunny differs from the female in being unprovided with the fin beneath the belly which is called *aphareus*.

10

Of cartilaginous fishes, the rhina or angel-fish is the only one that breeds twice; for it breeds at the beginning of autumn, and at the setting of the Pleiads: and, of the two seasons, it is in better condition in the autumn. It engenders at a birth seven or eight young. Certain of the dog-fishes, for example the spotted dog, seem to breed twice a month, and this results from the circumstance that the eggs do not all reach maturity at the same time.

Some fishes breed at all seasons, as the muraena. This animal lays a great number of eggs at a time; and the young when hatched are very small but grow with great rapidity, like the young of the hippurus, for these fishes from being diminutive at the outset grow with exceptional rapidity to an exceptional size. [Be it observed that the muraena breeds at all seasons, but the hippurus only in the spring. The smyrus differs from the smyraena; for the muraena is mottled and weakly, whereas the smyrus is strong and of one uniform colour, and the colour resembles that of the pine-tree, and the animal has teeth inside and out. They say that in this case, as in other similar ones, the one is the male, and the other the female, of a single species. They come out on to the land, and are frequently caught.]

Fishes, then, as a general rule, attain their full growth with great rapidity, but this is especially the case, among small fishes, with the coracine or crow-fish: it spawns, by the way, **543b** near the shore, in weedy and tangled spots. The orphus also, or sea-perch, is small at first, and rapidly attains a great size. The pelamys and the tunny breed in the Euxine, and nowhere else. The cestreus or mullet, the chrysophrys or gilt-head, and the labrax or basse, breed best where rivers run into the sea. The orcys or large-sized tunny, the scorpis, and many other species spawn in the open sea.

11

Fish for the most part breed some time or other during the three months between the middle of March and the middle of June. Some few breed in autumn: as, for instance, the saupe and the sargus, and such others of this sort as breed shortly before the autumn equinox; likewise the electric ray and the angel-fish. Other fishes breed both in winter and in summer, as was previously observed: as, for instance, in winter-time the basse, the grey mullet, and the belone or pipe-fish; and in summer-time, from the middle of June to the middle of July, the female tunny, about the time of the summer solstice; and the tunny lays a sac-like enclosure in which are contained a number of small eggs. The ryades or shoal-fishes breed in summer.

Of the grey mullets, the chelon begins to be in roe between the middle of November and the middle of December; as also the sargue, and the smyxon or myxon, and the cephalus; and their period of gestation is thirty days. And, by the way, some of the grey mullet species are not produced from copulation, but grow spontaneously from mud and sand.

As a general rule, then, fishes are in roe in the spring-time; while some, as has been said, are so in summer, in autumn, or in winter. But whereas the impregnation in the spring-time follows a general law, impregnation in the other seasons does not follow the same rule either throughout or within the limits of one genus; and, further, conception in these variant seasons is not so prolific. And, indeed, we must bear this in mind, that just as with plants and quadrupeds diversity of locality has much to do not only with general physical health but also with the comparative frequency of sexual intercourse and generation, so also with regard to fishes locality of itself has much to do not only in regard to the size and vigour of the creature, but also in regard to its parturition and its copulations, causing the same species to breed oftener in one place and seldomer in another.

12

544a The molluscs also breed in spring. Of the marine molluscs one of the first to breed is the sepia. It spawns at all times of the day and its period of gestation is fifteen days. After the female has laid her eggs, the male comes and discharges the milt over the eggs, and the eggs thereupon harden. And the two sexes of this animal go about in pairs, side by side; and the male is more mottled and more black on the back than the female.

The octopus pairs in winter and breeds in spring, lying hidden for about two months. Its spawn is shaped like a vine-tendril, and resembles the fruit of the white poplar; the creature is extraordinarily prolific, for the number of individuals that come from the spawn is something incalculable. The male differs from the female in the fact that its head is longer, and that the organ called by the fishermen its penis, in the tentacle, is white. The female, after laying her eggs, broods over them, and in consequence gets out of condition, by reason of not going in quest of food during the hatching period.

The purple murex breeds about spring-time, and the ceryx at the close of the winter. And, as a general rule, the testaceans are found to be furnished with their so-called eggs in spring-time and in autumn, with the exception of the edible urchin; for this animal has the so-called eggs in most abundance in these seasons, but at no season is unfurnished with them; and it is furnished with them in especial abundance in warm weather or when a full moon is in the sky. Only, by the way, these remarks do not apply to the sea-urchin found in the Pyrrhaean Straits, for this urchin is at its best for table purposes in the winter; and these urchins are small but full of eggs.

Snails are found by observations to become in all cases impregnated about the same season.

13

[Of birds the wild species, as has been stated, as a general rule pair and breed only once a year. The swallow, however, and the blackbird breed twice. With regard to the blackbird, however, its first brood is killed by inclemency of weather (for it is the earliest of all birds to breed), but the second brood it usually succeeds in rearing.

Birds that are domesticated or that are capable of domestication breed frequently, just as the common pigeon breeds all through the summer, and as is seen in the barn-door hen; for the barn-door cock and hen have intercourse, and the hen breeds, at all seasons alike: excepting by the way, during the days about the winter solstice.

544b Of the pigeon family there are many diversities; for the peristera or common pigeon is not identical with the peleias or rock-pigeon. In other words, the rock-pigeon is smaller than the common pigeon, and is less easily domesticated; it is also black, and small, red-footed and rough-footed; and in consequence of these peculiarities it is neglected by the pigeon-fancier. The largest of all the pigeon species is the phatta or ring-dove; and the next in size is the oenas or stock-dove; and the stock-dove is a little larger than the common pigeon. The smallest of all the species is the turtle-dove. Pigeons breed and hatch at all seasons, if they are furnished with a sunny place and all requisites; unless they are so furnished, they breed only in the summer. The spring brood is the best, or the autumn brood. At all events, without doubt, the produce of the hot season, the summer brood, is the poorest of the three.]

14

Further, animals differ from one another in regard to the time of life that is best adapted for sexual intercourse.

To begin with, in most animals the secretion of the seminal fluid and its generative capacity are not phenomena simultaneously manifested, but manifested successively. Thus, in all animals, the earliest secretion of sperm is unfruitful, or if it be fruitful the issue is comparatively poor and small. And this phenomenon is especially observable in man, in viviparous quadrupeds, and in birds; for in the case of man and the quadruped the offspring is smaller, and in the case of the bird, the egg.

For animals that copulate, of one and the same species, the age for maturity is in most species tolerably uniform, unless it occurs prematurely by reason of abnormality, or is postponed by physical injury.

In man, then, maturity is indicated by a change of the tone of voice, by an increase in size and an alteration in appearance of the sexual organs, as also in an increase of size and alteration in appearance of the breasts; and above all, in the hair-growth at the pubes. Man begins to possess seminal fluid about the age of fourteen, and becomes generatively capable at about the age of twenty-one years.

In other animals there is no hair-growth at the pubes (for some animals have no hair at all, and others have none on the belly, or less on the belly than on the back), but still, in some animals the change of voice is quite obvious; and in some animals other organs give indication of the commencing secretion of the sperm and the onset of generative capacity. As a general rule the female is sharper-toned in voice than the male, and the young animal **545a** than the elder; for, by the way, the stag has a much deeper-toned bay than the hind. Moreover, the male cries chiefly at rutting time, and the female under terror and alarm; and the cry of the female is short, and that of the male prolonged. With dogs also, as they grow old, the tone of the bark gets deeper.

There is a difference observable also in the neighings of horses. That is to say, the female foal has a thin small neigh, and the male foal a small neigh, yet bigger and deeper-toned than that of the female, and a louder one as time goes on. And when the young male and female are two years old and take to breeding, the neighing of the stallion becomes loud and deep, and that of the mare louder and shriller than heretofore; and this change goes on until they reach the age of about twenty years; and after this time the neighing in both sexes becomes weaker and weaker.

As a rule, then, as was stated, the voice of the male differs from the voice of the female, in animals where the voice admits of a continuous and prolonged sound, in the fact that the note in the male voice is more deep and bass; not, however, in all animals, for the contrary holds good in the case of some, as for instance in kine: for here the cow has a deeper note than the bull, and the calves a deeper note than the cattle. And we can thus understand the change of voice in animals that undergo gelding; for male animals that undergo this process assume the characters of the female.

The following are the ages at which various animals become capacitated for sexual commerce. The ewe and the she-goat are sexually mature when one year old, and this statement is made more confidently in respect to the she-goat than to the ewe; the ram and the he-goat are sexually mature at the same age. The progeny of very young individuals among these animals differs from that of other males: for the males improve in the course of the second year, when they become fully mature. The boar and the sow are capable of intercourse when eight months old, and the female brings forth when one year old, the difference corresponding to her period of gestation. The boar is capable of generation when eight months old, but, with a sire under a year in age, the litter is apt to be a poor one. The ages, however, are not invariable; now and then the **545b** boar and the sow are capable of intercourse when four months old, and are capable of producing a litter which can be reared when six months old; but at times the boar begins to be capable of intercourse when ten months. He continues sexually mature until he is three years old. The dog and the bitch are, as a rule, sexually capable and sexually receptive when a year old, and sometimes when eight months old; but the priority in date is more common with the dog than with the bitch. The period of gestation with the bitch is sixty days, or sixty-one, or sixty-two, or sixty-three at the utmost; the period is never under sixty days, or, if it is, the litter comes to no good. The bitch, after delivering a litter, submits to the male in six months, but not before. The horse and the mare are, at the earliest, sexually capable and sexually mature when two years old; the issue, however, of parents of this age is small and poor. As a general rule these animals are sexually capable when three years old, and they grow better for breeding purposes until they reach twenty years. The stallion is sexually capable up to the age of thirty-three years, and the mare up to forty, so that, in point of fact, the animals are sexually capable all their lives long; for the stallion, as a rule, lives for about thirty-five years, and the mare for a little over forty; although, by the way, a horse has been known to live to the age of seventy-five. The ass and the she-ass are sexually capable when thirty months old; but, as a rule, they are not generatively mature until they are three years old, or three years and a half. An instance has been known of a she-ass bearing and bringing forth a foal when only a year old. A cow has been known to calve when only a year old, and the calf grew as big as might be expected, but no more. So much for the dates in time at which these animals attain to generative capacity.

In the human species, the male is generative, at the longest, up to seventy years, and the female up to fifty; but such extended periods are rare. As a rule, the male is generative up to the age of sixty-five, and to the age of forty-five the female is capable of conception.

The ewe bears up to eight years, and, if she be carefully tended, up to eleven years; in fact, the ram and the ewe are sexually capable pretty **546a** well all their lives long. He-goats, if they be fat, are more or less unserviceable for breeding; and this, by the way, is the reason why country folk say of a vine when it stops bearing that it is 'running the goat'. However, if an over-fat he-goat be thinned down, he becomes sexually capable and generative.

Rams single out the oldest ewes for copulation, and show no regard for the young ones. And, as has been stated, the issue of the younger ewes is poorer than that of the older ones.

The boar is good for breeding purposes until he is three years of age; but after that age his issue deteriorates, for after that age his vigour is on the decline. The boar is most capable after a good feed, and with the first sow it mounts; if poorly fed or put to many females, the copulation is abbreviated, and the litter is comparatively poor. The first litter of the sow is the fewest in number; at the second litter she is at her prime. The animal, as it grows old, continues to breed, but the sexual desire abates. When they reach fifteen years, they become unproductive, and are getting old. If a sow be highly fed, it is all the more eager for sexual commerce, whether old or young; but, if it be over-fattened in pregnancy, it gives the less milk after parturition. With regard to the age of the parents, the litter is the best when they are in their prime; but with regard to the seasons of the year, the litter is the best that comes at the beginning of winter; and the summer litter the poorest, consisting as it usually does of animals small and thin and flaccid. The boar, if it be well fed, is sexually capable at all hours, night and day; but otherwise is peculiarly salacious early in the morning. As it grows old the sexual passion dies away, as we have already remarked. Very often a boar, when more or less impotent from age or debility, finding itself unable to accomplish the sexual commerce with due speed, and growing fatigued with the standing posture, will roll the sow over on the ground, and the pair will conclude the operation side by side of one another. The sow is sure of conception if it drops its lugs in rutting time; if the ears do not thus drop, it may have to rut a second time before impregnation takes place.

Bitches do not submit to the male throughout their lives, but only until they reach a certain maturity of years. As a general rule, they are sexually receptive and conceptive until they are twelve years old; although, by the way, cases have been known where dogs and bitches have been respectively procreative and conceptive to the ages of eighteen and even of twenty years. But, as a rule, age diminishes the capability of generation and of conception with these animals as with all others.

546b The female of the camel is opisthuretic, and submits to the male in the way above described;[1] and the season for copulation in Arabia is about the month of October. Its period of gestation is twelve months; and it is never delivered of more than one foal at a time. The female becomes sexually receptive and the male sexually capable at the age of three years. After parturition, an interval of a year elapses before the female is again receptive to the male.

The female elephant becomes sexually receptive when ten years old at the youngest, and when fifteen at the oldest; and the male is sexually capable when five years old, or six. The season for intercourse is spring. The male allows an interval of three years to elapse after commerce with a female: and, after it has once impregnated a female, it has no intercourse with her again. The period of gestation with the female is two years; and only one young animal is produced at a time, in other words it is uniparous. And the embryo is the size of a calf two or three months old.

15

So much for the copulations of such animals as copulate.

We now proceed to treat of generation both with respect to copulating and non-copulating animals, and we shall commence with discussing the subject of generation in the case of the testaceans.

[1] v. 2 (510a 8).

The testacean is almost the only genus that throughout all its species is non-copulative.

The porphyrae, or purple murices, gather together to some one place in the spring-time, and deposit the so-called 'honeycomb'. This substance resembles the comb, only that it is not so neat and delicate; and looks as though a number of husks of white chick-peas were all stuck together. But none of these structures has any open passage, and the porphyra does not grow out of them, but these and all other testaceans grow out of mud and decaying matter. The substance, is, in fact, an excretion of the porphyra and the ceryx; for it is deposited by the ceryx as well. Such, then, of the testaceans as deposit the honeycomb are generated spontaneously like all other testaceans, but they certainly come in greater abundance in places where their congeners have been living previously. At the commencement of the process of depositing the honeycomb, they throw off a slippery mucus, and of this the husklike formations are composed. These formations, then, all melt and deposit their contents on the ground, and at this spot there are found on the ground a number of minute porphyrae, and porphyrae are caught at times with these animalculae upon them, some of which are too small to be differentiated in **547a** form. If the porphyrae are caught before producing this honey-comb, they sometimes go through the process in fishing-creels, not here and there in the baskets, but gathering to some one spot all together, just as they do in the sea; and owing to the narrowness of their new quarters they cluster together like a bunch of grapes.

There are many species of the purple murex; and some are large, as those found off Sigeum and Lectum; others are small, as those found in the Euripus, and on the coast of Caria. And those that are found in bays are large and rough; in most of them the peculiar bloom from which their name is derived is dark to blackness, in others it is reddish and small in size; some of the large ones weigh upwards of a mina apiece. But the specimens that are found along the coast and on the rocks are small-sized, and the bloom in their case is of a reddish hue. Further, as a general rule, in northern waters the bloom is blackish, and in southern waters of a reddish hue. The murex is caught in the spring-time when engaged in the construction of the honeycomb; but it is not caught at any time about the rising of the dog-star, for at that period it does not feed, but con-

ceals itself and burrows. The bloom of the animal is situated between the mecon (or quasi-liver) and the neck, and the co-attachment of these is an intimate one. In colour it looks like a white membrane, and this is what people extract; and if it be removed and squeezed it stains your hand with the colour of the bloom. There is a kind of vein that runs through it, and this quasi-vein would appear to be in itself the bloom. And the qualities, by the way, of this organ are astringent. It is after the murex has constructed the honeycomb that the bloom is at its worst. Small specimens they break in pieces, shells and all, for it is no easy matter to extract the organ; but in dealing with the larger ones they first strip off the shell and then abstract the bloom. For this purpose the neck and mecon are separated, for the bloom lies in between them, above the so-called stomach; hence the necessity of separating them in abstracting the bloom. Fishermen are anxious always to break the animal in pieces while it is yet alive, for, if it die before the process is completed, it vomits out the bloom; and for this reason the fishermen keep the animals in creels, until they have collected a sufficient number and can attend to them at their leisure. Fishermen in past times used not to lower creels or attach them to the bait, so that very often the animal got dropped off in the pulling up; at present, however, they always attach a basket, so that if the animal fall off it is not lost. The animal is more inclined to slip off the bait if it be full inside; if it be empty it is difficult to shake it off. Such are the phenom-
547b ena connected with the porphyra or murex.

The same phenomena are manifested by the ceryx or trumpet-shell; and the seasons are the same in which the phenomena are observable. Both animals, also, the murex and the ceryx, have their opercula similarly situated—and, in fact, all the stromboids, and this is congenital with them all; and they feed by protruding the so-called tongue underneath the operculum. The tongue of the murex is bigger than one's finger, and by means of it, it feeds, and perforates conchylia and the shells of its own kind. Both the murex and the ceryx are long-lived. The murex lives for about six years; and the yearly increase is indicated by a distinct interval in the spiral convolution of the shell.

The mussel also constructs a honeycomb.

With regard to the limnostreae, or lagoon oysters, wherever you have slimy mud there you are sure to find them beginning to grow. Cockles and clams and razor-fishes and scallops grow spontaneously in sandy places. The pinna grows straight up from its tuft of anchoring fibres in sandy and slimy places; these creatures have inside them a parasite nicknamed the pinna-guard, in some cases a small carid and in other cases a little crab; if the pinna be deprived of this pinna-guard it soon dies.

As a general rule, then, all testaceans grow by spontaneous generation in mud, differing from one another according to the differences of the material; oysters growing in slime, and cockles and the other testaceans above mentioned on sandy bottoms; and in the hollows of the rocks the ascidian and the barnacle, and common sorts, such as the limpet and the nerites. All these animals grow with great rapidity, especially the murex and the scallop; for the murex and the scallop attain their full growth in a year. In some of the testaceans white crabs are found, very diminutive in size; they are most numerous in the trough-shaped mussel. In the pinna also is found the so-called pinna-guard. They are found also in the scallop and in the oyster; these parasites never appear to grow in size. Fishermen declare that the parasite is congenital with the larger animal. [Scallops burrow for a time in the sand, like the murex.]

[Shell-fish, then, grow in the way above mentioned; and some of them grow in shallow
548a water, some on the sea-shore, some in rocky places, some on hard and stony ground, and some in sandy places.] Some shift about from place to place, others remain permanent on one spot. Of those that keep to one spot the pinnae are rooted to the ground; the razor-fish and the clam keep to the same locality, but are not so rooted; but still, if forcibly removed they die.

[The star-fish is naturally so warm that whatever it lays hold of is found, when suddenly taken away from the animal, to have undergone a process like boiling. Fishermen say that the star-fish is a great pest in the Strait of Pyrrha. In shape it resembles a star as seen in an ordinary drawing. The so-called 'lungs' are generated spontaneously. The shells that painters use are a good deal thicker, and the bloom is outside the shell on the surface. These creatures are mostly found on the coast of Caria.]

The hermit-crab grows spontaneously out of soil and slime, and finds its way into untenanted shells. As it grows it shifts to a larger shell, as for instance into the shell of the nerites, or of the strombus or the like, and very often into the shell of the small ceryx. After entering a new shell, it carries it about, and begins again to feed, and, by and by, as it grows, it shifts again into another larger one.

16

Moreover, the animals that are unfurnished with shells grow spontaneously, like the testaceans, as, for instance, the sea-nettles and the sponges in rocky caves.

Of the sea-nettle, or sea-anemone, there are two species; and of these one species lives in hollows and never loosens its hold upon the rocks, and the other lives on smooth flat reefs, free and detached, and shifts its position from time to time. [Limpets also detach themselves, and shift from place to place.]

In the chambered cavities of sponges pinna-guards or parasites are found. And over the chambers there is a kind of spider's web, by the opening and closing of which they catch minute fishes; that is to say, they open the web to let the fish get in, and close it again to entrap them.

Of sponges there are three species; the first is of loose porous texture, the second is close-textured, the third, which is nicknamed 'the **548b** sponge of Achilles', is exceptionally fine and close-textured and strong. This sponge is used as a lining to helmets and greaves, for the purpose of deadening the sound of the blow; and this is a very scarce species. Of the close-textured sponges such as are particularly hard and rough are nicknamed 'goats'.

Sponges grow spontaneously either attached to a rock or on sea-beaches, and they get their nutriment in slime: a proof of this statement is the fact that when they are first secured they are found to be full of slime. This is characteristic of all living creatures that get their nutriment by close local attachment. And, by the way, the close-textured sponges are weaker than the more openly porous ones because their attachment extends over a smaller area.

It is said that the sponge is sensitive; and as a proof of this statement they say that if the sponge is made aware of an attempt being made to pluck it from its place of attachment it draws itself together, and it becomes a difficult task to detach it. It makes a similar contractile movement in windy and boisterous weather, obviously with the object of tightening its hold. Some persons express doubts as to the truth of this assertion; as, for instance, the people of Torone.

The sponge breeds parasites, worms, and other creatures, on which, if they be detached, the rock-fishes prey, as they prey also on the remaining stumps of the sponge; but, if the sponge be broken off, it grows again from the remaining stump and the place is soon as well covered as before.

The largest of all sponges are the loose-textured ones, and these are peculiarly abundant on the coast of Lycia. The softest are the close-textured sponges; for, by the way, the so-called sponges of Achilles are harder than these. As a general rule, sponges that are found in deep calm waters are the softest; for usually windy and stormy weather has a tendency to harden them (as it has to harden all similar growing things), and to arrest their growth. And this accounts for the fact that the sponges found in the Hellespont are rough and close-textured; and, as a general rule, sponges found beyond or inside Cape Malea are, respectively, comparatively soft or comparatively hard. But, by the way, the habitat of the sponge should not be too sheltered and warm, for it has a tendency to decay, like all similar vegetable-like growths. And this accounts for the fact that the sponge is at its best when found in deep water close to shore; for owing to the depth of the water they enjoy shelter alike from stormy winds and from excessive heat.

Whilst they are still alive and before they are washed and cleaned, they are blackish in colour. Their attachment is not made at one particular spot, nor is it made all over their bodies; for vacant pore-spaces intervene. There is a kind of membrane stretched over the under parts; and in the under parts the points of attachment are the more numerous. On the top **549a** most of the pores are closed, but four or five are open and visible; and we are told by some that it is through these pores that the animal takes its food.

There is a particular species that is named the 'aplysia' or the 'unwashable', from the circumstance that it cannot be cleaned. This species has the large open and visible pores, but all the rest of the body is close-textured; and, if it be dissected, it is found to be closer and more glutinous than the ordinary sponge, and, in a word, something lunglike in consistency. And, on all hands, it is allowed that this species is sensitive and long-lived. They are distinguished in the sea from ordinary sponges from the circumstance that the ordinary sponges are white while the slime is in them, but that these sponges are under any circumstances black.

And so much with regard to sponges and to generation in the testaceans.

17

Of crustaceans, the female crawfish after copulation conceives and retains its eggs for about three months, from about the middle of May to about the middle of August; they then lay the eggs into the folds underneath the belly, and their eggs grow like grubs. This same phenomenon is observable in molluscs also, and in such fishes as are oviparous; for in all these cases the egg continues to grow.

The spawn of the crawfish is of a loose or granular consistency, and is divided into eight parts; for corresponding to each of the flaps on the side there is a gristly formation to which the spawn is attached, and the entire structure resembles a cluster of grapes; for each gristly formation is split into several parts. This is obvious enough if you draw the parts asunder; but at first sight the whole appears to be one and indivisible. And the largest are not those nearest to the outlet but those in the middle, and the farthest off are the smallest. The size of the small eggs is that of a small seed in a fig; and they are not quite close to the outlet, but placed middleways; for at both ends, tailwards and trunkwards, there are two intervals devoid of eggs; for it is thus that the flaps also grow. The side flaps, then, cannot close, but by placing the end flap on them the animal can close up all, and this end-flap serves
549b them for a lid. And in the act of laying its eggs it seems to bring them towards the gristly formations by curving the flap of its tail, and then, squeezing the eggs towards the said gristly formations and maintaining a bent posture, it performs the act of laying. The gristly formations at these seasons increase in size and become receptive of the eggs; for the animal lays its eggs into these formations, just as the sepia lays its eggs among twigs and driftwood.

It lays its eggs, then, in this manner, and after hatching them for about twenty days it rids itself of them all in one solid lump, as is quite plain from outside. And out of these eggs crawfish form in about fifteen days, and these crawfish are caught at times less then a finger's breadth, or seven-tenths of an inch, in length. The animal, then, lays its eggs before the middle of September, and after the middle of that month throws off its eggs in a lump. With the humped carids or prawns the time for gestation is four months or thereabouts.

Crawfish are found in rough and rocky places, lobsters in smooth places, and neither crawfish nor lobsters are found in muddy ones; and this accounts for the fact that lobsters are found in the Hellespont and on the coast of Thasos, and crawfish in the neighbourhood of Sigeum and Mount Athos. Fishermen, accordingly, when they want to catch these various creatures out at sea, take bearings on the beach and elsewhere that tell them where the ground at the bottom is stony and where soft with slime. In winter and spring these animals keep in near to land, in summer they keep in deep water; thus at various times seeking respectively for warmth or coolness.

The so-called arctus or bear-crab lays its eggs at about the same time as the crawfish; and consequently in winter and in the spring-time, before laying their eggs, they are at their best, and after laying at their worst.

They cast their shell in the spring-time (just as serpents shed their so-called 'old-age' or slough), both directly after birth and in later life; this is true both of crabs and crawfish. And, by the way, all crawfish are longlived.

18

Molluscs, after pairing and copulation, lay a white spawn; and this spawn, as in the case of the testacean, gets granular in time. The octopus discharges into its hole, or into a potsherd or into any similar cavity, a structure resembling the tendrils of a young vine or the fruit of the white poplar, as has been previously observed. The eggs, when the female has laid them, are clustered round the sides of the
550a hole. They are so numerous that, if they be removed they suffice to fill a vessel much larger than the animal's body in which they were contained. Some fifty days later, the eggs burst and the little polypuses creep out, like little spiders, in great numbers; the characteristic form of their limbs is not yet to be discerned in detail, but their general outline is clear enough. And, by the way, they are so small and helpless that the greater number perish; it is a fact that they have been seen so extremely minute as to be absolutely without organization, but nevertheless when touched they moved. The eggs of the sepia look like big black myrtle-berries, and they are linked all together like a bunch of grapes, clustered round a centre, and are not easily sundered

from one another: for the male exudes over them some moist glairy stuff, which constitutes the sticky gum. These eggs increase in size; and they are white at the outset, but black and larger after the sprinkling of the male seminal fluid.

When it has come into being the young sepia is first distinctly formed inside out of the white substance, and when the egg bursts it comes out. The inner part is formed as soon as the female lays the egg, something like a hail-stone; and out of this substance the young sepia grows by a head-attachment, just as young birds grow by a belly-attachment. What is the exact nature of the navel-attachment has not yet been observed, except that as the young sepia grows the white substance grows less and less in size, and at length, as happens with the yolk in the case of birds, the white substance in the case of the young sepia disappears. In the case of the

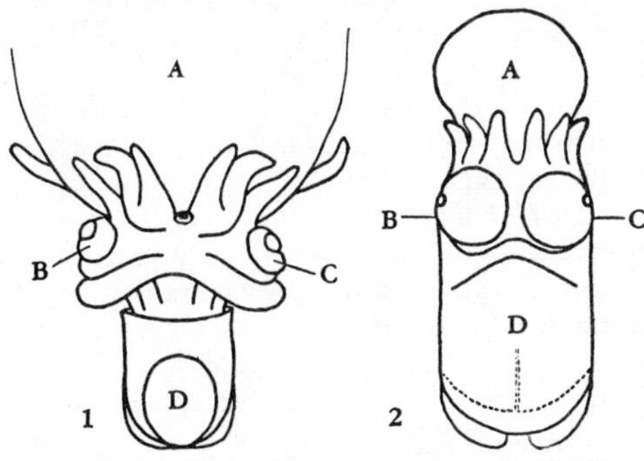

1. Younger, and 2, older, stages in the development of Sepia. A. 'Ovum,' or remains of the yolk-sac. B, C. Eyes. D. τὸ σηπίδιον, or body of the little Sepia.

young sepia, as in the case of the young of most animals, the eyes at first seem very large. To illustrate this by way of a figure, let A represent the ovum, B and C the eyes, and D the sepidium, or body of the little sepia.

The female sepia goes pregnant in the spring-time, and lays its eggs after fifteen days of gestation; after the eggs are laid there comes in another fifteen days something like a bunch of grapes, and at the bursting of these the young sepiae issue forth. But if, when the young ones are fully formed, you sever the outer covering a moment too soon, the young creatures eject excrement, and their colour changes from white to red in their alarm.

Crustaceans, then, hatch their eggs by brood-
550b ing over them as they carry them about beneath their bodies; but the octopus, the sepia, and the like hatch their eggs without stirring from the spot where they may have laid them, and this statement is particularly applicable to the sepia; in fact, the nest of the female sepia is often seen exposed to view close in to shore. The female octopus at times sits brooding over her eggs, and at other times squats in front of her hole, stretching out her tentacles on guard.

The sepia lays her spawn near to land in the neighbourhood of sea-weed or reeds or any off-sweepings such as brushwood, twigs, or stones; and fishermen place heaps of faggots here and there on purpose, and on to such heaps the female deposits a long continuous roe in shape like a vine tendril. It lays or spirts out the spawn with an effort, as though there were difficulty in the process. The female calamary spawns at sea; and it emits the spawn, as does the sepia, in the mass.

The calamary and the cuttle-fish are short-lived, as, with few exceptions, they never see the year out; and the same statement is applicable to the octopus.

From one single egg comes one single sepia; and this is likewise true of the young calamary.

The male calamary differs from the female; for if its gill-region be dilated and examined there are found two red formations resembling breasts, with which the male is unprovided. In the sepia, apart from this distinction in the sexes, the male, as has been stated,[1] is more mottled than the female.

19

With regard to insects, that the male is less than the female and that he mounts upon her back, and how he performs the act of copulation and the circumstance that he gives over reluctantly, all this has already been set forth,[2] in most cases of insect copulation this process is speedily followed up by parturition.

All insects engender grubs, with the exception of a species of butterfly; and the female of this species lays a hard egg, resembling the seed of the cnecus, with a juice inside it. But from the grub, the young animal does not grow out of a mere portion of it, as a young animal grows from a portion only of an egg, but the grub entire grows and the animal becomes differentiated out of it.

And of insects some are derived from insect congeners, as the venom-spider and the common-spider from the venom-spider and the common-spider, and so with the attelabus or

[1] 524b 30. [2] v. 8.

locust, the acris or grasshopper, and the tettix 551a or cicada. Other insects are not derived from living parentage, but are generated spontaneously: some out of dew falling on leaves, ordinarily in spring-time, but not seldom in winter when there has been a stretch of fair weather and southerly winds; others grow in decaying mud or dung; others in timber, green or dry; some in the hair of animals; some in the flesh of animals; some in excrements: and some from excrement after it has been voided, and some from excrement yet within the living animal, like the helminthes or intestinal worms. And of these intestinal worms there are three species: one named the flat-worm, another the round worm, and the third the ascarid. These intestinal worms do not in any case propagate their kind. The flat-worm, however, in an exceptional way, clings fast to the gut, and lays a thing like a melon-seed, by observing which indication the physician concludes that his patient is troubled with the worm.

The so-called psyche or butterfly is generated from caterpillars which grow on green leaves, chiefly leaves of the raphanus, which some call crambe or cabbage. At first it is less than a grain of millet; it then grows into a small grub; and in three days it is a tiny caterpillar. After this it grows on and on, and becomes quiescent and changes its shape, and is now called a chrysalis. The outer shell is hard, and the chrysalis moves if you touch it. It attaches itself by cobweb-like filaments, and is unfurnished with mouth or any other apparent organ. After a little while the outer covering bursts asunder, and out flies the winged creature that we call the psyche or butterfly. At first, when it is a caterpillar, it feeds and ejects excrement; but when it turns into the chrysalis it neither feeds nor ejects excrement.

The same remarks are applicable to all such insects as are developed out of the grub, both such grubs as are derived from the copulation of living animals and such as are generated without copulation on the part of parents. For the grub of the bee, the anthrena, and the wasp, 551b whilst it is young, takes food and voids excrement; but when it has passed from the grub shape to its defined form and become what is termed a 'nympha', it ceases to take food and to void excrement, and remains tightly wrapped up and motionless until it has reached its full size, when it breaks the formation with which the cell is closed, and issues forth. The insects named the hypera and the penia are derived from similar caterpillars, which move in an undulatory way, progressing with one part and then pulling up the hinder parts by a bend of the body. The developed insect in each case takes its peculiar colour from the parent caterpillar.

From one particular large grub, which has as it were horns, and in other respects differs from grubs in general, there comes, by a metamorphosis of the grub, first a caterpillar, then the cocoon, then the *necydalus;* and the creature passes through all these transformations within six months. A class of women unwind and reel off the cocoons of these creatures, and afterwards weave a fabric with the threads thus unwound; a Coan woman of the name of Pamphila, daughter of Plateus, being credited with the first invention of the fabric. After the same fashion the carabus or stag-beetle comes from grubs that live in dry wood: at first the grub is motionless, but after a while the shell bursts and the stag-beetle issues forth.

From the cabbage is engendered the cabbage-worm, and from the leek the prasocuris or leekbane; this creature is also winged. From the flat animalcule that skims over the surface of rivers comes the oestrus or gadfly; and this accounts for the fact that gadflies most abound in the neighbourhood of waters on whose surface these animalcules are observed. From a certain small, black and hairy caterpillar comes first a wingless glow-worm; and this creature again suffers a metamorphosis, and transforms into a winged insect named the bostrychus (or hair-curl).

Gnats grow from ascarids; and ascarids are engendered in the slime of wells, or in places where there is a deposit left by the draining off of water. This slime decays, and first turns 552a white, then black, and finally blood-red; and at this stage there originate in it, as it were, little tiny bits of red weed, which at first wriggle about all clinging together, and finally break loose and swim in the water, and are hereupon known as ascarids. After a few days they stand straight up on the water motionless and hard, and by and by the husk breaks off and the gnats are seen sitting upon it, until the sun's heat or a puff of wind sets them in motion, when they fly away.

With all grubs and all animals that break out from the grub state, generation is due primarily to the heat of the sun or to wind.

Ascarids are more likely to be found, and grow with unusual rapidity, in places where there is a deposit of a mixed and heterogeneous kind, as in kitchens and in ploughed fields, for the contents of such places are disposed to rapid putrefaction. In autumn, also, owing to the drying up of moisture, they grow in unusual numbers.

The tick is generated from couch-grass. The cockchafer comes from a grub that is generated in the dung of the cow or the ass. The cantharus or scarabeus rolls a piece of dung into a ball, lies hidden within it during the winter, and gives birth therein to small grubs, from which grubs come new canthari. Certain winged insects also come from the grubs that are found in pulse, in the same fashion as in the cases described.

Flies grow from grubs in the dung that farmers have gathered up into heaps: for those who are engaged in this work assiduously gather up the compost, and this they technically term 'working-up' the manure. The grub is exceedingly minute to begin with; first—even at this stage—it assumes a reddish colour, and then from a quiescent state it takes on the power of motion, as though born to it; it then becomes a small motionless grub; it then moves again, and again relapses into immobility; it then comes out a perfect fly, and moves away under the influence of the sun's heat or of a puff of air. The myops or horse-fly is engendered in timber. The orsodacna or budbane is a transformed grub; and this grub is engendered in cabbage-stalks. The cantharis **552ᵇ** comes from the caterpillars that are found on fig-trees or pear-trees or fir-trees—for on all these grubs are engendered—and also from caterpillars found on the dog-rose; and the cantharis takes eagerly to ill-scented substances, from the fact of its having been engendered in ill-scented woods. The conops comes from a grub that is engendered in the slime of vinegar.

And, by the way, living animals are found in substances that are usually supposed to be incapable of putrefaction; for instance, worms are found in long-lying snow; and snow of this description gets reddish in colour, and the grub that is engendered in it is red, as might have been expected, and it is also hairy. The grubs found in the snows of Media are large and white; and all such grubs are little disposed to motion. In Cyprus, in places where copper-ore is smelted, with heaps of the ore piled on day after day, an animal is engendered in the fire, somewhat larger than a bluebottle fly, furnished with wings, which can hop or crawl through the fire. And the grubs and these latter animals perish when you keep the one away from the fire and the other from the snow. Now the salamander is a clear case in point, to show us that animals do actually exist that fire cannot destroy; for this creature, so the story goes, not only walks through the fire but puts it out in doing so.

On the river Hypanis in the Cimmerian Bosphorus, about the time of the summer solstice, there are brought down towards the sea by the stream what look like little sacks rather bigger than grapes, out of which at their bursting issues a winged quadruped. The insect lives and flies about until the evening, but as the sun goes down it pines away, and dies at sunset having lived just one day, from which circumstance it is called the ephemeron.

As a rule, insects that come from caterpillars and grubs are held at first by filaments resembling the threads of a spider's web.

Such is the mode of generation of the insects above enumerated.

20

The wasps that are nicknamed 'the ichneumons' (or hunters), less in size, by the way, than the ordinary wasp, kill spiders and carry off the dead bodies to a wall or some such place with a hole in it; this hole they smear over with mud and lay their grubs inside it, and from the grubs come the hunter-wasps. Some of the coleoptera and of the small and nameless insects make small holes or cells of mud on a **553ᵃ** wall or on a grave-stone, and there deposit their grubs.

With insects, as a general rule, the time of generation from its commencement to its completion comprises three or four weeks. With grubs and grub-like creatures the time is usually three weeks, and in the oviparous insects as a rule four. But, in the case of oviparous insects, the egg-formation comes at the close of seven days from copulation, and during the remaining three weeks the parent broods over and hatches its young; i.e. where this is the result of copulation, as in the case of the spider and its congeners. As a rule, the transformations take place in intervals of three or four days, corresponding to the lengths of interval at which the crises recur in intermittent fevers.

So much for the generation of insects. Their death is due to the shrivelling of their organs, just as the larger animals die of old age. Winged insects die in autumn from the shrinking of their wings. The myops dies from dropsy in the eyes.

21

With regard to the generation of bees different hypotheses are in vogue. Some affirm that bees neither copulate nor give birth to young, but that they fetch their young. And some say that they fetch their young from the flower of the callyntrum; others assert that they bring them from the flower of the reed, others, from the flower of the olive. And in respect to the olive theory, it is stated as a proof that, when the olive harvest is most abundant, the swarms are most numerous. Others declare that they fetch the brood of the drones from such things as above mentioned, but that the working bees are engendered by the rulers of the hive.

Now of these rulers there are two kinds: the better kind is red in colour, the inferior kind is black and variegated; the ruler is double the size of the working bee. These rulers have the abdomen or part below the waist half as large again, and they are called by some the 'mothers', from an idea that they bear or generate the bees; and, as a proof of this theory of their motherhood, they declare that the brood of the drones appears even when there is no ruler-bee in the hive, but that the bees do not appear in his absence. Others, again, assert that these in-
553b sects copulate, and that the drones are male and the bees female.

The ordinary bee is generated in the cells of the comb, but the ruler-bees in cells down below attached to the comb, suspended from it, apart from the rest, six or seven in number, and growing in a way quite different from the mode of growth of the ordinary brood.

Bees are provided with a sting, but the drones are not so provided. The rulers are provided with stings, but they never use them; and this latter circumstance will account for the belief of some people that they have no stings at all.

22

Of bees there are various species. The best kind is a little round mottled insect; another is long, and resembles the anthrena; a third is black and flat-bellied, and is nick-named the 'robber'; a fourth kind is the drone, the largest of all, but stingless and inactive. And this proportionate size of the drone explains why some bee-masters place a net-work in front of the hives; for the network is put to keep the big drones out while it lets the little bees go in.

Of the king bees there are, as has been stated, two kinds. In every hive there are more kings than one; and a hive goes to ruin if there be too few kings, not because of anarchy thereby ensuing, but, as we are told, because these creatures contribute in some way to the generation of the common bees. A hive will go also to ruin if there be too large a number of kings in it; for the members of the hives are thereby subdivided into too many separate factions.

Whenever the spring-time is late a-coming, and when there is drought and mildew, then the progeny of the hive is small in number. But when the weather is dry they attend to the honey, and in rainy weather their attention is concentrated on the brood; and this will account for the coincidence of rich olive-harvests and abundant swarms.

The bees first work at the honeycomb, and then put the pupae in it: by the mouth, say those who hold the theory of their bringing them from elsewhere. After putting in the pupae they put in the honey for subsistence, and this they do in the summer and autumn; and, by the way, the autumn honey is the better of the two.

The honeycomb is made from flowers, and the materials for the wax they gather from the resinous gum of trees, while honey is distilled from dew, and is deposited chiefly at the risings of the constellations or when a rainbow is in the sky: and as a general rule there is no honey before the rising of the Pleiads. [The bee, then, makes the wax from flowers. The honey, however, it does not make, but
554a merely gathers what is deposited out of the atmosphere; and as a proof of this statement we have the known fact that occasionally bee-keepers find the hives filled with honey within the space of two or three days. Furthermore, in autumn flowers are found, but honey, if it be withdrawn, is not replaced; now, after the withdrawal of the original honey, when no food or very little is in the hives, there would be a fresh stock of honey, if the bees made it from flowers.] Honey, if allowed to ripen and mature, gathers consistency; for at first it is like water and remains liquid for several days. If it be drawn off during these days it has no consistency; but it attains consistency in about twenty days. The taste of thyme-honey is discernible at once, from its peculiar sweetness and consistency.

The bee gathers from every flower that is furnished with a calyx or cup, and from all other flowers that are sweet-tasted, without doing injury to any fruit; and the juices of the flowers it takes up with the organ that resembles a tongue and carries off to the hive.

Swarms are robbed of their honey on the appearance of the wild fig. They produce the best larvae at the time the honey is a-making. The bee carries wax and bees' bread round its legs, but vomits the honey into the cell. After depositing its young, it broods over it like a bird. The grub when it is small lies slantwise in the comb, but by and by rises up straight by an effort of its own and takes food, and holds on so tightly to the honeycomb as actually to cling to it.

The young of bees and of drones is white, and from the young come the grubs; and the grubs grow into bees and drones. The egg of the king bee is reddish in colour, and its substance is about as consistent as thick honey; and from the first it is about as big as the bee that is produced from it. From the young of the king bee there is no intermediate stage, it is said, of the grub, but the bee comes at once.

Whenever the bee lays an egg in the comb there is always a drop of honey set against it. The larva of the bee gets feet and wings as soon as the cell has been stopped up with wax, and when it arrives at its completed form it breaks **554b** its membrane and flies away. It ejects excrement in the grub state, but not afterwards; that is, not until it has got out of the encasing membrane, as we have already described. If you remove the heads from off the larvae before the coming of the wings, the bees will eat them up; and if you nip off the wings from a drone and let it go, the bees will spontaneously bite off the wings from off all the remaining drones.

The bee lives for six years as a rule, as an exception for seven years. If a swarm lasts for nine years, or ten, great credit is considered due to its management.

In Pontus are found bees exceedingly white in colour, and these bees produce their honey twice a month. (The bees in Themiscyra, on the banks of the river Thermodon, build honeycombs in the ground and in hives, and these honeycombs are furnished with very little wax but with honey of great consistency; and the honeycomb, by the way, is smooth and level.) But this is not always the case with these bees, but only in the winter season; for in Pontus the ivy is abundant, and it flowers at this time of the year, and it is from the ivy-flower that they derive their honey. A white and very consistent honey is brought down from the upper country to Amisus, which is deposited by bees on trees without the employment of honeycombs: and this kind of honey is produced in other districts in Pontus.

There are bees also that construct triple honeycombs in the ground; and these honeycombs supply honey but never contain grubs. But the honeycombs in these places are not all of this sort, nor do all the bees construct them.

23

Anthrenae and wasps construct combs for their young. When they have no king, but are wandering about in search of one, the anthrene constructs its comb on some high place, and the wasp inside a hole. When the anthrene and the wasp have a king, they construct their combs underground. Their combs are in all cases hexagonal like the comb of the bee. They are composed, however, not of wax, but of a bark-like filamented fibre, and the comb of the anthrene is much neater than the comb of the wasp. Like the bee, they put their young just like a drop of liquid on to the side of the cell, **555a** and the egg clings to the wall of the cell. But the eggs are not deposited in the cells simultaneously; on the contrary, in some cells are creatures big enough to fly, in others are nymphae, and in others are mere grubs. As in the case of bees, excrement is observed only in the cells where the grubs are found. As long as the creatures are in the nymph condition they are motionless, and the cell is cemented over. In the comb of the anthrene there is found in the cell of the young a drop of honey in front of it. The larvae of the anthrene and the wasp make their appearance not in the spring but in the autumn; and their growth is especially discernible in times of full moon. And, by the way, the eggs and the grubs never rest at the bottom of the cells, but always cling on to the side wall.

24

There is a kind of humble-bee that builds a cone-shaped nest of clay against a stone or in some similar situation, besmearing the clay with something like spittle. And this nest or hive is exceedingly thick and hard; in point of fact, one can hardly break it open with a spike. Here the insects lay their eggs, and white grubs are produced wrapped in a black membrane. Apart from the membrane there is found some wax in the honeycomb; and this wax is much sallower in hue than the wax in the honeycomb of the bee.

25

Ants copulate and engender grubs; and these grubs attach themselves to nothing in particular, but grow on and on from small and rounded shapes until they become elongated and defined in shape: and they are engendered in spring-time.

26

The land-scorpion also lays a number of egg-shaped grubs, and broods over them. When the hatching is completed, the parent animal, as happens with the parent spider, is ejected and put to death by the young ones; for very often the young ones are about eleven in number.

27

Spiders in all cases copulate in the way above mentioned, and generate at first small grubs. And these grubs metamorphose in their entirety, and not partially, into spiders; for, by the way, the grubs are round-shaped at the outset. And the spider, when it lays its eggs, broods
555b over them, and in three days the eggs or grubs take definite shape.

All spiders lay their eggs in a web; but some spiders lay in a small and fine web, and others in a thick one; and some, as a rule, lay in a round-shaped case or capsule, and some are only partially enveloped in the web. The young grubs are not all developed at one and the same time into young spiders; but the moment the development takes place, the young spider makes a leap and begins to spin his web. The juice of the grub, if you squeeze it, is the same as the juice found in the spider when young; that is to say, it is thick and white.

The meadow spider lays its eggs into a web, one half of which is attached to itself and the other half is free; and on this the parent broods until the eggs are hatched. The phalangia lay their eggs in a sort of strong basket which they have woven, and brood over it until the eggs are hatched. The smooth spider is much less prolific than the phalangium or hairy spider. These phalangia, when they grow to full size, very often envelop the mother phalangium and eject and kill her; and not seldom they kill the father-phalangium as well, if they catch him: for, by the way, he has the habit of co-operating with the mother in the hatching. The brood of a single phalangium is sometimes three hundred in number. The spider attains its full growth in about four weeks.

28

Grasshoppers [or locusts] copulate in the same way as other insects; that is to say, with the lesser covering the larger, for the male is smaller than the female. The females first insert the hollow tube, which they have at their tails, in the ground, and then lay their eggs: and the male, by the way, is not furnished with this tube. The females lay their eggs all in a lump together, and in one spot, so that the entire lump of eggs resembles a honeycomb. After they have laid their eggs, the eggs assume the shape of oval grubs that are enveloped by a sort of thin clay, like a membrane; in this membrane-like formation they grow on to maturity. The larva is so soft that it collapses at a touch. The larva is not placed on the surface of the ground, but a little beneath the surface; and, when it reaches maturity, it comes out of its clayey investiture in the shape of a little black grasshopper; by and by, the skin integument strips off, and it grows larger and larger.

The grasshopper lays its eggs at the close of
556a summer, and dies after laying them. The fact is that, at the time of laying the eggs, grubs are engendered in the region of the mother grasshopper's neck; and the male grasshoppers die about the same time. In spring-time they come out of the ground; and, by the way, no grasshoppers are found in mountainous land or in poor land, but only in flat and loamy land, for the fact is they lay their eggs in cracks of the soil. During the winter their eggs remain in the ground; and with the coming of summer the last year's larva develops into the perfect grasshopper.

29

The attelabi or locusts lay their eggs and die in like manner after laying them. Their eggs are subject to destruction by the autumn rains, when the rains are unusually heavy; but in seasons of drought the locusts are exceedingly numerous, from the absence of any destructive cause, since their destruction seems then to be a matter of accident and to depend on luck.

30

Of the cicada there are two kinds; one, small in size, the first to come and the last to disappear; the other, large, the singing one, that comes last and first disappears. Both in the small and the large species some are divided at the waist, to wit, the singing ones, and some are undivided; and these latter have no song. The large and singing cicada is by some designated the 'chirper', and the small cicada the 'tettigonium' or cicadelle. And, by the way, such of the tettigonia as are divided at the waist can sing just a little.

The cicada is not found where there are no trees; and this accounts for the fact that in the district surrounding the city of Cyrene it is not found at all in the plain country, but is found in great numbers in the neighbourhood of the city, and especially where olive-trees are growing: for an olive grove is not thickly shaded. And the cicada is not found in cold places, and consequently is not found in any grove that keeps out the sunlight.

The large and the small cicada copulate alike, belly to belly. The male discharges sperm into the female, as is the case with insects in general, and the female cicada has a cleft generative organ; and it is the female into which the male discharges the sperm.

They lay their eggs in fallow lands, boring a hole with the pointed organ they carry in the rear, as do the locusts likewise; for the locust
556b lays its eggs in untilled lands, and this fact may account for their numbers in the territory adjacent to the city of Cyrene. The cicadae also lay their eggs in the canes on which husbandmen prop vines, perforating the canes; and also in the stalks of the squill. This brood runs into the ground. And they are most numerous in rainy weather. The grub, on attaining full size in the ground, becomes a tettigometra (or nymph), and the creature is sweetest to the taste at this stage before the husk is broken. When the summer solstice comes, the creature issues from the husk at night-time, and in a moment, as the husk breaks, the larva becomes the perfect cicada. The creature, also, at once turns black in colour and harder and larger, and takes to singing. In both species, the larger and the smaller, it is the male that sings, and the female that is unvocal. At first, the males are the sweeter eating; but, after copulation, the females, as they are full then of white eggs.

If you make a sudden noise as they are flying overhead they let drop something like water. Country people, in regard to this, say that they are voiding urine, i.e. that they have an excrement, and that they feed upon dew.

If you present your finger to a cicada and bend back the tip of it and then extend it again, it will endure the presentation more quietly than if you were to keep your finger outstretched altogether; and it will set to climbing your finger: for the creature is so weak-sighted that it will take to climbing your finger as though that were a moving leaf.

31

Of insects that are not carnivorous but that live on the juices of living flesh, such as lice and fleas and bugs, all, without exception, generate what are called 'nits', and these nits generate nothing.

Of these insects the flea is generated out of the slightest amount of putrefying matter; for wherever there is any dry excrement, a flea is sure to be found. Bugs are generated from the moisture of living animals, as it dries up outside their bodies. Lice are generated out of the flesh of animals.

When lice are coming there is a kind of small eruption visible, unaccompanied by any discharge of purulent matter; and, if you prick an animal when in this condition at the spot of
557a eruption, the lice jump out. In some men the appearance of lice is a disease, in cases where the body is surcharged with moisture; and, indeed, men have been known to succumb to this louse-disease, as Alcman the poet and the Syrian Pherecydes are said to have done. Moreover, in certain diseases lice appear in great abundance.

There is also a species of louse called the 'wild louse', and this is harder than the ordinary louse, and there is exceptional difficulty in getting the skin rid of it. Boys' heads are apt to be lousy, but men's in less degree; and women are more subject to lice than men. But, whenever people are troubled with lousy heads, they are less than ordinarily troubled with headache. And lice are generated in other animals than man. For birds are infested with them; and pheasants, unless they clean themselves in the dust, are actually destroyed by them. All other winged animals that are furnished with feathers are similarly infested, and all hair-coated creatures also, with the single exception of the ass, which is infested neither with lice nor with ticks.

Cattle suffer both from lice and from ticks. Sheep and goats breed ticks, but do not breed lice. Pigs breed lice large and hard. In dogs are found the flea peculiar to the animal, the *Cynoroestes*. In all animals that are subject to lice, the latter originate from the animals themselves. Moreover, in animals that bathe at all, lice are more than usually abundant when they change the water in which they bathe.

In the sea, lice are found on fishes, but they are generated not out of the fish but out of slime; and they resemble multipedal woodlice, only that their tail is flat. Sea-lice are uniform in shape and universal in locality, and are particularly numerous on the body of the red mullet. And all these insects are multipedal and devoid of blood.

The parasite that feeds on the tunny is found in the region of the fins; it resembles a scorpion, and is about the size of a spider. In the seas between Cyrene and Egypt there is a fish that attends on the dolphin, which is called the 'dolphin's louse'. This fish gets exceedingly fat from enjoying an abundance of food while the dolphin is out in pursuit of its prey.

32

557b Other animalcules besides these are generated, as we have already remarked, some in wool or in articles made of wool, as the *ses* or clothes-moth. And these animalcules come in greater numbers if the woollen substances are dusty; and they come in especially large numbers if a spider be shut up in the cloth or wool, for the creature drinks up any moisture that may be there, and dries up the woollen substance. This grub is found also in men's clothes.

A creature is also found in wax long laid by, just as in wood, and it is the smallest of animalcules and is white in colour, and is designated the acari or mite. In books also other animalcules are found, some resembling the grubs found in garments, and some resembling tailless scorpions, but very small. As a general rule we may state that such animalcules are found in practically anything, both in dry things that are becoming moist and in moist things that are drying, provided they contain the conditions of life.

There is a grub entitled the 'faggot-bearer', as strange a creature as is known. Its head projects outside its shell, mottled in colour, and its feet are near the end or apex, as is the case with grubs in general; but the rest of its body is cased in a tunic as it were of spider's web, and there are little dry twigs about it, that look as though they had stuck by accident to the creature as it went walking about. But these twig-like formations are naturally connected with the tunic, for just as the shell is with the body of the snail so is the whole superstructure with our grub; and they do not drop off, but can only be torn off, as though they were all of a piece with him, and the removal of the tunic is as fatal to this grub as the removal of the shell would be to the snail. In course of time this grub becomes a chrysalis, as is the case with the silkworm, and lives in a motionless condition. But as yet it is not known into what winged condition it is transformed.

The fruit of the wild fig contains the psen, or fig-wasp. This creature is a grub at first; but in due time the husk peels off and the psen leaves the husk behind it and flies away, and enters into the fruit of the fig-tree through its orifice, and causes the fruit not to drop off; and with a view to this phenomenon, country folk are in the habit of tying wild figs on to fig-trees, and of planting wild fig-trees near domesticated ones.

33

In the case of animals that are quadrupeds and red-blooded and oviparous, generation
558a takes place in the spring, but copulation does not take place in an uniform season. In some cases it takes place in the spring, in others in summer time, and in others in the autumn, according as the subsequent season may be favourable for the young.

The tortoise lays eggs with a hard shell and of two colours within, like birds' eggs, and after laying them buries them in the ground and treads the ground hard over them; it then broods over the eggs on the surface of the ground, and hatches the eggs the next year. The hemys, or fresh-water tortoise, leaves the water and lays its eggs. It digs a hole of a cask-like shape, and deposits therein the eggs; after rather less than thirty days it digs the eggs up again and hatches them with great rapidity, and leads its young at once off to the water. The sea-turtle lays on the ground eggs just like the eggs of domesticated birds, buries the eggs in the ground, and broods over them in the night-time. It lays a very great number of eggs, amounting at times to one hundred.

Lizards and crocodiles, terrestrial and fluvial, lay eggs on land. The eggs of lizards hatch spontaneously on land, for the lizard does not live on into the next year; in fact, the life of the animal is said not to exceed six months. The river-crocodile lays a number of eggs, sixty at the most, white in colour, and broods over them for sixty days: for, by the way, the creature is very long-lived. And the disproportion is more marked in this animal than in any other between the smallness of the original egg and the huge size of the full-grown animal. For the egg is not larger than that of the goose, and the young crocodile is small, answering to the egg in size, but the full-grown animal attains the length of twenty-six feet; in fact, it is actually stated that the animal goes on growing to the end of its days.

34

With regard to serpents or snakes, the viper is externally viviparous, having been previously oviparous internally. The egg, as with the egg of fishes, is uniform in colour and soft-skinned. The young serpent grows on the surface of the egg, and, like the young of fishes, has no shell-like envelopment. The young of the viper is born inside a membrane that bursts from off the young creature in three days; and at times the young viper eats its way out from the inside of the egg. The mother viper brings forth all its young in one day, twenty in number, and one at a time. The other serpents **558b** are externally oviparous, and their eggs are strung on to one another like a lady's necklace; after the dam has laid her eggs in the ground she broods over them, and hatches the eggs in the following year.

BOOK VI

1

So much for the generative processes in snakes and insects, and also in oviparous quadrupeds. Birds without exception lay eggs, but the pairing season and the times of parturition are not alike for all. Some birds couple and lay at almost any time in the year, as for instance the barn-door hen and the pigeon: the former of these coupling and laying during the entire year, with the exception of the month before and the month after the winter solstice. Some hens, even in the high breeds, lay a large quantity of eggs before brooding, amounting to as many as sixty; and, by the way, the higher breeds are less prolific than the inferior ones. The Adrian hens are small-sized, but they lay every day; they are cross-tempered, and often kill their chickens; they are of all colours. Some domesticated hens lay twice a day; indeed, instances have been known where hens, after exhibiting extreme fecundity, have died suddenly. Hens, then, lay eggs, as has been stated, at all times indiscriminately; the pigeon, the ring-dove, the turtle-dove, and the stock-dove lay twice a year, and the pigeon actually lays ten times a year. The great majority of birds lay during the spring-time. Some birds are prolific, and prolific in either of two ways—either by laying often, as the pigeon, or by laying many eggs at a sitting, as the barn-door hen. All birds of prey, or birds with crooked talons, are unprolific, except the kestrel: this bird is the most prolific of birds of prey; as many as four eggs have been observed in the nest, and occasionally it lays even more.

Birds in general lay their eggs in nests, but **559a** such as are disqualified for flight, as the partridge and the quail, do not lay them in nests but on the ground, and cover them over with loose material. The same is the case with the lark and the tetrix. These birds hatch in sheltered places; but the bird called merops in Boeotia, alone of all birds, burrows into holes in the ground and hatches there.

Thrushes, like swallows, build nests of clay, on high trees, and build them in rows all close together, so that from their continuity the structure resembles a necklace of nests. Of all birds that hatch for themselves the hoopoe is the only one that builds no nest whatever; it gets into the hollow of the trunk of a tree, and lays its eggs there without making any sort of nest. The circus builds either under a dwelling-roof or on cliffs. The tetrix, called ourax in Athens, builds neither on the ground nor on trees, but on low-lying shrubs.

2

The egg in the case of all birds alike is hard-shelled, if it be the produce of copulation and be laid by a healthy hen—for some hens lay soft eggs. The interior of the egg is of two colours, and the white part is outside and the yellow part within.

The eggs of birds that frequent rivers and marshes differ from those of birds that live on dry land; that is to say, the eggs of water-birds have comparatively more of the yellow or yolk and less of the white. Eggs vary in colour according to their kind. Some eggs are white, as those of the pigeon and of the partridge; others are yellowish, as the eggs of marsh birds; in some cases the eggs are mottled, as the eggs of the guinea-fowl and the pheasant; while the eggs of the kestrel are red, like vermilion.

Eggs are not symmetrically shaped at both ends: in other words, one end is comparatively sharp, and the other end is comparatively blunt; and it is the latter end that protrudes first at the time of laying. Long and pointed eggs are female; those that are round, or more rounded at the narrow end, are male. Eggs are hatched by the incubation of the mother-bird. **559b** In some cases, as in Egypt, they are hatched spontaneously in the ground, by being buried in dung heaps. A story is told of a toper in Syracuse, how he used to put eggs into the ground under his rush-mat and to keep on drinking until he hatched them. Instances have occurred of eggs being deposited in warm vessels and getting hatched spontaneously.

The sperm of birds, as of animals in general, is white. After the female has submitted to the male, she draws up the sperm to underneath her midriff. At first it is little in size and white in colour; by and by it is red, the colour of blood; as it grows, it becomes pale and yellow all over. When at length it is getting ripe for hatching, it is subject to differentiation of substance, and the yolk gathers together within and the white settles round it on the outside. When the full time is come, the egg detaches itself and protrudes, changing from soft to hard with such temporal exactitude that, whereas it is not hard during the process of protrusion, it hardens immediately after the process is completed: that is if there be no concomitant pathological circumstances. Cases have occurred where substances resembling the egg at a critical point of its growth—that is, when it is yellow all over, as the yolk is subsequently—have been found in the cock when cut open, underneath his midriff, just where the hen has her eggs; and these are entirely yellow in appearance and of the same size as ordinary eggs. Such phenomena are regarded as unnatural and portentous.

Such as affirm that wind-eggs are the residua of eggs previously begotten from copulation are mistaken in this assertion, for we have cases well authenticated where chickens of the common hen and goose have laid wind-eggs without ever having been subjected to copulation. Wind-eggs are smaller, less palatable, and more liquid than true eggs, and are produced in greater numbers. When they are put under the mother bird, the liquid contents never coagulate, but both the yellow and the white remain as they were. Wind-eggs are laid by a number of birds: as for instance by the common hen, the hen partridge, the hen pigeon, the peahen, the goose, and the vulpanser. Eggs are hatched under brooding hens more rapidly in summer than in winter; that is to say, hens **560a** hatch in eighteen days in summer, but occasionally in winter take as many as twenty-five. And by the way for brooding purposes some birds make better mothers than others. If it thunders while a hen-bird is brooding, the eggs get addled. Wind-eggs that are called by some *cynosura* and *uria* are produced chiefly in summer. Wind-eggs are called by some zephyr-eggs, because at spring-time hen-birds are observed to inhale the breezes; they do the same if they be stroked in a peculiar way by hand. Wind-eggs can turn into fertile eggs, and eggs due to previous copulation can change breed, if before the change of the yellow to the white the hen that contains wind-eggs, or eggs begotten of copulation be trodden by another cock-bird. Under these circumstances the wind-eggs turn into fertile eggs, and the previously impregnated eggs follow the breed of the impregnator; but if the latter impregnation takes place during the change of the yellow to the white, then no change in the egg takes place: the wind-egg does not become a true egg, and the true egg does not take on the breed of the latter impregnator. If when the egg-substance is small copulation be intermitted, the previously existing egg-substance exhibits no increase; but if the hen be again submitted to the male the increase in size proceeds with rapidity.

The yolk and the white are diverse not only in colour but also in properties. Thus, the yolk congeals under the influence of cold, whereas the white instead of congealing is inclined rather to liquefy. Again, the white stiffens under the influence of fire, whereas the yolk does not stiffen; but, unless it be burnt through and through, it remains soft, and in point of fact is inclined to set or to harden more from the boiling than from the roasting of the egg. The yolk and the white are separated by a membrane from one another. The so-called 'hail-stones', or treadles, that are found at the extremity of the yellow in no way contribute towards generation, as some erroneously suppose: they are two in number, one below and the other above. If you take out of the shells a number of yolks and a number **560b** of whites and pour them into a saucepan and boil them slowly over a low fire, the yolks will gather into the centre and the whites will set all around them.

Young hens are the first to lay, and they do so at the beginning of spring and lay more eggs than the older hens, but the eggs of the younger hens are comparatively small. As a general rule, if hens get no brooding they pine and sicken. After copulation hens shiver and shake themselves, and often kick rubbish about all round them—and this, by the way, they do sometimes after laying—whereas pigeons trail their rumps on the ground, and geese dive under the water. Conception of the true egg and conformation of the wind-egg take place rapidly with most birds; as for instance with the hen-partridge when in heat. The fact is that, when she stands to windward and within scent of the male, she conceives, and becomes useless for decoy purposes: for, by the way, the partridge appears to have a very acute sense of smell.

The generation of the egg after copulation and the generation of the chick from the subsequent hatching of the egg are not brought about within equal periods for all birds, but differ as to time according to the size of the parent-birds. The egg of the common hen after copulation sets and matures in ten days as a general rule; the egg of the pigeon in a somewhat lesser period. Pigeons have the faculty of holding back the egg at the very moment of parturition; if a hen pigeon be put about by any one, for instance if it be disturbed on its nest, or have a feather plucked out, or sustain any other annoyance or disturbance, then even though she had made up her mind to lay she can keep the egg back in abeyance. A singular phenomenon is observed in pigeons with regard to pairing: that is, they kiss one another just when the male is on the point of mounting the female, and without this preliminary the male would decline to perform his function. With the older males the preliminary kiss is only given to begin with, and subsequently he mounts without previously kissing; with younger males the preliminary is never omitted. Another singularity in these birds is that the hens tread one another when a cock is not forthcoming, after kissing one another just as takes place in the normal pairing. Though they do not impregnate one
561a another they lay more eggs under these than under ordinary circumstances; no chicks, however, result therefrom, but all such eggs are wind-eggs.

3

Generation from the egg proceeds in an identical manner with all birds, but the full periods from conception to birth differ, as has been said. With the common hen after three days and three nights there is the first indication of the embryo; with larger birds the interval being longer, with smaller birds shorter. Meanwhile the yolk comes into being, rising towards the sharp end, where the primal element of the egg is situated, and where the egg gets hatched; and the heart appears, like a speck of blood, in the white of the egg. This point beats and moves as though endowed with life, and from it two vein-ducts with blood in them trend in a convoluted course [as the egg-substance goes on growing, towards each of the two circumjacent integuments]; and a membrane carrying bloody fibres now envelops the yolk, leading off from the vein-ducts. A little afterwards the body is differentiated, at first very small and white. The head is clearly distinguished, and in it the eyes, swollen out to a great extent. This condition of the eyes lasts on for a good while, as it is only by degrees that they diminish in size and collapse. At the outset the under portion of the body appears insignificant in comparison with the upper portion. Of the two ducts that lead from the heart, the one proceeds towards the circumjacent integument, and the other, like a navel-string, towards the yolk. The life-element of the chick is in the white of the egg, and the nutriment comes through the navel-string out of the yolk.

When the egg is now ten days old the chick and all its parts are distinctly visible. The head is still larger than the rest of its body, and the eyes larger than the head, but still devoid of vision. The eyes, if removed about this time, are found to be larger than beans, and black; if the cuticle be peeled off them there is a white and cold liquid inside, quite glittering in the sunlight, but there is no hard substance whatsoever. Such is the condition of the head
561b and eyes. At this time also the larger internal organs are visible, as also the stomach and the arrangement of the viscera; and veins that seem to proceed from the heart are now close to the navel. From the navel there stretch a pair of veins; one towards the membrane that envelops the yolk (and, by the way, the yolk is now liquid, or more so than is normal), and the other towards that membrane which envelops collectively the membrane wherein the

chick lies, the membrane of the yolk, and the intervening liquid. [For, as the chick grows, little by little one part of the yolk goes upward, and another part downward, and the white liquid is between them; and the white of the egg is underneath the lower part of the yolk, as it was at the outset.] On the tenth day the white is at the extreme outer surface, reduced in amount, glutinous, firm in substance, and sallow in colour.

The disposition of the several constituent parts is as follows. First and outermost comes the membrane of the egg, not that of the shell, but underneath it. Inside this membrane is a white liquid; then comes the chick, and a membrane round about it, separating it off so as to keep the chick free from the liquid; next after the chick comes the yolk, into which one of the two veins was described as leading, the other one leading into the enveloping white substance. [A membrane with a liquid resembling serum envelops the entire structure. Then comes another membrane right round the embryo, as has been described, separating it off against the liquid. Underneath this comes the yolk, enveloped in another membrane (into which yolk proceeds the navel-string that leads from the heart and the big vein), so as to keep the embryo free of both liquids.]

About the twentieth day, if you open the egg and touch the chick, it moves inside and chirps; and it is already coming to be covered with down, when, after the twentieth day is past, the chick begins to break the shell. The head is situated over the right leg close to the flank, and the wing is placed over the head; and about this time is plain to be seen the membrane resembling an after-birth that comes next after the outermost membrane of the shell, **562a** into which membrane the one of the navel-strings was described as leading (and, by the way, the chick in its entirety is now within it), and so also is the other membrane resembling an after-birth, namely that surrounding the yolk, into which the second navel-string was described as leading; and both of them were described as being connected with the heart and the big vein. At this conjuncture the navel-string that leads to the outer after-birth collapses and becomes detached from the chick, and the membrane that leads into the yolk is fastened on to the thin gut of the creature, and by this time a considerable amount of the yolk is inside the chick and a yellow sediment is in its stomach. About this time it discharges residuum in the direction of the outer after-birth, and has residuum inside its stomach; and the outer residuum is white [and there comes a white substance inside]. By and by the yolk, diminishing gradually in size, at length becomes entirely used up and comprehended within the chick (so that, ten days after hatching, if you cut open the chick, a small remnant of the yolk is still left in connexion with the gut), but it is detached from the navel, and there is nothing in the interval between, but it has been used up entirely. During the period above referred to the chick sleeps, wakes up, makes a move and looks up and chirps; and the heart and the navel together palpitate as though the creature were respiring. So much as to generation from the egg in the case of birds.

Birds lay some eggs that are unfruitful, even eggs that are the result of copulation, and no life comes from such eggs by incubation; and this phenomenon is observed especially with pigeons.

Twin eggs have two yolks. In some twin eggs a thin partition of white intervenes to prevent the yolks mixing with each other, but some twin eggs are unprovided with such partition, and the yokes run into one another. There are some hens that lay nothing but twin eggs, and in their case the phenomenon regarding the yolks has been observed. For instance, a hen has been known to lay eighteen eggs, and to hatch twins out of them all, except those that were wind-eggs; the rest were fertile (though, by the way, one of the twins is **562b** always bigger than the other), but the eighteenth was abnormal or monstrous.

4

Birds of the pigeon kind, such as the ring-dove and the turtle-dove, lay two eggs at a time; that is to say, they do so as a general rule, and they never lay more than three. The pigeon, as has been said, lays at all seasons; the ring-dove and the turtle-dove lay in the spring-time, and they never lay more than twice in the same season. The hen-bird lays the second pair of eggs when the first pair happens to have been destroyed, for many of the hen-pigeons destroy the first brood. The hen-pigeon, as has been said, occasionally lays three eggs, but it never rears more than two chicks, and sometimes rears only one; and the odd one is always a wind-egg.

Very few birds propagate within their first year. All birds, after once they have begun laying, keep on having eggs, though in the case of some birds it is difficult to detect the fact from the minute size of the creature.

The pigeon, as a rule, lays a male and a female egg, and generally lays the male egg first; after laying it allows a day's interval to ensue and then lays the second egg. The male takes its turn of sitting during the daytime; the female sits during the night. The first-laid egg is hatched and brought to birth within twenty days; and the mother bird pecks a hole in the egg the day before she hatches it out. The two parent birds brood for some time over the chicks in the way in which they brooded previously over the eggs. In all connected with the rearing of the young the female parent is more cross-tempered than the male, as is the case with most animals after parturition. The hens lay as many as ten times in the year; occasional instances have been known of their laying eleven times, and in Egypt they actually lay twelve times. The pigeon, male and female, couples within the year; in fact, it couples when only six months old. Some assert that ring-doves and turtle-doves pair and procreate when only three months old, and instance their superabundant numbers by way of proof of the assertion. The hen-pigeon carries her eggs fourteen days; for as many more days the parent birds hatch the eggs; by the end of another fourteen days the chicks are so far capa- **563a** ble of flight as to be overtaken with difficulty. [The ring-dove, according to all accounts, lives up to forty years. The partridge lives over sixteen.] [After one brood the pigeon is ready for another within thirty days.]

5

The vulture builds its nest on inaccessible cliffs; for which reason its nest and young are rarely seen. And therefore Herodorus, father of Bryson the Sophist, declares that vultures belong to some foreign country unknown to us, stating as a proof of the assertion that no one has ever seen a vulture's nest, and also that vultures in great numbers make a sudden appearance in the rear of armies. However, difficult as it is to get a sight of it, a vulture's nest has been seen. The vulture lays two eggs.

[Carnivorous birds in general are observed to lay but once a year. The swallow is the only carnivorous bird that builds a nest twice. If you prick out the eyes of swallow chicks while they are yet young, the birds will get well again and will see by and by.]

6

The eagle lays three eggs and hatches two of them, as it is said in the verses ascribed to Musaeus:

That lays three, hatches two, and cares for one.

This is the case in most instances, though occasionally a brood of three has been observed. As the young ones grow, the mother becomes wearied with feeding them and extrudes one of the pair from the nest. At the same time the bird is said to abstain from food, to avoid harrying the young of wild animals. That is to say, its wings blanch, and for some days its talons get turned awry. It is in consequence about this time cross-tempered to its own young. The phene is said to rear the young one that has been expelled the nest. The eagle broods for about thirty days.

The hatching period is about the same for the larger birds, such as the goose and the great bustard; for the middle-sized birds it extends over about twenty days, as in the case of the kite and the hawk. The kite in general lays two eggs, but occasionally rears three young ones. The so-called aegolius at times rears four. It is not true that, as some aver, the **563b** raven lays only two eggs; it lays a larger number. It broods for about twenty days and then extrudes its young. Other birds perform the same operation; at all events mother birds that lay several eggs often extrude one of their young.

Birds of the eagle species are not alike in the treatment of their young. The white-tailed eagle is cross, the black eagle is affectionate in the feeding of the young; though, by the way, all birds of prey, when their brood is rather forward in being able to fly, beat and extrude them from the nest. The majority of birds other than birds of prey, as has been said, also act in this manner, and after feeding their young take no further care of them; but the crow is an exception. This bird for a considerable time takes charge of her young; for, even when her young can fly, she flies alongside of them and supplies them with food.

7

The cuckoo is said by some to be a hawk transformed, because at the time of the cuckoo's coming, the hawk, which it resembles, is never seen; and indeed it is only for a few days that you will see hawks about when

the cuckoo's note sounds early in the season. The cuckoo appears only for a short time in summer, and in winter disappears. The hawk has crooked talons, which the cuckoo has not; neither with regard to the head does the cuckoo resemble the hawk. In point of fact, both as regards the head and the claws it more resembles the pigeon. However, in colour and in colour alone it does resemble the hawk, only that the markings of the hawk are striped, and of the cuckoo mottled. And, by the way, in size and flight it resembles the smallest of the hawk tribe, which bird disappears as a rule about the time of the appearance of the cuckoo, though the two have been seen simultaneously. The cuckoo has been seen to be preyed on by the hawk; and this never happens between birds of the same species. They say no one has ever seen the young of the cuckoo. The bird lays eggs, but does not build a nest. Sometimes it lays its eggs in the nest of a smaller bird after first devouring the eggs of this bird; it lays by preference in the nest of the ring-
564a dove, after first devouring the eggs of the pigeon. (It occasionally lays two, but usually one.) It lays also in the nest of the hypolais, and the hypolais hatches and rears the brood. It is about this time that the bird becomes fat and palatable. [The young of hawks also get palatable and fat. One species builds a nest in the wilderness and on sheer and inaccessible cliffs.]

8

With most birds, as has been said of the pigeon, the hatching is carried on by the male and the female in turns: with some birds, however, the male only sits long enough to allow the female to provide herself with food. In the goose tribe the female alone incubates, and after once sitting on the eggs she continues brooding until they are hatched.

The nests of all marsh-birds are built in districts fenny and well supplied with grass; consequently, the mother-bird while sitting quiet on her eggs can provide herself with food without having to submit to absolute fasting.

With the crow also the female alone broods, and broods throughout the whole period; the male bird supports the female, bringing her food and feeding her. The female of the ring-dove begins to brood in the afternoon and broods through the entire night until breakfast-time of the following day; the male broods during the rest of the time. Partridges build a nest in two compartments; the male broods on the one and the female on the other. After hatching, each of the parent birds rears its brood. But the male, when he first takes his young out of the nest, treads them.

9

Peafowl live for about twenty-five years, breed about the third year, and at the same time take on their spangled plumage. They hatch their eggs within thirty days or rather more. The peahen lays but once a year, and lays twelve eggs, or may be a slightly lesser number: she does not lay all the eggs there and then one after the other, but at intervals of two or three days. Such as lay for the first time lay about eight eggs. The peahen lays wind-eggs. They pair in the spring; and laying begins immediately after pairing. The bird moults when
564b the earliest trees are shedding their leaves, and recovers its plumage when the same trees are recovering their foliage. People that rear peafowl put the eggs under the barn-door hen, owing to the fact that when the peahen is brooding over them the peacock attacks her and tries to trample on them; owing to this circumstance some birds of wild varieties run away from the males and lay their eggs and brood in solitude. Only two eggs are put under a barn-door hen, for she could not brood over and hatch a large number. They take every precaution, by supplying her with food, to prevent her going off the eggs and discontinuing the brooding.

With male birds about pairing time the testicles are obviously larger than at other times, and this is conspicuously the case with the more salacious birds, such as the barn-door cock and the cock partridge; the peculiarity is less conspicuous in such birds as are intermittent in regard to pairing.

10

So much for the conception and generation of birds.

It has been previously stated that fishes are not all oviparous. Fishes of the cartilaginous genus are viviparous; the rest are oviparous. And cartilaginous fishes are first oviparous internally and subsequently viviparous; they rear the embryos internally, the batrachus or fishing-frog being an exception.

Fishes also, as was above stated, are provided with wombs, and wombs of diverse kinds. The oviparous genera have wombs bifurcate in shape and low down in position; the cartilaginous genus have wombs shaped like those of birds. The womb, however, in the cartilaginous fishes differs in this respect from the womb of birds, that with some cartilaginous fishes the eggs do not settle close to the diaphragm but middle-ways along the backbone, and as they grow they shift their position.

The egg with all fishes is not of two colours within but is of even hue; and the colour is nearer to white than to yellow, and that both when the young is inside it and previously as well.

Development from the egg in fishes differs from that in birds in this respect, that it does not exhibit that one of the two navel-strings that leads off to the membrane that lies close under the shell, while it does exhibit that one of the two that in the case of birds leads off to the yolk. In a general way the rest of the development from the egg onwards is identical in birds and fishes. That is to say, development takes place at the upper part of the egg, and the veins extend in like manner, at first from the heart; and at first the head, the eyes, and the upper parts are largest; and as the crea- **565a** ture grows the egg-substance decreases and eventually disappears, and becomes absorbed within the embryo, just as takes place with the yolk in birds.

The navel-string is attached a little way below the aperture of the belly. When the creatures are young the navel-string is long, but as they grow it diminishes in size; at length it gets small and becomes incorporated, as was described in the case of birds. The embryo and the egg are enveloped by a common membrane, and just under this is another membrane that envelops the embryo by itself; and in between the two membranes is a liquid. The food inside the stomach of the little fishes resembles that inside the stomach of young chicks, and is partly white and partly yellow.

As regards the shape of the womb, the reader is referred to my treatise on Anatomy. The womb, however, is diverse in diverse fishes, as for instance in the sharks as compared one with another or as compared with the skate. That is to say, in some sharks the eggs adhere in the middle of the womb round about the backbone, as has been stated, and this is the case with the dog-fish; as the eggs grow they shift their place; and since the womb is bifurcate and adheres to the midriff, as in the rest of similar creatures, the eggs pass into one or other of the two compartments. This womb and the womb of the other sharks exhibit, as you go a little way off from the midriff, something resembling white breasts, which never make their appearance unless there be conception.

Dog-fish and skate have a kind of egg-shell, in the which is found an egg-like liquid. The shape of the egg-shell resembles the tongue of a bagpipe, and hair-like ducts are attached to the shell. With the dog-fish which is called by some the 'dappled shark', the young are born when the shell-formation breaks in pieces and falls out; with the ray, after it has laid the egg the shell-formation breaks up and the young move out. The spiny dog-fish has its eggs close to the midriff above the breast-like formations; when the egg descends, as soon as it gets detached the young is born. The **565b** mode of generation is the same in the case of the fox-shark.

The so-called smooth shark has its eggs in betwixt the wombs like the dog-fish; these eggs shift into each of the two horns of the womb and descend, and the young develop with the navel-string attached to the womb, so that, as the egg-substance gets used up, the embryo is sustained to all appearance just as in the case of quadrupeds. The navel-string is long and adheres to the under part of the womb (each navel-string being attached as it were by a sucker), and also to the centre of the embryo in the place where the liver is situated. If the embryo be cut open, even though it has the egg-substance no longer, the food inside is egg-like in appearance. Each embryo, as in the case of quadrupeds, is provided with a chorion and separate membranes. When young the embryo has its head upwards, but downwards when it gets strong and is completed in form. Males are generated on the left-hand side of the womb, and females on the right-hand side, and males and females on the same side together. If the embryo be cut open, then, as with quadrupeds, such internal organs as it is furnished with, as for instance the liver, are found to be large and supplied with blood.

All cartilaginous fishes have at one and the same time eggs above close to the midriff (some larger, some smaller), in considerable numbers, and also embryos lower down. And this circumstance leads many to suppose that fishes of this species pair and bear young every month, inasmuch as they do not produce all their young at once, but now and again and over a lengthened period. But such eggs as have come down below within the womb are simultaneously ripened and completed in growth.

Dog-fish in general can extrude and take in again their young, as can also the angel-fish and the electric ray—and, by the way, a large electric ray has been seen with about eighty embryos inside it—but the spiny dog-fish is an exception to the rule, being prevented by the spine of the young fish from so doing. Of the flat cartilaginous fish, the trygon and the ray cannot extrude and take in again in consequence of the roughness of the tails of the young. The batrachus or fishing-frog also is unable to take in its young owing to the size of the head and the prickles; and, by the way, as was previously remarked, it is the only one of these fishes that is not viviparous.

566a So much for the varieties of the cartilaginous species and for their modes of generation from the egg.

11

At the breeding season the sperm-ducts of the male are filled with sperm, so much so that if they be squeezed the sperm flows out spontaneously as a white fluid; the ducts are bifurcate, and start from the midriff and the great vein. About this period the sperm-ducts of the male are quite distinct [from the womb of the female], but at any other than the actual breeding time their distinctness is not obvious to a non-expert. The fact is that in certain fishes at certain times these organs are imperceptible, as was stated regarding the testicles of birds.

Among other distinctions observed between the thoric ducts and the womb-ducts is the circumstance that the thoric ducts are attached to the loins, while the womb-ducts move about freely and are attached by a thin membrane. The particulars regarding the thoric ducts may be studied by a reference to the diagrams in my treatise on Anatomy.

Cartilaginous fishes are capable of superfoetation, and their period of gestation is six months at the longest. The so-called starry dog-fish bears young the most frequently; in other words it bears twice a month. The breeding-season is in the month of Maemacterion. The dog-fish as a general rule bear twice in the year, with the exception of the little dog-fish, which bears only once a year. Some of them bring forth in the springtime. The rhine, or angel-fish, bears its first brood in the springtime, and its second in the autumn, about the winter setting of the Pleiads; the second brood is the stronger of the two. The electric ray brings forth in the late autumn.

Cartilaginous fishes come out from the main seas and deep waters towards the shore and there bring forth their young, and they do so for the sake of warmth and by way of protection for their young.

Observations would lead to the general rule that no one variety of fish pairs with another variety. The angel-fish, however, and the batus or skate appear to pair with one another; for there is a fish called the rhinobatus, with the head and front parts of the skate and the after parts of the rhine or angel-fish, just as though it were made up of both fishes together.

Sharks then and their congeners, as the fox-shark and the dog-fish, and the flat fishes, such as the electric ray, the ray, the smooth skate, **566b** and the trygon, are first oviparous and then viviparous in the way above mentioned, [as are also the saw-fish and the ox-ray].

12

The dolphin, the whale, and all the rest of the Cetacea, all, that is to say, that are provided with a blow-hole instead of gills, are viviparous. That is to say, no one of all these fishes is ever seen to be supplied with eggs, but directly with an embryo from whose differentiation comes the fish, just as in the case of mankind and the viviparous quadrupeds.

The dolphin bears one at a time generally, but occasionally two. The whale bears one or at the most two, generally two. The porpoise in this respect resembles the dolphin, and, by the way, it is in form like a little dolphin, and is found in the Euxine; it differs, however, from the dolphin as being less in size and broader in the back; its colour is leaden-black. Many people are of opinion that the porpoise is a variety of the dolphin.

All creatures that have a blow-hole respire and inspire, for they are provided with lungs. The dolphin has been seen asleep with his nose above water, and when asleep he snores.

The dolphin and the porpoise are provided with milk, and suckle their young. They also take their young, when small, inside them. The young of the dolphin grow rapidly, being full-grown at ten years of age. Its period of gestation is ten months. It brings forth its young in summer, and never at any other season; [and, singularly enough, under the Dog-star it disappears for about thirty days]. Its young accompany it for a considerable period; and, in fact, the creature is remarkable for the strength of its parental affection. It lives for many years; some are known to have lived for more than twenty-five, and some for thirty years; the fact is fishermen nick their tails sometimes and set them adrift again, and by this expedient their ages are ascertained.

The seal is an amphibious animal: that is to say, it cannot take in water, but breathes and sleeps and brings forth on dry land—only close to the shore—as being an animal furnished with feet; it spends, however, the greater part of its time in the sea and derives its food from it, so that it must be classed in the category of marine animals. It is viviparous by immediate conception and brings forth its young alive, and exhibits an after-birth and all else **567a** just like a ewe. It bears one or two at a time, and three at the most. It has two teats, and suckles its young like a quadruped. Like the human species it brings forth at all seasons of the year, but especially at the time when the earliest kids are forthcoming. It conducts its young ones, when they are about twelve days old, over and over again during the day down to the sea, accustoming them by slow degrees to the water. It slips down steep places instead of walking, from the fact that it cannot steady itself by its feet. It can contract and draw itself in, for it is fleshy and soft and its bones are gristly. Owing to the flabbiness of its body it is difficult to kill a seal by a blow, unless you strike it on the temple. It looks like a cow. The female in regard to its genital organs resembles the female of the ray; in all other respects it resembles the female of the human species.

So much for the phenomena of generation and of parturition in animals that live in water and are viviparous either internally or externally.

13

Oviparous fishes have their womb bifurcate and placed low down, as was said previously[1]—and, by the way, all scaly fish are oviparous, as the basse, the mullet, the grey mullet, and the etelis, and all the so-called white-fish, and all the smooth or slippery fish except the eel—and their roe is of a crumbling or granular substance. This appearance is due to the fact that the whole womb of such fishes is full of eggs, so that in little fishes there seem to be only a couple of eggs there; for in small fishes the womb is indistinguishable, from its diminutive size and thin contexture. The pairing of fishes has been discussed previously.

Fishes for the most part are divided into males and females, but one is puzzled to account for the erythrinus and the channa, for specimens of these species are never caught except in a condition of pregnancy.

With such fish as pair, eggs are the result of copulation, but such fish have them also without copulation; and this is shown in the case of some river-fish, for the minnow has eggs when quite small,—almost, one may say, as soon as it is born. These fishes shed their eggs little by little, and, as is stated, the males swallow the greater part of them, and some portion of them goes to waste in the water; but such of **567b** the eggs as the female deposits on the spawning beds are saved. If all the eggs were preserved, each species would be infinite in number. The greater number of these eggs so deposited are not productive, but only those over which the male sheds the milt or sperm; for when the female has laid her eggs, the male follows and sheds its sperm over them, and from all the eggs so besprinkled young fishes proceed, while the rest are left to their fate.

The same phenomenon is observed in the case of molluscs also; for in the case of the cuttlefish or sepia, after the female has deposited her eggs, the male besprinkles them. It is highly probable that a similar phenomenon takes place in regard to molluscs in general, though up to the present time the phenomenon has been observed only in the case of the cuttlefish.

Fishes deposit their eggs close in to shore, the goby close to stones; and, by the way, the spawn of the goby is flat and crumbly. Fish in general so deposit their eggs; for the water close in to shore is warm and is better supplied with food than the outer sea, and serves as a protection to the spawn against the voracity of the larger fish. And it is for this reason that in the Euxine most fishes spawn near the mouth of the river Thermodon, because the locality is sheltered, genial, and supplied with fresh water.

Oviparous fish as a rule spawn only once a year. The little phycis or black goby is an exception, as it spawns twice; the male of the black goby differs from the female as being blacker and having larger scales.

Fishes then in general produce their young by copulation, and lay their eggs; but the pipefish, as some call it, when the time of parturition arrives, bursts in two, and the eggs escape out. For the fish has a diaphysis or cloven growth under the belly and abdomen (like the blind snakes), and, after it has spawned by the splitting of this diaphysis, the sides of the split grow together again.

Development from the egg takes place simi-

[1] III. 1 (510b 20); VI. 10 (564b 19).

larly with fishes that are oviparous internally and with fishes that are oviparous externally; that is to say, the embryo comes at the upper end of the egg and is enveloped in a membrane, and the eyes, large and spherical, are the first organs visible. From this circumstance it is plain that the assertion is untenable which is made by some writers, to wit, that the young of oviparous fishes are generated like the grubs of worms; for the opposite phenomena are observed in the case of these grubs, in that their lower extremities are the larger at the outset, and that the eyes and the head appear later on. **568a** After the egg has been used up, the young fishes are like tadpoles in shape, and at first, without taking any nutriment, they grow by sustenance derived from the juice oozing from the egg; by and by, they are nourished up to full growth by the river-waters.

When the Euxine is 'purged' a substance called phycus is carried into the Hellespont, and this substance is of a pale yellow colour. Some writers aver that it is the flower of the phycus, from which rouge is made; it comes at the beginning of summer. Oysters and the small fish of these localities feed on this substance, and some of the inhabitants of these maritime districts say that the purple murex derives its peculiar colour from it.

14

Marsh-fishes and river-fishes conceive at the age of five months as a general rule, and deposit their spawn towards the close of the year without exception. And with these fishes, like as with the marine fishes, the female does not void all her eggs at one time, nor the male his sperm; but they are at all times more or less provided, the female with eggs, and the male with sperm. The carp spawns as the seasons come round, five or six times, and follows in spawning the rising of the greater constellations. The chalcis spawns three times, and the other fishes once only in the year. They all spawn in pools left by the overflowing of rivers, and near to reedy places in marshes; as for instance the phoxinus or minnow and the perch.

The glanis or sheat-fish and the perch deposit their spawn in one continuous string, like the frog; so continuous, in fact, is the convoluted spawn of the perch that, by reason of its smoothness, the fishermen in the marshes can unwind it off the reeds like threads off a reel. The larger individuals of the sheat-fish spawn in deep waters, some in water of a fathom's depth, the smaller in shallower water, generally close to the roots of the willow or of some other tree, or close to reeds or to moss. At times these fishes intertwine with one another, a big with a little one, and bring into juxtaposition the ducts—which some writers designate as navels—at the point where they **568b** emit the generative products and discharge the egg in the case of the female and the milt in the case of the male. Such eggs as are besprinkled with the milt grow, in a day or thereabouts, whiter and larger, and in a little while afterwards the fish's eyes become visible, for these organs in all fishes, as for that matter in all other animals, are early conspicuous and seem disproportionately big. But such eggs as the milt fails to touch remain, as with marine fishes, useless and infertile. From the fertile eggs, as the little fish grow, a kind of sheath detaches itself; this is a membrane that envelops the egg and the young fish. When the milt has mingled with the eggs, the resulting product becomes very sticky or viscous, and adheres to the roots of trees or wherever it may have been laid. The male keeps on guard at the principal spawning-place, and the female after spawning goes away.

In the case of the sheat-fish the growth from the egg is exceptionally slow, and, in consequence, the male has to keep watch for forty or fifty days to prevent the spawn being devoured by such little fishes as chance to come by. Next in point of slowness is the generation of the carp. As with fishes in general, so even with these, the spawn thus protected disappears and gets lost rapidly.

In the case of some of the smaller fishes when they are only three days old young fishes are generated. Eggs touched by the male sperm take on increase both the same day and also later. The egg of the sheat-fish is as big as a vetch-seed; the egg of the carp and of the carp-species as big as a millet-seed.

These fishes then spawn and generate in the way here described. The chalcis, however, spawns in deep water in dense shoals of fish; and the so-called tilon spawns near to beaches in sheltered spots in shoals likewise. The carp, the baleros, and fishes in general push eagerly into the shallows for the purpose of spawning, and very often thirteen or fourteen males are seen following a single female. When the female deposits her spawn and departs, the males follow on and shed the milt. The greater portion of the spawn gets wasted; because, owing to the fact that the female

569a moves about while spawning, the spawn scatters, or so much of it as is caught in the stream and does not get entangled with some rubbish. For, with the exception of the sheat-fish, no fish keeps on guard; unless, by the way, it be the carp, which is said to remain on guard, if it so happen that its spawn lies in a solid mass.

All male fishes are supplied with milt, excepting the eel: with the eel, the male is devoid of milt, and the female of spawn. The mullet goes up from the sea to marshes and rivers; the eels, on the contrary, make their way down from the marshes and rivers to the sea.

15

The great majority of fish, then, as has been stated, proceed from eggs. However, there are some fish that proceed from mud and sand, even of those kinds that proceed also from pairing and the egg. This occurs in ponds here and there, and especially in a pond in the neighbourhood of Cnidos. This pond, it is said, at one time ran dry about the rising of the Dog-star, and the mud had all dried up; at the first fall of the rains there was a show of water in the pond, and on the first appearance of the water shoals of tiny fish were found in the pond. The fish in question was a kind of mullet, one which does not proceed from normal pairing, about the size of a small sprat, and not one of these fishes was provided with either spawn or milt. There are found also in Asia Minor, in rivers not communicating with the sea, little fishes like whitebait, differing from the small fry found near Cnidos but found under similar circumstances. Some writers actually aver that mullet all grow spontaneously. In this assertion they are mistaken, for the female of the fish is found provided with spawn, and the male with milt. However, there is a species of mullet that grows spontaneously out of mud and sand.

From the facts above enumerated it is quite proved that certain fishes come spontaneously into existence, not being derived from eggs or from copulation. Such fish as are neither oviparous nor viviparous arise all from one of two sources, from mud, or from sand and from decayed matter that rises thence as a scum; for instance, the so-called froth of the small fry comes out of sandy ground. This fry is incapable of growth and of propagating its 569b kind; after living for a while it dies away and another creature takes its place, and so, with short intervals excepted, it may be said to last the whole year through. At all events, it lasts from the autumn rising of Arcturus up to the spring-time. As a proof that these fish occasionally come out of the ground we have the fact that in cold weather they are not caught, and that they are caught in warm weather, obviously coming up out of the ground to catch the heat; also, when the fishermen use dredges and the ground is scraped up fairly often, the fishes appear in larger numbers and of superior quality. All other small fry are inferior in quality owing to rapidity of growth. The fry are found in sheltered and marshy districts, when after a spell of fine weather the ground is getting warmer, as, for instance, in the neighbourhood of Athens, at Salamis and near the tomb of Themistocles and at Marathon; for in these districts the froth is found. It appears, then, in such districts and during such weather, and occasionally appears after a heavy fall of rain in the froth that is thrown up by the falling rain, from which circumstance the substance derives its specific name. Foam is occasionally brought in on the surface of the sea in fair weather. [And in this, where it has formed on the surface, the so-called froth collects, as grubs swarm in manure; for which reason this fry is often brought in from the open sea. The fish is at its best in quality and quantity in moist warm weather.]

The ordinary fry is the normal issue of parent fishes: the so-called gudgeon-fry of small insignificant gudgeon-like fish that burrow under the ground. From the Phaleric fry comes the membras, from the membras the trichis, from the trichis the trichias, and from one particular sort of fry, to wit from that found in the harbour of Athens, comes what is called the encrasicholus, or anchovy. There is another fry, derived from the maenis and the mullet.

The unfertile fry is watery and keeps only a short time, as has been stated, for at last only head and eyes are left. However, the fish-570a ermen of late have hit upon a method of transporting it to a distance, as when salted it keeps for a considerable time.

16

Eels are not the issue of pairing, neither are they oviparous; nor was an eel ever found supplied with either milt or spawn, nor are they when cut open found to have within them passages for spawn or for eggs. In point of fact, this entire species of blooded animals proceeds neither from pair nor from the egg.

There can be no doubt that the case is so. For in some standing pools, after the water has been drained off and the mud has been dredged away, the eels appear again after a fall of rain. In time of drought they do not appear even in stagnant ponds, for the simple reason that their existence and sustenance is derived from rain-water.

There is no doubt, then, that they proceed neither from pairing nor from an egg. Some writers, however, are of opinion that they generate their kind, because in some eels little worms are found, from which they suppose that eels are derived. But this opinion is not founded on fact. Eels are derived from the so-called 'earth's guts' that grow spontaneously in mud and in humid ground; in fact, eels have at times been seen to emerge out of such earthworms, and on other occasions have been rendered visible when the earthworms were laid open by either scraping or cutting. Such earthworms are found both in the sea and in rivers, especially where there is decayed matter: in the sea in places where sea-weed abounds, and in rivers and marshes near to the edge; for it is near to the water's edge that sun-heat has its chief power and produces putrefaction. So much for the generation of the eel.

17

Fish do not all bring forth their young at the same season nor all in like manner, neither is the period of gestation for all of the same duration.

Before pairing the males and females gather together in shoals; at the time for copulation and parturition they pair off. With some fishes the time of gestation is not longer than thirty days, with others it is a lesser period; but with all it extends over a number of days divisible by seven. The longest period of gestation is that of the species which some call a *marinus*.

The sargue conceives during the month of **570b** Poseideon (or December), and carries its spawn for thirty days; and the species of mullet named by some the chelon, and the myxon, go with spawn at the same period and over the same length of time.

All fish suffer greatly during the period of gestation, and are in consequence very apt to be thrown up on shore at this time. In some cases they are driven frantic with pain and throw themselves on land. At all events they are throughout this time continually in motion until parturition is over (this being especially true of the mullet), and after parturition they are in repose. With many fish the time for parturition terminates on the appearance of grubs within the belly; for small living grubs get generated there and eat up the spawn.

With shoal fishes parturition takes place in the spring, and indeed, with most fishes, about the time of the spring equinox; with others it is at different times, in summer with some, and with others about the autumn equinox.

The first of shoal fishes to spawn is the atherine, and it spawns close to land; the last is the cephalus: and this is inferred from the fact that the brood of the atherine appears first of all and the brood of the cephalus last. The mullet also spawns early. The saupe spawns usually at the beginning of summer, but occasionally in the autumn. The aulopias, which some call the anthias, spawns in the summer. Next in order of spawning comes the chrysophrys or gilthead, the basse, the mormyrus, and in general such fish as are nicknamed 'runners'. Latest in order of the shoal fish come the red mullet and the coracine; these spawn in autumn. The red mullet spawns on mud, and consequently, as the mud continues cold for a long while, spawns late in the year. The coracine carries its spawn for a long time; but, as it lives usually on rocky ground, it goes to a distance and spawns in places abounding in sea-weed, at a period later than the red mullet. The maenis spawns about the winter solstice. Of the others, such as are pelagic spawn for the most part in summer; which fact is proved by their not being caught by fishermen during this period.

Of ordinary fishes the most prolific is the sprat; of cartilaginous fishes, the fishing-frog. Specimens, however, of the fishing-frog are rare from the facility with which the young are destroyed, as the female lays her spawn all in a lump close in to shore. As a rule, cartilaginous fish are less prolific than other fish owing to their being viviparous; and their young by **571a** reason of their size have a better chance of escaping destruction.

The so-called needle-fish (or pipe-fish) is late in spawning, and the greater portion of them are burst asunder by the eggs before spawning; and the eggs are not so many in number as large in size. The young fish cluster round the parent like so many young spiders, for the fish spawns on to herself; and, if any one touch the young, they swim away. The atherine spawns by rubbing its belly against the sand.

Tunny fish also burst asunder by reason of

their fat. They live for two years; and the fishermen infer this age from the circumstance that once when there was a failure of the young tunny fish for a year there was a failure of the full-grown tunny the next summer. They are of opinion that the tunny is a fish a year older than the pelamyd. The tunny and the mackerel pair about the close of the month of Elaphebolion, and spawn about the commencement of the month of Hecatombaeon; they deposit their spawn in a sort of bag. The growth of the young tunny is rapid. After the females have spawned in the Euxine, there comes from the egg what some call scordylae, but what the Byzantines nickname the 'auxids' or 'growers', from their growing to a considerable size in a few days; these fish go out of the Pontus in autumn along with the young tunnies, and enter Pontus in the spring as pelamyds. Fishes as a rule take on growth with rapidity, but this is peculiarly the case with all species of fish found in the Pontus; the growth, for instance, of the amia-tunny is quite visible from day to day.

To resume, we must bear in mind that the same fish in the same localities have not the same season for pairing, for conception, for parturition, or for favouring weather. The coracine, for instance, in some places spawns about wheat-harvest. The statements here given pretend only to give the results of general observation.

The conger also spawns, but the fact is not equally obvious in all localities, nor is the spawn plainly visible owing to the fat of the fish; for the spawn is lanky in shape as it is with serpents. However, if it be put on the fire it shows its nature; for the fat evaporates and melts, while the eggs dance about and explode with a crack. Further, if you touch the substances and rub them with your fingers, the fat feels smooth and the egg rough. Some con- **571b** gers are provided with fat but not with any spawn, others are unprovided with fat but have egg-spawn as here described.

18

We have, then, treated pretty fully of the animals that fly in the air or swim in the water, and of such of those that walk on dry land as are oviparous, to wit of their pairing, conception, and the like phenomena; it now remains to treat of the same phenomena in connexion with viviparous land animals and with man.

The statements made in regard to the pairing of the sexes apply partly to the particular kinds of animal and partly to all in general. It is common to all animals to be most excited by the desire of one sex for the other and by the pleasure derived from copulation. The female is most cross-tempered just after parturition, the male during the time of pairing; for instance, stallions at this period bite one another, throw their riders, and chase them. Wild boars, though usually enfeebled at this time as the result of copulation, are now unusually fierce, and fight with one another in an extraordinary way, clothing themselves with defensive armour, or in other words deliberately thickening their hide by rubbing against trees or by coating themselves repeatedly all over with mud and then drying themselves in the sun. They drive one another away from the swine pastures, and fight with such fury that very often both combatants succumb. The case is similar with bulls, rams, and he-goats; for, though at ordinary times they herd together, at breeding time they hold aloof from and quarrel with one another. The male camel also is cross-tempered at pairing time if either a man or a camel comes near him; as for a horse, a camel is ready to fight him at any time. It is the same with wild animals. The bear, the wolf, and the lion are all at this time ferocious towards such as come in their way, but the males of these animals are less given to fight with one another from the fact that they are at no time gregarious. The she-bear is fierce after cubbing, and the bitch after pupping.

Male elephants get savage about pairing time, and for this reason it is stated that men who have charge of elephants in India never allow the males to have intercourse with the females; on the ground that the males go wild **572a** at this time and turn topsy-turvy the dwellings of their keepers, lightly constructed as they are, and commit all kinds of havoc. They also state that abundancy of food has a tendency to tame the males. They further introduce other elephants amongst the wild ones, and punish and break them in by setting on the new-comers to chastise the others.

Animals that pair frequently and not at a single specific season, as for instance animals domesticated by man, such as swine and dogs, are found to indulge in such freaks to a lesser degree owing to the frequency of their sexual intercourse.

Of female animals the mare is the most sexually wanton, and next in order comes the cow. In fact, the mare is said to go a-horsing; and the term derived from the habits of this one animal serves as a term of abuse applicable to such females of the human species as are unbridled in the way of sexual appetite. This is the common phenomenon as observed in the sow when she is said to go a-boaring. The mare is said also about this time to get wind-impregnated if not impregnated by the stallion, and for this reason in Crete they never remove the stallion from the mares; for when the mare gets into this condition she runs away from all other horses. The mares under these circumstances fly invariably either northwards or southwards, and never towards either east or west. When this complaint is on them they allow no one to approach, until either they are exhausted with fatigue or have reached the sea. Under either of these circumstances they discharge a certain substance called 'hippomanes', the title given to a growth on a new-born foal; this resembles the sow-virus, and is in great request amongst women who deal in drugs and potions. About horsing time the mares huddle closer together, are continually switching their tails, their neigh is abnormal in sound, and from the sexual organ there flows a liquid resembling genital sperm, but much thinner than the sperm of the male. It is this substance that some call hippomanes, instead of the growth found on the foal; they say it is extremely difficult to get as it oozes out only in small drops at a time. Mares also, when in heat, discharge urine frequently, and frisk with one another. Such are the phenomena connected with the horse.

Cows go a-bulling; and so completely are they under the influence of the sexual excitement that the herdsmen have no control over them and cannot catch hold of them in the
572b fields. Mares and kine alike, when in heat, indicate the fact by the upraising of their genital organs, and by continually voiding urine. Further, kine mount the bulls, follow them about, and keep standing beside them. The younger females both with horses and oxen are the first to get in heat; and their sexual appetites are all the keener if the weather be warm and their bodily condition be healthy. Mares, when clipt of their coat, have the sexual feeling checked, and assume a downcast drooping appearance. The stallion recognizes by the scent the mares that form his company, even though they have been together only a few days before breeding time: if they get mixed up with other mares, the stallion bites and drives away the interlopers. He feeds apart, accompanied by his own troop of mares. Each stallion has assigned to him about thirty mares or even somewhat more; when a strange stallion approaches, he huddles his mares into a close ring, runs round them, then advances to the encounter of the newcomer; if one of the mares make a movement, he bites her and drives her back. The bull in breeding time begins to graze with the cows, and fights with other bulls (having hitherto grazed with them), which is termed by graziers 'herd-spurning'. Often in Epirus a bull disappears for three months together. In a general way one may state that of male animals either none or few herd with their respective females before breeding time; but they keep separate after reaching maturity, and the two sexes feed apart. Sows, when they are moved by sexual desire, or are, as it is called, a-boaring, will attack even human beings.

With bitches the same sexual condition is termed 'getting into heat'. The sexual organ rises at this time, and there is a moisture about the parts. Mares drip with a white liquid at this season.

Female animals are subject to menstrual discharges, but never in such abundance as is the female of the human species. With ewes and she-goats there are signs of menstruation in breeding time, just before the time for submitting to the male; after copulation also the signs are manifest, and then cease for an interval until the period of parturition arrives; the
573a process then supervenes, and it is by this supervention that the shepherd knows that such and such an ewe is about to bring forth. After parturition comes copious menstruation, not at first much tinged with blood, but deeply dyed with it by and by. With the cow, the she-ass, and the mare, the discharge is more copious actually, owing to their greater bulk, but proportionally to the greater bulk it is far less copious. The cow, for instance, when in heat, exhibits a small discharge to the extent of a quarter of a pint of liquid or a little less; and the time when this discharge takes place is the best time for her to be covered by the bull. Of all quadrupeds the mare is the most easily delivered of its young, exhibits the least amount of discharge after parturition, and emits the least amount of blood; that is to say, of all animals in proportion to size. With kine and mares menstruation usually manifests itself at intervals of two, four, and six months; but, unless one be constantly attending to and thoroughly acquainted with such animals, it is difficult to verify the circumstance, and the result

is that many people are under the belief that the process never takes place with these animals at all.

With mules menstruation never takes place, but the urine of the female is thicker than the urine of the male. As a general rule the discharge from the bladder in the case of quadrupeds is thicker than it is in the human species, and this discharge with ewes and she-goats is thicker than with rams and he-goats; but the urine of the jackass is thicker than the urine of the she-ass, and the urine of the bull is more pungent than the urine of the cow. After parturition the urine of all quadrupeds becomes thicker, especially with such animals as exhibit comparatively slight discharges. At breeding time the milk become purulent, but after parturition it becomes wholesome. During pregnancy ewes and she-goats get fatter and eat more; as is also the case with cows, and, indeed, with the females of all quadrupeds.

In general the sexual appetites of animals are keenest in spring-time; the time of pairing, however, is not the same for all, but is adapted so as to ensure the rearing of the young at a convenient season.

Domesticated swine carry their young for four months, and bring forth a litter of twenty at the utmost; and, by the way, if the litter be exceedingly numerous they cannot rear all the young. As the sow grows old she continues to bear, but grows indifferent to the boar; she conceives after a single copulation, but they have to put the boar to her repeatedly owing to her
573b dropping after intercourse what is called the sow-virus. This incident befalls all sows, but some of them discharge the genital sperm as well. During conception any one of the litter that gets injured or dwarfed is called an after-pig or scut: such injury may occur at any part of the womb. After littering the mother offers the foremost teat to the first-born. When the sow is in heat, she must not at once be put to the boar, but only after she lets her lugs drop, for otherwise she is apt to get into heat again; if she be put to the boar when in full condition of heat, one copulation, as has been said, is sufficient. It is as well to supply the boar at the period of copulation with barley, and the sow at the time of parturition with boiled barley. Some swine give fine litters only at the beginning, with others the litters improve as the mothers grow in age and size. It is said that a sow, if she have one of her eyes knocked out, is almost sure to die soon afterwards. Swine for the most part live for fifteen years, but some fall little short of the twenty.

19

Ewes conceive after three or four copulations with the ram. If rain falls after intercourse, the ram impregnates the ewe again; and it is the same with the she-goat. The ewe bears usually two lambs, sometimes three or four. Both ewe and she-goat carry their young for five months; consequently wherever a district is sunny and the animals are used to comfort and well fed, they bear twice in the year. The goat lives for eight years and the sheep for ten, but in most cases not so long; the bell-wether, however, lives to fifteen years. In every flock they train one of the rams for bell-wether. When he is called on by name by the shepherd, he takes the lead of the flock: and to this duty the creature is trained from its earliest years. Sheep in Ethiopia live for twelve or thirteen years, goats for ten or eleven. In the case of the sheep and the goat the two sexes have intercourse all their lives long.

Twins with sheep and goats may be due to richness of pasturage, or to the fact that either the ram or the he-goat is a twin-begetter or that the ewe or the she-goat is a twin-bearer. Of these animals some give birth to males and others to females; and the difference in this respect depends on the waters they drink and also on the sires. And if they submit to the male when north winds are blowing, they are apt to bear
574a males; if when south winds are blowing, females. Such as bear females may get to bear males, due regard being paid to their looking northwards when put to the male. Ewes accustomed to be put to the ram early will refuse him if he attempt to mount them late. Lambs are born white and black according as white or black veins are under the ram's tongue; the lambs are white if the veins are white, and black if the veins are black, and white and black if the veins are white and black; and red if the veins are red. The females that drink salted waters are the first to take the male; the water should be salted before and after parturition, and again in the spring-time. With goats the shepherds appoint no bell-wether, as the animal is not capable of repose but frisky and apt to ramble. If at the appointed season the elders of the flock are eager for intercourse, the shepherds say that it bodes well for the flock; if the younger ones, that the flock is going to be bad.

20

Of dogs there are several breeds. Of these the Laconian hound of either sex is fit for breeding purposes when eight months old: at about the same age some dogs lift the leg when voiding urine. The bitch conceives with one lining; this is clearly seen in the case where a dog contrives to line a bitch by stealth, as they impregnate after mounting only once. The Laconian bitch carries her young the sixth part of a year or sixty days: or more by one, two, or three, or less by one; the pups are blind for twelve days after birth. After pupping, the bitch gets in heat again in six months, but not before. Some bitches carry their young for the fifth part of the year or for seventy-two days; and their pups are blind for fourteen days. Other bitches carry their young for a quarter of a year or for three whole months; and the whelps of these are blind for seventeen days. The bitch appears to go in heat for the same length of time. Menstruation continues for seven days, and a swelling of the genital organ occurs simultaneously; it is not during this period that the bitch is disposed to submit to the dog, but in the seven days that follow. The bitch as a rule **574b** goes in heat for fourteen days, but occasionally for sixteen. The birth-discharge occurs simultaneously with the delivery of the whelps, and the substance of it is thick and mucous. [The falling-off in bulk on the part of the mother is not so great as might have been inferred from the size of her frame.] The bitch is usually supplied with milk five days before parturition; some seven days previously, some four; and the milk is serviceable immediately after birth. The Laconian bitch is supplied with milk thirty days after lining. The milk at first is thickish, but gets thinner by degrees; with the bitch the milk is thicker than with the female of any other animal excepting the sow and the hare. When the bitch arrives at full growth an indication is given of her capacity for the male; that is to say, just as occurs in the female of the human species, a swelling takes place in the teats of the breasts, and the breasts take on gristle. This incident, however, it is difficult for any but an expert to detect, as the part that gives the indication is inconsiderable. The preceding statements relate to the female, and not one of them to the male. The male as a rule lifts his leg to void urine when six months old; some at a later period, when eight months old, some before they reach six months. In a general way one may put it that they do so when they are out of puppyhood. The bitch squats down when she voids urine; it is a rare exception that she lifts the leg to do so. The bitch bears twelve pups at the most, but usually five or six; occasionally a bitch will bear one only. The bitch of the Laconian breed generally bears eight. The two sexes have intercourse with each other at all periods of life. A very remarkable phenomenon is observed in the case of the Laconian hound: in other words, he is found to be more vigorous in commerce with the female after being hard-worked than when allowed to live idle.

The dog of the Laconian breed lives ten years, and the bitch twelve. The bitch of other breeds usually lives for fourteen or fifteen years, but some live to twenty; and for this reason certain critics consider that Homer did well **575a** in representing the dog of Ulysses as having died in his twentieth year. With the Laconian hound, owing to the hardships to which the male is put, he is less long-lived than the female; with other breeds the distinction as to longevity is not very apparent, though as a general rule the male is the longer-lived.

The dog sheds no teeth except the so-called 'canines'; these a dog of either sex sheds when four months old. As they shed these only, many people are in doubt as to the fact, and some people, owing to their shedding but two and its being hard to hit upon the time when they do so, fancy that the animal sheds no teeth at all; others, after observing the shedding of two, come to the conclusion that the creature sheds the rest in due turn. Men discern the age of a dog by inspection of its teeth; with young dogs the teeth are white and sharp pointed, with old dogs black and blunted.

21

The bull impregnates the cow at a single mount, and mounts with such vigour as to weigh down the cow; if his effort be unsuccessful, the cow must be allowed an interval of twenty days before being again submitted. Bulls of mature age decline to mount the same cow several times on one day, except, by the way, at considerable intervals. Young bulls by reason of their vigour are enabled to mount the same cow several times in one day, and a good many cows besides. The bull is the least salacious of male animals. . . . The victor among the bulls is the one that mounts the females; when he gets exhausted by his amorous efforts, his beaten antagonist sets on him and very often gets the better of the conflict. The bull and the cow are about a year old when it is possible for them to have commerce with chance of offspring: as a rule, however, they are about twenty months old, but it is universally allowed that they are capable in this respect at the age of two years. The cow goes with calf for nine months, and she calves in the tenth month; some maintain that they go in calf for ten months, to the very day. A calf delivered before the times here specified is an abortion and never lives, however little premature its birth may have been, as its hooves are weak and imperfect. The cow as a rule bears but one calf, very seldom two; she submits to the bull and bears as long as she lives.

Cows live for about fifteen years, and the bulls too, if they have been castrated; but some live for twenty years or even more, if their bodily constitutions be sound. The herdsmen
575ᵇ tame the castrated bulls, and give them an office in the herd analogous to the office of the bell-wether in a flock; and these bulls live to an exceptionally advanced age, owing to their exemption from hardship and to their browsing on pasture of good quality. The bull is in fullest vigour when five years old, which leads the critics to commend Homer for applying to the bull the epithets of 'five-year-old', or 'of nine seasons', which epithets are alike in meaning. The ox sheds his teeth at the age of two years, not all together but just as the horse sheds his. When the animal suffers from podagra it does not shed the hoof, but is subject to a painful swelling in the feet. The milk of the cow is serviceable after parturition, and before parturition there is no milk at all. The milk that first presents itself becomes as hard as stone when it clots; this result ensues unless it be previously diluted with water. Oxen younger than a year old do not copulate unless under circumstances of an unnatural and portentous kind: instances have been recorded of copulation in both sexes at the age of four months. Kine in general begin to submit to the male about the month of Thargelion or of Scirophorion; some, however, are capable of conception right on to the autumn. When kine in large numbers receive the bull and conceive, it is looked upon as prognostic of rain and stormy weather. Kine herd together like mares, but in lesser degree.

22

In the case of horses, the stallion and the mare are first fitted for breeding purposes when two years old. Instances, however, of such early maturity are rare, and their young are exceptionally small and weak; the ordinary age for sexual maturity is three years, and from that age to twenty the two sexes go on improving in the quality of their offspring. The mare carries her foal for eleven months, and casts it in the twelfth. It is not a fixed number of days that the stallion takes to impregnate the mare; it may be one, two, three, or more. An ass in covering will impregnate more expeditiously than a stallion. The act of intercourse with horses is not laborious as it is with oxen. In both sexes the horse is the most salacious of animals next after the human species. The breeding faculties of the younger horses may be stimulated beyond their years if they be supplied with good feeding in abundance. The mare as
576ª a rule bears only one foal; occasionally she has two, but never more. A mare has been known to cast two mules; but such a circumstance was regarded as unnatural and portentous.

The horse then is first fitted for breeding purposes at the age of two and a half years, but achieves full sexual maturity when it has ceased to shed teeth, except it be naturally infertile; it must be added, however, that some horses have been known to impregnate the mare while the teeth were in process of shedding.

The horse has forty teeth. It sheds its first set of four, two from the upper jaw and two from the lower, when two and a half years old. After a year's interval, it sheds another set of four in like manner, and another set of four after yet another year's interval; after arriving at the age of four years and six months it sheds no more. An instance has occurred where a horse shed all his teeth at once, and another instance of a horse shedding all his teeth with his last set of four; but such instances are very rare. It consequently happens that a horse when four and a half years old is in excellent condition for breeding purposes.

The older horses, whether of the male or female, are the more generatively productive. Horses will cover mares from which they have been foaled and mares which they have begotten; and, indeed, a troop of horses is only considered perfect when such promiscuity of intercourse occurs. Scythians use pregnant mares for riding when the embryo has turned rather soon in the womb, and they assert that thereby the mothers have all the easier delivery. Quadrupeds as a rule lie down for parturition, and in consequence the young of them all come out of the womb sideways. The mare, however, when the time for parturition arrives, stands erect and in that posture casts its foal.

The horse in general lives for eighteen or twenty years; some horses live for twenty-five or even thirty, and if a horse be treated with extreme care, it may last on to the age of fifty years; a horse, however, when it reaches thirty
576b years is regarded as exceptionally old. The mare lives usually for twenty-five years, though instances have occurred of their attaining the age of forty. The male is less long-lived than the female by reason of the sexual service he is called on to render; and horses that are reared in a private stable live longer than such as are reared in troops. The mare attains her full length and height at five years old, the stallion at six; in another six years the animal reaches its full bulk, and goes on improving until it is twenty years old. The female, then, reaches maturity more rapidly than the male, but in the womb the case is reversed, just as is observed in regard to the sexes of the human species; and the same phenomenon is observed in the case of all animals that bear several young.

The mare is said to suckle a mule-foal for six months, but not to allow its approach for any longer on account of the pain it is put to by the hard tugging of the young; an ordinary foal it allows to suck for a longer period.

Horse and mule are at their best after the shedding of the teeth. After they have shed them all, it is not easy to distinguish their age; hence they are said to carry their mark before the shedding, but not after. However, even after the shedding their age is pretty well recognized by the aid of the canines; for in the case of horses much ridden these teeth are worn away by attrition caused by the insertion of the bit; in the case of horses not ridden the teeth are large and detached, and in young horses they are sharp and small.

The male of the horse will breed at all seasons and during its whole life; the mare can take the horse all its life long, but is not thus ready to pair at all seasons unless it be held in check by a halter or some other compulsion be brought to bear. There is no fixed time at which intercourse of the two sexes cannot take place; and accordingly intercourse may chance to take place at a time that may render difficult the rearing of the future progeny. In a stable in Opus there was a stallion that used to serve mares when forty years old: his fore legs had to be lifted up for the operation.

Mares first take the horse in the spring-time. After a mare has foaled she does not get impregnated at once again, but only after a considerable interval; in fact, the foals will be all the better if the interval extend over four or five years. It is, at all events, absolutely necessary to allow an interval of one year, and for
577a that period to let her lie fallow. A mare, then, breeds at intervals; a she-ass breeds on and on without intermission. Of mares some are absolutely sterile, others are capable of conception but incapable of bringing the foal to full term; it is said to be an indication of this condition in a mare, that her foal if dissected is found to have other kidney-shaped substances round about its kidneys, presenting the appearance of having four kidneys.

After parturition the mare at once swallows the after-birth, and bites off the growth, called the 'hippomanes', that is found on the forehead of the foal. This growth is somewhat smaller than a dried fig; and in shape is broad and round, and in colour black. If any bystander gets possession of it before the mare, and the mare gets a smell of it, she goes wild and frantic at the smell. And it is for this reason that venders of drugs and simples hold the substance in high request and include it among their stores.

If an ass cover a mare after the mare has been covered by a horse, the ass will destroy the previously formed embryo.

[Horse-trainers do not appoint a horse as leader to a troop, as herdsmen appoint a bull as leader to a herd, and for this reason that the horse is not steady but quick-tempered and skittish.]

23

The ass of both sexes is capable of breeding, and sheds its first teeth at the age of two and a half years; it sheds its second teeth within six months, its third within another six months, and the fourth after the like interval. These fourth teeth are termed the gnomons or age-indicators.

A she-ass has been known to conceive when a year old, and the foal to be reared. After intercourse with the male it will discharge the genital sperm unless it be hindered, and for this reason it is usually beaten after such intercourse and chased about. It casts its young in the twelfth month. It usually bears but one foal, and that is its natural number, occasionally however it bears twins. The ass if it cover a mare destroys, as has been said, the embryo previously begotten by the horse; but, after the mare has been covered by the ass, the horse supervening will not spoil the embryo. The she-ass has milk in the tenth month of pregnancy. Seven days after casting a foal the she-ass submits to the male, and is almost sure to conceive if put to the male on this particular day; the same result, however, is quite possible later on. The she-ass will refuse to cast 577b her foal with any one looking on or in the daylight and just before foaling she has to be led away into a dark place. If the she-ass has had young before the shedding of the index-teeth, she will bear all her life through; but if not, then she will neither conceive nor bear for the rest of her days. The ass lives for more than thirty years, and the she-ass lives longer than the male.

When there is a cross between a horse and a she-ass or a jackass and a mare, there is much greater chance of a miscarriage than where the commerce is normal. The period for gestation in the case of a cross depends on the male, and is just what it would have been if the male had had commerce with a female of his own kind. In regard to size, looks, and vigour, the foal is more apt to resemble the mother than the sire. If such hybrid connexions be continued without intermittence, the female will soon go sterile; and for this reason trainers always allow of intervals between breeding times. A mare will not take the ass, nor a she-ass the horse, unless the ass or she-ass shall have been suckled by a mare; and for this reason trainers put foals of the she-ass under mares, which foals are technically spoken of as 'mare-suckled'. These asses, thus reared, mount the mares in the open pastures, mastering them by force as the stallions do.

24

A mule is fitted for commerce with the female after the first shedding of its teeth, and at the age of seven will impregnate effectually; and where connexion has taken place with a mare, a 'hinny' has been known to be produced. After the seventh year it has no further intercourse with the female. A female mule has been known to be impregnated, but without the impregnation being followed up by parturition. In Syrophoenicia she-mules submit to the mule and bear young; but the breed, though it resembles the ordinary one, is different and specific. The hinny or stunted mule is foaled by a mare when she has gone sick during gestation, and corresponds to the dwarf in the human species and to the after-pig or scut in swine; and as is the case with dwarfs, the sexual organ of the hinny is abnormally large.

The mule lives for a number of years. There are on record cases of mules living to the age of eighty, as did one in Athens at the time of the building of the temple; this mule on account of its age was let go free, but continued to assist in dragging burdens, and would go side by side with the other draught-beasts and stimulate them to their work; and in consequence a public decree was passed forbidding 578a any baker driving the creature away from his bread-tray. The she-mule grows old more slowly than the mule. Some assert that the she-mule menstruates by the act of voiding her urine, and that the mule owes the prematurity of his decay to his habit of smelling at the urine. So much for the modes of generation in connexion with these animals.

25

Breeders and trainers can distinguish between young and old quadrupeds. If, when drawn back from the jaw, the skin at once goes back to its place, the animal is young; if it remains long wrinkled up, the animal is old.

26

The camel carries its young for ten months, and bears but one at a time and never more; the young camel is removed from the mother when a year old. The animal lives for a long period, more than fifty years. It bears in spring-time, and gives milk until the time of the next conception. Its flesh and milk are exceptionally palatable. The milk is drunk mixed with water in the proportion of either two to one or three to one.

27

The elephant of either sex is fitted for breeding before reaching the age of twenty. The female carries her young, according to some accounts, for two and a half years; according to others, for three years; and the discrepancy in the assigned periods is due to the fact that there are never human eyewitnesses to the commerce between the sexes. The female settles down on its rear to cast its young, and obviously suffers greatly during the process. The young one, immediately after birth, sucks the mother, not with its trunk but with the mouth; and can walk about and see distinctly the moment it is born.

28

The wild sow submits to the boar at the beginning of winter, and in the spring-time retreats for parturition to a lair in some district inaccessible to intrusion, hemmed in with sheer cliffs and chasms and overshadowed by trees. The boar usually remains by the sow for thirty days. The number of the litter and the period of gestation is the same as in the case of the domesticated congener. The sound of the grunt also is similar; only that the sow grunts continually, and the boar but seldom. Of the wild boars such as are castrated grow to the largest size and become fiercest: to which cir-
578b cumstance Homer alludes when he says:—

'He reared against him a wild castrated boar: it was not like a food-devouring brute, but like a forest-clad promontory.'[1]

Wild boars become castrated owing to an itch befalling them in early life in the region of the testicles, and the castration is superinduced by their rubbing themselves against the trunks of trees.

29

The hind, as has been stated, submits to the stag as a rule only under compulsion, as she is unable to endure the male often owing to the rigidity of the penis. However, they do occasionally submit to the stag as the ewe submits to ram; and when they are in heat the hinds avoid one another. The stag is not constant to one particular hind, but after a while quits one and mates with others. The breeding time is after the rising of Arcturus, during the months of Boedromion and Maimacterion. The period of gestation lasts for eight months. Conception comes on a few days after intercourse; and a number of hinds can be impregnated by a single male. The hind, as a rule, bears but one fawn, although instances have been known of her casting two. Out of dread of wild beasts she casts her young by the side of the high-road. The young fawn grows with rapidity. Menstruation occurs at no other time with the hind; it takes place only after parturition, and the substance is phlegm-like.

The hind leads the fawn to her lair; this is her place of refuge, a cave with a single inlet, inside which she shelters herself against attack.

Fabulous stories are told concerning the longevity of the animal, but the stories have never been verified, and the brevity of the period of gestation and the rapidity of growth in the fawn would not lead one to attribute extreme longevity to this creature.

In the mountain called Elaphoeis or Deer Mountain, which is in Arginussa in Asia Minor—the place, by the way, where Alcibiades was assassinated—all the hinds have the ear split, so that, if they stray to a distance, they can be recognized by this mark; and the embryo actually has the mark while yet in the womb of the mother.

The hind has four teats like the cow. After the hinds have become pregnant, the males all segregate one by one, and in consequence of the violence of their sexual passions they keep
579a each one to himself, dig a hole in the ground, and bellow from time to time; in all these particulars they resemble the goat, and their foreheads from getting wetted become black, as is also the case with the goat. In this way they pass the time until the rain falls, after which time they turn to pasture. The animal acts in this way owing to its sexual wantonness and also to its obesity; for in summer-time it becomes so exceptionally fat as to be unable to run: in fact at this period they can be overtaken by the hunters that pursue them on foot in the second or third run; and, by the way, in consequence of the heat of the weather and their getting out of breath they always make for water in their runs. In the rutting season, the flesh of the deer is unsavoury and rank, like the flesh of the he-goat. In winter-time the deer becomes thin and weak, but towards the approach of the spring he is at his best for running. When on the run the deer keeps pausing from time to time, and waits until his pursuer draws upon him, whereupon he starts off again. This habit appears due to some internal pain: at all events, the gut is so slender and weak that, if you strike the animal ever so softly, it is apt to break asunder, though the hide of the animal remains sound and uninjured.

30

Bears, as has been previously stated, do not copulate with the male mounting the back of the female, but with the female lying down under the male. The she-bear goes with young for thirty days. She brings forth sometimes one cub, sometimes two cubs, and at most five. Of all animals the newly born cub of the she-bear is the smallest in proportion to the size of

[1] The quotation is a travesty of *Iliad*, IX. 539, and *Odyssey*, IX. 190.

the mother; that is to say, it is larger than a mouse but smaller than a weasel. It is also smooth and blind, and its legs and most of its organs are as yet inarticulate. Pairing takes place in the month of Elaphebolion, and parturition about the time for retiring into winter quarters; about this time the bear and the she-bear are at the fattest. After the she-bear has reared her young, she comes out of her winter lair in the third month, when it is already spring. The female porcupine, by the way, hibernates and goes with young the same number of days as the she-bear, and in all respects as to parturition resembles this animal. When a she-bear is with young, it is a very hard task to catch her.

31

It has already been stated that the lion and lioness copulate rearwards, and that these animals are opisthuretic. They do not copulate nor bring forth at all seasons indiscriminately, but once in the year only. The lioness brings forth **579b** in the spring, generally two cubs at a time, and six at the very most; but sometimes only one. The story about the lioness discharging her womb in the act of parturition is a pure fable, and was merely invented to account for the scarcity of the animal; for the animal is, as is well known, a rare animal, and is not found in many countries. In fact, in the whole of Europe it is only found in the strip between the rivers Achelous and Nessus. The cubs of the lioness when newly born are exceedingly small, and can scarcely walk when two months old. The Syrian lion bears cubs five times: five cubs at the first litter, then four, then three, then two, and lastly one; after this the lioness ceases to bear for the rest of her days. The lioness has no mane, but this appendage is peculiar to the lion. The lion sheds only the four so-called canines, two in the upper jaw and two in the lower; and it sheds them when it is six months old.

32

The hyena in colour resembles the wolf, but is more shaggy, and is furnished with a mane running all along the spine. What is recounted concerning its genital organs, to the effect that every hyena is furnished with the organ both of the male and the female, is untrue. The fact is that the sexual organ of the male hyena resembles the same organ in the wolf and in the dog; the part resembling the female genital organ lies underneath the tail, and does to some extent resemble the female organ, but it is unprovided with duct or passage, and the passage for the residuum comes underneath it. The female hyena has the part that resembles the organ of the male, and, as in the case of the male, has it underneath her tail, unprovided with duct or passage; and after it the passage for the residuum, and underneath this the true female genital organ. The female hyena has a womb, like all other female animals of the same kind. It is an exceedingly rare circumstance to meet with a female hyena. At least a hunter said that out of eleven hyenas he had caught, only one was a female.

33

Hares copulate in a rearward posture, as has been stated,[1] for the animal is opisthuretic. They breed and bear at all seasons, superfoetate during pregnancy, and bear young every month. They do not give birth to their young ones all together at one time, but bring them **580a** forth at intervals over as many days as the circumstances of each case may require. The female is supplied with milk before parturition; and after bearing submits immediately to the male, and is capable of conception while suckling her young. The milk in consistency resembles sow's milk. The young are born blind, as is the case with the greater part of the fissipeds or toed animals.

34

The fox mounts the vixen in copulation, and the vixen bears young like the she-bear; in fact, her young ones are even more inarticulately formed. Before parturition she retires to sequestered places, so that it is a great rarity for a vixen to be caught while pregnant. After parturition she warms her young and gets them into shape by licking them. She bears four at most at a birth.

35

The wolf resembles the dog in regard to the time of conception and parturition, the number of the litter, and the blindness of the new-born young. The sexes couple at one special period, and the female brings forth at the beginning of the summer. There is an account given of the parturition of the she-wolf that borders on the fabulous, to the effect that she confines her lying-in to within twelve particular days of the year. And they give the rea-

[1] v. 2(539b 22); II. 1(500b 15).

son for this in the form of a myth, viz. that when they transported Leto in so many days from the land of the Hyperboreans to the island of Delos, she assumed the form of a she-wolf to escape the anger of Here. Whether the account be correct or not has not yet been verified; I give it merely as it is currently told. There is no more of truth in the current statement that the she-wolf bears once and only once in her lifetime.

The cat and the ichneumon bear as many young as the dog, and live on the same food; they live about six years. The cubs of the panther are born blind like those of the wolf, and the female bears four at the most at one birth. The particulars of conception are the same for the thos, or civet, as for the dog; the cubs of the animal are born blind, and the female bears two, or three, or four at a birth. It is long in the body and low in stature; but notwithstanding the shortness of its legs it is exceptionally fleet of foot, owing to the suppleness of its frame and its capacity for leaping.

36

580b There is found in Syria a so-called mule. It is not the same as the cross between the horse and ass, but resembles it just as a wild ass resembles the domesticated congener, and derives its name from the resemblance. Like the wild ass, this wild mule is remarkable for its speed. The animals of this species interbreed with one another; and a proof of this statement may be gathered from the fact that a certain number of them were brought into Phrygia in the time of Pharnaces, the father of Pharnabazus, and the animal is there still. The number originally introduced was nine, and there are three there at the present day.

37

The phenomena of generation in regard to the mouse are the most astonishing both for the number of the young and for the rapidity of recurrence in the births. On one occasion a she-mouse in a state of pregnancy was shut up by accident in a jar containing millet-seed, and after a little while the lid of the jar was removed and upwards of one hundred and twenty mice were found inside it.

The rate of propagation of field mice in country places, and the destruction that they cause, are beyond all telling. In many places their number is so incalculable that but very little of the corn-crop is left to the farmer; and so rapid is their mode of proceeding that sometimes a small farmer will one day observe that it is time for reaping, and on the following morning, when he takes his reapers afield, he finds his entire crop devoured. Their disappearance is unaccountable: in a few days not a mouse will there be to be seen. And yet in the time before these few days men fail to keep down their numbers by fumigating and unearthing them, or by regularly hunting them and turning in swine upon them; for pigs, by the way, turn up the mouse-holes by rooting with their snouts. Foxes also hunt them, and the wild ferrets in particular destroy them, but they make no way against the prolific qualities of the animal and the rapidity of its breeding. When they are super-abundant, nothing succeeds in thinning them down except the rain; but after heavy rains they disappear rapidly.

In a certain district of Persia when a female mouse is dissected the female embryos appear to be pregnant. Some people assert, and positively assert, that a female mouse by lick-
581a ing salt can become pregnant without the intervention of the male.

Mice in Egypt are covered with bristles like the hedgehog. There is also a different breed of mice that walk on their two hind-legs; their front legs are small and their hind-legs long; the breed is exceedingly numerous. There are many other breeds of mice than are here referred to.

BOOK VII

I

As to Man's growth, first within his mother's womb and afterward to old age, the course of nature, in so far as man is specially concerned, is after the following manner. And, by the way, the difference of male and female and of their respective organs has been dealt with heretofore.[1] When twice seven years old, in the most of cases, the male begins to engender seed; and at the same time hair appears upon the pubes, in like manner, so Alcmaeon of Croton remarks, as plants first blossom and then seed. About the same time, the voice begins to alter, getting harsher and more uneven, neither shrill as formerly nor deep as afterward, nor yet of any even tone, but like an instrument whose strings are frayed and

[1] III. I.

out of tune; and it is called, by way of by-word, the bleat of the billy-goat. Now this breaking of the voice is the more apparent in those who are making trial of their sexual powers; for in those who are prone to lustfulness the voice turns into the voice of a man, but not so in the continent. For if a lad strive diligently to hinder his voice from breaking, as some do of those who devote themselves to music, the voice lasts a long while unbroken and may even persist with little change. And the breasts swell and likewise the private parts, altering in size and shape. (And by the way, at this time of life those who try by friction to provoke emission of seed are apt to experience pain as well as voluptuous sensations.) At the same age in the female, the breasts swell and the so-
581b called catamenia commence to flow; and this fluid resembles fresh blood. There is another discharge, a white one, by the way, which occurs in girls even at a very early age, more especially if their diet be largely of a fluid nature; and this malady causes arrest of growth and loss of flesh. In the majority of cases the catamenia are noticed by the time the breasts have grown to the height of two fingers' breadth. In girls, too, about this time the voice changes to a deeper note; for while in general the woman's voice is higher than the man's, so also the voices of girls are pitched in a higher key than the elder women's, just as the boy's are higher than the men's; and the girls' voices are shriller than the boys', and a maid's flute is tuned sharper than a lad's.

Girls of this age have much need of surveillance. For then in particular they feel a natural impulse to make usage of the sexual faculties that are developing in them; so that unless they guard against any further impulse beyond that inevitable one which their bodily development of itself supplies, even in the case of those who abstain altogether from passionate indulgence, they contract habits which are apt to continue into later life. For girls who give way to wantonness grow more and more wanton; and the same is true of boys, unless they be safeguarded from one temptation and another; for the passages become dilated and set up a local flux or running, and besides this the recollection of pleasure associated with former indulgence creates a longing for its repetition.

Some men are congenitally impotent owing to structural defect; and in like manner women also may suffer from congenital incapacity. Both men and women are liable to constitutional change, growing healthier or more sickly, or altering in the way of leanness, stoutness, and vigour; thus, after puberty some lads who were thin before grow stout and healthy, and the converse also happens; and the same is equally true of girls. For when in boy or girl the body is loaded with superfluous matter, then, when such superfluities are got rid of in the spermatic or catamenial discharge, their bodies improve in health and condition owing
582a to the removal of what had acted as an impediment to health and proper nutrition; but in such as are of opposite habit their bodies become emaciated and out of health, for then the spermatic discharge in the one case and the catamenial flow in the other take place at the cost of natural healthy conditions.

Furthermore, in the case of maidens the condition of the breasts is diverse in different individuals, for they are sometimes quite big and sometimes little; and as a general rule their size depends on whether or not the body was burthened in childhood with superfluous material. For when the signs of womanhood are nigh but not come, the more there be of moisture the more will it cause the breasts to swell, even to the bursting point; and the result is that the breasts remain during after-life of the bulk that they then acquired. And among men, the breasts grow more conspicuous and more like to those of women, both in young men and old, when the individual temperament is moist and sleek and the reverse of sinewy, and all the more among the dark-complexioned than the fair.

At the outset and till the age of one and twenty the spermatic discharge is devoid of fecundity; afterwards it becomes fertile, but young men and women produce undersized and imperfect progeny, as is the case also with the common run of animals. Young women conceive readily, but, having conceived, their labour in childbed is apt to be difficult.

The frame fails of reaching its full development and ages quickly in men of intemperate lusts and in women who become mothers of many children; for it appears to be the case that growth ceases when the woman has given birth to three children. Women of a lascivious disposition grow more sedate and virtuous after they have borne several children.

After the age of twenty-one women are fully ripe for child-bearing, but men go on increasing in vigour. When the spermatic fluid is of a thin consistency it is infertile; when granular it is fertile and likely to produce male children, but when thin and unclotted it is apt to produce female offspring. And it is about this time of life that in men the beard makes its appearance.

2

The onset of the catamenia in women takes place towards the end of the month; and on this account the wiseacres assert that the moon is **582b** feminine, because the discharge in women and the waning of the moon happen at one and the same time, and after the wane and the discharge both one and the other grow whole again. [In some women the catamenia occur regularly but sparsely every month, and more abundantly every third month.] With those in whom the ailment lasts but a little while, two days or three, recovery is easy; but where the duration is longer, the ailment is more troublesome. For women are ailing during these days; and sometimes the discharge is sudden and sometimes gradual, but in all cases alike there is bodily distress until the attack be over. In many cases at the commencement of the attack, when the discharge is about to appear, there occur spasms and rumbling noises within the womb until such time as the discharge manifests itself.

Under natural conditions it is after recovery from these symptoms that conception takes place in women, and women in whom the signs do not manifest themselves for the most part remain childless. But the rule is not without exception, for some conceive in spite of the absence of these symptoms; and these are cases in which a secretion accumulates, not in such a way as actually to issue forth, but in amount equal to the residuum left in the case of child-bearing women after the normal discharge has taken place. And some conceive while the signs are on but not afterwards, those namely in whom the womb closes up immediately after the discharge. In some cases the menses persist during pregnancy up to the very last; but the result in these cases is that the offspring are poor, and either fail to survive or grow up weakly.

In many cases, owing to excessive desire, arising either from youthful impetuosity or from lengthened abstinence, prolapsion of the womb takes place and the catamenia appear repeatedly, thrice in the month, until conception occurs; and then the womb withdraws upwards again to its proper place. . . .

As we have remarked above, the discharge is wont to be more abundant in women than in the females of any other animals.[1] In creatures that do not bring forth their young alive nothing of the sort manifests itself, this particular superfluity being converted into bodily substance; and by the way, in such animals the females are sometimes larger than the males; and moreover, the material is used up sometimes for scutes and sometimes for scales, and sometimes for the abundant covering of feathers, whereas in the vivipara possessed of limbs it is turned into hair and into bodily substance **583a** (for man alone among them is smooth-skinned), and into urine, for this excretion is in the majority of such animals thick and copious. Only in the case of women is the superfluity turned into a discharge instead of being utilized in these other ways.

There is something similar to be remarked of men: for in proportion to his size man emits more seminal fluid than any other animal (for which reason man is the smoothest of animals), especially such men as are of a moist habit and not over corpulent, and fair men in greater degree than dark. It is likewise with women; for in the stout, great part of the excretion goes to nourish the body. In the act of intercourse, women of a fair complexion discharge a more plentiful secretion than the dark; and furthermore, a watery and pungent diet conduces to this phenomenon.

3

It is a sign of conception in women when the place is dry immediately after intercourse. If the lips of the orifice be smooth conception is difficult, for the matter slips off; and if they be thick it is also difficult. But if on digital examination the lips feel somewhat rough and adherent, and if they be likewise thin, then the chances are in favour of conception. Accordingly, if conception be desired, we must bring the parts into such a condition as we have just described; but if on the contrary we want to avoid conception then we must bring about a contrary disposition. Wherefore, since if the parts be smooth conception is prevented, some anoint that part of the womb on which the seed falls with oil of cedar, or with ointment of lead or with frankincense, commingled with olive oil. If the seed remain within for seven days then it is certain that conception has taken place; for it is during that period that what is known as effluxion takes place.

In most cases the menstrual discharge recurs for some time after conception has taken place,

[1] III. 19(521a); VI. 18(572b).

its duration being mostly thirty days in the case of a female and about forty days in the case of a male child. After parturition also it is common for the discharge to be withheld for an equal number of days, but not in all cases with equal exactitude. After conception, and when the above-mentioned days are past, the discharge no longer takes its natural course but finds its way to the breasts and turns to milk. The first appearance of milk in the breasts is scant in quantity and so to speak cobwebby or interspersed with little threads. And when conception has taken place, there is apt to be a sort of feeling in the region of the flanks, which in some cases quickly swell up a little, especi-
583b ally in thin persons, and also in the groin.

In the case of male children the first movement usually occurs on the right-hand side of the womb and about the fortieth day, but if the child be a female then on the left-hand side and about the ninetieth day. However, we must by no means assume this to be an accurate statement of fact, for there are many exceptions, in which the movement is manifested on the right-hand side though a female child be coming, and on the left-hand side though the infant be a male. And in short, these and all suchlike phenomena are usually subject to differences that may be summed up as differences of degree.

About this period the embryo begins to resolve into distinct parts, it having hitherto consisted of a fleshlike substance without distinction of parts.

What is called effluxion is a destruction of the embryo within the first week, while abortion occurs up to the fortieth day; and the greater number of such embryos as perish do so within the space of these forty days.

In the case of a male embryo aborted at the fortieth day, if it be placed in cold water it holds together in a sort of membrane, but if it be placed in any other fluid it dissolves and disappears. If the membrane be pulled to bits the embryo is revealed, as big as one of the large kind of ants; and all the limbs are plain to see, including the penis, and the eyes also, which as in other animals are of great size. But the female embryo, if it suffer abortion during the first three months, is as a rule found to be undifferentiated; if however it reach the fourth month it comes to be subdivided and quickly attains further differentiation. In short, while within the womb, the female infant accomplishes the whole development of its parts more slowly than the male, and more frequently than the man-child takes ten months to come to perfection. But after birth, the females pass more quickly than the males through youth and maturity and age; and this is especially true of those that bear many children, as indeed I have already said.

4

When the womb has conceived the seed, straightway in the majority of cases it closes up until seven months are fulfilled; but in the eighth month it opens, and the embryo, if it be fertile, descends in the eighth month. But such embryos as are not fertile but are devoid of breath at eight months old, their mothers do not bring into the world by parturition at eight months, neither does the embryo descend within the womb at that period nor does
584a the womb open. And it is a sign that the embryo is not capable of life if it be formed without the above-named circumstances taking place.

After conception women are prone to a feeling of heaviness in all parts of their bodies, and for instance they experience a sensation of darkness in front of the eyes and suffer also from headache. These symptoms appear sooner or later, sometimes as early as the tenth day, according as the patient be more or less burthened with superfluous humours. Nausea also and sickness affect the most of women, and especially such as those that we have just now mentioned, after the menstrual discharge has ceased and before it is yet turned in the direction of the breasts.

Moreover, some women suffer most at the beginning of their pregnancy and some at a later period when the embryo has had time to grow; and in some women it is a common occurrence to suffer from strangury towards the end of their time. As a general rule women who are pregnant of a male child escape comparatively easily and retain a comparatively healthy look, but it is otherwise with those whose infant is a female; for these latter look as a rule paler and suffer more pain, and in many cases they are subject to swellings of the legs and eruptions on the body. Nevertheless the rule is subject to exceptions.

Women in pregnancy are a prey to all sorts of longings and to rapid changes of mood, and some folks call this the 'ivy-sickness'; and with the mothers of female infants the longings are more acute, and they are less contented when they have got what they desired.

In a certain few cases the patient feels unusually well during pregnancy. The worst time of all is just when the child's hair is beginning to grow.

In pregnant women their own natural hair is inclined to grow thin and fall out, but on the other hand hair tends to grow on parts of the body where it was not wont to be. As a general rule, a man-child is more prone to movement within its mother's womb than a female child, and it is usually born sooner. And labour in the case of female children is apt to be protracted and sluggish, while in the case of male children it is acute and by a long way more difficult. Women who have connexion with their husbands shortly before childbirth are delivered all the more quickly. Occasionally women seem to be in the pains of labour though labour has not in fact commenced, what seemed like the commencement of labour being really the result of the foetus turning its head.

Now all other animals bring the time of pregnancy to an end in a uniform way; in other words, one single term of pregnancy is defined for each of them. But in the case of mankind alone of all animals the times are diverse; for pregnancy may be of seven months' duration, or of eight months or of nine, and still more commonly of ten [lunar] months, **584b** while some few women go even into the eleventh month.

Children that come into the world before seven months can under no circumstances survive. The seven-months' children are the earliest that are capable of life, and most of them are weakly—for which reason, by the way, it is customary to swaddle them in wool,—and many of them are born with some of the orifices of the body imperforate, for instance the ears or the nostrils. But as they get bigger they become more perfectly developed, and many of them grow up.

In Egypt, and in some other places where the women are fruitful and are wont to bear and bring forth many children without difficulty, and where the children when born are capable of living even if they be born subject to deformity, in these places the eight-months' children live and are brought up, but in Greece it is only a few of them that survive while most perish. And this being the general experience, when such a child does happen to survive the mother is apt to think that it was not an eight-months' child after all, but that she had conceived at an earlier period without being aware of it.

Women suffer most pain about the fourth and the eighth months, and if the foetus perishes in the fourth or in the eighth month the mother also succumbs as a general rule; so that not only do the eight-months' children not live, but when they die their mothers are in great danger of their own lives. In like manner children that are apparently born at a later term than eleven months are held to be in doubtful case; inasmuch as with them also the beginning of conception may have escaped the notice of the mother. What I mean to say is that often the womb gets filled with wind, and then when at a later period connexion and conception take place, they think that the former circumstance was the beginning of conception from the similarity of the symptoms that they experienced.

Such then are the differences between mankind and other animals in regard to the many various modes of completion of the term of pregnancy. Furthermore, some animals produce one and some produce many at a birth, but the human species does sometimes the one and sometimes the other. As a general rule and among most nations the women bear one child at a birth; but frequently and in many lands they bear twins, as for instance in Egypt especially. Sometimes women bring forth three and even four children, and especially in certain parts of the world, as has already been stated. The largest number ever brought forth is five, and such an occurrence has been witnessed on several occasions. There was once upon a time a certain women who had twenty children at four births; each time she had five, and most of them grew up.

Now among other animals, if a pair of twins happen to be male and female they have as good a chance of surviving as though both had been males or both females; but among man- **585a** kind very few twins survive if one happen to be a boy and the other a girl.

Of all animals the woman and the mare are most inclined to receive the commerce of the male during pregnancy; while all other animals when they are pregnant avoid the male, save those in which the phenomenon of superfoetation occurs, such as the hare. Unlike that animal, the mare after once conceiving cannot be rendered pregnant again, but brings forth one foal only, at least as a general rule; in the human species cases of superfoetation are rare, but they do happen now and then.

An embryo conceived some considerable time after a previous conception does not come to perfection, but gives rise to pain and causes the destruction of the earlier embryo; and, by the way, a case has been known to occur where owing to this destructive influence no less than twelve embryos conceived by superfoetation have been discharged. But if the second conception take place at a short interval, then the mother bears that which was later conceived, and brings forth the two children like actual twins, as happened, according to the legend, in the case of Iphicles and Hercules. The following also is a striking example: a certain woman, having committed adultery, brought forth the one child resembling her husband and the other resembling the adulterous lover.

The case has also occurred where a woman, being pregnant of twins, has subsequently conceived a third child; and in course of time she brought forth the twins perfect and at full term, but the third a five-months' child; and this last died there and then. And in another case it happened that the woman was first delivered of a seven-months' child, and then of two which were of full term; and of these the first died and the other two survived.

Some also have been known to conceive while about to miscarry, and they have lost the one child and been delivered of the other.

If women while going with child cohabit after the eighth month the child is in most cases born covered over with a slimy fluid. Often also the child is found to be replete with food of which the mother had partaken.

When women have partaken of salt in overabundance their children are apt to be born destitute of nails.

5

Milk that is produced earlier than the seventh month is unfit for use; but as soon as the child is fit to live the milk is fit to use. The first of the milk is saltish, as it is likewise with sheep. Most women are sensibly affected by wine during pregnancy, for if they partake of it they grow relaxed and debilitated.

The beginning of child-bearing in women and of the capacity to procreate in men, and the cessation of these functions in both cases, coincide in the one case with the emission of seed and in the other with the discharge of the catamenia: with this qualification that there is a lack of fertility at the commencement of these symptoms, and again towards their close when the emissions become scanty and weak. The
585b age at which the sexual powers begin has been related already.[1] As for their end, the menstrual discharges ceases in most women about their fortieth year; but with those in whom it goes on longer it lasts even to the fiftieth year, and women of that age have been known to bear children. But beyond that age there is no case on record.

6

Men in most cases continue to be sexually competent until they are sixty years old, and if that limit be overpassed then until seventy years; and men have been actually known to procreate children at seventy years of age. With many men and many women it so happens that they are unable to produce children to one another, while they are able to do so in union with other individuals. The same thing happens with regard to the production of male and female offspring; for sometimes men and women in union with one another produce male children or female, as the case may be, but children of the opposite sex when otherwise mated. And they are apt to change in this respect with advancing age: for sometimes a husband and wife while they are young produce female children and in later life male children; and in other cases the very contrary occurs. And just the same thing is true in regard to the generative faculty: for some while young are childless, but have children when they grow older; and some have children to begin with, and later on no more.

There are certain women who conceive with difficulty, but if they do conceive, bring the child to maturity; while others again conceive readily, but are unable to bring the child to birth. Furthermore, some men and some women produce female offspring and some male, as for instance in the story of Hercules, who among all his two and seventy children is said to have begotten but one girl. Those women who are unable to conceive, save with the help of medical treatment or some other adventitious circumstance, are as a general rule apt to bear female children rather than male.

It is a common thing with men to be at first sexually competent and afterwards impotent, and then again to revert to their former powers.

From deformed parents come deformed children, lame from lame and blind from blind, and, speaking generally, children often inherit anything that is peculiar in their parents and are born with similar marks, such as

[1] v. 1.

pimples or scars. Such things have been known to be handed down through three generations; for instance, a certain man had a mark on his arm which his son did not possess, but his grandson had it in the same spot though not very distinct.

Such cases, however, are few; for the children of cripples are mostly sound, and there is no hard and fast rule regarding them. While children mostly resemble their parents or their **586a** ancestors, it sometimes happens that no such resemblance is to be traced. But parents may pass on resemblance after several generations, as in the case of the woman in Elis, who committed adultery with a negro; in this case it was not the woman's own daughter but the daughter's child that was a blackamoor.

As a rule the daughters have a tendency to take after the mother, and the boys after the father; but sometimes it is the other way, the boys taking after the mother and the girls after the father. And they may resemble both parents in particular features.

There have been known cases of twins that had no resemblance to one another, but they are alike as a general rule. There was once upon a time a woman who had intercourse with her husband a week after giving birth to a child, and she conceived and bore a second child as like the first as any twin. Some women have a tendency to produce children that take after themselves, and others children that take after the husband; and this latter case is like that of the celebrated mare in Pharsalus, that got the name of the Honest Wife.

7

In the emission of sperm there is a preliminary discharge of air, and the outflow is manifestly caused by a blast of air; for nothing is cast to a distance save by pneumatic pressure. After the seed reaches the womb and remains there for a while, a membrane forms around it; for when it happens to escape before it is distinctly formed, it looks like an egg enveloped in its membrane after removal of the egg-shell; and the membrane is full of veins.

All animals whatsoever, whether they fly or swim or walk upon dry land, whether they bring forth their young alive or in the egg, develop in the same way: save only that some have the navel attached to the womb, namely the viviparous animals, and some have it attached to the egg, and some to both parts alike, as in a certain sort of fishes. And in some cases membranous envelopes surround the egg, and in other cases the chorion surrounds it. And first of all the animal develops within the innermost envelope, and then another membrane appears around the former one, which latter is for the most part attached to the womb, but is in part separated from it and contains fluid. In between is a watery or sanguineous fluid, which the women folk call the fore-waters.

8

All animals, or all such as have a navel, grow by the navel. And the navel is attached to the cotyledon in all such as possess cotyledons, and to the womb itself by a vein in all such as have the womb smooth. And as regards their shape within the womb, the four-footed animals all lie stretched out, and the footless animals lie on **586b** their sides, as for instance fishes; but two-legged animals lie in a bent position, as for instance birds; and human embryos lie bent, with nose between the knees and eyes upon the knees, and the ears free at the sides.

All animals alike have the head upwards to begin with; but as they grow and approach the term of egress from the womb they turn downwards, and birth in the natural course of things takes place in all animals head foremost; but in abnormal cases it may take place in a bent position, or feet foremost.

The young of quadrupeds when they are near their full time contain excrements, both liquid and in the form of solid lumps, the latter in the lower part of the bowel and the urine in the bladder.

In those animals that have cotyledons in the womb the cotyledons grow less as the embryo grows bigger, and at length they disappear altogether. The navel-string is a sheath wrapped about blood-vessels which have their origin in the womb, from the cotyledons in those animals which possess them and from a blood-vessel in those which do not. In the larger animals, such as the embryos of oxen, the vessels are four in number, and in smaller animals two; in the very little ones, such as fowls, one vessel only.

Of the four vessels that run into the embryo, two pass through the liver where the so-called gates or 'portae' are, running in the direction of the great vein, and the other two run in the direction of the aorta towards the point where it divides and becomes two vessels instead of one. Around each pair of blood-vessels are membranes, and surrounding these membranes is the navel-string itself, after the manner of a sheath. And as the embryo grows, the veins themselves tend more and more to dwindle in size. And also as the embryo matures it comes down into the hollow of the womb and is observed to move here, and sometimes rolls over in the vicinity of the groin.

9

When women are in labour, their pains determine towards many divers parts of the body, and in most cases to one or other of the thighs. Those are the quickest to be delivered who experience severe pains in the region of the belly; and parturition is difficult in those who begin by suffering pain in the loins, and speedy when the pain is abdominal. If the child about to be born be a male, the preliminary flood is watery and pale in colour, but if a girl it is tinged with blood, though still watery. In some cases of labour these latter phenomena do not occur, either one way or the other.

In other animals parturition is unaccompanied by pain, and the dam is plainly seen to suffer but moderate inconvenience. In women, however, the pains are more severe, and this is especially the case in persons of sedentary habits, and in those who are weak-chested and short of breath. Labour is apt to be especially difficult if during the process the woman while exerting force with her breath fails to hold it in.

First of all, when the embryo starts to move and the membranes burst, there issues forth the watery flood; then afterwards comes the embryo, while the womb everts and the afterbirth comes out from within.

10

The cutting of the navel-string, which is the nurse's duty, is a matter calling for no little care and skill. For not only in cases of difficult labour must she be able to render assistance with skilful hand, but she must also have her wits about her in all contingencies, and especially in the operation of tying the cord. For if the afterbirth have come away, the navel is ligatured off from the afterbirth with a woollen thread and is then cut above the ligature; and at the place where it has been tied it heals up, and the remaining portion drops off. (If the ligature come loose the child dies from loss of blood.) But if the afterbirth has not yet come away, but remains after the child itself is extruded, it is cut away within after the ligaturing of the cord.

It often happens that the child appears to have been born dead when it is merely weak, and when, before the umbilical cord has been ligatured, the blood has run out into the cord and its surroundings. But experienced midwives have been known to squeeze back the blood into the child's body from the cord, and immediately the child that a moment before was bloodless came back to life again.

It is the natural rule, as we have mentioned above, for all animals to come into the world head foremost, and children, moreover, have their hands stretched out by their sides. And the child gives a cry and puts its hands up to its mouth as soon as it issues forth.

Moreover the child voids excrement sometimes at once, sometimes a little later, but in all cases during the first day; and this excrement is unduly copious in comparison with the size of the child; it is what the midwives call the meconium or 'poppy-juice'. In colour it resembles blood, extremely dark and pitch-like, but later on it becomes milky, for the child takes at once to the breast. Before birth the child makes no sound, even though in difficult labour it put forth its head while the rest of the body remains within.

In cases where flooding takes place rather before its time, it is apt to be followed by difficult parturition. But if discharge take place after birth in small quantity, and in cases where it only takes place at the beginning and does not continue till the fortieth day, then in such cases women make a better recovery and are the sooner ready to conceive again.

Until the child is forty days old it neither laughs nor weeps during waking hours, but of nights it sometimes does both; and for the most part it does not even notice being tickled, but passes most of its time in sleep. As it keeps on growing it gets more and more wakeful; and moreover it shows signs of dreaming, though it is long afterwards before it remembers what it dreams.

In other animals there is no contrasting difference between one bone and another, but all are properly formed; but in children the front part of the head is soft and late of ossifying. And by the way, some animals are born with teeth, but children begin to cut their teeth in the seventh month; and the front teeth are the first to come through, sometimes the upper and sometimes the lower ones. And the warmer the nurses' milk so much the quicker are the children's teeth to come.

11

After parturition and the cleasing flood the milk comes in plenty, and in some women it flows not only from the nipples but at divers parts of the breasts, and in some cases even from the armpits. And for some time afterwards there continue to be certain indurated parts of the breast called strangalides, or 'knots', which occur when it so happens that the moisture is not concocted, or when it finds no outlet but accumulates within. For the whole breast is so spongy that if a woman in drinking happen to swallow a hair, she gets a pain in her breast, which ailment is called 'trichia'; and the pain lasts till the hair either find its own way out or be sucked out with the milk. Women continue to have milk until their next conception; and then the milk stops coming and goes dry, alike in the human species and in the quadrupedal vivipara. So long as there is a flow of milk the menstrual purgations do not take place, at least as a general rule, though the discharge has been known to occur during the period of suckling. For, speaking generally, a determination of moisture does not take place at one and the same time in several directions; as for instance the menstrual purgations tend to be scanty in persons suffering from haemorrhoids. And in some women the like happens owing to their suffering from varices, when the fluids issue from the pelvic region before entering into the womb. And patients who during suppression **588a** of the menses happen to vomit blood are no whit the worse.

12

Children are very commonly subject to convulsions, more especially such of them as are more than ordinarily well-nourished on rich or unusually plentiful milk from a stout nurse. Wine is bad for infants, in that it tends to excite this malady, and red wine is worse than white, especially when taken undiluted; and most things that tend to induce flatulency are also bad, and constipation too is prejudicial. The majority of deaths in infancy occur before the child is a week old, hence it is customary to name the child at that age, from a belief that it has now a better chance of survival. This malady is worst at the full of the moon; and by the way, it is a dangerous symptom when the spasms begin in the child's back.

BOOK VIII

1

We have now discussed the physical characteristics of animals and their methods of generation. Their habits and their modes of living vary according to their character and their food.

In the great majority of animals there are traces of psychical qualities or attitudes, which qualities are more markedly differentiated in the case of human beings. For just as we pointed out resemblances in the physical organs, so in a number of animals we observe gentleness or fierceness, mildness or cross temper, courage, or timidity, fear or confidence, high spirit or low cunning, and, with regard to intelligence, something equivalent to sagacity. Some of these qualities in man, as compared with the corresponding qualities in animals, differ only quantitatively: that is to say, a man has more or less of this quality, and an animal has more or less of some other; other qualities in man are represented by analogous and not identical qualities: for instance, just as in man we find knowledge, wisdom, and sagacity, so in certain animals there exists some other natural potentiality akin to these. The truth of this statement will be the more clearly apprehended if we have regard to the phenomena of childhood: for in children may be observed the traces and seeds of what will **588b** one day be settled psychological habits, though psychologically a child hardly differs for the time being from an animal; so that one is quite justified in saying that, as regards man and animals, certain psychical qualities are identical with one another, whilst others resemble, and others are analogous to, each other.

Nature proceeds little by little from things lifeless to animal life in such a way that it is impossible to determine the exact line of demarcation, nor on which side thereof an intermediate form should lie. Thus, next after lifeless things in the upward scale comes the plant, and of plants one will differ from another as to its amount of apparent vitality; and, in a word, the whole genus of plants, whilst it is devoid of life as compared with an animal, is endowed with life as compared with other corporeal entities. Indeed, as we just remarked, there is observed in plants a continuous scale of ascent towards the animal. So, in the sea, there are certain objects concerning which one would be at a loss to determine whether they be animal or vegetable. For instance, certain of these objects are fairly rooted, and in several cases perish if detached; thus the pinna is rooted to a particular spot, and the solen (or razor-shell) cannot survive withdrawal from its burrow. Indeed, broadly speaking, the entire genus of testaceans have a resemblance to vegetables, if they be contrasted with such animals as are capable of progression.

In regard to sensibility, some animals give no indication whatsoever of it, whilst others indicate it but indistinctly. Further, the substance of some of these intermediate creatures is flesh-like, as is the case with the so-called tethya (or ascidians) and the acalephae (or sea-anemones); but the sponge is in every respect like a vegetable. And so throughout the entire animal scale there is a graduated differentiation in amount of vitality and in capacity for motion.

A similar statement holds good with regard to habits of life. Thus of plants that spring from seed the one function seems to be the reproduction of their own particular species, and the sphere of action with certain animals is similarly limited. The faculty of reproduction, then, is common to all alike. If sensibility be superadded, then their lives will differ from one another in respect to sexual intercourse through the varying amount of pleasure derived therefrom, and also in regard to modes of parturition and ways of rearing their young. Some animals, like plants, simply procreate their own species at definite seasons; other animals busy themselves also in procuring food for their young, and after they are reared quit them and have no further dealings with
589a them; other animals are more intelligent and endowed with memory, and they live with their offspring for a longer period and on a more social footing.

The life of animals, then, may be divided into two acts—procreation and feeding; for on these two acts all their interests and life concentrate. Their food depends chiefly on the substance of which they are severally constituted; for the source of their growth in all cases will be this substance. And whatsoever is in conformity with nature is pleasant, and all animals pursue pleasure in keeping with their nature.

2

Animals are also differentiated locally: that is to say, some live upon dry land, while others live in the water. And this differentiation may be interpreted in two different ways. Thus, some animals are termed terrestrial as inhaling air, and others aquatic as taking in water; and there are others which do not actually take in these elements, but nevertheless are constitutionally adapted to the cooling influence, so far as is needful to them, of one element or the other, and hence are called terrestrial or aquatic though they neither breathe air nor take in water. Again, other animals are so called from their finding their food and fixing their habitat on land or in water: for many animals, although they inhale air and breed on land, yet derive their food from the water, and live in water for the greater part of their lives; and these are the only animals to which as living in and on two elements the term 'amphibious' is applicable. There is no animal taking in water that is terrestrial or aerial or that derives its food from the land, whereas of the great number of land animals inhaling air many get their food from the water; moreover some are so peculiarly organized that if they be shut off altogether from the water they cannot possibly live, as for instance, the so-called sea-turtle, the crocodile, the hippopotamus, the seal, and some of the smaller creatures, such as the fresh-water tortoise and the frog: now all these animals choke or drown if they do not from time to time breathe atmospheric air: they breed and rear their young on dry land, or near the land, but they pass their lives in water.

But the dolphin is equipped in the most remarkable way of all animals: the dolphin and other similar aquatic animals, including the other cetaceans which resemble it; that is to say,
589b the whale, and all the other creatures that are furnished with a blow-hole. One can hardly allow that such an animal is terrestrial and terrestrial only, or aquatic and aquatic only, if by terrestrial we mean an animal that inhales air, and if by aquatic we mean an animal that takes in water. For the fact is the dolphin performs both these processes: he takes in water and discharges it by his blow-hole, and he also inhales air into his lungs; for, by the way, the creature is furnished with this organ and respires thereby, and accordingly, when caught in the nets, he is quickly suffocated for lack of air. He can also live for a consid-

erable while out of the water, but all this while he keeps up a dull moaning sound corresponding to the noise made by air-breathing animals in general; furthermore, when sleeping, the animal keeps his nose above water, and he does so that he may breathe the air. Now it would be unreasonable to assign one and the same class of animals to both categories, terrestrial and aquatic, seeing that these categories are more or less exclusive of one another; we must accordingly supplement our definition of the term 'aquatic' or 'marine'. For the fact is, some aquatic animals take in water and discharge it again, for the same reason that leads air-breathing animals to inhale air: in other words, with the object of cooling the blood. Others take in water as incidental to their mode of feeding; for as they get their food in the water they cannot but take in water along with their food, and if they take in water they must be provided with some organ for discharging it. Those blooded animals, then, that use water for a purpose analogous to respiration are provided with gills; and such as take in water when catching their prey, with the blow-hole. Similar remarks are applicable to molluscs and crustaceans; for again it is by way of procuring food that these creatures take in water.

Aquatic in different ways, the differences depending on bodily relation to external temperature and on habit of life, are such animals on the one hand as take in air but live in water, and such on the other hand as take in water and are furnished with gills but go upon dry land and get their living there. At present only one animal of the latter kind is known, the so-called cordylus or water-newt; this creature is furnished not with lungs but with gills, but for all that it is a quadruped and fitted for walking on dry land.

In the case of all these animals their nature appears in some kind of a way to have got warped, just as some male animals get to resemble the female, and some female animals the male. The fact is that animals, if they be subjected to a modification in minute organs, are liable to immense modifications in their general configuration. This phenomenon may be observed in the case of gelded animals: only **590a** a minute organ of the animal is mutilated, and the creature passes from the male to the female form. We may infer, then, that if in the primary conformation of the embryo an infinitesimally minute but absolutely essential organ sustain a change of magnitude one way or the other, the animal will in one case turn to male and in the other to female; and also that, if the said organ be obliterated altogether, the animal will be of neither one sex nor the other. And so by the occurrence of modification in minute organs it comes to pass that one animal is terrestrial and another aquatic, in both senses of these terms. And, again, some animals are amphibious whilst other animals are not amphibious, owing to the circumstance that in their conformation while in the embryonic condition there got intermixed into them some portion of the matter of which their subsequent food is constituted; for, as was said above,[1] what is in conformity with nature is to every single animal pleasant and agreeable.

Animals then have been categorized into terrestrial and aquatic in three ways, according to their assumption of air or of water, the temperament of their bodies, or the character of their food; and the mode of life of an animal corresponds to the category in which it is found. That is to say, in some cases the animal depends for its terrestrial or aquatic nature on temperament and diet combined, as well as upon its method of respiration; and sometimes on temperament and habits alone.

Of testaceans, some, that are incapable of motion, subsist on fresh water, for, as the sea water dissolves into its constituents, the fresh water from its greater thinness percolates through the grosser parts; in fact, they live on fresh water just as they were originally engendered from the same. Now that fresh water is contained in the sea and can be strained off from it can be proved in a thoroughly practical way. Take a thin vessel of moulded wax, attach a cord to it, and let it down quite empty into the sea: in twenty-four hours it will be found to contain a quantity of water, and the water will be fresh and drinkable.

Sea-anemones feed on such small fishes as come in their way. The mouth of this creature is in the middle of its body; and this fact may be clearly observed in the case of the larger varieties. Like the oyster it has a duct for the outlet of the residuum; and this duct is at the top of the animal. In other words, the sea-anemone corresponds to the inner fleshy part of the oyster, and the stone to which the one creature clings corresponds to the shell which encases the other.

The limpet detaches itself from the rock and goes about in quest of food. Of shell-fish that are mobile, some are carnivorous and live on

[1] 589a 9.

590b little fishes, as for instance, the purple murex—and there can be no doubt that the purple murex is carnivorous, as it is caught by a bait of fish; others are carnivorous, but feed also on marine vegetation.

The sea-turtles feed on shell-fish—for, by the way, their mouths are extraordinarily hard; (whatever object it seizes, stone or other, it crunches into bits, but when it leaves the water for dry land it browses on grass). These creatures suffer greatly, and oftentimes die when they lie on the surface of the water exposed to a scorching sun; for, when once they have risen to the surface, they find a difficulty in sinking again.

Crustaceans feed in like manner. They are omnivorous; that is to say, they live on stones, slime, sea-weed, and excrement—as for instance the rock-crab—and are also carnivorous. The crawfish or spiny-lobster can get the better of fishes even of the larger species, though in some of them it occasionally finds more than its match. Thus, this animal is so overmastered and cowed by the octopus that it dies of terror if it become aware of an octopus in the same net with itself. The crawfish can master the conger-eel, for owing to the rough spines of the crawfish the eel cannot slip away and elude its hold. The conger-eel, however, devours the octopus, for owing to the slipperiness of its antagonist the octopus can make nothing of it. The crawfish feeds on little fish, capturing them beside its hole or dwelling-place; for, by the way, it is found out at sea on rough and stony bottoms, and in such places it makes its den. Whatever it catches, it puts into its mouth with its pincer-like claws, like the common crab. Its nature is to walk straight forward when it has nothing to fear, with its feelers hanging sideways; if it be frightened, it makes its escape backwards, darting off to a great distance. These animals fight one another with their claws, just as rams fight with their horns, raising them and striking their opponents; they are often also seen crowded together in herds. So much for the mode of life of the crustacean.

Molluscs are all carnivorous; and of molluscs the calamary and the sepia are more than a
591a match for fishes even of the large species. The octopus for the most part gathers shell-fish, extracts the flesh, and feeds on that; in fact, fishermen recognize their holes by the number of shells lying about. Some say that the octopus devours its own species, but this statement is incorrect; it is doubtless founded on the fact that the creature is often found with its tentacles removed, which tentacles have really been eaten off by the conger.

Fishes, all without exception, feed on spawn in the spawning season; but in other respects the food varies with the varying species. Some fishes are exclusively carnivorous, as the cartilaginous genus, the conger, the channa or *Serranus,* the tunny, the bass, the synodon or *Dentex,* the amia, the sea-perch, and the muraena. The red mullet is carnivorous, but feeds also on sea-weed, on shell-fish, and on mud. The grey mullet feeds on mud, the dascyllus on mud and offal, the scarus or parrot-fish and the melanurus on sea-weed, the saupe on offal and sea-weed; the saupe feeds also on zostera, and is the only fish that is captured with a gourd. All fishes devour their own species, with the single exception of the cestreus or mullet; and the conger is especially ravenous in this respect. The cephalus and the mullet in general are the only fish that eat no flesh; this may be inferred from the facts that when caught they are never found with flesh in their intestines, and that the bait used to catch them is not flesh but barley-cake. Every fish of the mullet-kind lives on sea-weed and sand. The cephalus, called by some the 'chelon', keeps near in to the shore, the peraeas keeps out at a distance from it, and feeds on a mucous substance exuding from itself, and consequently is always in a starved condition. The cephalus lives in mud, and is in consequence heavy and slimy; it never feeds on any other fish. As it lives in mud, it has every now and then to make a leap upwards out of the mud so as to wash the slime from off its body. There is no creature known to prey upon the spawn of the cephalus, so that the species is exceedingly numerous; when, however, the fish is full-grown it is preyed upon by a number of fishes, and especially by the achar-
591b nas or bass. Of all fishes the mullet is the most voracious and insatiable, and in consequence its belly is kept at full stretch; whenever it is not starving, it may be considered as out of condition. When it is frightened, it hides its head in mud, under the notion that it is hiding its whole body. The synodon is carnivorous and feeds on molluscs. Very often the synodon and the channa cast up their stomachs while chasing smaller fishes; for, be it remembered, fishes have their stomachs close to the mouth, and are not furnished with a gullet.

Some fishes then, as has been stated, are carnivorous, and carnivorous only, as the dolphin, the synodon, the gilt-head, the selachians, and the molluscs. Other fishes feed habitually on mud or sea-weed or sea-moss or the so-called stalk-weed or growing plants; as for instance, the phycis, the goby, and the rock-fish; and, by the way, the only meat that the phycis will touch is that of prawns. Very often, however, as has been stated, they devour one another, and especially do the larger ones devour the smaller. The proof of their being carnivorous is the fact that they can be caught with flesh for a bait. The mackerel, the tunny, and the bass are for the most part carnivorous, but they do occasionally feed on sea-weed. The sargue feeds on the leavings of the trigle or red mullet. The red mullet burrows in the mud, and when it sets the mud in motion and quits its haunt, the sargue settles down into the place and feeds on what is left behind, and prevents any smaller fish from settling in the immediate vicinity.

Of all fishes the so-called scarus, or parrot-wrasse, is the only one known to chew the cud like a quadruped.

As a general rule the larger fishes catch the smaller ones in their mouths whilst swimming straight after them in the ordinary position; but the selachians, the dolphin, and all the cetacea must first turn over on their backs, as their mouths are placed down below; this allows a fair chance of escape to the smaller fishes, and, indeed, if it were not so, there would be very few of the little fishes left, for the speed and voracity of the dolphin is something marvellous.

Of eels a few here and there feed on mud **592a** and on chance morsels of food thrown to them; the greater part of them subsist on fresh water. Eel-breeders are particularly careful to have the water kept perfectly clear, by its perpetually flowing on to flat slabs of stone and then flowing off again; sometimes they coat the eel-tanks with plaster. The fact is that the eel will soon choke if the water is not clear as his gills are peculiarly small. On this account, when fishing for eels, they disturb the water. In the river Strymon eel-fishing takes place at the rising of the Pleiads, because at this period the water is troubled and the mud raised up by contrary winds; unless the water be in this condition, it is as well to leave the eels alone. When dead the eel, unlike the majority of fishes, neither floats on nor rises to the surface; and this is owing to the smallness of the stomach. A few eels are supplied with fat, but the greater part have no fat whatsoever. When removed from the water they can live for five or six days; for a longer period if north winds prevail, for a shorter if south winds. If they are removed in summer from the pools to the tanks they will die; but not so if removed in the winter. They are not capable of holding out against any abrupt change; consequently they often die in large numbers when men engaged in transporting them from one place to another dip them into water particularly cold. They will also die of suffocation if they be kept in a scanty supply of water. This same remark will hold good for fishes in general; for they are suffocated if they be long confined in a short supply of water, with the water kept unchanged—just as animals that respire are suffocated if they be shut up with a scanty supply of air. The eel in some cases lives for seven or eight years. The river-eel feeds on his own species, on grass, or on roots, or on any chance food found in the mud. Their usual feeding-time is at night, and during the day-time they retreat into deep water. And so much for the food of fishes.

3

Of birds, such as have crooked talons are carnivorous without exception, and cannot swallow corn or bread-food even if it be put into their bills in tit-bits; as for instance, the eagle **592b** of every variety, the kite, the two species of hawks, to wit, the dove-hawk and the sparrow-hawk—and, by the way, these two hawks differ greatly in size from one another—and the buzzard. The buzzard is of the same size as the kite, and is visible at all seasons of the year. There is also the phene (or lämmergeier) and the vulture. The phene is larger than the common eagle and is ashen in colour. Of the vulture there are two varieties: one small and whitish, the other comparatively large and rather more ashen-coloured than white. Further, of birds that fly by night, some have crooked talons, such as the night-raven, the owl, and the eagle-owl. The eagle-owl resembles the common owl in shape, but it is quite as large as the eagle. Again, there is the eleus, the Aegolian owl, and the little horned owl. Of these birds, the eleus is somewhat larger than the barn-door cock, and the Aegolian owl is of about the same size as the eleus, and both these birds hunt the jay; the little horned owl is smaller than the common owl. All these three birds are alike in appearance, and all three are carnivorous.

Again, of birds that have not crooked talons some are carnivorous, such as the swallow. Others feed on grubs, such as the chaffinch, the sparrow, the 'batis', the green linnet, and the titmouse. Of the titmouse there are three varieties. The largest is the finch-titmouse—for it is about the size of a finch; the second has a long tail, and from its habitat is called the hill-titmouse; the third resembles the other two in appearance, but is less in size than either of them. Then come the becca-fico, the black-cap, the bull-finch, the robin, the epilais, the midget-bird, and the golden-crested wren. This wren is little larger than a locust, has a crest of bright red gold, and is in every way a beautiful and graceful little bird. Then the anthus, a bird about the size of a finch; and the mountain-finch, which resembles a finch and is of much the same size, but its neck is blue, and it is named from its habitat; and lastly the wren and the rook. The above-enumerated birds and the like of them feed either wholly or for the most part on grubs, but the following and the like feed on thistles; to wit, the linnet, the thraupis, and the goldfinch. All these birds **593a** feed on thistles, but never on grubs or any living thing whatever; they live and roost also on the plants from which they derive their food.

There are other birds whose favourite food consists of insects found beneath the bark of trees; as for instance, the great and the small pie, which are nicknamed the woodpeckers. These two birds resemble one another in plumage and in note, only that the note of the larger bird is the louder of the two; they both frequent the trunks of trees in quest of food. There is also the greenpie, a bird about the size of a turtle-dove, green-coloured all over, that pecks at the bark of trees with extraordinary vigour, lives generally on the branch of a tree, has a loud note, and is mostly found in the Peloponnese. There is another bird called the 'grub-picker' (or tree-creeper), about as small as the penduline titmouse, with speckled plumage of an ashen colour, and with a poor note; it is a variety of the woodpecker.

There are other birds that live on fruit and herbage, such as the wild pigeon or ring-dove, the common pigeon, the rock-dove, and the turtle-dove. The ring-dove and the common pigeon are visible at all seasons; the turtle-dove only in the summer, for in winter it lurks in some hole or other and is never seen. The rock-dove is chiefly visible in the autumn, and is caught at that season; it is larger than the common pigeon but smaller than the wild one; it is generally caught while drinking. These pigeons bring their young ones with them when they visit this country. All our other birds come to us in the early summer and build their nests here, and the greater part of them rear their young on animal food, with the sole exception of the pigeon and its varieties.

The whole genus of birds may be pretty well divided into such as procure their food on dry land, such as frequent rivers and lakes, and such as live on or by the sea.

Of water-birds such as are web-footed live actually on the water, while such as are split-footed live by the edge of it—and, by the way, water-birds that are not carnivorous live on water-plants, ⟨but most of them live on fish⟩, **593b** like the heron and the spoonbill that frequent the banks of lakes and rivers; and the spoonbill, by the way, is less than the common heron, and has a long flat bill. There are furthermore the stork and the seamew; and the seamew, by the way, is ashen-coloured. There is also the schoenilus, the cinclus, and the white-rump. Of these smaller birds the last mentioned is the largest, being about the size of the common thrush; all three may be described as 'wag-tails'. Then there is the scalidris, with plumage ashen-grey, but speckled. Moreover, the family of the halcyons or kingfishers live by the waterside. Of kingfishers there are two varieties; one that sits on reeds and sings; the other, the larger of the two, is without a note. Both these varieties are blue on the back. There is also the trochilus (or sandpiper). The halcyon also, including a variety termed the cerylus, is found near the seaside. The crow also feeds on such animal life as is cast up on the beach, for the bird is omnivorous. There are also the white gull, the cepphus, the aethyia, and the charadrius.

Of web-footed birds, the larger species live on the banks of rivers and lakes; as the swan, the duck, the coot, the grebe, and the teal—a bird resembling the duck but less in size—and the water-raven or cormorant. This bird is the size of a stork, only that its legs are shorter; it is web-footed and is a good swimmer; its plumage is black. It roosts on trees, and is the only one of all such birds as these that is found to build its nest in a tree. Further there is the large goose, the little gregarious goose, the vulpanser, the horned grebe, and the penelops. The sea-eagle lives in the neighbourhood of the sea and seeks its quarry in lagoons.

A great number of birds are omnivorous.

Birds of prey feed on any animal or bird, other than a bird of prey, that they may catch. These birds never touch one of their own genus, whereas fishes often devour members actually of their own species.

Birds, as a rule, are very spare drinkers. In **594a** fact birds of prey never drink at all, excepting a very few, and these drink very rarely; and this last observation is peculiarly applicable to the kestrel. The kite has been seen to drink, but he certainly drinks very seldom.

4

Animals that are coated with tessellates—such as the lizard and the other quadrupeds, and the serpents—are omnivorous: at all events they are carnivorous and graminivorous; and serpents, by the way, are of all animals the greatest gluttons.

Tessellated animals are spare drinkers, as are also all such animals as have a spongy lung, and such a lung, scantily supplied with blood, is found in all oviparous animals. Serpents, by the by, have an insatiate appetite for wine; consequently, at times men hunt for snakes by pouring wine into saucers and putting them into the interstices of walls, and the creatures are caught when inebriated. Serpents are carnivorous, and whenever they catch an animal they extract all its juices and eject the creature whole. And, by the way, this is done by all other creatures of similar habits, as for instance the spider; only that the spider sucks out the juices of its prey outside, and the serpent does so in its belly. The serpent takes any food presented to him, eats birds and animals, and swallows eggs entire. But after taking his prey he stretches himself until he stands straight out to the very tip, and then he contracts and squeezes himself into little compass, so that the swallowed mass may pass down his outstretched body; and this action on his part is due to the tenuity and length of his gullet. Spiders and snakes can both go without food for a long time; and this remark may be verified by observation of specimens kept alive in the shops of the apothecaries.

5

Of viviparous quadrupeds such as are fierce and jag-toothed are without exception carnivorous; though, by the way, it is stated of the wolf, but of no other animal, that in extremity of hunger it will eat a certain kind of earth. These carnivorous animals never eat grass except when they are sick, just as dogs bring on a vomit by eating grass and thereby purge themselves.

The solitary wolf is more apt to attack man than the wolf that goes with a pack.

The animal called 'glanus' by some and **594b** 'hyaena' by others is as large as a wolf, with a mane like a horse, only that the hair is stiffer and longer and extends over the entire length of the chine. It will lie in wait for a man and chase him, and will inveigle a dog within its reach by making a noise that resembles the retching noise of a man vomiting. It is exceedingly fond of putrefied flesh, and will burrow in a graveyard to gratify this propensity.

The bear is omnivorous. It eats fruit, and is enabled by the suppleness of its body to climb a tree; it also eats vegetables, and it will break up a hive to get at the honey; it eats crabs and ants also, and is in a general way carnivorous. It is so powerful that it will attack not only the deer but the wild boar, if it can take it unawares, and also the bull. After coming to close quarters with the bull it falls on its back in front of the animal, and, when the bull proceeds to butt, the bear seizes hold of the bull's horns with its front paws, fastens its teeth into his shoulder, and drags him down to the ground. For a short time together it can walk erect on its hind legs. All the flesh it eats it first allows to become carrion.

The lion, like all other savage and jag-toothed animals, is carnivorous. It devours its food greedily and fiercely, and often swallows its prey entire without rending it at all; it will then go fasting for two or three days together, being rendered capable of this abstinence by its previous surfeit. It is a spare drinker. It discharges the solid residuum in small quantities, about every other day or at irregular intervals, and the substance of it is hard and dry like the excrement of a dog. The wind discharged from off its stomach is pungent, and its urine emits a strong odour, a phenomenon which, in the case of dogs, accounts for their habit of sniffing at trees; for, by the way, the lion, like the dog, lifts its leg to void its urine. It infects the food it eats with a strong smell by breathing on it, and when the animal is cut open an overpowering vapour exhales from its inside.

Some wild quadrupeds feed in lakes and rivers; the seal is the only one that gets its living on the sea. To the former class of animals belong the so-called castor, the satyrium, the otter, and the so-called latax, or beaver. The beaver is flatter than the otter and has strong

595a teeth; it often at night-time emerges from the water and goes nibbling at the bark of the aspens that fringe the riversides. The otter will bite a man, and it is said that whenever it bites it will never let go until it hears a bone crack. The hair of the beaver is rough, intermediate in appearance between the hair of the seal and the hair of the deer.

6

Jag-toothed animals drink by lapping, as do also some animals with teeth differently formed, as the mouse. Animals whose upper and lower teeth meet evenly drink by suction, as the horse and the ox; the bear neither laps nor sucks, but gulps down his drink. Birds, as a rule, drink by suction, but the long-necked birds stop and elevate their heads at intervals; the purple coot is the only one (of the long-necked birds) that swallows water by gulps.

Horned animals, domesticated or wild, and all such as are not jag-toothed, are all frugivorous and graminivorous, save under great stress of hunger. The pig is an exception, it cares little for grass or fruit, but of all animals it is the fondest of roots, owing to the fact that its snout is peculiarly adapted for digging them out of the ground; it is also of all animals the most easily pleased in the matter of food. It takes on fat more rapidly in proportion to its size than any other animal; in fact, a pig can be fattened for the market in sixty days. Pig-dealers can tell the amount of flesh taken on, by having first weighed the animal while it was being starved. Before the fattening process begins, the creature must be starved for three days; and, by the way, animals in general will take on fat if subjected previously to a course of starvation; after the three days of starvation, pig-breeders feed the animal lavishly. Breeders in Thrace, when fattening pigs, give them a drink on the first day; then they miss one, and then two days, then three and four, until the interval extends over seven days. The pigs' meat used for fattening is composed of barley, millet, figs, acorns, wild pears, and cucumbers. These animals—and other animals that have warm bellies—are fattened by repose. [Pigs also fatten the better by being allowed to wallow in mud. They like to feed in batches 595b of the same age. A pig will give battle even to a wolf.] If a pig be weighed when living, you may calculate that after death its flesh will weigh five-sixths of that weight, and the hair, the blood, and the rest will weigh the other sixth. When suckling their young, swine—like all other animals—get attenuated. So much for these animals.

7

Cattle feed on corn and grass, and fatten on vegetables that tend to cause flatulency, such as bitter vetch or bruised beans or bean-stalks. The older ones also will fatten if they be fed up after an incision has been made into their hide, and air blown thereinto. Cattle will fatten also on barley in its natural state or on barley finely winnowed, or on sweet food, such as figs, or pulp from the wine-press, or on elm-leaves. But nothing is so fattening as the heat of the sun and wallowing in warm waters. If the horns of young cattle be smeared with hot wax, you may mold them to any shape you please, and cattle are less subject to disease of the hoof if you smear the horny parts with wax, pitch, or olive oil. Herded cattle suffer more when they are forced to change their pasture-ground by frost than when snow is the cause of change. Cattle grow all the more in size when they are kept from sexual commerce over a number of years; and it is with a view to growth in size that in Epirus the so-called Pyrrhic kine are not allowed intercourse with the bull until they are nine years old; from which circumstance they are nicknamed the 'unbulled' kine. Of these Pyrrhic cattle, by the way, they say that there are only about four hundred in the world, that they are the private property of the Epirote royal family, that they cannot thrive out of Epirus, and that people elsewhere have tried to rear them, but without success.

8

Horses, mules, and asses feed on corn and grass, but are fattened chiefly by drink. Just in proportion as beasts of burden drink water, so will they more or less enjoy their food, and a place will give good or bad feeding according as the water is good or bad. Green corn, while ripening, will give a smooth coat; but such corn is injurious if the spikes are too stiff and sharp. The first crop of clover is unwholesome, and so is clover over which ill-scented water runs; for the clover is sure to get the taint of the water. Cattle like clear water for drinking; but the horse in this respect resembles the camel, for the camel likes turbid and thick water, and will never drink from a 596a stream until he has trampled it into a turbid condition. And, by the way, the camel can go without water for as much as four days, but after that when he drinks, he drinks in immense quantities.

9

The elephant at the most can eat nine Macedonian medimni of fodder at one meal; but so large an amount is unwholesome. As a general rule it can take six or seven medimni of fodder, five medimni of wheat, and five *mareis* of wine—six cotylae going to the *maris*. An elephant has been known to drink right off fourteen Macedonian *metretae* of water, and another *metretae* later in the day.

Camels live for about thirty years; in some exceptional cases they live much longer, and instances have been known of their living to the age of a hundred. The elephant is said by some to live for about two hundred years; by others, for three hundred.

10

Sheep and goats are graminivorous, but sheep browse assiduously and steadily, whereas goats shift their ground rapidly, and browse only on the tips of the herbage. Sheep are much improved in condition by drinking, and accordingly they give the flocks salt every five days in summer, to the extent of one medimnus to the hundred sheep, and this is found to render a flock healthier and fatter. In fact they mix salt with the greater part of their food; a large amount of salt is mixed into their bran (for the reason that they drink more when thirsty), and in autumn they get cucumbers with a sprinkling of salt on them; this admixture of salt in their food tends also to increase the quantity of milk in the ewes. If sheep be kept on the move at midday they will drink more copiously towards evening; and if the ewes be fed with salted food as the lambing season draws near they will get larger udders. Sheep are fattened by twigs of the olive or of the oleaster, by vetch, and bran of every kind; and these articles of food fatten all the more if they be first sprinkled with brine. Sheep will take on flesh all the better if they be first put for three days through a process of starving. In autumn, water from the north is more wholesome for sheep than water from the south. Pasture grounds are all the better if they have a westerly aspect.

Sheep will lose flesh if they be kept overmuch on the move or be subjected to any hardship. In winter time shepherds can easily distinguish the vigorous sheep from the weakly, from the fact that the vigorous sheep are covered with hoar-frost while the weakly ones
596b are quite free of it; the fact being that the weakly ones feeling oppressed with the burden shake themselves and so get rid of it. The flesh of all quadrupeds deteriorates in marshy pastures, and is the better on high grounds. Sheep that have flat tails can stand the winter better than long-tailed sheep, and short-fleeced sheep than the shaggy-fleeced; and sheep with crisp wool stand the rigour of winter very poorly. Sheep are healthier than goats, but goats are stronger than sheep. [The fleeces and the wool of sheep that have been killed by wolves, as also the clothes made from them, are exceptionally infested with lice.]

11

Of insects, such as have teeth are omnivorous; such as have a tongue feed on liquids only, extracting with that organ juices from all quarters. And of these latter some may be called omnivorous, inasmuch as they feed on every kind of juice, as for instance, the common fly; others are blood-suckers, such as the gadfly and the horse-fly, others again live on the juices of fruits and plants. The bee is the only insect that invariably eschews whatever is rotten; it will touch no article of food unless it have a sweet-tasting juice, and it is particularly fond of drinking water if it be found bubbling up clear from a spring underground.

So much for the food of animals of the leading genera.

12

The habits of animals are all connected with either breeding and the rearing of young, or with the procuring a due supply of food; and these habits are modified so as to suit cold and heat and the variations of the seasons. For all animals have an instinctive perception of the changes of temperature, and, just as men seek shelter in houses in winter, or as men of great possessions spend their summer in cool places and their winter in sunny ones, so also all animals that can do so shift their habitat at various seasons.

Some creatures can make provision against change without stirring from their ordinary haunts; others migrate, quitting Pontus and the cold countries after the autumnal equi-
597a nox to avoid the approaching winter, and after the spring equinox migrating from warm lands to cool lands to avoid the coming heat. In some cases they migrate from places near at

hand, in others they may be said to come from the ends of the world, as in the case of the crane; for these birds migrate from the steppes of Scythia to the marshlands south of Egypt where the Nile has its source. And it is here, by the way, that they are said to fight with the pygmies; and the story is not fabulous, but there is in reality a race of dwarfish men, and the horses are little in proportion, and the men live in caves underground. Pelicans also migrate, and fly from the Strymon to the Ister, and breed on the banks of this river. They depart in flocks, and the birds in front wait for those in the rear, owing to the fact that when the flock is passing over the intervening mountain range, the birds in the rear lose sight of their companions in the van.

Fishes also in a similar manner shift their habitat now out of the Euxine and now into it. In winter they move from the outer sea in towards land in quest of heat; in summer they shift from shallow waters to the deep sea to escape the heat.

Weakly birds in winter and in frosty weather come down to the plains for warmth, and in summer migrate to the hills for coolness. The more weakly an animal is the greater hurry will it be in to migrate on account of extremes of temperature, either hot or cold; thus the mackerel migrates in advance of the tunnies, and the quail in advance of the cranes. The former migrates in the month of Boedromion, and the latter in the month of Maemacterion. All creatures are fatter in migrating from cold to heat than in migrating from heat to cold; thus the quail is fatter when he emigrates in autumn than when he arrives in spring. The migration from cold countries is contemporaneous with the close of the hot season. Animals are in better trim for breeding purposes in spring-time, when they change from hot to cool lands.

Of birds, the crane, as has been said, migrates from one end of the world to the other; they fly against the wind. The story told about
597b the stone is untrue: to wit, that the bird, so the story goes, carries in its inside a stone by way of ballast, and that the stone when vomited up is a touchstone for gold.

The cushat and the rock-dove migrate, and never winter in our country, as is the case also with the turtle-dove; the common pigeon, however, stays behind. The quail also migrates; only, by the way, a few quails and turtle-doves may stay behind here and there in sunny districts. Cushats and turtle-doves flock together, both when they arrive and when the season for migration comes round again. When quails come to land, if it be fair weather or if a north wind is blowing, they will pair off and manage pretty comfortably; but if a southerly wind prevail they are greatly distressed owing to the difficulties in the way of flight, for a southerly wind is wet and violent. For this reason bird-catchers are never on the alert for these birds during fine weather, but only during the prevalence of southerly winds, when the bird from the violence of the wind is unable to fly. And, by the way, it is owing to the distress occasioned by the bulkiness of its body that the bird always screams while flying: for the labour is severe. When the quails come from abroad they have no leaders, but when they migrate hence, the glottis flits along with them, as does also the landrail, and the eared owl, and the corncrake. The corncrake calls them in the night, and when the bird-catchers hear the croak of the bird in the night-time they know that the quails are on the move. The landrail is like a marsh bird, and the glottis has a tongue that can project far out of its beak. The eared owl is like an ordinary owl, only that it has feathers about its ears; by some it is called the night-raven. It is a great rogue of a bird, and is a capital mimic; a bird-catcher will dance before it and, while the bird is mimicking his gestures, the accomplice comes behind and catches it. The common owl is caught by a similar trick.

As a general rule all birds with crooked talons are short-necked, flat-tongued, and disposed to mimicry. The Indian bird, the parrot, which is said to have a man's tongue, answers to this description; and, by the way, after drinking wine, the parrot becomes more saucy than ever.

Of birds, the following are migratory—the crane, the swan, the pelican, and the lesser goose.

13

Of fishes, some, as has been observed, migrate from the outer seas in towards shore, and from the shore towards the outer seas, to avoid the
598a extremes of cold and heat.

Fish living near to the shore are better eating than deep-sea fish. The fact is they have more abundant and better feeding, for wherever the sun's heat can reach vegetation is more abundant, better in quality, and more delicate, as is seen in any ordinary garden. Further, the black shore-weed grows near to shore; the other shore-weed is like wild weed. Besides, the parts of the sea near to shore are subjected to a more equable temperature; and consequently the flesh of shallow-water fishes is firm and consistent, whereas the flesh of deep-water fishes is flaccid and watery.

The following fishes are found near into shore—the synodon, the black bream, the merou, the gilthead, the mullet, the red mullet, the wrasse, the weaver, the callionymus, the goby, and rock-fishes of all kinds. The following are deep-sea fishes—the trygon, the cartilaginous fishes, the white conger, the serranus, the erythrinus, and the glaucus. The braize, the sea-scorpion, the black conger, the muraena, and the piper or sea-cuckoo are found alike in shallow and deep waters. These fishes, however, vary for various localities; for instance, the goby and all rock-fish are fat off the coast of Crete. Again, the tunny is out of season in summer, when it is being preyed on by its own peculiar louse-parasite, but after the rising of Arcturus, when the parasite has left it, it comes into season again. A number of fish also are found in sea-estuaries; such as the saupe, the gilthead, the red mullet, and, in point of fact, the greater part of the gregarious fishes. The bonito also is found in such waters, as, for instance, off the coast of Alopeconnesus; and most species of fishes are found in Lake Bistonis. The coly-mackerel as a rule does not enter the Euxine, but passes the summer in the Propontis, where it spawns, and winters in the Aegean. The tunny proper, the pelamys, and the bonito penetrate into the Euxine in summer and pass the summer there; as do also the greater part of such fish as swim in shoals with the currents, or congregate in shoals together. And most fish congregate in shoals, and shoal-fishes in all cases have leaders.

Fish penetrate into the Euxine for two reasons, and firstly for food. For the feeding is more abundant and better in quality owing to the amount of fresh river-water that discharges into the sea, and moreover, the large fishes of **598b** this inland sea are smaller than the large fishes of the outer sea. In point of fact, there is no large fish in the Euxine excepting the dolphin and the porpoise, and the dolphin is a small variety; but as soon as you get into the outer sea the big fishes are on the big scale. Furthermore, fish penetrate into this sea for the purpose of breeding; for there are recesses there favourable for spawning, and the fresh and exceptionally sweet water has an invigorating effect upon the spawn. After spawning, when the young fishes have attained some size, the parent fish swim out of the Euxine immediately after the rising of the Pleiads. If winter comes in with a southerly wind, they swim out with more or less of deliberation; but, if a north wind be blowing, they swim out with greater rapidity, from the fact that the breeze is favourable to their own course. And, by the way, the young fish are caught about this time in the neighbourhood of Byzantium very small in size, as might have been expected from the shortness of their sojourn in the Euxine. The shoals in general are visible both as they quit and enter the Euxine. The trichiae, however, only can be caught during their entry, but are never visible during their exit; in point of fact, when a trichia is caught running outwards in the neighbourhood of Byzantium, the fishermen are particularly careful to cleanse their nets, as the circumstance is so singular and exceptional. The way of accounting for this phenomenon is that this fish, and this one only, swims northwards into the Danube, and then at the point of its bifurcation swims down southwards into the Adriatic. And, as a proof that this theory is correct, the very opposite phenomenon presents itself in the Adriatic; that is to say, they are not caught in that sea during their entry, but are caught during their exit.

Tunny-fish swim into the Euxine keeping the shore on their right, and swim out of it with the shore upon their left. It is stated that they do so as being naturally weak-sighted, and seeing better with the right eye.

During the daytime shoal-fish continue on their way, but during the night they rest and feed. But if there be moonlight, they continue their journey without resting at all. Some people accustomed to sea-life assert that shoal-fish at the period of the winter solstice never move at all, but keep perfectly still wherever they may happen to have been overtaken by the solstice, and this lasts until the equinox.

The coly-mackerel is caught more frequently on entering than on quitting the Euxine. And in the Propontis the fish is at its best before the spawning season. Shoal-fish, as a rule, are caught in greater quantities as they leave the Euxine, and at that season they are in the best condition. At the time of their entrance they are caught in very plump condition close to shore, but those are in comparatively poor condition that are caught farther out to **599a** sea. Very often, when the coly-mackerel and the mackerel are met by a south wind in their exit, there are better catches to the southward than in the neighbourhood of Byzantium. So much then for the phenomenon of migration of fishes.

Now the same phenomenon is observed in fishes as in terrestrial animals in regard to hibernation: in other words, during winter fishes take to concealing themselves in out of the way places, and quit their places of concealment in the warmer season. But, by the way, animals go into concealment by way of refuge against extreme heat, as well as against extreme cold. Sometimes an entire genus will thus seek concealment; in other cases some species will do so and others will not. For instance, the shell-fish seek concealment without exception, as is seen in the case of those dwelling in the sea, the purple murex, the ceryx, and all such like; but though in the case of the detached species the phenomenon is obvious—for they hide themselves, as is seen in the scallop, or they are provided with an operculum on the free surface, as in the case of land snails—in the case of the non-detached the concealment is not so clearly observed. They do not go into hiding at one and the same season; but the snails go in winter, the purple murex and the ceryx for about thirty days at the rising of the Dog-star, and the scallop at about the same period. But for the most part they go into concealment when the weather is either extremely cold or extremely hot.

14

Insects almost all go into hiding, with the exception of such of them as live in human habitations or perish before the completion of the year. They hide in the winter; some of them for several days, others for only the coldest days, as the bee. For the bee also goes into hiding: and the proof that it does so is that during a certain period bees never touch the food set before them, and if a bee creeps out of the hive, it is quite transparent, with nothing whatsoever in its stomach; and the period of its rest and hiding lasts from the setting of the Pleiads until springtime.

Animals take their winter-sleep or summer-sleep by concealing themselves in warm places, or in places where they have been used to lie concealed.

15

Several blooded animals take this sleep, such as the pholidotes or tessellates, namely, the serpent, the lizard, the gecko, and the river-crocodile, all of which go into hiding for four months in the depth of winter, and during that
599b time eat nothing. Serpents in general burrow under ground for this purpose; the viper conceals itself under a stone.

A great number of fishes also take this sleep, and notably, the hippurus and coracinus in winter time; for, whereas fish in general may be caught at all periods of the year more or less, there is this singularity observed in these fishes, that they are caught within a certain fixed period of the year, and never by any chance out of it. The muraena also hides, and the orphus or sea-perch, and the conger. Rock-fish pair off, male and female, for hiding (just as for breeding); as is observed in the case of the species of wrasse called the thrush and the owzel, and in the perch.

The tunny also takes a sleep in winter in deep waters, and gets exceedingly fat after the sleep. The fishing season for the tunny begins at the rising of the Pleiads and lasts, at the longest, down to the setting of Arcturus; during the rest of the year they are hid and enjoying immunity. About the time of hibernation a few tunnies or other hibernating fishes are caught while swimming about, in particularly warm localities and in exceptionally fine weather, or on nights of full moon; for the fishes are induced (by the warmth or the light) to emerge for a while from their lair in quest of food.

Most fishes are at their best for the table during the summer or winter sleep.

The primas-tunny conceals itself in the mud; this may be inferred from the fact that during a particular period the fish is never caught, and that, when it is caught after that period, it is covered with mud and has its fins damaged. In the spring these tunnies get in motion and proceed towards the coast, coupling and breeding, and the females are now caught full of spawn. At this time they are considered as in season, but in autumn and in winter as of inferior quality; at this time also the males are full of milt. When the spawn is small, the fish is hard to catch, but it is easily caught when the spawn gets large, as the fish is then infested by its parasite. Some fish burrow for sleep in the sand and some in mud, just keeping their mouths outside.

Most fishes hide, then, during the winter only, but crustaceans, the rock-fish, the ray, and the cartilaginous species hide only during extremely severe weather, and this may be in-

ferred from the fact that these fishes are never by any chance caught when the weather is extremely cold. Some fishes, however, hide during the summer, as the glaucus or grey-back; this fish hides in summer for about sixty days. The hake also and the gilthead hide; and we infer that the hake hides over a lengthened
600a period from the fact that it is only caught at long intervals. We are led also to infer that fishes hide in summer from the circumstance that the takes of certain fish are made between the rise and setting of certain constellations: of the Dog-star in particular, the sea at this period being upturned from the lower depths. This phenomenon may be observed to best advantage in the Bosporus; for the mud is there brought up to the surface and the fish are brought up along with it. They say also that very often, when the sea-bottom is dredged, more fish will be caught by the second haul than by the first one. Furthermore, after very heavy rains numerous specimens become visible of creatures that at other times are never seen at all or seen only at intervals.

16

A great number of birds also go into hiding; they do not all migrate, as is generally supposed, to warmer countries. Thus, certain birds (as the kite and the swallow) when they are not far off from places of this kind, in which they have their permanent abode, betake themselves thither; others, that are at a distance from such places, decline the trouble of migration and simply hide themselves where they are. Swallows, for instance, have been often found in holes, quite denuded of their feathers, and the kite on its first emergence from torpidity has been seen to fly from out some such hiding-place. And with regard to this phenomenon of periodic torpor there is no distinction observed, whether the talons of a bird be crooked or straight; for instance, the stork, the owzel, the turtle-dove, and the lark, all go into hiding. The case of the turtle-dove is the most notorious of all, for we would defy any one to assert that he had anywhere seen a turtle-dove in winter-time; at the beginning of the hiding time it is exceedingly plump, and during this period it moults, but retains its plumpness. Some cushats hide; others, instead of hiding, migrate at the same time as the swallow. The thrush and the starling hide; and of birds with crooked talons the kite and the owl hide for a few days.

17

Of viviparous quadrupeds the porcupine and the bear retire into concealment. The fact that the bear hides is well established, but there are doubts as to its motive for so doing, whether it be by reason of the cold or from some other cause. About this period the male and the female become so fat as to be hardly capable of motion. The female brings forth her young at this time, and remains in concealment until it
600b is time to bring the cubs out; and she brings them out in spring, about three months after the winter solstice. The bear hides for at least forty days; during fourteen of these days it is said not to move at all, but during most of the subsequent days it moves, and from time to time wakes up. A she-bear in pregnancy has either never been caught at all or has been caught very seldom. There can be no doubt but that during this period they eat nothing; for in the first place they never emerge from their hiding-place, and further, when they are caught, their belly and intestines are found to be quite empty. It is also said that from no food being taken the gut almost closes up, and that in consequence the animal on first emerging takes to eating arum with the view of opening up and distending the gut.

The dormouse actually hides in a tree, and gets very fat at that period; as does also the white mouse of Pontus.

[Of animals that hide or go torpid some slough off what is called their 'old-age'. This name is applied to the outermost skin, and to the casing that envelops the developing organism.]

In discussing the case of terrestrial vivipara we stated that the reason for the bear's seeking concealment is an open question. We now proceed to treat of the tessellates. The tessellates for the most part go into hiding, and if their skin is soft they slough off their 'old-age', but not if the skin is shell-like, as is the shell of the tortoise—for, by the way, the tortoise and the freshwater tortoise belong to the tessellates. Thus, the old-age is sloughed off by the gecko, the lizard, and above all, by serpents; and they slough off the skin in springtime when emerging from their torpor, and again in the autumn. Vipers also slough off their skin both in spring and in autumn, and it is not the case, as some aver, that this species of the serpent family is exceptional in not sloughing. When the serpent begins to slough, the skin peels off at first from the eyes, so that any one ignorant

of the phenomenon would suppose the animal were going blind; after that it peels off the head, and so on, until the creature presents to view only a white surface all over. The sloughing goes on for a day and a night, beginning with the head and ending with the tail. During the sloughing of the skin an inner layer comes to the surface, for the creature emerges
601a just as the embryo from its afterbirth.

All insects that slough at all slough in the same way; as the silphe, and the empis or midge, and all the coleoptera, as for instance the cantharus-beetle. They all slough after the period of development; for just as the afterbirth breaks from off the young of the vivipara so the outer husk breaks off from around the young of the vermipara, in the same way both with the bee and the grasshopper. The cicada the moment after issuing from the husk goes and sits upon an olive tree or a reed; after the breaking up of the husk the creature issues out, leaving a little moisture behind, and after a short interval flies up into the air and sets a-chirping.

Of marine animals the crawfish and the lobster slough sometimes in the spring, and sometimes in autumn after parturition. Lobsters have been caught occasionally with the parts about the thorax soft, from the shell having there peeled off, and the lower parts hard, from the shell having not yet peeled off there; for, by the way, they do not slough in the same manner as the serpent. The crawfish hides for about five months. Crabs also slough off their old-age; this is generally allowed with regard to the soft-shelled crabs, and it is said to be the case with the testaceous kind, as for instance with the large 'granny' crab. When these animals slough their shell becomes soft all over, and as for the crab, it can scarcely crawl. These animals also do not cast their skins once and for all, but over and over again.

So much for the animals that go into hiding or torpidity, for the times at which, and the ways in which, they go; and so much also for the animals that slough off their old-age, and for the times at which they undergo the process.

18

Animals do not all thrive at the same seasons, nor do they thrive alike during all extremes of weather. Further animals of diverse species are in a diverse way healthy or sickly at certain seasons; and, in point of fact, some animals have ailments that are unknown to others. Birds thrive in times of drought, both in their general health and in regard to parturition, and this is especially the case with the cushat; fishes, however, with a few exceptions, thrive best in rainy weather; on the contrary, rainy seasons are bad for birds—and so by the way is much drinking—and drought is bad for fishes. Birds of prey, as has been already stated, may in a general way be said nev-
601b er to drink at all, though Hesiod appears to have been ignorant of the fact, for in his story about the siege of Ninus he represents the eagle that presided over the auguries as in the act of drinking; all other birds drink, but drink sparingly, as is the case also with all other spongy-lunged oviparous animals. Sickness in birds may be diagnosed from their plumage, which is ruffled when they are sickly instead of lying smooth as when they are well.

19

The majority of fishes, as has been stated, thrive best in rainy seasons. Not only have they food in greater abundance at this time, but in a general way rain is wholesome for them just as it is for vegetation—for, by the way, kitchen vegetables, though artificially watered, derive benefit from rain; and the same remark applies even to reeds that grow in marshes, as they hardly grow at all without a rainfall. That rain is good for fishes may be inferred from the fact that most fishes migrate to the Euxine for the summer; for owing to the number of the rivers that discharge into this sea its water is exceptionally fresh, and the rivers bring down a large supply of food. Besides, a great number of fishes, such as the bonito and the mullet, swim up the rivers and thrive in the rivers and marshes. The sea-gudgeon also fattens in the rivers, and, as a rule, countries abounding in lagoons furnish unusually excellent fish. While most fishes, then, are benefited by rain, they are chiefly benefited by summer rain; or we may state the case thus, that rain is good for fishes in spring, summer, and autumn, and fine dry weather in winter. As a general rule what is good for men is good for fishes also.

Fishes do not thrive in cold places, and those fishes suffer most in severe winters that have a stone in their head, as the chromis, the basse, the sciaena, and the braize; for owing to the stone they get frozen with the cold, and are thrown up on shore.

Whilst rain is wholesome for most fishes, it
602a is, on the contrary, unwholesome for the

mullet, the cephalus, and the so-called marinus, for rain superinduces blindness in most of these fishes, and all the more rapidly if the rainfall be superabundant. The cephalus is peculiarly subject to this malady in severe winters; their eyes grow white, and when caught they are in poor condition, and eventually the disease kills them. It would appear that this disease is due to extreme cold even more than to an excessive rainfall; for instance, in many places and more especially in shallows off the coast of Nauplia, in the Argolid, a number of fishes have been known to be caught out at sea in seasons of severe cold. The gilthead also suffers in winter; the acharnas suffers in summer, and loses condition. The coracine is exceptional among fishes in deriving benefit from drought, and this is due to the fact that heat and drought are apt to come together.

Particular places suit particular fishes; some are naturally fishes of the shore, and some of the deep sea, and some are at home in one or the other of these regions, and others are common to the two and are at home in both. Some fishes will thrive in one particular spot, and in that spot only. As a general rule it may be said that places abounding in weeds are wholesome; at all events, fishes caught in such places are exceptionally fat: that is, such fishes as inhabit all sorts of localities as well. The fact is that weed-eating fishes find abundance of their special food in such localities, and carnivorous fish find an unusually large number of smaller fish. It matters also whether the wind be from the north or south: the longer fish thrive better when a north wind prevails, and in summer at one and the same spot more long fish will be caught than flat fish with a north wind blowing.

The tunny and the sword-fish are infested with a parasite about the rising of the Dog-star; that is to say, about this time both these fishes have a grub beside their fins that is nicknamed the 'gadfly'. It resembles the scorpion in shape, and is about the size of the spider. So acute is the pain it inflicts that the sword-fish will often leap as high out of the water as a dolphin; in fact, it sometimes leaps over the bulwarks of a vessel and falls back on the deck. The tunny delights more than any other fish in the heat of the sun. It will burrow for warmth
602b in the sand in shallow waters near to shore, or will, because it is warm, disport itself on the surface of the sea.

The fry of little fishes escape by being overlooked, for it is only the larger ones of the small species that fishes of the large species will pursue. The greater part of the spawn and the fry of fishes is destroyed by the heat of the sun, for whatever of them the sun reaches it spoils.

Fishes are caught in greatest abundance before sunrise and after sunset, or, speaking generally, just about sunset and sunrise. Fishermen haul up their nets at these times, and speak of the hauls then made as the 'nick-of-time' hauls. The fact is, that at these times fishes are particularly weaksighted; at night they are at rest, and as the light grows stronger they see comparatively well.

We know of no pestilential malady attacking fishes, such as those which attack man, and horses and oxen among the quadrupedal vivipara, and certain species of other genera, domesticated and wild; but fishes do seem to suffer from sickness; and fishermen infer this from the fact that at times fishes in poor condition, and looking as though they were sick, and of altered colour, are caught in a large haul of well-conditioned fish of their own species. So much for sea-fishes.

20

River-fish and lake-fish also are exempt from diseases of a pestilential character, but certain species are subject to special and peculiar maladies. For instance, the sheat-fish just before the rising of the Dog-star, owing to its swimming near the surface of the water, is liable to sunstroke, and is paralysed by a loud peal of thunder. The carp is subject to the same eventualities, but in a lesser degree. The sheat-fish is destroyed in great quantities in shallow waters by the serpent called the dragon. In the balerus and tilon a worm is engendered about the rising of the Dog-star, that sickens these fish and causes them to rise towards the surface, where they are killed by the excessive heat. The chalcis is subject to a very violent malady; lice are engendered underneath their gills in great numbers, and cause destruction among them; but no other species of fish is subject to any such malady.

If mullein be introduced into water it will kill fish in its vicinity. It is used extensively for catching fish in rivers and ponds; by the Phoe-
603a nicians it is made use of also in the sea.

There are two other methods employed for catching fish. It is a known fact that in winter fishes emerge from the deep parts of rivers—and, by the way, at all seasons fresh water is tolerably cold. A trench accordingly is dug leading into a river, and wattled at the river end with reeds and stones, an aperture being left in the wattling through which the river water flows into the trench; when the frost comes on the fish can be taken out of the trench in weels. Another method is adopted in summer and winter alike. They run across a stream a dam composed of brushwood and stones, leaving a small open space, and in this space they insert a weel; they then coop the fish in towards this place, and draw them up in the weel as they swim through the open space.

Shell-fish, as a rule, are benefited by rainy weather. The purple murex is an exception; if it be placed on a shore near to where a river discharges, it will die within a day after tasting the fresh water. The murex lives for about fifty days after capture; during this period they feed off one another, as there grows on the shell a kind of sea-weed or sea-moss; if any food is thrown to them during this period, it is said to be done not to keep them alive, but to make them weigh more.

To shell-fish in general drought is unwholesome. During dry weather they decrease in size and degenerate in quality; and it is during such weather that the red scallop is found in more than usual abundance. In the Pyrrhaean Strait the clam was exterminated, partly by the dredging-machine used in their capture, and partly by long-continued droughts. Rainy weather is wholesome to the generality of shell-fish owing to the fact that the sea-water then becomes exceptionally sweet. In the Euxine, owing to the coldness of the climate, shell-fish are not found: nor yet in rivers, excepting a few bivalves here and there. Univalves, by the way, are very apt to freeze to death in extremely cold weather. So much for animals that live in water.

21

To turn to quadrupeds, the pig suffers from three diseases, one of which is called branchos, a disease attended with swellings about the windpipe and the jaws. It may break **603b** out in any part of the body; very often it attacks the foot, and occasionally the ear; the neighbouring parts also soon rot, and the decay goes on until it reaches the lungs, when the animal succumbs. The disease develops with great rapidity, and the moment it sets in the animal gives up eating. The swineherds know but one way to cure it, namely, by complete excision, when they detect the first signs of the disease. There are two other diseases, which are both alike termed craurus. The one is attended with pain and heaviness in the head, and this is the commoner of the two, the other with diarrhoea. The latter is incurable, the former is treated by applying wine fomentations to the snout and rinsing the nostrils with wine. Even this disease is very hard to cure; it has been known to kill within three or four days. The animal is chiefly subject to branchos when it gets extremely fat, and when the heat has brought a good supply of figs. The treatment is to feed on mashed mulberries, to give repeated warm baths, and to lance the under part of the tongue.

Pigs with flabby flesh are subject to measles about the legs, neck, and shoulders, for the pimples develop chiefly in these parts. If the pimples are few in number the flesh is comparatively sweet, but if they be numerous it gets watery and flaccid. The symptoms of measles are obvious, for the pimples show chiefly on the under side of the tongue, and if you pluck the bristles off the chine the skin will appear suffused with blood, and further the animal will be unable to keep its hind-feet at rest. Pigs never take this disease while they are mere sucklings. The pimples may be got rid of by feeding on a kind of spelt called tiphe; and this spelt, by the way, is very good for ordinary food. The best food for rearing and fattening pigs is chickpeas and figs, but the one thing essential is to vary the food as much as possible, for this animal, like animals in general, delights in a change of diet; and it is said that one kind of food blows the animal out, that another superinduces flesh, and that another puts on fat, and that acorns, though liked by the animal, render the flesh flaccid. Besides, if a sow eats acorns in great quantities, it will miscarry, as is also the case with the ewe; and, **604a** indeed, the miscarriage is more certain in the case of the ewe than in the case of the sow. The pig is the only animal known to be subject to measles.

22

Dogs suffer from three diseases; rabies, quinsy, and sore feet. Rabies drives the animal mad, and any animal whatever, excepting man, will take the disease if bitten by a dog so afflicted; the disease is fatal to the dog itself, and to any animal it may bite, man excepted. Quinsy also is fatal to dogs; and only a few recover from disease of the feet. The camel, like the dog, is subject to rabies. The elephant, which is reputed to enjoy immunity from all other illnesses, is occasionally subject to flatulency.

23

Cattle in herds are liable to two diseases, foot-sickness and craurus. In the former their feet suffer from eruptions, but the animal recovers from the disease without even the loss of the hoof. It is found of service to smear the horny parts with warm pitch. In craurus, the breath comes warm at short intervals; in fact, craurus in cattle answers to fever in man. The symptoms of the disease are drooping of the ears and disinclination for food. The animal soon succumbs, and when the carcase is opened the lungs are found to be rotten.

24

Horses out at pasture are free from all diseases excepting disease of the feet. From this disease they sometimes lose thir hooves: but after losing them they grow them soon again, for as one hoof is decaying it is being replaced by another. Symptoms of the malady are a sinking in and wrinkling of the lip in the middle under the nostrils, and in the case of the male, a twitching of the right testicle.

Stall-reared horses are subject to very numerous forms of disease. They are liable to disease **604b** called 'eileus'. Under this disease the animal trails its hind-legs under its belly so far forward as almost to fall back on its haunches; if it goes without food for several days and turns rabid, it may be of service to draw blood, or to castrate the male. The animal is subject also to tetanus: the veins get rigid, as also the head and neck, and the animal walks with its legs stretched out straight. The horse suffers also from abscesses. Another painful illness afflicts them called the 'barley-surfeit'. The symptoms are a softening of the palate and heat of the breath; the animal may recover through the strength of its own constitution, but no formal remedies are of any avail.

There is also a disease called nymphia, in which the animal is said to stand still and droop its head on hearing flute-music; if during this ailment the horse be mounted, it will run off at a gallop until it is pulled. Even with this rabies in full force, it preserves a dejected spiritless appearance; some of the symptoms are a throwing back of the ears followed by a projection of them, great languor, and heavy breathing. Heart-ache also is incurable, of which the symptom is a drawing in of the flanks; and so is displacement of the bladder, which is accompanied by a retention of urine and a drawing up of the hooves and haunches. Neither is there any cure if the animal swallow the grape-beetle, which is about the size of the sphondyle or knuckle-beetle. The bite of the shrewmouse is dangerous to horses and other draught animals as well; it is followed by boils. The bite is all the more dangerous if the mouse be pregnant when she bites, for the boils then burst, but do not burst otherwise. The cicigna—called 'chalcis' by some, and 'zignis' by others—either causes death by its bite or, at all events, intense pain; it is like a small lizard, with the colour of the blind snake. In point of fact, according to experts, the horse and the sheep have pretty well as many ailments as the human species. The drug known under the name of 'sandarace' or realgar, is extremely injurious to a horse, and to all draught animals; it is given to the animal as a medicine in a solution of water, the liquid being filtered through a colander. The mare when pregnant is apt to miscarry when disturbed by the odour of an extinguished candle; and a similar **605a** accident happens occasionally to women in their pregnancy. So much for the diseases of the horse.

The so-called hippomanes grows, as has been stated, on the foal, and the mare nibbles it off as she licks and cleans the foal. All the curious stories connected with the hippomanes are due to old wives and to the venders of charms. What is called the 'polium' or foal's membrane, is, as all the accounts state, delivered by the mother before the foal appears.

A horse will recognize the neighing of any other horse with which it may have fought at any previous period. The horse delights in meadows and marshes, and likes to drink muddy water; in fact, if water be clear, the horse will trample in it to make it turbid, will then drink it, and afterwards will wallow in it. The animal is fond of water in every way, whether for drinking or for bathing purposes; and this explains the peculiar constitution of the hippopotamus or river-horse. In regard to water the ox is the opposite of the horse; for if the water be impure or cold, or mixed up with alien matter, it will refuse to drink it.

25

The ass suffers chiefly from one particular disease which they call 'melis'. It arises first in the head, and a clammy humour runs down the nostrils, thick and red; if it stays in the head the animal may recover, but if it descends into the lungs the animal will die. Of all animals of its kind it is the least capable of enduring extreme cold, which circumstance will account for the fact that the animal is not found on the shores of the Euxine, nor in Scythia.

26

Elephants suffer from flatulence, and when thus afflicted can void neither solid nor liquid residuum. If the elephant swallow earth-mould it suffers from relaxation; but if it go on taking it steadily, it will experience no harm. From time to time it takes to swallowing stones. It suffers also from diarrhoea: in this case they administer draughts of lukewarm water or dip its fodder in honey, and either one or the other prescription will prove a costive. When they suffer from insomnia, they will be restored to health if their shoulders be rubbed with salt, olive-oil, and warm water; when they have aches in their shoulders they will derive great benefit from the application
605b of roast pork. Some elephants like olive-oil, and others do not. If there is a bit of iron in the inside of an elephant it is said that it will pass out if the animal takes a drink of olive-oil; if the animal refuses olive-oil, they soak a root in the oil and give it the root to swallow.

So much, then, for quadrupeds.

27

Insects, as a general rule, thrive best in the time of year in which they come into being, especially if the season be moist and warm, as in spring.

In bee-hives are found creatures that do great damage to the combs; for instance, the grub that spins a web and ruins the honey-comb: it is called the 'cleros'. It engenders an insect like itself, of a spider-shape, and brings disease into the swarm. There is another insect resembling the moth, called by some the 'pyraustes', that flies about a lighted candle: this creature engenders a brood full of a fine down. It is never stung by a bee, and can only be got out of a hive by fumigation. A caterpillar also is engendered in hives, of a species nicknamed the teredo, or 'borer', with which creature the bee never interferes. Bees suffer most when flowers are covered with mildew, or in seasons of drought.

All insects, without exception, die if they be smeared over with oil; and they die all the more rapidly if you smear their head with the oil and lay them out in the sun.

28

Variety in animal life may be produced by variety of locality: thus in one place an animal will not be found at all, in another it will be small, or short-lived, or will not thrive. Sometimes this sort of difference is observed in closely adjacent districts. Thus, in the territory of Miletus, in one district cicadas are found while there are none in the district close adjoining; and in Cephalenia there is a river on one side of which the cicada is found and not on the other. In Pordoselene there is a public road one side of which the weasel is found but not on the other. In Boeotia the mole is found in great abundance in the neighbourhood of Orchomenus, but there are none in
606a Lebadia though it is in the immediate vicinity, and if a mole be transported from the one district to the other it will refuse to burrow in the soil. The hare cannot live in Ithaca if introduced there; in fact it will be found dead, turned towards the point of the beach where it was landed. The horseman-ant is not found in Sicily; the croaking frog has only recently appeared in the neighbourhood of Cyrene. In the whole of Libya there is neither wild boar, nor stag, nor wild goat; and in India, according to Ctesias—no very good authority, by the way—there are no swine, wild or tame, but animals that are devoid of blood and such as go into hiding or go torpid are all of immense size there. In the Euxine there are no small molluscs nor testaceans, except a few here and there; but in the Red Sea all the testaceans are exceedingly large. In Syria the sheep have tails a cubit in breadth; the goats have ears a span and a palm long, and some have ears that flap down to the ground; and the cattle have humps on their shoulders, like the camel. In Lycia goats are shorn for their fleece, just as sheep are in all other countries. In Libya the long-horned ram is born with horns, and not the ram only, as Homer[1] words it, but the ewe as well; in Pontus, on the confines of Scythia, the ram is without horns.

In Egypt animals, as a rule, are larger than their congeners in Greece, as the cow and the sheep; but some are less, as the dog, the wolf, the hare, the fox, the raven, and the hawk; others are of pretty much the same size, as the crow and the goat. The difference, where it exists, is attributed to the food, as being abundant in one case and insufficient in another, for instance for the wolf and the hawk; for

[1] *Odyssey*, IV. 85.

provision is scanty for the carnivorous animals, **606b** small birds being scarce; food is scanty also for the hare and for all frugivorous animals, because neither the nuts nor the fruit last long.

In many places the climate will account for peculiarities; thus in Illyria, Thrace, and Epirus the ass is small, and in Gaul and in Scythia the ass is not found at all owing to the coldness of the climate of these countries. In Arabia the lizard is more than a cubit in length, and the mouse is much larger than our field-mouse, with its hind-legs a span long and its front legs the length of the first finger-joint. In Libya, according to all accounts, the length of the serpents is something appalling; sailors spin a yarn to the effect that some crews once put ashore and saw the bones of a number of oxen, and that they were sure that the oxen had been devoured by serpents, for, just as they were putting out to sea, serpents came chasing their galleys at full speed and overturned one galley and set upon the crew. Again, lions are more numerous in Libya, and in that district of Europe that lies between the Achelous and the Nessus; the leopard is more abundant in Asia Minor, and is not found in Europe at all. As a general rule, wild animals are at their wildest in Asia, at their boldest in Europe, and most diverse in form in Libya; in fact, there is an old saying, 'Always something fresh in Libya.'

It would appear that in that country animals of diverse species meet, on account of the rainless climate, at the watering-places, and there pair together; and that such pairs will often breed if they be nearly of the same size and have periods of gestation of the same length. For it is said that they are tamed down in their behaviour towards each other by extremity of thirst. And, by the way, unlike animals elsewhere, they require to drink more in wintertime than in summer: for they acquire the habit of not drinking in summer, owing to the circumstance that there is usually no water then; and the mice, if they drink, die. Else- **607a** where also bastard-animals are born to heterogeneous pairs; thus in Cyrene the wolf and the bitch will couple and breed; and the Laconian hound is a cross between the fox and the dog. They say that the Indian dog is a cross between the tiger and the bitch, not the first cross, but a cross in the third generation; for they say that the first cross is a savage creature. They take the bitch to a lonely spot and tie her up: if the tiger be in an amorous mood he will pair with her; if not he will eat her up, and this casualty is of frequent occurrence.

29

Locality will differentiate habits also: for instance, rugged highlands will not produce the same results as the soft lowlands. The animals of the highlands look fiercer and bolder, as is seen in the swine of Mount Athos; for a lowland boar is no match even for a mountain sow.

Again, locality is an important element in regard to the bite of an animal. Thus, in Pharos and other places, the bite of the scorpion is not dangerous; elsewhere—in Caria, for instance,—where scorpions are venomous as well as plentiful and of large size, the sting is fatal to man or beast, even to the pig, and especially to a black pig, though the pig, by the way, is in general most singularly indifferent to the bite of any other creature. If a pig goes into water after being struck by the scorpion of Caria, it will surely die.

There is great variety in the effects produced by the bites of serpents. The asp is found in Libya; the so-called 'septic' drug is made from the body of the animal, and is the only remedy known for the bite of the original. Among the silphium, also, a snake is found, for the bite of which a certain stone is said to be a cure: a stone that is brought from the grave of an ancient king, which stone is put into water and drunk off. In certain parts of Italy the bite of the gecko is fatal. But the deadliest of all bites of venomous creatures is when one venomous animal has bitten another; as, for instance, a viper's after it has bitten a scorpion. To the great majority of such creatures man's spittle is fatal. There is a very little snake, by some entitled the 'holy-snake', which is dreaded by even the largest serpents. It is about an ell long, and hairy-looking; whenever it bites an animal, the flesh all round the wound will at once mortify. There is in India a small snake which is exceptional in this respect, that for its bite no specific whatever is known.

30

607b Animals also vary as to their condition of health in connexion with their pregnancy.

Testaceans, such as scallops and all the oyster-family, and crustaceans, such as the lobster-family, are best when with spawn. Even in the case of the testacean we speak of spawning (or pregnancy); but whereas the crustaceans may be seen coupling and laying their spawn, this is never the case with testaceans. Molluscs are best in the breeding time, as the calamary, the sepia, and the octopus.

Fishes, when they begin to breed, are nearly all good for the table; but after the female has gone long with spawn they are good in some cases, and in others are out of season. The maenis, for instance, is good at the breeding time. The female of this fish is round, the male longer and flatter; when the female is beginning to breed the male turns black and mottled, and is quite unfit for the table; at this period he is nicknamed the 'goat'.

The wrasses called the owzel and the thrush, and the smaris have different colours at different seasons, as is the case with the plumage of certain birds; that is to say, they become black in the spring and after the spring get white again. The phycis also changes its hue: in general it is white, but in spring it is mottled; it is the only sea-fish which is said to make a bed for itself, and the female lays her spawn in this bed or nest. The maenis, as was observed, changes its colour as does the smaris, and in summer-time changes back from whitish to black, the change being especially marked about the fins and gills. The coracine, like the maenis, is in best condition at breeding time; the mullet, the basse, and scaly fishes in general are in bad condition at this period. A few fish are in much the same condition at all times, whether with spawn or not, as the glaucus. Old fishes also are bad eating; the old tunny is unfit even for pickling, as a great part of its flesh wastes away with age, and the same wasting is observed in all old fishes. The age of a scaly fish may be told by the size and the hardness of its scales. An old tunny has been caught weighing fifteen talents, with the span of its tail two cubits and a palm broad.

River-fish and lake-fish are best after they **608a** have discharged the spawn in the case of the female and the milt in the case of the male: that is, when they have fully recovered from the exhaustion of such discharge. Some are good in the breeding time, as the saperdis, and some bad, as the sheat-fish. As a general rule, the male fish is better eating than the female; but the reverse holds good of the sheat-fish. The eels that are called females are the best for the table: they look as though they were female, but they really are not so.

BOOK IX

I

Of the animals that are comparatively obscure and short-lived the characters or dispositions are not so obvious to recognition as are those of animals that are longer-lived. These latter animals appear to have a natural capacity corresponding to each of the passions: to cunning or simplicity, courage or timidity, to good temper or to bad, and to other similar dispositions of mind.

Some also are capable of giving or receiving instruction—of receiving it from one another or from man: those that have the faculty of hearing, for instance; and, not to limit the matter to audible sound, such as can differentiate the suggested meanings of word and gesture.

In all genera in which the distinction of male and female is found, Nature makes a similar differentiation in the mental characteristics of the two sexes. This differentiation is the most obvious in the case of human kind and in that of the larger animals and the viviparous quadrupeds. In the case of these latter the female is softer in character, is the sooner tamed, admits more readily of caressing, is more apt in the way of learning; as, for instance, in the Laconian breed of dogs the female is cleverer than the male. Of the Molossian breed of dogs, such as are employed in the chase are pretty much the same as those elsewhere; but the sheep-dogs of this breed are superior to the others in size, and in the courage with which they face the attacks of wild animals.

Dogs that are born of a mixed breed between these two kinds are remarkable for courage and endurance of hard labour.

In all cases, excepting those of the bear and leopard, the female is less spirited than the male; in regard to the two exceptional cases, the superiority in courage rests with the female. With all other animals the female is softer in **608b** disposition than the male, is more mischievous, less simple, more impulsive, and more attentive to the nurture of the young; the male, on the other hand, is more spirited than the female, more savage, more simple and less cunning. The traces of these differentiated characteristics are more or less visible everywhere, but they are especially visible where character is the more developed, and most of all in man.

The fact is, the nature of man is the most rounded off and complete, and consequently in man the qualities or capacities above referred to are found in their perfection. Hence woman is more compassionate than man, more easily moved to tears, at the same time is more jealous, more querulous, more apt to scold and to strike. She is, furthermore, more prone to despondency and less hopeful than the man, more void of shame or self-respect, more false of speech, more deceptive, and of more retentive memory. She is also more wakeful, more shrinking, more difficult to rouse to action, and requires a smaller quantity of nutriment.

As was previously stated, the male is more courageous than the female, and more sympathetic in the way of standing by to help. Even in the case of molluscs, when the cuttle-fish is struck with the trident the male stands by to help the female; but when the male is struck the female runs away.

There is enmity between such animals as dwell in the same localities or subsist on the same food. If the means of subsistence run short, creatures of like kind will fight together. Thus it is said that seals which inhabit one and the same district will fight, male with male, and female with female, until one combatant kills the other, or one is driven away by the other; and their young do even in like manner.

All creatures are at enmity with the carnivores, and the carnivores with all the rest, for they all subsist on living creatures. Soothsayers take notice of cases where animals keep apart from one another, and cases where they congregate together; calling those that live at war with one another 'dissociates', and those that dwell in peace with one another 'associates'. One may go so far as to say that if there were no lack or stint of food, then those animals that are now afraid of man or are wild by nature would be tame and familiar with him, and in like manner with one another. This is shown by the way animals are treated in Egypt, for owing to the fact that food is constantly supplied to them the very fiercest creatures live peaceably together. The fact is they are tamed by kindness, and in some places
609a crocodiles are tame to their priestly keeper from being fed by him. And elsewhere also the same phenomenon is to be observed.

The eagle and the snake are enemies, for the eagle lives on snakes; so are the ichneumon and the venom-spider, for the ichneumon preys upon the latter. In the case of birds, there is mutual enmity between the poecilis, the crested lark, the woodpecker (?), and the chloreus, for they devour one another's eggs; so also between the crow and the owl; for, owing to the fact that the owl is dim-sighted by day, the crow at midday preys upon the owl's eggs, and the owl at night upon the crow's, each having the whip-hand of the other, turn and turn about, night and day.

There is enmity also between the owl and the wren; for the latter also devours the owl's eggs. In the daytime all other little birds flutter round the owl—a practice which is popularly termed 'admiring him'—buffet him, and pluck out his feathers; in consequence of this habit, bird-catchers use the owl as a decoy for catching little birds of all kinds.

The so-called presbys or 'old man' is at war with the weasel and the crow, for they prey on her eggs and her brood; and so the turtle-dove with the pyrallis, for they live in the same districts and on the same food; and so with the green woodpecker and the libyus; and so with the kite and the raven, for, owing to his having the advantage from stronger talons and more rapid flight the former can steal whatever the latter is holding, so that it is food also that makes enemies of these. In like manner there is war between birds that get their living from the sea, as between the brenthus, the gull, and the harpe; and so between the buzzard on one side and the toad and snake on the other, for the buzzard preys upon the eggs of the two others; and so between the turtle-dove and the chloreus; the chloreus kills the dove, and the crow kills the so-called drummer-bird.

The aegolius, and birds of prey in general, prey upon the calaris, and consequently there is war between it and them; and so is there war between the gecko-lizard and the spider, for the former preys upon the latter; and so between the woodpecker and the heron, for the former preys upon the eggs and brood of the latter. And so between the aegithus and the ass, owing to the fact that the ass, in passing a furze-bush, rubs its sore and itching parts against the prickles; by so doing, and all the more if it brays, it topples the eggs and the brood out of the nest, the young ones tumble out in fright, and the mother-bird, to avenge this wrong, flies at the beast and pecks at his sore places.
609b The wolf is at war with the ass, the bull, and the fox, for as being a carnivore, he attacks these other animals; and so for the same reason with the fox and the circus, for the circus, be-

ing carnivorous and furnished with crooked talons, attacks and maims the animal. And so the raven is at war with the bull and the ass, for it flies at them, and strikes them, and pecks at their eyes; and so with the eagle and the heron, for the former, having crooked talons, attacks the latter, and the latter usually succumbs to the attack; and so the merlin with the vulture; and the crex with the eleus-owl, the blackbird, and the oriole (of this latter bird, by the way, the story goes that he was originally born out of a funeral pyre): the cause of warfare is that the crex injures both them and their young. The nuthatch and the wren are at war with the eagle; the nuthatch breaks the eagle's eggs, so the eagle is at war with it on special grounds, though, as a bird of prey, it carries on a general war all round. The horse and the anthus are enemies, and the horse will drive the bird out of the field where he is grazing: the bird feeds on grass, and sees too dimly to foresee an attack; it mimics the whinnying of the horse, flies at him, and tries to frighten him away; but the horse drives the bird away, and whenever he catches it he kills it: this bird lives beside rivers or on marsh ground; it has pretty plumage, and finds its food without trouble. The ass is at enmity with the lizard, for the lizard sleeps in his manger, gets into his nostril, and prevents his eating.

Of herons there are three kinds: the ash-coloured, the white, and the starry heron (or bittern). Of these the first mentioned submits with reluctance to the duties of incubation, or to union of the sexes; in fact, it screams during the union, and it is said drips blood from its eyes; it lays its eggs also in an awkward manner, not unattended with pain. It is at war with certain creatures that do it injury: with the eagle for robbing it, with the fox for worrying it at night, and with the lark for stealing its eggs.

The snake is at war with the weasel and the pig; with the weasel when they are both at home, for they live on the same food; with the pig for preying on her kind. The merlin is at war with the fox; it strikes and claws it, and, as it has crooked talons, it kills the animal's young. The raven and the fox are good friends, for the raven is at enmity with the merlin; and so when the merlin assails the fox the raven comes and helps the animal. The vulture and the merlin are mutual enemies, as being both furnished with crooked talons. The vulture fights with the eagle, and so, by the way,
610a does the swan; and the swan is often victorious: moreover, of all birds swans are most prone to the killing of one another.

In regard to wild creatures, some sets are at enmity with other sets at all times and under all circumstances; others, as in the case of man and man, at special times and under incidental circumstances. The ass and the acanthis are enemies; for the bird lives on thistles, and the ass browses on thistles when they are young and tender. The anthus, the acanthis, and the aegithus are at enmity with one another; it is said that the blood of the anthus will not intercommingle with the blood of the aegithus. The crow and the heron are friends, as also are the sedge-bird and lark, the laedus and the celeus or green woodpecker; the woodpecker lives on the banks of rivers and beside brakes, the laedus lives on rocks and hills, and is greatly attached to its nesting-place. The piphinx, the harpe, and the kite are friends; as are the fox and the snake, for both burrow underground; so also are the blackbird and the turtle-dove. The lion and the thos or civet are enemies, for both are carnivorous and live on the same food. Elephants fight fiercely with one another, and stab one another with their tusks; of two combatants the beaten one gets completely cowed, and dreads the sound of his conqueror's voice. These animals differ from one another to an extraordinary extent in the way of courage. Indians employ these animals for war purposes, irrespective of sex; the females, however, are less in size and much inferior in point of spirit. An elephant by pushing with his big tusks can batter down a wall, and will butt with his forehead at a palm until he brings it down, when he stamps on it and lays it in orderly fashion on the ground. Men hunt the elephant in the following way: they mount tame elephants of approved spirit and proceed in quest of wild animals; when they come up with these they bid the tame brutes to beat the wild ones until they tire the latter completely. Hereupon the driver mounts a wild brute and guides him with the application of his metal prong; after this the creature soon becomes tame, and obeys guidance. Now when the driver is on their back they are all tractable, but after he has dismounted, some are tame and others vicious; in the case of these latter, they tie their front-legs with ropes to keep them quiet. The animal is hunted whether young or full grown.

Thus we see that in the case of the creatures above mentioned their mutual friendship or enmity is due to the food they feed on and the life they lead.

2

610b Of fishes, such as swim in shoals together are friendly to one another; such as do not so swim are enemies. Some fishes swarm during the spawning season; others after they have spawned. To state the matter comprehensively, we may say that the following are shoaling fish: the tunny, the maenis, the sea-gudgeon, the bogue, the horse-mackerel, the coracine, the synodon or dentex, the red mullet, the sphyraena, the anthias, the eleginus, the atherine, the sarginus, the gar-fish, [the squid,] the rainbow-wrasse, the pelamyd, the mackerel, the coly-mackerel. Of these some not only swim in shoals, but go in pairs inside the shoal; the rest without exception swim in pairs, and only swim in shoals at certain periods: that is, as has been said, when they are heavy with spawn or after they have spawned.

The basse and the grey mullet are bitter enemies, but they swarm together at certain times; for at times not only do fishes of the same species swarm together, but also those whose feeding-grounds are identical or adjacent, if the food-supply be abundant. The grey mullet is often found alive with its tail lopped off, and the conger with all that part of its body removed that lies to the rear of the vent; in the case of the mullet the injury is wrought by the basse, in that of the conger-eel by the muraena. There is war between the larger and the lesser fishes: for the big fishes prey on the little ones. So much on the subject of marine animals.

3

The characters of animals, as has been observed,[1] differ in respect to timidity, to gentleness, to courage, to tameness, to intelligence, and to stupidity.

The sheep is said to be naturally dull and stupid. Of all quadrupeds it is the most foolish: it will saunter away to lonely places with no object in view; oftentimes in stormy weather it will stray from shelter; if it be overtaken by a snowstorm, it will stand still unless the shepherd sets it in motion; it will stay behind and perish unless the shepherd brings up the rams; it will then follow home.

If you catch hold of a goat's beard at the extremity—the beard is of a substance resembling hair—all the companion goats will stand stock still, staring at this particular goat in a kind of dumbfounderment.

[1] IX. 1(608a 11).

You will have a warmer bed in amongst the goats than among the sheep, because the goats will be quieter and will creep up towards you; for the goat is more impatient of cold than the sheep.

Shepherds train sheep to close in together at a clap of their hands, for if, when a thunderstorm comes on, a ewe stays behind without closing in, the storm will kill it if it be with **611a** young; consequently if a sudden clap or noise is made, they close in together within the sheepfold by reason of their training.

Even bulls, when they are roaming by themselves apart from the herd, are killed by wild animals.

Sheep and goats lie crowded together, kin by kin. When the sun turns early towards its setting, the goats are said to lie no longer face to face, but back to back.

4

Cattle at pasture keep together in their accustomed herds, and if one animal strays away the rest will follow; consequently if the herdsmen lose one particular animal, they keep close watch on all the rest.

When mares with their colts pasture together in the same field, if one dam dies the others will take up the rearing of the colt. In point of fact, the mare appears to be singularly prone by nature to maternal fondness; in proof whereof a barren mare will steal the foal from its dam, will tend it with all the solicitude of a mother, but, as it will be unprovided with mother's milk, its solicitude will prove fatal to its charge.

5

Among wild quadrupeds the hind appears to be pre-eminently intelligent; for example, in its habit of bringing forth its young on the sides of public roads, where the fear of man forbids the approach of wild animals. Again, after parturition, it first swallows the afterbirth, then goes in quest of the seseli shrub, and after eating of it returns to its young. The mother takes its young betimes to her lair, so leading it to know its place of refuge in time of danger; this lair is a precipitous rock, with only one approach, and there it is said to hold its own against all comers. The male when it gets fat, which it does in a high degree in autumn, disappears, abandoning its usual resorts, apparently under an idea that its fatness facilitates its capture. They shed their horns in places difficult of access or discovery, whence the proverbial expression of 'the place where the stag sheds his horns'; the fact being that, as having parted with their weapons, they take care not to be seen. The saying is that no man has ever seen the animal's left horn; that the creature keeps it out of sight because it possesses some medicinal property.

In their first year stags grow no horns, but only an excrescence indicating where horns will be, this excrescence being short and thick. In their second year they grow their horns for the first time, straight in shape, like pegs for hanging clothes on; and on this account they have an appropriate nickname. In the third year the antlers are bifurcate; in the fourth year they grow trifurcate; and so they go on increasing in complexity until the creature is six years **611b** old: after this they grow their horns without any specific differentiation, so that you cannot by observation of them tell the animal's age. But the patriarchs of the herd may be told chiefly by two signs; in the first place they have few teeth or none at all, and, in the second place, they have ceased to grow the pointed tips to their antlers. The forward-pointing tips of the growing horns ⟨that is to say the brow-antlers⟩, with which the animal meets attack, are technically termed its 'defenders'; with these the patriarchs are unprovided, and their antlers merely grow straight upwards. Stags shed their horns annually, in or about the month of May; after shedding, they conceal themselves, it is said, during the daytime, and, to avoid the flies, hide in thick copses; during this time, until they have grown their horns, they feed at night-time. The horns at first grow in a kind of skin envelope, and get rough by degrees; when they reach their full size the animal basks in the sun, to mature and dry them. When they need no longer rub them against tree-trunks they quit their hiding-places, from a sense of security based upon the possession of arms defensive and offensive. An Achaeine stag has been caught with a quantity of green ivy grown over its horns, it having grown apparently, as on fresh green wood, when the horns were young and tender. When a stag is stung by a venom-spider or similar insect, it gathers crabs and eats them; it is said to be a good thing for man to drink the juice, but the taste is disagreeable. The hinds after parturition at once swallow the afterbirth, and it is impossible to secure it, for the hind catches it before it falls to the ground: now this substance is supposed to have medicinal properties. When hunted the creatures are caught by singing or pipe-playing on the part of the hunters; they are so pleased with the music that they lie down on the grass. If there be two hunters, one before their eyes sings or plays the pipe, the other keeps out of sight and shoots, at a signal given by the confederate. If the animal has its ears cocked, it can hear well and you cannot escape its ken; if its ears are down, you can.

6

When bears are running away from their pursuers they push their cubs in front of them, or take them up and carry them; when they are being overtaken they climb up a tree. When emerging from their winter-den, they at once take to eating cuckoo-pint, as has been said,[1] **612a** and chew sticks of wood as though they were cutting teeth.

Many other quadrupeds help themselves in clever ways. Wild goats in Crete are said, when wounded by arrows, to go in search of dittany, which is supposed to have the property of ejecting arrows in the body. Dogs, when they are ill, eat some kind of grass and produce vomiting. The panther, after eating panther's-bane, tries to find some human excrement, which is said to heal its pain. This panther's-bane kills lions as well. Hunters hang up human excrement in a vessel attached to the boughs of a tree, to keep the animal from straying to any distance; the animal meets its end in leaping up to the branch and trying to get at the medicine. They say that the panther has found out that wild animals are fond of the scent it emits; that, when it goes a-hunting, it hides itself; that the other animals come nearer and nearer, and that by this stratagem it can catch even animals as swift of foot as stags.

The Egyptian ichneumon, when it sees the serpent called the asp, does not attack it until it has called in other ichneumons to help; to meet the blows and bites of their enemy the assailants beplaster themselves with mud, by first soaking in the river and then rolling on the ground.

When the crocodile yawns, the trochilus flies into his mouth and cleans his teeth. The trochilus gets his food thereby, and the crocodile gets ease and comfort; it makes no attempt to injure its little friend, but, when it wants it

[1] VIII. 17(600b 11).

to go, it shakes its neck in warning, lest it should accidentally bite the bird.

The tortoise, when it has partaken of a snake, eats marjoram; this action has been actually observed. A man saw a tortoise perform this operation over and over again, and every time it plucked up some marjoram go back to partake of its prey; he thereupon pulled the marjoram up by the roots, and the consequence was the tortoise died. The weasel, when it fights with a snake, first eats wild rue, the smell of which is noxious to the snake. The dragon, when it eats fruit, swallows endive-juice; it has been seen in the act. Dogs, when they suffer from worms, eat the standing corn. Storks, and all other birds, when they get a wound fighting, apply marjoram to the place injured.

Many have seen the locust, when fighting with the snake get a tight hold of the snake by the neck. The weasel has a clever way of get-
612b ting the better of birds; it tears their throats open, as wolves do with sheep. Weasels fight desperately with mice-catching snakes, as they both prey on the same animal.

In regard to the instinct of hedgehogs, it has been observed in many places that, when the wind is shifting from north to south, and from south to north, they shift the outlook of their earth-holes, and those that are kept in domestication shift over from one wall to the other. The story goes that a man in Byzantium got into high repute for foretelling a change of weather, all owing to his having noticed this habit of the hedgehog.

The polecat or marten is about as large as the smaller breed of Maltese dogs. In the thickness of its fur, in its look, in the white of its belly, and in its love of mischief, it resembles the weasel; it is easily tamed; from its liking for honey it is a plague to bee-hives; it preys on birds like the cat. Its genital organ, as has been said, consists of bone: the organ of the male is supposed to be a cure for strangury; doctors scrape it into powder, and administer it in that form.

7

In a general way in the lives of animals many resemblances to human life may be observed. Pre-eminent intelligence will be seen more in small creatures than in large ones, as is exemplified in the case of birds by the nest-building of the swallow. In the same way as men do, the bird mixes mud and chaff together; if it runs short of mud, it souses its body in water and rolls about in the dry dust with wet feathers; furthermore, just as man does, it makes a bed of straw, putting hard material below for a foundation, and adapting all to suit its own size. Both parents co-operate in the rearing of the young; each of the parents will detect, with practised eye, the young one that has had a helping, and will take care it is not helped twice over; at first the parents will rid the nest of excrement, but, when the young are grown, they will teach their young to shift their position and let their excrement fall over the side of the nest.

Pigeons exhibit other phenomena with a similar likeness to the ways of humankind. In pairing the same male and the same female keep together; and the union is only broken by the death of one of the two parties. At the time of parturition in the female the sympathetic attentions of the male are extraordinary;
613a if the female is afraid on account of the impending parturition to enter the nest, the male will beat her and force her to come in. When the young are born, he will take and masticate pieces of suitable food, will open the beaks of the fledglings, and inject these pieces, thus preparing them betimes to take food. [When the male bird is about to expel the young ones from the nest, he cohabits with them all.] As a general rule these birds show this conjugal fidelity, but occasionally a female will cohabit with other than her mate. These birds are combative, and quarrel with one another, and enter each other's nests, though this occurs but seldom; at a distance from their nests this quarrelsomeness is less marked, but in the close neighbourhood of their nests they will fight desperately. A peculiarity common to the tame pigeon, the ring-dove and the turtle-dove is that they do not lean the head back when they are in the act of drinking, but only when they have fully quenched their thirst. The turtle-dove and the ring-dove both have but one mate, and let no other come nigh; both sexes co-operate in the process of incubation. It is difficult to distinguish between the sexes except by an examination of their interiors. Ring-doves are long-lived; cases have been known where such birds were twenty-five years old, thirty years old, and in some cases forty. As they grow old their claws increase in size, and pigeon-fanciers cut the claws; as far as one can see, the birds suffer no other perceptible disfigurement by their increase in age. Turtle-doves and pigeons that are blinded by fanciers for use as decoys, live for eight

years. Partridges live for about fifteen years. Ring-doves and turtle-doves always build their nests in the same place year after year. The male, as a general rule, is more long-lived than the female; but in the case of pigeons some assert that the male dies before the female, taking their inference from the statements of persons who keep decoy-birds in captivity. Some declare that the male sparrow lives only for a year, pointing to the fact that early in spring the male sparrow has no black beard, but has one later on, as though the black-bearded birds of the last year had all died out; they also say that the females are the longer lived, on the grounds that they are caught in **613b** amongst the young birds and that their age is rendered manifest by the hardness about their beaks. Turtle-doves in summer live in cold places, ⟨and in warm places during the winter⟩; chaffinches affect warm habitations in summer and cold ones in winter.

8

Birds of a heavy build, such as quails, partridges, and the like, build no nests; indeed, where they are incapable of flight, it would be of no use if they could do so. After scraping a hole on a level piece of ground—and it is only in such a place that they lay their eggs—they cover it over with thorns and sticks for security against hawks and eagles, and there lay their eggs and hatch them; after the hatching is over, they at once lead the young out from the nest, as they are not able to fly afield for food for them. Quails and partridges, like barn-door hens, when they go to rest, gather their brood under their wings. Not to be discovered, as might be the case if they stayed long in one spot, they do not hatch the eggs where they laid them. When a man comes by chance upon a young brood, and tries to catch them, the hen-bird rolls in front of the hunter, pretending to be lame: the man every moment thinks he is on the point of catching her, and so she draws him on and on, until every one of her brood has had time to escape; hereupon she returns to the nest and calls the young back. The partridge lays not less than ten eggs, and often lays as many as sixteen. As has been observed, the bird has mischievous and deceitful habits. In the spring-time, a noisy scrimmage takes place, out of which the male-birds emerge each with a hen. Owing to the lecherous nature of the bird, and from a dislike to the hen sitting, the males, if they find any eggs, roll them over and over until they break them in pieces; to provide against this the female goes to a distance and lays the eggs, and often, under the stress of parturition, lays them in any chance spot that offers; if the male bird be near at hand, then to keep the eggs intact she refrains from visiting them. If she be seen by a man, then, just as with her fledged brood, she entices him off by showing herself close at his feet until she has drawn him to a di tance. When the females have run away and taken to sitting, the males in a pack take **614a** to screaming and fighting; when thus engaged, they have the nickname of 'widowers'. The bird who is beaten follows his victor, and submits to be covered by him only; and the beaten bird is covered by a second one or by any other, only clandestinely without the victor's knowledge; this is so, not at all times, but at a particular season of the year, and with quails as well as with partridges. A similar proceeding takes place occasionally with barn-door cocks: for in temples, where cocks are set apart as dedicate without hens, they all as a matter of course tread any new-comer. Tame partridges tread wild birds, peck at their heads, and treat them with every possible outrage. The leader of the wild birds, with a counter-note of challenge, pushes forward to attack the decoy-bird, and after he has been netted, another advances with a similar note. This is what is done if the decoy be a male; but if it be a female that is the decoy and gives the note, and the leader of the wild birds give a counter one, the rest of the males set upon him and chase him away from the female for making advances to her instead of to them; in consequence of this the male often advances without uttering any cry, so that no other may hear him and come and give him battle; and experienced fowlers assert that sometimes the male bird, when he approaches the female, makes her keep silence, to avoid having to give battle to other males who might have heard him. The partridge has not only the note here referred to, but also a thin shrill cry and other notes. Oftentimes the hen-bird rises from off her brood when she sees the male showing attentions to the female decoy; she will give the counter-note and remain still, so as to be trodden by him and divert him from the decoy. The quail and the partridge are so intent upon sexual union that they often come right in the way of the decoy-birds, and not seldom alight upon their heads. So much for the sexual proclivities of the partridge, for the way in which it is hunted, and the general nasty habits of the bird.

As has been said, quails and partridges build their nests upon the ground, and so also do some of the birds that are capable of sustained flight. Further, for instance, of such birds, the lark and the woodcock, as well as the quail, do not perch on a branch, but squat upon the ground.

9

614ᵇ The woodpecker does not squat on the ground, but pecks at the bark of trees to drive out from under it maggots and gnats; when they emerge, it licks them up with its tongue, which is large and flat. It can run up and down a tree in any way, even with the head downwards, like the gecko-lizard. For secure hold upon a tree, its claws are better adapted than those of the daw; it makes its way by sticking these claws into the bark. One species of woodpecker is smaller than a blackbird, and has small reddish speckles; a second species is larger than the blackbird, and a third is not much smaller than a barn-door hen. It builds a nest on trees, as has been said, on olive trees amongst others. It feeds on the maggots and ants that are under the bark: it is so eager in the search for maggots that it is said sometimes to hollow a tree out to its downfall. A woodpecker once, in course of domestication, was seen to insert an almond into a hole in a piece of timber, so that it might remain steady under its pecking; at the third peck it split the shell of the fruit, and then ate the kernel.

10

Many indications of high intelligence are given by cranes. They will fly to a great distance and high up in the air, to command an extensive view; if they see clouds and signs of bad weather they fly down again and remain still. They, furthermore, have a leader in their flight, and patrols that scream on the confines of the flock so as to be heard by all. When they settle down, the main body go to sleep with their heads under their wing, standing first on one leg and then on the other, while their leader, with his head uncovered, keeps a sharp look out, and when he sees anything of importance signals it with a cry.

Pelicans that live beside rivers swallow the large smooth mussel-shells: after cooking them inside the crop that precedes the stomach, they spit them out, so that, now when their shells are open, they may pick the flesh out and eat it.

11

Of wild birds, the nests are fashioned to meet the exigencies of existence and ensure the security of the young. Some of these birds are fond of their young and take great care of them, others are quite the reverse; some are clever in procuring subsistence, others are not so. Some of these birds build in ravines and clefts, and on cliffs, as, for instance, the so-
615ᵃ called charadrius, or stone-curlew; this bird is in no way noteworthy for plumage or voice; it makes an appearance at night, but in the daytime keeps out of sight.

The hawk also builds in inaccessible places. Although a ravenous bird, it will never eat the heart of any bird it catches; this has been observed in the case of the quail, the thrush, and other birds. They modify betimes their method of hunting, for in summer they do not grab their prey as they do at other seasons.

Of the vulture, it is said that no one has ever seen either its young or its nest; on this account and on the ground that all of a sudden great numbers of them will appear without any one being able to tell from whence they come, Herodorus, the father of Bryson the sophist, says that it belongs to some distant and elevated land. The reason is that the bird has its nest on inaccessible crags, and is found only in a few localities. The female lays one egg as a rule, and two at the most.

Some birds live on mountains or in forests, as the hoopoe and the brenthus; this latter bird finds his food with ease and has a musical voice. The wren lives in brakes and crevices; it is difficult of capture, keeps out of sight, is gentle of disposition, finds its food with ease, and is something of a mechanic. It goes by the nickname of 'old man' or 'king'; and the story goes that for this reason the eagle is at war with him.

12

Some birds live on the sea-shore, as the wagtail; the bird is of a mischievous nature, hard to capture, but when caught capable of complete domestication; it is a cripple, as being weak in its hinder quarters.

Web-footed birds without exception live near the sea or rivers or pools, as they naturally resort to places adapted to their structure. Several birds, however, with cloven toes live near pools or marshes, as, for instance, the anthus lives by the side of rivers; the plumage of this bird is pretty, and it finds its food with ease. The catarrhactes lives near the sea; when it makes a dive, it will keep under water for as long as it would take a man to walk a furlong; it is less than the common hawk. Swans are web-footed, and live near pools and marshes; they find their food with ease, are good-tempered, are fond of their young, and live to a green old age. If the eagle attacks them they **615b** will repel the attack and get the better of their assailant, but they are never the first to attack. They are musical, and sing chiefly at the approach of death; at this time they fly out to sea, and men, when sailing past the coast of Libya, have fallen in with many of them out at sea singing in mournful strains, and have actually seen some of them dying.

The cymindis is seldom seen, as it lives on mountains; it is black in colour, and about the size of the hawk called the 'dove-killer'; it is long and slender in form. The Ionians call the bird by this name; Homer in the *Iliad* mentions it in the line[1]:—

Chalcis *its name with those of heav'nly birth*,
But called Cymindis *by the sons of earth*.

The hybris, said by some to be the same as the eagle-owl, is never seen by daylight, as it is dim-sighted, but during the night it hunts like the eagle; it will fight the eagle with such desperation that the two combatants are often captured alive by shepherds; it lays two eggs, and, like others we have mentioned, it builds on rocks and in caverns. Cranes also fight so desperately among themselves as to be caught when fighting, for they will not leave off; the crane lays two eggs.

13

The jay has a great variety of notes: indeed, one might almost say it had a different note for every day in the year. It lays about nine eggs; builds its nest on trees, out of hair and tags of wool; when acorns are getting scarce, it lays up a store of them in hiding.

It is a common story of the stork that the old birds are fed by their grateful progeny. Some tell a similar story of the bee-eater, and declare that the parents are fed by their young not only when growing old, but at an early period, as soon as the young are capable of feeding them; and the parent-birds stay inside the nest. The under part of the bird's wing is pale yellow; the upper part is dark blue, like that of the halcyon; the tips of the wings are red. About autumn-time it lays six or seven eggs, in overhanging banks where the soil is soft; there it burrows into the ground to a depth of six feet.

The greenfinch, so called from the colour of its belly, is as large as a lark; it lays four or five **616a** eggs, builds its nest out of the plant called comfrey, pulling it up by the roots, and makes an under-mattress to lie on of hair and wool. The blackbird and the jay build their nests after the same fashion. The nest of the penduline tit shows great mechanical skill; it has the appearance of a ball of flax, and the hole for entry is very small.

People who live where the bird comes from say that there exists a cinnamon bird which brings the cinnamon from some unknown localities, and builds its nest out of it; it builds on high trees on the slender top branches. They say that the inhabitants attach leaden weights to the tips of their arrows and therewith bring down the nests, and from the intertexture collect the cinnamon sticks.

14

The halcyon is not much larger than the sparrow. Its colour is dark blue, green, and light purple; the whole body and wings, and especially parts about the neck, show these colours in a mixed way, without any colour being sharply defined; the beak is light green, long and slender: such, then, is the look of the bird. Its nest is like sea-balls, i.e. the things that go by the name of halosachne or sea-foam, only the colour is not the same. The colour of the nest is light red, and the shape is that of the long-necked gourd. The nests are larger than the largest sponge, though they vary in size; they are roofed over, and great part of them is solid and great part hollow. If you use a sharp knife it is not easy to cut the nest through; but if you cut it, and at the same time bruise it with your hand, it will soon crumble to pieces, like the halosachne. The opening is small, just enough for a tiny entrance, so that even if the nest upset the sea does not enter in; the hollow channels are like those in sponges. It is not known for certain of what material the nest is constructed; it is possibly made of the backbones of the gar-fish; for, by the way, the bird lives on fish. Besides living on the shore, it ascends fresh-water streams. It lays generally about five eggs, and lays eggs all its life long, beginning to do so at the age of four months.

[1] *Iliad*, XIV. 291.

15

The hoopoe usually constructs its nest out of 616b human excrement. It changes its appearance in summer and in winter, as in fact do the great majority of wild birds. (The titmouse is said to lay a very large quantity of eggs: next to the ostrich the blackheaded tit is said by some to lay the largest number of eggs; seventeen eggs have been seen; it lays, however, more than twenty; it is said always to lay an odd number. Like others we have mentioned, it builds in trees; it feeds on caterpillars.) A peculiarity of this bird and of the nightingale is that the outer extremity of the tongue is not sharp-pointed.

The aegithus finds its food with ease, has many young, and walks with a limp. The golden oriole is apt at learning, is clever at making a living, but is awkward in flight and has an ugly plumage.

16

The reed-warbler makes its living as easily as any other bird, sits in summer in a shady spot facing the wind, in winter in a sunny and sheltered place among reeds in a marsh; it is small in size, with a pleasant note. The so-called chatterer has a pleasant note, beautiful plumage, makes a living cleverly, and is graceful in form; it appears to be alien to our country; at all events it is seldom seen at a distance from its own immediate home.

17

The crake is quarrelsome, clever at making a living, but in other ways an unlucky bird. The bird called sitta is quarrelsome, but clever and tidy, makes its living with ease, and for its knowingness is regarded as uncanny; it has a numerous brood, of which it is fond, and lives by pecking the bark of trees. The aegolius-owl flies by night, is seldom seen by day; like others we have mentioned, it lives on cliffs or in caverns; it feeds on two kinds of food; it has a strong hold on life and is full of resource. The tree-creeper is a little bird, of fearless disposition; it lives among trees, feeds on caterpillars, makes a living with ease, and has a loud clear note. The acanthis finds its food with difficulty; its plumage is poor, but its note is musical.

18

Of the herons, the ashen-coloured one, as has been said, unites with the female not without pain;[1] it is full of resource, carries its food with it, is eager in the quest of it, and works by day; its plumage is poor, and its excrement is always 617a wet. Of the other two species—for there are three in all—the white heron has handsome plumage, unites without harm to itself with the female, builds a nest and lays its eggs neatly in trees; it frequents marshes and lakes and plains and meadow land. The speckled heron, which is nicknamed 'the skulker', is said in folklore stories to be of servile origin, and, as its nickname implies, it is the laziest bird of the three species. Such are the habits of herons. The bird that is called the poynx has this peculiarity, that it is more prone than any other bird to peck at the eyes of an assailant or its prey; it is at war with the harpy, as the two birds live on the same food.

19

There are two kinds of owsels; the one is black, and is found everywhere, the other is quite white, about the same size as the other, and with the same pipe. This latter is found on Cyllene in Arcadia, and is found nowhere else. The laius, or blue-thrush, is like the black owsel, only a little smaller; it lives on cliffs or on tile roofings; it has not a red beak as the black owsel has.

20

Of thrushes there are three species. One is the misselthrush; it feeds only on mistletoe and resin; it is about the size of the jay. A second kind is the song-thrush; it has a sharp pipe, and is about the size of the owsel. There is another species called the Illas; it is the smallest species of the three, and is less variegated in plumage than the others.

21

There is a bird that lives on rocks, called the blue-bird from its colour. It is comparatively common in Nisyros, and is somewhat less than the owsel and a little bigger than the chaffinch. It has large claws, and climbs on the face of the rocks. It is steel-blue all over; its beak is long and slender; its legs are short, like those of the woodpecker.

22

The oriole is yellow all over; it is not visible during winter, but puts in an appearance about the time of the summer solstice, and departs again at the rising of Arcturus; it is the

[1] IX. 2(609b 21).

size of the turtle-dove. The so-called soft-head (or shrike) always settles on one and the same **617b** branch, where it falls a prey to the bird-catcher. Its head is big, and composed of gristle; it is a little smaller than the thrush; its beak is strong, small, and round; it is ashen-coloured all over; is fleet of foot, but slow of wing. The bird-catcher usually catches it by help of the owl.

23

There is also the pardalus. As a rule, it is seen in flocks and not singly; it is ashen-coloured all over, and about the size of the birds last described; it is fleet of foot and strong of wing, and its pipe is loud and high-pitched. The collyrion (or fieldfare) feeds on the same food as the owsel; is of the same size as the above-mentioned birds; and is trapped usually in the winter. All these birds are found at all times. Further, there are the birds that live as a rule in towns, the raven and the crow. These also are visible at all seasons, never shift their place of abode, and never go into winter quarters.

24

Of daws there are three species. One is the chough; it is as large as the crow, but has a red beak. There is another, called the 'wolf'; and further there is the little daw, called the 'railer'. There is another kind of daw found in Lybia and Phrygia, which is web-footed.

25

Of larks there are two kinds. One lives on the ground and has a crest on its head; the other is gregarious, and not sporadic like the first; it is, however, of the same coloured plumage, but is smaller, and has no crest; it is an article of human food.

26

The woodcock is caught with nets in gardens. It is about the size of a barn-door hen; it has a long beak, and in plumage is like the francolin-partridge. It runs quickly, and is pretty easily domesticated. The starling is speckled; it is of the same size as the owsel.

27

Of the Egyptian ibis there are two kinds, the white and the black. The white ones are found all over Egypt, excepting in Pelusium; the black ones are found in Pelusium, and nowhere else in Egypt.

28

Of the little horned owls there are two kinds, and one is visible at all seasons, and for that reason has the nickname of 'all-the-year-round owl'; it is not sufficiently palatable to come to **618a** table; another species makes its appearance sometimes in the autumn, is seen for a single day or at the most for two days, and is regarded as a table delicacy; it scarcely differs from the first species save only in being fatter; it has no note, but the other species has. With regard to their origin, nothing is known from ocular observation; the only fact known for certain is that they are first seen when a west wind is blowing.

29

The cuckoo, as has been said elsewhere, makes no nest, but deposits its eggs in an alien nest, generally in the nest of the ring-dove, or on the ground in the nest of the hypolais or lark, or on a tree in the nest of the green linnet. It lays only one egg and does not hatch it itself, but the mother-bird in whose nest it has deposited it hatches and rears it; and, as they say, this mother bird, when the young cuckoo has grown big, thrusts her own brood out of the nest and lets them perish; others say that this mother-bird kills her own brood and gives them to the alien to devour, despising her own young owing to the beauty of the cuckoo. Personal observers agree in telling most of these stories, but are not in agreement as to the destruction of the young. Some say that the mother-cuckoo comes and devours the brood of the rearing mother; others say that the young cuckoo from its superior size snaps up the food brought before the smaller brood have a chance, and that in consequence the smaller brood die of hunger; others say that, by its superior strength, it actually kills the other ones whilst it is being reared up with them. The cuckoo shows great sagacity in the disposal of its progeny; the fact is, the mother-cuckoo is quite conscious of her own cowardice and of the fact that she could never help her young one in an emergency, and so, for the security of the young one, she makes of him a supposititious child in an alien nest. The truth is, this bird is pre-eminent among birds in the way of cowardice; it allows itself to be pecked at by little birds, and flies away from their attacks.

30

It has already been stated that the footless bird, which some term the cypselus,[1] resembles the swallow; indeed, it is not easy to distinguish between the two birds, excepting in the fact that the cypselus has feathers on the shank. These birds rear their young in long cells made of mud, and furnished with a hole just big enough for entry and exit; they build under **618b** cover of some roofing—under a rock or in a cavern—for protection against animals and men.

The so-called goat-sucker lives on mountains; it is a little larger than the owsel, and less than the cuckoo; it lays two eggs, or three at the most, and is of a sluggish disposition. It flies up to the she-goat and sucks its milk, from which habit it derives its name; it is said that, after it has sucked the teat of the animal, the teat dries up and the animal goes blind. It is dim-sighted in the day-time, but sees well enough by night.

31

In narrow circumscribed districts where the food would be insufficient for more birds than two, ravens are only found in isolated pairs; when their young are old enough to fly, the parent couple first eject them from the nest, and by and by chase them from the neighbourhood. The raven lays four or five eggs. About the time when the mercenaries under Medius were slaughtered at Pharsalus, the districts about Athens and the Peloponnese were left destitute of ravens, from which it would appear that these birds have some means of intercommunicating with one another.

32

Of eagles there are several species. One of them, called 'the white-tailed eagle', is found on low lands, in groves, and in the neighbourhood of cities; some call it the 'heron-killer'. It is bold enough to fly to mountains and the interior of forests. The other eagles seldom visit groves or low-lying land. There is another species called the 'plangus'; it ranks second in point of size and strength; it lives in mountain combes and glens, and by marshy lakes, and goes by the name of 'duck-killer' and 'swart-eagle.' It is mentioned by Homer[2] in his account of the visit made by Priam to the tent of Achilles. There is another species with black plumage, the smallest but boldest of all the kinds. It dwells on mountains or in forests, and is called 'the black-eagle' or 'the hare-killer'; it is the only eagle that rears its young thoroughly and takes them out with it. It is swift of flight, is neat and tidy in its habits, too proud for jealousy, fearless, quarrelsome; it is also silent, for it neither whimpers nor screams. There is another species, the percnopterus, very large, with white head, very short wings, long tail-feathers, in appearance like a vulture. It goes by the name of 'mountain-stork' or 'half-eagle'. It lives in groves; has all the bad qualities of the other species, and none of the good **619a** ones; for it lets itself be chased and caught by the raven and the other birds. It is clumsy in its movements, has difficulty in procuring its food, preys on dead animals, is always hungry, and at all times whining and screaming. There is another species, called the 'sea-eagle' or 'osprey'. This bird has a large thick neck, curved wings, and broad tailfeathers; it lives near the sea, grasps its prey with its talons, and often, from inability to carry it, tumbles down into the water. There is another species called the 'true-bred'; people say that these are the only true-bred birds to be found, that all other birds—eagles, hawks, and the smallest birds—are all spoilt by the interbreeding of different species. The true-bred eagle is the largest of all eagles; it is larger than the phene; is half as large again as the ordinary eagle, and has yellow plumage; it is seldom seen, as is the case with the so-called cymindis. The time for an eagle to be on the wing in search of prey is from midday to evening; in the morning until the market-hour it remains on the nest. In old age the upper beak of the eagle grows gradually longer and more crooked, and the bird dies eventually of starvation; there is a folklore story that the eagle is thus punished because it once was a man and refused entertainment to a stranger. The eagle puts aside its superfluous food for its young; for owing to the difficulty in procuring food day by day, it at times may come back to the nest with nothing. If it catch a man prowling about in the neighbourhood of its nest, it will strike him with its wings and scratch him with its talons. The nest is built not on low ground but on an elevated spot, generally on an inaccessible ledge of a cliff; it does, however, build upon a tree. The young are fed until they can fly; hereupon the parent-birds topple them out of the nest, and chase them completely out of the locality. The fact is that a pair of eagles demands an extensive space for its maintenance, and conse-

[1] Cf. I. 1(487b 25).

[2] *Iliad*, XXIV. 316.

quently cannot allow other birds to quarter themselves in close neighbourhood. They do not hunt in the vicinity of their nest, but go to a great distance to find their prey. When the eagle has captured a beast, it puts it down without attempting to carry it off at once; if on trial it finds the burden too heavy, it will leave it. When it has spied a hare, it does not swoop on
619b it at once, but lets it go on into the open ground; neither does it descend to the ground at one swoop, but goes gradually down from higher flights to lower and lower: these devices it adopts by way of security against the stratagem of the hunter. It alights on high places by reason of the difficulty it experiences in soaring up from the level ground; it flies high in the air to have the more extensive view; from its high flight it is said to be the only bird that resembles the gods. Birds of prey, as a rule, seldom alight upon rock, as the crookedness of their talons prevents a stable footing on hard stone. The eagle hunts hares, fawns, foxes, and in general all such animals as he can master with ease. It is a long-lived bird, and this fact might be inferred from the length of time during which the same nest is maintained in its place.

33

In Scythia there is found a bird as large as the great bustard. The female lays two eggs, but does not hatch them, but hides them in the skin of a hare or fox and leaves them there, and, when it is not in quest of prey, it keeps a watch on them on a high tree; if any man tries to climb the tree, it fights and strikes him with its wing, just as eagles do.

34

The owl and the night-raven and all the birds that see poorly in the daytime seek their prey in the night, but not all the night through, but at evening and dawn. Their food consists of mice, lizards, chafers and the like little creatures. The so-called phene, or lämmergeier, is fond of its young, provides its food with ease, fetches food to its nest, and is of a kindly disposition. It rears its own young and those of the eagle as well; for when the eagle ejects its young from the nest, this bird catches them up as they fall and feeds them. For the eagle, by the way, ejects the young birds prematurely, before they are able to feed themselves, or to fly. It appears to do so from jealousy; for it is by nature jealous, and is so ravenous as to grab furiously at its food; and when it does grab at its food, it grabs it in large morsels. It is accordingly jealous of the young birds as they approach maturity, since they are getting good appetites, and so it scratches them with its talons. The young birds fight also with one another, to secure a morsel of food or a comfortable position, whereupon the mother-bird beats them and ejects them from the nest; the young ones scream at this treatment, and the phene hearing them catches them as they fall. The
620a phene has a film over its eyes and sees badly, but the sea-eagle is very keen-sighted, and before its young are fledged tries to make them stare at the sun, and beats the one that refuses to do so, and twists him back in the sun's direction; and if one of them gets watery eyes in the process, it kills him, and rears the other. It lives near the sea, and feeds, as has been said, on sea-birds; when in pursuit of them it catches them one by one, watching the moment when the bird rises to the surface from its dive. When a sea-bird, emerging from the water, sees the sea-eagle, he in terror dives under, intending to rise again elsewhere; the eagle, however, owing to its keenness of vision, keeps flying after him until he either drowns the bird or catches him on the surface. The eagle never attacks these birds when they are in a swarm, for they keep him off by raising a shower of water-drops with their wings.

35

The cepphus is caught by means of sea-foam; the bird snaps at the foam, and consequently fishermen catch it by sluicing with showers of sea-water. These birds grow to be plump and fat; their flesh has a good odour, excepting the hinder quarters, which smell of shoreweed.

36

Of hawks, the strongest is the buzzard; the next in point of courage is the merlin; and the circus ranks third; other diverse kinds are the asterias, the pigeon-hawk, and the pternis; the broaded-winged hawk is called the half-buzzard; others go by the name of hobby-hawk, or sparrow-hawk, or 'smooth-feathered', or 'toad-catcher'. Birds of this latter species find their food with very little difficulty, and flutter along the ground. Some say that there are ten species of hawks, all differing from one another. One hawk, they say, will strike and grab the pigeon as it rests on the ground, but never touch it while it is in flight; another hawk attacks the pigeon when it is perched upon a tree or any elevation, but never touches it when it is on the ground or on the wing; other hawks attack their prey only when it is on the wing. They say that pigeons can distinguish the various species: so that, when a hawk is an assailant, if it be one that attacks its prey when the prey is on the wing, the pigeon will sit still; if it be one that attacks sitting prey, the pigeon will rise up and fly away.

In Thrace, in the district sometimes called that of Cedripolis, men hunt for little birds in the marshes with the aid of hawks. The men with sticks in their hands go beating at the **620b** reeds and brushwood to frighten the birds out, and the hawks show themselves overhead and frighten them down. The men then strike them with their sticks and capture them. They give a portion of their booty to the hawks; that is, they throw some of the birds up in the air, and the hawks catch them.

In the neighbourhood of Lake Maeotis, it is said, wolves act in concert with the fishermen, and if the fishermen decline to share with them, they tear their nets in pieces as they lie drying on the shore of the lake.

37

So much for the habits of birds.

In marine creatures, also, one may observe many ingenious devices adapted to the circumstances of their lives. For the accounts commonly given of the so-called fishing-frog are quite true; as are also those given of the torpedo. The fishing-frog has a set of filaments that project in front of its eyes; they are long and thin like hairs, and are round at the tips; they lie on either side, and are used as baits. Accordingly, when the animal stirs up a place full of sand and mud and conceals itself therein, it raises the filaments, and, when the little fish strike against them, it draws them in underneath into its mouth. The torpedo narcotizes the creatures that it wants to catch, overpowering them by the power of shock that is resident in its body, and feeds upon them; it also hides in the sand and mud, and catches all the creatures that swim in its way and come under its narcotizing influence. This phenomenon has been actually observed in operation. The sting-ray also conceals itself, but not exactly in the same way. That the creatures get their living by this means is obvious from the fact that, whereas they are peculiarly inactive, they are often caught with mullets in their interior, the swiftest of fishes. Furthermore, the fishing-frog is unusually thin when he is caught after losing the tips of his filaments, and the torpedo is known to cause a numbness even in human beings. Again, the hake, the ray, the flat-fish, and the angel-fish burrow in the sand, and after concealing themselves angle with the filaments on their mouths, that fishermen call their fishing-rods, and the little creatures on which they feed swim up to the filaments taking them for bits of sea-weed, such as they feed upon.

Wherever an anthias-fish is seen, there will be no dangerous creatures in the vicinity, and sponge-divers will dive in security, and they call these signal-fishes 'holy-fish'. It is a sort of perpetual coincidence, like the fact that **621a** wherever snails are present you may be sure there is neither pig nor partridge in the neighbourhood; for both pig and partridge eat up the snails.

The sea-serpent resembles the conger in colour and shape, but is of lesser bulk and more rapid in its movements. If it be caught and thrown away, it will bore a hole with its snout and burrow rapidly in the sand; its snout, by the way, is sharper than that of ordinary serpents. The so-called sea-scolopendra, after swallowing the hook, turns itself inside out until it ejects it, and then it again turns itself outside in. The sea-scolopendra, like the land-scolopendra, will come to a savoury bait; the creature does not bite with its teeth, but stings by contact with its entire body, like the so-called sea-nettle. The so-called fox-shark, when it finds it has swallowed the hook, tries to get rid of it as the scolopendra does, but not in the same way; in other words, it runs up the fishing-line, and bites it off short; it is caught in some districts in deep and rapid waters, with night-lines.

The bonitos swarm together when they espy a dangerous creature, and the largest of them swim round it, and if it touches one of the shoal they try to repel it; they have strong teeth. Amongst other large fish, a lamia-shark, after falling in amongst a shoal, has been seen to be covered with wounds.

Of river-fish, the male of the sheat-fish is remarkably attentive to the young. The female after parturition goes away; the male stays and keeps on guard where the spawn is most abundant, contenting himself with keeping off all other little fishes that might steal the spawn or fry, and this he does for forty or fifty days, until the young are sufficiently grown to make away from the other fishes for them-

selves. The fishermen can tell where he is on guard: for, in warding off the little fishes, he makes a rush in the water and gives utterance to a kind of muttering noise. He is so earnest in the performance of his parental duties that the fishermen at times, if the eggs be attached to the roots of water-plants deep in the water, drag them into as shallow a place as possible; the male fish will still keep by the young, and, if it so happen, will be caught by the hook when snapping at the little fish that come by; if, however, he be sensible by experience of the
621b danger of the hook, he will still keep by his charge, and with his extremely strong teeth will bite the hook in pieces.

All fishes, both those that wander about and those that are stationary, occupy the districts where they were born or very similar places, for their natural food is found there. Carnivorous fish wander most; and all fish are carnivorous with the exception of a few, such as the mullet, the saupe, the red mullet, and the chalcis. The so-called pholis gives out a mucous discharge, which envelops the creature in a kind of nest. Of shell-fish, and fish that are finless, the scallop moves with greatest force and to the greatest distance, impelled along by some internal energy; the murex or purple-fish, and others that resemble it, move hardly at all. Out of the lagoon of Pyrrha all the fishes swim in winter-time, except the sea-gudgeon; they swim out owing to the cold, for the narrow waters are colder than the outer sea, and on the return of the early summer they all swim back again. In the lagoon no scarus is found, nor thritta, nor any other species of the spiny fish, no spotted dogfish, no spiny dogfish, no sea-crawfish, no octopus either of the common or the musky kinds, and certain other fish are also absent; but of fish that are found in the lagoon the white gudgeon is not a marine fish. Of fishes the oviparous are in their prime in the early summer until the spawning time; the viviparous in the autumn, as is also the case with the mullet, the red mullet, and all such fish. In the neighbourhood of Lesbos, the fishes of the outer sea, or of the lagoon, bring forth their eggs or young in the lagoon; sexual union takes place in the autumn, and parturition in the spring. With fishes of the cartilaginous kind, the males and females swarm together in the autumn for the sake of sexual union; in the early summer they come swimming in, and keep apart until after parturition; the two sexes are often taken linked together in sexual union.

Of molluscs the sepia is the most cunning, and is the only species that employs its dark liquid for the sake of concealment as well as from fear: the octopus and calamary make the discharge solely from fear. These creatures never discharge the pigment in its entirety; and after a discharge the pigment accumulates again. The sepia, as has been said, often uses its colouring pigment for concealment; it shows itself in front of the pigment and then
622a retreats back into it; it also hunts with its long tentacles not only little fishes, but oftentimes even mullets. The octopus is a stupid creature, for it will approach a man's hand if it be lowered in the water; but it is neat and thrifty in its habits: that is, it lays up stores in its nest, and, after eating up all that is eatable, it ejects the shells and sheaths of crabs and shell-fish, and the skeletons of little fishes. It seeks its prey by so changing its colour as to render it like the colour of the stones adjacent to it; it does so also when alarmed. By some the sepia is said to perform the same trick; that is, they say it can change its colour so as to make it resemble the colour of its habitat. The only fish that can do this is the angel-fish, that is, it can change its colour like the octopus. The octopus as a rule does not live the year out. It has a natural tendency to run off into liquid; for, if beaten and squeezed, it keeps losing substance and at last disappears. The female after parturition is peculiarly subject to this colliquefaction; it becomes stupid; if tossed about by waves, it submits impassively; a man, if he dived, could catch it with the hand; it gets covered over with slime, and makes no effort to catch its wonted prey. The male becomes leathery and clammy. As a proof that they do not live into a second year there is the fact that, after the birth of the little octopuses in the late summer or beginning of autumn, it is seldom that a large-sized octopus is visible, whereas a little before this time of year the creature is at its largest. After the eggs are laid, they say that both the male and the female grow so old and feeble that they are preyed upon by little fish, and with ease dragged from their holes; and that this could not have been done previously; they say also that this is not the case with the small and young octopus, but that the young creature is much stronger than the grown-up one. Neither does the sepia live into a second year. The octopus is the only mollusc that ventures on to dry land; it walks by preference on rough ground; it is firm all over when you squeeze it,

excepting in the neck. So much for the mollusca.

622b It is also said that they make a thin rough shell about them like a hard sheath, and that this is made larger and larger as the animal grows larger, and that it comes out of the sheath as though out of a den or dwelling-place.

The nautilus (or argonaut) is a poulpe or octopus, but one peculiar both in its nature and its habits. It rises up from deep water and swims on the surface; it rises with its shell down-turned in order that it may rise the more easily and swim with it empty, but after reaching the surface it shifts the position of the shell. In between its feelers it has a certain amount of web-growth, resembling the substance between the toes of web-footed birds; only that with these latter the substance is thick, while with the nautilus it is thin and like a spider's web. It uses this structure, when a breeze is blowing, for a sail, and lets down some of its feelers alongside as rudder-oars. If it be frightened it fills its shell with water and sinks. With regard to the mode of generation and the growth of the shell knowledge from observation is not yet satisfactory; the shell, however, does not appear to be there from the beginning, but to grow in their case as in that of other shell-fish; neither is it ascertained for certain whether the animal can live when stripped of the shell.

38

Of all insects, one may also say of all living creatures, the most industrious are the ant, the bee, the hornet, the wasp, and in point of fact all creatures akin to these; of spiders some are more skilful and more resourceful than others. The way in which ants work is open to ordinary observation; how they all march one after the other when they are engaged in putting away and storing up their food; all this may be seen, for they carry on their work even during bright moonlight nights.

39

Of spiders and phalangia there are many species. Of the venomous phalangia there are two; one that resembles the so-called wolf-spider, small, speckled, and tapering to a point; it moves with leaps, from which habit it is nicknamed 'the flea': the other kind is large, black in colour, with long front legs; it is heavy in its movements, walks slowly, is not very strong, and never leaps. (Of all the other species wherewith poison-vendors supply themselves, 623a some give a weak bite, and others never bite at all. There is another kind, comprising the so-called wolf-spiders.) Of these spiders the small one weaves no web, and the large weaves a rude and poorly built one on the ground or on dry stone walls. It always builds its web over hollow places inside of which it keeps a watch on the end-threads, until some creature gets into the web and begins to struggle, when out the spider pounces. The speckled kind makes a little shabby web under trees.

There is a third species of this animal, pre-eminently clever and artistic. It first weaves a thread stretching to all the exterior ends of the future web; then from the centre, which it hits upon with great accuracy, it stretches the warp; on the warp it puts what corresponds to the woof, and then weaves the whole together. It sleeps and stores its food away from the centre, but it is at the centre that it keeps watch for its prey. Then, when any creature touches the web and the centre is set in motion, it first ties and wraps the creature round with threads until it renders it helpless, then lifts it and carries it off, and, if it happens to be hungry, sucks out the life-juices—for that is the way it feeds; but, if it be not hungry, it first mends any damage done and then hastens again to its quest of prey. If something comes meanwhile into the net, the spider at first makes for the centre, and then goes back to its entangled prey as from a fixed starting-point. If any one injures a portion of the web, it recommences weaving at sunrise or at sunset, because it is chiefly at these periods that creatures are caught in the web. It is the female that does the weaving and the hunting, but the male takes a share of the booty captured.

Of the skilful spiders, weaving a substantial web, there are two kinds, the larger and the smaller. The one has long legs and keeps watch while swinging downwards from the web: from its large size it cannot easily conceal itself, and so it keeps underneath, so that its prey may not be frightened off, but may strike upon the web's upper surface; the less awkwardly formed one lies in wait on the top, using a little hole for a lurking-place. Spiders can spin webs from the time of their birth, not from their interior as a superfluity or excretion, as Democritus avers, but off their body as a kind of tree-bark, like the creatures that shoot out with their hair, as for instance the porcupine. The creature can attack animals larger than itself, and enwrap them with its threads: in other words, it will attack a small 623b lizard, run round and draw threads about its mouth until it closes the mouth up; then it comes up and bites it.

40

So much for the spider. Of insects, there is a genus that has no one name that comprehends all the species, though all the species are akin to one another in form; it consists of all the insects that construct a honeycomb: to wit, the bee, and all the insects that resemble it in form. There are nine varieties, of which six are gregarious—the bee, the king-bee, the drone-bee, the annual wasp, and, furthermore, the anthrene (or hornet), and the tenthredo (or ground-wasp); three are solitary—the smaller siren, of a dun colour, the larger siren, black and speckled, and the third, the largest of all, that is called the humble-bee. Now ants never go a-hunting, but gather up what is ready to hand; the spider makes nothing, and lays up no store, but simply goes a-hunting for its food; while the bee—for we shall by and by treat of the nine varieties—does not go a-hunting, but constructs its food out of gathered material and stores it away, for honey is the bee's food. This fact is shown by the bee-keepers' attempt to remove the combs; for the bees, when they are fumigated, and are suffering great distress from the process, then devour the honey most ravenously, whereas at other times they are never observed to be so greedy, but apparently are thrifty and disposed to lay by for their future sustenance. They have also another food which is called bee-bread; this is scarcer than honey and has a sweet fig-like taste; this they carry as they do the wax on their legs.

Very remarkable diversity is observed in their methods of working and their general habits. When the hive has been delivered to them clean and empty, they build their waxen cells, bringing in the juice of all kinds of flowers and the 'tears' or exuding sap of trees, such as willows and elms and such others as are particularly given to the exudation of gum. With this material they besmear the groundwork, to provide against attacks of other creatures; the bee-keepers call this stuff 'stop-wax'. They also with the same material narrow by side-building the entrances to the hive if they are too wide. They first build cells for themselves; then for the so-called kings and the 624a drones; for themselves they are always building, for the kings only when the brood of young is numerous, and cells for the drones they build if a superabundance of honey should suggest their doing so. They build the royal cells next to their own, and they are of small bulk; the drones' cells they build near by, and these latter are less in bulk than the bee's cells. They begin building the combs downwards from the top of the hive, and go down and down building many combs connected together until they reach the bottom. The cells, both those for the honey and those also for the grubs, are double-doored; for two cells are ranged about a single base, one pointing one way and one the other, after the manner of a double (or hour-glass-shaped) goblet. The cells that lie at the commencement of the combs and are attached to the hives, to the extent of two or three concentric circular rows, are small and devoid of honey; the cells that are well filled with honey are most thoroughly luted with wax. At the entry to the hive the aperture of the doorway is smeared with mitys; this substance is a deep black, and is a sort of dross or residual by-product of wax; it has a pungent odour, and is a cure for bruises and suppurating sores. The greasy stuff that comes next is pitch-wax; it has a less pungent odour and is less medicinal than the mitys. Some say that the drones construct combs by themselves in the same hive and in the same comb that they share with the bees; but that they make no honey, but subsist, they and their grubs also, on the honey made by the bees. The drones, as a rule, keep inside the hive; when they go out of doors, they soar up in the air in a stream, whirling round and round in a kind of gymnastic exercise; when this is over, they come inside the hive and feed to repletion ravenously. The kings never quit the hive, except in conjunction with the entire swarm, either for food or for any other reason. They say that, if a young swarm go astray, it will turn back upon its route and by the aid of scent seek out its leader. It is said that if he is unable to fly he is carried by the swarm, and that if he dies the swarm perishes; and that, if this swarm outlives the king for a while and constructs combs, no honey is produced and the bees soon die out. Bees scramble up the stalks of flowers and rapidly gather the bees-wax with their front legs; the front legs 624b wipe it off on to the middle legs, and these pass it on to the hollow curves of the hind-legs; when thus laden, they fly away home, and one may see plainly that their load is a heavy one. On each expedition the bee does not fly from a flower of one kind to a flower of another, but flies from one violet, say, to another violet, and never meddles with another flower until it has got back to the hive; on reaching the hive they throw off their load, and each bee on his return is accompanied by three or four companions. One cannot well tell what is the substance they gather, nor the exact process of their work. Their mode of gathering wax has been observed on olive-trees, as owing to the thickness of the leaves the bees remain stationary for a considerable while. After this work is over, they attend to the grubs. There is nothing to prevent grubs, honey, and drones being all found in one and the same comb. As long as the leader is alive, the drones are said to be produced apart by themselves; if he be no longer living, they are said to be reared by the bees in their own cells, and under these circumstances to become more spirited: for this reason they are called 'sting-drones', not that they really have stings, but that they have the wish, without the power, to use such weapons. The cells for the drones are larger than the others; sometimes the bees construct cells for the drones apart, but usually they put them in amongst their own; and when this is the case the bee-keepers cut the drone-cells out of the combs. There are several species of bees, as has been said; two of 'kings', the better kind red, the other black and variegated, and twice as big as the working-bee. The best working-bee is small, round, and speckled: another kind is long and like an anthrene wasp; another kind is what is called the robber-bee, black and flat-bellied; then there is the drone, the largest of all, but devoid of sting, and lazy. There is a difference between the progeny of bees that inhabit cultivated land and of those from the mountains: the forest-bees are more shaggy, smaller, more industrious and more fierce. Working-bees make their combs all even, with the superficial covering quite smooth. Each comb is of one kind only: that is, it contains either bees only, or grubs only, or drones only; if it happen, however, that they make in one and the same comb all these kinds of cells, each separate kind will be built in a **625a** continuous row right through. The long bees build uneven combs, with the lids of the cells protuberant, like those of the anthrene; grubs and everything else have no fixed places, but are put anywhere; from these bees come inferior kings, a large quantity of drones, and the so-called robber-bee; they produce either no honey at all, or honey in very small quantities. Bees brood over the combs and so mature them; if they fail to do so, the combs are said to go bad and to get covered with a sort of spider's web. If they can keep brooding over the part undamaged, the damaged part simply eats itself away; if they cannot so brood, the entire comb perishes; in the damaged combs small worms are engendered, which take on wings and fly away. When the combs keep settling down, the bees restore the level surface, and put props underneath the combs to give themselves free passage-room; for if such free passage be lacking they cannot brood, and the cobwebs come on. When the robber-bee and the drone appear, not only do they do no work themselves, but they actually damage the work of the other bees; if they are caught in the act, they are killed by the working-bees. These bees also kill without mercy most of their kings, and especially kings of the inferior sort; and this they do for fear a multiplicity of kings should lead to a dismemberment of the hive. They kill them especially when the hive is deficient in grubs, and a swarm is not intended to take place; under these circumstances they destroy the cells of the kings if they have been prepared, on the ground that these kings are always ready to lead out swarms. They destroy also the combs of the drones if a failure in the honey supply be threatening and the hive runs short of provisions; under such circumstances they fight desperately with all who try to take their honey, and eject from the hive all the resident drones; and oftentimes the drones are to be seen sitting apart in the hive. The little bees fight vigorously with the long kind, and try to banish them from the hives; if they succeed, the hive will be unusually productive, but if the bigger bees get left mistresses of the field they pass the time in idleness, and do no good at all but die out before the autumn. Whenever the working-bees kill an enemy they try to do so out of doors; and whenever one of their own body dies, they carry the dead bee out of doors also. The so-called robber-bees spoil their own combs, and, if they can **625b** do so unnoticed, enter and spoil the combs of other bees; if they are caught in the act they are put to death. It is no easy task for them to escape detection, for there are sentinels on guard at every entry; and, even if they do escape detection on entering, afterwards from a surfeit of food they cannot fly, but go rolling about in front of the hive, so that their chances of escape are small indeed. The kings are never themselves seen outside the hive except with a swarm in flight: during which time all the other bees cluster around them. When the flight of a swarm is imminent, a monotonous and quite peculiar sound made by all the bees is heard for several days, and for two or three days in advance a few bees are seen flying round the hive; it has never as yet been ascertained, owing to the difficulty of the observation, whether or no the king is among these. When they have swarmed, they fly away and separate off to each of the kings; if a small swarm happens to settle near to a large one, it will shift to join this large one, and if the king whom they have abandoned follows them, they put him to death. So much for the quitting of the hive and the swarm-flight. Separate detachments of bees are told off for diverse operations; that is, some carry flower-produce, others carry water, others smooth and arrange the combs. A bee carries water when it is rearing grubs. No bee ever settles on the flesh of any creature, or ever eats animal food. They have no fixed date for commencing work; but when their provender is forthcoming and they are in comfortable trim, and by preference in summer, they set to work, and when the weather is fine they work incessantly. The bee, when quite young and in fact only three days old, after shedding its chrysalis-case, begins to work if it be well fed. When a swarm is settling, some bees detach themselves in search of food and return back to the swarm. In hives that are in good condition the production of young bees is discontinued only for the forty days that follow the winter solstice. When the grubs are grown, the bees put food beside them and cover them with a coating of wax; and, as soon as the grub is strong enough, he of his own accord breaks the lid and comes out. Creatures that make their appearance in hives and spoil the combs the working-bees clear out, but the other bees from sheer laziness look with indifference on damage done to their produce. When the bee-mas-

626a ters take out the combs, they leave enough food behind for winter use; if it be sufficient in quantity, the occupants of the hive will survive; if it be insufficient, then, if the weather be rough, they die on the spot, but if it be fair, they fly away and desert the hive. They feed on honey summer and winter; but they store up another article of food resembling wax in hardness, which by some is called sandarace, or bee-bread. Their worst enemies are wasps and the birds named titmice, and furthermore the swallow and the bee-eater. The frogs in the marsh also catch them if they come in their way by the water-side, and for this reason bee-keepers chase the frogs from the ponds from which the bees take water; they destroy also wasps' nests, and the nests of swallows, in the neighbourhood of the hives, and also the nests of bee-eaters. Bees have fear only of one another. They fight with one another and with wasps. Away from the hive they attack neither their own species nor any other creature, but in the close proximity of the hive they kill whatever they get hold of. Bees that sting die from their inability to extract the sting without at the same time extracting their intestines. True, they often recover, if the person stung takes the trouble to press the sting out; but once it loses its sting the bee must die. They can kill with their stings even large animals; in fact, a horse has been known to have been stung to death by them. The kings are the least disposed to show anger or to inflict a sting. Bees that die are removed from the hive, and in every way the creature is remarkable for its cleanly habits; in point of fact, they often fly away to a distance to void their excrement because it is malodorous; and, as has been said, they are annoyed by all bad smells and by the scent of perfumes, so much so that they sting people that use perfumes. They perish from a number of accidental causes, and when their kings become too numerous and try each to carry away a portion of the swarm. The toad also feeds on bees; he comes to the doorway of the hive, puffs himself out as he sits on the watch, and devours the creatures as they come flying out; the bees can in no way

626b retaliate, but the bee-keeper makes a point of killing him. As for the class of bee that has been spoken of as inferior or good-for-nothing, and as constructing its combs so roughly, some bee-keepers say that it is the young bees that act so from inexperience; and the bees of the current year are termed young. The young bees do not sting as the others do; and it is for this reason that swarms may be safely carried, as it is of young bees that they are composed. When honey runs short they expel the drones, and the bee-keepers supply the bees with figs and sweet-tasting articles of food. The elder bees do the indoor work, and are rough and hairy from staying indoors; the young bees do the outer carrying, and are comparatively smooth. They kill the drones also when in their work they are confined for room; the drones, by the way, live in the innermost recess of the hive. On one occasion, when a hive was in a poor condition, some of the occupants assailed a foreign hive; proving victorious in a combat they took to carrying off the honey; when the bee-keeper tried to kill them, the other bees came out and tried to beat off the enemy but made no attempt to sting the man. The diseases that chiefly attack prosperous hives are first of all the clerus—this consists in a growth of little worms on the floor, from which, as they develop, a kind of cobweb grows over the entire hive, and the combs decay; another diseased condition is indicated in a lassitude on the part of the bees and in malodorousness of the hive. Bees feed on thyme; and the white thyme is better than the red. In summer the place for the hive should be cool, and in winter warm. They are very apt to fall sick if the plant they are at work on be mildewed. In a high wind they carry a stone by way of ballast to steady them. If a stream be near at hand, they drink from it and from it only, but before they drink they first deposit their load; if there be no water near at hand, they disgorge their honey as they drink elsewhere, and at once make off to work. There are two seasons for making honey, spring and autumn; the spring honey is sweeter, whiter, and in every way better than the autumn honey. Superior honey comes from fresh comb, and from young shoots; the red honey is inferior, and owes its inferiority to the comb in which it is deposited, just as wine is apt to be spoiled by its cask; consequently, one should **627a** have it looked to and dried. When the thyme is in flower and the comb is full, the honey does not harden. The honey that is golden in hue is excellent. White honey does not come from thyme pure and simple; it is good as a salve for sore eyes and wounds. Poor honey always floats on the surface and should be skimmed off; the fine clear honey rests below. When the floral world is in full bloom, then they make wax; consequently you must then take the wax out of the hive, for they go to work on new wax at once. The flowers from which they gather honey are as follows: the spindle-tree, the melilot-clover, king's-spear, myrtle, flowering-reed, withy, and broom. When they work at thyme,they mix in water before sealing up the comb. As has been already stated, they all either fly to a distance to discharge their excrement or make the discharge into one single comb. The little bees, as has been said, are more industrious than the big ones; their wings are battered; their colour is black, and they have a burnt-up aspect. Gaudy and showy bees, like gaudy and showy women, are good-for-nothings. Bees seem to take a pleasure in listening to a rattling noise; and consequently men say that they can muster them into a hive by rattling with crockery or stones; it is uncertain, however, whether or no they can hear the noise at all and also whether their procedure is due to pleasure or alarm. They expel from the hive all idlers and unthrifts. As has been said, they differentiate their work; some make wax, some make honey, some make bee-bread, some shape and mould combs, some bring water to the cells and mingle it with the honey, some engage in out-of-door work. At early dawn they make no noise, until some one particular bee makes a buzzing noise two or three times and thereby awakes the rest; hereupon they all fly in a body to work. By and by they return and at first are noisy; then the noise gradually decreases, until at last some one bee flies round about, making a buzzing noise, and apparently calling on the others to go to sleep; then all of a sudden there is a dead silence. The hive is known to be in good condition if the noise heard within it is loud, and if the bees make a flutter as they go out and in; for at this time they are constructing brood-cells. They suffer most from hunger when they recommence work after winter. They become somewhat lazy if the bee-keeper, in robbing the hive, leave behind too much honey; still one should leave cells numerous in proportion to the population, for the bees work in a spiritless **627b** way if too few combs are left. They become idle also, as being dispirited, if the hive be too big. A hive yields to the bee-keeper six or nine pints of honey; a prosperous hive will yield twelve or fifteen pints, exceptionally good hives eighteen. Sheep and, as has been said, wasps are enemies to the bees. Bee-keepers entrap the latter, by putting a flat dish on the ground with pieces of meat on it; when a number of the wasps settle on it, they cover them with a lid and put the dish and its contents on the fire. It is a good thing to have a few drones in a hive, as their presence increases the industry of the workers. Bees can tell the approach of rough weather or of rain; and the proof is that they will not fly away, but even while it is as yet fine they go fluttering about within a restricted space, and the bee-keeper knows from this that they are expecting bad weather. When the bees inside the hive hang clustering to one another, it is a sign that the swarm is intending to quit; consequently, bee-keepers, on seeing this, besprinkle the hive with sweet wine. It is advisable to plant about the hives pear-trees, beans, Median-grass, Syrian-grass, yellow pulse, myrtle, poppies, creeping-thyme, and almond-trees. Some bee-keepers sprinkle their bees with flour, and can distinguish them from others when they are at work out of doors. If the spring be late, or if there be drought or blight, then grubs are all the fewer in the hives. So much for the habits of bees.

41

Of wasps, there are two kinds. Of these kinds one is wild and scarce, lives on the mountains, engenders grubs not underground but on oak-trees, is larger, longer, and blacker than the other kind, is invariably speckled and furnished with a sting, and is remarkably courageous. The pain from its sting is more severe than that caused by the others, for the instrument that causes the pain is larger, in proportion to its own larger size. These wild wasps live over into a second year, and in winter time, when oaks have been in course of felling, they may be seen coming out and flying away. They lie concealed during the winter, and live in the interior of logs of wood. Some of them are mother-wasps and some are workers, as with the tamer kind; but it is by observation of the tame wasps that one may learn the varied characteristics of the mothers **628a** and the workers. For in the case of the tame wasps also there are two kinds; one consists of leaders, who are called mothers, and the other of workers. The leaders are far larger and milder-tempered than the others. The workers do not live over into a second year, but all die when winter comes on; and this can be proved, for at the commencement of winter the workers become drowsy, and about the time of the winter solstice they are never seen at all. The leaders, the so-called mothers, are seen all through the winter, and live in holes underground; for men when ploughing or digging in winter have often come upon mother-wasps, but never upon workers. The mode of reproduction of wasps is as follows. At the approach of summer, when the leaders have found a sheltered spot, they take to moulding their combs, and construct the so-called *sphecons,*—little nests containing four cells or thereabouts, and in these are produced working-wasps but not mothers. When these are grown up, then they construct other larger combs upon the first, and then again in like manner others; so that by the close of autumn there are numerous large combs in which the leader, the so-called mother, engenders no longer working-wasps but mothers. These develop high up in the nest as large grubs, in cells that occur in groups of four or rather more, pretty much in the same way as we have seen the grubs of the king-bees to be produced in their cells. After the birth of the working-grubs in the cells, the leaders do nothing and the workers have to supply them with nourishment; and this is inferred from the fact that the leaders [of the working-wasps] no longer fly out at this time, but rest quietly indoors. Whether the leaders of last year after engendering new leaders are killed by the new brood, and whether this occurs invariably or whether they can live for a longer time, has not been ascertained by actual observation; neither can we speak with certainty, as from observation, as to the age attained by the mother-wasp or by the wild wasps, or as to any other similar phenomenon. The mother-wasp is broad and heavy, fatter and larger than the ordinary wasp, and from its weight not very strong on the wing; these wasps cannot fly far, and for this reason they always rest inside the nest, building and managing its indoor arrangements. The so-called mother-wasps are found in most of the nests; it is a matter of doubt **628b** whether or no they are provided with stings; in all probability, like the king-bees, they have stings, but never protrude them for offence. Of the ordinary wasps some are destitute of stings, like the drone-bees, and some are provided with them. Those unprovided therewith are smaller and less spirited and never fight, while the others are big and courageous; and these latter, by some, are called males, and the stingless, females. At the approach of winter many of the wasps that have stings appear to lose them; but we have never met an eyewitness of this phenomenon. Wasps are more abundant in times of drought and in wild localities. They live underground; their combs they mould out of chips and earth, each comb from a single origin, like a kind of root. They feed on certain flowers and fruits, but for the most part on animal food. Some of the tame wasps have been observed when sexually united, but it was not determined whether both, or neither, had stings, or whether one had a sting and the other had not; wild wasps have been seen under similar circumstances, when one was seen to have a sting but the case of the other was left undetermined. The wasp-grub does not appear to come into existence by parturition, for at the outset the grub is too big to be the offspring of a wasp. If you take a wasp by the feet and let him buzz with the vibration of his wings, wasps that have no stings will fly toward it, and wasps that have stings will not; from which fact it is inferred by some that one set are males and the other females. In holes in the ground in winter-time wasps are found, some with stings, and some without. Some build cells, small and few in number; others build many and large ones. The so-called mothers are caught at the change of season, mostly on elm-trees, while gathering a substance sticky and gumlike. A large number of mother-wasps are found when in the previous year wasps have been numerous and the weather rainy; they are captured in precipitous places, or in vertical clefts in the ground, and they all appear to be furnished with stings.

42

So much for the habits of wasps.

Anthrenae do not subsist by culling from flowers as bees do, but for the most part on animal food: for this reason they hover about dung; for they chase the large flies, and after catching them lop off their heads and fly away **629a** with the rest of the carcases; they are furthermore fond of sweet fruits. Such is their food. They have also kings or leaders like bees and wasps; and their leaders are larger in proportion to themselves than are wasp-kings to wasps or bee-kings to bees. The anthrena-king, like the wasp-king, lives indoors. Anthrenae build their nests underground, scraping out the soil like ants; for neither anthrenae nor wasps go off in swarms as bees do, but successive layers of young anthrenae keep to the same habitat, and go on enlarging their nest by scraping out more and more of soil. The nest accordingly attains a great size; in fact, from a particularly prosperous nest have been removed three and even four baskets full of combs. They do not, like bees, store up food, but pass the winter in a torpid condition; the greater part of them die in the winter, but it is uncertain whether that can be said of them all. In the hives of bees several kings are found and they lead off detachments in swarms, but in the anthrena's nest only one king is found. When individual anthrenae have strayed from their nest, they cluster on a tree and construct combs, as may be often seen above-ground, and in this nest they produce a king; when the king is full-grown, he leads them away and settles them along with himself in a hive or nest. With regard to their sexual unions, and the method of their reproduction, nothing is known from actual observation. Among bees both the drones and the kings are stingless, and so are certain wasps, as has been said; but anthrenae appear to be all furnished with stings: though, by the way, it would well be worth while to carry out investigation as to whether the anthrena-king has a sting or not.

43

Humble-bees produce their young under a stone, right on the ground, in a couple of cells or little more; in these cells is found an attempt at honey, of a poor description. The tenthredon is like the anthrena, but speckled, and about as broad as a bee. Being epicures as to their food, they fly, one at a time, into kitchens and on to slices of fish and the like dainties. The tenthredon brings forth, like the wasp, underground, and is very prolific; its **629b** nest is much bigger and longer than that of the wasp. So much for the methods of working and the habits of life of the bee, the wasp, and all the other similar insects.

44

As regards the disposition or temper of animals, as has been previously observed,[1] one may detect great differences in respect to courage and timidity, as also, even among wild animals, in regard to tameness and wildness. The lion, while he is eating, is most ferocious; but when he is not hungry and has had a good meal, he is quite gentle. He is totally devoid of suspicion or nervous fear, is fond of romping with animals that have been reared along with him and to whom he is accustomed, and manifests great affection towards them. In the chase, as long as he is in view, he makes no attempt to run and shows no fear, but even if he be compelled by the multitude of the hunters to retreat, he withdraws deliberately, step by step, every now and then turning his head to regard his pursuers. If, however, he reach wooded cover, then he runs at full speed, until he comes to open ground, when he resumes his leisurely retreat. When, in the open, he is forced by the number of the hunters to run while in full view, he does run at the top of his speed, but without leaping and bound-

[1] VIII. 1(588a 14); IX. 3(610b 20).

ing. This running of his is evenly and continuously kept up like the running of a dog; but when he is in pursuit of his prey and is close behind, he makes a sudden pounce upon it. The two statements made regarding him are quite true; the one that he is especially afraid of fire, as Homer pictures him in the line—'and glowing torches, which, though fierce he dreads,' [1]—and the other, that he keeps a steady eye upon the hunter who hits him, and flings himself upon him. If a hunter hit him, without hurting him, then if with a bound he gets hold of him, he will do him no harm, not even with his claws, but after shaking him and giving him a fright will let him go again. They invade the cattle-folds and attack human beings when they are grown old and so by reason of old age and the diseased condition of their teeth are unable to pursue their wonted prey. They live to a good old age. The lion who was captured when lame, had a number of his teeth broken; which fact was regarded by some as a proof of the longevity of lions, as he could hardly have been reduced to this condition except at an advanced age. There are two species of lions, the plump, curly-maned, and the long-bodied, straight-maned; the latter kind is courageous, and the former comparatively timid; sometimes they **630a** run away with their tail between their legs, like a dog. A lion was once seen to be on the point of attacking a boar, but to run away when the boar stiffened his bristles in defence. It is susceptible of hurt from a wound in the flank, but on any other part of its frame will endure any number of blows, and its head is especially hard. Whenever it inflicts a wound, either by its teeth or its claws, there flows from the wounded parts suppurating matter, quite yellow, and not to be stanched by bandage or sponge; the treatment for such a wound is the same as that for the bite of a dog.

The thos, or civet, is fond of man's company; it does him no harm and is not much afraid of him, but it is an enemy to the dog and the lion, and consequently is not found in the same habitat with them. The little ones are the best. Some say that there are two species of the animal, and some say, three; there are probably not more than three, but, as is the case with certain of the fishes, birds, and quadrupeds, this animal changes in appearance with the change of season. His colour in winter is not the same as it is in summer; in summer the animal is smooth-haired, in winter he is clothed in fur.

[1] *Iliad*, XI. 533; XVII. 633.

45

The bison is found in Paeonia on Mount Messapium, which separates Paeonia from Maedica; and the Paeonians call it the *monapos*. It is the size of a bull, but stouter in build, and not long in the body; its skin, stretched tight on a frame, would give sitting room for seven people. In general it resembles the ox in appearance, except that it has a mane that reaches down to the point of the shoulder, as that of the horse reaches down to its withers; but the hair in its mane is softer than the hair in the horse's mane, and clings more closely. The colour of the hair is brown-yellow; the mane reaches down to the eyes, and is deep and thick. The colour of the body is half red, half ashen-grey, like that of the so-called chestnut horse, but rougher. It has an undercoat of woolly hair. The animal is not found either very black or very red. It has the bellow of a bull. Its horns are crooked, turned inwards towards each other and useless for purposes of self-defence; they are a span broad, or a little more, and in volume each horn would hold about three pints of liquid; the black colour of the horn is beautiful and bright. The tuft of hair on the forehead reaches down to the eyes, **630b** so that the animal sees objects on either flank better than objects right in front. It has no upper teeth, as is the case also with kine and all other horned animals. Its legs are hairy; it is cloven-footed, and the tail, which resembles that of the ox, seems not big enough for the size of its body. It tosses up dust and scoops out the ground with its hooves, like the bull. Its skin is impervious to blows. Owing to the savour of its flesh it is sought for in the chase. When it is wounded it runs away, and stops only when thoroughly exhausted. It defends itself against an assailant by kicking and projecting its excrement to a distance of eight yards; this device it can easily adopt over and over again, and the excrement is so pungent that the hair of hunting-dogs is burnt off by it. It is only when the animal is disturbed or alarmed that the dung has this property; when the animal is undisturbed it has no blistering effect. So much for the shape and habits of the animal. When the season comes for parturition the mothers give birth to their young in troops upon the mountains. Before dropping their young they scatter their dung in all directions, making a kind of circular rampart around them; for the animal has the faculty of ejecting excrement in most extraordinary quantities.

46

Of all wild animals the most easily tamed and the gentlest is the elephant. It can be taught a number of tricks, the drift and meaning of which it understands; as, for instance, it can be taught to kneel in presence of the king. It is very sensitive, and possessed of an intelligence superior to that of other animals. When the male has had sexual union with the female, and the female has conceived, the male has no further intercourse with her.

Some say that the elephant lives for two hundred years; others, for one hundred and twenty; that the female lives nearly as long as the male; that they reach their prime about the age of sixty, and that they are sensitive to inclement weather and frost. The elephant is found by the banks of rivers, but he is not a river animal; he can make his way through water, as long as the tip of his trunk can be above the surface, for he blows with his trunk and breathes through it. The animal is a poor swimmer owing to the heavy weight of his body.

47

The male camel declines intercourse with its mother; if his keeper tries compulsion, he evinces disinclination. On one occasion, when intercourse was being declined by the young male, the keeper covered over the mother and put the young male to her; but, when after the intercourse the wrapping had been removed, though the operation was completed and could not be revoked, still by and by he bit his keeper
631a to death. A story goes that the king of Scythia had a highly-bred mare, and that all her foals were splendid; that wishing to mate the best of the young males with the mother, he had him brought to the stall for the purpose; that the young horse declined; that, after the mother's head had been concealed in a wrapper he, in ignorance, had intercourse; and that, when immediately afterwards the wrapper was removed and the head of the mare was rendered visible, the young horse ran way and hurled himself down a precipice.

48

Among the sea-fishes many stories are told about the dolphin, indicative of his gentle and kindly nature, and of manifestations of passionate attachment to boys, in and about Tarentum, Caria, and other places. The story goes that, after a dolphin had been caught and wounded off the coast of Caria, a shoal of dolphins came into the harbour and stopped there until the fisherman let his captive go free; whereupon the shoal departed. A shoal of young dolphins is always, by way of protection, followed by a large one. On one occasion a shoal of dolphins, large and small, was seen, and two dolphins at a little distance appeared swimming in underneath a little dead dolphin when it was sinking, and supporting it on their backs, trying out of compassion to prevent its being devoured by some predaceous fish. Incredible stories are told regarding the rapidity of movement of this creature. It appears to be the fleetest of all animals, marine and terrestrial, and it can leap over the masts of large vessels. This speed is chiefly manifested when they are pursuing a fish for food; then, if the fish endeavours to escape, they pursue him in their ravenous hunger down to deep waters; but, when the necessary return swim is getting too long, they hold in their breath, as though calculating the length of it, and then draw themselves together for an effort and shoot up like arrows, trying to make the long ascent rapidly in order to breathe, and in the effort they spring right over a ship's masts if a ship be in the vicinity. This same phenomenon is observed in divers, when they have plunged into deep water; that is, they pull themselves together and rise with a
631b speed proportional to their strength. Dolphins live together in pairs, male and female. It is not known for what reason they run themselves aground on dry land; at all events, it is said that they do so at times, and for no obvious reason.

49

Just as with all animals a change of action follows a change of circumstance, so also a change of character follows a change of action, and often some portions of the physical frame undergo a change, as occurs in the case of birds. Hens, for instance, when they have beaten the cock in a fight, will crow like the cock and endeavour to tread him; the crest rises up on their head and the tail-feathers on the rump, so that it becomes difficult to recognize that they are hens; in some cases there is a growth of small spurs. On the death of a hen a cock has been seen to undertake the maternal duties, leading the chickens about and providing them with food, and so intent upon these duties as to cease crowing and indulging his sexual propensities. Some cock-birds are congenitally so feminine that they will submit patiently to other males who attempt to tread them.

50

Some animals change their form and character, not only at certain ages and at certain seasons, but in consequence of being castrated; and all animals possessed of testicles may be submitted to this operation. Birds have their testicles inside, and oviparous quadrupeds close to the loins; and of viviparous animals that walk some have them inside, and most have them outside, but all have them at the lower end of the belly. Birds are castrated at the rump at the part where the two sexes unite in copulation. If you burn this twice or thrice with hot irons, then, if the bird be full-grown, his crest grows sallow, he ceases to crow, and foregoes sexual passion; but if you cauterize the bird when young, none of these male attributes or propensities will come to him as he grows up. The case is the same with men: if you mutilate them in boyhood, the later-growing hair never comes, and the voice never changes but remains high-pitched; if they be **632a** mutilated in early manhood, the late growths of hair quit them except the growth on the groin, and that diminishes but does not entirely depart. The congenital growths of hair never fall out, for a eunuch never grows bald. In the case of all castrated or mutilated male quadrupeds the voice changes to the feminine voice. All other quadrupeds when castrated, unless the operation be performed when they are young, invariably die; but in the case of boars, and in their case only, the age at which the operation is performed produces no difference. All animals, if operated on when they are young, become bigger and better looking than their unmutilated fellows; if they be mutilated when full-grown, they do not take on any increase of size. If stags be mutilated, when, by reason of their age, they have as yet no horns, they never grow horns at all; if they be mutilated when they have horns, the horns remain unchanged in size, and the animal does not lose them. Calves are mutilated when a year old; otherwise, they turn out uglier and smaller. Steers are mutilated in the following way: they turn the animal over on its back, cut a little off the scrotum at the lower end, and squeeze out the testicles, then push back the roots of them as far as they can, and stop up the incision with hair to give an outlet to suppurating matter; if inflammation ensues, they cauterize the scrotum and put on a plaster. If a full-grown bull be mutilated, he can still to all appearance unite sexually with the cow. The ovaries of sows are excised with the view of quenching in them sexual appetites and of stimulating growth in size and fatness. The sow has first to be kept two days without food, and, after being hung up by the hind legs, it is operated on; they cut the lower belly, about the place where the boars have their testicles, for it is there that the ovary grows, adhering to the two divisions (or horns) of the womb; they cut off a little piece and stitch up the incision. Female camels are mutilated when they are wanted for war purposes, and are mutilated to prevent their being got with young. Some of the inhabitants of Upper Asia have as many as three thousand camels: when they run, they run, in consequence of the length of their stride, much quicker than the horses of Nisaea. As a general rule, mutilated animals grow to a greater length than the unmutilated.

All animals that ruminate derive profit and pleasure from the process of rumination, as they do from the process of eating. It is the **632b** animals that lack the upper teeth that ruminate, such as kine, sheep, and goats. In the case of wild animals no observation has been possible; save in the case of animals that are occasionally domesticated, such as the stag, and it, we know, chews the cud. All animals that ruminate generally do so when lying down on the ground. They carry on the process to the greatest extent in winter, and stall-fed ruminants carry it on for about seven months in the year; beasts that go in herds, as they get their food out of doors, ruminate to a lesser degree and over a lesser period. Some, also, of the animals that have teeth in both jaws ruminate; as, for instance, the Pontic mice, and the fish which from the habit is by some called 'the Ruminant', [as well as other fish].

Long-limbed animals have loose faeces, and broad-chested animals vomit with comparative facility, and these remarks are, in a general way, applicable to quadrupeds, birds, and men.

49B

A considerable number of birds change according to season the colour of their plumage and their note; as, for instance, the owsel becomes yellow instead of black, and its note gets altered, for in summer it has a musical note and in winter a discordant chatter. The thrush also changes its colour; about the throat it is marked in winter with speckles like a starling, in summer distinctly spotted: however, it never alters its note. The nightingale, when the hills are taking on verdure, sings continually for fifteen days and fifteen nights; afterwards it sings, but not continuously. As summer advances it has a different song, not so varied as before, nor so deep, nor so intricately modulated, but simple; it also changes its colour, and in Italy about this season it goes by a different name. It goes into hiding, and is consequently visible only for a brief period.

The erithacus (or redbreast) and the so-called redstart change into one another; the former is a winter bird, the latter a summer one, and the difference between them is practically limited to the coloration of their plumage. In the same way with the beccafico and the blackcap; these change into one another. The beccafico appears about autumn, and the blackcap as soon as autumn has ended. **633a** These birds, also, differ from one another only in colour and note; that these birds, two in name, are one in reality is proved by the fact that at the period when the change is in progress each one has been seen with the change as yet incomplete. It is not so very strange that in these cases there is a change in note and in plumage, for even the ring-dove ceases to coo in winter, and recommences cooing when spring comes in; in winter, however, when fine weather has succeeded to very stormy weather, this bird has been known to give its cooing note, to the astonishment of such as were acquainted with its usual winter silence. As a general rule, birds sing most loudly and most diversely in the pairing season. The cuckoo changes its colour, and its note is not clearly heard for a short time previous to its departure. It departs about the rising of the Dog-star, and it reappears from springtime to the rising of the Dog-star. At the rise of this star the bird called by some oenanthe disappears, and reappears when it is setting: thus keeping clear at one time of extreme cold, and at another time of extreme heat. The hoopoe also changes its colour and appearance, as Aeschylus has represented in the following lines[1]:—

The Hoopoe, witness to his own distress,
Is clad by Zeus in variable dress:—
Now a gay mountain-bird, with knightly crest,
Now in the white hawk's silver plumage drest;
For, timely changing, on the hawk's white wing
He greets the apparition of the Spring.
Thus twofold form and colour are conferred,
In youth and age, upon the selfsame bird.
The spangled raiment marks his youthful days,
The argent his maturity displays;
And when the fields are yellow with ripe corn
Again his particoloured plumes are worn.
But evermore, in sullen discontent,
He seeks the lonely hills, in self-sought banishment.

Of birds, some take a dust-bath by rolling in dust, some take a water-bath, and some take neither the one bath nor the other. Birds that do not fly but keep on the ground take the dust-**633b** bath, as for instance the hen, the partridge, the francolin, the crested lark, the pheasant; some of the straight-taloned birds, and such as live on the banks of a river, in marshes, or by the sea, take a water-bath; some birds take both the dust-bath and the water-bath, as for instance the pigeon and the sparrow; of the crooked-taloned birds the greater part take neither the one bath nor the other. So much for the ways of the above-mentioned,—but some birds have a peculiar habit of making a noise at their hinder quarters, as, for instance, the turtle-dove; and they make a violent movement of their tails at the same time that they produce this peculiar sound.

[1] Nauck, fr. 297.

CONTENTS: ON THE PARTS OF ANIMALS

ON THE PARTS OF ANIMALS

BOOK I

I

639a Every systematic science, the humblest and the noblest alike, seems to admit of two distinct kinds of proficiency; one of which may be properly called scientific knowledge of the subject, while the other is a kind of educational acquaintance with it. For an educated man should be able to form a fair off-hand judgement as to the goodness or badness of the method used by a professor in his exposition. To be educated is in fact to be able to do this; and even the man of universal education we deem to be such in virtue of his having this ability. It will, however, of course, be understood that we only ascribe universal education to one who in his own individual person is thus critical in all or nearly all branches of knowledge, and not to one who has a like ability merely in some special subject. For it is possible for a man to have this competence in some one branch of knowledge without having it in all.

It is plain then that, as in other sciences, so in that which inquires into nature, there must be certain canons, by reference to which a hearer shall be able to criticize the method of a professed exposition, quite independently of the question whether the statements made be true or false. Ought we, for instance (to give an illustration of what I mean), to begin by discussing each separate species—man, lion, ox, and the like—taking each kind in hand independently of the rest, or ought we rather to deal first with the attributes which they have in common in virtue of some common element of their nature, and proceed from this as a basis for the consideration of them separately? For genera that are quite distinct yet oftentimes present many identical phenomena, sleep, for instance, respiration, growth, decay, death, and other similar affections and conditions, which may be passed over for the present, as we are not yet prepared to treat of them with clearness and precision. Now it is plain that if we deal with each species independently of the rest, we shall frequently be obliged to repeat the same statements over and over again; for horse and dog and man present, each and all, every one of the phenomena just enumerated. A discussion therefore of the attributes of each such species separately would necessarily involve frequent repetitions as to characters, themselves identical but recurring in animals specifically distinct. (Very possibly also there may be other characters which, **639b** though they present specific differences, yet come under one and the same category. For instance, flying, swimming, walking, creeping, are plainly specifically distinct, but yet are all forms of animal progression.) We must, then, have some clear understanding as to the manner in which our investigation is to be conducted; whether, I mean, we are first to deal with the common or generic characters, and afterwards to take into consideration special peculiarities; or whether we are to start straight off with the ultimate species. For as yet no definite rule has been laid down in this matter. So also there is a like uncertainty as to another point now to be mentioned. Ought the writer who deals with the works of nature to follow the plan adopted by the mathematicians in their astronomical demonstrations, and after considering the phenomena presented by animals, and their several parts, proceed subsequently to treat of the causes and the reason why; or ought he to follow some other method? And when these questions are answered, there yet remains another. The causes concerned in the generation of the works of nature are, as we see, more than one. There is the final cause and there is the motor cause. Now we must decide which of these two causes comes first, which second. Plainly, however, that cause is the first which we call the final one. For this is the Reason, and the Reason forms the starting-point, alike in the works of art and in works of nature. For consider how the physician or how the builder sets about his work. He starts by forming for himself a definite picture, in the one case perceptible to mind, in the other to sense, of his end—the

NOTE: The bold face numbers and letters are approximate indications of the pages and columns of the standard Berlin Greek text; the bracketed numbers, of the lines in the Greek text; they are here assigned as they are assigned in the Oxford translation.

physician of health, the builder of a house—and this he holds forward as the reason and explanation of each subsequent step that he takes, and of his acting in this or that way as the case may be. Now in the works of nature the good end and the final cause is still more dominant than in works of art such as these, nor is necessity a factor with the same significance in them all; though almost all writers, while they try to refer their origin to this cause, do so without distinguishing the various senses in which the term necessity is used. For there is absolute necessity, manifested in eternal phenomena; and there is hypothetical necessity, manifested in everything that is generated by nature as in everything that is produced by art, be it a house or what it may. For if a house or other such final object is to be realized, it is necessary that such and such material shall exist; and it is necessary that first this then that shall be produced, and first this and then that set in motion, and so on in continuous succession, until the end and final result is reached, for the sake of which each prior thing is produced and exists. As with these productions of art, so also is it with the productions of nature. The mode of necessity, however, and the mode **640a** of ratiocination are different in natural science from what they are in the theoretical sciences; of which we have spoken elsewhere. For in the latter the starting-point is that which is; in the former that which is to be. For it is that which is yet to be—health, let us say, or a man—that, owing to its being of such and such characters, necessitates the pre-existence or previous production of this and that antecedent; and not this or that antecedent which, because it exists or has been generated, makes it necessary that health or a man is in, or shall come into, existence. Nor is it possible to track back the series of necessary antecedents to a starting-point, of which you can say that, existing itself from eternity, it has determined their existence as its consequent. These however, again, are matters that have been dealt with in another treatise. There too it was stated in what cases absolute and hypothetical necessity exist; in what cases also the proposition expressing hypothetical necessity is simply convertible, and what cause it is that determines this convertibility.[1]

Another matter which must not be passed over without consideration is, whether the proper subject of our exposition is that with which the ancient writers concerned themselves, namely, what is the process of formation of each animal; or whether it is not rather, what are the characters of a given creature when formed. For there is no small difference between these two views. The best course appears to be that we should follow the method already mentioned, and begin with the phenomena presented by each group of animals, and, when this is done, proceed afterwards to state the causes of those phenomena, and to deal with their evolution. For elsewhere, as for instance in house building, this is the true sequence. The plan of the house, or the house, has this and that form; and because it has this and that form, therefore is its construction carried out in this or that manner. For the process of evolution is for the sake of the thing finally evolved, and not this for the sake of the process. Empedocles, then, was in error when he said that many of the characters presented by animals were merely the results of incidental occurrences during their development; for instance, that the backbone was divided as it is into vertebrae, because it happened to be broken owing to the contorted position of the foetus in the womb. In so saying he overlooked the fact that propagation implies a creative seed endowed with certain formative properties. Secondly, he neglected another fact, namely, that the parent animal pre-exists, not only in idea, but actually in time. For man is generated from man; and thus it is the possession of certain characters by the parent that determines the development of like characters in the child. The same statement holds good also for the operations of art, and even for those which are apparently spontaneous. For the same result as is produced by art may occur spontaneously. Spontaneity, for instance, may bring about the restoration of health. The products of art, however, require the pre-existence of an efficient cause homogeneous with themselves, such as the statuary's art, which must necessarily precede the statue; for this cannot possibly be produced spontaneously. Art indeed consists in the conception of the result to be produced before its realization in the material. As with spontaneity, so with chance; for this also produces the same result as art, and by the same process.

The fittest mode, then, of treatment is to say, a man has such and such parts, because the conception of a man includes their presence, and because they are necessary conditions of his existence, or, if we cannot quite say this, which would be best of all, then the next thing

[1] Cf. *On Generation and Corruption*, II. 9-11.

to it, namely, that it is either quite impossible for him to exist without them, or, at any rate, that it is better for him that they should be there; and their existence involves the existence **640b** of other antecedents. Thus we should say, because man is an animal with such and such characters, therefore is the process of his development necessarily such as it is; and therefore is it accomplished in such and such an order, this part being formed first, that next, and so on in succession; and after a like fashion should we explain the evolution of all other works of nature.

Now that with which the ancient writers, who first philosophized about Nature, busied themselves, was the material principle and the material cause. They inquired what this is, and what its character; how the universe is generated out of it, and by what motor influence, whether, for instance, by antagonism or friendship, whether by intelligence or spontaneous action, the substratum of matter being assumed to have certain inseparable properties; fire, for instance, to have a hot nature, earth a cold one; the former to be light, the latter heavy. For even the genesis of the universe is thus explained by them. After a like fashion do they deal also with the development of plants and of animals. They say, for instance, that the water contained in the body causes by its currents the formation of the stomach and the other receptacles of food or of excretion; and that the breath by its passage breaks open the outlets of the nostrils; air and water being the materials of which bodies are made; for all represent nature as composed of such or similar substances.

But if men and animals and their several parts are natural phenomena, then the natural philosopher must take into consideration not merely the ultimate substances of which they are made, but also flesh, bone, blood, and all the other homogeneous parts; not only these, but also the heterogeneous parts, such as face, hand, foot; and must examine how each of these comes to be what it is, and in virtue of what force. For to say what are the ultimate substances out of which an animal is formed, to state, for instance, that it is made of fire or earth, is no more sufficient than would be a similar account in the case of a couch or the like. For we should not be content with saying that the couch was made of bronze or wood or whatever it might be, but should try to describe its design or mode of composition in preference to the material; or, if we did deal with the material, it would at any rate be with the concretion of material and form. For a couch is such and such a form embodied in this or that matter, or such and such a matter with this or that form; so that its shape and structure must be included in our description. For the formal nature is of greater importance than the material nature.

Does, then, configuration and colour constitute the essence of the various animals and of their several parts? For if so, what Democritus says will be strictly correct. For such appears to have been his notion. At any rate he says that it is evident to every one what form it is that makes the man, seeing that he is recognizable by his shape and colour. And yet a dead body has exactly the same configuration as a living one; but for all that is not a man. So also no hand of bronze or wood or constituted in any but the appropriate way can possibly be a hand in more than name. For like a physician **641a** in a painting, or like a flute in a sculpture, in spite of its name it will be unable to do the office which that name implies. Precisely in the same way no part of a dead body, such I mean as its eye or its hand, is really an eye or a hand. To say, then, that shape and colour constitute the animal is an inadequate statement, and is much the same as if a woodcarver were to insist that the hand he had cut out was really a hand. Yet the physiologists, when they give an account of the development and causes of the animal form, speak very much like such a craftsman. What, however, I would ask, are the forces by which the hand or the body was fashioned into its shape? The woodcarver will perhaps say, by the axe or the auger; the physiologist, by air and by earth. Of these two answers the artificer's is the better, but it is nevertheless insufficient. For it is not enough for him to say that by the stroke of his tool this part was formed into a concavity, that into a flat surface; but he must state the reasons why he struck his blow in such a way as to effect this, and what his final object was; namely, that the piece of wood should develop eventually into this or that shape. It is plain, then, that the teaching of the old physiologists is inadequate, and that the true method is to state what the definitive characters are that distinguish the animal as a whole; to explain what it is both in substance and in form, and to deal after the same fashion with its several organs; in fact, to proceed in exactly the same way as we should do, were we giving a complete description of a couch.

If now this something that constitutes the

form of the living being be the soul, or part of the soul, or something that without the soul cannot exist; as would seem to be the case, seeing at any rate that when the soul departs, what is left is no longer a living animal, and that none of the parts remain what they were before, excepting in mere configuration, like the animals that in the fable are turned into stone; if, I say, this be so, then it will come within the province of the natural philosopher to inform himself concerning the soul, and to treat of it, either in its entirety, or, at any rate, of that part of it which constitutes the essential character of an animal; and it will be his duty to say what this soul or this part of a soul is; and to discuss the attributes that attach to this essential character, especially as nature is spoken of in two senses, and the nature of a thing is either its matter or its essence; nature as essence including both the motor cause and the final cause. Now it is in the latter of these two senses that either the whole soul or some part of it constitutes the nature of an animal; and inasmuch as it is the presence of the soul that enables matter to constitute the animal nature, much more than it is the presence of matter which so enables the soul, the inquirer into nature is bound on every ground to treat of the soul rather than of the matter. For though the wood of which they are made constitutes the couch and the tripod, it only does so because it is capable of receiving such and such a form.

What has been said suggests the question, whether it is the whole soul or only some part of it, the consideration of which comes within the province of natural science. Now if it be of the whole soul that this should treat, then **641b** there is no place for any other philosophy beside it. For as it belongs in all cases to one and the same science to deal with correlated subjects—one and the same science, for instance, deals with sensation and with the objects of sense—and as therefore the intelligent soul and the objects of intellect, being correlated, must belong to one and the same science, it follows that natural science will have to include the whole universe in its province. But perhaps it is not the whole soul, nor all its parts collectively, that constitutes the source of motion; but there may be one part, identical with that in plants, which is the source of growth, another, namely the sensory part, which is the source of change of quality, while still another, and this not the intellectual part, is the source of locomotion. I say not the intellectual part; for other animals than man have the power of locomotion, but in none but him is there intellect. Thus then it is plain that it is not of the whole soul that we have to treat. For it is not the whole soul that constitutes the animal nature, but only some part or parts of it. Moreover, it is impossible that any abstraction can form a subject of natural science, seeing that everything that Nature makes is means to an end. For just as human creations are the products of art, so living objects are manifestly the products of an analogous cause or principle, not external but internal, derived like the hot and the cold from the environing universe. And that the heaven, if it had an origin, was evolved and is maintained by such a cause, there is therefore even more reason to believe, than that mortal animals so originated. For order and definiteness are much more plainly manifest in the celestial bodies than in our own frame; while change and chance are characteristic of the perishable things of earth. Yet there are some who, while they allow that every animal exists and was generated by nature, nevertheless hold that the heaven was constructed to be what it is by chance and spontaneity; the heaven, in which not the faintest sign of haphazard or of disorder is discernible! Again, whenever there is plainly some final end, to which a motion tends should nothing stand in the way, we always say that such final end is the aim or purpose of the motion; and from this it is evident that there must be a something or other really existing, corresponding to what we call by the name of Nature. For a given germ does not give rise to any chance living being, nor spring from any chance one; but each germ springs from a definite parent and gives rise to a definite progeny. And thus it is the germ that is the ruling influence and fabricator of the offspring. For these it is by nature, the offspring being at any rate that which in nature will spring from it. At the same time the offspring is anterior to the germ; for germ and perfected progeny are related as the developmental process and the result. Anterior, however, to both germ and product is the organism from which the germ was derived. For every germ implies two organisms, the parent and the progeny. For germ or seed is both the seed of the organism from which it came, of the horse, for instance, from which it was derived, and the seed of the organism that will eventually arise from it, of the mule, for example, which is developed from the seed of the horse. The same seed then is the seed both of the horse and of the mule, though in different ways as here set forth. Moreover, the seed is potentially that which will spring from it, and the relation of potentiality to actuality we know.

642a There are then two causes, namely, necessity and the final end. For many things are produced, simply as the results of necessity. It may, however, be asked, of what mode of necessity are we speaking when we say this. For it can be of neither of those two modes which are set forth in the philosophical treatises. There is, however, the third mode, in such things at any rate as are generated. For instance, we say that food is necessary; because an animal cannot possibly do without it. This third mode is what may be called hypothetical necessity. Here is another example of it. If a piece of wood is to be split with an axe, the axe must of necessity be hard; and, if hard, must of necessity be made of bronze or iron. Now exactly in the same way the body, which like the axe is an instrument—for both the body as a whole and its several parts individually have definite operations for which they are made—just in the same way, I say, the body, if it is to do its work, must of necessity be of such and such a character, and made of such and such materials.

It is plain then that there are two modes of causation, and that both of these must, so far as possible, be taken into account in explaining the works of nature, or that at any rate an attempt must be made to include them both; and that those who fail in this tell us in reality nothing about nature. For primary cause constitutes the nature of an animal much more than does its matter. There are indeed passages in which even Empedocles hits upon this, and following the guidance of fact, finds himself constrained to speak of the ratio (ὁ λύγος) as constituting the essence and real nature of things. Such, for instance, is the case when he explains what is a bone. For he does not merely describe its material, and say it is this one element, or those two or three elements, or a compound of all the elements, but states the ratio (ὁ λύγος) of their combination. As with a bone, so manifestly is it with the flesh and all other similar parts.

The reason why our predecessors failed in hitting upon this method of treatment was, that they were not in possession of the notion of essence, nor of any definition of substance. The first who came near it was Democritus, and he was far from adopting it as a necessary method in natural science, but was merely brought to it, spite of himself, by constraint of facts. In the time of Socrates a nearer approach was made to the method. But at this period men gave up inquiring into the works of nature, and philosophers diverted their attention to political science and to the virtues which benefit mankind.

Of the method itself the following is an example. In dealing with respiration we must show that it takes place for such or such a final object; and we must also show that this and that part of the process is necessitated by this and that other stage of it. By necessity we shall sometimes mean hypothetical necessity, the necessity, that is, that the requisite antecedants shall be there, if the final end is to be reached; and sometimes absolute necessity, such necessity as that which connects substances and their inherent properties and characters. For the alternate discharge and re-entrance of heat and the inflow of air are necessary if we are to live. Here we have at once a necessity in the **642b** former of the two senses. But the alternation of heat and refrigeration produces of necessity an alternate admission and discharge of the outer air, and this is a necessity of the second kind.

In the foregoing we have an example of the method which we must adopt, and also an example of the kind of phenomena, the causes of which we have to investigate.

2

Some[1] writers propose to reach the definitions of the ultimate forms of animal life by bipartite division. But this method is often difficult, and often impracticable.

Sometimes the final differentia of the subdivision is sufficient by itself, and the antecedent differentiae are mere surplusage. Thus in the series Footed, Two-footed, Cleft-footed, the last term is all-expressive by itself, and to append the higher terms is only an idle iteration. Again it is not permissible to break up a natural group, Birds for instance, by putting its members under different bifurcations, as is done in the published dichotomies, where some birds are ranked with animals of the water, and others placed in a different class. The group Birds and the group Fishes happen to be named, while other natural groups have no popular names; for instance, the groups that we may call Sanguineous and Bloodless are not known popularly by any designations.

[1] Plato, *Sophist*.

If such natural groups are not to be broken up, the method of Dichotomy cannot be employed, for it necessarily involves such breaking up and dislocation. The group of the Many-footed, for instance, would, under this method, have to be dismembered, and some of its kinds distributed among land animals, others among water animals.

3

Again, privative terms inevitably form one branch of dichotomous division, as we see in the proposed dichotomies. But privative terms in their character of privatives admit of no subdivision. For there can be no specific forms of a negation, of Featherless for instance or of Footless, as there are of Feathered and of Footed. Yet a generic differentia must be subdivisible; for otherwise what is there that makes it generic rather than specific? There are to be found generic, that is specifically subdivisible, differentiae; Feathered for instance and Footed. For feathers are divisible into Barbed and Unbarbed, and feet into Manycleft, and Twocleft, like those of animals with bifid hoofs, and Uncleft or Undivided, like those of animals with solid hoofs. Now even with differentiae capable of this specific subdivision it is difficult enough so to make the classification, as that each animal shall be comprehended in some one subdivision and in not more than one; but far more difficult, nay impossible, is it to do this, if we start with a dichotomy into two contradictories. (Suppose for instance we start with the two contradictories, Feathered and Unfeathered; we shall find that the ant, the glow-worm, and some other animals fall under both divisions.) For each differentia must be presented by some species. There must be some species, therefore, under **643a** the privative heading. Now specifically distinct animals cannot present in their essence a common undifferentiated element, but any apparently common element must really be differentiated. (Bird and Man for instance are both Two-footed, but their two-footedness is diverse and differentiated. So any two sanguineous groups must have some difference in their blood, if their blood is part of their essence.) From this it follows that a privative term, being insusceptible of differentiation, cannot be a generic differentia; for, if it were, there would be a common undifferentiated element in two different groups.

Again, if the species are ultimate indivisible groups, that is, are groups with indivisible differentiae, and if no differentia be common to several groups, the number of differentiae must be equal to the number of species. If a differentia though not divisible could yet be common to several groups, then it is plain that in virtue of that common differentia specifically distinct animals would fall into the same division. It is necessary then, if the differentiae, under which are ranged all the ultimate and indivisible groups, are specific characters, that none of them shall be common; for otherwise, as already said, specifically distinct animals will come into one and the same division. But this would violate one of the requisite conditions, which are as follows. No ultimate group must be included in more than a single division; different groups must not be included in the same division; and every group must be found in some division. It is plain then that we cannot get at the ultimate specific forms of the animal, or any other, kingdom by bifurcate division. If we could, the number of ultimate differentiae would equal the number of ultimate animal forms. For assume an order of beings whose prime differentiae are White and Black. Each of these branches will bifurcate, and their branches again, and so on till we reach the ultimate differentiae, whose number will be four or some other power of two, and will also be the number of the ultimate species comprehended in the order.

(A species is constituted by the combination of differentia and matter. For no part of an animal is purely material or purely immaterial; nor can a body, independently of its condition, constitute an animal or any of its parts, as has repeatedly been observed.)[1]

Further, the differentiae must be elements of the essence, and not merely essential attributes. Thus if Figure is the term to be divided, it must not be divided into figures whose angles are equal to two right angles, and figures whose angles are together greater than two right angles. For it is only an attribute of a triangle and not part of its essence that its angles are equal to two right angles.

Again, the bifurcations must be opposites, like White and Black, Straight and Bent; and if we characterize one branch by either term, we must characterize the other by its opposite, and not, for example, characterize one branch by a colour, the other by a mode of progression, swimming for instance.

Furthermore, living beings cannot be divided by the functions common to body and

[1] e.g., at I. 1 (641a 19).

soul, by Flying, for instance, and Walking, as we see them divided in the dichotomies already 643b referred to. For some groups, Ants for instance, fall under both divisions, some ants flying while others do not. Similarly as regards the division into Wild and Tame; for it also would involve the disruption of a species into different groups. For in almost all species in which some members are tame, there are other members that are wild. Such, for example, is the case with Men, Horses, Oxen, Dogs in India, Pigs, Goats, Sheep; groups which, if double, ought to have what they have not, namely, different appellations; and which, if single, prove that Wildness and Tameness do not amount to specific differences. And whatever single element we take as a basis of division the same difficulty will occur.

The method then that we must adopt is to attempt to recognize the natural groups, following the indications afforded by the instincts of mankind, which led them for instance to form the class of Birds and the class of Fishes, each of which groups combines a multitude of differentiae, and is not defined by a single one as in dichotomy. The method of dichotomy is either impossible (for it would put a single group under different divisions or contrary groups under the same division), or it only furnishes a single ultimate differentia for each species, which either alone or with its series of antecedents has to constitute the ultimate species.

If, again, a new differential character be introduced at any stage into the division, the necessary result is that the continuity of the division becomes merely a unity and continuity of agglomeration, like the unity and continuity of a series of sentences coupled together by conjunctive particles. For instance, suppose we have the bifurcation Feathered and Featherless, and then divide Feathered into Wild and Tame, or into White and Black. Tame and White are not a differentiation of Feathered, but are the commencement of an independent bifurcation, and are foreign to the series at the end of which they are introduced.

As we said then, we must define at the outset by a multiplicity of differentiae. If we do so, privative terms will be available, which are unavailable to the dichotomist.

The impossibility of reaching the definition of any of the ultimate forms by dichotomy of the larger group, as some propose, is manifest also from the following considerations. It is impossible that a single differentia, either by itself or with its antecedents, shall express the whole essence of a species. (In saying a single differentia by itself I mean such an isolated differentia as Cleft-footed; in saying a single differentia with antecedent I mean, to give an instance, Many-cleft-footed preceded by Cleft-footed. The very continuity of a series of successive differentiae in a division is intended to show that it is their combination that expresses the character of the resulting unit, or ultimate group. But one is misled by the usages of language into imagining that it is merely the final term of the series, Many-cleft-footed for instance, that constitutes the whole differentia, and that the antecedent terms, Footed, Cleft-footed, are superfluous. 644a Now it is evident that such a series cannot consist of many terms. For if one divides and subdivides, one soon reaches the final differential term, but for all that will not have got to the ultimate division, that is, to the species.) No single differentia, I repeat, either by itself or with its antecedents, can possibly express the essence of a species. Suppose, for example, Man to be the animal to be defined; the single differentia will be Cleft-footed, either by itself or with its antecedents, Footed and Two-footed. Now if man was nothing more than a Cleft-footed animal, this single differentia would duly represent his essence. But seeing that this is not the case, more differentiae than this one will necessarily be required to define him; and these cannot come under one division; for each single branch of a dichotomy ends in a single differentia, and cannot possibly include several differentiae belonging to one and the same animal.

It is impossible then to reach any of the ultimate animal forms by dichotomous division.

4

It deserves inquiry why a single name denoting a higher group was not invented by mankind, as an appellation to comprehend the two groups of Water animals and Winged animals. For even these have certain attributes in common. However, the present nomenclature is just. Groups that only differ in degree, and in the more or less of an identical element that they possess, are aggregated under a single class; groups whose attributes are not identical but analogous are separated. For instance, bird differs from bird by gradation, or by excess and defect; some birds have long feathers, others short ones, but all are feathered. Bird and Fish are more remote and only agree in having analogous organs; for what in the bird is feather, in the fish is scale. Such analogies can scarcely, however, serve universally as indications for the formation of groups, for almost all animals present analogies in their corresponding parts.

The individuals comprised within a species, such as Socrates and Coriscus, are the real existences; but inasmuch as these individuals possess one common specific form, it will suffice to state the universal attributes of the species, that is, the attributes common to all its individuals, once for all, as otherwise there will be endless reiteration, as has already been pointed out.[1]

But as regards the larger groups—such as Birds—which comprehend many species, there may be a question. For on the one hand it may be urged that as the ultimate species represent the real existences, it will be well, if practicable, to examine these ultimate species separately, just as we examine the species Man separately; to examine, that is, not the whole class Birds collectively, but the Ostrich, the Crane, and the other indivisible groups or species belonging to the class.

On the other hand, however, this course would involve repeated mention of the same attribute, as the same attribute is common **644b** to many species, and so far would be somewhat irrational and tedious. Perhaps, then, it will be best to treat generically the universal attributes of the groups that have a common nature and contain closely allied subordinate forms, whether they are groups recognized by a true instinct of mankind, such as Birds and Fishes, or groups not popularly known by a common appellation, but withal composed of closely allied subordinate groups; and only to deal individually with the attributes of a single species, when such species —man, for instance, and any other such, if such there be—stands apart from others, and does not constitute with them a larger natural group.

It is generally similarity in the shape of particular organs, or of the whole body, that has determined the formation of the larger groups. It is in virtue of such a similarity that Birds, Fishes, Cephalopoda, and Testacea have been made to form each a separate class. For within the limits of each such class, the parts do not differ in that they have no nearer resemblance than that of analogy—such as exists between the bone of man and the spine of fish—but differ merely in respect of such corporeal conditions as largeness smallness, softness hardness, smoothness roughness, and other similar oppositions, or, in one word, in respect of degree.

We have now touched upon the canons for criticizing the method of natural science, and have considered what is the most systematic and easy course of investigation; we have also dealt with division, and the mode of conducting it so as best to attain the ends of science, and have shown why dichotomy is either impracticable or inefficacious for its professed purposes.

Having laid this foundation, let us pass on to our next topic.

5

Of things constituted by nature some are ungenerated, imperishable, and eternal, while others are subject to generation and decay. The former are excellent beyond compare and divine, but less accessible to knowledge. The evidence that might throw light on them, and on the problems which we long to solve respecting them, is furnished but scantily by sensation; whereas respecting perishable plants and animals we have abundant information, living as we do in their midst, and ample data may be collected concerning all their various kinds, if only we are willing to take sufficient pains. Both departments, however, have their special charm. The scanty conceptions to which we can attain of celestial things give us, from their excellence, more pleasure than all our knowledge of the world in which we live; just as a half glimpse of persons that we love is more delightful than a leisurely view of **645a** other things, whatever their number and dimensions. On the other hand, in certitude and in completeness our knowledge of terrestrial things has the advantage. Moreover, their greater nearness and affinity to us balances somewhat the loftier interest of the heavenly things that are the objects of the higher philosophy. Having already treated of the celestial world, as far as our conjectures could reach, we proceed to treat of animals, without omitting, to the best of our ability, any member of the kingdom, however ignoble. For if some have no graces to charm the sense, yet even these, by disclosing to intellectual perception the artistic spirit that designed them, give immense pleasure to all who can

[1] Cf. I. 1 (639a 27).

trace links of causation, and are inclined to philosophy. Indeed, it would be strange if mimic representations of them were attractive, because they disclose the mimetic skill of the painter or sculptor, and the original realities themselves were not more interesting, to all at any rate who have eyes to discern the reasons that determined their formation. We therefore must not recoil with childish aversion from the examination of the humbler animals. Every realm of nature is marvellous: and as Heraclitus, when the strangers who came to visit him found him warming himself at the furnace in the kitchen and hesitated to go in, is reported to have bidden them not to be afraid to enter, as even in that kitchen divinities were present, so we should venture on the study of every kind of animal without distaste; for each and all will reveal to us something natural and something beautiful. Absence of haphazard and conduciveness of everything to an end are to be found in Nature's works in the highest degree, and the resultant end of her generations and combinations is a form of the beautiful.

If any person thinks the examination of the rest of the animal kingdom an unworthy task, he must hold in like disesteem the study of man. For no one can look at the primordia of the human frame—blood, flesh, bones, vessels, and the like—without much repugnance. Moreover, when any one of the parts or structures, be it which it may, is under discussion, it must not be supposed that it is its material composition to which attention is being directed or which is the object of the discussion, but the relation of such part to the total form. Similarly, the true object of architecture is not bricks, mortar, or timber, but the house; and so the principal object of natural philosophy is not the material elements, but their composition, and the totality of the form, independently of which they have no existence.

645b The course of exposition must be first to state the attributes common to whole groups of animals, and then to attempt to give their explanation. Many groups, as already noticed,[1] present common attributes, that is to say, in some cases absolutely identical affections, and absolutely identical organs,—feet, feathers, scales, and the like; while in other groups the affections and organs are only so far identical as that they are analogous. For instance, some groups have lungs, others have no lung, but an organ analogous to a lung in its place; some have blood, others have no blood, but a fluid analogous to blood, and with the same office. To treat of the common attributes in connexion with each individual group would involve, as already suggested, useless iteration. For many groups have common attributes. So much for this topic.

As every instrument and every bodily member subserves some partial end, that is to say, some special action, so the whole body must be destined to minister to some plenary sphere of action. Thus the saw is made for sawing, for sawing is a function, and not sawing for the saw. Similarly, the body too must somehow or other be made for the soul, and each part of it for some subordinate function, to which it is adapted.

We have, then, first to describe the common functions, common, that is, to the whole animal kingdom, or to certain large groups, or to the members of a species. In other words, we have to describe the attributes common to all animals, or to assemblages, like the class of Birds, of closely allied groups differentiated by gradation, or to groups like Man not differentiated into subordinate groups. In the first case the common attributes may be called analogous, in the second generic, in the third specific.

When a function is ancillary to another, a like relation manifestly obtains between the organs which discharge these functions; and similarly, if one function is prior to and the end of another, their respective organs will stand to each other in the same relation. Thirdly, the existence of these parts involves that of other things as their necessary consequents.

Instances of what I mean by functions and affections are Reproduction, Growth, Copulation, Waking, Sleep, Locomotion, and other similar vital actions. Instances of what I mean by parts are Nose, Eye, Face, and other **646a** so-called members or limbs, and also the more elementary parts of which these are made. So much for the method to be pursued. Let us now try to set forth the causes of all vital phenomena, whether universal or particular, and in so doing let us follow that order of exposition which conforms, as we have indicated, to the order of nature.

[1] Cf. I. 1 (639a 18 and 27).

BOOK II

I

THE nature and the number of the parts of which animals are severally composed are matters which have already been set forth in detail in the book of Researches about Animals. We have now to inquire what are the causes that in each case have determined this composition, a subject quite distinct from that dealt with in the Researches.

Now there are three degrees of composition; and of these the first in order, as all will allow, is composition out of what some call the elements, such as earth, air, water, fire. Perhaps, however, it would be more accurate to say composition out of the elementary forces; nor indeed out of all of these, but out of a limited number of them, as defined in previous treatises. For fluid and solid, hot and cold, form the material of all composite bodies; and all other differences are secondary to these, such differences, that is, as heaviness or lightness, density or rarity, roughness or smoothness, and any other such properties of matter as there may be. The second degree of composition is that by which the homogeneous parts of animals, such as bone, flesh, and the like, are constituted out of the primary substances. The third and last stage is the composition which forms the heterogeneous parts, such as face, hand, and the rest.

Now the order of actual development and the order of logical existence are always the inverse of each other. For that which is posterior in the order of development is antecedent in the order of nature, and that is genetically last which in nature is first.

(That this is so is manifest by induction; for a house does not exist for the sake of bricks and stones, but these materials for the sake of the house; and the same is the case with the materials of other bodies. Nor is induction required to show this. It is included in our conception of generation. For generation is a process from a something to a something; that which is generated having a cause in which it originates and a cause in which it ends. The originating cause is the primary efficient cause, which is something already endowed with tangible existence, while the final cause is some definite form or similar end; for man generates man, and plant generates plant, in each case out of the underlying material.)

In order of time, then, the material and the generative process must necessarily be anterior to the being that is generated; but in logical or-
646b der the definitive character and form of each being precedes the material. This is evident if one only tries to define the process of formation. For the definition of house-building includes and presupposes that of the house; but the definition of the house does not include nor presuppose that of house-building; and the same is true of all other productions. So that it must necessarily be that the elementary material exists for the sake of the homogeneous parts, seeing that these are genetically posterior to it, just as the heterogeneous parts are posterior genetically to them. For these heterogeneous parts have reached the end and goal, having the third degree of composition, in which degree generation or development often attains its final term.

Animals, then, are composed of homogeneous parts, and are also composed of heterogeneous parts. The former, however, exist for the sake of the latter. For the active functions and operations of the body are carried on by these; that is, by the heterogeneous parts, such as the eye, the nostril, the whole face, the fingers, the hand, and the whole arm. But inasmuch as there is a great variety in the functions and motions not only of aggregate animals but also of the individual organs, it is necessary that the substances out of which these are composed shall present a diversity of properties. For some purposes softness is advantageous, for others hardness; some parts must be capable of extension, others of flexion. Such properties, then, are distributed separately to the different homogeneous parts, one being soft another hard, one fluid another solid, one viscous another brittle; whereas each of the heterogeneous parts presents a combination of multifarious properties. For the hand, to take an example, requires one property to enable it to effect pressure, and another and different property for simple prehension. For this reason the active or executive parts of the body are compounded out of bones, sinews, flesh, and the like, but not these latter out of the former.

So far, then, as has yet been stated, the relations between these two orders of parts are determined by a final cause. We have, however, to inquire whether necessity may not also have a share in the matter; and it must be admitted that these mutual relations could not from the very beginning have possibly been other than they are. For heterogeneous parts can be made up out of homogeneous parts, either from a plurality of them, or from a single one, as is the case with some of the viscera which, varying in configuration, are yet, to speak broadly, formed from a single homogeneous substance; but that homogeneous substances should be formed out of a combination **647a** of heterogeneous parts is clearly an impossibility. For these causes, then, some parts of animals are simple and homogeneous, while others are composite and heterogeneous; and dividing the parts into the active or executive and the sensitive, each one of the former is, as before said, heterogeneous, and each one of the latter homogeneous. For it is in homogeneous parts alone that sensation can occur, as the following considerations show.

Each sense is confined to a single order of sensibles, and its organ must be such as to admit the action of that kind or order. But it is only that which is endowed with a property *in posse* that is acted on by that which has the like property *in esse,* so that the two are the same in kind, and if the latter is single so also is the former. Thus it is that while no physiologists ever dream of saying of the hand or face or other such part that one is earth, another water, another fire, they couple each separate sense-organ with a separate element, asserting this one to be air and that other to be fire. Sensation, then, is confined to the simple or homogeneous parts. But, as might reasonably be expected, the organ of touch, though still homogeneous, is yet the least simple of all the sense-organs. For touch more than any other sense appears to be correlated to several distinct kinds of objects, and to recognize more than one category of contrasts, heat and cold, for instance, solidity and fluidity, and other similar oppositions. Accordingly, the organ which deals with these varied objects is of all the sense-organs the most corporeal, being either the flesh, or the substance which in some animals takes the place of flesh.

Now as there cannot possibly be an animal without sensation, it follows as a necessary consequence that every animal must have some homogeneous parts; for these alone are capable of sensation, the heterogeneous parts serving for the active functions. Again, as the sensory faculty, the motor faculty, and the nutritive faculty are all lodged in one and the same part of the body, as was stated in a former treatise,[1] it is necessary that the part which is the primary seat of these principles shall on the one hand, in its character of general sensory recipient, be one of the simple parts; and on the other hand shall, in its motor and active character, be one of the heterogeneous parts. For this reason it is the heart which in sanguineous animals constitutes this central part, and in bloodless animals it is that which takes the place of a heart. For the heart, like the other viscera, is one of the homogeneous parts; for, if cut up, its pieces are homogeneous in substance with each other. But it is at the same time heterogeneous in virtue of its definite configuration. And the same is true of the other so-called viscera, which are indeed formed from the **647b** same material as the heart. For all these viscera have a sanguineous character owing to their being situated upon vascular ducts and branches. For just as a stream of water deposits mud, so the various viscera, the heart excepted, are, as it were, deposits from the stream of blood in the vessels. And as to the heart, the very starting-point of the vessels, and the actual seat of the force by which the blood is first fabricated, it is but what one would naturally expect, that out of the selfsame nutriment of which it is the recipient its own proper substance shall be formed. Such, then, are the reasons why the viscera are of sanguineous aspect; and why in one point of view they are homogeneous, in another heterogeneous.

2

Of the homogeneous parts of animals, some are soft and fluid, others hard and solid; and of the former some are fluid permanently, others only so long as they are in the living body. Such are blood, serum, lard, suet, marrow, semen, bile, milk when present, flesh, and their various analogues. For the parts enumerated are not to be found in all animals, some animals only having parts analogous to them. Of the hard and solid homogeneous parts bone, fish-spine, sinew, blood-vessel, are examples. The last of these points to a sub-division that may be made in the class of homogeneous parts. For in some of them the whole and a portion of the whole in one sense are designated by the same term—as, for example, is the case with blood-vessel and bit of blood-vessel—while in another sense they are not; but a portion of a heterogeneous part, such as face, in no sense has the same designation as the whole.

[1] Cf. *On Sleep and Sleeplessness*, 2, 455b 34, 456a 5.

The first question to be asked is what are the causes to which these homogeneous parts owe their existence? The causes are various; and this whether the parts be solid or fluid. Thus one set of homogeneous parts represent the material out of which the heterogeneous parts are formed; for each separate organ is constructed of bones, sinews, flesh, and the like; which are either essential elements in its formation, or contribute to the proper discharge of its function. A second set are the nutriment of the first, and are invariably fluid, for all growth occurs at the expense of fluid matter; while a third set are the residue of the second. Such, for instance, are the faeces and, in animals that have a bladder, the urine; the former being the dregs of the solid nutriment, the latter of the fluid.

Even the individual homogeneous parts present variations, which are intended in each case to render them more serviceable for their purpose. The variations of the blood may be selected to illustrate this. For different bloods differ in their degrees of thinness or thickness, of clearness or turbidity, of coldness or heat; and this whether we compare the bloods from different parts of the same individual or the bloods of different animals. For, in the individual, all the differences just enumerated distinguish the blood of the upper and **648a** of the lower halves of the body; and, dealing with classes, one section of animals is sanguineous, while the other has no blood, but only something resembling it in its place. As regards the results of such differences, the thicker and the hotter blood is, the more conducive is it to strength, while in proportion to its thinness and its coldness is its suitability for sensation and intelligence. A like distinction exists also in the fluid which is analogous to blood. This explains how it is that bees and other similar creatures are of a more intelligent nature than many sanguineous animals; and that, of sanguineous animals, those are the most intelligent whose blood is thin and cold. Noblest of all are those whose blood is hot, and at the same time thin and clear. For such are suited alike for the development of courage and of intelligence. Accordingly, the upper parts are superior in these respects to the lower, the male superior to the female, and the right side to the left. As with the blood so also with the other parts, homogeneous and heterogeneous alike. For here also such variations as occur must be held either to be related to the essential constitution and mode of life of the several animals, or, in other cases, to be merely matters of slightly better or slightly worse. Two animals, for instance, may have eyes. But in one these eyes may be of fluid consistency, while in the other they are hard; and in one there may be eyelids, in the other no such appendages. In such a case, the fluid consistency and the presence of eyelids, which are intended to add to the accuracy of vision, are differences of degree. As to why all animals must of necessity have blood or something of a similar character, and what the nature of blood may be, these are matters which can only be considered when we have first discussed hot and cold. For the natural properties of many substances are referable to these two elementary principles; and it is a matter of frequent dispute what animals or what parts of animals are hot and what cold. For some maintain that water animals are hotter than such as live on land, asserting that their natural heat counterbalances the coldness of their medium; and again, that bloodless animals are hotter than those with blood, and females than males. Parmenides, for instance, and some others declare that women are hotter than men, and that it is the warmth and abundance of their blood which causes their menstrual flow, while Empedocles maintains the opposite opinion. Again, comparing the blood and the bile, some speak of the former as hot and of the latter as cold, while others invert the description. If there be this endless disputing about hot and cold, which of all things that affect our senses are the most distinct, what are we to think as to our other sensory impressions?

The explanation of the difficulty appears to **648b** be that the term 'hotter' is used in several senses; so that different statements, though in verbal contradiction with each other, may yet all be more or less true. There ought, then, to be some clear understanding as to the sense in which natural substances are to be termed hot or cold, solid or fluid. For it appears manifest that these are properties on which even life and death are largely dependent, and that they are moreover the causes of sleep and waking, of maturity and old age, of health and disease; while no similar influence belongs to roughness and smoothness, to heaviness and lightness, nor, in short, to any other such properties of matter. That this should be so is but in accordance with rational expectation. For hot and cold, solid and fluid, as was stated in a former treatise,[1] are the foundations of the physical elements.

[1] *On Generation and Corruption*, II. 2-3.

Is then the term hot used in one sense or in many? To answer this we must ascertain what special effect is attributed to a hotter substance, and if there be several such, how many these may be. A body then is in one sense said to be hotter than another, if it impart a greater amount of heat to an object in contact with it. In a second sense, that is said to be hotter which causes the keener sensation when touched, and especially if the sensation be attended with pain. This criterion, however, would seem sometimes to be a false one; for occasionally it is the idiosyncrasy of the individual that causes the sensation to be painful. Again, of two things, that is the hotter which the more readily melts a fusible substance, or sets on fire an inflammable one. Again, of two masses of one and the same substance, the larger is said to have more heat than the smaller. Again, of two bodies, that is said to be the hotter which takes the longer time in cooling, as also we call that which is rapidly heated hotter than that which is long about it; as though the rapidity implied proximity and this again similarity of nature, while the want of rapidity implied distance and this again dissimilarity of nature. The term hotter is used then in all the various senses that have been mentioned, and perhaps in still more. Now it is impossible for one body to be hotter than another in all these different fashions. Boiling water for instance, though it is more scalding than flame, yet has no power of burning or melting combustible or fusible matter, while flame has. So again this boiling water is hotter than a small fire, and yet gets cold more rapidly and completely. For in fact fire never becomes cold; whereas water invariably does so. Boiling water, again, is hotter to the touch than oil; yet it gets cold and solid more rapidly than this other fluid. Blood, again, is hotter to the touch than either water or oil, and yet coagulates before them. Iron, again, and stones and other similar bodies are longer in getting heated than water, but when once heated burn other substances with a much greater intensity. Another distinction is this. In some of the bodies which are called hot the heat is derived from without,
649a while in others it belongs to the bodies themselves; and it makes a most important difference whether the heat has the former or the latter origin. For to call that one of two bodies the hotter, which is possessed of heat, we may almost say, accidentally and not of its own essence, is very much the same thing as if, finding that some man in a fever was a musician, one were to say that musicians are hotter than healthy men. Of that which is hot *per se* and that which is hot *per accidens*, the former is the slower to cool, while not rarely the latter is the hotter to the touch. The former again is the more burning of the two—flame, for instance, as compared with boiling water—while the latter, as the boiling water, which is hot *per accidens,* is the more heating to the touch. From all this it is clear that it is no simple matter to decide which of two bodies is the hotter. For the first may be the hotter in one sense, the second the hotter in another. Indeed in some of these cases it is impossible to say simply even whether a thing is hot or not. For the actual substratum may not itself be hot, but may be hot when coupled with heat as an attribute, as would be the case if one attached a single name to hot water or hot iron. It is after this manner that blood is hot. In such cases, in those, that is, in which the substratum owes its heat to an external influence, it is plain that cold is not a mere privation, but an actual existence.

There is no knowing but that even fire may be another of these cases. For the substratum of fire may be smoke or charcoal, and though the former of these is always hot, smoke being an uprising vapour, yet the latter becomes cold when its flame is extinguished, as also would oil and pinewood under similar circumstances. But even substances that have been burnt nearly all possess some heat, cinders, for example, and ashes, the dejections also of animals, and, among the excretions, bile; because some residue of heat has been left in them after their combustion. It is in another sense that pinewood and fat substances are hot; namely, because they rapidly assume the actuality of fire.

Heat appears to cause both coagulation and melting. Now such things as are formed merely of water are solidified by cold, while such as are formed of nothing but earth are solidified by fire. Hot substances again are solidified by cold, and, when they consist chiefly of earth, the process of solidification is rapid, and the resulting substance is insoluble; but, when their main constituent is water, the solid matter is again soluble. What kinds of substances, however, admit of being solidified, and what are the causes of solidification, are questions that have already been dealt with more precisely in another treatise.[1]

In conclusion, then, seeing that the terms hot

[1] Cf. *Meteorology*, IV. 6-8, 10.

649b and hotter are used in many different senses, and that no one substance can be hotter than others in all these senses, we must, when we attribute this character to an object, add such further statements as that this substance is hotter *per se*, though that other is often hotter *per accidens;* or again, that this substance is potentially hot, that other actually so; or again, that this substance is hotter in the sense of causing a greater feeling of heat when touched, while that other is hotter in the sense of producing flame and burning. The term hot being used in all these various senses, it plainly follows that the term cold will also be used with like ambiguity.

So much then as to the signification of the terms hot and cold, hotter and colder.

3

In natural sequence we have next to treat of solid and fluid. These terms are used in various senses. Sometimes, for instance, they denote things that are potentially, at other times things that are actually, solid or fluid. Ice for example, or any other solidified fluid, is spoken of as being actually and accidentally solid, while potentially and essentially it is fluid. Similarly earth and ashes and the like, when mixed with water, are actually and accidentally fluid, but potentially and essentially are solid. Now separate the constituents in such a mixture and you have on the one hand the watery components to which its fluidity was due, and these are both actually and potentially fluid, and on the other hand the earthy components, and these are in every way solid; and it is to bodies that are solid in this complete manner that the term 'solid' is most properly and absolutely applicable. So also the opposite term 'fluid' is strictly and absolutely applicable to that only which is both potentially and actually fluid. The same remark applies also to hot bodies and to cold.

These distinctions, then, being laid down, it is plain that blood is essentially hot in so far as that heat is connoted in its name; just as if boiling water were denoted by a single term, boiling would be connoted in that term. But the substratum of blood, that which it is in substance while it is blood in form, is not hot. Blood then in a certain sense is essentially hot, and in another sense is not so. For heat is included in the definition of blood, just as whiteness is included in the definition of a white man, and so far therefore blood is essentially hot. But so far as blood becomes hot from some external influence, it is not hot essentially.

As with hot and cold, so also is it with solid and fluid. We can therefore understand how some substances are hot and fluid so long as they remain in the living body, but become perceptibly cold and coagulate so soon as they are separated from it; while others are hot and consistent while in the body, but when withdrawn under a change to the opposite condition, and become cold and fluid. Of the former blood is an example, of the latter bile; for while blood solidifies when thus separated, yellow bile under the same circumstances becomes more fluid. We must attribute to such substances the possession of opposite properties in a greater or less degree.

650a In what sense, then, the blood is hot and in what sense fluid, and how far it partakes of the opposite properties, has now been fairly explained. Now since everything that grows must take nourishment, and nutriment in all cases consists of fluid and solid substances, and since it is by the force of heat that these are concocted and changed, it follows that all living things, animals and plants alike, must on this account, if on no other, have a natural source of heat. This natural heat, moreover, must belong to many parts, seeing that the organs by which the various elaborations of the food are effected are many in number. For first of all there is the mouth and the parts inside the mouth, on which the first share in the duty clearly devolves, in such animals at least as live on food which requires disintegration. The mouth, however, does not actually concoct the food, but merely facilitates concoction; for the subdivision of the food into small bits facilitates the action of heat upon it. After the mouth come the upper and the lower abdominal cavities, and here it is that concoction is effected by the aid of natural heat. Again, just as there is a channel for the admission of the unconcocted food into the stomach, namely the mouth, and in some animals the so-called oesophagus, which is continuous with the mouth and reaches to the stomach, so must there also be other and more numerous channels by which the concocted food or nutriment shall pass out of the stomach and intestines into the body at large, and to which these cavities shall serve as a kind of manger. For plants get their food from the earth by means of their roots; and this food is already elaborated when taken in, which is the reason why plants produce no excrement, the earth and its heat serv-

ing them in the stead of a stomach. But animals, with scarcely an exception, and conspicuously all such as are capable of locomotion, are provided with a stomachal sac, which is as it were an internal substitute for the earth. They must therefore have some instrument which shall correspond to the roots of plants, with which they may absorb their food from this sac, so that the proper end of the successive stages of concoction may at last be attained. The mouth then, its duty done, passes over the food to the stomach, and there must necessarily be something to receive it in turn from this. This something is furnished by the blood-vessels, which run throughout the whole extent of the mesentery from its lowest part right up to the stomach. A description of these will be found in the treatises on Anatomy and Natural History.[1] Now as there is a receptacle for the entire matter taken as food, and also a receptacle for its excremental residue, and again a third receptacle, namely the vessels, which serve as such for the blood, it is plain that this blood must be the final nutritive material in such animals as have it; while in bloodless animals the same is the case with the fluid which represents the blood. This explains why the blood diminishes in quantity when no food is taken, and increases when much is con-
650b sumed, and also why it becomes healthy and unhealthy according as the food is of the one or the other character. These facts, then, and others of a like kind, make it plain that the purpose of the blood in sanguineous animals is to subserve the nutrition of the body. They also explain why no more sensation is produced by touching the blood than by touching one of the excretions or the food, whereas when the flesh is touched sensation is produced. For the blood is not continuous nor united by growth with the flesh, but simply lies loose in its receptacle, that is in the heart and vessels. The manner in which the parts grow at the expense of the blood, and indeed the whole question of nutrition, will find a more suitable place for exposition in the treatise on Generation, and in other writings. For our present purpose all that need be said is that the blood exists for the sake of nutrition, that is the nutrition of the parts; and with this much let us therefore content ourselves.

4

What are called fibres are found in the blood of some animals but not of all. There are none, for instance, in the blood of deer and of roes; and for this reason the blood of such animals as these never coagulates. For one part of the blood consists mainly of water and therefore does not coagulate, this process occurring only in the other and earthy constituent, that is to say in the fibres, while the fluid part is evaporating.

Some at any rate of the animals with watery blood have a keener intellect than those whose blood is of an earthier nature. This is due not to the coldness of their blood, but rather to its thinness and purity; neither of which qualities belongs to the earthy matter. For the thinner and purer its fluid is, the more easily affected is an animal's sensibility. Thus it is that some bloodless animals, notwithstanding their want of blood, are yet more intelligent than some among the sanguineous kinds. Such for instance, as already said,[2] is the case with the bee and the tribe of ants, and whatever other animals there may be of a like nature. At the same time too great an excess of water makes animals timorous. For fear chills the body; so that in animals whose heart contains so watery a mixture the way is prepared for the operation of this emotion. For water is congealed by cold. This also explains why bloodless animals are, as a general rule, more timorous than such as have blood, so that they remain motionless, when frightened, and discharge their excretions, and in some instances change colour. Such animals, on the other hand, as have thick and abundant fibres in their blood are of a more earthy nature, and of a choleric temperament, and liable to bursts of passion. For anger is productive of heat; and solids, when they have been made hot, give
651a off more heat than fluids. The fibres therefore, being earthy and solid, are turned into so many hot embers in the blood, like the embers in a vapour-bath, and cause ebullition in the fits of passion.

This explains why bulls and boars are so choleric and so passionate. For their blood is exceedingly rich in fibres, and the bull's at any rate coagulates more rapidly than that of any other animal. If these fibres, that is to say if the earthy constituents of which we are speaking, are taken out of the blood, the fluid that remains behind will no longer coagulate; just as the watery residue of mud will not coagulate after removal of the earth. But if the fibres are left the fluid coagulates, as also does mud, under the influence of cold. For when the heat

[1] Cf. *History of Animals*, I. 16; III. 4 (514b 12).

[2] Cf. II. 2 (648a 6).

is expelled by the cold, the fluid, as has been already stated, passes off with it by evaporation, and the residue is dried up and solidified, not by heat but by cold. So long, however, as the blood is in the body, it is kept fluid by animal heat.

The character of the blood affects both the temperament and the sensory faculties of animals in many ways. This is indeed what might reasonably be expected, seeing that the blood is the material of which the whole body is made. For nutriment supplies the material, and the blood is the ultimate nutriment. It makes then a considerable difference whether the blood be hot or cold, thin or thick, turbid or clear.

The watery part of the blood is serum; and it is watery, either owing to its not being yet concocted, or owing to its having become corrupted; so that one part of the serum is the resultant of a necessary process, while another part is material intended to serve for the formation of the blood.

5

The differences between lard and suet correspond to differences of blood. For both are blood concocted into these forms as a result of abundant nutrition, being that surplus blood that is not expended on the fleshy part of the body, and is of an easily concocted and fatty character. This is shown by the unctuous aspect of these substances; for such unctuous aspect in fluids is due to a combination of air and fire. It follows from what has been said that no non-sanguineous animals have either lard or suet; for they have no blood. Among sanguineous animals those whose blood is dense have suet rather than lard. For suet is of an earthy nature, that is to say, it contains but a small proportion of water and is chiefly composed of earth; and this it is that makes it coagulate, just as the fibrous matter of blood coagulates, or broths which contain such fibrous matter. Thus it is that in those horned animals that have no front teeth in the upper jaw the fat consists of suet. For the very fact that they have horns and huckle-bones shows that their composition is rich in this earthy element; for all such appurtenances are solid and earthy in character. On the other hand in those hornless animals that have front teeth in both jaws, and whose feet are divided into toes, there is no suet, but in its place lard; and this, not being of an earthy character, neither coagulates nor dries up into a friable mass.

Both lard and suet when present in moderate amount are beneficial; for they contribute to health and strength, while they are no hin-
651b drance to sensation. But when they are present in great excess, they are injurious and destructive. For were the whole body formed of them it would perish. For an animal is an animal in virtue of its sensory part, that is in virtue of its flesh, or of the substance analogous to flesh. But the blood, as before stated, is not sensitive; as therefore is neither lard nor suet, seeing that they are nothing but concocted blood. Were then the whole body composed of these substances, it would be utterly without sensation. Such animals, again, as are excessively fat age rapidly. For so much of their blood is used in forming fat, that they have but little left; and when there is but little blood the way is already open for decay. For decay may be said to be deficiency of blood, the scantiness of which renders it liable, like all bodies of small bulk, to be injuriously affected by any chance excess of heat or cold. For the same reason fat animals are less prolific than others. For that part of the blood which should go to form semen and seed is used up in the production of lard and suet, which are nothing but concocted blood; so that in these animals there is either no reproductive excretion at all, or only a scanty amount.

6

So much then of blood and serum, and of lard and suet. Each of these has been described, and the purposes told for which they severally exist. The marrow also is of the nature of blood, and not, as some [1] think, the germinal force of the semen. That this is the case is quite evident in very young animals. For in the embryo the marrow of the bones has a blood-like appearance, which is but natural, seeing that the parts are all constructed out of blood, and that it is on blood that the embryo is nourished. But, as the young animal grows up and ripens into maturity, the marrow changes its colour, just as do the external parts and the viscera. For the viscera also in animals, so long as they are young, have each and all a blood-like look, owing to the large amount of this fluid which they contain.

The consistency of the marrow agrees with that of the fat. For when the fat consists of lard, then the marrow also is unctuous and lard-like; but when the blood is converted by concoction

[1] Plato, *Timaeus*, 73.

into suet, and does not assume the form of lard, then the marrow also has a suety character. In those animals, therefore, that have horns and are without upper front teeth, the marrow has the character of suet; while it takes the form of lard in those that have front teeth in both jaws, and that also have the foot divided into toes. What has ben said hardly applies to the spinal marrow. For it is necessary that this shall be continuous and extend without break through the whole backbone, inasmuch as this bone consists of separate vertebrae. But were the spinal marrow either of unctuous fat or of suet, it could not hold together in such a continuous mass as it does, but would either be too fluid or too frangible.

There are some animals that can hardly be said to have any marrow. These are those whose bones are strong and solid, as is the case **652a** with the lion. For in this animal the marrow is so utterly insignificant that the bones look as though they had none at all. However, as it is necessary that animals shall have bones or something analogous to them, such as the fish-spines of water-animals, it is also a matter of necessity that some of these bones shall contain marrow; for the substance contained within the bones is the nutriment out of which these are formed. Now the universal nutriment, as already stated,[1] is blood; and the blood within the bone, owing to the heat which is developed in it from its being thus surrounded, undergoes concoction, and self-concocted blood is suet or lard; so that it is perfectly intelligible how the marrow within the bone comes to have the character of these substances. So also it is easy to understand why, in those animals that have strong and compact bones, some of these should be entirely void of marrow, while the rest contain but little of it; for here the nutriment is spent in forming the bones.

Those animals that have fish-spines in place of bones have no other marrow than that of the chine. For in the first place they have naturally but a small amount of blood; and secondly the only hollow fish-spine is that of the chine. In this then marrow is formed; this being the only spine in which there is space for it, and, moreover, being the only one which owing to its division into parts requires a connecting bond. This too is the reason why the marrow of the chine, as already mentioned, is somewhat different from that of other bones. For, having to act the part of a clasp, it must be of glutinous character, and at the same time sinewy so as to admit of stretching.

Such then are the reasons for the existence of marrow, in those animals that have any, and such its nature. It is evidently the surplus of the sanguineous nutriment apportioned to the bones and fish-spines, which has undergone concoction owing to its being enclosed within them.

7

From the marrow we pass on in natural sequence to the brain. For there are many[2] who think that the brain itself consists of marrow, and that it forms the commencement of that substance, because they see that the spinal marrow is continuous with it. In reality the two may be said to be utterly opposite to each other in character. For of all the parts of the body there is none so cold as the brain; whereas the marrow is of a hot nature, as is plainly shown by its fat and unctuous character. Indeed this is the very reason why the brain and spinal marrow are continuous with each other. For, wherever the action of any part is in excess, nature so contrives as to set by it another part with an excess of contrary action, so that the excesses of the two may counterbalance each other. Now that the marrow is hot is clearly shown by many indications. The coldness of the brain is also manifest enough. For in the first place it is cold even to the touch; and, secondly, of all the fluid parts of the body it is the driest and the one that has the least blood; for in fact it has no blood at all in **652b** its proper substance. This brain is not residual matter, nor yet is it one of the parts which are anatomically continuous with each other; but it has a character peculiar to itself, as might indeed be expected. That it has no continuity with the organs of sense is plain from simple inspection, and is still more clearly shown by the fact, that, when it is touched, no sensation is produced; in which respect it resembles the blood of animals and their excrement. The purpose of its presence in animals is no less than the preservation of the whole body. For some writers assert that the soul is fire or some such force. This, however, is but a rough and inaccurate assertion; and it would perhaps be better to say that the soul is incorporate in some substance of a fiery character. The reason for this being so is that of all substances there is none so suitable for ministering to the operations of the soul as that which is possessed

[1] Cf. II. 4 (651a 14).

[2] As Plato in the *Timaeus*, 73.

of heat. For nutrition and the imparting of motion are offices of the soul, and it is by heat that these are most readily effected. To say then that the soul is fire is much the same thing as to confound the auger or the saw with the carpenter or his craft, simply because the work is wrought by the two in conjunction. So far then this much is plain, that all animals must necessarily have a certain amount of heat. But as all influences require to be counterbalanced, so that they may be reduced to moderation and brought to the mean (for in the mean, and not in either extreme, lies the true and rational position), nature has contrived the brain as a counterpoise to the region of the heart with its contained heat, and has given it to animals to moderate the latter, combining in it the properties of earth and water. For this reason it is, that every sanguineous animal has a brain; whereas no bloodless creature has such an organ, unless indeed it be, as the Poulp, by analogy. For where there is no blood, there in consequence there is but little heat. The brain, then, tempers the heat and seething of the heart. In order, however, that it may not itself be absolutely without heat, but may have a moderate amount, branches run from both blood-vessels, that is to say from the great vessel and from what is called the aorta, and end in the membrane which surrounds the brain; while at the same time, in order to prevent any injury from the heat, these encompassing vessels, instead of being few and large, are numerous and small, and their blood scanty and clear, instead of being abundant and thick. We can now understand why defluxions have their origin in the head, and occur whenever the parts about the brain have more than a due proportion of coldness. For when the nutriment **653a** steams upwards through the blood-vessels, its refuse portion is chilled by the influence of this region, and forms defluxions of phlegm and serum. We must suppose, to compare small things with great, that the like happens here as occurs in the production of showers. For when vapour steams up from the earth and is carried by the heat into the upper regions, so soon as it reaches the cold air that is above the earth, it condenses again into water owing to the refrigeration, and falls back to the earth as rain. These, however, are matters which may be suitably considered in the Principles of Diseases, so far as natural philosophy has anything to say to them.

It is the brain again—or, in animals that have no brain, the part analogous to it—which is the cause of sleep. For either by chilling the blood that streams upwards after food, or by some other similar influences, it produces heaviness in the region in which it lies (which is the reason why drowsy persons hang the head), and causes the heat to escape downwards in company with the blood. It is the accumulation of this in excess in the lower region that produces complete sleep, taking away the power of standing upright from those animals to whom that posture is natural, and from the rest the power of holding up the head. These, however, are matters which have been separately considered in the treatises on Sensation and on Sleep.[1]

That the brain is a compound of earth and water is shown by what occurs when it is boiled. For, when so treated, it turns hard and solid, inasmuch as the water is evaporated by the heat, and leaves the earthy part behind. Just the same occurs when pulse and other fruits are boiled. For these also are hardened by the process, because the water which enters into their composition is driven off and leaves the earth, which is their main constituent, behind.

Of all animals, man has the largest brain in proportion to his size; and it is larger in men than in women. This is because the region of the heart and of the lung is hotter and richer in blood in man than in any other animal; and in men than in women. This again explains why man, alone of animals, stands erect. For the heat, overcoming any opposite inclination, makes growth take its own line of direction, which is from the centre of the body upwards. It is then as a counterpoise to his excessive heat that in man's brain there is this superabundant fluidity and coldness; and it is again owing to this superabundance that the cranial bone, which some call the Bregma, is the last to become solidified; so long does evaporation continue to occur through it under the influence of heat. Man is the only sanguineous animal in which this takes place. Man, **653b** again, has more sutures in his skull than any other animal, and the male more than the female. The explanation is again to be found in the greater size of the brain, which demands free ventilation, proportionate to its bulk. For if the brain be either too fluid or too solid, it will not perform its office, but in the one case will freeze the blood, and in the other will not cool it at all; and thus will cause disease, madness, and death. For the cardiac heat and

[1] *On Sleep and Sleeplessness*, 2 (455^b 28)-3 (458^a 32).

the centre of life is most delicate in its sympathies, and is immediately sensitive to the slightest change or affection of the blood on the outer surface of the brain.

The fluids which are present in the animal body at the time of birth have now nearly all been considered. Amongst those that appear only at a later period are the residua of the food, which include the deposits of the belly and also those of the bladder. Besides these there is the semen and the milk, one or the other of which makes its appearance in appropriate animals. Of these fluids, the excremental residua of the food may be suitably discussed by themselves, when we come to examine and consider the subject of nutrition. Then will be the proper time to explain in what animals they are found, and what are the reasons for their presence. Similarly all questions concerning the semen and the milk may be dealt with in the treatise on Generation,[1] for the former of these fluids is the very starting-point of the generative process, and the latter has no other ground of existence than generative purposes.

8

We have now to consider the remaining homogeneous parts, and will begin with flesh, and with the substance that, in animals that have no flesh, takes its place. The reason for so beginning is that flesh forms the very basis of animals, and is the essential constituent of their body. Its right to this precedence can also be demonstrated logically. For an animal is by our definition something that has sensibility and chief of all the primary sensibility, which is that of Touch; and it is the flesh, or analogous substance, which is the organ of this sense. And it is the organ, either in the same way as the pupil is the organ of sight, that is it constitutes the primary organ of the sense; or it is the organ and the medium through which the object acts combined, that is it answers to the pupil with the whole transparent medium attached to it. Now in the case of the other senses it was impossible for nature to unite the medium with the sense-organ, nor would such a junction have served any purpose; but in the case of touch she was compelled by necessity to do so. For of all the sense-organs that of touch is the only one that has corporeal substance, or at any rate it is more corporeal than any other, and its medium must be corporeal like itself.

It is obvious also to sense that it is for the sake of the flesh that all the other parts exist. By the other parts I mean the bones, the skin, the sinews, and the blood-vessels, and, again, the hair and the various kinds of nails, and anything else there may be of a like character. Thus the bones are a contrivance to give security to the soft parts, to which purpose they are adapted by their hardness; and in animals that have no bones the same office is fulfilled by some analogous substance, as by fish-spine in some fishes, and by cartilage in others.

Now in some animals this supporting sub-
654a stance is situated within the body, while in some of the bloodless species it is placed on the outside. The latter is the case in all the Crustacea, as the Carcini (*Crabs*) and the Carabi (*Prickly Lobsters*); it is the case also in the Testacea, as for instance in the several species known by the general name of oysters. For in all these animals the fleshy substance is within, and the earthy matter, which holds the soft parts together and keeps them from injury, is on the outside. For the shell not only enables the soft parts to hold together, but also, as the animal is bloodless and so has but little natural warmth, surrounds it, as a chaufferette does the embers, and keeps in the smouldering heat. Similar to this seems to be the arrangement in another and distinct tribe of animals, namely the Tortoises, including the Chelone and the several kinds of Emys. But in Insects and in Cephalopods the plan is entirely different, there being moreover a contrast between these two themselves. For in neither of these does there appear to be any bony or earthy part, worthy of notice, distinctly separated from the rest of the body. Thus in the Cephalopods the main bulk of the body consists of a soft flesh-like substance, or rather of a substance which is intermediate to flesh and sinew, so as not to be so readily destructible as actual flesh. I call this substance intermediate to flesh and sinew, because it is soft like the former, while it admits of stretching like the latter. Its cleavage, however, is such that it splits not longitudinally, like sinew, but into circular segments, this being the most advantageous condition, so far as strength is concerned. These animals have also a part inside them corresponding to the spinous bones of fishes. For instance, in the Cuttle-fishes there is what is known as the *os sepiae*, and in the Calamaries there is the so-called *gladius*. In the Poulps, on the other hand, there is no such internal part, because the body, or, as it is termed in them, the head, forms but a short sac, whereas it is of considerable length in the other two;

[1] *On the Generation of Animals*, I. 17-II. 3; IV. 8.

and it was this length which led nature to assign to them their hard support, so as to ensure their straightness and inflexibility; just as she has assigned to sanguineous animals their bones or their fish-spines, as the case may be. To come now to Insects. In these the arrangement is quite different from that of the Cephalopods; quite different also from that which obtains in sanguineous animals, as indeed has been already stated. For in an insect there is no distinction into soft and hard parts, but the whole body is hard, the hardness, however, being of such a character as to be more flesh-like than bone, and more earthy and bone-like than flesh. The purpose of this is to make the body of the insect less liable to get broken into pieces.

9

There is a resemblance between the osseous and the vascular systems; for each has a central part in which it begins, and each forms a continuous whole. For no bone in the body exists as a separate thing in itself, but each is either a portion of what may be considered a continuous whole, or at any rate is linked with the rest by contact and by attachments; so that nature may use adjoining bones either as **654b** though they were actually continuous and formed a single bone, or, for purposes of flexure, as though they were two and distinct. And similarly no blood-vessel has in itself a separate individuality; but they all form parts of one whole. For an isolated bone, if such there were, would in the first place be unable to perform the office for the sake of which bones exist; for, were it discontinuous and separated from the rest by a gap, it would be perfectly unable to produce either flexure or extension; nor only so, but it would actually be injurious, acting like a thorn or an arrow lodged in the flesh. Similarly if a vessel were isolated, and not continuous with the vascular centre, it would be unable to retain the blood within it in a proper state. For it is the warmth derived from this centre that hinders the blood from coagulating; indeed the blood, when withdrawn from its influence, becomes manifestly putrid. Now the centre or origin of the blood-vessels is the heart, and the centre or origin of the bones, in all animals that have bones, is what is called the chine. With this all the other bones of the body are in continuity; for it is the chine that holds together the whole length of an animal and preserves its straightness. But since it is necessary that the body of an animal shall bend during locomotion, this chine, while it is one in virtue of the continuity of its parts, yet by its division into vertebrae is made to consist of many segments. It is from this chine that the bones of the limbs, in such animals as have these parts, proceed, and with it they are continuous, being fastened together by the sinews where the limbs admit of flexure, and having their extremities adapted to each other, either by the one being hollowed and the other rounded, or by both being hollowed and including between them a hucklebone, as a connecting bolt, so as to allow of flexure and extension. For without some such arrangement these movements would be utterly impossible, or at any rate would be performed with great difficulty. There are some joints, again, in which the lower end of the one bone and the upper end of the other are alike in shape. In these cases the bones are bound together by sinews, and cartilaginous pieces are interposed in the joint, to serve as a kind of padding, and prevent the two extremities from grating against each other.

Round about the bones, and attached to them by thin fibrous bands, grow the fleshy parts, for the sake of which the bones themselves exist. For just as an artist, when he is moulding an animal out of clay or other soft substance, takes first some solid body as a basis, and round this moulds the clay, so also has nature acted in fashioning the animal body out of flesh. Thus we find all the fleshy parts, with one exception, supported by bones, which serve, when the parts are organs of motion, to facilitate flexure, and, when the parts are motionless, act as a protection. The ribs, for example, which enclose the chest are intended to ensure the safety of the heart and neighbouring viscera. The exception of which mention was made is the belly. The walls of this are in all animals devoid of bones; in order that there may be no hindrance to the expansion which necessarily occurs in this part after a meal, nor, in females, any interference with the growth of the foetus, which is lodged here.

655a Now the bones of viviparous animals, of such, that is, as are not merely externally but also internally viviparous, vary but very little from each other in point of strength, which in all of them is considerable. For the Vivipara in their bodily proportions are far above other animals, and many of them occasionally grow to an enormous size, as is the case in Libya and in hot and dry countries generally. But the greater the bulk of an animal, the stronger, the bigger, and the harder, are the supports which it requires; and comparing the big animals with each other, this requirement will be most marked in those that live a life of rapine. Thus it is that the bones of males are harder than those of females; and the bones of flesh-eaters, that get their food by fighting, are harder than those of Herbivora. Of this the Lion is an example; for so hard are its bones, that, when struck, they give off sparks, as though they were stones. It may be mentioned also that the Dolphin, inasmuch as it is viviparous, is provided with bones and not with fish-spines.

In those sanguineous animals, on the other hand, that are oviparous, the bones present successive slight variations of character. Thus in Birds there are bones, but these are not so strong as the bones of the Vivipara. Then come the Oviparous fishes, where there is no bone, but merely fish-spine. In the Serpents too the bones have the character of fish-spine, excepting in the very large species, where the solid foundation of the body requires to be stronger, in order that the animal itself may be strong, the same reason prevailing as in the case of the Vivipara. Lastly, in the Selachia, as they are called, the fish-spines are replaced by cartilage. For it is necessary that the movements of these animals shall be of an undulating character; and this again requires the framework that supports the body to be made of a pliable and not of a brittle substance. Moreover, in these Selachia nature has used all the earthy matter on the skin; and she is unable to allot to many different parts one and the same superfluity of material. Even in viviparous animals many of the bones are cartilaginous. This happens in those parts where it is to the advantage of the surrounding flesh that its solid base shall be soft and mucilaginous. Such, for instance, is the case with the ears and nostrils; for in projecting parts, such as these, brittle substances would soon get broken. Cartilage and bone are indeed fundamentally the same thing, the differences between them being merely matters of degree. Thus neither cartilage nor bone, when once cut off, grows again. Now the cartilages of these land animals are without marrow, that is without any distinctly separate marrow. For the marrow, which in bones is distinctly separate, is here mixed up with the whole mass, and gives a soft and mucilaginous consistence to the cartilage. But in the Selachia
655b the chine, though it is cartilaginous, yet contains marrow; for here it stands in the stead of a bone.

Very nearly resembling the bones to the touch are such parts as nails, hoofs, whether solid or cloven, horns, and the beaks of birds, all of which are intended to serve as means of defence. For the organs which are made out of these substances, and which are called by the same names as the substances themselves, the organ hoof, for instance, and the organ horn, are contrivances to ensure the preservation of the animals to which they severally belong. In this class too must be reckoned the teeth, which in some animals have but a single function, namely the mastication of the food, while in others they have an additional office, namely to serve as weapons; as is the case with all animals that have sharp interfitting teeth or that have tusks. All these parts are necessarily of solid and earthy character; for the value of a weapon depends on such properties. Their earthy character explains how it is that all such parts are more developed in four-footed vivipara than in man. For there is always more earth in the composition of these animals than in that of the human body. However, not only all these parts but such others as are nearly connected with them, skin for instance, bladder, membrane, hairs, feathers, and their analogues, and any other similar parts that there may be, will be considered farther on with the heterogeneous parts. There we shall inquire into the causes which produce them, and into the objects of their presence severally in the bodies of animals. For, as with the heterogeneous parts, so with these, it is from a consideration of their functions that alone we can derive any knowledge of them. The reason for dealing with them at all in this part of the treatise, and classifying them with the homogeneous parts, is that under one and the same name are confounded the entire organs and the substances of which they are composed. But of all these substances flesh and bone form the basis. Semen and milk were also passed over when we were considering the homogeneous fluids. For the treatise on Generation[1] will afford a more suitable place for their examination, seeing that the former of the two is the very foundation of the thing generated, while the latter is its nourishment.

10

Let us now make, as it were, a fresh beginning, and consider the heterogeneous parts, taking those first which are the first in importance. For in all animals, at least in all the perfect

[1] *On the Generation of Animals*, I. 17-II. 3; IV. 8.

kinds, there are two parts more essential than the rest, namely the part which serves for the ingestion of food, and the part which serves for the discharge of its residue. For without food growth and even existence is impossible. Intervening again between these two parts there is invariably a third, in which is lodged the vital principle. As for plants, though they also are included by us among things that have life, yet are they without any part for the discharge of waste residue. For the food which they absorb from the ground is already concocted, and they give off as its equivalent **656a** their seeds and fruits. Plants, again, inasmuch as they are without locomotion, present no great variety in their heterogeneous parts. For, where the functions are but few, few also are the organs required to effect them. The configuration of plants is a matter then for separate consideration. Animals, however, that not only live but feel, present a greater multiformity of parts, and this diversity is greater in some animals than in others, being most varied in those to whose share has fallen not mere life but life of high degree. Now such an animal is man. For of all living beings with which we are acquainted man alone partakes of the divine, or at any rate partakes of it in a fuller measure than the rest. For this reason, then, and also because his external parts and their forms are more familiar to us than those of other animals, we must speak of man first; and this the more fitly, because in him alone do the natural parts hold the natural position; his upper part being turned towards that which is upper in the universe. For, of all animals, man alone stands erect.

In man, then, the head is destitute of flesh; this being the necessary consequence of what has already been stated[1] concerning the brain. There are, indeed, some[2] who hold that the life of man would be longer than it is, were his head more abundantly furnished with flesh; and they account for the absence of this substance by saying that it is intended to add to the perfection of sensation. For the brain they assert to be the organ of sensation; and sensation, they say, cannot penetrate to parts that are too thickly covered with flesh. But neither part of this statement is true. On the contrary, were the region of the brain thickly covered with flesh, the very purpose for which animals are provided with a brain would be directly contravened. For the brain would itself be heated to excess and so unable to cool any other part; and, as to the other half of their statement, the brain cannot be the cause of any of the sensations, seeing that it is itself as utterly without feeling as any one of the excretions. These writers see that certain of the senses are located in the head, and are unable to discern the reason for this; they see also that the brain is the most peculiar of all the animal organs; and out of these facts they form an argument, by which they link sensation and brain together. It has, however, already been clearly set forth in the treatise on Sensation, that it is the region of the heart that constitutes the sensory centre. There also it was stated that two of the senses, namely touch and taste, are manifestly in immediate connexion with the heart; and that as regards the other three, namely hearing, sight, and the centrally placed sense of smell, it is the character of their sense-organs which causes them to be lodged as a rule in the head. Vision is so placed in all animals. But such is not invariably the case with hearing or with smell. For fishes and the like hear and smell, and yet have no visible organs for these senses in the head; a fact which demonstrates the accuracy of the opinion here maintained. Now that vision, whenever it exists, should be in the neighbourhood of the brain is **656b** but what one would rationally expect. For the brain is fluid and cold, and vision is of the nature of water, water being of all transparent substances the one most easily confined. Moreover it cannot but necessarily be that the more precise senses will have their precision rendered still greater if ministered to by parts that have the purest blood. For the motion of the heat of blood destroys sensory activity. For these reasons the organs of the precise senses are lodged in the head.

It is not only the fore part of the head that is destitute of flesh, but the hind part also. For, in all animals that have a head, it is this head which more than any other part requires to be held up. But, were the head heavily laden with flesh, this would be impossible; for nothing so burdened can be held upright. This is an additional proof that the absence of flesh from the head has no reference to brain sensation. For there is no brain in the hinder part of the head, and yet this is as much without flesh as is the front.

In some animals hearing as well as vision is lodged in the region of the head. Nor is this without a rational explanation. For what is called the empty space is full of air, and the organ of hearing is, as we say, of the nature of

[1] Cf. II. 7. [2] e. g. Plato in the *Timaeus*, 75.

air. Now there are channels which lead from the eyes to the blood-vessels that surround the brain; and similarly there is a channel which leads back again from each ear and connects it with the hinder part of the head. But no part that is without blood is endowed with sensation, as neither is the blood itself, but only some one of the parts that are formed of blood.

The brain in all animals that have one is placed in the front part of the head; because the direction in which sensation acts is in front; and because the heart, from which sensation proceeds, is in the front part of the body; and lastly because the instruments of sensation are the blood-containing parts, and the cavity in the posterior part of the skull is destitute of blood-vessels.

As to the position of the sense-organs, they have been arranged by nature in the following well-ordered manner. The organs of hearing are so placed as to divide the circumference of the head into two equal halves; for they have to hear not only sounds which are directly in a line with themselves, but sounds from all quarters. The organs of vision are placed in front, because sight is exercised only in a straight line, and moving as we do in a forward direction it is necessary that we should see before us, in the direction of our motion. Lastly, the organs of smell are placed with good reason between the eyes. For as the body consists of two parts, a right half and a left, so also each organ of sense is double. In the case of touch this is not apparent, the reason being that the primary organ of this sense is not the flesh or analogous part, but lies internally. In the case of taste, which is merely a modification of touch and which is placed in the tongue, the fact is more apparent than in the case of touch,
657a but still not so manifest as in the case of the other senses. However, even in taste it is evident enough; for in some animals the tongue is plainly forked. The double character of the sensations is, however, more conspicuous in the other organs of sense. For there are two ears and two eyes, and the nostrils, though joined together, are also two. Were these latter otherwise disposed, and separated from each other as are the ears, neither they nor the nose in which they are placed would be able to perform their office. For in such animals as have nostrils olfaction is effected by means of inspiration, and the organ of inspiration is placed in front and in the middle line. This is the reason why nature has brought the two nostrils together and placed them as the central of the three sense-organs, setting them side by side on a level with each other, to avail themselves of the inspiratory motion. In other animals than man the arrangement of these sense-organs is also such as is adapted in each case to the special requirements.

11

For instance, in quadrupeds the ears stand out freely from the head and are set to all appearance above the eyes. Not that they are in reality above the eyes; but they seem to be so, because the animal does not stand erect, but has its head hung downwards. This being the usual attitude of the animal when in motion, it is of advantage that its ears shall be high up and movable; for by turning themselves about they can the better take in sounds from every quarter.

12

In birds, on the other hand, there are no ears, but only the auditory passages. This is because their skin is hard and because they have feathers instead of hairs, so that they have not got the proper material for the formation of ears. Exactly the same is the case with such oviparous quadrupeds as are clad with scaly plates, and the same explanation applies to them. There is also one of the viviparous quadrupeds, namely the seal, that has no ears but only the auditory passages. The explanation of this is that the seal, though a quadruped, is a quadruped of stunted formation.

13

Men, and Birds, and Quadrupeds, viviparous and oviparous alike, have their eyes protected by lids. In the Vivipara there are two of these; and both are used by these animals not only in closing the eyes, but also in the act of blinking; whereas the oviparous quadrupeds, and the heavy-bodied birds as well as some others, use only the lower lid to close the eye; while birds blink by means of a membrane that issues from the canthus. The reason for the eyes being thus protected is that nature has made them of fluid consistency, in order to ensure keenness of vision. For had they been covered with hard skin, they would, it is true, have been less liable to get injured by anything falling into them from without, but they would not have been sharp-sighted. It is then to ensure keenness of vision that the skin over the pupil is fine and delicate; while the lids are superadded as a protection from injury. It is as a still further safeguard that all these animals **657b** blink, and man most of all; this action (which is not performed from deliberate intention but from a natural instinct) serving to keep objects from falling into the eyes; and being more frequent in man than in the rest of these animals, because of the greater delicacy of his skin. These lids are made of a roll of skin; and it is because they are made of skin and contain no flesh that neither they, nor the similarly constructed prepuce, unite again when once cut.

As to the oviparous quadrupeds, and such birds as resemble them in closing the eye with the lower lid, it is the hardness of the skin of their heads which makes them do so. For such birds as have heavy bodies are not made for flight; and so the materials which would otherwise have gone to increase the growth of the feathers are diverted thence, and used to augment the thickness of the skin. Birds therefore of this kind close the eye with the lower lid; whereas pigeons and the like use both upper and lower lids for the purpose. As birds are covered with feathers, so oviparous quadrupeds are covered with scaly plates; and these in all their forms are harder than hairs, so that the skin also to which they belong is harder than the skin of hairy animals. In these animals, then, the skin on the head is hard, and so does not allow of the formation of an upper eyelid, whereas lower down the integument is of a flesh-like character, so that the lower lid can be thin and extensible.

The act of blinking is performed by the heavy-bodied birds by means of the membrane already mentioned, and not by this lower lid. For in blinking rapid motion is required, and such is the motion of this membrane, whereas that of the lower lid is slow. It is from the canthus that is nearest to the nostrils that the membrane comes. For it is better to have one starting-point for nictitation than two; and in these birds this starting-point is the junction of eye and nostrils, an anterior starting-point being preferable to a lateral one. Oviparous quadrupeds do not blink in like manner as the birds; for, living as they do on the ground, they are free from the necessity of having eyes of fluid consistency and of keen sight, whereas these are essential requisites for birds, inasmuch as they have to use their eyes at long distances. This too explains why birds with talons, that have to search for prey by eye from aloft, and therefore soar to greater heights than other birds, are sharp-sighted; while common fowls and the like, that live on the ground and are not made for flight, have no such keenness of vision. For there is nothing in their mode of life which imperatively requires it.

Fishes and Insects and the hard-skinned Crustacea present certain differences in their eyes, but so far resemble each other as that none of them have eyelids. As for the hard-skinned Crustacea it is utterly out of the question that they should have any; for an eyelid, to be of use, requires the action of the skin to be rapid. These animals then have no eyelids and, in default of this protection, their eyes are hard, just as though the lid were attached to the surface of the eye, and the animal saw through it. Inasmuch, however, as such hardness must necessarily blunt the sharpness of vision, nature has endowed the eyes of Insects, **658a** and still more those of Crustacea, with mobility (just as she has given some quadrupeds movable ears), in order that they may be able to turn to the light and catch its rays, and so see more plainly. Fishes, however, have eyes of a fluid consistency. For animals that move much about have to use their vision at considerable distances. If now they live on land, the air in which they move is transparent enough. But the water in which fishes live is a hindrance to sharp sight, though it has this advantage over the air, that it does not contain so many objects to knock against the eyes. The risk of collision being thus small, nature, who makes nothing in vain, has given no eyelids to fishes, while to counterbalance the opacity of the water she has made their eyes of fluid consistency.

14

All animals that have hairs on the body have lashes on the eyelids; but birds and animals with scale-like plates, being hairless, have none. The Libyan ostrich, indeed, forms an exception; for, though a bird, it is furnished with eyelashes. This exception, however, will be explained hereafter. Of hairy animals, man alone has lashes on both lids. For in quadrupeds there is a greater abundance of hair on the back than on the under side of the body; whereas in man the contrary is the case, and the hair is more abundant on the front surface than on the back. The reason for this is that hair is intended to serve as a protection to its possessor. Now, in quadrupeds, owing to their inclined attitude, the under or anterior surface does not require so much protection as the back, and is therefore left comparatively bald, in spite of its being the nobler of the two sides. But in man, owing to his upright attitude, the anterior and posterior surfaces of the body are on an equality as regards need of protection. Nature therefore has assigned the protective covering to the nobler of the two surfaces; for invariably she brings about the best arrangement of such as are possible. This then is the reason that there is no lower eyelash in any quadruped; though in some a few scattered hairs sprout out under the lower lid. This also is the reason that they never have hair in the axillae, nor on the pubes, as man has. Their hair, then, instead of being collected in these parts, is either thickly set over the whole dorsal surface, as is the case for instance in dogs, or, sometimes, forms a mane, as in horses and the like, or as in the male lion, where the mane is still more flowing and ample. So, again, whenever there is a tail of any length, nature decks it with hair, with long hair if the stem of the tail be short, as in horses, with short hair if the stem be long, regard also being had to the condition of the rest of the body. For nature invariably gives to one part what she subtracts from another. Thus when she has covered the general surface of an animal's body with an excess of hair, she leaves a deficiency in **658b** the region of the tail. This, for instance, in the case with bears.

No animal has so much hair on the head as man. This, in the first place, is the necessary result of the fluid character of his brain, and of the presence of so many sutures in his skull. For wherever there is the most fluid and the most heat, there also must necessarily occur the greatest outgrowth. But, secondly, the thickness of the hair in this part has a final cause, being intended to protect the head, by preserving it from excess of either heat or cold. And as the brain of man is larger and more fluid than that of any other animal, it requires a proportionately greater amount of protection. For the more fluid a substance is, the more readily does it get excessively heated or excessively chilled, while substances of an opposite character are less liable to such injurious affections.

These, however, are matters which by their close connexion with eyelashes have led us to digress from our real topic, namely the cause to which these lashes owe their existence. We must therefore defer any further remarks we may have to make on these matters till the proper occasion arises and then return to their consideration.

15

Both eyebrows and eyelashes exist for the protection of the eyes; the former that they may shelter them, like the eaves of a house, from any fluids that trickle down from the head; the latter to act like the palisades which are sometimes placed in front of enclosures, and keep out any objects which might otherwise get in. The brows are placed over the junction of two bones, which is the reason that in old age they often become so bushy as to require cutting. The lashes are set at the terminations of small blood-vessels. For the vessels come to an end where the skin itself terminates; and, in all places where these endings occur, the exudation of moisture of a corporeal character necessitates the growth of hairs, unless there be some operation of nature which interferes, by diverting the moisture to another purpose.

16

Viviparous quadrupeds, as a rule, present no great variety of form in the organ of smell. In those of them, however, whose jaws project forwards and taper to a narrow end, so as to form what is called a snout, the nostrils are placed in this projection, there being no other available plan; while, in the rest, there is a more definite demarcation between nostrils and jaws. But in no animal is this part so peculiar as in the elephant, where it attains an extraordinary size and strength. For the elephant uses its **659a** nostril as a hand; this being the instrument with which it conveys food, fluid and solid alike, to its mouth. With it, too, it tears up trees, coiling it round their stems. In fact it applies it generally to the purposes of a hand. For the elephant has the double character of a land animal, and of one that lives in swamps. Seeing then that it has to get its food from the water, and yet must necessarily breathe, inasmuch as it is a land animal and has blood; seeing, also, that its excessive weight prevents it from passing rapidly from water to land, as some other sanguineous vivipara that breathe can do, it becomes necessary that it shall be suited alike for life in the water and for life on dry land. Just then as divers are sometimes provided with instruments for respiration, through which they can draw air from above the water, and thus may remain for a long time under the sea, so also have elephants been furnished by nature with their lengthened nostril; and, whenever they have to traverse the water, they lift this up above the surface and breathe through it. For the elephant's proboscis, as already said, is a nostril. Now it would have been impossible for this nostril to have the form of a proboscis, had it been hard and incapable of bending. For its very length would then have prevented the animal from supplying itself with food, being as great an impediment as the horns of certain oxen, that are said to be obliged to walk backwards while they are grazing. It is therefore soft and flexible, and, being such, is made, in addition to its own proper functions, to serve the office of the fore-feet; nature in this following her wonted plan of using one and the same part for several purposes. For in polydactylous quadrupeds the fore-feet are intended not merely to support the weight of the body, but to serve as hands. But in elephants, though they must be reckoned polydactylous, as their foot has neither cloven nor solid hoof, the fore-feet, owing to the great size and weight of the body, are reduced to the condition of mere supports; and indeed their slow motion and unfitness for bending make them useless for any other purpose. A nostril, then, is given to the elephant for respiration, as to every other animal that has a lung, and is lengthened out and endowed with its power of coiling because the animal has to remain for considerable periods of time in the water, and is unable to pass thence to dry ground with any rapidity. But as the feet are shorn of their full office, this same part is also, as already said, made by nature to supply their place, and give such help as otherwise would be rendered by them.

As to other sanguineous animals, the Birds,
659b the Serpents, and the Oviparous quadrupeds, in all of them there are the nostril-holes, placed in front of the mouth; but in none are there any distinctly formed nostrils, nothing in fact which can be called nostrils except from a functional point of view. A bird at any rate has nothing which can properly be called a nose. For its so-called beak is a substitute for jaws. The reason for this is to be found in the natural conformation of birds. For they are winged bipeds; and this makes it necessary that their heads and neck shall be of light weight; just as it makes it necessary that their breast shall be narrow. The beak therefore with which they are provided is formed of a bone-like substance, in order that it may serve as a weapon as well as for nutritive purposes, but is made of narrow dimensions to suit the small size of the head. In this beak are placed the olfactory passages. But there are no nostrils; for such could not possibly be placed there.

As for those animals that have no respiration, it has already been explained[1] why it is that they are without nostrils, and perceive odours either through gills, or through a blowhole, or, if they are insects, by the hypozoma; and how the power of smelling depends, like their motion, upon the innate spirit of their bodies, which in all of them is implanted by nature and not introduced from without.

Under the nostrils are the lips, in such sanguineous animals, that is, as have teeth. For in birds, as already has been said, the purposes of nutrition and defence are fulfilled by a bone-like beak, which forms a compound substitute for teeth and lips. For supposing that one were to cut off a man's lips, unite his upper teeth together, and similarly his under ones, and then were to lengthen out the two separate pieces thus formed, narrowing them on either side and making them project forwards, supposing, I say, this to be done, we should at once have a bird-like beak.

The use of the lips in all animals except man is to preserve and guard the teeth; and thus it is that the distinctness with which the lips are formed is in direct proportion to the degree of nicety and perfection with which the teeth are fashioned. In man the lips are soft and flesh-like and capable of separating from each other. Their purpose, as in other animals, is to guard the teeth, but they are more especially intended to serve a higher office, contributing in common with other parts to man's faculty of speech. For just as nature has made man's tongue unlike that of other animals, and, in ac-
660a cordance with what I have said[2] is her not uncommon practice, has used it for two distinct operations, namely for the perception of savours and for speech, so also has she acted with regard to the lips, and made them serve both for speech and for the protection of the teeth. For vocal speech consists of combinations of the letters, and most of these would be impossible to pronounce, were the lips not moist, nor the tongue such as it is. For some letters are formed by closures of the lips and others by applications of the tongue. But what are the differences presented by these and what the nature and extent of such differences, are questions to

[1] Perhaps this refers to *Sense and the Sensible*, 5. 444b 6 sqq.

[2] Cf. 659a 21.

which answers must be sought from those who are versed in metrical science. It was necessary that the two parts which we are discussing should, in conformity with the requirements, be severally adapted to fulfil the office mentioned above, and be of appropriate character. Therefore are they made of flesh, and flesh is softer in man than in any other animal, the reason for this being that of all animals man has the most delicate sense of touch.

17

The tongue is placed under the vaulted roof of the mouth. In land animals it presents but little diversity. But in other animals it is variable, and this whether we compare them as a class with such as live on land, or compare their several species with each other. It is in man that the tongue attains its greatest degree of freedom, of softness, and of breadth; the object of this being to render it suitable for its double function. For its softness fits it for the perception of savours, a sense which is more delicate in man than in any other animal, softness being most impressionable by touch, of which sense taste is but a variety. This same softness again, together with its breadth, adapts it for the articulation of letters and for speech. For these qualities, combined with its freedom from attachment, are those which suit it best for advancing and retiring in every direction. That this is so is plain, if we consider the case of those who are tongue-tied in however slight a degree. For their speech is indistinct and lisping; that is to say there are certain letters which they cannot pronounce. In being broad is comprised the possibility of becoming narrow; for in the great the small is included, but not the great in the small.

What has been said explains why, even among birds, those that are most capable of pronouncing letters are such as have the broadest tongues; and why the viviparous and sanguineous quadrupeds, where the tongue is hard and thick and not free in its motions, have a very limited vocal articulation. Some birds have a considerable variety of notes. These are the smaller kinds. But it is the birds with talons that have the broader tongues. All birds use their tongues to communicate with each
660b other. But some do this in a greater degree than the rest; so that in some cases it even seems as though actual instruction were imparted from one to another by its agency. These, however, are matters which have already been discussed in the Researches concerning Animals.[1]

As to those oviparous and sanguineous animals that live not in the air but on the earth, their tongue in most cases is tied down and hard, and is therefore useless for vocal purposes; in the serpents, however, and in the lizards it is long and forked, so as to be suited for the perception of savours. So long indeed is this part in serpents, that though small while in the mouth it can be protruded to a great distance. In these animals it is forked and has a fine and hair-like extremity, because of their great liking for dainty food. For by this arrangement they derive a twofold pleasure from savours, their gustatory sensation being as it were doubled.

Even some bloodless animals have an organ that serves for the perception of savours; and in sanguineous animals such an organ is invariably present. For even in such of these as would seem to an ordinary observer to have nothing of the kind, some of the fishes for example, there is a kind of shabby representative of a tongue, much like what exists in river crocodiles. In most of these cases the apparent absence of the part can be rationally explained on some ground or other. For in the first place the interior of the mouth in animals of this character is invariably spinous. Secondly, in water animals there is but short space of time for the perception of savours, and as the use of this sense is thus of short duration, shortened also is the separate part which subserves it. The reason for their food being so rapidly transmitted to the stomach is that they cannot possibly spend any time in sucking out the juices; for were they to attempt to do so, the water would make its way in during the process. Unless therefore one pulls their mouth very widely open, the projection of this part is quite invisible. The region exposed by thus opening the mouth is spinous; for it is formed by the close apposition of the gills, which are of a spinous character.

In crocodiles the immobility of the lower jaw also contributes in some measure to stunt the development of the tongue. For the crocodile's tongue is adherent to the lower jaw. For its upper and lower jaws are, as it were, inverted, it being the upper jaw which in other animals is the immovable one. The tongue, however, of this animal is not attached to the upper jaw, because that would interfere with the in-

[1] Cf. *History of Animals*, II. 12 (504b 1); IV. 9 (536a 20-b 19); IX. 1 (608a 17).

gestion of food, but adheres to the lower jaw, because this is, as it were, the upper one which has changed its place. Moreover, it is the crocodile's lot, though a land animal, to live the life of a fish, and this again necessarily involves an indistinct formation of the part in question. The roof of the mouth resembles flesh, even in many of the fishes; and in some of the river species, as for instance in the fishes known as Cyprini, is so very flesh-like and soft as **661a** to be taken by careless observers for a tongue. The tongue of fishes, however, though it exists as a separate part, is never formed with such distinctness as this, as has been already explained. Again, as the gustatory sensibility is intended to serve animals in the selection of food, it is not diffused equally over the whole surface of the tongue-like organ, but is placed chiefly in the tip; and for this reason it is the tip which is the only part of the tongue separated in fishes from the rest of the mouth. As all animals are sensible to the pleasure derivable from food, they all feel a desire for it. For the object of desire is the pleasant. The part, however, by which food produces the sensation is not precisely alike in all of them, but while in some it is free from attachments, in others, where it is not required for vocal purposes, it is adherent. In some again it is hard, in others soft or flesh-like. Thus even the Crustacea, the Carabi for instance and the like, and the Cephalopods, such as the Sepias and the Poulps, have some such part inside the mouth. As for the Insects, some of them have the part which serves as tongue inside the mouth, as is the case with ants, and as is also the case with many Testacea, while in others it is placed externally. In this latter case it resembles a sting, and is hollow and spongy, so as to serve at one and the same time for the tasting and for the sucking up of nutriment. This is plainly to be seen in flies and bees and all such animals, and likewise in some of the Testacea. In the Purpurae, for instance, so strong is this part that it enables them to bore holes through the hard covering of shell-fish, of the spiral snails, for example, that are used as bait to catch them. So also the gad-flies and cattle-flies can pierce through the skin of man, and some of them even through the skins of other animals. Such, then, in these animals is the nature of the tongue, which is thus as it were the counterpart of the elephant's nostril. For as in the elephant the nostril is used as a weapon, so in these animals the tongue serves as a sting.

In all other animals the tongue agrees with the description already given.

BOOK III

I

We have next to consider the teeth, and with these the mouth, that is the cavity which they enclose and form. The teeth have one in- **661b** variable office, namely the reduction of food; but besides this general function they have other special ones, and these differ in different groups. Thus in some animals the teeth serve as weapons; but this with a distinction. For there are offensive weapons and there are defensive weapons; and while in some animals, as the wild Carnivora, the teeth answer both purposes, in many others, both wild and domesticated, they serve only for defence. In man the teeth are admirably constructed for their general office, the front ones being sharp, so as to cut the food into bits, and the hinder ones broad and flat, so as to grind it to a pulp; while between these and separating them are the dog-teeth, which, in accordance with the rule that the mean partakes of both extremes, share in the characters of those on either side, being broad in one part but sharp in another. Similar distinctions of shape are presented by the teeth of other animals, with the exception of those whose teeth are one and all of the sharp kind. In man, however, the number and the character even of these sharp teeth have been mainly determined by the requirements of speech. For the front teeth of man contribute in many ways to the formation of letter-sounds.

In some animals, however, the teeth, as already said, serve merely for the reduction of food. When, besides this, they serve as offensive and defensive weapons, they may either be formed into tusks, as for instance is the case in swine, or may be sharp-pointed and interlock with those of the opposite jaw, in which case the animal is said to be saw-toothed. The explanation of this latter arrangement is as follows. The strength of such an animal is in its teeth, and these depend for their efficiency on their sharpness. In order, then, to prevent their getting blunted by mutual friction, such of them as serve for weapons fit into each other's interspaces, and are so kept in proper condition. No animal that has sharp interfitting teeth is at the same time furnished with tusks. For nature never makes anything superfluous or in vain. She gives, therefore, tusks to such animals as strike in fighting, and serrated teeth to such as bite. Sows, for instance, have no tusks, and accordingly sows bite instead of striking.

A general principle must here be noted, which will be found applicable not only in this instance but in many others that will occur later on. Nature allots each weapon, offensive and defensive alike, to those animals alone that can use it; or, if not to them alone, to them in a more marked degree; and she allots it in its most perfect state to those that can use it best; and this whether it be a sting, or a spur, or horns, or tusks, or what it may of a like kind.

Thus as males are stronger and more choleric than females, it is in males that such parts as those just mentioned are found, either exclusively, as in some species, or more fully developed, as in others. For though females are of course provided with such parts as are no less necessary to them than to males, the parts, for instance, which subserve nutrition, they have even these in an inferior degree, and the parts which answer no such necessary purpose **662a** they do not possess at all. This explains why stags have horns, while does have none; why the horns of cows are different from those of bulls, and, similarly, the horns of ewes from those of rams. It explains also why the females are often without spurs in species where the males are provided with them, and accounts for similar facts relating to all other such parts.

All fishes have teeth of the serrated form, with the single exception of the fish known as the Scarus. In many of them there are teeth even on the tongue and on the roof of the mouth. The reason for this is that, living as they do in the water, they cannot but allow this fluid to pass into the mouth with the food. The fluid thus admitted they must necessarily discharge again without delay. For were they not to do so, but to retain it for a time while triturating the food, the water would run into their digestive cavities. Their teeth therefore are all sharp, being adapted only for cutting, and are numerous and set in many parts, that their abundance may serve in lieu of any grinding faculty, to mince the food into small bits. They are also curved, because these are almost the only weapons which fishes possess.

In all these offices of the teeth the mouth also takes its part; but besides these functions it is subservient to respiration, in all such animals as breathe and are cooled by external agency. For nature, as already said,[1] uses the parts which are common to all animals for many special purposes, and this of her own accord. Thus the mouth has one universal function in all animals alike, namely its alimentary office; but in some, besides this, the special duty of serving as a weapon is attached to it; in others that of ministering to speech; and again in many, though not in all, the office of respiration. All these functions are thrown by nature upon one single organ, the construction of which she varies so as to suit the variations of office. Therefore it is that in some animals the mouth is contracted, while in others it is of wide dimensions. The contracted form belongs to such animals as use the mouth merely for nutritive, respiratory, and vocal purposes; whereas in such as use it as a means of defence it has a wide gape. This is its invariable form in such animals as are saw-toothed. For seeing that their mode of warfare consists in biting, it is advantageous to them that their mouth shall have a wide opening; for the wider it opens, the greater will be the extent of the bite, and the more numerous will be the teeth called into play.

What has just been said applies to fishes as well as to other animals; and thus in such of them as are carnivorous, and made for biting, the mouth has a wide gape; whereas in the rest it is small, being placed at the extremity of a tapering snout. For this form is suited for their purposes, while the other would be useless.

In birds the mouth consists of what is called the beak, which in them is a substitute for lips and teeth. This beak presents variations in harmony with the functions and protective **662b** purposes which it serves. Thus in those birds that are called Crooked-clawed it is invariably hooked, inasmuch as these birds are carnivorous, and eat no kind of vegetable food whatsoever. For this form renders it serviceable to them in obtaining the mastery over their prey, and is better suited for deeds of violence than any other. Moreover, as their weapons of offence consist of this beak and of their claws, these latter also are more crooked in them than in the generality of birds. Similarly in each other kind of bird the beak is suited to the mode of life. Thus, in woodpeckers it is hard and strong, as also in crows and birds of crow-like habit, while in the smaller birds it is deli-

[1] Namely, at II. 16. (658b 35), when speaking of the elephant's trunk.

cate, so as to be of use in collecting seeds and picking up minute animals. In such birds, again, as eat herbage, and such as live about marshes—those, for example, that swim and have webbed feet—the bill is broad, or adapted in some other way to the mode of life. For a broad bill enables a bird to dig into the ground with ease, just as, among quadrupeds, does the broad snout of the pig, an animal which, like the birds in question, lives on roots. Moreover, in these root-eating birds and in some others of like habits of life, the tips of the bill end in hard points, which gives them additional facility in dealing with herbaceous food.

The several parts which are set on the head have now, pretty nearly all, been considered. In man, however, the part which lies between the head and the neck is called the face, this name (*prosōpon*) being, it would seem, derived from the function of the part. For as man is the only animal that stands erect, he is also the only one that looks directly in front (*prosō*); and the only one whose voice is emitted in that direction.

2

We have now to treat of horns; for these also, when present, are appendages of the head. They exist in none but viviparous animals; though in some ovipara certain parts are metaphorically spoken of as horns, in virtue of a certain resemblance. To none of such parts, however, does the proper office of a horn belong; for they are never used, as are the horns of vivipara, for purposes which require strength, whether it be in self-protection or in offensive strife. So also no polydactylous animal is furnished with horns. For horns are defensive weapons, and these polydactylous animals possess other means of security. For to some of them nature has given claws, to others teeth suited for combat, and to the rest some other adequate defensive appliance. There are horns, however, in most of the cloven-
663a hoofed animals, and in some of those that have a solid hoof, serving them as an offensive weapon, and in some cases also as a defensive one. There are horns also in all animals that have not been provided by nature with some other means of security; such means, for instance, as speed, which has been given to horses; or great size, as in camels; for excessive bulk, such as has been given to these animals, and in a still greater measure to elephants, is sufficient in itself to protect an animal from being destroyed by others. Other animals again are protected by the possession of tusks; and among these are the swine, though they have a cloven hoof.

All animals again, whose horns are but useless appendages, have been provided by nature with some additional means of security. Thus deer are endowed with speed; for the large size and great branching of their horns makes these a source of detriment rather than of profit to their possessors. Similarly endowed are the Bubalus and gazelle; for though these animals will stand up against some enemies and defend themselves with their horns, yet they run away from such as are fierce and pugnacious. The Bonasus again, whose horns curve inwards towards each other, is provided with a means of protection in the discharge of its excrement; and of this it avails itself when frightened. There are some other animals besides the Bonasus that have a similar mode of defence. In no case, however, does nature ever give more than one adequate means of protection to one and the same animal.

Most of the animals that have horns are cloven-hoofed; but the Indian ass, as they call it, is also reported to be horned, though its hoof is solid.

Again as the body, so far as regards its organs of motion, consists of two distinct parts, the right and the left, so also and for like reasons the horns of animals are, in the great majority of cases, two in number. Still there are some that have but a single horn; the Oryx, for instance, and the so-called Indian ass; in the former of which the hoof is cloven, while in the latter it is solid. In such animals the horn is set in the centre of the head; for as the middle belongs equally to both extremes, this arrangement is the one that comes nearest to each side having its own horn.

Again, it would appear consistent with reason that the single horn should go with the solid rather than with the cloven hoof. For hoof, whether solid or cloven, is of the same nature as horn; so that the two naturally undergo division simultaneously and in the same animals. Again, since the division of the cloven hoof depends on deficiency of material, it is but rationally consistent, that nature, when she gave an animal an excess of material for the hoofs, which thus became solid, should have taken away something from the upper parts and so made the animal to have but one horn. Rightly too did she act when she chose the head whereon to set the horns; and Æsop's Momus is beside the mark, when he finds fault with the bull for not having its horns upon its shoulders. For from this position, says he, they would have delivered their blow with the **663b** greatest force, whereas on the head they occupy the weakest part of the whole body. Momus was but dull-sighted in making this hostile criticism. For had the horns been set on the shoulders, or had they been set on any other part than they are, the encumbrance of their weight would have been increased, not only without any compensating gain whatsoever, but with the disadvantage of impeding many bodily operations. For the point whence the blows could be delivered with the greatest force was not the only matter to be considered, but the point also whence they could be delivered with the widest range. But as the bull has no hands and cannot possibly have its horns on its feet or on its knees, where they would prevent flexion, there remains no other site for them but the head; and this therefore they necessarily occupy. In this position, moreover, they are much less in the way of the movements of the body than they would be elsewhere.

Deer are the only animals in which the horns are solid throughout, and are also the only animals that cast them. This casting is not simply advantageous to the deer from the increased lightness which it produces, but, seeing how heavy the horns are, is a matter of actual necessity.

In all other animals the horns are hollow for a certain distance, and the end alone is solid, this being the part of use in a blow. At the same time, to prevent even the hollow part from being weak, the horn, though it grows out of the skin, has a solid piece from the bones fitted into its cavity. For this arrangement is not only that which makes the horns of the greatest service in fighting, but that which causes them to be as little of an impediment as possible in the other actions of life.

Such then are the reasons for which horns exist; and such the reasons why they are present in some animals, absent from others.

Let us now consider the character of the material nature whose necessary results have been made available by rational nature for a final cause.

In the first place, then, the larger the bulk of animals, the greater is the proportion of corporeal and earthy matter which they contain. Thus no very small animal is known to have horns, the smallest horned animal that we are acquainted with being the gazelle. But in all our speculations concerning nature, what we have to consider is the general rule; for that is natural which applies either universally or generally. And thus when we say that the largest animals have most earthy matter, we say so because such is the general rule. Now this earthy matter is used in the animal body to form bone. But in the larger animals there is an excess of it, and this excess is turned by nature to useful account, being converted into weapons of defence. Part of it necessarily flows to the upper portion of the body, and this is allotted by her in some cases to the formation of tusks and teeth, in others to the formation of horns. Thus it is that no animal that has horns has also front teeth in both jaws, those in **664a** the upper jaw being deficient. For nature by subtracting from the teeth adds to the horns; the nutriment which in most animals goes to the former being here spent on the augmentation of the latter. Does, it is true, have no horns and yet are equally deficient with the males as regards the teeth. The reason, however, for this is that they, as much as the males, are naturally horn-bearing animals; but they have been stripped of their horns, because these would not only be useless to them but actually baneful; whereas the greater strength of the males causes these organs, though equally useless, to be less of an impediment. In other animals, where this material is not secreted from the body in the shape of horns, it is used to increase the size of the teeth; in some cases of all the teeth, in others merely of the tusks, which thus become so long as to resemble horns projecting from the jaws.

So much, then, of the parts which appertain to the head.

3

Below the head lies the neck, in such animals as have one. This is the case with those only that have the parts to which a neck is subservient. These parts are the larynx and what is called the oesophagus. Of these the former, or larynx, exists for the sake of respiration, being the instrument by which such animals as breathe inhale and discharge the air. Therefore it is that, when there is no lung, there is also no neck. Of this condition the Fishes are an example. The other part, or oesophagus, is the channel through which food is conveyed to the stomach; so that all animals that are without a neck are also without a distinct oesophagus; Such a part is in fact not required of necessity for nutritive purposes; for it has no action whatsoever on the food. Indeed there is nothing to prevent the stomach from being placed directly after the mouth. This, however, is quite impossible in the case of the lung. For there must be some sort of tube common to the two divisions of the lung, by which—it being bipartite—the breath may be apportioned to their respective bronchi, and thence pass into the air-pipes; and such an arrangement will be the best for giving perfection to inspiration and expiration. The organ then concerned in respiration must of necessity be of some length; and this, again, necessitates there being an oesophagus to unite mouth and stomach. This oesophagus is of a flesh-like character, and yet admits of extension like a sinew. This latter property is given to it, that it may stretch when food is introduced; while the flesh-like character is intended to make it soft and yielding, and to prevent it from being rasped by particles as they pass downwards, and so suffering damage. On the other hand, the windpipe and the so-called larynx are constructed **664b** out of a cartilaginous substance. For they have to serve not only for respiration, but also for vocal purposes; and an instrument that is to produce sounds must necessarily be not only smooth but firm. The windpipe lies in front of the oesophagus, although this position causes it to be some hindrance to the latter in the act of deglutition. For if a morsel of food, fluid or solid, slips into it by accident, choking and much distress and violent fits of coughing ensue. This must be a matter of astonishment to any of those who assert that it is by the windpipe that an animal imbibes fluid. For the consequences just mentioned occur invariably, whenever a particle of food slips in, and are quite obvious. Indeed on many grounds it is ridiculous to say that this is the channel through which animals imbibe fluid. For there is no passage leading from the lung to the stomach, such as the oesophagus which we see leading thither from the mouth. Moreover, when any cause produces sickness and vomiting, it is plain enough when the fluid is discharged. It is manifest also that fluid, when swallowed, does not pass directly into the bladder and collect there, but goes first into the stomach. For, when red wine is taken, the dejections of the stomach are seen to be coloured by its dregs; and such discoloration has been even seen on many occasions inside the stomach itself, in cases where there have been wounds opening into that organ. However, it is perhaps silly to be minutely particular in dealing with silly statements such as this.

The windpipe then, owing to its position in front of the oesophagus, is exposed, as we have said, to annoyance from the food. To obviate this, however, nature has contrived the epiglottis. This part is not found in all sanguineous animals, but only in such of them as have a lung; nor in all of these, but only in such as at the same time have their skin covered with hairs, and not either with scaly plates or with feathers. In such scaly and feathered animals there is no epiglottis, but its office is supplied by the larynx, which closes and opens, just as in the other case the epiglottis falls down and rises up; rising up during the ingress or egress of breath, and falling down during the ingestion of food, so as to prevent any particle from slipping into the windpipe. Should there be the slightest want of accuracy in this movement, or should an inspiration be made during the ingestion of food, choking and coughing ensue, as already has been noticed. So admirably contrived, however, is the movement both of the epiglottis and of the tongue, that, while the food is being ground to a pulp in the mouth, the tongue very rarely gets caught between the teeth; and, while the food is passing over the epiglottis seldom does a particle of it slip into the windpipe.

665a The animals which have been mentioned as having no epiglottis owe this deficiency to the dryness of their flesh and to the hardness of their skin. For an epiglottis made of such materials would not admit of easy motion. It would, indeed, take a longer time to shut down an epiglottis made of the peculiar flesh of these animals, and shaped like that of those with hairy skins, than to bring the edges of the windpipe itself into contact with each other.

Thus much then as to the reason why some animals have an epiglottis while others have none, and thus much also as to its use. It is a contrivance of nature to remedy the vicious position of the windpipe in front of the oesophagus. That position is the result of necessity. For it is in the front and centre of the body that the heart is situated, in which we say is the principle of life and the source of all motion and sensation. (For sensation and motion are exercised in the direction which we term forwards, and it is on this very relation that the distinction of before and behind is founded.) But where the heart is, there and surrounding it is the lung. Now inspiration, which occurs for the sake of the lung and for the sake of the principle which has its seat in the heart, is effected through the windpipe. Since then the heart must of necessity lie in the very front place of all, it follows that the larynx also and the windpipe must of necessity lie in front of the oesophagus. For they lead to the lung and heart, whereas the oesophagus leads to the stomach. And it is a universal law that, as regards above and below, front and back, right and left, the nobler and more honourable part invariably is placed uppermost, in front, and on the right, rather than in the opposite positions, unless some more important object stands in the way.

4

We have now dealt with the neck, the oesophagus, and the windpipe, and have next to treat of the viscera. These are peculiar to sanguineous animals, some of which have all of them, others only a part, while no bloodless animals have any at all. Democritus then seems to have been mistaken in the notion he formed of the viscera, if, that is to say, he fancied that the reason why none were discoverable in bloodless animals was that these animals were too small to allow them to be seen. For, in sanguineous animals, both heart and liver are visible enough when the body is only just formed, and while it is still extremely small. For these parts are to be seen in the egg sometimes as early as the third day, being then no bigger **665b** than a point; and are visible also in aborted embryos, while still excessively minute. Moreover, as the external organs are not precisely alike in all animals, but each creature is provided with such as are suited to its special mode of life and motion, so is it with the internal parts, these also differing in different animals. Viscera, then, are peculiar to sanguineous animals; and therefore are each and all formed from sanguineous material, as is plainly to be seen in the new-born young of these animals. For in such the viscera are more sanguineous, and of greater bulk in proportion to the body, than at any later period of life, it being in the earliest stage of formation that the nature of the material and its abundance are most conspicuous. There is a heart, then, in all sanguineous animals, and the reason for this has already been given.[1] For that sanguineous animals must necessarily have blood is self-evident. And, as the blood is fluid, it is also a matter of necessity that there shall be a receptacle for it; and it is apparently to meet this requirement that nature has devised the blood-vessels. These, again, must necessarily have one primary source. For it is preferable that there shall be one such, when possible, rather than several. This primary source of the vessels is the heart. For the vessels manifestly issue from it and do not go through it. Moreover, being as it is homogeneous, it has the character of a blood-vessel. Again its position is that of a primary or dominating part. For nature, when no other more important purpose stands in her way, places the more honourable part in the more honourable position; and the heart lies about the centre of the body, but rather in its upper than its lower half, and also more in front than behind. This is most evident in the case of man, but even in other animals there is a tendency in the heart to assume a similar position, in the centre of the necessary part of the body, that is to say of the part which terminates in the vent for excrement. For the limbs vary in position in different animals, and are not to be counted with the parts which are necessary for life. For life can be maintained even when they are removed; while it is self-evident that the addition of them to an animal is not destructive of it.

There are some who say that the vessels commence in the head. In this they are clearly mistaken. For in the first place, according to their representation, there would be many sources for the vessels, and these scattered; and secondly, these sources would be in a region that is manifestly cold, as is shown by its intolerance of chill, whereas the region of the heart is as manifestly hot. Again, as already said, the vessels continue their course through the other viscera, but no vessel spreads through the heart. From this it is quite evident that the heart is a part of the vessels and their origin; and for this it is well suited by its structure. For its central part consists of a dense and hollow substance, and is moreover full of blood, as though **666a** the vessels took thence their origin. It is hollow to serve for the reception of the blood, while its wall is dense, that it may serve to protect the source of heat. For here, and here alone in all the viscera and indeed in all the body, there is blood without blood-vessels, the blood elsewhere being always contained within vessels. Nor is this but consistent with reason. For the blood is conveyed into the vessels from the heart, but none passes into the heart from without. For in itself it constitutes the origin and fountain, or primary receptacle, of the blood. It is however, from dissections and from observations on the process of development that the truth of these statements receives its clearest demonstration. For the heart is

[1] Cf. III. 3 (665a 12).

the first of all the parts to be formed; and no sooner is it formed than it contains blood. Moreover, the motions of pain and pleasure, and generally of all sensation, plainly have their source in the heart, and find in it their ultimate termination. This, indeed, reason would lead us to expect. For the source must, whenever possible, be one; and, of all places, the best suited for a source is the centre. For the centre is one, and is equally or almost equally within reach of every part. Again, as neither the blood itself, nor yet any part which is bloodless, is endowed with sensation, it is plain that that part which first has blood, and which holds it as it were in a receptacle, must be the primary source of sensation. And that this part is the heart is not only a rational inference, but is also evident to the senses. For no sooner is the embryo formed, than its heart is seen in motion as though it were a living creature, and this before any of the other parts, it being, as thus shown, the starting-point of their nature in all animals that have blood. A further evidence of the truth of what has been stated is the fact that no sanguineous animal is without a heart. For the primary source of blood must of necessity be present in them all. It is true that sanguineous animals not only have a heart but also invariably have a liver. But no one could ever deem the liver to be the primary organ either of the whole body or of the blood. For the position in which it is placed is far from being that of a primary or dominating part; and, moreover, in the most perfectly finished animals there is another part, the spleen, which as it were counterbalances it. Still further, the liver contains no spacious receptacle in its substance, as does the heart; but its blood is in a vessel as in all the other viscera. The vessel, moreover, extends through it, and no vessel whatsoever originates in it; for it is from the heart that all the vessels take their rise. Since then one or other of these two parts must be the central source, and since it is not the liver which is such, it follows of necessity that it is the heart which is the source of the blood, as also the primary organ in other respects. For the definitive characteristic of an animal is the possession of sensation; and the first sensory part is that which first has blood; that is to say is the heart, which is the source of blood
666b and the first of the parts to contain it.

The apex of the heart is pointed and more solid than the rest of the organ. It lies against the breast, and entirely in the anterior part of the body, in order to prevent that region from getting chilled. For in all animals there is comparatively little flesh over the breast, whereas there is a more abundant covering of that substance on the posterior surface, so that the heat has in the back a sufficient amount of protection. In all animals but man the heart is placed in the centre of the pectoral region; but in man it inclines a little towards the left, so that it may counterbalance the chilliness of that side. For the left side is colder in man, as compared with the right, than in any other animal. It has been stated in an earlier treatise[1] that even in fishes the heart holds the same position as in other animals; and the reason has been given why it appears not to do so. The apex of the heart, it is true, is in them turned towards the head, but this in fishes is the front aspect, for it is the direction in which their motion occurs.

The heart again is abundantly supplied with sinews, as might reasonably be expected. For the motions of the body commence from the heart, and are brought about by traction and relaxation. The heart therefore, which, as already said,[2] is as it were a living creature inside its possessor, requires some such subservient and strengthening parts.

In no animals does the heart contain a bone, certainly in none of those that we have ourselves inspected, with the exception of the horse and a certain kind of ox. In these exceptional cases the heart, owing to its large bulk, is provided with a bone as a support; just as the bones serve as supports for the body generally.

In animals of great size the heart has three cavities; in smaller animals it has two; and in all has at least one, for, as already stated,[3] there must be some place in the heart to serve as a receptacle for the first blood; which, as has been mentioned more than once, is formed in this organ. But inasmuch as the main blood-vessels are two in number, namely the so-called great vessel and the aorta, each of which is the origin of other vessels; inasmuch, moreover, as these two vessels present differences, hereafter to be discussed,[4] when compared with each other, it is of advantage that they also shall themselves have distinct origins. This advantage will be obtained if each side have its own blood, and the blood of one side be kept separate from that of the other. For this reason the heart, whenever it is possible, has two receptacles. And this possibility exists in the case of large animals, for in them the heart, as the

[1] *On Breathing*, 16, 478b 3. [2] III. 666a 22.
[3] Cf. 666a 7. [4] Cf. III. 5 (667b 15).

body generally, is of large size. Again it is still better that there shall be three cavities, so that the middle and odd one may serve as a centre common to both sides. But this requires the heart to be of greater magnitude, so that it is only in the largest hearts that there are three cavities.

667a Of these three cavities it is the right that has the most abundant and the hottest blood, and this explains why the limbs also on the right side of the body are warmer than those on the left. The left cavity has the least blood of all, and the coldest; while in the middle cavity the blood, as regards quantity and heat, is intermediate to the other two, being however of purer quality than either. For it behoves the supreme part to be as tranquil as possible, and this tranquillity can be ensured by the blood being pure, and of moderate amount and warmth.

In the heart of animals there is also a kind of joint-like division, something like the sutures of the skull. This is not, however, attributable to the heart being formed by the union of several parts into a compound whole, but is rather, as already said, the result of a joint-like division. These jointings are most distinct in animals of keen sensibility, and less so in those that are of duller feeling, in swine for instance. Different hearts differ also from each other in their sizes, and in their degrees of firmness; and these differences somehow extend their influence to the temperaments of the animals. For in animals of low sensibility the heart is hard and dense in texture, while it is softer in such as are endowed with keener feeling. So also when the heart is of large size the animal is timorous, while it is more courageous if the organ be smaller and of moderate bulk. For in the former the bodily affection which results from terror already pre-exists; for the bulk of the heart is out of all proportion to the animal's heat, which being small is reduced to insignificance in the large space, and thus the blood is made colder than it would otherwise be.

The heart is of large size in the hare, the deer, the mouse, the hyena, the ass, the leopard, the marten, and in pretty nearly all other animals that either are manifestly timorous, or betray their cowardice by their spitefulness.

What has been said of the heart as a whole is no less true of its cavities and of the blood-vessels; these also if of large size being cold. For just as a fire of equal size gives less heat in a large room than in a small one, so also does the heat in a large cavity or a large blood-vessel, that is in a large receptacle, have less effect than in a small one. Moreover, all hot bodies are cooled by motions external to themselves, and the more spacious the cavities and vessels are, the greater the amount of spirit they contain, and the more potent its action. Thus it is that no animal that has large cavities in its heart, or large blood-vessels, is ever fat, the vessels being indistinct and the cavities small in all or most fat animals.

The heart again is the only one of the viscera, and indeed the only part of the body, that is unable to tolerate any serious affection. This is but what might reasonably be expected. For, if the primary or dominant part be diseased, there is nothing from which the other parts which depend upon it can derive succour. A **667b** proof that the heart is thus unable to tolerate any morbid affection is furnished by the fact that in no sacrificial victim has it ever been seen to be affected with those diseases that are observable in the other viscera. For the kidneys are frequently found to be full of stones, and growths, and small abscesses, as also are the liver, the lung, and more than all the spleen. There are also many other morbid conditions which are seen to occur in these parts, those which are least liable to such being the portion of the lung which is close to the windpipe, and the portion of the liver which lies about the junction with the great blood-vessel. This again admits of a rational explanation. For it is in these parts that the lung and liver are most closely in communion with the heart. On the other hand, when animals die not by sacrifice but from disease, and from affections such as are mentioned above, they are found on dissection to have morbid affections of the heart.

Thus much of the heart, its nature, and the end and cause of its existence in such animals as have it.

5

In due sequence we have next to discuss the blood-vessels, that is to say the great vessel and the aorta. For it is into these two that the blood first passes when it quits the heart; and all the other vessels are but offshoots from them. Now that these vessels exist on account of the blood has already been stated. For every fluid requires a receptacle, and in the case of the blood the vessels are that receptacle. Let us now explain why these vessels are two, and why they spring from one single source, and extend throughout the whole body.

The reason, then, why these two vessels coalesce into one centre, and spring from one source, is that the sensory soul is in all animals actually one; and this one-ness of the sensory soul determines a corresponding one-ness of the part in which it primarily abides. In sanguineous animals this one-ness is not only actual but potential, whereas in some bloodless animals it is only actual. Where, however, the sensory soul is lodged, there also and in the selfsame place must necessarily be the source of heat; and, again, where this is there also must be the source of the blood, seeing that it thence derives its warmth and fluidity. Thus, then, in the oneness of the part in which is lodged the prime source of sensation and of heat is involved the one-ness of the source in which the blood originates; and this, again, explains why the blood-vessels have one common starting-point.

The vessels, again, are two, because the body of every sanguineous animal that is capable of locomotion is bilateral; for in all such animals there is a distinguishable before and behind, a right and left, an above and below. Now as the front is more honourable and of higher supremacy than the hinder aspect, so also **668a** and in like degree is the great vessel superior to the aorta. For the great vessel is placed in front, while the aorta is behind; the former again is plainly visible in all sanguineous animals, while the latter is in some indistinct and in some not discernible at all.

Lastly, the reason for the vessels being distributed throughout the entire body is that in them, or in parts analogous to them, is contained the blood, or the fluid which in bloodless animals takes the place of blood, and that the blood or analogous fluid is the material from which the whole body is made. Now as to the manner in which animals are nourished, and as to the source from which they obtain nutriment and as to the way in which they absorb this from the stomach, these are matters which may be more suitably considered and explained in the treatise on Generation.[1] But inasmuch as the parts are, as already said, formed out of the blood, it is but rational that the flow of the blood should extend, as it does, throughout the whole of the body. For since each part is formed of blood, each must have blood about and in its substance.

To give an illustration of this. The water-courses in gardens are so constructed as to distribute water from one single source or fount into numerous channels, which divide and subdivide so as to convey it to all parts; and, again, in house-building stones are thrown down along the whole ground-plan of the foundation walls; because the garden-plants in the one case grow at the expense of the water, and the foundation walls in the other are built out of the stones. Now just after the same fashion has nature laid down channels for the conveyance of the blood throughout the whole body, because this blood is the material out of which the whole fabric is made. This becomes very evident in bodies that have undergone great emaciation. For in such there is nothing to be seen but the blood-vessels; just as when fig-leaves or vine-leaves or the like have dried up, there is nothing left of them but their vessels. The explanation of this is that the blood, or fluid which takes its place, is potentially body and flesh, or substance analogous to flesh. Now just as in irrigation the largest dykes are permanent, while the smallest are soon filled up with mud and disappear, again to become visible when the deposit of mud ceases; so also do the largest blood-vessels remain permanently open, while the smallest are converted actually into flesh, though potentially they are no whit less vessels than before. This too explains why, so long as the flesh of an animal is in its integrity, blood will flow from any part of it whatsoever that is cut, though no vessel, however small, be visible in it. Yet there can be no blood, unless there be a blood-vessel. The vessels then are there, but are invisible owing to their being clogged up, just as the dykes for irrigation are invisible until they have been cleared of mud.

668b As the blood-vessels advance, they become gradually smaller and smaller, until at last their tubes are too fine to admit the blood. This fluid can therefore no longer find its way through them, though they still give passage to the humour which we call sweat; and especially so when the body is heated, and the mouths of the small vessels are dilated. Instances, indeed, are not unknown of persons who in consequence of a cachectic state have secreted sweat that resembled blood, their body having become loose and flabby, and their blood watery, owing to the heat in the small vessels having been too scanty for its concoction. For, as was before said, every compound of earth and water—and both nutriment and blood are such—becomes thicker from concoction. The

[1] *On the Generation of Animals*, II. 4 (740a 21-b 12); 6 (743a 8)-7 (746a 28).

inability of the heat to effect concoction may be due either to its being absolutely small in amount, or to its being small in proportion to the quantity of food, when this has been taken in excess. This excess again may be of two kinds, either quantitative or qualitative; for all substances are not equally amenable to concoction.

The widest passages in the body are of all parts the most liable to haemorrhage; so that bleeding occurs not infrequently from the nostrils, the gums, and the fundament, occasionally also from the mouth. Such haemorrhages are of a passive kind, and not violent as are those from the windpipe.

The great vessel and the aorta, which above lie somewhat apart, lower down exchange positions, and by so doing give compactness to the body. For when they reach the point where the legs diverge, they each split into two, and the great vessel passes from the front to the rear, and the aorta from the rear to the front. By this they contribute to the unity of the whole fabric. For as in plaited work the parts hold more firmly together because of the interweaving, so also by the interchange of position between the blood-vessels are the anterior and posterior parts of the body more closely knit together. A similar exchange of position occurs also in the upper part of the body, between the vessels that have issued from the heart. The details however of the mutual relations of the different vessels must be looked for in the treatises on Anatomy and the Researches concerning Animals.[1]

So much, then, as concerns the heart and the blood-vessels. We must now pass on to the other viscera and apply the same method of inquiry to them.

6

The lung, then, is an organ found in all the animals of a certain class, because they live on land. For there must of necessity be some means or other of tempering the heat of the body; and in sanguineous animals, as they are of an especially hot nature, the cooling agency must be external, whereas in the blood- **669a** less kinds the innate spirit is sufficient of itself for the purpose. The external cooling agent must be either air or water. In fishes the agent is water. Fishes therefore never have a lung, but have gills in its place, as was stated in the treatise on Respiration.[2] But animals that breathe are cooled by air. These therefore are all provided with a lung.

All land animals breathe, and even some water animals, such as the whale, the dolphin, and all the spouting Cetacea. For many animals lie half-way between terrestrial and aquatic; some that are terrestrial and that inspire air being nevertheless of such a bodily constitution that they abide for the most time in the water; and some that are aquatic partaking so largely of the land character, that respiration constitutes for them the man condition of life.

The organ of respiration is the lung. This derives its motion from the heart; but it is its own large size and spongy texture that affords amplitude of space for the entrance of the breath. For when the lung rises up the breath streams in, and is again expelled when the lung collapses. It has been said[3] that the lung exists as a provision to meet the jumping of the heart. But this is out of the question. For man is practically the only animal whose heart presents this phenomenon of jumping, inasmuch as he alone is influenced by hope and anticipation of the future. Moreover, in most animals the lung is separated from the heart by a considerable interval and lies above it, so that it can contribute nothing to mitigate any jumping.

The lung differs much in different animals. For in some it is of large size and contains blood; while in others it is smaller and of spongy texture. In the vivipara it is large and rich in blood, because of their natural heat; while in the ovipara it is small and dry but capable of expanding to a vast extent when inflated. Among terrestrial animals, the oviparous quadrupeds, such as lizards, tortoises, and the like, have this kind of lung; and, among inhabitants of the air, the animals known as birds. For in all these the lung is spongy, and like foam. For it is membranous and collapses from a large bulk to a small one, as does foam when it runs together. In this too lies the explanation of the fact that these animals are little liable to thirst and drink but sparingly, and that they are able to remain **669b** for a considerable time under water. For, inasmuch as they have but little heat, the very motion of the lung, airlike and void, suffices by itself to cool them for a considerable period.

These animals, speaking generally, are also distinguished from others by their smaller bulk. For heat promotes growth, and abundance of blood is a sure indication of heat. Heat, again,

[1] Cf. *History of Animals*, I. 17; III. 2-4.

[2] *On Breathing*, 10, 475b 15 sqq.

[3] Plato, *Timaeus*, 70.

tends to make the body erect; and thus it is that man is the most erect of animals, and the vivipara more erect than other quadrupeds. For no viviparous animal, be it apodous or be it possessed of feet, is so given to creep into holes as are the ovipara.

The lung, then, exists for respiration; and this is its universal office; but in one order of animals it is bloodless and has the structure described above, to suit the special requirements. There is, however, no one term to denote all animals that have a lung; no designation, that is, like the term Bird, applicable to the whole of a certain class. Yet the possession of a lung is a part of their essence, just as much as the presence of certain characters constitutes the essence of a bird.

7

Of the viscera some appear to be single, as the heart and lung; others to be double, as the kidneys; while of a third kind it is doubtful in which class they should be reckoned. For the liver and the spleen would seem to lie half-way between the single and the double organs. For they may be regarded either as constituting each a single organ, or as a pair of organs resembling each other in character.

In reality, however, all the organs are double. The reason for this is that the body itself is double, consisting of two halves, which are however combined together under one supreme centre. For there is an upper and a lower half, a front and a rear, a right side and a left.

This explains why it is that even the brain and the several organs of sense tend in all animals to consist of two parts; and the same explanation applies to the heart with its cavities. The lung again in Ovipara is divided to such an extent that these animals look as though they had actually two lungs. As to the kidneys, no one can overlook their double character. But when we come to the liver and the spleen, any one might fairly be in doubt. The reason of this is, that, in animals that necessarily have a spleen, this organ is such that it might be taken for a kind of bastard liver; while in those in which a spleen is not an actual necessity but is merely present, as it were, by way of token, in an extremely minute form, the liver plainly consists of two parts; of which the larger tends to lie on the right side and the smaller on the left. Not but what there are some even of the Ovipara in which this condition is comparatively indistinctly marked; while, on the other hand, there are some Vivipara in which the liver is manifestly divided into two parts. Examples of such division are furnished by the hares of certain regions, which have the appearance of having two livers, and by the cartilaginous and some other fishes.

It is the position of the liver on the right side
670a of the body that is the main cause for the formation of the spleen; the existence of which thus becomes to a certain extent a matter of necessity in all animals, though not of very stringent necessity.

The reason, then, why the viscera are bilateral is, as we have said, that there are two sides to the body, a right and a left. For each of these sides aims at similarity with the other, and so likewise do their several viscera; and as the sides, though dual, are knit together into unity, so also do the viscera tend to be bilateral and yet one by unity of constitution.

Those viscera which lie below the diaphragm exist one and all on account of the blood-vessels; serving as a bond, by which these vessels, while floating freely, are yet held in connexion with the body. For the vessels give off branches which run to the body through the outstretched structures, like so many anchor-lines thrown out from a ship. The great vessel sends such branches to the liver and the spleen; and these viscera—the liver and spleen on either side with the kidneys behind—attach the great vessel to the body with the firmness of nails. The aorta sends similar branches to each kidney, but none to the liver or spleen.

These viscera, then, contribute in this manner to the compactness of the animal body. The liver and spleen assist, moreover, in the concoction of the food; for both are of a hot character, owing to the blood which they contain. The kidneys, on the other hand, take part in the separation of the excretion which flows into the bladder.

The heart then and the liver are essential constituents of every animal; the liver that it may effect concoction, the heart that it may lodge the central source of heat. For some part or other there must be which, like a hearth, shall hold the kindling fire; and this part must be well protected, seeing that it is, as it were, the citadel of the body.

All sanguineous animals, then, need these two parts; and this explains why these two viscera, and these two alone, are invariably found in them all. In such of them, however, as breathe, there is also as invariably a third, namely the lung. The spleen, on the other hand, is not invariably present; and, in those animals that have it, is only present of necessity in the same sense as the excretions of the belly and of the bladder are necessary, in the sense, that is, of being an inevitable concomitant. Therefore it is that in some animals the spleen is but scantily developed as regards size. This, for instance, is the case in such feathered animals as have a hot stomach. Such are the **670b** pigeon, the hawk, and the kite. It is the case also in oviparous quadrupeds, where the spleen is excessively minute, and in many of the scaly fishes. These same animals are also without a blader, because the loose texture of their flesh allows the residual fluid to pass through and to be applied to the formation of feathers and scales. For the spleen attracts the residual humours from the stomach, and owing to its bloodlike character is enabled to assist in their concoction. Should, however, this residual fluid be too abundant, or the heat of the spleen be too scanty, the body becomes sickly from over-repletion with nutriment. Often, too, when the spleen is affected by disease, the belly becomes hard owing to the reflux into it of the fluid; just as happens to those who form too much urine, for they also are liable to a similar diversion of the fluids into the belly. But in those animals that have but little superfluous fluid to excrete, such as birds and fishes, the spleen is never large, and in some exists no more than by way of token. So also in the oviparous quadrupeds it is small, compact, and like a kidney. For their lung is spongy, and they drink but little, and such superfluous fluid as they have is applied to the growth of the body and the formation of scaly plates, just as in birds it is applied to the formation of feathers.

On the other hand, in such animals as have a bladder, and whose lung contains blood, the spleen is watery, both for the reason already mentioned, and also because the left side of the body is more watery and colder than the right. For each of two contraries has been so placed as to go together with that which is akin to it in another pair of contraries. Thus right and left, hot and cold, are pairs of contraries; and right is conjoined with hot, after the manner described, and left with cold.

The kidneys when they are present exist not of actual necessity, but as matters of greater finish and perfection. For by their special character they are suited to serve in the excretion of the fluid which collects in the bladder. In animals therefore where this fluid is very abundantly formed, their presence enables the bladder to perform its proper office with greater perfection.

Since then both kidneys and bladder exist in animals for one and the same function, we must next treat of the bladder, though in so doing we disregard the due order of succession in which the parts should be enumerated. For not a word has yet been said of the midriff, which is one of the parts that environ the viscera and therefore has to be considered with them.

8

It is not every animal that has a bladder; those only being apparently intended by nature to have one, whose lung contains blood. To such **671a** it was but reasonable that she should give this part. For the superabundance in their lung of its natural constituents causes them to be the thirstiest of animals, and makes them require a more than ordinary quantity not merely of solid but also of liquid nutriment. This increased consumption necessarily entails the production of an increased amount of residue; which thus becomes too abundant to be concocted by the stomach and excreted with its own residual matter. The residual fluid must therefore of necessity have a receptacle of its own; and thus it comes to pass that all animals whose lung contains blood are provided with a bladder. Those animals, on the other hand, that are without a lung of this character, and that either drink but sparingly owing to their lung being of a spongy texture, or never imbibe fluid at all for drinking's sake but only as nutriment, insects for instance and fishes, and that are moreover clad with feathers or scales or scaly plates—all these animals, owing to the small amount of fluid which they imbibe, and owing also to such residue as there may be being converted into feathers and the like, are invariably without a bladder. The Tortoises, which are comprised among animals with scaly plates, form the only exception; and this is merely due to the imperfect development of their natural conformation; the explanation of the matter being that in the sea-tortoises the lung is flesh-like and contains blood, resembling the lung of the ox, and that in the land-tortoises it is of disproportionately large size. Moreover, inasmuch as the covering which invests them is dense and shell-like, so that the moisture cannot exhale through the porous flesh, as it does in birds and in snakes and other animals with scaly plates, such an amount of secretion is formed that some special part is required to receive and hold it. This then is the reason why these animals, alone of their kind, have a bladder, the sea-tortoise a large one, the land-tortoises an extremely small one.

9

What has been said of the bladder is equally true of the kidneys. For these also are wanting in all animals that are clad with feathers or with scales or with scale-like plates; the sea and land tortoises forming the only exception. In some of the birds, however, there are flattened kidney-like bodies, as though the flesh allotted to the formation of the kidneys, unable to find one single place of sufficient size, had been scattered over several.

The Emys has neither bladder nor kidneys. For the softness of its shell allows of the ready transpiration of fluid; and for this reason neither of the organs mentioned exists in this animal. All other animals, however, whose lung contains blood are, as before said, provid-
671b ed with kidneys. For nature uses these organs for two separate purposes, namely for the excretion of the residual fluid, and to subserve the blood-vessels, a channel leading to them from the great vessel.

In the centre of the kidney is a cavity of variable size. This is the case in all animals, excepting the seal. The kidneys of this animal are more solid than those of any other, and in form resemble the kidneys of the ox. The human kidneys are of similar shape; being as it were made up of numerous small kidneys, and not presenting one unbroken surface like the kidneys of sheep and other quadrupeds. For this reason, should the kidneys of a man be once attacked by disease, the malady is not easily expelled. For it is as though many kidneys were diseased and not merely one; which naturally enhances the difficulties of a cure.

The duct which runs to the kidney from the great vessel does not terminate in the central cavity, but is expended on the substance of the organ, so that there is no blood in the cavity, nor is any coagulum found there after death. A pair of stout ducts, void of blood, run, one from the cavity of each kidney, to the bladder; and other ducts, strong and continuous, lead into the kidneys from the aorta. The purpose of this arrangement is to allow the superfluous fluid to pass from the blood-vessel into the kidney, and the resulting renal excretion to collect by the percolation of the fluid through the solid substance of the organ, in its centre, where as a general rule there is a cavity. (This by the way explains why the kidney is the most ill-savoured of all the viscera.) From the central cavity the fluid is discharged into the bladder by the ducts that have been mentioned, having already assumed in great degree the character of excremental residue. The bladder is as it were moored to the kidneys; for, as already has been stated, it is attached to them by strong ducts. These then are the purposes for which the kidneys exist, and such the functions of these organs.

In all animals that have kidneys, that on the right is placed higher than that on the left. For, inasmuch as motion commences from the right, and the organs on this side are in consequence stronger than those on the left, they must all push upwards in advance of their opposite fellows; as may be seen in the fact that men even raise the right eyebrow more than the left, and that the former is more arched than the latter. The right kidney being thus drawn upwards is in all animals brought into contact with the liver; for the liver lies on the right side.

672a Of all the viscera the kidneys are those that have the most fat. This is in the first place the result of necessity, because the kidneys are the parts through which the residual matters percolate. For the blood which is left behind after this excretion, being of pure quality, is of easy concoction, and the final result of thorough blood-concoction is lard and suet. For just as a certain amount of fire is left in the ashes of solid substances after combustion, so also does a remnant of the heat that has been developed remain in fluids after concoction; and this is the reason why oily matter is light, and floats on the surface of other fluids. The fat is not formed in the kidneys themselves, the density of their substance forbidding this, but is deposited about their external surface. It consists of lard or of suet, according as the animal's fat is of the former or latter character. The difference between these two kinds of fat has already been set forth in other passages.[1] The formation, then, of fat in the kidneys is the result of necessity; being, as explained, a consequence of the necessary conditions which accompany the possession of such organs. But at the same time the fat has a final cause, namely to ensure the safety of the kidneys, and to maintain their natural heat. For placed, as these organs are, close to the surface, they require a

[1] Cf. II. 5; *History of Animals*, III. 17.

greater supply of heat than other parts. For while the back is thickly covered with flesh, so as to form a shield for the heart and neighbouring viscera, the loins, in accordance with a rule that applies to all bendings, are destitute of flesh; and fat is therefore formed as a substitute for it, so that the kidneys may not be without protection. The kidneys, moreover, by being fat are the better enabled to secrete and concoct their fluid; for fat is hot, and it is heat that effects concoction.

Such, then, are the reasons why the kidneys are fat. But in all animals the right kidney is less fat than its fellow. The reason for this is, that the parts on the right side are naturally more solid and more suited for motion than those on the left. But motion is antagonistic to fat, for it tends to melt it.

Animals then, as a general rule, derive advantage from their kidneys being fat; and the fat is often very abundant and extends over the whole of these organs. But, should the like occur in the sheep, death ensues. Be its kidneys, however, as fat as they may, they are never so fat but that some part, if not in both at any rate in the right one, is left free. The reason why sheep are the only animals that suffer in this manner, or suffer more than others, is that in animals whose fat is composed of lard this is of fluid consistency, so that there is not the same chance in their case of wind getting shut in and causing mischief. But it is to such an enclosure of wind that rot is due. And thus even in men, though it is beneficial to them to have fat kidneys, yet should these organs become over-fat and diseased, deadly pains ensue. As to those animals whose fat con-
672b sists of suet, in none is the suet so dense as in the sheep, neither is it nearly so abundant; for of all animals there is none in which the kidneys become so soon gorged with fat as in the sheep. Rot, then, is produced by the moisture and the wind getting shut up in the kidneys, and is a malady that carries off sheep with great rapidity. For the disease forthwith reaches the heart, passing thither by the aorta and the great vessel, the ducts which connect these with the kidneys being of unbroken continuity.

10

We have now dealt with the heart and the lung, as also with the liver, spleen, and kidneys. The latter are separated from the former by the midriff or, as some call it, the *Phrenes*. This divides off the heart and lung, and, as already said, is called *Phrenes* in sanguineous animals, all of which have a midriff, just as they all have a heart and a liver. For they require a midriff to divide the region of the heart from the region of the stomach, so that the centre wherein abides the sensory soul may be undisturbed, and not be overwhelmed, directly food is taken, by its up-steaming vapour and by the abundance of heat then superinduced. For it was to guard against this that nature made a division, constructing the midriff as a kind of partition-wall and fence, and so separated the nobler from the less noble parts, in all cases where a separation of upper from lower is possible. For the upper part is the more honourable, and is that for the sake of which the rest exists; while the lower part exists for the sake of the upper and constitutes the necessary element in the body, inasmuch as it is the recipient of the food.

That portion of the midriff which is near the ribs is fleshier and stronger than the rest, but the central part has more of a membranous character; for this structure conduces best to its strength and its extensibility. Now that the midriff, which is a kind of outgrowth from the sides of the thorax, acts as a screen to prevent heat mounting up from below, is shown by what happens, should it, owing to its proximity to the stomach, attract thence the hot and residual fluid. For when this occurs there ensues forthwith a marked disturbance of intellect and of sensation. It is indeed because of this that the midriff is called *Phrenes,* as though it had some share in the process of thinking (*Phronein*). In reality, however, it has no part whatsoever itself in the matter, but, lying in close proximity to organs that have, it brings about the manifest changes of intelligence in question by acting upon them. This too explains why its central part is thin. For though this is in some measure the result of necessity, inasmuch as those portions of the fleshy whole which lie nearest to the ribs must necessarily be fleshier than the rest, yet besides this there is a final cause, namely to give it as small a proportion of humour as possible;
673a for, had it been made of flesh throughout, it would have been more likely to attract and hold a large amount of this. That heating of it affects sensation rapidly and in a notable manner is shown by the phenomena of laughing. For when men are tickled they are quickly set a-laughing, because the motion quickly reaches this part, and heating it though but slightly nevertheless manifestly so disturbs the

mental action as to occasion movements that are independent of the will. That man alone is affected by tickling is due firstly to the delicacy of his skin, and secondly to his being the only animal that laughs. For to be tickled is to be set in laughter, the laughter being produced by such a motion as mentioned of the region of the armpit.

It is said also that when men in battle are wounded anywhere near the midriff, they are seen to laugh, owing to the heat produced by the wound. This may possibly be the case. At any rate it is a statement made by much more credible persons than those who tell the story of the human head, how it speaks after it is cut off. For so some assert, and even call in Homer to support them, representing him as alluding to this when he wrote,[1] 'His head still speaking rolled into the dust,' instead of 'The head of the speaker'. So fully was the possibility of such an occurrence accepted in Caria, that one of that country was actually brought to trial under the following circumstances. The priest of Zeus Hoplosmios had been murdered; but as yet it had not been ascertained who was the assassin; when certain persons asserted that they had heard the murdered man's head, which had been severed from the body, repeat several times the words, 'Cercidas slew man on man.' Search was thereupon made and a man of those parts who bore the name of Cercidas hunted out and put upon his trial. But it is impossible that any one should utter a word when the windpipe is severed and no motion any longer derived from the lung. Moreover, among the Barbarians, where heads are chopped off with great rapidity, nothing of the kind has ever yet occurred. Why, again, does not the like occur in the case of other animals than man? For that none of them should laugh, when their midriff is wounded, is but what one would expect; for no animal but man ever laughs. So, too, there is nothing irrational in supposing that the trunk may run forwards to a certain distance after the head has been cut off; seeing that bloodless animals at any rate can live, and that for a considerable time, after decapitation, as has been set forth and explained in other passages.[2]

The purposes, then, for which the viscera severally exist have now been stated. It is of necessity upon the inner terminations of the vessels that they are developed; for humour, and that of a bloody character, cannot but exude at **673b** these points, and it is of this, solidified and coagulated, that the substance of the viscera is formed. Thus they are of a bloody character, and in substance resemble each other while they differ from other parts.

[1] *Iliad*, x. 457; *Odyssey*, xxii. 329.

[2] Cf. iii. 5 (677b 27); *On the Soul*, i. 5 (411b 19); ii. 2 (413b 20); *On Longevity and the Shortness of Life*, 6 (467a 19); *On Life and Death*, 2 (468a 25, b 2); *On Breathing*, 3 (471b 20); *History of Animals*, iv. 7 (531b 30-532a 5); *On the Gait of Animals*, 7 (707a 27).

11

The viscera are enclosed each in a membrane. For they require some covering to protect them from injury, and require, moreover, that this covering shall be light. To such requirements membrane is well adapted; for it is close in texture so as to form a good protection, destitute of flesh so as neither to attract humour nor retain it, and thin so as to be light and not add to the weight of the body. Of the membranes those are the stoutest and strongest which invest the heart and the brain; as is but consistent with reason. For these are the parts which require most protection, seeing that they are the main governing powers of life, and that it is to governing powers that guard is due.

12

Some animals have all the viscera that have been enumerated; others have only some of them. In what kind of animals this latter is the case, and what is the explanation, has already been stated.[3] Moreover, the self-same viscera present differences in different possessors. For the heart is not precisely alike in all animals that have one; nor, in fact, is any viscus whatsoever. Thus the liver is in some animals split into several parts, while in others it is comparatively undivided. Such differences in its form present themselves even among those sanguineous animals that are viviparous, but are more marked in fishes and in the oviparous quadrupeds, and this whether we compare them with each other or with the Vivipara. As for birds, their liver very nearly resembles that of the Vivipara; for in them, as in these, it is of a pure and blood-like colour. The reason of this is that the body in both these classes of animals admits of the freest exhalation, so that the amount of foul residual matter within is but small. Hence it is that some of the Vivipara are without any gall-bladder at all. For the liver takes a large share in maintaining the purity of composition and the healthiness of the body. For these are conditions that depend fi-

[3] Cf. iii. 4 (665a 29).

nally and in the main upon the blood, and there is more blood in the liver than in any of the other viscera, the heart only excepted. On the other hand, the liver of oviparous quadrupeds and fishes inclines, as a rule, to a yellow hue, and there are even some of them in which it is entirely of this bad colour, in accordance with the bad composition of their bodies generally. Such, for instance, is the case in the toad, the tortoise, and other similar animals.

The spleen, again, varies in different animals. For in those that have horns and cloven hoofs, such as the goat, the sheep, and the like, it is of a rounded form; excepting when increased size has caused some part of it to ex- **674a** tend its growth longitudinally, as has happened in the case of the ox. On the other hand, it is elongated in all polydactylous animals. Such, for instance, is the case in the pig, in man, and in the dog. While in animals with solid hoofs it is of a form intermediate to these two, being broad in one part, narrow in another. Such, for example, is its shape in the horse, the mule, and the ass.

13

The viscera differ from the flesh not only in the turgid aspect of their substance, but also in position; for they lie within the body, whereas the flesh is placed on the outside. The explanation of this is that these parts partake of the character of blood-vessels, and that while the former exist for the sake of the vessels, the latter cannot exist without them.

14

Below the midriff lies the stomach, placed at the end of the oesophagus when there is one, and in immediate contiguity with the mouth when the oesophagus is wanting. Continuous with this stomach is what is called the gut. These parts are present in all animals, for reasons that are self-evident. For it is a matter of necessity that an animal shall receive the incoming food; and necessary also that it shall discharge the same when its goodness is exhausted. This residual matter, again, must not occupy the same place as the yet unconcocted nutriment. For as the ingress of food and the discharge of the residue occur at distinct periods, so also must they necessarily occur in distinct places. Thus there must be one receptacle for the ingoing food and another for the useless residue, and between these, therefore, a part in which the change from one condition to the other may be effected. These, however, are matters which will be more suitably set forth when we come to deal with Generation and Nutrition.[1] What we have at present to consider are the variations presented by the stomach and its subsidiary parts. For neither in size nor in shape are these parts uniformly alike in all animals. Thus the stomach is single in all such sanguineous and viviparous animals as have teeth in front of both jaws. It is single therefore in all the polydactylous kinds, such as man, dog, lion, and the rest; in all the solid-hoofed animals also, such as horse, mule, ass; and in all those which, like the pig, though their hoof is cloven, yet have front teeth in both jaws. When, however, an animal is of large size, and feeds on substances of so thorny and ligneous a character as to be difficult of concoction, it may in consequence have several stomachs, as for instance is the case with the camel. A similar multiplicity of stomachs exists also in the horned animals; the reason being that horn-bearing animals have no front teeth in the upper jaw. The camel also, though it has no horns, is yet without upper front teeth. The explanation of this is that it is more essential for the camel to have a multiple stomach than to have these teeth. Its stomach, then, is constructed like that of animals without up- **674b** per front teeth, and, its dental arrangements being such as to match its stomach, the teeth in question are wanting. They would indeed be of no service. Its food, moreover, being of a thorny character, and its tongue necessarily made of a fleshy substance, nature uses the earthy matter which is saved from the teeth to give hardness to the palate. The camel ruminates like the horned animals, because its multiple stomach resembles theirs. For all animals that have horns, the sheep for instance, the ox, the goat, the deer, and the like, have several stomachs. For since the mouth, owing to its lack of teeth, only imperfectly performs its office as regards the food, this multiplicity of stomachs is intended to make up for its shortcomings; the several cavities receiving the food one from the other in succession; the first taking the unreduced substances, the second the same when somewhat reduced, the third when reduction is complete, and the fourth when the whole has become a smooth pulp. Such is the reason why there is this multiplicity of parts and cavities in animals with such dentition. The names given to the several cavities are the paunch, the honeycomb bag,

[1] *On the Generation of Animals*, II. 4 (740a 21-b 12); 6 (743a 8)-7 (746a 28).

the manyplies, and the reed. How these parts are related to each other, in position and in shape, must be looked for in the treatises on Anatomy and the Researches concerning Animals.[1]

Birds also present variations in the part which acts as a recipient of the food; and the reason for these variations is the same as in the animals just mentioned. For here again it is because the mouth fails to perform its office and fails even more completely—for birds have no teeth at all, nor any instrument whatsoever with which to comminute or grind down their food—it is, I say, because of this, that in some of them what is called the crop precedes the stomach and does the work of the mouth; while in others the oesophagus is either wide throughout or a part of it bulges just before it enters the stomach, so as to form a preparatory store-house for the unreduced food; or the stomach itself has a protuberance in some part, or is strong and fleshy, so as to be able to store up the food for a considerable period and to concoct it, in spite of its not having been ground into a pulp. For nature retrieves the inefficiency of the mouth by increasing the efficiency and heat of the stomach. Other birds there are, such, namely, as have long legs and live in marshes, that have none of these provisions, but merely an elongated oesophagus. The explanation of this is to be found in the moist character of their food. For all these birds feed on substances easy of reduction, and their food being moist and not requiring much concoction, their digestive cavities are of a corresponding character.

675a Fishes are provided with teeth, which in almost all of them are of the sharp interfitting kind. For there is but one small section in which it is otherwise. Of these the fish called Scarus (*Parrot-fish*) is an example. And this is probably the reason why this fish apparently ruminates, though no other fishes do so. For those horned animals that have no front teeth in the upper jaw also ruminate.

In fishes the teeth are all sharp; so that these animals can divide their food, though imperfectly. For it is impossible for a fish to linger or spend time in the act of mastication, and therefore they have no teeth that are flat or suitable for grinding; for such teeth would be to no purpose. The oesophagus again in some fishes is entirely wanting, and in the rest is but short. In order, however, to facilitate the concoction of the food, some of them, as the Cestreus (*mullet*), have a fleshy stomach resembling that of a bird; while most of them have numerous processes close against the stomach, to serve as a sort of antechamber in which the food may be stored up and undergo putrefaction and concoction. There is a contrast between fishes and birds in the position of these processes. For in fishes they are placed close to the stomach; while in birds, if present at all, they are lower down, near the end of the gut. Some of the Vivipara also have processes connected with the lower part of the gut which serve the same purpose as that stated above.

The whole tribe of fishes is of gluttonous appetite, owing to the arrangements for the reduction of their food being very imperfect, and much of it consequently passing through them without undergoing concoction; and, of all, those are the most gluttonous that have a straight intestine. For as the passage of food in such cases is rapid, and the enjoyment derived from it in consequence but brief, it follows of necessity that the return of appetite is also speedy.

It has already been mentioned that in animals with front teeth in both jaws the stomach is of small size. It may be classed pretty nearly always under one or other of two headings, namely as resembling the stomach of the dog, or as resembling the stomach of the pig. In the pig the stomach is larger than in the dog, and presents certain folds of moderate size, the purpose of which is to lengthen out the period of concoction; while the stomach of the dog is of small size, not much larger in calibre than the gut, and smooth on the internal surface.

Not much larger, I say, than the gut; for in all animals after the stomach comes the gut. This, like the stomach, presents numerous modifications. For in some animals it is uniform, when uncoiled, and alike throughout, while in others it differs in different portions. Thus in some cases it is wider in the neighbourhood of the stomach, and narrower towards the other end; and this explains by the way why dogs have to strain so much in discharging **675b** their excrement. But in most animals it is the upper portion that is the narrower and the lower that is of greater width.

Of greater length than in other animals, and much convoluted, are the intestines of those that have horns. These intestines, moreover, as also the stomach, are of ampler volume, in accordance with the larger size of the body. For animals with horns are, as a rule, animals of no small bulk, because of the thorough elab-

[1] Cf. *History of Animals*, II. 17 (507^a 34-^{b} 15).

oration which their food undergoes. The gut, except in those animals where it is straight, invariably widens out as we get farther from the stomach and come to what is called the colon, and to a kind of caecal dilatation. After this it again becomes narrower and convoluted. Then succeeds a straight portion which runs right on to the vent. This vent is known as the anus, and is in some animals surrounded by fat, in others not so. All these parts have been so contrived by nature as to harmonize with the various operations that relate to the food and its residue. For, as the residual food gets farther on and lower down, the space to contain it enlarges, allowing it to remain stationary and undergo conversion. Thus is it in those animals which, owing either to their large size, or to the heat of the parts concerned, require more nutriment, and consume more fodder than the rest.

Neither is it without a purpose, that, just as a narrower gut succeeds to the upper stomach, so also does the residual food, when its goodness is thoroughly exhausted, pass from the colon and the ample space of the lower stomach into a narrower channel and into the spiral coil. For so nature can regulate her expenditure and prevent the excremental residue from being discharged all at once.

In all such animals, however, as have to be comparatively moderate in their alimentation, the lower stomach presents no wide and roomy spaces, though their gut is not straight, but has a number of convolutions. For amplitude of space causes desire for ample food, and straightness of the intestine causes quick return of appetite. And thus it is that all animals whose food receptacles are either simple or spacious are of gluttonous habits, the latter eating enormously at a meal, the former making meals at short intervals.

Again, since the food in the upper stomach, having just been swallowed, must of necessity be quite fresh, while that which has reached the lower stomach must have had its juices exhausted and resemble dung, it follows of necessity that there must also be some intermediate part, in which the change may be effected, and where the food will be neither perfectly fresh nor yet dung. And thus it is that, in all such animals as we are now considering, there is found what is called the jejunum; which is a part of the small gut, of the gut, that is, which comes next to the stomach. For this jejunum lies between the upper cavity which contains the yet unconcocted food and the lower cavity which holds the residual matter, which by the time it has got here has become worthless. There is a jejunum in all these

676a animals, but it is only plainly discernible in those of large size, and this only when they have abstained from food for a certain time. For then alone can one hit on the exact period when the food lies half-way between the upper and lower cavities; a period which is very short, for the time occupied in the transition of food is but brief. In females this jejunum may occupy any part whatsoever of the upper intestine, but in males it comes just before the caecum and the lower stomach.

15

What is known as rennet is found in all animals that have a multiple stomach, and in the hare among animals whose stomach is single. In the former the rennet neither occupies the large paunch, nor the honeycomb bag, nor the terminal reed, but is found in the cavity which separates this terminal one from the two first, namely in the so-called manyplies. It is the thick character of their milk which causes all these animals to have rennet; whereas in animals with a single stomach the milk is thin, and consequently no rennet is formed. It is this difference in thickness which makes the milk of horned animals coagulate, while that of animals without horns does not. Rennet forms in the hare because it feeds on herbage that has juice like that of the fig; for juice of this kind coagulates the milk in the stomach of the sucklings. Why it is in the manyplies that rennet is formed in animals with multiple stomachs has been stated in the Problems.

BOOK IV

1

The account which has now been given of the viscera, the stomach, and the other several parts holds equally good not only for the oviparous quadrupeds, but also for such apodous animals as the Serpents. These two classes of animals are indeed nearly akin, a serpent resembling a lizard which has been lengthened out and deprived of its feet. Fishes, again, resemble these two groups in all their parts, excepting that, while these, being land animals, have a lung, fishes have no lung, but gills in its place. None of these animals, excepting the tortoise, as also no fish, has a urinary bladder. For owing to the bloodlessness of their lung, they drink but sparingly; and such fluid as they have is diverted to the scaly plates, as in birds it is diverted to the feathers, and thus they come to have the same white matter on the surface of their excrement as we see on that of birds. For in animals that have a bladder, its excretion when voided throws down a deposit of earthy brine in the containing vessel. For the sweet and fresh elements, being light, are expended on the flesh.

676b Among the Serpents, the same peculiarity attaches to vipers, as among fishes attaches to Selachia. For both these and vipers are externally viviparous, but previously produce ova internally.

The stomach in all these animals is single, just as it is single in all other animals that have teeth in front of both jaws; and their viscera are excessively small, as always happens when there is no bladder. In serpents these viscera are, moreover, differently shaped from those of other animals. For, a serpent's body being long and narrow, its contents are as it were moulded into a similar form, and thus come to be themselves elongated.

All animals that have blood possess an omentum, a mesentery, intestines with their appendages, and, moreover, a diaphragm and a heart; and all, excepting fishes, a lung and a windpipe. The relative positions, moreover, of the windpipe and the oesophagus are precisely similar in them all; and the reason is the same as has already been given.[1]

2

Almost all sanguineous animals have a gall-bladder. In some this is attached to the liver, in others separated from that organ and attached to the intestines, being apparently in the latter case no less than in the former an appendage of the lower stomach. It is in fishes that this is most clearly seen. For all fishes have a gall-bladder; and in most of them it is attached to the intestine, being in some, as in the Amia, united with this, like a border, along its whole length. It is similarly placed in most serpents. There are therefore no good grounds for the view entertained by some writers, that the gall exists for the sake of some sensory action. For they say that its use is to affect that part of the soul which is lodged in the neighbourhood of the liver, vexing this part when it is congealed, and restoring it to cheerfulness when it again flows free. But this cannot be. For in some animals there is absolutely no gall-bladder at all—in the horse, for instance, the mule, the ass, the deer, and the roe; and in others, as the camel, there is no distinct bladder, but merely small vessels of a biliary character. Again, there is no such organ in the seal, nor, of purely sea-animals, in the dolphin. Even within the limits of the same genus, some animals appear to have and others to be without it. Such, for instance, is the case with mice; such also with man. For in some individuals there is a distinct gall-bladder attached to the liver, while in others there is no gall-bladder at all. This explains how the existence of this part in the whole genus has been a matter of dispute. For each observer, according as he has found it present or absent in the individual cases he has examined, has supposed it to be present or absent in the whole genus. The same has occurred in the case of sheep and of **677a** goats. For these animals usually have a gall-bladder; but, while in some localities it is so enormously big as to appear a monstrosity, as is the case in Naxos, in others it is altogether wanting, as is the case in a certain district belonging to the inhabitants of Chalcis in Euboea. Moreover, the gall-bladder in fishes is separated, as already mentioned,[2] by a considerable interval from the liver. No less mistaken seems to be the opinion of Anaxagoras and his followers, that the gall-bladder is the cause of acute diseases, inasmuch as it becomes over-full, and spirts out its excess on to the lung, the blood-vessels, and the ribs. For, almost invariably, those who suffer from these forms of disease are persons who have no gall-bladder at all, as would be quite evident were they to be dissected. Moreover, there is no kind of correspondence between the amount of bile which is present in these diseases and the amount which is exuded. The most probable opinion is that, as the bile when it is present in any other part of the body is a mere residuum or a product of decay, so also when it is present in the region of the liver it is equally excremental and has no further use; just as is the case with the dejections of the stomach and intestines. For though even the residua are occasionally used by nature for some useful purpose, yet we must not in all cases expect to find such a final cause; for granted the existence in the body of this or that constituent,

[1] Cf. III. 3 (664b 3).

[2] Cf. IV. 2 (676b 19).

with such and such properties, many results must ensue merely as necessary consequences of these properties. All animals, then, whose liver is healthy in composition and supplied with none but sweet blood, are either entirely without a gall-bladder on this organ, or have merely small bile-containing vessels; or are some with and some without such parts. Thus it is that the liver in animals that have no gall-bladder is, as a rule, of good colour and sweet; and that, when there is a gall-bladder, that part of the liver is sweetest which lies immediately underneath it. But, when animals are formed of blood less pure in composition, the bile serves for the excretion of its impure residue. For the very meaning of excrement is that it is the opposite of nutriment, and of bitter that it is the opposite of sweet; and healthy blood is sweet. So that it is evident that the bile, which is bitter, cannot have any useful end, but must simply be a purifying excretion. It was therefore no bad saying of old writers that the absence of a gall-bladder gave long life. In so saying they had in mind deer and animals with solid hoofs. For such have no gall-bladder and live long. But besides these there are other animals that have no gall-bladder, though those old writers had not noticed the fact, such as the camel and the dolphin; and these also are, as it happens, long-lived. Seeing, indeed, that the liver is not only useful, but a necessary and vital part in all

677b animals that have blood, it is but reasonable that on its character should depend the length or the shortness of life. Nor less reasonable is it that this organ and none other should have such an excretion as the bile. For the heart, unable as it is to stand any violent affection, would be utterly intolerant of the proximity of such a fluid; and, as to the rest of the viscera, none excepting the liver are necessary parts of an animal. It is the liver therefore that alone has this provision. In conclusion, wherever we see bile we must take it to be excremental. For to suppose that it has one character in this part, another in that, would be as great an absurdity as to suppose mucus or the dejections of the stomach to vary in character according to locality and not to be excremental wherever found.

3

So much then of the gall-bladder, and of the reasons why some animals have one, while others have not. We have still to speak of the mesentery and the omentum; for these are associated with the parts already described and contained in the same cavity. The omentum, then, is a membrane containing fat; the fat being suet or lard, according as the fat of the animal generally is of the former or latter description. What kinds of animals are so distinguished has been already set forth in an earlier part of this treatise.[1] This membrane, alike in animals that have a single and in those that have a multiple stomach, grows from the middle of that organ, along a line which is marked on it like a seam. Thus attached, it covers the rest of the stomach and the greater part of the bowels, and this alike in all sanguineous animals, whether they live on land or in water. Now the development of this part into such a form as has been described is the result of necessity. For, whenever solid and fluid are mixed together and heated, the surface invariably becomes membranous and skin-like. But the region in which the omentum lies is full of nutriment of such a mixed character. Moreover, in consequence of the close texture of the membrane, that portion of the sanguineous nutriment will alone filter into it which is of a greasy character; for this portion is composed of the finest particles; and when it has so filtered in, it will be concocted by the heat of the part, and will be converted into suet or lard, and will not acquire a flesh-like or sanguineous constitution. The development, then, of the omentum is simply the result of necessity. But when once formed, it is used by nature for an end, namely, to facilitate and to hasten the concoction of food. For all that is hot aids concoction; and fat is hot, and the omentum is fat. This too explains why it hangs from the middle of the stomach; for the upper part of the stomach has no need of it, being assisted in concoction by the adjacent liver. Thus much as concerns the omentum.

4

The so-called mesentery is also a membrane; and extends continuously from the long stretch

678a of intestine to the great vessel and the aorta. In it are numerous and close-packed vessels, which run from the intestines to the great vessel and to the aorta. The formation of this membrane we shall find to be the result of necessity, as is that of the other [similar] parts. What, however, is the final cause of its existence in sanguineous animals is manifest on reflection. For it is necessary that animals shall get nutriment from without; and, again, that

[1] Cf. II. 5 (657a 35).

this shall be converted into the ultimate nutriment, which is then distributed as sustenance to the various parts; this ultimate nutriment being, in sanguineous animals, what we call blood, and having, in bloodless animals, no definite name. This being so, there must be channels through which the nutriment shall pass, as it were through roots, from the stomach into the blood-vessels. Now the roots of plants are in the ground; for thence their nutriment is derived. But in animals the stomach and intestines represent the ground from which the nutriment is to be taken. The mesentery, then, is an organ to contain the roots; and these roots are the vessels that traverse it. This then is the final cause of its existence. But how it absorbs nutriment, and how that portion of the food which enters into the vessels is distributed by them to the various parts of the body, are questions which will be considered when we come to deal with the generation and nutrition of animals.

The constitution of sanguineous animals, so far as the parts as yet mentioned are concerned, and the reasons for such constitution, have now been set forth. In natural sequence we should next go on to the organs of generation, as yet undescribed, on which depend the distinctions of male and female. But, inasmuch as we shall have to deal specially with generation hereafter, it will be more convenient to defer the consideration of these parts to that occasion.

5

Very different from the animals we have as yet considered are the Cephalopoda and the Crustacea. For these have absolutely no viscera whatsoever; as is indeed the case with all bloodless animals, in which are included two other genera, namely the Testacea and the Insects. For in none of them does the material out of which viscera are formed exist. None of them, that is, have blood. The cause of this lies in their essential constitution. For the presence of blood in some animals, its absence from others, must be included in the conception which determines their respective essences. Moreover, in the animals we are now considering, none of those final causes will be found to exist which in sanguineous animals determine the presence of viscera. For they have no blood-
678b vessels nor urinary bladder, nor do they breathe; the only part that it is necessary for them to have being that which is analogous to a heart. For in all animals there must be some central and commanding part of the body, to lodge the sensory portion of the soul and the source of life. The organs of nutrition are also of necessity present in them all. They differ, however, in character because of differences of the habitats in which they get their subsistence.

In the Cephalopoda there are two teeth, enclosing what is called the mouth; and inside this mouth is a flesh-like substance which represents a tongue and serves for the discrimination of pleasant and unpleasant food. The Crustacea have teeth corresponding to those of the Cephalopoda, namely their anterior teeth, and also have the fleshy representative of a tongue. This latter part is found, moreover, in all Testacea, and serves, as in sanguineous animals, for gustatory sensations. Similarly provided also are the Insects. For some of these, such as the Bees and the Flies, have, as already described,[1] their proboscis protruding from the mouth; while those others that have no such instrument in front have a part which acts as a tongue inside the mouth. Such, for instance, is the case in the Ants and the like. As for teeth, some insects have them, the Bees and the Ants for instance, though in a somewhat modified form, while others that live on fluid nutriment are without them. For in many insects the teeth are not meant to deal with the food, but to serve as weapons.

In some Testacea, as was said in the first treatise, the organ which is called the tongue is of considerable strength; and in the Cochli (*Sea-snails*) there are also two teeth, just as in the Crustacea. The mouth in the Cephalopoda is succeeded by a long gullet. This leads to a crop, like that of a bird, and directly continuous with this is the stomach, from which a gut runs without windings to the vent. The Sepias and the Poulps resemble each other completely, so far as regards the shape and consistency of these parts. But not so the Teuthides (*Calamaries*). Here, as in the other groups, there are the two stomach-like receptacles; but the first of these cavities has less resemblance to a crop, and in neither is the form [or the consistency] the same as in the other kinds, the whole body indeed being made of a softer kind of flesh.

The object of this arrangement of the parts in question is the same in the Cephalopoda as in Birds; for these also are all unable to masticate their food; and therefore it is that a crop precedes their stomach.

[1] Cf. *History of Animals*, IV. 4 (528b 29).

For purposes of defence, and to enable them to escape from their foes, the Cephalopoda have what is called their ink. This is contained **679a** in a membranous pouch, which is attached to the body and provided with a terminal outlet just at the point where what is termed the funnel gives issue to the residua of the stomach. This funnel is placed on the ventral surface of the animal. All Cephalopoda alike have this characteristic ink, but chief of all the Sepia, where it is more abundant than in the rest. When the animal is disturbed and frightened it uses this ink to make the surrounding water black and turbid, and so, as it were, puts a shield in front of its body.

In the Calamaries and the Poulps the ink-bag is placed in the upper part of the body, in close proximity to the *mytis,* whereas in the Sepia it is lower down, against the stomach. For the Sepia has a more plentiful supply of ink than the rest, inasmuch as it makes more use of it. The reasons for this are, firstly, that it lives near the shore, and, secondly, that it has no other means of protection; whereas the Poulp has its long twining feet to use in its defence, and is, moreover, endowed with the power of changing colour. This changing of colour, like the discharge of ink, occurs as the result of fright. As to the Calamary, it lives far out at sea, being the only one of the Cephalopoda that does so; and this gives it protection. These then are the reasons why the ink is more abundant in the Sepia than in the Calamary, and this greater abundance explains the lower position; for it allows the ink to be ejected with ease even from a distance. The ink itself is of an earthy character, in this resembling the white deposit on the surface of a bird's excrement and the explanation in both cases is the same, namely, the absence of a urinary bladder. For, in default of this, it is the ink that serves for the excretion of the earthiest matter. And this is more especially the case in the Sepia, because there is a greater proportion of earth in its composition than in that of the other Cephalopoda. The earthy character of its bone is a clear indication of this. For in the Poulp there is no bone at all, and in the Calamary it is thin and cartilaginous. Why this bone should be present in some Cephalopoda, and wanting in others, and how its character varies in those that have it, has now been set forth.

These animals, having no blood, are in consequence cold and of a timid character. Now, in some animals, fear causes a disturbance of the bowels, and, in others, a flow of urine from the bladder. Similarly in these it produces a discharge of ink, and, though the ejection of this ink in fright, like that of the urine, is the result of necessity, and, though it is of excremental character, yet it is used by nature for a purpose, namely, the protection and safety of the animal that excretes it.

The Crustacea also, both the Caraboid forms and the Crabs, are provided with teeth, namely their two anterior teeth; and between these they also present the tongue-like piece of flesh, as has indeed been already mentioned.[1] Directly after their mouth comes a gullet, which, if we compare relative sizes, is but small in proportion to the body: and then a stomach, which in the Carabi and some of the Crabs is furnished with a second set of teeth, the anterior **679b** teeth being insufficient for adequate mastication. From the stomach a uniform gut runs in a direct line to the excremental vent.

The parts described are to be found also in all the various Testacea. The degree of distinctness, however, with which they are formed varies in the different kinds, and the larger the size of the animal the more easily distinguishable are all these parts severally. In the Sea-snails, for example, we find teeth, hard and sharp, as before mentioned,[2] and between them the flesh-like substance, just as in the Crustacea and Cephalopoda, and again the proboscis, which, as has been stated,[3] is something between a sting and a tongue. Directly after the mouth comes a kind of bird-like crop, then a gullet, succeeded by a stomach, in which is the *mecon,* as it is styled; and continuous with this *mecon* is an intestine, starting directly from it. It is this residual substance which appears in all the Testacea to form the most palatable morsel. Purpuras and Whelks, and all other Testacea that have turbinate shells, in structure resemble the Sea-snail. The genera and species of Testacea are very numerous. For there are those with turbinate shells, of which some have just been mentioned; and, besides these, there are bivalves and univalves. Those with turbinate shells may, indeed, after a certain fashion be said to resemble bivalves. For they all from their very birth have an operculum to protect that part of their body which is exposed to view. This is the case with the Purpuras, with Whelks, with the Nerites, and the like. Were it not for this, the part which is undefended by the shell would be very liable to injury by collision with external ob-

[1] Cf. 678b 10. [2] Cf. IV. 5 (678b 23).
[3] Cf. *History of Animals,* IV. 4 (528b 30).

jects. The univalves also are not without protection. For on their dorsal surface they have a shell, and by the under surface they attach themselves to the rocks, and so after a manner become bivalved, the rock representing the second valve. Of these the animals known as Limpets are an example. The bivalves, scallops and mussels, for instance, are protected by the power they have of closing their valves; and the Turbinata by the operculum just mentioned, which transforms them, as it were, from univalves into bivalves. But of all there is none so perfectly protected as the sea-urchin. For here there is a globular shell which encloses the body completely, and which is, moreover, set with sharp spines. This peculiarity distinguishes the sea-urchin from all other Testacea, as has already been mentioned.

The structure of the Testacea and of the Crustacea is exactly the reverse of that of the Cephalopoda. For in the latter the fleshy substance is on the outside and the earthy substance within, whereas in the former the soft parts are inside and the hard part without. In the sea-urchin, however, there is no fleshy part whatsoever.

All the Testacea then, those that have not been mentioned as well as those that have, agree as stated in possessing a mouth with the tongue-like body, a stomach, and a vent for excrement, but they differ from each other in the positions and proportions of these parts. The details, however, of these differences must be **680a** looked for in the Researches concerning Animals and the treatises on Anatomy.[1] For while there are some points which can be made clear by verbal description, there are others which are more suited for ocular demonstration.

Peculiar among the Testacea are the sea-urchins and the animals known as Tethya (*Ascidians*). The sea-urchins have five teeth, and in the centre of these the fleshy body which is common to all the animals we have been discussing. Immediately after this comes a gullet, and then the stomach, divided into a number of separate compartments, which look like so many distinct stomachs; for the cavities are separate and all contain abundant residual matter. They are all, however, connected with one and the same oesophagus, and they all end in one and the same excremental vent. There is nothing besides the stomach of a fleshy character, as has already been stated.[2] All that can be seen are the so-called ova, of which there are several, contained each in a separate membrane, and certain black bodies which have no name, and which, beginning at the animal's mouth, are scattered round its body here and there promiscuously. These sea-urchins are not all of one species, but there are several different kinds, and in all of them the parts mentioned are to be found. It is not, however, in every kind that the so-called ova are edible. Neither do these attain to any size in any other species than that with which we are all familiar. A similar distinction may be made generally in the case of all Testacea. For there is a great difference in the edible qualities of the flesh of different kinds; and in some, moreover, the residual substance known as the *mecon* is good for food, while in others it is uneatable. This *mecon* in the turbinated genera is lodged in the spiral part of the shell, while in univalves, such as limpets, it occupies the fundus, and in bivalves is placed near the hinge, the so-called ovum lying on the right; while on the opposite side is the vent. The former is incorrectly termed ovum, for it merely corresponds to what in well-fed sanguineous animals is fat; and thus it is that it makes its appearance in Testacea at those seasons of the year when they are in good condition, namely, spring and autumn. For no Testacea can abide extremes of temperature, and they are therefore in evil plight in seasons of great cold or heat. This is clearly shown by what occurs in the case of the sea-urchins. For though the ova are to be found in these animals even directly they are born, yet they acquire a greater size than usual at the time of full moon; not, as some think, because sea-urchins eat more at that season, but because the nights are then warmer, owing to the moonlight. For these creatures are bloodless, and so are unable to stand cold and require warmth. Therefore it is that they are found in better condition in summer than at any other **680b** season; and this all over the world excepting in the Pyrrhean tidal strait. There the sea-urchins flourish as well in winter as in summer. But the reason for this is that they have a greater abundance of food in the winter, because the fish desert the strait at that season.

The number of the ova is the same in all sea-urchins, and is an odd one. For there are five ova, just as there are also five teeth and five stomachs; and the explanation of this is to be found in the fact that the so-called ova are not really ova, but merely, as was said before,

[1] Cf. *History of Animals*, IV. 4 (528^b 10 sqq.).

[2] Cf. 679^b 34.

the result of the animal's well-fed condition. Oysters also have a so-called ovum, corresponding in character to that of the sea-urchins, but existing only on one side of their body. Now inasmuch as the sea-urchin is of a spherical form, and not merely a single disk like the oyster, and in virtue of its spherical shape is the same from whatever side it be examined, its ovum must necessarily be of a corresponding symmetry. For the spherical shape has not the asymmetry of the disk-shaped body of the oysters. For in all these animals the head is central, but in the sea-urchin the so-called ovum is above [and symmetrical, while in the oyster it is only on one side]. Now the necessary symmetry would be observed were the ovum to form a continuous ring. But this may not be. For it would be in opposition to what prevails in the whole tribe of Testacea; for in all the ovum is discontinuous, and in all excepting the sea-urchins asymmetrical, being placed only on one side of the body. Owing then to this necessary discontinuity of the ovum, which belongs to the sea-urchin as a member of the class, and owing to the spherical shape of its body, which is its individual peculiarity, this animal cannot possibly have an even number of ova. For were they an even number, they would have to be arranged exactly opposite to each other, in pairs, so as to keep the necessary symmetry; one ovum of each pair being placed at one end, the other ovum at the other end of a transverse diameter. This again would violate the universal provision in Testacea. For both in the oysters and in the scallops we find the ovum only on one side of the circumference. The number then of the ova must be uneven, three for instance, or five. But if there were only three they would be much too far apart; while, if there were more than five, they would come to form a continuous mass. The former arrangement would be disadvantageous to the animal, the latter an impossibility. There can therefore be neither more nor less than five. For the same reason the stomach is divided into five parts, and there is a corresponding number of teeth. For seeing that the ova represent each of them a kind of body for the animal, their disposition must conform to that of the stomach, seeing that it is from this that they derive the material for their growth. Now if there were only one stomach, either the ova would be too far off from it, or it would be so big as to fill up the whole cavity, and the sea-urchin would have great difficulty in moving about and finding due nourishment for its repletion. As then there are five intervals between the five ova, so are there of necessity five divisions of the stomach, one for each interval. So also, and on like grounds, there are
681ª five teeth. For nature is thus enabled to allot to each stomachal compartment and ovum its separate and similar tooth. These, then, are the reasons why the number of ova in the sea-urchin is an odd one, and why that odd number is five. In some sea-urchins the ova are excessively small, in others of considerable size, the explanation being that the latter are of a warmer constitution, and so are able to concoct their food more thoroughly; while in the former concoction is less perfect, so that the stomach is found full of residual matter, while the ova are small and uneatable. Those of a warmer constitution are, moreover, in virtue of their warmth more given to motion, so that they make expeditions in search of food, instead of remaining stationary like the rest. As evidence of this, it will be found that they always have something or other sticking to their spines, as though they moved much about; for they use their spines as feet.

The Ascidians differ but slightly from plants, and yet have more of an animal nature than the sponges, which are virtually plants and nothing more. For nature passes from lifeless objects to animals in such unbroken sequence, interposing between them beings which live and yet are not animals, that scarcely any difference seems to exist between two neighbouring groups owing to their close proximity.

A sponge, then, as already said, in these respects completely resembles a plant, that throughout its life it is attached to a rock, and that when separated from this it dies. Slightly different from the sponges are the so-called Holothurias and the sea-lungs, as also sundry other sea-animals that resemble them. For these are free and unattached. Yet they have no feeling, and their life is simply that of a plant separated from the ground. For even among land-plants there are some that are independent of the soil, and that spring up and grow, either upon other plants, or even entirely free. Such, for example, is the plant which is found on Parnassus, and which some call the Epipetrum. This you may hang up on a peg and it will yet live for a considerable time. Sometimes it is a matter of doubt whether a given organism should be classed with plants or with animals. The Ascidians, for instance, and the like so far resemble plants as that they never live free and unattached, but, on the other hand, inasmuch as they have a certain flesh-like substance, they must be supposed to possess some degree of sensibility.

An Ascidian has a body divided by a single septum and with two orifices, one where it takes in the fluid matter that ministers to its nutrition, the other where it discharges the surplus of unused juice, for it has no visible residual substance, such as have the other Testacea. This is itself a very strong justification for considering an Ascidian, and anything else there may be among animals that resembles it, to be of a vegetable character; for plants also never have any residuum. Across the middle of the body of these Ascidians there runs a thin transverse partition, and here it is that we may reasonably suppose the part on which life depends to be situated.

The Acalephae, or Sea-nettles, as they are **681b** variously called, are not Testacea at all, but lie outside the recognized groups. Their constitution, like that of the Ascidians, approximates them on one side to plants, on the other to animals. For seeing that some of them can detach themselves and can fasten upon their food, and that they are sensible of objects which come in contact with them, they must be considered to have an animal nature. The like conclusion follows from their using the asperity of their bodies as a protection against their enemies. But, on the other hand, they are closely allied to plants, firstly by the imperfection of their structure, secondly by their being able to attach themselves to the rocks, which they do with great rapidity, and lastly by their having no visible residuum notwithstanding that they possess a mouth.

Very similar again to the Acalephae are the Starfishes. For these also fasten on their prey, and suck out its juices, and thus destroy a vast number of oysters. At the same time they present a certain resemblance to such of the animals we have described as the Cephalopoda and Crustacea, inasmuch as they are free and unattached. The same may also be said of the Testacea.

Such, then, is the structure of the parts that minister to nutrition and which every animal must necessarily possess. But besides these organs it is quite plain that in every animal there must be some part or other which shall be analogous to what in sanguineous animals is the presiding seat of sensation. Whether an animal has or has not blood, it cannot possibly be without this. In the Cephalopoda this part consists of a fluid substance contained in a membrane, through which runs the gullet on its way to the stomach. It is attached to the body rather towards its dorsal surface, and by some is called the *mytis*. Just such another organ is found also in the Crustacea and there too is known by the same name. This part is at once fluid and corporeal and, as before said, is traversed by the gullet. For had the gullet been placed between the *mytis* and the dorsal surface of the animal, the hardness of the back would have interfered with its due dilatation in the act of deglutition. On the outer surface of the *mytis* runs the intestine; and in contact with this latter is placed the ink-bag, so that it may be removed as far as possible from the mouth and its obnoxious fluid be kept at a distance from the nobler and sovereign part. The position of the *mytis* shows that it corresponds to the heart of sanguineous animals; for it occupies the self-same place. The same is shown by the sweetness of its fluid, which has the character of concocted matter and resembles blood.

In the Testacea the presiding seat of sensation is in a corresponding position, but is less easily made out. It should, however, always be looked for in some midway position; namely, in such Testacea as are stationary, midway between the part by which food is taken in and the channel through which either the excrement or the spermatic fluid is voided, and, in those species which are capable of locomotion, **682a** invariably midway between the right and left sides.

In Insects this organ, which is the seat of sensation, lies, as was stated in the first treatise,[1] between the head and the cavity which contains the stomach. In most of them it consists of a single part; but in others, for instance in such as have long bodies and resemble the Juli (*Millipedes*), it is made up of several parts, so that such insects continue to live after they have been cut in pieces. For the aim of nature is to give to each animal only one such dominant part; and when she is unable to carry out this intention she causes the parts, though potentially many, to work together actually as one. This is much more clearly marked in some insects than in others.

The parts concerned in nutrition are not alike in all insects, but show considerable diversity. Thus some have what is called a sting in the mouth, which is a kind of compound instrument that combines in itself the character

[1] *History of Animals*, IV. 7 (531b 34).

of a tongue and of lips. In others that have no such instrument in front there is a part inside the mouth that answers the same sensory purposes. Immediately after the mouth comes the intestine, which is never wanting in any insect. This runs in a straight line and without further complication to the vent; occasionally, however, it has a spiral coil. There are, moreover, some insects in which a stomach succeeds to the mouth, and is itself succeeded by a convoluted intestine, so that the larger and more voracious insects may be enabled to take in a more abundant supply of food. More curious than any are the Cicadae. For here the mouth and the tongue are united so as to form a single part, through which, as through a root, the insect sucks up the fluids on which it lives. Insects are always small eaters, not so much because of their diminutive size as because of their cold temperament. For it is heat which requires sustenance; just as it is heat which speedily concocts it. But cold requires no sustenance. In no insects is this so conspicuous as in these Cicadae. For they find enough to live on in the moisture which is deposited from the air. So also do the Ephemera that are found about the Black sea. But while these latter only live for a single day, the Cicadae subsist on such food for several days, though still not many.

We have now done with the internal parts of animals, and must therefore return to the consideration of the external parts which have not yet been described. It will be better to change our order of exposition and begin with the animals we have just been describing, so that proceeding from these, which require less discussion, our account may have more time to spend on the perfect kinds of animals, those namely that have blood.

6

We will begin with Insects. These animals, though they present no great multiplicity of parts, are not without diversities when compared with each other. They are all many-footed; the object of this being to compensate
682b their natural slowness and frigidity, and give greater activity to their motions. Accordingly we find that those which, as the Juli (*Millipedes*), have long bodies, and are therefore the most liable to refrigeration, have also the greatest number of feet. Again, the body in these animals is insected—the reason for this being that they have not got one vital centre but many—and the number of their feet corresponds to that of the insections.

Should the feet fall short of this, their deficiency is compensated by the power of flight. Of such flying insects some live a wandering life, and are forced to make long expeditions in search of food. These have a body of light weight, and four feathers, two on either side, to support it. Such are bees and the insects akin to them. When, however, such insects are of very small bulk, their feathers are reduced to two, as is the case with flies. Insects with heavy bodies and of stationary habits, though not polypterous in the same way as bees, yet have sheaths to their feathers to maintain their efficiency. Such are the Melolonthae and the like. For their stationary habits expose their feathers to much greater risks than are run by those of insects that are more constantly in flight, and on this account they are provided with this protecting shield. The feather of an insect has neither barbs nor shaft. For, though it is called a feather, it is no feather at all, but merely a skin-like membrane that, owing to its dryness, necessarily becomes detached from the surface of the body, as the fleshy substance grows cold.

These animals then have their bodies insected, not only for the reasons already assigned, but also to enable them to curl round in such a manner as may protect them from injury; for such insects as have long bodies can roll themselves up, which would be impossible were it not for the insections; and those that cannot do this can yet draw their segments up into the insected spaces, and so increase the hardness of their bodies. This can be felt quite plainly by putting the finger on one of the insects, for instance, known as Canthari. The touch frightens the insect, and it remains motionless, while its body becomes hard. The division of the body into segments is also a necessary result of there being several supreme organs in place of one; and this again is a part of the essential constitution of insects, and is a character which approximates them to plants. For as plants, though cut into pieces, can still live, so also can insects. There is, however, this difference between the two cases, that the portions of the divided insect live only for a limited time, whereas the portions of the plant live on and attain the perfect form of the whole, so that from one single plant you may obtain two or more.

Some insects are also provided with another means of protection against their enemies, namely a sting. In some this is in front, connected with the tongue, in others behind at the posterior end. For just as the organ of smell in elephants answers several uses, serving alike as a weapon and for purposes of **683a** nutrition, so does also the sting, when placed in connexion with the tongue, as in some insects, answer more than one end. For it is the instrument through which they derive their sensations of food, as well as that with which they suck it up and bring it to the mouth. Such of these insects as have no anterior sting are provided with teeth, which serve in some of them for biting the food, and in others for its prehension and conveyance to the mouth. Such are their uses, for instance, in ants and all the various kinds of bees. As for the insects that have a sting behind, this weapon is given them because they are of a fierce disposition. In some of them the sting is lodged inside the body, in bees, for example, and wasps. For these insects are made for flight, and were their sting external and of delicate make it would soon get spoiled; and if, on the other hand, it were of thicker build, as in scorpions, its weight would be an incumbrance. As for scorpions that live on the ground and have a tail, their sting must be set upon this, as otherwise it would be of no use as a weapon. Dipterous insects never have a posterior sting. For the very reason of their being dipterous is that they are small and weak, and therefore require no more than two feathers to support their light weight; and the same reason which reduces their feathers to two causes their sting to be in front; for their strength is not sufficient to allow them to strike efficiently with the hinder part of the body. Polypterous insects, on the other hand, are of greater bulk—indeed it is this which causes them to have so many feathers; and their greater size makes them stronger in their hinder parts. The sting of such insects is therefore placed behind. Now it is better, when possible, that one and the same instrument shall not be made to serve several dissimilar uses; but that there shall be one organ to serve as a weapon, which can then be very sharp, and a distinct one to serve as a tongue, which can then be of spongy texture and fit to absorb nutriment. Whenever, therefore, nature is able to provide two separate instruments for two separate uses, without the one hampering the other, she does so, instead of acting like a coppersmith who for cheapness makes a spit and lampholder in one. It is only when this is impossible that she uses one organ for several functions.

The anterior legs are in some cases longer than the others, that they may serve to wipe away any foreign matter that may lodge on the insect's eyes and obstruct its sight, which already is not very distinct owing to the eyes being made of a hard substance. Flies and bees and the like may be constantly seen thus dressing themselves with crossed forelegs. Of the other legs, the hinder are bigger than the middle pair, both to aid in running and also that the insect, when it takes flight, may spring more easily from the ground. This difference is still more marked in such insects as leap, in locusts for instance, and in the various kinds of fleas. For these first bend and then extend the legs, and, by doing so, are necessarily shot up from the ground. It is only the hind legs of locusts, and not the front ones, that **683b** resemble the steering oars of a ship. For this requires that the joint shall be deflected inwards, and such is never the case with the anterior limbs. The whole number of legs, including those used in leaping, is six in all these insects.

7

In the Testacea the body consists of but few parts, the reason being that these animals live a stationary life. For such animals as move much about must of necessity have more numerous parts than such as remain quiet; for their activities are many, and the more diversified the movements the greater the number of organs required to effect them. Some species of Testacea are absolutely motionless, and others not quite but nearly so. Nature, however, has provided them with a protection in the hardness of the shell with which she has invested their body. This shell, as already has been said,[1] may have one valve, or two valves, or be turbinate. In the latter case it may be either spiral, as in whelks, or merely globular, as in sea-urchins. When it has two valves, these may be gaping, as in scallops and mussels, where the valves are united together on one side only, so as to open and shut on the other; or they may be united together on both sides, as in the Solens (*razor-fishes*). In all cases alike the Testacea have, like plants, the head downwards. The reason for this is, that they take in their nourishment from below, just as do plants with their roots. Thus the under parts come in them to be above, and the upper parts to be below. The body is enclosed in a membrane, and through this the animal filters fluid

[1] Cf. iv. 5 (679b 16).

free from salt and absorbs its nutriment. In all there is a head; but none of the parts, excepting this recipient of food, has any distinctive name.

8

All the Crustacea can crawl as well as swim, and accordingly they are provided with numerous feet. There are four main genera, viz. the Carabi, as they are called, the Astaci, the Carides, and the Carcini. In each of these genera, again, there are numerous species, which differ from each other not only as regards shape, but also very considerably as regards size. For, while in some species the individuals are large, in others they are excessively minute. The Carcinoid and Caraboid Crustacea resemble each other in possessing claws. These claws are not for locomotion, but to serve in place of hands for seizing and holding objects; and they are therefore bent in the opposite direction to the feet, being so twisted as to turn their convexity towards the body, while their feet turn towards it their concavity. For in this position the claws are best suited for laying hold of the food and carrying it to the mouth. The distinction between the Carabi and the Carcini (*Crabs*) consists in the former having a tail while the latter have none. For the Carabi swim about and a tail is therefore of use to them, serving for their propulsion like the blade of an oar. But it would be of no use to the Crabs; for these animals live habitually close to the shore, and creep into holes and corners. In such of them as live out at sea, the feet are much less adapted for locomotion than in the rest, because they are little given to moving about but depend for protection on their shell-like covering. The Maiae and the crabs known as Heracleotic are examples of this; the legs in the former being very thin, in the latter very short.

The very minute crabs that are found among the small fry at the bottom of the net have their hindermost feet flattened out into the semblance of fins or oar-blades, so as to help the animal in swimming.

The Carides are distinguished from the Carcinoid species by the presence of a tail; and from the Caraboids by the absence of claws. This is explained by their large number of feet, on which has been expended the material for the growth of claws. Their feet again are numerous to suit their mode of progression, which is mainly by swimming.

Of the parts on the ventral surface, those near the head are in some of these animals formed like gills, for the admission and discharge of water; while the parts lower down differ in the two sexes. For in the female Carabi these are more laminar than in the males, and in the female crabs the flap is furnished with hairier appendages. This gives ampler space for the disposal of the ova, which the females retain in these parts instead of letting them go free, as do fishes and all other oviparous animals. In the Carabi and in the Crabs the right claw is invariably the larger and the stronger. For it is natural to every animal in active operations to use the parts on its right side in preference to those on its left; and nature, in distributing the organs, invariably assigns each, either exclusively or in a more perfect condition, to such animals as can use it. So it is with tusks, and teeth, and horns, and spurs, and all such defensive and offensive weapons.

In the Lobsters alone it is a matter of chance which claw is the larger, and this in either sex. Claws they must have, because they belong to a genus in which this is a constant character; but they have them in this indeterminate way, owing to imperfect formation and to their not using them for their natural purpose, but for locomotion.

For a detailed account of the several parts of these animals, of their position and their differences, those parts being also included which distinguish the sexes, reference must be made to the treatises on Anatomy and to the Researches concerning Animals.[1]

9

We come now to the Cephalopoda. Their internal organs have already been described[2] with those of other animals. Externally there is the trunk of the body, not distinctly defined, and in front of this the head surrounded by feet, which form a circle about the mouth and teeth, and are set beween these and the eyes. Now in all other animals the feet, if there are any, are disposed in one of two ways; either before and behind or along the sides, the latter being the plan in such of them, for instance, as are bloodless and have numerous feet. But in the Cephalopoda there is a peculiar arrangement, different from either of these. For their feet are all placed at what may be called the fore end. The reason for this is that the hind part of their body has been drawn up close to

[1] *History of Animals*, IV. 2, 3; V. 7 (541^b 29).
[2] Cf. IV. 5 (678^b 24–679^a 31).

the fore part, as is also the case in the turbinated Testacea. For the Testacea, while in some points they resemble the Crustacea, in others resemble the Cephalopoda. Their earthy matter is on the outside, and their fleshy substance within. So far they are like the Crustacea. But the general plan of their body is that of the Cephalopoda; and, though this is true in a certain degree of all the Testacea, it is more especially true of those turbinated species that have a spiral shell. Of this general plan, common to the two, we will speak presently. But let us first consider the case of quadrupeds and of man, where the arrangement is that of a straight line. Let *A* at the upper end of such a line be supposed to represent the mouth, then *B* the gullet, and *C* the stomach, and the intestine to run from this *C* to the excremental vent where *D* is inscribed. Such is the plan in sanguineous animals; and round this straight line as an axis are disposed the head and so-called trunk; the remaining parts, such as the anterior and posterior limbs, having been superadded by nature, merely to minister to these and for locomotion.

In the Crustacea also and in Insects there is a tendency to a similar arrangement of the internal parts in a straight line; the distinction between these groups and the sanguineous animals depending on differences of the external organs which minister to locomotion. But the Cephalopoda and the turbinated Testacea have in common an arrangement which stands in **685a** contrast with this. For here the two extremities are brought together by a curve, as if one were to bend the straight line marked *E* until *D* came close to *A*. Such, then, is the disposition of the internal parts; and round these, in the Cephalopoda, is placed the sac (in the Poulps alone called a head), and, in the Testacea, the turbinate shell which corresponds to the sac. There is, in fact, only this difference between them, that the investing substance of the Cephalopoda is soft while the shell of the Testacea is hard, nature having surrounded their fleshy part with this hard coating as a protection because of their limited power of locomotion. In both classes, owing to this arrangement of the internal organs, the excrement is voided near the mouth; at a point below this orifice in the Cephalopoda, and in the Turbinata on one side of it.

Such, then, is the explanation of the position of the feet in the Cephalopoda, and of the contrast they present to other animals in this matter. The arrangement, however, in the Sepias and the Calamaries is not precisely the same as in the Poulps, owing to the former having no other mode of progression than by swimming, while the latter not only swim but crawl. For in the former six of the feet are above the teeth and small, the outer one on either side being the biggest; while the remaining two, which make up the total eight, are below the mouth and are the biggest of all, just as the hind limbs in quadrupeds are stronger than the fore limbs. For it is these that have to support the weight, and to take the main part in locomotion. And the outer two of the upper six are bigger than the pair which intervene between them and the uppermost of all, because they have to assist the lowermost pair in their office. In the Poulps, on the other hand, the four central feet are the biggest. Again, though the number of feet is the same in all the Cephalopoda, namely eight, their length varies in different kinds, being short in the Sepias and the Calamaries, but greater in the Poulps. For in these latter the trunk of the body is of small bulk, while in the former it is of considerable size; and so in the one case nature has used the materials subtracted from the body to give length to the feet, while in the other she has acted in precisely the opposite way, and has given to the growth of the body what she has first taken from the feet. The Poulps, then, owing to the length of their feet, can not only swim but crawl, whereas in the other genera the feet are useless for the latter mode of progression, being small while the bulk of the body is considerable. These short feet would not enable their possessors to cling to the rocks and keep themselves from being torn off by the waves when these run high in times of storm; neither would they serve to lay hold of objects at all remote and bring them in; but, to supply these defects, the animal is furnished with two long proboscises, by which it can moor itself and ride at anchor like a ship in rough **685b** weather. These same processes serve also to catch prey at a distance and to bring it to the mouth. They are so used by both the Sepias and the Calamaries. In the Poulps the feet are themselves able to perform these offices, and there are consequently no proboscises. Proboscises and twining tentacles, with acetabula set upon them, act in the same way and have the same structure as those plaited instruments which were used by physicians of old to reduce dislocations of the fingers. Like these they are made by the interlacing of their fibres, and they act by pulling upon pieces of flesh and yielding substances. For the plaited fibres encircle an object in a slackened condition, and when they are put on the stretch they grasp and cling tightly to whatever it may be that is in contact with their inner surface. Since, then, the Cephalopoda have no other instruments with which to convey anything to themselves from without, than either twining tentacles, as in some species, or proboscises as in others, they are provided with these to serve as hands for offence and defence and other necessary uses.

The acetabula are set in double line in all the Cephalopoda excepting in one kind of poulp, where there is but a single row. The length and the slimness which is part of the nature of this kind of poulp explain the exception. For a narrow space cannot possibly admit of more than a single row. This exceptional character, then, belongs to them, not because it is the most advantageous arrangement, but because it is the necessary consequence of their essential specific constitution.

In all these animals there is a fin, encircling the sac. In the Poulps and the Sepias this fin is unbroken and continuous, as is also the case in the larger calamaries known as Teuthi. But in the smaller kind, called Teuthides, the fin is not only broader than in the Sepias and the Poulps, where it is very narrow, but, moreover, does not encircle the entire sac, but only begins in the middle of the side. The use of this fin is to enable the animal to swim, and also to direct its course. It acts, that is, like the rump-feathers in birds, or the tail-fin in fishes. In none is it so small or so indistinct as in the Poulps. For in these the body is of small bulk and can be steered by the feet sufficiently well without other assistance.

The Insects, the Crustacea, the Testacea, and the Cephalopoda, have now been dealt with in turn; and their parts have been described, whether internal or external.

10

We must now go back to the animals that have blood, and consider such of their parts, already enumerated, as were before passed over. We will take the viviparous animals first, and, when we have done with these, will pass on to the oviparous, and treat of them in like manner.

The parts that border on the head, and on what is known as the neck and throat, have already been taken into consideration.[1] All animals that have blood have a head; whereas in

[1] Cf. II. 10–III. 3.

686a some bloodless animals, such as crabs, the part which represents a head is not clearly defined. As to the neck, it is present in all the Vivipara, but only in some of the Ovipara; for while those that have a lung also have a neck, those that do not inhale the outer air have none. The head exists mainly for the sake of the brain. For every animal that has blood must of necessity have a brain; and must, moreover, for reasons already given,[2] have it placed in an opposite region to the heart. But the head has also been chosen by nature as the part in which to set some of the senses; because its blood is mixed in such suitable proportions as to ensure their tranquillity and precision, while at the same time it can supply the brain with such warmth as it requires. There is yet a third constituent superadded to the head, namely the part which ministers to the ingestion of food. This has been placed here by nature, because such a situation accords best with the general configuration of the body. For the stomach could not possibly be placed above the heart, seeing that this is the sovereign organ; and if placed below, as in fact it is, then the mouth could not possibly be placed there also. For this would have necessitated a great increase in the length of the body; and the stomach, moreover, would have been removed too far from the source of motion and of concoction.

The head, then, exists for the sake of these three parts; while the neck, again, exists for the sake of the windpipe. For it acts as a defence to this and to the oesophagus, encircling them and keeping them from injury. In all other animals this neck is flexible and contains several vertebrae; but in wolves and lions it contains only a single bone. For the object of nature was to give these animals an organ which should be serviceable in the way of strength, rather than one that should be useful for any of the other purposes to which necks are subservient.

Continuous with the head and neck is the trunk with the anterior limbs. In man the forelegs and forefeet are replaced by arms and by what we call hands. For of all animals man alone stands erect, in accordance with his god-like nature and essence. For it is the function of the god-like to think and to be wise; and no easy task were this under the burden of a heavy body, pressing down from above and obstructing by its weight the motions of the intellect and of the general sense. When, more-

[2] Cf. II. 7 (652^b 17).

over, the weight and corporeal substance become excessive, the body must of necessity incline towards the ground. In such cases therefore nature, in order to give support to the body, has replaced the arms and hands by forefeet, and has thus converted the animal into a quadruped. For, as every animal that walks **686b** must of necessity have the two hinder feet, such an animal becomes a quadruped, its body inclining downwards in front from the weight which its soul cannot sustain. For all animals, man alone excepted, are dwarf-like in form. For the dwarf-like is that in which the upper part is large, while that which bears the weight and is used in progression is small. This upper part is what we call the trunk, which reaches from the mouth to the vent. In man it is duly proportionate to the part below, and diminishes much in its comparative size as the man attains to full growth. But in his infancy the contrary obtains, and the upper parts are large, while the lower part is small; so that the infant can only crawl, and is unable to walk; nay, at first cannot even crawl, but remains without motion. For all children are dwarfs in shape, but cease to be so as they become men, from the growth of their lower part; whereas in quadrupeds the reverse occurs, their lower parts being largest in youth, and advance of years bringing increased growth above, that is in the trunk, which extends from the rump to the head. Thus it is that colts are scarcely, if at all, below full-grown horses in height; and that while still young they can touch their heads with the hind legs, though this is no longer possible when they are older. Such, then, is the form of animals that have either a solid or a cloven hoof. But such as are polydactylous and without horns, though they too are of dwarf-like shape, are so in a less degree; and therefore the greater growth of the lower parts as compared with the upper is also small, being proportionate to this smaller deficiency.

Dwarf-like again is the race of birds and fishes; and so in fact, as already has been said, is every animal that has blood. This is the reason why no other animal is so intelligent as man. For even among men themselves if we compare children with adults, or such adults as are of dwarf-like shape with such as are not, we find that, whatever other superiority the former may possess, they are at any rate deficient as compared with the latter in intelligence. The explanation, as already stated, is that their psychical principle is corporeal, and much impeded in its motions. Let now a further decrease occur in the elevating heat, and a further increase in the earthy matter, and the animals become smaller in bulk, and their feet more numerous, until at a later stage they become apodous, and extended full length on the ground. Then, by further small successions of change, they come to have their principal organ below; and at last their cephalic part becomes motionless and destitute of sensation. Thus the animal becomes a plant, that has its upper parts downwards and its lower parts above. For in plants the roots are the equivalents of mouth and head, while the seed **687a** has an opposite significance, for it is produced above at the extremities of the twigs.

The reasons have now been stated why some animals have many feet, some only two, and others none; why, also, some living things are plants and others animals; and, lastly, why man alone of all animals stands erect. Standing thus erect, man has no need of legs in front, and in their stead has been endowed by nature with arms and hands. Now it is the opinion of Anaxagoras that the possession of these hands is the cause of man being of all animals the most intelligent. But it is more rational to suppose that his endowment with hands is the consequence rather than the cause of his superior intelligence. For the hands are instruments or organs, and the invariable plan of nature in distributing the organs is to give each to such animal as can make use of it; nature acting in this matter as any prudent man would do. For it is a better plan to take a person who is already a flute-player and give him a flute, than to take one who possesses a flute and teach him the art of flute-playing. For nature adds that which is less to that which is greater and more important, and not that which is more valuable and greater to that which is less. Seeing then that such is the better course, and seeing also that of what is possible nature invariably brings about the best, we must conclude that man does not owe his superior intelligence to his hands, but his hands to his superior intelligence. For the most intelligent of animals is the one who would put the most organs to use; and the hand is not to be looked on as one organ but as many; for it is, as it were, an instrument for further instruments. This instrument, therefore,—the hand—of all instruments the most variously serviceable, has been given by nature to man, the animal of all animals the most capable of acquiring the most varied handicrafts.

Much in error, then, are they who say that the construction of man is not only faulty, but inferior to that of all other animals; seeing that he is, as they point out, bare-footed, naked, and without weapon of which to avail himself. For other animals have each but one mode of defence, and this they can never change; so that they must perform all the offices of life and even, so to speak, sleep with sandals on, never laying aside whatever serves as a protection to their bodies, nor changing such single weapon as they may chance to possess. But to man numerous modes of defence are open, and **687b** these, moreover, he may change at will; as also he may adopt such weapon as he pleases, and at such times as suit him. For the hand is talon, hoof, and horn, at will. So too it is spear, and sword, and whatsoever other weapon or instrument you please; for all these can it be from its power of grasping and holding them all. In harmony with this varied office is the form which nature has contrived for it. For it is split into several divisions, and these are capable of divergence. Such capacity of divergence does not prevent their again converging so as to form a single compact body, whereas had the hand been an undivided mass, divergence would have been impossible. The divisions also may be used singly or two together and in various combinations. The joints, moreover, of the fingers are well constructed for prehension and for pressure. One of these also, and this not long like the rest but short and thick, is placed laterally. For were it not so placed all prehension would be as impossible, as were there no hand at all. For the pressure of this digit is applied from below upwards, while the rest act from above downwards; an arrangement which is essential, if the grasp is to be firm and hold like a tight clamp. As for the shortness of this digit, the object is to increase its strength, so that it may be able, though but one, to counterbalance its more numerous opponents. Moreover, were it long it would be of no use. This is the explanation of its being sometimes called the great digit, in spite of its small size; for without it all the rest would be practically useless. The finger which stands at the other end of the row is small, while the central one of all is long, like a centre oar in a ship. This is rightly so; for it is mainly by the central part of the encircling grasp that a tool must be held when put to use.

No less skilfully contrived are the nails. For, while in man these serve simply as coverings to protect the tips of the fingers, in other animals they are also used for active purposes; and their form in each case is suited to their office.

The arms in man and the fore limbs in quadrupeds bend in contrary directions, this difference having reference to the ingestion of food and to the other offices which belong to these parts. For quadrupeds must of necessity bend their anterior limbs inwards that they may serve in locomotion, for they use them as feet. Not but what even among quadrupeds there is at any rate a tendency for such as are polydactylous to use their forefeet not only **688a** for locomotion but as hands. And they are in fact so used, as any one may see. For these animals seize hold of objects, and also repel assailants with their anterior limbs; whereas quadrupeds with solid hoofs use their hind legs for this latter purpose. For their fore limbs are not analogous to the arms and hands of man.

It is this hand-like office of the anterior limbs which explains why in some of the polydactylous quadrupeds, such as wolves, lions, dogs, and leopards, there are actually five digits on each forefoot, though there are only four on each hind one. For the fifth digit of the foot corresponds to the fifth digit of the hand, and like it is called the big one. It is true that in the smaller polydactylous quadrupeds the hind feet also have each five toes. But this is because these animals are creepers; and the increased number of nails serves to give them a tighter grip, and so enables them to creep up steep places with greater facility, or even to run head downwards.

In man between the arms, and in other animals between the forelegs, lies what is called the breast. This in man is broad, as one might expect; for as the arms are set laterally on the body, they offer no impediment to such expansion in this part. But in quadrupeds the breast is narrow, owing to the legs having to be extended in a forward direction in progression and locomotion.

Owing to this narrowness the mammae of quadrupeds are never placed on the breast. But in the human body there is ample space in this part; moreover, the heart and neighbouring organs require protection, and for these reasons this part is fleshy and the mammae are placed upon it separately, side by side, being themselves of a fleshy substance in the male and therefore of use in the way just stated; while in the female, nature, in accordance with what we say is her frequent practice, makes them minister to an additional function, employing them as a store-place of nutriment for the offspring. The human mammae are two in number, in accordance with the division of the body into two halves, a right and a left. They are somewhat firmer than they would otherwise be, because the ribs in this region are joined together; while they form two separate masses, because their presence is in no wise burdensome. In other animals than man, it is impossible for the mammae to be placed on the breast between the forelegs, for they would interfere with locomotion; they are therefore disposed of otherwise, and in a variety of ways. Thus in such animals as produce but few at a birth, whether horned quadrupeds or those with solid hoofs, the mammae are placed in the region of the thighs, and are two in number, while in such as produce litters, or such as are polydactylous, the dugs are either numerous and placed laterally on the belly, as in swine and dogs, or are only two in number, being set, however, in the centre of the abdomen, as is the case in the lion. The **688b** explanation of this latter condition is not that the lion produces few at a birth, for sometimes it has more than two cubs at a time, but is to be found in the fact that this animal has no plentiful supply of milk. For, being a flesh-eater, it gets food at but rare intervals, and such nourishment as it obtains is all expended on the growth of its body.

In the elephant also there are but two mammae, which are placed under the axillae of the fore limbs. The mammae are not more than two, because this animal has only a single young one at a birth; and they are not placed in the region of the thighs, because they never occupy that position in any polydactylous animal such as this. Lastly, they are placed above, close to the axillae, because this is the position of the foremost dugs in all animals whose dugs are numerous, and the dugs so placed give the most milk. Evidence of this is furnished by the sow. For she always presents these foremost dugs to the first-born of her litter. A single young one is of course a first-born, and so such animals as only produce a single young one must have these anterior dugs to present to it; that is they must have the dugs which are under the axillae. This, then, is the reason why the elephant has but two mammae, and why they are so placed. But, in such animals as have litters of young, the dugs are disposed about the belly; the reason being that more dugs are required by those that will have more young to nourish. Now it is impossible that these dugs should be set transversely in rows of more than two, one, that is, for each side of the body, the right and the left; they must therefore be placed lengthways, and the only place where there is sufficient length for this is the region between the front and hind legs. As to the animals that are not polydactylous but produce few at a birth, or have horns, their dugs are placed in the region of the thighs. The horse, the ass, the camel are examples; all of which bear but a single young one at a time, and of which the two former have solid hoofs, while in the last the hoof is cloven. As still further examples may be mentioned the deer, the ox, the goat, and all other similar animals.

The explanation is that in these animals growth takes place in an upward direction; so that there must be an abundant collection of residual matter and of blood in the lower region, that is to say in the neighbourhood of the orifices for efflux, and here therefore nature has placed the mammae. For the place in which the nutriment is set in motion must also be the place whence nutriment can be derived by them. In man there are mammae in the male as well as in the female; but some of the males of other animals are without them. Such, for instance, is the case with horses, some stallions being destitute of these parts, while others that resemble their dams have them. Thus much then concerning the mammae.

Next after the breast comes the region of **689a** the belly, which is left unenclosed by the ribs for a reason which has already been given;[1] namely that there may be no impediment to the swelling which necessarily occurs in the food as it gets heated, nor to the expansion of the womb in pregnancy.

At the extreme end of what is called the trunk are the parts concerned in the evacuation of the solid and also of the fluid residue. In all sanguineous animals with some few exceptions, and in all Vivipara without any exception at all, the same part which serves for the evacuation of the fluid residue is also made by nature to serve in sexual congress, and this alike in male and female. For the semen is a kind of fluid and residual matter. The proof of this will be given hereafter,[2] but for the present let it be taken for granted. (The like holds good of the menstrual fluid in women, and of the part where they emit semen. This also, however, is a matter of which a more accurate

[1] Cf. II. 9 (655a 2).

[2] *On the Generation of Animals*, I. 18 (724b 21–726a 25).

account will be given hereafter. For the present let it be simply stated as a fact, that the catamenia of the female like the semen of the male are residual matter. Both of them, moreover, being fluid, it is only natural that the parts which serve for voidance of the urine should give issue to residues which resemble it in character.) Of the internal structure of these parts, and of the differences which exist between the parts concerned with semen and the parts concerned with conception, a clear account is given in the book of Researches concerning Animals and in the treatises on Anatomy. Moreover, I shall have to speak of them again when I come to deal with Generation.[1] As regards, however, the external shape of these parts, it is plain enough that they are adapted to their operations, as indeed of necessity they must be. There are, however, differences in the male organ corresponding to differences in the body generally. For all animals are not of an equally sinewy nature. This organ, again, is the only one that, independently of any morbid change, admits of augmentation and of diminution of bulk. The former condition is of service in copulation, while the other is required for the advantage of the body at large. For, were the organ constantly in the former condition, it would be an incumbrance. The organ therefore has been formed of such constituents as will admit of either state. For it is partly sinewy, partly cartilaginous, and thus is enabled either to contract or to become extended, and is capable of admitting air.

All female quadrupeds void their urine backwards, because the position of the parts which this implies is useful to them in the act of copulation. This is the case with only some few males, such as the lynx, the lion, the camel, and the hare. No quadruped with a solid hoof is retromingent.

689b The posterior portion of the body and the parts about the legs are peculiar in man as compared with quadrupeds. Nearly all these latter have a tail, and this whether they are viviparous or oviparous. For, even if the tail be of no great size, yet they have a kind of scut, as at any rate a small representative of it. But man is tail-less. He has, however, buttocks, which exist in none of the quadrupeds. His legs also are fleshy (as too are his thighs and feet); while the legs in all other animals that have any, whether viviparous or not, are fleshless, being made of sinew and bone and spinous substance. For all these differences there is, so to say, one common explanation, and this is that of all animals man alone stands erect. It was to facilitate the maintenance of this position that Nature made his upper parts light, taking away some of their corporeal substance, and using it to increase the weight of the parts below, so that the buttocks, the thighs, and the calves of the legs were all made fleshy. The character which she thus gave to the buttocks renders them at the same time useful in resting the body. For standing causes no fatigue to quadrupeds, and even the long continuance of this posture produces in them no weariness; for they are supported the whole time by four props, which is much as though they were lying down. But to man it is no easy task to remain for any length of time on his feet, his body demanding rest in a sitting position. This, then, is the reason why man has buttocks and fleshy legs; and the presence of these fleshy parts explains why he has no tail. For the nutriment which would otherwise go to the tail is used up in the production of these parts, while at the same time the existence of buttocks does away with the necessity of a tail. But in quadrupeds and other animals the reverse obtains. For they are of dwarf-like form, so that all the pressure of their weight and corporeal substance is on their upper part, and is withdrawn from the parts below. On this account they are without buttocks and have hard legs. In order, however, to cover and protect that part which serves for the evacuation of excrement, nature has given them a tail of some kind or other, subtracting for the purpose some of the nutriment which would otherwise go to the legs. Intermediate in shape between man and quadrupeds is the ape, belonging therefore to neither or to both, and having on this account neither tail nor buttocks; no tail in its character of biped, no buttocks in its character of quadruped. There is **690a** a great diversity of so-called tails; and this organ like others is sometimes used by nature for by-purposes, being made to serve not only as a covering and protection to the fundament, but also for other uses and advantages of its possessor.

There are differences in the feet of quadrupeds. For in some of these animals there is a solid hoof, and in others a hoof cloven into two, and again in others a foot divided into many parts.

The hoof is solid when the body is large and

[1] *History of Animals*, I. 13, 14; I. 17 (497a 27); III. 1; *On the Generation of Animals*, I. 2–16.

the earthy matter present in great abundance; in which case the earth, instead of forming teeth and horns, is separated in the character of a nail, and being very abundant forms one continuous nail, that is a hoof, in place of several. This consumption of the earthy matter on the hoof explains why these animals, as a rule, have no huckle-bones; a second reason being that the presence of such a bone in the joint of the hind leg somewhat impedes its free motion. For extension and flexion can be made more rapidly in parts that have but one angle than in parts that have several. But the presence of a huckle-bone, as a connecting bolt, is the introduction as it were of a new limb-segment between the two ordinary ones. Such an addition adds to the weight of the foot, but renders the act of progression more secure. Thus it is that in such animals as have a huckle-bone, it is only in the posterior and not in the anterior limbs that this bone is found. For the anterior limbs, moving as they do in advance of the others, require to be light and capable of ready flexion, whereas firmness and extensibility are what are wanted in the hind limbs. Moreover, a huckle-bone adds weight to the blow of a limb, and so renders it a suitable weapon of defence; and these animals all use their hind legs to protect themselves, kicking out with their heels against anything which annoys them. In the cloven-hoofed quadrupeds the lighter character of the hind legs admits of there being a huckle-bone; and the presence of the huckle-bone prevents them from having a solid hoof, the bony substance remaining in the joint, and therefore being deficient in the foot. As to the polydactylous quadrupeds, none of them have huckle-bones. For if they had they would not be polydactylous, but the divisions of the foot would only extend to that amount of its breadth which was covered by the huckle-bone. Thus it is that most of the animals that have huckle-bones are cloven-hoofed.

Of all animals man has the largest foot in proportion to the size of the body. This is only what might be expected. For seeing that he is the only animal that stands erect, the two feet which are intended to bear all the weight of the body must be both long and broad. Equally intelligible is it that the proportion between the size of the fingers and that of the whole hand should be inverted in the case of the toes and feet. For the function of the hands is to take hold of objects and retain them by pressure; so that the fingers require to be long. For it is by its flexed portion that the hand

690b grasps an object. But the function of the feet is to enable us to stand securely, and for this the undivided part of the foot requires to be of larger size than the toes. However, it is better for the extremity to be divided than to be undivided. For in an undivided foot disease of any one part would extend to the whole organ; whereas, if the foot be divided into separate digits, there is not an equal liability to such an occurrence. The digits, again, by being short would be less liable to injury. For these reasons the feet in man are many-toed, while the separate digits are of no great length. The toes, finally, are furnished with nails for the same reason as are the fingers, namely because such projecting parts are weak and therefore require special protection.

11

We have now done with such sanguineous animals as live on land and bring forth their young alive; and, having dealt with all their main kinds, we may pass on to such sanguineous animals as are oviparous. Of these some have four feet, while others have none. The latter form a single genus, namely the Serpents; and why these are apodous has been already explained in the dissertation on Animal Progression.[1] Irrespective of this absence of feet, serpents resemble the oviparous quadrupeds in their conformation.

In all these animals there is a head with its component parts; its presence being determined by the same causes as obtain in the case of other sanguineous animals; and in all, with the single exception of the river crocodile, there is a tongue inside the mouth. In this one exception there would seem to be no actual tongue, but merely a space left vacant for it. The reason is that a crocodile is in a way a land-animal and a water-animal combined. In its character of land-animal it has a space for a tongue; but in its character of water-animal it is without the tongue itself. For in some fishes, as has already been mentioned,[2] there is no appearance whatsoever of a tongue, unless the mouth be stretched open very widely indeed; while in others it is indistinctly separated from the rest of the mouth. The reason for this is that a tongue would be of but little service to such animals, seeing that they are unable to chew their food or to taste it before swallowing, the pleasurable sensations they derive from

[1] *On the Gait of Animals*, 8 (708a 9–20).

[2] Cf. II. 17 (660b 13).

it being limited to the act of deglutition. For it is in their passage down the gullet that solid edibles cause enjoyment, while it is by the tongue that the savour of fluids is perceived. Thus it is during deglutition that the oiliness, the heat, and other such qualities of food are recognized; and, in fact, the satisfaction from most solid edibles and dainties is derived al- **691a** most entirely from the dilatation of the oesophagus during deglutition. This sensation, then, belongs even to animals that have no tongue, but while other animals have in addition the sensations of taste, tongueless animals have, we may say, no other satisfaction than it. What has now been said explains why intemperance as regards drinks and savoury fluids does not go hand in hand with intemperance as regards eating and solid relishes.

In some oviparous quadrupeds, namely in lizards, the tongue is bifid, as also it is in serpents, and its terminal divisions are of hair-like fineness, as has already been described.[1] (Seals also have a forked tongue.) This it is which accounts for all these animals being so fond of dainty food. The teeth in the four-footed Ovipara are of the sharp interfitting kind, like the teeth of fishes. The organs of all the senses are present and resemble those of other animals. Thus there are nostrils for smell, eyes for vision, and ears for hearing. The latter organs, however, do not project from the sides of the head, but consist simply of the duct, as also is the case in birds. This is due in both cases to the hardness of the integument; birds having their bodies covered with feathers, and these oviparous quadrupeds with horny plates. These plates are equivalent to scales, but of a harder character. This is manifest in tortoises and river crocodiles, and also in the large serpents. For here the plates become stronger than the bones, being seemingly of the same substance as these.

These animals have no upper eyelid, but close the eye with the lower lid. In this they resemble birds, and the reason is the same as was assigned in their case. Among birds there are some that can not only thus close the eye, but can also blink by means of a membrane which comes from its corner. But none of the oviparous quadrupeds blink; for their eyes are harder than those of birds. The reason for this is that keen vision and far-sightedness are of very considerable service to birds, flying as they do in the air, whereas they would be of comparatively small use to the oviparous quadrupeds, seeing that they are all of troglodytic habits.

Of the two separate portions which constitute the head, namely the upper part and the lower jaw, the latter in man and in the viviparous quadrupeds moves not only upwards and downwards, but also from side to side; while in fishes, and birds and oviparous quadrupeds, the only movement is up and down. The reason is that this latter movement is the **691b** one required in biting and dividing food, while the lateral movement serve to reduce substances to a pulp. To such animals, therefore, as have grinder-teeth this lateral motion is of service; but to those animals that have no grinders it would be quite useless, and they are therefore invariably without it. For nature never makes anything that is superfluous. While in all other animals it is the lower jaw that is movable, in the river crocodile it is exceptionally the upper. This is because the feet in this creature are so excessively small as to be useless for seizing and holding prey; on which account nature has given it a mouth that can serve for these purposes in their stead. For that direction of motion which will give the greater force to a blow will be the more serviceable one in holding or in seizing prey; and a blow from above is always more forcible than one from below. Seeing, then, that both the prehension and the mastication of food are offices of the mouth, and that the former of these two is the more essential in an animal that has neither hands nor suitably formed feet, these crocodiles will derive greater benefit from a motion of the upper jaw downwards than from a motion of the lower jaw upwards. The same considerations explain why crabs also move the upper division of each claw and not the lower. For their claws are substitutes for hands, and so require to be suitable for the prehension of food, and not for its comminution; for such comminution and biting is the office of teeth. In crabs, then, and in such other animals as are able to seize their food in a leisurely manner, inasmuch as their mouth is not called on to perform its office while they are still in the water, the two functions are assigned to different parts, prehension to the hands or feet, biting and comminution of food to the mouth. But in crocodiles the mouth has been so framed by nature as to serve both purposes, the jaws being made to move in the manner just described.

Another part present in these animals is a neck, this being the necessary consequence of

[1] Cf. II. 17 (660b 9).

their having a lung. For the windpipe by which the air is admitted to the lung is of some length. If, however, the definition of a neck be correct, which calls it the portion between the head and the shoulders, a serpent can scarcely be said with the same right as the rest of these animals to have a neck, but only to have something analogous to that part of the body. It is a peculiarity of serpents, as compared with other animals allied to them, that **692a** they are able to turn their head backwards without stirring the rest of the body. The reason of this is that a serpent, like an insect, has a body that admits of being curled up, its vertebrae being cartilaginous and easily bent. The faculty in question belongs then to serpents simply as a necessary consequence of this character of their vertebrae; but at the same time it has a final cause, for it enables them to guard against attacks from behind. For their body, owing to its length and the absence of feet, is ill-suited for turning round and protecting the hinder parts; and merely to lift the head, without the power of turning it round, would be of no use whatsoever.

The animals with which we are dealing have, moreover, a part which corresponds to the breast; but neither here nor elsewhere in their body have they any mammae, as neither has any bird or fish. This is a consequence of their having no milk; for a mamma is a receptacle for milk and, as it were, a vessel to contain it. This absence of milk is not peculiar to these animals, but is common to all such as are not internally viviparous. For all such produce eggs, and the nutriment which in Vivipara has the character of milk is in them engendered in the egg. Of all this, however, a clearer account will be given in the treatise on Generation.[1] As to the mode in which the legs bend, a general account, in which all animals are considered, has already been given in the dissertation on Progression.[2] These animals also have a tail, larger in some of them, smaller in others, and the reason for this has been stated in general terms in an earlier passage.[3]

Of all oviparous animals that live on land there is none so lean as the Chamaeleon. For there is none that has so little blood. The explanation of this is to be found in the psychical temperament of the creature. For it is of a timid nature, as the frequent changes it undergoes in its outward aspect testify. But fear is a refrigeration, and results from deficiency of natural heat and scantiness of blood.

692b We have now done with such sanguineous animals as are quadrupedous and also such as are apodous, and have stated with sufficient completeness what external parts they possess, and for what reason they have them.

12

The differences of birds compared one with another are differences of magnitude, and of the greater or smaller development of parts. Thus some have long legs, others short legs; some have a broad tongue, others a narrow tongue; and so on with the other parts. There are few of their parts that differ save in size, taking birds by themselves. But when birds are compared with other animals the parts present differences of form also. For in some animals these are hairy, in others scaly, and in others have scale-like plates, while birds are feathered.

Birds, then, are feathered, and this is a character common to them all and peculiar to them. Their feathers, too, are split and distinct in kind from the undivided feathers of insects; for the bird's feather is barbed, these are not; the bird's feather has a shaft, these have none. A second strange peculiarity which distinguishes birds from all other animals is their beak. For as in elephants the nostril serves in place of hands, and as in some insects the tongue serves in place of mouth, so in birds there is a beak, which, being bony, serves in place of teeth and lips. Their organs of sense have already been considered.[4]

All birds have a neck extending from the body; and the purpose of this neck is the same as in such other animals as have one. This neck in some birds is long, in others short; its length, as a general rule, being pretty nearly determined by that of the legs. For long-legged birds have a long neck, short-legged birds a short one, to which rule, however, the web-footed **693a** birds form an exception. For to a bird perched up on long legs a short neck would be of no use whatsoever in collecting food from the ground; and equally useless would be a long neck, if the legs were short. Such birds, again, as are carnivorous would find length in this part interfere greatly with their habits of life. For a long neck is weak, and it is on their superior strength that carnivorous birds depend for their subsistence. No bird, therefore, that has talons ever has an elongated neck.

[1] *On the Generation of Animals*, III. 2 (752b 15 sqq.).

[2] Cf. *On the Gait of Animals*, 13.

[3] Cf. IV. 10 (689b 3–690a 4).

[4] Cf. II. 12–17.

In web-footed birds, however, and in those other birds belonging to the same class, whose toes though actually separate have flat marginal lobes, the neck is elongated, so as to be suitable for collecting food from the water; while the legs are short, so as to serve in swimming. The beaks of birds, as their feet, vary with their modes of life. For in some the beak is straight, in others crooked; straight, in those who use it merely for eating; crooked, in those that live on raw flesh. For a crooked beak is an advantage in fighting; and these birds must, of course, get their food from the bodies of other animals, and in most cases by violence. In such birds, again, as live in marshes and are herbivorous the beak is broad and flat, this form being best suited for digging and cropping, and for pulling up plants. In some of these marsh birds, however, the beak is elongated, as too is the neck, the reason for this being that the bird get its food from some depth below the surface. For most birds of this kind, and most of those whose feet are webbed, either in their entirety or each part separately, live by preying on some of the smaller animals that are to be found in water, and use these parts for their capture, the neck acting as a fishing-rod, and the beak representing the line and hook.

The upper and under sides of the body, that is of what in quadrupeds is called the trunk, present in birds one unbroken surface, and they have no arms or forelegs attached to it, but in their stead wings, which are a distinc-
693b tive peculiarity of these animals; and, as these wings are substitutes for arms, their terminal segments lie on the back in the place of a shoulder-blade.

The legs are two in number, as in man; not however, as in man, bent outwards, but bent inwards like the [hind] legs of a quadruped. The wings are bent like the forelegs of a quadruped, having their convexity turned outwards. That the feet should be two in number is a matter of necessity. For a bird is essentially a sanguineous animal, and at the same time essentially a winged animal; and no sanguineous animal has more than four points for motion. In birds, then, as in those other sanguineous animals that live and move upon the ground, the limbs attached to the trunk are four in number. But, while in all the rest these four limbs consist of a pair of arms and a pair of legs, or of four legs as in quadrupeds, in birds the arms or forelegs are replaced by a pair of wings, and this is their distinctive character. For it is of the essence of a bird that it shall be able to fly; and it is by the extension of wings that this is made possible. Of all arrangements, then, the only possible, and so the necessary, one is that birds shall have two feet; for this with the wings will give them four points for motion. The breast in all birds is sharp-edged, and fleshy. The sharp edge is to minister to flight, for broad surfaces move with considerable difficulty, owing to the large quantity of air which they have to displace; while the fleshy character acts as a protection, for the breast, owing to its form, would be weak, were it not amply covered.

Below the breast lies the belly, extending, as in quadrupeds and in man, to the vent and to the place where the legs are jointed to the trunk.

Such, then, are the parts which lie between the wings and the legs. Birds like all other animals, whether produced viviparously or from eggs, have an umbilicus during their development, but, when the bird has attained to fuller growth, no signs of this remain visible. The cause of this is plainly to be seen during the process of development; for in birds the umbilical cord unites with the intestine, and is not a portion of the vascular system, as is the case in viviparous animals.

Some birds, again, are well adapted for
694a flight, their wings being large and strong. Such, for instance, are those that have talons and live on flesh. For their mode of life renders the power of flight a necessity, and it is on this account that their feathers are so abundant and their wings so large. Besides these, however, there are also other genera of birds that can fly well; all those, namely, that depend on speed for security, or that are of migratory habits. On the other hand, some kinds of birds have heavy bodies and are not constructed for flight. These are birds that are frugivorous and live on the ground, or that are able to swim and get their living in watery places. In those that have talons the body, without the wings, is small; for the nutriment is consumed in the production of these wings, and of the weapons and defensive appliances; whereas in birds that are not made for flight the contrary obtains, and the body is bulky and so of heavy weight. In some of these heavy-bodied birds the legs are furnished with what are called spurs, which replace the wings as a means of defence. Spurs and talons never co-exist in the same bird. For nature never makes anything superfluous; and if a bird can fly, and has talons, it has no

use for spurs; for these are weapons for fighting on the ground, and on this account are an appanage of certain heavy-bodied birds. These latter, again, would find the possession of talons not only useless but actually injurious; for the claws would stick into the ground and interfere with progression. This is the reason why all birds with talons walk so badly, and why they never settle upon rocks. For the character of their claws is ill-suited for either action.

All this is the necessary consequence of the process of development. For the earthy matter in the body issuing from it is converted into parts that are useful as weapons. That which flows upwards gives hardness or size to the beak; and, should any flow downwards, it either forms spurs upon the legs or gives size and strength to the claws upon the feet. But it does not at one and the same time produce both these results, one in the legs, the other in the claws; for such a dispersion of this residual matter would destroy all its efficiency. In other birds this earthy residue furnishes the legs with
694b the material for their elongation; or sometimes, in place of this, fills up the interspaces between the toes. Thus it is simply a matter of necessity, that such birds as swim shall either be actually web-footed, or shall have a kind of broad blade-like margin running along the whole length of each distinct toe. The forms, then, of these feet are simply the necessary results of the causes that have been mentioned. Yet at the same time they are intended for the animal's advantage. For they are in harmony with the mode of life of these birds, who, living on the water, where their wings are useless, require that their feet shall be such as to serve in swimming. For these feet are so developed as to resemble the oars of a boat, or the fins of a fish; and the destruction of the foot-web has the same effect as the destruction of the fins; that is to say, it puts an end to all power of swimming.

In some birds the legs are very long, the cause of this being that they inhabit marshes. I say the cause, because nature makes the organs for the function, and not the function for the organs. It is, then, because these birds are not meant for swimming that their feet are without webs, and it is because they live on ground that gives way under the foot that their legs and toes are elongated, and that these latter in most of them have an extra number of joints. Again, though all birds have the same material composition, they are not all made for flight; and in these, therefore, the nutriment that should go to their tail-feathers is spent on the legs and used to increase their size. This is the reason why these birds when they fly make use of their legs as a tail, stretching them out behind, and so rendering them serviceable, whereas in any other position they would be simply an impediment.

In other birds, where the legs are short, these are held close against the belly during flight. In some cases this is merely to keep the feet out of the way, but in birds that have talons the position has a further purpose, being the one best suited for rapine. Birds that have a long and a thick neck keep it stretched out during flight; but those whose neck though long is slender fly with it coiled up. For in this position it is protected, and less likely to get broken, should the bird fly against any obstacle.

695a In all birds there is an ischium, but so placed and of such length that it would scarcely be taken for an ischium, but rather for a second thigh-bone; for it extends as far as to the middle of the belly. The reason for this is that the bird is a biped, and yet is unable to stand erect. For if its ischium extended but a short way from the fundament, and then immediately came the leg, as is the case in man and in quadrupeds, the bird would be unable to stand up at all. For while man stands erect, and while quadrupeds have their heavy bodies propped up in front by the forelegs, birds can neither stand erect owing to their dwarf-like shape, nor have anterior legs to prop them up, these legs being replaced by wings. As a remedy for this Nature has given them a long ischium, and brought it to the centre of the body, fixing it firmly; and she has placed the legs under this central point, that the weight on either side may be equally balanced, and standing or progression rendered possible. Such then is the reason why a bird, though it is a biped, does not stand erect. Why its legs are destitute of flesh has also already been stated;[1] for the reasons are the same as in the case of quadrupeds.

In all birds alike, whether web-footed or not, the number of toes in each foot is four. For the Libyan ostrich may be disregarded for the present, and its cloven hoof and other discrepancies of structure as compared with the tribe of birds will be considered further on.[2] Of these four toes three are in front, while the fourth points backward, serving, as a heel, to give steadiness. In the long-legged birds this fourth

[1] Cf. iv. 10 (689b 7). [2] Cf. iv. 14.

toe is much shorter than the others, as is the case with the Crex, but the number of their toes is not increased. The arrangement of the toes is such as has been described in all birds with the exception of the wryneck. Here only two of the toes are in front, the other two behind; and the reason for this is that the body of the wryneck is not inclined forward so much as that of other birds. All birds have testicles; but they are inside the body. The reason for this will be given in the treatise *On the Generation of Animals*.[1]

13

695b Thus then are fashioned the parts of birds. But in fishes a still further stunting has occurred in the external parts. For here, for reasons already given, there are neither legs nor hands nor wings, the whole body from head to tail presenting one unbroken surface. This tail differs in different fishes, in some approximating in character to the fins, while in others, namely in some of the flat kinds, it is spinous and elongated, because the material which should have gone to the tail has been diverted thence and used to increase the breadth of the body. Such, for instance, is the case with the Torpedos, the Trygons, and whatever other Selachia there may be of like nature. In such fishes, then, the tail is spinous and long; while in some others it is short and fleshy, for the same reason which makes it spinous and long in the Torpedo. For to be short and fleshy comes to the same thing as to be long and less amply furnished with flesh.

What has occurred in the Fishing-frog is the reverse of what has occurred in the other instances just given. For here the anterior and broad part of the body is not of a fleshy character, and so all the fleshy substance which has been thence diverted has been placed by nature in the tail and hinder portion of the body.

In fishes there are no limbs attached to the body. For in accordance with their essential constitution they are swimming animals; and nature never makes anything superfluous or void of use. Now inasmuch as fishes are made for swimming they have fins, and as they are not made for walking they are without feet; for feet are attached to the body that they may be of use in progression on land. Moreover, fishes cannot have feet, or any other similar limbs, as well as four fins; for they are essentially sanguineous animals. The Cordylus, though it has gills, has feet, for it has no fins but merely has its tail flattened out and loose in texture.

Fishes, unless, like the Batos and the Trygon, **696a** they are broad and flat, have four fins, two on the upper and two on the under side of the body; and no fish ever has more than these. For, if it had, it would be a bloodless animal.

The upper pair of fins is present in nearly all fishes, but not so the under pair; for these are wanting in some of those fishes that have long thick bodies, such as the eel, the conger, and a certain kind of Cestreus that is found in the lake at Siphae. When the body is still more elongated, and resembles that of a serpent rather than that of a fish, as is the case in the Smuraena, there are absolutely no fins at all; and locomotion is effected by the flexures of the body, the water being put to the same use by these fishes as is the ground by serpents. For serpents swim in water exactly in the same way as they glide on the ground. The reason for these serpent-like fishes being without fins is the same as that which causes serpents to be without feet; and what this is has been already stated in the dissertations on the Progression and the Motion of Animals.[2] The reason was this. If the points of motion were four, motion would be effected under difficulties; for either the two pairs of fins would be close to each other, in which case motion would scarcely be possible, or they would be at a very considerable distance apart, in which case the long interval between them would be just as great an evil. On the other hand, to have more than four such motor points would convert the fishes into bloodless animals. A similar explanation applies to the case of those fishes that have only two fins. For here again the body is of great length and like that of a serpent, and its undulations do the office of the two missing fins. It is owing to this that such fishes can even crawl on dry ground, and can live there for a considerable time; and do not begin to gasp until they have been for a considerable time out of the water, while others, whose nature is akin to that of land-animals, do not even do as much as that. In such fishes as have but two fins it is the upper pair (*pectorals*) that is present, excepting when the flat broad shape of the body prevents this. The fins in such cases are placed at the head, because in this region there is no elongation, which might serve in the absence of fins as a means of locomotion; whereas in the direction of the tail there is a

[1] *On the Generation of Animals*, I. 4 (717^{b} 4), 12.

[2] Cf. *On the Gait of Animals*, 7, 709^{b} 7 sqq.

considerable lengthening out in fishes of this conformation. As for the Bati and the like, they use the marginal part of their flattened bodies in place of fins for swimming.

In the Torpedo and the Fishing-frog the breadth of the anterior part of the body is not so great as to render locomotion by fins impossible, but in consequence of it the upper pair (*pectorals*) are placed further back and the under pair (*ventrals*) are placed close to the head, while to compensate for this advancement they are reduced in size so as to be smaller than the upper ones. In the Torpedo the two upper fins (*pectorals*) are placed on the tail, and the fish uses the broad expansion of its body to supply their place, each lateral half of its circumference serving the office of a fin.

The head, with its several parts, as also the organs of sense, have already come under consideration.[1]

There is one peculiarity which distinguishes fishes from all other sanguineous animals, namely, the possession of gills. Why they have
696^b these organs has been set forth in the treatise on Respiration.[2] These gills are in most fishes covered by opercula, but in the Selachia, owing to the skeleton being cartilaginous, there are no such coverings. For an operculum requires fish-spine for its formation, and in other fishes the skeleton is made of this substance, whereas in the Selachia it is invariably formed of cartilage. Again, while the motions of spinous fishes are rapid, those of the Selachia are sluggish, inasmuch as they have neither fish-spine nor sinew; but an operculum requires rapidity of motion, seeing that the office of the gills is to minister as it were to expiration. For this reason in Selachia the branchial orifices themselves effect their own closure, and thus there is no need for an operculum to ensure its taking place with due rapidity. In some fishes the gills are numerous, in others few in number; in some again they are double, in others single. The last gill in most cases is single. For a detailed account of all this, reference must be made to the treatises on Anatomy, and to the book of Researches concerning Animals.[3]

It is the abundance or the deficiency of the cardiac heat which determines the numerical abundance or deficiency of the gills. For, the greater an animal's heat, the more rapid and the more forcible does it require the branchial movement to be; and numerous and double gills act with more force and rapidity than such as are few and single. Thus, too, it is that some fishes that have but few gills, and those of comparatively small efficacy, can live out of water for a considerable time; for in them there is no great demand for refrigeration. Such, for example, are the eel and all other fishes of serpent-like form.

Fishes also present diversities as regards the mouth. For in some this is placed in front, at the very extremity of the body, while in others, as the dolphin and the Selachia, it is placed on the under surface; so that these fishes turn on the back in order to take their food. The purpose of Nature in this was apparently not merely to provide a means of salvation for other animals, by allowing them opportunity of escape during the time lost in the act of turning—for all the fishes with this kind of mouth prey on living animals—but also to prevent these fishes from giving way too much to their gluttonous ravening after food. For had they been able to seize their prey more easily than they do, they would soon have perished from over-repletion. An additional reason is that the projecting extremity of the head in these fishes is round and small, and therefore cannot admit of a wide opening.

Again, even when the mouth is not placed on the under surface, there are differences in the extent to which it can open. For in some cases it can gape widely, while in others it is
697^a set at the point of a small tapering snout; the former being the case in carnivorous fishes, such as those with sharp interfitting teeth, whose strength lies in their mouth, while the latter is its form in all such as are not carnivorous.

The skin is in some fishes covered with scales (the scale of a fish is a thin and shiny film, and therefore easily becomes detached from the surface of the body). In others it is rough, as for instance in the Rhine, the Batos, and the like. Fewest of all are those whose skin is smooth. The Selachia have no scales, but a rough skin. This is explained by their cartilaginous skeleton. For the earthy material which has been thence diverted is expended by nature upon the skin.

No fish has testicles either externally or internally; as indeed have no apodous animals, among which of course are included the serpents. One and the same orifice serves both for the excrement and for the generative secre-

[1] Namely, in the latter part of the second book and beginning of the third book.

[2] *On Breathing*, 10, 476^a 1 sqq.; and 21, 480^b 13.

[3] Cf. *History of Animals*, II. 13 (504^b 28–505^a 20).

tions, as is the case also in all other oviparous animals, whether two-footed or four-footed, inasmuch as they have no urinary bladder and form no fluid excretion.

Such then are the characters which distinguish fishes from all other animals. But dolphins and whales and all such Cetacea are without gills; and, having a lung, are provided with a blow-hole; for this serves them to discharge the sea-water which has been taken into the mouth. For, feeding as they do in the water, they cannot but let this fluid enter into their mouth, and, having let it in, they must of necessity let it out again. The use of gills, however, as has been explained in the treatise on Respiration,[1] is limited to such animals as do not breathe; for no animal can possibly possess gills and at the same time be a respiratory animal. In order, therefore, that these Cetacea may discharge the water, they are provided with a blow-hole. This is placed in front of the brain; for otherwise it would have cut off the brain from the spine. The reason for these animals having a lung and breathing, is that animals of large size require an excess of heat, to facilitate their motion. A lung, therefore, is placed within their body, and is fully supplied with blood-heat. These creatures are after a fashion land and water animals in one. For so far as they are inhalers of air they resemble land-animals, while they resemble water-animals in having no feet and in deriving their **697b** food from the sea. So also seals lie half-way between land and water animals, and bats half-way between animals that live on the ground and animals that fly; and so belong to both kinds or to neither. For seals, if looked on as water-animals, are yet found to have feet; and, if looked on as land-animals, are yet found to have fins. For their hind feet are exactly like the fins of fishes; and their teeth also are sharp and interfitting as in fishes. Bats again, if regarded as winged animals, have feet; and, if regarded as quadrupeds, are without them. So also they have neither the tail of a quadruped nor the tail of a bird; no quadruped's tail, because they are winged animals; no bird's tail, because they are terrestrial. This absence of tail is the result of necessity. For bats fly by means of a membrane, but no animal, unless it has barbed feathers, has the tail of a bird; for a bird's tail is composed of such feathers. As for a quadruped's tail, it would be an actual impediment, if present among the feathers.

[1] *On Breathing*, 10, 476^a 1 sqq.; 21, 480^b 13.

14

Much the same may be said also of the Libyan ostrich. For it has some of the characters of a bird, some of the characters of a quadruped. It differs from a quadruped in being feathered; and from a bird in being unable to soar aloft, and in having feathers that resemble hair and are useless for flight. Again, it agrees with quadrupeds in having upper eyelashes, which are the more richly supplied with hairs because the parts about the head and the upper portion of the neck are bare; and it agrees with birds in being feathered in all the parts posterior to these. Further, it resembles a bird in being a biped, and a quadruped in having a cloven hoof; for it has hoofs and not toes. The explanation of these peculiarities is to be found in its bulk, which is that of a quadruped rather than that of a bird. For, speaking generally, a bird must necessarily be of very small size. For a body of heavy bulk can with difficulty be raised into the air.

Thus much then as regards the parts of animals. We have discussed them all, and set forth the cause why each exists; and in so doing we have severally considered each group of animals. We must now pass on, and in due sequence must next deal with the question of their generation.

CONTENTS: ON THE MOTION OF ANIMALS

ON THE MOTION OF ANIMALS

1

698a ELSEWHERE we have investigated in detail[1] the movement of animals after their various kinds, the differences between them, and the reasons for their particular characters (for some animals fly, some swim, some walk, others move in various other ways); there remains an investigation of the common ground of any sort of animal movement whatsoever.

Now we have already determined (when we were discussing[2] whether eternal motion exists or not, and its definition, if it does exist) that the origin of all other motions is that which moves itself, and that the origin of this is the immovable, and that the prime mover must of necessity be immovable. And we must grasp this not only generally in theory, but also by reference to individuals in the world of sense, for with these in view we seek general theories, and with these we believe that general theories ought to harmonize. Now in the world of sense too it is plainly impossible for movement to be initiated if there is nothing at rest, and before all else in our present subject—animal life. For if one of the parts of an animal be moved, another must be at rest, and this is the purpose of their joints; animals use joints like a centre, and the whole member, in which the joint is, becomes both one and two, both straight and bent, changing potentially and actually by reason of the joint. And when it is bending and being moved one of the points in the joint is moved and one is at rest, just as if the points A and D of a diameter were at rest, and B were moved, and DAC were generated. However, in the geometrical illustration, the centre is held to be altogether indivisible (for in mathematics motion is a fiction, as the phrase goes, no mathematical entity being really moved), whereas in the case of joints the centres become now one potentially and divided actually, and now one actually and **698b** divided potentially. But still the origin of movement, qua origin, always remains at rest when the lower part of a limb is moved; for example, the elbow joint, when the forearm is moved, and the shoulder, when the whole arm; the knee when the tibia is moved, and the hip when the whole leg. Accordingly it is plain that each animal as a whole must have within itself a point at rest, whence will be the origin of that which is moved, and supporting itself upon which it will be moved both as a complete whole and in its members.

2

But the point of rest in the animal is still quite ineffectual unless there be something without which is absolutely at rest and immovable. Now it is worth while to pause and consider what has been said, for it involves a speculation which extends beyond animals even to the motion and march of the universe. For just as there must be something immovable within the animal, if it is to be moved, so even more must there be without it something immovable, by supporting itself upon which that which is moved moves. For were that something always to give way (as it does for mice walking in grain or persons walking in sand) advance would be impossible, and neither would there be any walking unless the ground were to remain still, nor any flying or swimming were not the air and the sea to resist. And this which resists must needs be different from what is moved, the whole of it from the whole of that, and what is thus immovable must be no part of what is moved; otherwise there will be no movement. Evidence of this lies in the problem why it is that a man easily moves a boat from outside, if he push with a pole, putting it against the mast or some other part, but if he tried to do this when in the boat itself he would never move it, no not giant Tityus himself nor Boreas blowing from inside the ship, if he really were blowing in the way painters represent him; for they paint him sending the breath out from the boat. For whether one blew gently or so stout-

[1] e. g., *On the Parts of Animals*, IV. 10-14, and *On the Gait of Animals*.

[2] Cf. *On the Soul*, III. 2, 9, 10; *Physics*, VIII. 5; *Metaphysics*, XII. 7 and 8.

NOTE: The bold face numbers and letters are approximate indications of the pages and columns of the standard Berlin Greek text; the bracketed numbers, of the lines in the Greek text; they are here assigned as they are assigned in the Oxford translation.

ly as to make a very great wind, and whether **699a** what were thrown or pushed were wind or something else, it is necessary in the first place to be supported upon one of one's own members which is at rest and so to push, and in the second place for this member, either itself, or that of which it is a part, to remain at rest, fixing itself against something external to itself. Now the man who is himself in the boat, if he pushes, fixing himself against the boat, very naturally does not move the boat, because what he pushes against should properly remain at rest. Now what he is trying to move, and what he is fixing himself against is in his case the same. If, however, he pushes or pulls from outside he does move it, for the ground is no part of the boat.

3

Here we may ask the difficult question whether if something moves the whole heavens this mover must be immovable, and moreover be no part of the heavens, nor in the heavens. For either it is moved itself and moves the heavens, in which case it must touch something immovable in order to create movement, and then this is no part of that which creates movement; or if the mover is from the first immovable it will equally be no part of that which is moved. In this point at least they argue correctly who say that as the Sphere is carried round in a circle no single part remains still, for then either the whole would necessarily stand still or its continuity be torn asunder; but they argue less well in supposing that the poles have a certain force, though conceived as having no magnitude, but as merely termini or points. For besides the fact that no such things have any substantial existence it is impossible for a single movement to be initiated by what is twofold; and yet they make the poles two. From a review of these difficulties we may conclude that there is something so related to the whole of Nature, as the earth is to animals and things moved by them.

And the mythologists with their fable of Atlas setting his feet upon the earth appear to have based the fable upon intelligent grounds. They make Atlas a kind of diameter twirling the heavens about the poles. Now as the earth remains still this would be reasonable enough, but their theory involves them in the position that the earth is no part of the universe. And further the force of that which initiates movement must be made equal to the force of that which remains at rest. For there is a definite quantity of force or power by dint of which that which remains at rest does so, just as there is of force by dint of which that which initiates movement does so; and as there is a necessary proportion between opposite motions, so there is between absences of motion. Now equal forces are unaffected by one another, but are overcome by a superiority of force. **699b** And so in their theory Atlas, or whatever similar power initiates movement from within, must exert no more force than will exactly balance the stability of the earth—otherwise the earth will be moved out of her place in the centre of things. For as the pusher pushes so is the pushed pushed, and with equal force. But the prime mover moves that which is to begin with at rest, so that the power it exerts is greater, rather than equal and like to the power which produces absence of motion in that which is moved. And similarly also the power of what is moved and so moves must be greater than the power of that which is moved but does not initiate movement. Therefore the force of the earth in its immobility will have to be as great as the force of the whole heavens, and of that which moves the heavens. But if that is impossible, it follows that the heavens cannot possibly be moved by any force of this kind inside them.

4

There is a further difficulty about the motions of the parts of the heavens which, as akin to what has gone before, may be considered next. For if one could overcome by force of motion the immobility of the earth he would clearly move it away from the centre. And it is plain that the power from which this force would originate will not be infinite, for the earth is not infinite and therefore its weight is not. Now there are more senses than one of the word 'impossible'. When we say it is impossible to see a sound, and when we say it is impossible to see the men in the moon, we use two senses of the word; the former is of necessity, the latter, though their nature is to be seen, cannot as a fact be seen by us. Now we suppose that the heavens are *of necessity* impossible to destroy and to dissolve, whereas the result of the present argument would be to do away with this necessity. For it is natural and possible for a motion to exist greater than the force by dint of which the earth is at rest, or than that by dint of which Fire and Aether are moved. If then there are superior motions, these will be dissolved in succession by one another: and if there actually are not, but might possibly be (for the earth cannot be infinite because no body can possibly be infinite), there is a possibility of the heavens being dissolved. For what is to prevent this coming to pass, unless it be impossible? And it is not impossible unless the opposite is necessary. This difficulty, however, we will discuss elsewhere.[1]

To resume, must there be something immovable and at rest outside of what is moved, and no part of it, or not? And must this necessarily be so also in the case of the universe? Perhaps it would be thought strange were the origin of movement inside. And to those who so conceive it the word of Homer[2] would appear to have been well spoken:

700a 'Nay, ye would not pull Zeus, highest of all from heaven to the plain, no not even if ye toiled right hard; come, all ye gods and goddesses! Set hands to the chain'; for that which is entirely immovable cannot possibly be moved by anything. And herein lies the solution of the difficulty stated some time back, the possibility or impossibility of dissolving the system of the heavens, in that it depends from an original which is immovable.

Now in the animal world there must be not only an immovable without, but also within those things which move in place, and initiate their own movement. For one part of an animal must be moved, and another be at rest, and against this the part which is moved will support itself and be moved; for example, if it move one of its parts; for one part, as it were, supports itself against another part at rest.

But about things without life which are moved one might ask the question whether all contain in themselves both that which is at rest and that which initiates movement, and whether they also, for instance fire, earth, or any other inanimate thing, must support themselves against something outside which is at rest. Or is this impossible and must it not be looked for rather in those primary causes by which they are set in motion? For all things without life are moved by something other, and the origin of all things so moved are things which move themselves. And out of these we have spoken about animals (for they must all have in themselves that which is at rest, and without them that against which they are supported); but whether there is some higher and prime mover is not clear, and an origin of that kind involves a different discussion. Animals at any rate which move themselves are all moved supporting themselves on what is outside them, even when they inspire and expire; for there is no essential difference between casting a great and a small weight, and this is what men do when they spit and cough and when they breathe in and breathe out.

5

But is it only in that which moves itself in place that there must be a point at rest, or does this hold also of that which causes its own qualitative changes, and its own growth? Now the question of original generation and decay is different; for if there is, as we hold, a primary movement, this would be the cause of generation and decay, and probably of all the secondary movements too. And as in the universe, so in the animal world this is the primary movement, when the creature attains maturity; and therefore it is the cause of growth, when the creature becomes the cause of its own growth, and the cause too of alteration. But if this is not the primary movement then the point at rest is not necessary. However, the earliest growth and alteration in the living creature arise through another and by other **700b** channels, nor can anything possibly be the cause of its own generation and decay, for the mover must exist before the moved, the begetter before the begotten, and nothing is prior to itself.

6

Now whether the soul is moved or not, and how it is moved if it be moved, has been stated before in our treatise concerning it.[3] And since all inorganic things are moved by some other thing—and the manner of the movement of the first and eternally moved, and how the first mover moves it, has been determined before in our *Metaphysics*,[4] it remains to inquire how the soul moves the body, and what is the origin of movement in a living creature. For, if we except the movement of the universe, things with life are the causes of the movement of all else, that is of all that are not moved by one another by mutual impact. And so all their motions have a term or limit, inasmuch as the movements of things with life have such. For all living things both move and are moved with some object, so that this is

[1] Cf. *Physics*, VIII, *passim; On the Heavens*, I.
[2] *Iliad*, VIII. 21.
[3] Cf. *On the Soul*, I. 3-5; II. 4; III. 9-end.
[4] Cf. *Metaphysics*, XII. 7.

the term of all their movement, the end, that is, in view. Now we see that the living creature is moved by intellect, imagination, purpose, wish, and appetite. And all these are reducible to mind and desire. For both imagination and sensation are on common ground with mind, since all three are faculties of judgement though differing according to distinctions stated elsewhere.[1] Will, however, impulse, and appetite, are all three forms of desire, while purpose belongs both to intellect and to desire. Therefore the object of desire or of intellect first initiates movement, not, that is, every object of intellect, only the end in the domain of conduct. Accordingly among goods that which moves is a practical end, not the good in its whole extent. For it initiates movement only so far as something else is for its sake, or so far as it is the object of that which is for the sake of something else. And we must suppose that a seeming good may take the room of actual good, and so may the pleasant, which is itself a seeming good. From these considerations it is clear that in one regard that which is eternally moved by the eternal mover is moved in the same way as every living creature, in another regard differently, and so while it is moved eternally, the movement of living creatures has a term. Now the eternal beautiful, and the truly and primarily good (which is not at one time good, at another time not good), is too divine and precious to be relative to anything else. The prime mover then moves, **701a** itself being unmoved, whereas desire and its faculty are moved and so move. But it is not necessary for the last in the chain of things moved to move something else; wherefore it is plainly reasonable that motion in place should be the last of what happens in the region of things happening, since the living creature is moved and goes forward by reason of desire or purpose, when some alteration has been set going on the occasion of sensation or imagination.

7

But how is it that thought ⟨viz. sense, imagination, and thought proper⟩ is sometimes followed by action, sometimes not; sometimes by movement, sometimes not? What happens seems parallel to the case of thinking and inferring about the immovable objects of science. There the end is the truth seen (for, when one conceives the two premisses, one at once conceives and comprehends the conclusion), but here the two premisses result in a conclusion which is an action—for example, one conceives that every man ought to walk, one is a man oneself: straightway one walks; or that, in this case, no man should walk, one is a man: straightway one remains at rest. And one so acts in the two cases provided that there is nothing in the one case to compel or in the other to prevent. Again, I ought to create a good, a house is good: straightway I make a house. I need a covering, a coat is a covering: I need a coat. What I need I ought to make, I need a coat: I make a coat. And the conclusion I must make a coat is an action. And the action goes back to the beginning or first step. If there is to be a coat, one must first have B, and if B then A, so one gets A to begin with. Now that the action is the conclusion is clear. But the premisses of action are of two kinds, of the good and of the possible.

And as in some cases of speculative inquiry we suppress one premise so here the mind does not stop to consider at all an obvious minor premise; for example if walking is good for man, one does not dwell upon the minor 'I am a man'. And so what we do without reflection, we do quickly. For when a man actualizes himself in relation to his object either by perceiving, or imagining or conceiving it, what he desires he does at once. For the actualizing of desire is a substitute for inquiry or reflection. I want to drink, says appetite; this is drink, says sense or imagination or mind: straightway I drink. In this way living creatures are impelled to move and to act, and desire is the last or immediate cause of movement, and desire arises after perception or after imagination and conception. And things that desire to act now create and now act under the influence of appetite or impulse or of desire or wish.

701b The movements of animals may be compared with those of automatic puppets, which are set going on the occasion of a tiny movement; the levers are released, and strike the twisted strings against one another; or with the toy wagon. For the child mounts on it and moves it straight forward, and then again it is moved in a circle owing to its wheels being of unequal diameter (the smaller acts like a centre on the same principle as the cylinders). Animals have parts of a similar kind, their organs, the sinewy tendons to wit and the bones; the bones are like the wooden levers in the automaton, and the iron; the tendons are like the

[1] Cf. *On the Soul*, III. 3.

strings, for when these are tightened or released movement begins. However, in the automata and the toy wagon there is no change of quality, though if the inner wheels became smaller and greater by turns there would be the same circular movement set up. In an animal the same part has the power of becoming now larger and now smaller, and changing its form, as the parts increase by warmth and again contract by cold and change their quality. This change of quality is caused by imaginations and sensations and by ideas. Sensations are obviously a form of change of quality, and imagination and conception have the same effect as the objects so imagined and conceived. For in a measure the form conceived be it of hot or cold or pleasant or fearful is like what the actual objects would be, and so we shudder and are frightened at a mere idea. Now all these affections involve changes of quality, and with those changes some parts of the body enlarge, others grow smaller. And it is not hard to see that a small change occurring at the centre makes great and numerous changes at the circumference, just as by shifting the rudder a hair's breadth you get a wide deviation at the prow. And further, when by reason of heat or cold or some kindred affection a change is set up in the region of the heart, even in an imperceptibly small part of the heart, it produces a vast difference in the periphery of the body,—blushing, let us say, or turning white, goose-skin and shivers and their opposites.

8

But to return, the object we pursue or avoid in the field of action is, as has been explained, the original of movement, and upon the conception and imagination of this there necessarily follows a change in the temperature of the body. For what is painful we avoid, what is pleasing we pursue. We are, however, unconscious of what happens in the minute parts; still **702a** anything painful or pleasing is generally speaking accompanied by a definite change of temperature in the body. One may see this by considering the affections. Blind courage and panic fears, erotic motions, and the rest of the corporeal affections, pleasant and painful, are all accompanied by a change of temperature, some in a particular member, others in the body generally. So, memories and anticipations, using as it were the reflected images of these pleasures and pains, are now more and now less causes of the same changes of temperature. And so we see the reason of nature's handiwork in the inward parts, and in the centres of movement of the organic members; they change from solid to moist, and from moist to solid, from soft to hard and vice versa. And so when these are affected in this way, and when besides the passive and active have the constitution we have many times described, as often as it comes to pass that one is active and the other passive, and neither of them falls short of the elements of its essence, straightway one acts and the other responds. And on this account thinking that one ought to go and going are virtually simultaneous, unless there be something else to hinder action. The organic parts are suitably prepared by the affections, these again by desire, and desire by imagination. Imagination in its turn depends either upon conception or sense-perception. And the simultaneity and speed are due to the natural correspondence of the active and passive.

However, that which first moves the animal organism must be situate in a definite original. Now we have said that a joint is the beginning of one part of a limb, the end of another. And so nature employs it sometimes as one, sometimes as two. When movement arises from a joint, one of the extreme points must remain at rest, and the other be moved (for as we explained above the mover must support itself against a point at rest); accordingly, in the case of the elbow-joint, the last point of the forearm is moved but does not move anything, while, in the flexion, one point of the elbow, which lies in the whole forearm that is being moved, is moved, but there must also be a point which is unmoved, and this is our meaning when we speak of a point which is in potency one, but which becomes two in actual exercise. Now if the arm were the living animal, somewhere in its elbow-joint would be situate the original seat of the moving soul. Since, however, it is possible for a lifeless thing to be so related to the hand as the forearm is to the upper (for example, when a man moves a stick in his hand), it is evident that the soul, the original of movement, could not lie in either of the two extreme points, neither, that is, in the last point of the stick which is moved, nor in the original point which causes move- **702b** ment. For the stick too has an end point and an originative point by reference to the hand. Accordingly, this example shows that the moving original which derives from the soul is not in the stick; and if not, then not in the hand; for a precisely similar relation obtains between the hand and the wrist, as between the wrist and the elbow. In this matter it makes no difference whether the part is a continuous part of the body or not; the stick may be looked at as a detached part of the whole. It follows then of necessity that the original cannot lie in any individual origin which is the end of another member, even though there may lie another part outside the one in question. For example, relatively to the end point of the stick the hand is the original, but the original of the hand's movement is in the wrist. And so if the true original is not in the hand, be- there is still something higher up, neither is the true original in the wrist, for once more if the elbow is at rest the whole part below it can be moved as a continuous whole.

9

Now since the left and the right sides are symmetrical, and these opposites are moved simultaneously, it cannot be that the left is moved by the right remaining stationary, nor vice versa; the original must always be in what lies above both. Therefore, the original seat of the moving soul must be in that which lies in the middle, for of both extremes the middle is the limiting point; and this is similarly related to the movements from above [and below,] those that is from the head, and to the bones which spring from the spinal column, in creatures that have a spinal column.

And this is a reasonable arrangement. For the sensorium is in our opinion in the centre too; and so, if the region of the original of movement is altered in structure through sense-perception and thus changes, it carries with it the parts that depend upon it and they too are extended or contracted, and in this way the movement of the creature necessarily follows. And the middle of the body must needs be in potency one but in action more than one; for the limbs are moved simultaneously from the original seat of movement, and when one is at rest the other is moved. For example, in the line BAC,[1] B is moved, and A is the mover. There must, however, be a point at rest if one is to move, the other to be moved. A ⟨AE⟩ then being one in potency must be two in action, and so be a definite spatial magnitude not a mathematical point. Again, C may be moved simultaneously with B. Both the originals then in A must move and be moved, and so there must be something other than them which moves but is not moved. For otherwise, when the movement begins, the extremes, i.e. the originals, in A would rest upon one another, like two men
703a putting themselves back to back and so moving their legs. There must then be some one thing which moves both. This something is the soul, distinct from the spatial magnitude just described and yet located therein.

10

Although from the point of view of the definition of movement—a definition which gives the cause—desire is the middle term or cause, and desire moves being moved, still in the material animated body there must be some material which itself moves being moved. Now that which is moved, but whose nature is not to initiate movement, is capable of being passive to an external force, while that which initiates movement must needs possess a kind of force and power. Now experience shows us that animals do both possess connatural spirit and derive power from this. (How this connatural spirit is maintained in the body is explained in other passages of our works.) And this spirit appears to stand to the soul-centre or original in a relation analogous to that between the point in a joint which moves being moved and the unmoved. Now since this centre is for some animals in the heart, in the rest in a part analogous with the heart, we further see the reason for the connatural spirit being situate where it actually is found. The question whether the spirit remains always the same or constantly changes and is renewed, like the cognate question about the rest of the parts of the body, is better postponed. At all events we see that it is well disposed to excite movement and to exert power; and the functions of movement are thrusting and pulling. Accordingly, the organ of movement must be capable of expanding and contracting; and this is precisely the characteristic of spirit. It contracts and expands naturally, and so is able to pull and to thrust from one and the same cause, exhibiting gravity compared with the fiery element, and levity by comparison with the opposites of fire. Now that which is to initiate movement without change of structure must be of the kind described, for the elementary bodies prevail over one another in a compound body by dint of disproportion; the light is over-

[1] Cf. 703b 30. The diagrams, so often mentioned (cf. *Short Physical Treatises*, 452b 17; *On the Generation of Animals*, 749b 8, 761a 10), are lost.

come and kept down by the heavier, and the heavy kept up by the lighter.

We have now explained what the part is which is moved when the soul originates movement in the body, and what is the reason for this. And the animal organism must be conceived after the similitude of a well-governed commonwealth. When order is once established in it there is no more need of a separate monarch to preside over each several task. The individuals each play their assigned part as it is ordered, and one thing follows another in its accustomed order. So in animals there is the same orderliness—nature taking the place of custom—and each part naturally doing his own work as nature has composed them. There is no need then of a soul in each part, but she resides in a kind of central governing place of the body, and the remaining parts
703b live by continuity of natural structure, and play the parts Nature would have them play.

11

So much then for the voluntary movements of animal bodies, and the reasons for them. These bodies, however, display in certain members involuntary movements too, but most often non-voluntary movements. By involuntary I mean motions of the heart and of the privy member; for often upon an image arising and without express mandate of the reason these parts are moved. By non-voluntary I mean sleep and waking and respiration, and other similar organic movements. For neither imagination nor desire is properly mistress of any of these; but since the animal body must undergo natural changes of quality, and when the parts are so altered some must increase and other decrease, the body must straightway be moved and change with the changes that nature makes dependent upon one another. Now the causes of the movements are natural changes of temperature, both those coming from outside the body, and those taking place within it. So the involuntary movements which occur in spite of reason in the aforesaid parts occur when a change of quality supervenes. For conception and imagination, as we said above, produce the conditions necessary to affections, since they bring to bear the images or forms which tend to create these states. And the two parts aforesaid display this motion more conspicuously than the rest, because each is in a sense a separate vital organism, the reason being that each contains vital moisture. In the case of the heart the cause is plain, for the heart is the seat of the senses, while an indication that the generative organ too is vital is that there flows from it the seminal potency, itself a kind of organism. Again, it is a reasonable arrangement that the movements arise in the centre upon movements in the parts, and in the parts upon movements in the centre, and so reach one another. Conceive A to be the centre or starting-point. The movements then arrive at the centre from each letter in the diagram we have drawn, and flow back again from the centre which is moved and changes, (for the centre is potentially multiple) the movement of B goes to B, that of C to C, the movement of both to both; but from B to C the movements flow by dint of going from B to A as to a centre, and then from A to C as from a centre.

Moreover a movement contrary to reason sometimes does and sometimes does not arise in the organs on the occasion of the same thoughts; the reason is that sometimes the mat-
704a ter which is passive to the impressions is there in sufficient quantity and of the right quality and sometimes not.

And so we have finished our account of the reasons for the parts of each kind of animal,
704b of the soul, and furthere of sense-perception, of sleep, of memory, and of movement in general; it remains to speak of animal generation.

CONTENTS: ON THE GAIT OF ANIMALS

ON THE GAIT OF ANIMALS

1

704a We have now to consider the parts which are useful to animals for movement in place (locomotion); first, why each part is such as it is and to what end they possess them; and second, the differences between these parts both in one and the same creature, and again by comparison of the parts of creatures of different species with one another. First then let us lay down how many questions we have to consider.

The first is what are the fewest points of motion necessary to animal progression, the second why sanguineous animals have four points and not more, but bloodless animals more than four, and generally why some animals are footless, others bipeds, others quadrupeds, others polypods, and why all have an even number of feet, if they have feet at all; why in fine the points on which progression depends are even in number.

Next, why are man and bird bipeds, but fish footless; and why do man and bird, though both bipeds, have an opposite curvature of the legs. For man bends his legs convexly, a bird has his bent concavely; again, man bends his arms and legs in opposite directions, for he has his arms bent convexly, but his legs concavely. And a viviparous quadruped bends his limbs in opposite directions to a man's, and in opposite directions to one another; for he has his forelegs bent convexly, his hind legs concavely. **704b** Again, quadrupeds which are not viviparous but oviparous have a peculiar curvature of the limbs laterally away from the body. Again, why do quadrupeds move their legs criss-cross?

We have to examine the reasons for all these facts, and others cognate to them; that the facts are such is clear from our Natural History, we have now to ask reasons for the facts.

2

At the beginning of the inquiry we must postulate the principles we are accustomed constantly to use for our scientific investigation of nature, that is we must take for granted principles of this universal character which appear in all Nature's work. Of these one is that Nature creates nothing without a purpose, but always the best possible in each kind of living creature by reference to its essential constitution. Accordingly if one way is better than another that is the way of Nature. Next we must take for granted the different species of dimensions which inhere in various things; of these there are three pairs of two each, superior and inferior, before and behind, to the right and to the left. Further we must assume that the originals of movements in place are thrusts and pulls. (These are the essential place-movements, it is only accidentally that what is carried by another is moved; it is not thought to **705a** move itself, but to be moved by something else.)

3

After these preliminaries, we go on to the next questions in order.

Now of animals which change their position some move with the whole body at once, for example jumping animals, others move one part first and then the other, for example walking ⟨and running⟩ animals. In both these changes the moving creature always changes its position by pressing against what lies below it. Accordingly if what is below gives way too quickly for that which is moving upon it to lean against it, or if it affords no resistance at all to what is moving, the latter can of itself effect no movement upon it. For an animal which jumps makes its jump both by leaning against its own upper part and also against what is beneath its feet; for at the joints the parts do in a sense lean upon one another, and in general that which pushes down leans upon what is pushed down. That is why athletes jump further with weights in their hands than without, and runners run faster if they swing their arms; there is in extending the arms a kind of leaning against the hands and

[1] *History of Animals*, 490b 4, 498a 3 sqq.

Note: The bold face numbers and letters are approximate indications of the pages and columns of the standard Berlin Greek text; the bracketed numbers, of the lines in the Greek text; they are here assigned as they are assigned in the Oxford translation.

wrists. In all cases then that which moves makes its change of position by the use of at least two parts of the body; one part so to speak squeezes, the other is squeezed; for the part that is still is squeezed as it has to carry the weight, the part that is lifted strains against that which carries the weight. It follows then that nothing without parts can move itself in this way, for it has not in it the distinction of the part which is passive and that which is active.

4

Again, the boundaries by which living beings are naturally determined are six in number, superior and inferior, before and behind, right and left. Of these all living beings have a superior and an inferior part; for superior and inferior is in plants too, not only in animals. And this distinction is one of function, not merely of position relatively to our earth and the sky above our heads. The superior is that from which flows in each kind the distribution **705b** of nutriment and the process of growth; the inferior is that to which the process flows and in which it ends. One is a starting-point, the other an end, and the starting-point is the superior. And yet it might be thought that in the case of plants at least the inferior is rather the appropriate starting-point, for in them the superior and inferior are in position other than in animals. Still they are similarly situated from the point of view of function, though not in their position relatively to the universe. The roots are the superior part of a plant, for from them the nutriment is distributed to the growing members, and a plant takes it with its roots as an animal does with its mouth.

Things that are not only alive but are animals have both a front and a back, because they all have sense, and front and back are distinguished by reference to sense. The front is the part in which sense is innate, and whence each thing gets its sensations, the opposite parts are the back.

All animals which partake not only in sense, but are able of themselves to make a change of place, have a further distinction of left and right besides those already enumerated; like the former these are distinctions of function and not of position. The right is that from which change of position naturally begins, the opposite which naturally depends upon this is the left.

This distinction (of right and left) is more articulate and detailed in some than in others. For animals which make the aforesaid change (of place) by the help of organized parts (I mean feet for example, or wings or similar organs) have the left and right distinguished in greater detail, while those which are not differentiated into such parts, but make the differentiation in the body itself and so progress, like some footless animals (for example snakes and caterpillars after their kind, and besides what men call earth-worms), all these have the distinction spoken of, although it is not made so manifest to us. That the beginning of movement is on the right is indicated by the fact that all men carry burdens on the left shoulder; in this way they set free the side which initiates movement and enable the side which bears the weight to be moved. And so men hop easier on the left leg; for the nature **706a** of the right is to initiate movement, that of the left to be moved. The burden then must rest on the side which is to be moved, not on that which is going to cause movement, and if it be set on the moving side, which is the original of movement, it will either not be moved at all or with more labour. Another indication that the right is the source of movement is the way we put our feet forward; all men lead off with the left, and after standing still prefer to put the left foot forward, unless something happens to prevent it. The reason is that their movement comes from the leg they step off, not from the one put forward. Again, men guard themselves with their right. And this is the reason why the right is the same in all, for that from which motion begins is the same for all, and has its natural position in the same place, and for this reason the spiral-shaped Testaceans have their shells on the right, for they do not move in the direction of the spire, but all go forward in the direction opposite to the spire. Examples are the murex and the ceryx. As all animals then start movement from the right, and the right moves in the same direction as the whole, it is necessary for all to be alike right-handed. And man has the left limbs detached more than any other animal because he is natural in a higher degree than the other animals; now the right is naturally both better than the left and separate from it, and so in man the right is more especially the right, more dextrous that is, than in other animals. The right then being differentiated it is only reasonable that in man the left should be most movable, and most detached. In man, too, the other starting-point are found most naturally and clearly distinct, the superior part that is and the front.

5

Animals which, like men and birds, have the superior part distinguished from the front are two-footed (biped). In them, of the four points of motion, two are wings in the one, hands and arms in the other. Animals which have the superior and the front parts identically situated are four-footed, many-footed, or footless (quadruped, polypod, limbless). I use the term foot for a member employed for movement in place connected with a point on the ground, for the feet appear to have got their name from the ground under our feet.

706b Some animals, too, have the front and back parts identically situated, for example, Cephalopods (molluscs) and spiral-shaped Testaceans, and these we have discussed elsewhere in another connexion.

Now there is in place a superior, an intermediate, and an inferior; in respect to place bipeds have their superior part corresponding to the superior part of the universe; quadrupeds, polypods, and footless animals to the intermediate part, and plants to the inferior. The reason is that these have no power of locomotion, and the superior part is determined relatively to the nutriment, and their nutriment is from the earth. Quadrupeds, polypods, and footless animals again have their superior part corresponding to the intermediate, because they are not erect. Bipeds have theirs corresponding to the superior part of the universe because they are erect, and of bipeds, man *par excellence;* for man is the most natural of bipeds. And it is reasonable for the starting-points to be in these parts; for the starting-point is honourable, and the superior is more honourable than the inferior, the front than the back, and the right than the left. Or we may reverse the argument and say quite well that these parts are more honourable than their opposites just because the starting-points are in them.

6

The above discussion has made it clear that the original of movement is in the parts on the right. Now every continuous whole, one part of which is moved while the other remains at rest must, in order to be able to move as a whole while one part stands still, have in the place where both parts have opposed movements some common part which connects the moving parts with one another. Further in this common part the original of the motion (and similarly of the absence of motion) of each of the parts must lie.

Clearly then if any of the opposite pairs of parts (right and left, that is, superior and inferior, before and behind) have a movement of their own, each of them has for common original of its movements the juncture of the parts in question.

Now before and behind are not distinctions relatively to that which sets up its own motion, because in nature nothing has a movement backwards, nor has a moving animal any division whereby it may make a change of position towards its front or back; but right and left, superior and inferior are so distinguished. Accordingly, all animals which progress by the

707a use of distinct members have these members distinguished not by the differences of before and behind, but only of the remaining two pairs; the prior difference dividing these members into right and left (a difference which must appear as soon as you have division into two), and the other difference appearing of necessity where there is division into four.

Since then these two pairs, the superior and inferior and the right and left, are linked to one another by the same common original (by which I mean that which controls their movement), and further, everything which is intended to make a movement in each such part properly must have the original cause of all the said movements arranged in a certain definite position relatively to the distances from it of the originals of the movements of the individual members (and these centres of the individual parts are in pairs arranged coordinately or diagonally, and the common centre is the original from which the animal's movements of right and left, and similarly of superior and inferior, start); each animal must have this original at a point where it is equally or nearly equally related to each of the centres in the four parts described.

7

It is clear then how locomotion belongs to those animals only which make their changes of place by means of two or four points in their structure, or to such animals *par excellence.* Moreover, since this property belongs almost peculiarly to Sanguineous animals, we see that no Sanguineous animal can progress at more points than four, and that if it is the nature of anything so to progress at four points it must of necessity be Sanguineous.

What we observe in the animal world is in agreement with the above account. For no Sanguineous animal if it be divided into more parts can live for any appreciable length of time, nor can it enjoy the power of locomotion which it possessed while it was a continuous and undivided whole. But some bloodless animals and polypods can live a long time, if divided, in each of the severed parts, and can move in the same way as before they were dismembered. Examples are what is termed the centipede and other insects that are long in **707b** shape, for even the hinder portion of all these goes on progressing in the same direction as before when they are cut in two.

The explanation of their living when thus divided is that each of them is constructed like a continuous body of many separate living beings. It is plain, too, from what was said above why they are like this. Animals constructed most naturally are made to move at two or four points, and even limbless Sanguinea are no exception. They too move by dint of four points, whereby they achieve progression. They go forward by means of two flexions. For in each of their flexions there is a right and a left, both before and behind in their flat surface, in the part towards the head a right and a left front point, and in the part towards the tail the two hinder points. They look as if they moved at two points only, where they touch before and behind, but that is only because they are narrow in breadth. Even in them the right is the sovereign part, and there is an alternate correspondence behind, exactly as in quadrupeds. The reason of their flexions is their great length, for just as tall men walk with their spines bellied (undulated) forward, and when their right shoulder is leading in a forward direction their left hip is rather inclined backwards, so that their middle becomes hollow and bellied (undulated), so we ought to conceive snakes as moving in concave curves (undulations) upon the ground. And this is evidence that they move themselves like the quadrupeds, for they make the concave in its turn convex and the convex concave. When in its turn the left of the forward parts is leading, the concavity is in its turn reversed, for the right becomes the inner. (Let the right front point be A, the left B, the right hind C, the left D.)

Among land animals this is the character of the movement of snakes, and among water animals of eels, and conger-eels and also lampreys, in fact of all that have their form snakelike. However, some marine animals of this **708a** shape have no fin, lampreys for example, but put the sea to the same use as snakes do both land and water (for snakes swim precisely as they move on the ground). Others have two fins only, for example conger-eels and eels and a kind of cestreus which breeds in the lake of Siphae. On this account too those that are accustomed to live on land, for example all the eels, move with fewer flexions in a fluid than on land, while the kind of cestreus which has two fins, by its flexion in a fluid makes up the remaining points.

8

The reason why snakes are limbless is first that nature makes nothing without purpose, but always regards what is the best possible for each individual, preserving the peculiar essence of each and its intended character, and secondly the principle we laid down above that no Sanguineous creature can move itself at more than four points. Granting this it is evident that Sanguineous animals like snakes, whose length is out of proportion to the rest of their dimensions, cannot possibly have limbs; for they cannot have more than four (or they would be bloodless), and if they had two or four they would be practically stationary; so slow and unprofitable would their movement necessarily be.

But every limbed animal has necessarily an even number of such limbs. For those which only jump and so move from place to place do not need limbs for this movement at least, but those which not only jump but also need to walk, finding that movement not sufficient for their purposes, evidently either are better able to progress with even limbs or cannot otherwise progress at all [for every animal which has limbs must have an even number], for as this kind of movement is effected by part of the body at a time, and not by the whole at once as in the movement of leaping, some of the limbs must in turn remain at rest, and others be moved, and the animal must act in each of these cases with opposite limbs, shifting the weight from the limbs that are being moved to those at rest. And so nothing can **708b** walk on three limbs or on one; in the latter case it has no support at all on which to rest the body's weight, in the former only in respect of one pair of opposites, and so it must necessarily fall in endeavouring so to move.

Polypods however, like the Centipede, can indeed make progress on an odd number of limbs, as may be seen by the experiment of wounding one of their limbs; for then the mutilation of one row of limbs is corrected by the number of limbs which remain on either side. Such mutilated creatures, however, drag the wounded limb after them with the remainder, and do not properly speaking walk. Moreover, it is plain that they, too, would make the change of place better if they had an even number, in fact if none were missing and they had the limbs which correspond to one another. In this way they could equalize their own weight, and not oscillate to one side, if they had corresponding supports instead of one section of the opposite sides being unoccupied by a limb. A walking creature advances from each of its members alternately, for in this way it recovers the same figure that it had at first.

9

The fact that all animals have an even number of feet, and the reasons for the fact have been set forth. What follows will explain that if there were no point at rest flexion and straightening would be impossible. Flexion is a change from a right line to an arc or an angle, straightening a change from either of these to a right line. Now in all such changes the flexion or the straightening must be relative to one point. Moreover, without flexion there could not be walking or swimming or flying. For since limbed creatures stand and take their weight alternately on one or other of the opposite legs, if one be thrust forward the other of necessity must be bent. For the opposite limbs are naturally of equal length, and the one which is under the weight must be a kind of perpendicular at right angles to the ground.

When then one leg is advanced it becomes the **709a** hypotenuse of a right-angled triangle. Its square then is equal to the square on the other side together with the square on the base. As the legs then are equal, the one at rest must bend either at the knee or, if there were any kneeless animal which walked, at some other articulation. The following experiment exhibits the fact. If a man were to walk parallel to a wall in sunshine, the line described ⟨by the shadow of his head⟩ would be not straight but zigzag, becoming lower as he bends, and higher when he stands and lifts himself up.

It is, indeed, possible to move oneself even if the leg be not bent, in the way in which children crawl. This was the old though erroneous account of the movement of elephants. But these kinds of movements involve a flexion in the shoulders or in the hips. Nothing at any rate could walk upright continuously and securely without flexions at the knee, but would have to move like men in the wrestling schools who crawl forward through the sand on their knees. For the upper part of the upright creature is long so that its leg has to be correspondingly long; in consequence there must be flexion. For since a stationary position is perpendicular, if that which moves cannot bend it will either fall forward as the right angle becomes acute or will not be able to progress. For if one leg is at right angles to the ground and the other is advanced, the latter will be at once equal and greater. For it will be equal to the stationary leg and also equivalent to the hypotenuse of a right-angled triangle. That which goes forward therefore must bend, and while bending one, extend the other leg simultaneously, so as to incline forward and make a stride and still remain above the perpendicular; for the legs form an isosceles triangle, and the head sinks lower when it is perpendicularly above the base on which it stands.

Of limbless animals, some progress by undulations (and this happens in two ways, either they undulate on the ground, like snakes, or up and down, like caterpillars), and undulation is a flexion; others by a telescopic action, like what are called earthworms and leeches. These go forward, first one part leading and then drawing the whole of the rest of the body up to this, and so they change from place to place. It is plain too that if the two curves were not greater than the one line which subtends them undulating animals could not move **709b** themselves; when the flexure is extended they would not have moved forward at all if the flexure or arc were equal to the chord subtended; as it is, it reaches further when it is straightened out, and then this part stays still and it draws up what is left behind.

In all the changes described that which moves now extends itself in a straight line to progress, and now is hooped; it straightens itself in its leading part, and is hooped in what follows behind. Even jumping animals all make a flexion in the part of the body which is underneath, and after this fashion make their leaps. So too flying and swimming things progress, the one straightening and bending their wings to fly, the other their fins to swim. Of the latter some have four fins, others which are rather long, for example eels, have only two. These swim by substituting a flexion of the rest of their body for the ⟨missing⟩ pair of fins to complete the movement, as we have said before.[1] Flat fish use two fins, and the flat of their body as a substitute for the absent pair of fins. Quite flat fish, like the Ray, produce their swimming movement with the actual fins and with the two extremes or semicircles of their body, bending and straightening themselves alternately.

10

A difficulty might perhaps be raised about birds. How, it may be said, can they, either when they fly or when they walk, be said to move at four points? Now we did not say that all Sanguinea move at four points, but merely at not more than four. Moreover, they cannot as a fact fly if their legs be removed, nor walk without their wings. Even a man does not walk without moving his shoulders. Everything indeed, as we have said, makes a change of place by flexion and straightening, for all things progress by pressing upon what being beneath them up to a point gives way as it were gradually; accordingly, even if there be no flexion in another member, there must be at least in the point whence motion begins, that is in feathered (flying) insects at the base of the 'scale-wing', in birds at the base of the wing, in others at the base of the corresponding member, the fins, for instance, in fish. In others, for example snakes, the flexion **710a** begins in the joints of the body.

In winged creatures the tail serves, like a ship's rudder, to keep the flying thing in its course. The tail then must like other limbs be able to bend at the point of attachment. And so flying insects, and birds (Schizoptera) whose tails are ill-adapted for the use in question, for example peacocks, and domestic cocks, and generally birds that hardly fly, cannot steer a straight course. Flying insects have absolutely no tail, and so drift along like a rudderless vessel, and beat against anything they happen upon; and this applies equally to sharded insects, like the scarab-beetle and the chafer, and to unsharded, like bees and wasps. Further, birds that are not made for flight have a tail that is of no use; for instance the purple coot and the heron and all water-fowl. These fly stretching out their feet as a substitute for a tail, and use their legs instead of a tail to direct their flight. The flight of insects is slow and frail because the character of their feathery wings is not proportionate to the bulk of their body; this is heavy, their wings small and frail, and so the flight they use is like a cargo boat attempting to make its voyage with oars; now the frailty both of the actual wings and of the outgrowths upon them contributes in a measure to the flight described. Among birds, the peacock's tail is at one time useless because of its size, at another because it is shed. But birds are in general at the opposite pole to flying insects as regards their feathers, but especially the swiftest flyers among them. (These are the birds with curved talons, for swiftness of wing is useful to their mode of life.) The rest of their bodily structure is in harmony with their peculiar movement: the small head, the slight neck, the strong and acute breastbone (acute like the prow of a clipper-built vessel, so as to be well-girt, and strong by dint of its mass of flesh), in order to **710b** be able to push away the air that beats against it, and that easily and without exhaustion. The hind-quarters, too, are light and taper again, in order to conform to the movement of the front and not by their breadth to suck the air.

11

So much then for these questions. But why an animal that is to stand erect must necessarily be not only a biped, but must also have the superior parts of the body lighter, and those that lie under these heavier, is plain. Only if situated like this could it possibly carry itself easily. And so man, the only erect animal, has legs longer and stouter relatively to the upper parts of his body than any other animal with legs. What we observe in children also is evidence of this. Children cannot walk erect because they are always dwarf-like, the upper parts of their bodies being longer and stouter than the lower. With advancing years the lower increase disproportionately, until the children get their appropriate size, and then and not till then they succeed in walking erect. Birds are hunchbacked yet stand on two legs because their weight is set back, after the principle of horses fashioned in bronze with their forelegs prancing. But their being biped and able to stand is above all due to their having the hip-bone shaped like a thigh, and so large that it looks as if they had two thighs, one in the leg before the knee-joint, the other

[1] Cf. 708a 7.

joining this part to the fundament. Really this is not a thigh but a hip, and if it were not so large the bird could not be a biped. As in a man or a quadruped, the thigh and the rest of the leg would be attached immediately to quite a small hip; consequently the whole body would be tilted forward. As it is, however, the hip is long and extends right along to the middle of the belly, so that the legs are attached at that point and carry as supports the whole frame. It is also evident from these considerations that a bird cannot possibly be erect in the sense in which man is. For as it holds its body now the wings are naturally useful to it, but if
711a it were erect they would be as useless as the wings of Cupids we see in pictures. It must have been clear as soon as we spoke that the form of no human nor any similar being permits of wings; not only because it would, though Sanguineous, be moved at more than four points, but also because to have wings would be useless to it when moving naturally. And Nature makes nothing contrary to her own nature.

12

We have stated above[1] that without flexion in the legs or shoulders and hips no Sanguineous animal with feet could progress, and that flexion is impossible except some point be at rest, and that men and birds, both bipeds, bend their legs in opposite directions, and further that quadrupeds bend their in opposite directions, and each pair in the opposite way to a man's limbs. For men bend their arms backwards, their legs forwards; quadrupeds their forelegs forwards, their back legs backwards, and in like manner also birds bend theirs. The reason is that Nature's workmanship is never purposeless, as we said above, but everything for the best possible in the circumstances. Inasmuch, therefore, as all creatures which naturally have the power of changing position by the use of limbs, must have one leg stationary with the weight of the body on it, and when they move forward the leg which has the leading position must be unencumbered, and the progression continuing the weight must shift and be taken off on this leading leg, it is evidently necessary for the back leg from being bent to become straight again, while the point of movement of the leg thrust forward and its lower part remain still. And so the legs must be jointed. And it is possible for this to take place and at the same time for the animal to go forward, if the leading leg has its articulation forwards, impossible if it be backwards. For, if it be forwards, the stretching out of the leg will be while the body is going forwards, but, if the other way, while it is going backwards. And again, if the flexion were backwards, the placing of the foot would be made by two movements and those con-
711b trary to one another, one, that is, backwards and one forwards; for in the bending together of the limb the lower end of the thigh would go backwards, and the shin would move the foot forwards away from the flexion; whereas, with the flexion forwards, the progression described will be performed not with contrary motions, but with one forward motion.

Now man, being a biped and making his change of position in the natural way with his two legs, bends them forward for the reasons set forth, but his arms bend backwards reasonably enough. If they bent the opposite way they would be useless for the work of the hands, and for taking food. But quadrupeds which are also viviparous necessarily bend their front legs forwards. For these lead off first when they move, and are also in the forepart of their body. The reason that they bend forward is the same as in the case of man, for in this respect they are like mankind. And so quadrupeds as well as men bend these legs forward in the manner described. Moreover, if the flexion is like this, they are enabled to lift their feet high; if they bent them in the opposite way they would only lift them a little way from the ground, because the whole thigh and the joint from which the shin-bone springs would lie under the belly as the beast moved forward. If, however, the flexion of the hind legs were forwards the lifting of these feet would be similar to that of the forefeet (for the hind legs, too, would in this case have only a little room for their lifting inasmuch as both the thigh and the knee-joint would fall under the position of the belly); but the flexion being backwards, as in fact it is, nothing comes in the way of their progression with this mode of moving the feet. Moreover, it is necessary or at least better for their legs to bend thus when they are suckling their young, with a view to such ministrations. If the flexion were inwards it would be difficult to keep their young under them and to shelter them.

13

712a Now there are four modes of flexion if we take the combinations in pairs. Fore and

[1] Cf. chapter 9.

hind may bend either both backwards, as the figures marked A, or in the opposite way both forwards, as in B, or in converse ways and not in the same direction, as in C where the fore bend forwards and the hind bend backwards, or as in D, the opposite way to C, where the convexities are turned towards one another and the concavities outwards. Now no biped or quadruped bends his limbs like the figures A or B, but the quadrupeds like C, and like D only the elephant among quadrupeds and man if you consider his arms as well as his legs. For he bends his arms concavely and his legs convexly.

In man, too, the flexions of the limbs are always alternately opposite, for example the elbow bends back, but the wrist of the hand forwards, and again the shoulder forwards. In like fashion, too, in the case of the legs, the hip backwards, the knee forwards, the ankle in the opposite way backwards. And plainly the lower limbs are opposed in this respect to the upper, because the first joints are opposites, the shoulder bending forwards, the hip backwards; wherefore also the ankle bends backwards, and the wrist of the hand forwards.

14

This is the way then the limbs bend, and for the reasons given. But the hind limbs move criss-cross with the fore limbs; after the off fore they move the near hind, then the near fore, and then the off hind. The reason is that (*a*) if they moved the forelegs together and first, the animal would be wrenched, and the progression would be a stumbling forwards with the hind parts as it were dragged after. Again, that would not be walking but jumping, and it is hard to make a continuous change of place, jumping all the time. Here is evidence of what I say; even as it is, all horses that move in this way soon begin to refuse, for example the horses in a religious procession. **712b** For these reasons the fore limbs and the hind limbs move in this separate way. Again, (*b*) if they moved both the right legs first the weight would be outside the supporting limbs and they would fall. If then it is necessary to move in one or other of these ways or criss-cross fashion, and neither of these two is satisfactory, they must move criss-cross; for moving in the way we have said they cannot possibly experience either of these untoward results. And this is why horses and such-like animals stand still with their legs put forward criss-cross, not with the right or the left put forward together at once. In the same fashion animals with more than four legs make their movements; if you take two consecutive pairs of legs the hind move criss-cross with the forelegs; you can see this if you watch them moving slowly. Even crabs move in this way, and they are polypods. They, too, always move criss-cross in whichever direction they are making progress. For in direction this animal has a movement all its own; it is the only animal that moves not forwards, but obliquely. Yet since forwards is a distinction relative to the line of vision, Nature has made its eyes able to conform to its limbs, for its eyes can move themselves obliquely, and therefore after a fashion crabs are no exception but in this sense move forwards.

15

Birds bend their legs in the same way as quadrupeds. For their natural construction is broadly speaking nearly the same. That is, in birds the wings are a substitute for the forelegs; and so they are bent in the same way as the forelegs of a quadruped, since when they move to progress the natural beginning of change is from the wings ⟨as in quadrupeds from the forelegs⟩. Flight in fact is their appropriate movement. And so if the wings be cut off a bird can neither stand still nor go forwards.

Again, the bird though a biped is not erect, and has the forward parts of the body lighter than the hind, and so it is necessary (or at least preferable for the standing posture) to have the thigh so placed below the body as it actually is, I mean growing towards the back. If then it must have this situation the flexion of the leg must be backwards, as in the hind legs **713a** of quadrupeds. The reasons are the same as those given in the case of viviparous quadrupeds.

If now we survey generally birds and winged insects, and animals which swim in a watery medium, all I mean that make their progress in water by dint of organs of movement, it is not difficult to see that it is better to have the attachment of the parts in question oblique to the frame, exactly as in fact we see it to be both in birds and insects. And this same arrangement obtains also among fishes. Among birds the wings are attached obliquely; so are the fins in water animals, and the feather-like wings of insects. In this way they divide the air or water most quickly and with most force and so effect their movement. For the hinder parts in this way would follow forwards as they are carried along in the yielding medium, fish in the water, birds in the air.

Of oviparous quadrupeds all those that live in holes, like crocodiles, lizards, spotted lizards, freshwater tortoises, and turtles, have their legs attached obliquely as their whole body sprawls over the ground, and bend them obliquely. The reason is that this is useful for ease in creeping into holes, and for sitting upon their eggs and guarding them. And as they are splayed outwards they must of necessity tuck in their thighs and put them under them in order to achieve the lifting of the whole body. In view of this they cannot bend them otherwise than outwards.

16

We have already stated the fact[1] that non-sanguineous animals with limbs are polypods and none of them quadrupeds. And the reason why their legs, except the extreme pairs, were necessarily attached obliquely and had their flexions upwards, and the legs themselves were somewhat turned under (bandy-shape) and backwards is plain. In all such creatures the intermediate legs both lead and follow. If then

713b they lay under them, they must have had their flexion both forwards and backwards; on account of leading, forwards; and on account of following, backwards. Now since they have to do both, for this reason their limbs are turned under and bent obliquely, except the two extreme pairs. (These two are more natural in their movement, the front leading and the back following.) Another reason for this kind of flexion is the number of their legs; arranged in this way they would interfere less with one another in progression and not knock together. But the reason that they are bandy is that all of them or most of them live in holes, for creatures living so cannot possibly be high above the ground.

But crabs are in nature the oddest of all polypods; they do not progress forwards except in the sense explained above,[2] and they are the only animals which have more than one pair of leading limbs. The explanation of this is the hardness of their limbs, and the fact that they use them not for swimming but for walking; they always keep on the ground. However, the flexion of the limbs of all polypods is oblique, like that of the quadrupeds which live in holes—for example lizards and crocodiles and most of the oviparous quadrupeds. And the explanation is that some of them in their breeding periods, and some all their life, live in holes.

17

Now the rest have bandy legs because they are soft-skinned, but the crayfish is hard-skinned and its limbs are for swimming and not for walking ⟨and so are not bandy⟩. Crabs, too, have their limbs bent obliquely, but not bandy like oviparous quadrupeds and non-sanguineous polypods, because their limbs have a hard and shell-like skin, although they don't swim but live in holes; they live in fact on the ground. Moreover, their shape is like a disk, as compared with the crayfish which is elongated, and they haven't a tail like the crayfish; a tail is useful to the crayfish for swimming, but the crab is not a swimming creature. Further, it alone has its side equivalent to a hinder part, because it has many leading feet. The explana-

714a tion of this is that its flexions are not forward nor its legs turned in under (bandy). We have given above the reason why its legs are not turned in under, that is the hardness and shell-like character of its integument.

For these reasons then it must lead off with more than one limb, and move obliquely; obliquely, because the flexion is oblique; and with more than one limb, because otherwise the limbs that were still would have got in the way of those that were moving.

Fishes of the flat kind swim with their heads twisted, as one-eyed men walk; they have their natural shape distorted. Web-footed birds swim with their feet; because they breathe the air and have lungs they are bipeds, but because they have their home in the water they are webbed; by this arrangement their feet serve them instead of fins. They have their legs too, not like the rest of birds in the centre of their body, but rather set back. Their legs are short, and being set back are serviceable for swimming. The reason for their having short legs is that nature has added to their feet by subtracting from the length of their limbs; instead of length she gives stoutness to the legs and breadth to the feet. Broad feet are more useful than long for pushing away the water when they are swimming.

18

There is reason, too, for winged creatures having feet, but fish none. The former have their home in the dry medium, and cannot remain always in mid air; they must therefore

[1] Above, 704a 11. [2] Above, 712b 20.

have feet. Fish on the contrary live in the wet **714b** medium, and take in water, not air. Fins are useful for swimming, but feet not. And if they had both they would be non-sanguineous. There is a broad similarity between birds and fishes in the organs of locomotion. Birds have their wings on the superior part, similarly fish have two pectoral fins; again, birds have legs on their under parts and near the wings; similarly, most fish have two fins on the under parts and near the pectorals. Birds, too, have a tail and fish a tail-fin.

19

A difficulty may be suggested as to the movements of molluscs, that is, as to where that movement originates; for they have no distinction of left and right. Now observation shows them moving. We must, I think, treat all this class as mutilated, and as moving in the way in which limbed creatures do when one cuts off their legs, or as analogous with the seal and the bat. Both the latter are quadrupeds but misshapen. Now molluscs do move, but move in a manner contrary to nature. They are not moving things, but are moving if as sedentary creatures they are compared with zoophytes, and sedentary if classed with progressing animals.

As to right and left, crabs, too, show the distinction poorly, still they do show it. You can see it in the claw; the right claw is larger and stronger, as though the right and left sides were trying to get distinguished.

The structure of animals, both in their other parts, and especially in those which concern progression and any movement in place, is as we have now described. It remains, after determining these questions, to investigate the problems of Life and Death.

CONTENTS:
ON THE GENERATION OF ANIMALS

PART IV

Book V

ON THE GENERATION OF ANIMALS

BOOK I

I

715ª We have now discussed the other parts of animals, both generally and with reference to the peculiarities of each kind, explaining how each part exists on account of such a cause, and I mean by this the final cause.

There are four causes underlying everything: first, the final cause, that for the sake of which a thing exists; secondly, the formal cause, the definition of its essence (and these two we may regard pretty much as one and the same); thirdly, the material; and fourthly, the moving principle or efficient cause.

We have then already discussed the other three causes, for the definition and the final cause are the same, and the material of animals is their parts—of the whole animal the non-homogeneous parts, of these again the homogeneous, and of these last the so-called elements of all matter. It remains to speak of those parts which contribute to the generation of animals and of which nothing definite has yet been said, and to explain what is the moving or efficient cause. To inquire into this last and to inquire into the generation of each animal is in a way the same thing; and, therefore, my plan has united them together, arranging the discussion of these parts last, and the beginning of the question of generation next to them.

Now some animals come into being from the union of male and female, i.e. all those kinds of animal which possess the two sexes. This is not the case with all of them; though in the sanguinea with few exceptions the creature, when its growth is complete, is either male or female, and though some bloodless animals have sexes so that they generate offspring of the same kind, yet other bloodless animals generate indeed, but not offspring of the same kind; such are all that come into being not from a union of the sexes, but from decaying earth and excrements. To speak generally, if we take all animals which change their locality, some by swimming, others by flying, others by walking, we find in these the two sexes, not only in the sanguinea but also in some of the bloodless animals; and this applies in the case of the latter sometimes to the whole class, as **715ᵇ** the cephalopoda and crustacea, but in the class of insects only to the majority. Of these, all which are produced by union of animals of the same kind generate also after their kind, but all which are not produced by animals, but from decaying matter, generate indeed, but produce another kind, and the offspring is neither male nor female; such are some of the insects. This is what might have been expected, for if those animals which are not produced by parents had themselves united and produced others, then their offspring must have been either like or unlike to themselves. If like, then their parents ought to have come into being in the same way; this is only a reasonable postulate to make, for it is plainly the case with other animals. If unlike, and yet able to copulate, then there would have come into being again from them another kind of creature and again another from these, and this would have gone on to infinity. But Nature flies from the infinite, for the infinite is unending or imperfect, and Nature ever seeks an end.

But all those creatures which do not move, as the testacea and animals that live by clinging to something else, inasmuch as their nature resembles that of plants, have no sex any more than plants have, but as applied to them the word is only used in virtue of a similarity and analogy. For there is a slight distinction of this sort, since even in plants we find in the same kind some trees which bear fruit and others which, while bearing none themselves, yet contribute to the ripening of the fruits of those which do, as in the case of the fig-tree and caprifig.

The same holds good also in plants, some coming into being from seed and others, as it were, by the spontaneous action of Nature, arising either from decomposition of the earth or of some parts in other plants, for some are not formed by themselves separately but are **716ª** produced upon other trees, as the mistle-

Note: The bold face numbers and letters are approximate indications of the pages and columns of the standard Berlin Greek text; the bracketed numbers, of the lines in the Greek text; they are here assigned as they are assigned in the Oxford translation.

toe. Plants, however, must be investigated separately.

2

Of the generation of animals we must speak as various questions arise in order in the case of each, and we must connect our account with what has been said. For, as we said above, the male and female principles may be put down first and foremost as origins of generation, the former as containing the efficient cause of generation, the latter the material of it. The most conclusive proof of this is drawn from considering how and whence comes the semen; for there is no doubt that it is out of this that those creatures are formed which are produced in the ordinary course of Nature; but we must observe carefully the way in which this semen actually comes into being from the male and female. For it is just because the semen is secreted from the two sexes, the secretion taking place *in* them and *from* them, that they are first principles of generation. For by a male animal we mean that which generates in another, and by a female that which generates in itself; wherefore men apply these terms to the macrocosm also, naming Earth *mother* as being female, but addressing Heaven and the Sun and other like entities as *fathers,* as causing generation.

Male and female differ in their essence by each having a separate ability or faculty, and anatomically by certain parts; essentially the male is that which is able to generate in another, as said above; the female is that which is able to generate in itself and out of which comes into being the offspring previously existing in the parent. And since they are differentiated by an ability or faculty and by their function, and since instruments or organs are needed for all functioning, and since the bodily parts are the instruments or organs to serve the faculties, it follows that certain parts must exist for union of parents and production of offspring. And these must differ from each other, so that consequently the male will differ from the female. (For even though we speak of the animal as a whole as male or female, yet really it is not male or female in virtue of the whole of itself, but only in virtue of a certain faculty and a certain part—just as with the part used for sight or locomotion—which part is also plain to sense-perception.)

Now as a matter of fact such parts are in the female the so-called uterus, in the male the testes and the penis, in all the sanguinea; for some of them have testes and others the corresponding passages. There are corresponding **716b** differences of male and female in all the bloodless animals also which have this division into opposite sexes. But if in the sanguinea it is the parts concerned in copulation that differ primarily in their forms, we must observe that a small change in a first principle is often attended by changes in other things depending on it. This is plain in the case of castrated animals, for, though only the generative part is disabled, yet pretty well the whole form of the animal changes in consequence so much that it seems to be female or not far short of it, and thus it is clear than an animal is not male or female in virtue of an isolated part or an isolated faculty. Clearly, then, the distinction of sex is a first principle; at any rate, when that which distinguishes male and female suffers change, many other changes accompany it, as would be the case if a first principle is changed.

3

The sanguinea are not all alike as regards testes and uterus. Taking the former first, we find that some of them have not testes at all, as the classes of fish and of serpents, but only two spermatic ducts. Others have testes indeed, but internally by the loin in the region of the kidneys, and from each of these a duct, as in the case of those animals which have no testes at all, these ducts unite also as with those animals; this applies (among animals breathing air and having a lung) to all birds and oviparous quadrupeds. For all these have their testes internal near the loin, and two ducts from these in the same way as serpents; I mean the lizards and tortoises and all the scaly reptiles. But all the vivipara have their testes in front; some of them inside at the end of the abdomen, as the dolphin, not with ducts but with a penis projecting externally from them; others outside, either pendent as in man or towards the fundament as in swine. They have been discriminated more accurately in the *Enquiries about Animals.*[1]

The uterus is always double, just as the testes are always two in the male. It is situated either near the pudendum (as in women, and all those animals which bring forth alive not only **717a** externally but also internally, and all fish that lay eggs externally) or up towards the hypozoma (as in all birds and in viviparous fishes). The uterus is also double in the crustacea and the cephalopoda, for the membranes which

[1] *History of Animals,* III. 1.

include their so-called eggs are of the nature of a uterus. It is particularly hard to distinguish in the case of the poulps, so that it seems to be single, but the reason of this is that the bulk of the body is everywhere similar.

It is double also in the larger insects; in the smaller the question is uncertain owing to the small size of the body.

Such is the description of the aforesaid parts of animals.

4

With regard to the difference of the spermatic organs in males, if we are to investigate the causes of their existence, we must first grasp the final cause of the testes. Now if Nature makes everything either because it is necessary or because it is better so, this part also must be for one of these two reasons. But that it is not necessary for generation is plain; else had it been possessed by all creatures that generate, but as it is neither serpents have testes nor have fish; for they have been seen uniting and with their ducts full of milt. It remains then that it must be because it is somehow better so. Now it is true that the business of most animals is, you may say, nothing else than to produce young, as the business of a plant is to produce seed and fruit. But still as, in the case of nutriment, animals with straight intestines are more violent in their desire for food, so those which have not testes but only ducts, or which have them indeed but internally, are all quicker in accomplishing copulation. But those which are to be more temperate in the one case have not straight intestines, and in the other have their ducts twisted to prevent their desire being too violent and hasty. It is for this that the testes are contrived; for they make the movement of the spermatic secretion steadier, preserving the folding back of the passages in the vivipara, as horses and the like, and in man. (For details see the *Enquiries about Animals.*[1]) For the testes are no part of the ducts but are only attached to them, as women fasten stones to the loom when weaving; if they are **717b** removed the ducts are drawn up internally, so that castrated animals are unable to generate; if they were not drawn up they would be able, and before now a bull mounting immediately after castration has caused conception in the cow because the ducts had not yet been drawn up. In birds and oviparous quadrupeds the testes receive the spermatic secretion, so that its expulsion is slower than in fishes. This is clear in the case of birds, for their testes are much enlarged at the time of copulation, and all those which pair at one season of the year have them so small when this time is past that they are almost indiscernible, but during the season they are very large. When the testes are internal the act of copulation is quicker than when they are external, for even in the latter case the semen is not emitted before the testes are drawn up.

5

Besides, quadrupeds have the organ of copulation, since it is possible for them to have it, but for birds and the footless animals it is not possible, because the former have their legs under the middle of the abdomen and the latter have no legs at all; now the penis depends from that region and is situated there. (Wherefore also the legs are strained in intercourse, both the penis and the legs being sinewy.) So that, since it is not possible for them to have this organ, they must necessarily either have no testes also, or at any rate not have them there, as those animals that have both penis and testes have them in the same situation.

Further, with those animals at any rate that have external testes, the semen is collected together before emission, and emission is due to the penis being heated by its movement; it is not ready for emission at immediate contact as in fishes.

All the vivipara have their testes in front, internally or externally, except the hedgehog; he alone has them near the loin. This is for the same reason as with birds, because their union must be quick, for the hedgehog does not, like the other quadrupeds, mount upon the back of the female, but they conjugate standing upright because of their spines.

So much for the reasons why those animals have testes which have them, and why they are sometimes external and sometimes internal.

6

All those animals which have no testes are deficient in this part, as has been said, not because it is better to be so but simply because of necessity, and secondly because it is necessary that their copulation should be speedy. Such is the **718a** nature of fish and serpents. Fish copulate throwing themselves alongside of the females and separating again quickly. For as men and all such creatures must hold their breath before emitting the semen, so fish at such times must cease taking in the sea-water, and then they

[1] *History of Animals*, III. 1.

perish easily. Therefore they must not mature the semen during copulation, as viviparous land-animals do, but they have it all matured together before the time, so as not to be maturing it while in contact but to emit it ready matured. So they have no testes, and the ducts are straight and simple. There is a small part similar to this connected with the testes in the system of quadrupeds, for part of the reflected duct is sanguineous and part is not; the fluid is already semen when it is received by and passes through this latter part, so that once it has arrived there it is soon emitted in these quadrupeds also. Now in fishes the *whole* passage resembles the last section of the reflected part of the duct in man and similar animals.

7

Serpents copulate twining round one another, and, as said above, have neither testes nor penis, the latter because they have no legs, the former because of their length, but they have ducts like fish; for on account of their extreme length the seminal fluid would take too long in its passage and be cooled if it were further delayed by testes. (This happens also if the penis is large; such men are less fertile than when it is smaller because the semen, if cold, is not generative, and that which is carried too far is cooled.) So much for the reason why some animals have testes and others not. Serpents intertwine because of their inaptitude to cast themselves alongside of one another. For they are too long to unite closely with so small a part and have no organs of attachment, so they make use of the suppleness of their bodies, intertwining. Wherefore also they seem to be slower in copulation than fish, not only on account of the length of the ducts but also of this elaborate arrangement in uniting.

8

It is not easy to state the facts about the uterus in female animals, for there are many points of difference. The vivipara are not alike in this part; women and all the vivipara with feet have the uterus low down by the puden-
718b dum, but the cartilaginous viviparous fish have it higher up near the hypozoma. In the ovipara, again, it is low in fish (as in women and the viviparous quadrupeds), high in birds and all oviparous quadrupeds. Yet even these differences are on a principle. To begin with the ovipara, they differ in the manner of laying their eggs, for some produce them imperfect, as fishes whose eggs increase and are finally developed outside of them. The reason is that they produce many young, and this is their function as it is with plants. If then they perfected the egg in themselves they must needs be few in number, but as it is, they have so many that each uterus seems to be an egg, at any rate in the small fishes. For these are the most productive, just as with the other animals and plants whose nature is analogous to theirs, for the increase of size turns with them to seed.

But the eggs of birds and the quadrupedal ovipara are perfect when produced. In order that these may be preserved they must have a hard covering (for their envelope is soft so long as they are increasing in size), and the shell is made by heat squeezing out the moisture from the earthy material; consequently the place must be hot in which this is to happen. But the part about the hypozoma *is* hot, as is shown by that being the part which concocts the food. If then the eggs must be within the uterus, then the uterus must be near the hypozoma in those creatures which produce their eggs in a perfect form. Similarly it must be low down in those which produce them imperfect, for it is profitable that it should be so. And it is more natural for the uterus to be low down than high up, when Nature has no other business in hand to hinder it; for its end is low down, and where is the end, there is the function, and the uterus itself is naturally where the function is.

9

We find differences in the vivipara also as compared with one another. Some produce their young alive, not only externally, but also internally, as men, horses, dogs, and all those which have hair, and among aquatic animals, dolphins, whales, and such cetacea.

10

But the cartilaginous fish and the vipers produce their young alive externally, but first produce eggs internally. The egg is perfect, for so only can an animal be generated from an egg, and nothing comes from an imperfect one. It is because they are of a cold nature, not hot as some assert, that they do not lay their eggs externally.

11

At least they certainly produce their eggs in a soft envelope, the reason being that they have

but little heat and so their nature does not complete the process of drying the egg-shell. Because, then, they are cold they produce soft-
719a shelled eggs, and because the eggs are soft they do not produce them externally; for that would have caused their destruction.

The process is for the most part the same as in birds, for the egg descends and the young is hatched from it near the vagina, where the young is produced in those animals which are viviparous from the beginning. Therefore in such animals the uterus is dissimilar to that of both the vivipara and ovipara, because they participate in both classes; for it is at once near the hypozoma and also stretching along downwards in all the cartilaginous fishes. But the facts about this and the other kinds of uterus must be gathered from inspection of the drawings of dissections and from the *Enquiries*.[1] Thus, because they are oviparous, laying perfect eggs, they have the uterus placed high, but, as being viviparous, low, participating in both classes.

Animals that are viviparous from the beginning all have it low, Nature here having no other business to interfere with her, and their production having no double character. Besides this, it is impossible for animals to be produced alive near the hypozoma, for the foetus must needs be heavy and move, and that region in the mother is vital and would not be able to bear the weight and the movement. Thirdly, parturition would be difficult because of the length of the passage to be traversed; even as it is there is difficulty with women if they draw up the uterus in parturition by yawning or anything of the kind, and even when empty it causes a feeling of suffocation if moved upwards. For if a uterus is to hold a living animal it must be stronger than in ovipara, and therefore in all the vivipara it is fleshy, whereas when the uterus is near the hypozoma it is membranous. And this is clear also in the case of the animals which produce young by the mixed method, for their eggs are high up and sideways, but the living young are produced in the lower part of the uterus.

So much for the reason why differences are found in the uterus of various animals, and generally why it is low in some and high in others near the hypozoma.

12

Why is the uterus always internal, but the testes sometimes internal, sometimes external? The reason for the uterus always being internal is that in this is contained the egg or foetus, which needs guarding, shelter, and maturation by concoction, while the outer surface of the body is easily injured and cold. The testes vary in position because they also need shelter and a
719b covering to preserve them and to mature the semen; for it would be impossible for them, if chilled and stiffened, to be drawn up and discharge it. Therefore, whenever the testes are visible, they have a cuticular covering known as the scrotum. If the nature of the skin is opposed to this, being too hard to be adapted for enclosing them or for being soft like a true 'skin', as with the scaly integument of fish and reptiles, then the testes must needs be internal. Therefore they are so in dolphins and all the cetacea which have them, and in the oviparous quadrupeds among the scaly animals. The skin of birds also is hard so that it will not conform to the size of anything and enclose it neatly. (This is another reason with all these animals for their testes being internal besides those previously mentioned[2] as arising necessarily from the details of copulation.) For the same reason they are internal in the elephant and hedgehog, for the skin of these, too, is not well suited to keep the protective part separate.

[The position of the uterus differs in animals viviparous within themselves and those externally oviparous, and in the latter class again it differs in those which have the uterus low and those which have it near the hypozoma, as in fishes compared with birds and oviparous quadrupeds. And it is different again in those which produce young in both ways, being oviparous internally and viviparous externally. For those which are viviparous both internally and externally have the uterus placed on the abdomen, as men, cattle, dogs, and the like, since it is expedient for the safety and growth of the foetus that no weight should be upon the uterus.]

13

The passages also are different through which the solid and liquid excreta pass out in all the vivipara. Wherefore both males and females in this class all have a part whereby the urine is voided, and this serves also for the issue of the semen in males, of the offspring in females. This passage is situated above and in front of the passage of the solid excreta. The
720a passage is the same as that of the solid

[1] *History of Animals*, III. 1.

[2] See chapter 5.

nutriment in all those animals that have no penis, in all the ovipara, even those of them that have a bladder, as the tortoises. For it is for the sake of generation, not for the evacuation of the urine, that the passages are double; but because the semen is naturally liquid, the liquid excretion also shares the same passage. This is clear from the fact that all animals produce semen, but all do not void liquid excrement. Now the spermatic passages of the male must be fixed and must not wander, and the same applies to the uterus of the female, and this fixing must take place at either the front or the back of the body. To take the uterus first, it is in the front of the body in vivipara because of the foetus, but at the loin and the back in ovipara. All animals which are internally oviparous and externally viviparous are in an intermediate condition because they participate in both classes, being at once oviparous and viviparous. For the upper part of the uterus, where the eggs are produced, is under the hypozoma by the loin and the back, but as it advances is low at the abdomen; for it is in that part that the animal is viviparous. In these also the passage for solid excrement and for copulation is the same, for none of these, as has been said already, has a separate pudendum.

The same applies to the passages in the male, whether they have testes or no, as to the uterus of the ovipara. For in all of them, not only in the ovipara, the ducts adhere to the back and the region of the spine. For they must not wander but be settled, and that is the character of the region of the back, which gives continuity and stability. Now in those which have internal testes, the ducts are fixed from the first, and they are fixed in like manner if the testes are external; then they meet together towards the region of the penis.

The like applies to the ducts in the dolphins, but they have their testes hidden under the abdominal cavity.

We have now discussed the situation of the **720b** parts contributing to generation, and the causes thereof.

14

The bloodless animals do not agree either with the sanguinea or with each other in the fashion of the parts contributing to generation. There are four classes still left to deal with, first the crustacea, secondly the cephalopoda, thirdly the insects, and fourthly the testacea. We cannot be certain about all of them, but that most of them copulate is plain; in what manner they unite must be stated later.

The crustacea copulate like the retromingent quadrupeds, fitting their tails to one another, the one supine and the other prone. For the flaps attached to the sides of the tail being long prevent them from uniting with the belly against the back. The males have fine spermatic ducts, the females a membranous uterus alongside the intestine, cloven on each side, in which the egg is produced.

15

The cephalopoda entwine together at the mouth, pushing against one another and enfolding their arms. This attitude is necessary, because Nature has bent backwards the end of the intestine and brought it round near the mouth, as has been said before in the treatise on the parts of animals.[1] The female has a part corresponding to the uterus, plainly to be seen in each of these animals, for it contains an egg which is at first indivisible to the eye but afterwards splits up into many; each of these eggs is imperfect when deposited, as with the oviparous fishes. In the cephalopoda (as also in the crustacea) the same passage serves to void the excrement and leads to the part like a uterus, for the male discharges the seminal fluid through this passage. And it is on the lower surface of the body, where the mantle is open and the sea-water enters the cavity. Hence the union of the male with the female takes place at this point, for it is necessary, if the male discharges either semen or a part of himself or any other force, that he should unite with her at the uterine passage. But the insertion, in the case of the poulps, of the arm of the male into the funnel of the female, by which arm the fishermen say the male copulates with her, is only for the sake of attachment, and it is not an organ useful for generation, for it is outside the passage in the male and indeed outside the body of the male altogether.

Sometimes also cephalopoda unite by the **721a** male mounting on the back of the female, but whether for generation or some other cause has not yet been observed.

16

Some insects copulate and the offspring are produced from animals of the same name, just as with the sanguinea; such are the locusts, cicadae, spiders, wasps, and ants. Others unite indeed and generate; but the result is not a

[1] *On the Parts of Animals*, IV. 9.

creature of the same kind, but only a scolex, and these insects do not come into being from animals but from putrefying matter, liquid or solid; such are fleas, flies, and cantharides. Others again are neither produced from animals nor unite with each other; such are gnats, 'conopes', and many similar kinds. In most of those which unite the female is larger than the male. The males do not appear to have spermatic passages. In most cases the male does not insert any part into the female, but the female from below upwards into the male; this has been observed in many cases (as also that the male mounts the female), the opposite in few cases; but observations are not yet comprehensive enough to enable us to make a distinction of classes. And generally it is the rule with most of the oviparous fish and oviparous quadrupeds that the female is larger than the male because this is expedient in view of the increase of bulk in conception by reason of the eggs. In the female the part analogous to the uterus is cleft and extends along the intestine, as with the other animals; in this are produced the results of conception. This is clear in locusts and all other large insects whose nature it is to unite; most insects are too small to be observed in this respect.

Such is the character of the generative organs in animals which were not spoken of before. It remains now to speak of the homogeneous parts concerned, the seminal fluid and milk. We will take the former first, and treat of milk afterwards.[1]

17

Some animals manifestly emit semen, as all the sanguinea, but whether the insects and cephalopoda do so is uncertain. Therefore this is a question to be considered, whether all males do so, or not all; and if not all, why some do and some not; and whether the female also **721ᵇ** contributes any semen or not; and, if not semen, whether she does not contribute anything else either, or whether she contributes something else which is not semen. We must also inquire what those animals which emit semen contribute by means of it to generation, and generally what is the nature of semen, and of the so-called catamenia in all animals which discharge this liquid.

Now it is thought that all animals are generated out of semen, and that the semen comes from the parents. Wherefore it is part of the same inquiry to ask whether both male and female produce it or only one of them, and to ask whether it comes from the whole of the body or not from the whole; for if the latter is true it is reasonable to suppose that it does not come from both parents either. Accordingly, since some say that it comes from the whole of the body, we must investigate this question first.

The proofs from which it can be argued that the semen comes from each and every part of the body may be reduced to four. First, the intensity of the pleasure of coition; for the same state of feeling is more pleasant if multiplied, and that which affects all the parts is multiplied as compared with that which affects only one or a few. Secondly, the alleged fact that mutilations are inherited, for they argue that since the parent is deficient in this part the semen does not come from thence, and the result is that the corresponding part is not formed in the offspring. Thirdly, the resemblances to the parents, for the young are born like them part for part as well as in the whole body; if then the coming of the semen from the whole body is cause of the resemblance of the whole, so the parts would be like because it comes from each of the parts. Fourthly, it would seem to be reasonable to say that as there is some first thing from which the whole arises, so it is also with each of the parts, and therefore if semen or seed is cause of the whole so each of the parts would have a seed peculiar to itself. And these opinions are plausibly supported by such evidence as that children are born with a likeness to their parents, not in congenital but also in acquired characteristics; for before now, when the parents have had scars, the children have been born with a mark in the form of the scar in the same place, and there was a case at Chalcedon where the father had a brand on his arm and the letter was marked on the child, only confused and not clearly articulated. That is pretty much the evidence on which some believe that **722ᵃ** the semen comes from all the body.

18

On examining the question, however, the opposite appears more likely, for it is not hard to refute the above arguments and the view involves impossibilities. First, then, the resemblance of children to parents is no proof that the semen comes from the whole body, because the resemblance is found also in voice, nails, hair, and way of moving, from which

1 iv. 8.

nothing comes. And men generate before they yet have certain characters, such as a beard or grey hair. Further, children are like their more remote ancestors from whom nothing has come, for the resemblances recur at an interval of many generations, as in the case of the woman in Elis who had intercourse with the Aethiop; her daughter was not an Aethiop but the son of that daughter was. The same thing applies also to plants, for it is clear that if this theory were true the seed would come from all parts of plants also; but often a plant does not possess one part, and another part may be removed, and a third grows afterwards. Besides, the seed does not come from the pericarp, and yet this also comes into being with the same form as in the parent plant.

We may also ask whether the semen comes from each of the homogeneous parts only, such as flesh and bone and sinew, or also from the heterogeneous, such as face and hands. For if (1) from the former only, we object that the resemblance exists rather in the heterogeneous parts, such as face and hands and feet; if then it is not because of the semen coming from all parts that children resemble their parents in *these,* what is there to stop the homogeneous parts also from being like for some other reason than this? If (2) the semen comes from the heterogeneous alone, then it does not come from all parts; but it is more fitting that it should come from the homogeneous parts, for they are prior to the heterogeneous which are composed of them; and as children are born like their parents in face and hands, so they are, necessarily, in flesh and nails. If (3) the semen comes from both, what would be the manner of generation? For the heterogeneous parts are composed of the homogeneous, so that to come from the former would be to come from the latter and from their composition. To make this clearer by an illustration, take a written name; if anything came from the whole of it, it would be from each of the syllables, and if from these, from the letters and their composition. So that if really flesh and bones are composed of fire and the like elements, the semen would come rather from the elements than anything else, for how can it come from their composition? Yet with-
722b out this composition there would be no resemblance. If again something creates this composition later, it would be *this* that would be the cause of the resemblance, not the coming of the semen from every part of the body.

Further, if the parts of the future animal are separated in the semen, how do they live? and if they are connected, they would form a small animal.

And what about the generative parts? For that which comes from the male is not similar to what comes from the female.

Again, if the semen comes from all parts of both parents alike, the result is *two* animals, for the offspring will have all the parts of both. Wherefore Empedocles seems to say what agrees pretty well with this view (if we are to adopt it), to a certain extent at any rate, but to be wrong if we think otherwise. What he says agrees with it when he declares that there is a sort of tally in the male and female, and that the whole offspring does not come from either, 'but sundered is the fashion of limbs, some in man's . . .' For why does not the female generate from herself if the semen comes from all parts alike and she has a receptacle ready in the uterus? But, it seems, either it does not come from all the parts, or if it does it is in the way Empedocles says, not the same parts coming from each parent, which is why they need intercourse with each other.

Yet this also is impossible, just as much as it is impossible for the parts when full grown to survive and have life in them when torn apart, as Empedocles accounts for the creation of animals; in the time of his 'Reign of Love', says he, 'many heads sprang up without necks,' and later on these isolated parts combined into animals. Now that *this* is impossible is plain, for neither would the separate parts be able to survive without having any soul or life in them, nor if they were living things, so to say, could several of them combine so as to become one animal again. Yet those who say that semen comes from the whole of the body really have to talk in that way, and as it happened then in the earth during the 'Reign of Love', so it happens according to them in the body. Now it is impossible that the parts should be united together when they come into being and should come from different parts of the parent, meeting together in one place. Then how can the upper and lower, right and left, front and back parts have been 'sundered'? All these points are unintelligible. Further, some parts are distinguished by possessing a faculty, others by being in certain states or conditions; the heterogeneous, as tongue and hand, by the faculty of doing something, the homogeneous by hardness and softness and the other similar states. Blood, then, will not be blood, nor flesh flesh, in any and every state. It is clear,

then, that that which comes from any part, as
723a blood from blood or flesh from flesh, will not be identical with that part. But if it is something different from which the blood of the offspring comes, the coming of the semen from all the parts will not be the cause of the resemblance, as is held by the supporters of this theory. For if blood is formed from something which is not blood, it is enough that the semen come from one part only, for why should not all the other parts of the offspring as well as blood be formed from one part of the parent? Indeed, this theory seems to be the same as that of Anaxagoras, that none of the homogeneous parts come into being, except that these theorists assume, in the case of the generation of animals, what he assumed of the universe.

Then, again, how will these parts that came from all the body of the parent be increased or grow? It is true that Anaxagoras plausibly says that particles of flesh out of the food are added to the flesh. But if we do not say this (while saying that semen comes from all parts of the body), how will the foetus become greater by the addition of something else if that which is added remain unchanged? But if that which is added *can* change, then why not say that the semen from the very first is of such a kind that blood and flesh can be made out of it, instead of saying that it itself *is* blood and flesh? Nor is there any other alternative, for surely we cannot say that it is increased later by a process of mixing, as wine when water is poured into it. For in that case each element of the mixture would be itself *at first* while still unmixed, but the fact rather is that flesh and bone and each of the other parts *is* such *later*. And to say that some part of the semen is sinew and bone is quite above us, as the saying is.

Besides all this there is a difficulty if the sex is determined in conception (as Empedocles says: 'it is shed in clean vessels; some wax female, if they fall in with cold').[1] Anyhow, it is plain that both men and women change not only from infertile to fertile, but also from bearing female to bearing male offspring, which looks as if the cause does not lie in the semen coming from all the parent or not, but in the mutual proportion or disproportion of that which comes from the woman and the man, or in something of this kind. It is clear, then, if we are to put this down as being so, that the female sex is not determined by the semen coming from any particular part, and consequently neither is the special sexual part so determined (if really the same semen can become either a male or female child, which shows that the sexual part does not exist in the semen). Why, then, should we assert this of
723b *this* part any more than of others? For if semen does not come from this part, the uterus, the same account may be given of the others.

Again, some creatures come into being neither from parents of the same kind nor from parents of a different kind, as flies and the various kinds of what are called fleas; from these are produced animals indeed, but not in this case of similar nature, but a kind of scolex. It is plain in this case that the young of a different kind are not produced by semen coming from all parts of the parent, for they would then resemble them, if indeed resemblance is a sign of its coming from all parts.

Further, even among animals some produce many young from a single coition (and something like this is universal among plants, for it is plain that they bear all the fruit of a whole season from a single movement). And yet how would this be possible if the semen were secreted from all the body? For from a single coition and a single segregation of the semen scattered throughout the body must needs follow only a single secretion. Nor is it possible for it to be separated in the uterus, for this would no longer be a mere separation of semen, but, as it were, a severance from a new plant or animal.

Again, the cuttings from a plant bear seed; clearly, therefore, even before they were cut from the parent plant, they bore their fruit from their own mass alone, and the seed did not come from *all* the plant.

But the greatest proof of all is derived from observations we have sufficiently established on insects. For, if not in all, at least in most of these, the female in the act of copulation inserts a part of herself into the male. This, as we said before, is the way they copulate, for the females manifestly insert this from below into the males above, not in all cases, but in most of those observed. Hence it seems clear that, when the males do emit semen, then also the cause of the generation is not its coming from all the body, but something else which must be investigated hereafter. For even if it were true that it comes from all the *body*, as they say, they ought not to claim that it comes from all *parts* of it, but only from the creative part—from the workman, so to

[1] Empedocles, fr. 67 (Diels).

say, not the material he works in. Instead of that, they talk as if one were to say that the semen comes from the shoes, for, generally speaking, if a son is like his father, the shoes he wears are like his father's shoes.

As to the vehemence of pleasure in sexual intercourse, it is not because the semen comes from all the body, but because there is a strong friction (wherefore if this intercourse is often **724a** repeated the pleasure is diminished in the persons concerned). Moreover, the pleasure is at the end of the act, but it ought, on the theory, to be in each of the parts, and not at the same time, but sooner in some and later in others.

If mutilated young are born of mutilated parents, it is for the same reason as that for which they are like them. And the young of mutilated parents are not always mutilated, just as they are not always like their parents; the cause of this must be inquired into later, for this problem is the same as that.

Again, if the female does not produce semen, it is reasonable to suppose it does not come from all the body of the male either. Conversely, if it does not come from all the male it is not unreasonable to suppose that it does not come from the female, but that the female is cause of the generation in some other way. Into this we must next inquire, since it is plain that the semen is not secreted from all the parts.

In this investigation and those which follow from it, the first thing to do is to understand what semen is, for then it will be easier to inquire into its operations and the phenomena connected with it. Now the object of semen is to be of such a nature that from it as their origin come into being those things which are naturally formed, not because there is any agent which makes them from it as . . . but simply because this is the semen. Now we speak of one thing coming *from* another in many senses; it is one thing when we say that night comes *from* day or a man becomes man *from* boy, meaning that A follows B; it is another if we say that a statue is made *from* bronze and a bed *from* wood, and so on in all the other cases where we say that the thing made is made *from* a material, meaning that the whole is formed from something pre-existing which is only put into shape. In a third sense a man becomes unmusical *from* being musical, sick *from* being well, and generally in this sense contraries arise from contraries. Fourthly, as in the 'climax' of Epicharmus; thus *from* slander comes railing and *from* this fighting, and all these are *from* something in the sense that it is the efficient cause. In this last class sometimes the efficient cause is in the things themselves, as in the last mentioned (for the slander is a part of the whole trouble), and sometimes external, as the art is external to the work of art or the torch to the burning house. Now the offspring comes *from* the semen, and it is plainly in one of the two following senses that it does so—either the semen is the material from which it is made, or it is the first **724b** efficient cause. For assuredly it is not in the sense of A being *after* B, as the voyage comes *from,* i.e. after, the Panathenaea; nor yet as contraries come from contraries, for then one of the two contraries ceases to be, and a third substance must exist as an immediate underlying basis from which the new thing comes into being. We must discover then, in which of the two other classes the semen is to be put, whether it is to be regarded as matter, and therefore acted upon by something else, or as a form, and therefore acting upon something else, or as both at once. For perhaps at the same time we shall see clearly also how all the products of semen come into being from contraries, since coming into being from contraries is also a natural process, for some animals do so, i.e. from male and female, others from only one parent, as is the case with plants and all those animals in which male and female are not separately differentiated. Now that which comes from the generating parent is called the seminal fluid, being that which first has in it a principle of generation, in the case of all animals whose nature it is to unite; semen is that which has in it the principles from *both* united parents, as the first mixture which arises from the union of male and female, be it a foetus or an ovum, for these already have in them that which comes from both. (Semen, or seed, and grain differ only in the one being earlier and the other later, grain in that it comes from something else, i.e. the seed, and seed in that something else, the grain, comes from *it,* for both are really the same thing.)

We must again take up the question what the primary nature of what is called semen is. Needs must everything which we find in the body either be (1) one of the natural parts, whether homogeneous or heterogeneous, or (2) an unnatural part such as a growth, or (3) a secretion or excretion, or (4) waste-product, or (5) nutriment. (By secretion or excretion I mean the residue of the nutriment, by waste-product that which is given off from the tissues by an unnatural decomposition.)

Now that semen cannot be a part of the body is plain, for it is homogeneous, and from the homogeneous nothing is composed, e.g. from only sinew or only flesh; nor is it separated as are all the other parts. But neither is it contrary to Nature nor a defect, for it exists in all alike, and the development of the young animal comes from it. Nutriment, again, is obviously introduced from without.

It remains, then, that it must be either a waste-product or a secretion or excretion. Now the ancients seem to think that it is a waste-product, for when they say that it comes from all the body by reason of the heat of the **725a** movement of the body in copulation, they imply that it is a kind of waste-product. But these are contrary to Nature, and from such arises nothing according to Nature. So then it must be a secretion or excretion.

But, to go further into it, every secretion or excretion is either of useless or useful nutriment; by 'useless' I mean that from which nothing further is contributed to natural growth, but which is particularly mischievous to the body if too much of it is consumed; by 'useful' I mean the opposite. Now it is evident that it cannot be of the former character, for such is most abundant in persons of the worst condition of body through age or sickness; semen, on the contrary, is least abundant in them, for either they have none at all or it is not fertile, because a useless and morbid secretion is mingled with it.

Semen, then, is part of a useful secretion. But the *most* useful is the last and that from which finally is formed each of the parts of the body. For secretions are either earlier or later; of the nutriment in the first stage the secretion is phlegm and the like, for phlegm also is a secretion of the useful nutriment, an indication of this being that if it is mixed with pure nutriment it is nourishing, and that it is used up in cases of illness. The final secretion is the smallest in proportion to the quantity of nutriment. But we must reflect that the daily nutriment by which animals and plants grow is but small, for if a very little be added continually to the same thing the size of it will become excessive.

So we must say the opposite of what the ancients said. For whereas *they* said that semen is that which comes *from* all the body, *we* shall say it is that whose nature is to go *to* all of it, and what they thought a waste-product seems rather to be a secretion. For it is more reasonable to suppose that the last extract of the nutriment which goes to all parts resembles that which is left over from it, just as part of a painter's colour is often left over resembling that which he has used up. Waste-products, on the contrary, are always due to corruption or decay and to a departure from Nature.

A further proof that it is not a waste-product, but rather a secretion, is the fact that the large animals have few young, the small many. For the large must have more waste and less secretion, since the great size of the body causes most of the nutriment to be used up, so that the residue or secretion is small.

Again, no place has been set apart by Nature for waste-products but they flow wherever they can find an easy passage in the body, but a place has been set apart for all the natural secretions; **725b** thus the lower intestine serves for the excretion of the solid nutriment, the bladder for that of the liquid; for the useful part of the nutriment we have the upper intestine, for the spermatic secretions the uterus and pudenda and breasts, for it is collected and flows together into them.

And the resulting phenomena are evidence that semen is what we have said, and these result because such is the nature of the secretion. For the exhaustion consequent on the loss of even a very little of the semen is conspicuous because the body is deprived of the ultimate gain drawn from the nutriment. With some few persons, it is true, during a short time in the flower of their youth the loss of it, if it be excessive in quantity, is an alleviation (just as in the case of the nutriment in its first stage, if too much have been taken, since getting rid of this also makes the body more comfortable), and so it may be also when other secretions come away with it, for in that case it is not only semen that is lost but also other influences come away mingled with it, and these are morbid. Wherefore, with some men at least, that which comes from them proves sometimes incapable of procreation because the seminal element in it is so small. But still in most men and as a general rule the result of intercourse is exhaustion and weakness rather than relief, for the reason given. Moreover, semen does not exist in them either in childhood or in old age or in sickness—in the last case because of weakness, in old age because they do not sufficiently concoct their food, and in childhood because they are growing and so all the nutriment is used up too soon, for in about five years, in the case of human beings at any rate, the body seems to gain half the height that is gained in all the rest of life.

In many animals and plants we find a difference in this connexion not only between kinds as compared with kinds, but also between similar individuals of the same kind as compared with each other, e.g. man with man or vine with vine. Some have much semen, others little, others again none at all, not through weakness but the contrary, at any rate in some cases. This is because the nutriment is used up to form the body, as with some human beings, who, being in good condition and developing much flesh or getting rather too fat, produce less semen and are less desirous of intercourse. Like this is what happens with those vines which 'play the goat', that is, luxuriate wan-
726a tonly through too much nutrition, for he-goats when fat are less inclined to mount the female; for which reason they thin them before breeding from them, and say that the vines 'play the goat', so calling it from the condition of the goats. And fat people, women as well as men, appear to be less fertile than others from the fact that the secretion when in process of concoction turns to fat with those who are too well-nourished. For fat also is a healthy secretion due to good living.

In some cases no semen is produced at all, as by the willow and poplar. This condition is due to each of the two causes, weakness and strength; the former prevents concoction of the nutriment, the latter causes it to be all consumed, as said above. In like manner other animals produce much semen through weakness as well as through strength, when a great quantity of a useless secretion is mixed with it; this sometimes results in actual disease when a passage is not found to carry off the impurity, and though some recover of this, others actually die of it. For corrupt humours collect here as in the urine, which also has been known to cause disease.

[Further, the same passage serves for urine and semen; and whatever animals have both kinds of excrement, that of liquid and that of solid nutriment, discharge the semen by the same passage as the liquid excrement (for it is a secretion of a liquid, since the nutriment of all animals is rather liquid than solid), but those which have no liquid excrement discharge it at the passage of the solid residua. Moreover, waste-products are always morbid, but the removal of the secretion is useful; now the discharge of the semen participates in both characteristics because it takes up some of the non-useful nutriment. But if it were a waste-product it would be always harmful; as it is, it is not so.]

From what has been said, it is clear that semen is a secretion of useful nutriment, and that in its last stage, whether it is produced by all or no.

19

After this we must distinguish of what sort of nutriment it is a secretion, and must discuss the catamenia which occur in certain of the vivipara. For thus we shall make it clear (1) whether the female also produces semen like the male and the foetus is a single mixture of two semens, or whether no semen is secreted by the female, and, (2) if not, whether she contrbutes nothing else either to generation but only provides a receptacle, or whether she does
726b contribute something, and, if so, how and in what manner she does so.

We have previously stated that the final nutriment is the blood in the sanguinea and the analogous fluid in the other animals. Since the semen is also a secretion of the nutriment, and that in its final stage, it follows that it will be either (1) blood or that which is analogous to blood, or (2) something formed from this. But since it is from the blood, when concocted and somehow divided up, that each part of the body is made, and since the semen if properly concocted is quite of a different character from the blood when it is separated from it, but if not properly concocted has been known in some cases to issue in a bloody condition if one forces oneself too often to coition, therefore it is plain that semen will be a secretion of the nutriment when reduced to blood, being that which is finally distributed to the parts of the body. And this is the reason why it has so great power, for the loss of the pure and healthy blood is an exhausting thing; for this reason also it is natural that the offspring should resemble the parents, for that which goes to all the parts of the body resembles that which is left over. So that the semen which is to form the hand or the face or the whole animal is already the hand or face or whole animal undifferentiated, and what each of them is actually such is the semen potentially, either in virtue of its own mass or because it has a certain power in itself. I mention these alternatives here because we have not yet made it clear from the distinctions drawn hitherto whether it is the matter of the semen that is the cause of generation, or whether it has in it some faculty and efficient cause thereof, for the hand also or any other bodily part is not hand or other part in a true sense if it be without soul or some other power, but is only called by the same name as the living hand.

On this subject, then, so much may be laid down. But since it is necessary (1) that the weaker animal also should have a secretion greater in quantity and less concocted, and (2) that being of such a nature it should be a mass of sanguineous liquid, and (3) since that which Nature endows with a smaller portion of heat is weaker, and (4) since it has already been stated that such is the character of the female—putting all these considerations together we see that the sanguineous matter discharged by the **727a** female is also a secretion. And such is the discharge of the so-called catamenia.

It is plain, then, that the catamenia are a secretion, and that they are analogous in females to the semen in males. The circumstances connected with them are evidence that this view is correct. For the semen begins to appear in males and to be emitted at the same time of life that the catamenia begin to flow in females, and that they change their voice and their breasts begin to develop. So, too, in the decline of life the generative power fails in the one sex and the catamenia in the other.

The following signs also indicate that this discharge in females is a secretion. Generally speaking women suffer neither from haemorrhoids nor bleeding at the nose nor anything else of the sort except when the catamenia are ceasing, and if anything of the kind occurs the flow is interfered with because the discharge is diverted to it.

Further, the blood-vessels of women stand out less than those of men, and women are rounder and smoother because the secretion which in men goes to these vessels is drained away with the catamenia. We must suppose, too, that the same cause accounts for the fact that the bulk of the body is smaller in females than in males among the vivipara, since this is the only class in which the catamenia are discharged from the body. And in this class the fact is clearest in women, for the discharge is greater in women than in the other animals. Wherefore her pallor and the absence of prominent blood-vessels is most conspicuous, and the deficient development of her body compared with a man's is obvious.

Now since this is what corresponds in the female to the semen in the male, and since it is not possible that two such discharges should be found together, it is plain that the female does not contribute semen to the generation of the offspring. For if she had semen she would not have the catamenia; but, as it is, because she has the latter she has not the former.

It has been stated then that the catamenia are a secretion as the semen is, and confirmation of this view may be drawn from some of the phenomena of animals. For fat creatures produce less semen than lean ones, as observed before. The reason is that fat also, like semen, is a secretion, is in fact concocted blood, only not concocted in the same way as the semen. Thus, if the secretion is consumed to form fat **727b** the semen is naturally deficient. And so among the bloodless animals the cephalopoda and crustacea are in best condition about the time of producing eggs, for, because they are bloodless and no fat is formed in them, that which is analogous in them to fat is at that season drawn off to form the spermatic secretion.

And a proof that the female does not emit similar semen to the male, and that the offspring is not formed by a mixture of both, as some say, is that often the female conceives without the sensation of pleasure in intercourse, and if again the pleasure is experienced by her no less than by the male and the two sexes reach their goal together, yet often no conception takes place unless the liquid of the so-called catamenia is present in a right proportion. Hence the female does not produce young if the catamenia are absent altogether, nor often when, they being present, the efflux still continues; but she does so *after* the purgation. For in the one case she has not the nutriment or material from which the foetus can be framed by the power coming from the male and inherent in the semen, and in the other it is washed away with the catamenia because of their abundance. But when after their occurrence the greater part has been evacuated, the remainder is formed into a foetus. Cases of conception when the catamenia do not occur at all, or of conception during their discharge instead of after it, are due to the fact that in the former instance there is only so much liquid to begin with as remains behind after the discharge in fertile women, and no greater quantity is secreted so as to come away from the body, while in the latter instance the mouth of the uterus closes after the discharge. When, therefore, the quantity already expelled from the body is great but the discharge still continues, only not on such a scale as to wash away the semen, then it is that conception accompanies coition. Nor is it at all strange that the catamenia should still continue after conception (for even after it they recur to some extent, but are scanty and do not last during all the period of gestation; this, however, is a morbid phenomenon, wherefore it is found only in a few cases and then seldom, whereas it is that which happens as a regular thing that is according to Nature).

It is clear then that the female contributes the material for generation, and that this is in the substance of the catamenia, and that they are a secretion.

20

Some think that the female contributes semen in coition because the pleasure she experiences is sometimes similar to that of the male, and also is attended by a liquid discharge. But this discharge is not seminal; it is merely **728a** proper to the part concerned in each case, for there is a discharge from the uterus which occurs in some women but not in others. It is found in those who are fair-skinned and of a feminine type generally, but not in those who are dark and of a masculine appearance. The amount of this discharge, when it occurs, is sometimes on a different scale from the emission of semen and far exceeds it. Moreover, different kinds of food cause a great difference in the quantity of such discharges; for instance some pungently-flavoured foods cause them to be conspicuously increased. And as to the pleasure which accompanies coition it is due to emission not only of semen, but also of a spiritus, the coming together of which precedes the emission. This is plain in the case of boys who are not yet able to emit semen, but are near the proper age, and of men who are impotent, for all these are capable of pleasure by attrition. And those who have been injured in the generative organs sometimes suffer from diarrhoea because the secretion, which they are not able to concoct and turn into semen, is diverted into the intestine. Now a boy is like a woman in form, and the woman is as it were an impotent male, for it is through a certain incapacity that the female is female, being incapable of concocting the nutriment in its last stage into semen (and this is either blood or that which is analogous to it in animals which are bloodless owing to the coldness of their nature). As then diarrhoea is caused in the bowels by the insufficient concoction of the blood, so are caused in the blood-vessels all discharges of blood, including that of the catamenia, for this also is such a discharge, only it is natural whereas the others are morbid.

Thus it is clear that it is reasonable to suppose that generation comes from this. For the catamenia are semen not in a pure state but in need of working up, just as in the formation of fruits the nutriment is present, when it is not yet sifted thoroughly, but needs working up to purify it. Thus the catamenia cause generation by mixture with the semen, as this impure nutriment in plants is nutritious when mixed with pure nutriment.

And a sign that the female does not emit semen is the fact that the pleasure of intercourse is caused by touch in the same region of the female as of the male; and yet is it not from thence that this flow proceeds. Further, it is not all females that have it at all, but only the sanguinea, and not all even of these, but only those whose uterus is not near the hypozoma **728b** and which do not lay eggs; it is not found in the animals which have no blood but only the analogous fluid (for what is blood in the former is represented by another fluid in the latter). The reason why neither the latter nor those sanguinea mentioned (i.e. those whose uterus is low and which do not lay eggs) have this effluxion is the dryness of their bodies; this allows but little matter to be secreted, only enough for generation but not enough to be discharged from the body. All animals that are viviparous without producing eggs first (such are man and all quadrupeds which bend their hind-legs outwards, for all these are viviparous without producing eggs)—all these have the catamenia, unless they are defective in development as the mule, only the efflux is not abundant as in women. Details of the facts in each animal have been given in the *Enquiries concerning animals*.[1]

The catamenia are more abundant in women than in the other animals, and men emit the most semen in proportion to their size. The reason is that the composition of their bodies is liquid and hot compared to others, for more matter must be secreted in such a case. Further, man has no such parts in his body as those to which the superfluous matter is diverted in the other animals; for he has no great quantity of hair in proportion to his body, nor outgrowths of bones, horns, and teeth.

There is evidence that the semen is in the catamenia, for, as said before, this secretion

[1] See *History of Animals*, vi. 18.

appears in the male at the same time of life as the catamenia in the female; this indicates that the parts destined to receive each of these secretions are differentiated at the same time in both sexes; and as the neighboring parts in both become swollen the hair of puberty springs forth in both alike. As the parts in question are on the point of differentiating they are distended by the spiritus; this is clearer in males in the testes, but appears also about the breasts; in females it is more marked in the breasts, for it is when they have risen two fingers' breadth that the catamenia generally begin.

Now, in all living things in which the male and female are not separated the semen (or seed) is a sort of embryo; by embryo I mean the first mixture of male and female; hence, from one semen comes one body,—for example, one stalk of wheat from one grain, as one animal from one egg (for twin eggs are **729a** really two eggs). But in whatever kinds the sexes are distinguished, in these many animals may come from one emission of semen, showing that the semen differs in its nature in plants and animals. A proof of this is that animals which can bear more than one young one at a time do so in consequence of only one coition. Whereby, too, it is plain that the semen does not come from the whole of the body; for neither would the different parts of the semen already be separated as soon as discharged from the same part, nor could they be separated in the uterus if they had once entered it all together; but what does happen is just what one would expect, since what the male contributes to generation is the form and the efficient cause, while the female contributes the material. In fact, as in the coagulation of milk, the milk being the material, the fig-juice or rennet is that which contains the curdling principle, so acts the secretion of the male, being divided into parts in the female. Why it is sometimes divided into more or fewer parts, and sometimes not divided at all, will be the subject of another discussion.[1] But because it does not differ in kind at any rate this does not matter, but what does matter is only that each part should correspond to the material, being neither too little to concoct it and fix it into form, nor too much so as to dry it up; it then generates a number of offspring. But from this first formative semen, if it remains one, and is not divided, only one young one comes into being.

[1] IV, 771b.

That, then, the female does not contribute semen to generation, but does contribute something, and that this is the matter of the catamenia, or that which is analogous to it in bloodless animals, is clear from what has been said, and also from a general and abstract survey of the question. For there must needs be that which generates and that from which it generates; even if these be one, still they must be distinct in form and their essence must be different; and in those animals that have these powers separate in two sexes the body and nature of the active and the passive sex must also differ. If, then, the male stands for the effective and active, and the female, considered as female, for the passive, it follows that what the female would contribute to the semen of the male would not be semen but material for the semen to work upon. This is just what we find to be the case, for the catamenia have in their nature an affinity to the primitive matter.

21

So much for the discussion of this question. At the same time the answer to the next question we have to investigate is clear from these con- **729b** siderations, I mean how it is that the male contributes to generation and how it is that the semen from the male is the cause of the offspring. Does it exist in the body of the embryo as a part of it from the first, mingling with the material which comes from the female? Or does the semen communicate nothing to the material body of the embryo but only to the power and movement in it? For this power is that which acts and makes, while that which is made and receives the form is the residue of the secretion in the female. Now the latter alternative appears to be the right one both *a priori* and in view of the facts. For, if we consider the question on general grounds, we find that, whenever one thing is made from two of which one is active and the other passive, the active agent does not exist in that which is made; and, still more generally, the same applies when one thing moves and another is moved; the moving thing does not exist in that which is moved. But the female, as female, is passive, and the male, as male, is active, and the principle of the movement comes from him. Therefore, if we take the highest genera under which they each fall, the one being active and motive and the other passive and moved, that one thing which is produced comes from them only in the sense in which a bed comes into being from the carpenter and the wood, or in which a ball comes into being from the wax and the form. It is plain then that it is not necessary that anything at all should come away from the male, and if anything does come away it does not follow that this gives rise to the embryo as being in the embryo, but only as that which imparts the motion and as the form; so the medical art cures the patient.

This *a priori* argument is confirmed by the facts. For it is for this reason that some males which unite with the female do not, it appears, insert any part of themselves into the female, but on the contrary the female inserts a part of herself into the male; this occurs in some insects. For the effect produced by the semen in the female (in the case of those animals whose males do insert a part) is produced in the case of these insects by the heat and power in the male animal itself when the female inserts that part of herself which receives the secretion. And therefore such animals remain united a long time, and when they are separated the young are produced quickly. For the union lasts until that which is analogous to the semen has done its work, and when they separate the female produces the embryo quickly; for the young is imperfect inasmuch as all such creatures give birth to scoleces.

What occurs in birds and oviparous fishes is the greatest proof that neither does the semen **730a** come from all parts of the male nor does he emit anything of such a nature as to exist within that which is generated, as part of the material embryo, but that he only makes a living creature by the power which resides in the semen (as we said in the case of those insects whose females insert a part of themselves into the male). For if a hen-bird is in process of producing wind-eggs and is then trodden by the cock before the egg has begun to whiten and while it is all still yellow, then they become fertile instead of being wind-eggs. And if while it is still yellow she be trodden by another cock, the whole brood of chicks turn out like the second cock. Hence some of those who are anxious to rear fine birds act thus; they change the cocks for the first and second treading, not as if they thought that the semen is mingled with the egg or exists in it, or that it comes from all parts of the cock; for if it did it would have come from both cocks, so that the chick would have all its parts doubled. But it is by its force that the semen of the male gives a certain quality to the material and the nutriment in the female, for the second semen added to the first can produce this effect by heat and concoction, as the egg acquires nutriment so long as it is growing.

The same conclusion is to be drawn from the generation of oviparous fishes. When the female has laid her eggs, the male spinkles the milt over them, and those eggs are fertilized which it reaches, but not the others; this shows that the male does not contribute anything to the quantity but only to the quality of the embryo.

From what has been said it is plain that the semen does not come from the whole of the body of the male in those animals which emit it, and that the contribution of the female to the generative product is not the same as that of the male, but the male contributes the principle of movement and the female the material. This is why the female does not produce offspring by herself, for she needs a principle, i.e. something to begin the movement in the embryo and to define the form it is to assume. Yet in some animals, as birds, the nature of the female unassisted can generate to a certain extent, for they do form something, only it is incomplete; I mean the so-called wind-eggs.

22

For the same reason the development of the embryo takes place in the female; neither the male himself nor the female emits semen into the male, but the female receives within herself **730b** the share contributed by both, because in the female is the material from which is made the resulting product. Not only must the mass of material exist there from which the embryo is formed in the first instance, but further material must constantly be added that it may increase in size. Therefore the birth must take place in the female. For the carpenter must keep in close connexion with his timber and the potter with his clay, and generally all workmanship and the ultimate movement imparted to matter must be connected with the material concerned, as, for instance, architecture is *in* the buildings it makes.

From these considerations we may also gather how it is that the male contributes to generation. The male does not emit semen at all in some animals, and where he does this is no part of the resulting embryo; just so no material part comes from the carpenter to the material, i.e. the wood in which he works, nor does any part of the carpenter's art exist within what he makes, but the shape and the form are imparted from him to the material by means of the motion he sets up. It is his hands that move his tools, his tools that move the material; it is his knowledge of his art, and his soul, in which is the form, that moves his hands or any other part of him with a motion of some definite kind, a motion varying with the varying nature of the object made. In like manner, in the male of those animals which emit semen, Nature uses the semen as a tool and as possessing motion in actuality, just as tools are used in the products of any art, for in them lies in a certain sense the motion of the art. Such, then, is the way in which these males contribute to generation. But when the male does not emit semen, but the female inserts some part of herself into the male, this is parallel to a case in which a man should carry the material to the workman. For by reason of weakness in such males Nature is not able to do anything by any secondary means, but the movements imparted to the material are scarcely strong enough when Nature herself watches over them. Thus here she resembles a modeller in clay rather than a carpenter, for she does not touch the work she is forming by means of tools, but, as it were, with her own hands.

23

In all animals which can move about, the sexes are separated, one individual being male and **731a** one female, though both are the same in species, as with man and horse. But in plants these powers are mingled, female not being separated from male. Wherefore they generate out of themselves, and do not emit semen but produce an embryo, what is called the seed. Empedocles puts this well in the line: 'and thus the tall trees oviposit; first olives . . .' For as the egg is an embryo, a certain part of it giving rise to the animal and the rest being nutriment, so also from a part of the seed springs the growing plant, and the rest is nutriment for the shoot and the first root.

In a certain sense the same thing happens also in those animals which have the sexes separate. For when there is need for them to generate the sexes are no longer separated any more than in plants, their nature desiring that they shall become one; and this is plain to view when they copulate and are united, that one animal is made out of both.

It is the nature of those creatures which do not emit semen to remain united a long time until the male element has formed the embryo, as with those insects which copulate. The others so remain only until the male has discharged from the parts of himself introduced something which will form the embryo in a longer time, as among the sanguinea. For the former remain paired some part of a day, while the semen forms the embryo in several days. And after emitting this they cease their union.

And animals seem literally to be like divided plants, as though one should separate and divide them, when they bear seed, into the male and female existing in them.

In all this Nature acts like an intelligent workman. For to the essence of plants belongs no other function or business than the production of seed; since, then, this is brought about by the union of male and female, Nature has mixed these and set them together in plants, so that the sexes are not divided in them. Plants, however, have been investigated elsewhere. But the function of the animal is not only to generate (which is common to all living things), but they all of them participate also in a kind of knowledge, some more and some less, and some very little indeed. For they have sense-perception, and this is a kind of knowledge. (If we consider the value of this we find that it is of great importance compared with the class of lifeless objects, but of little compared with the use of the intellect. For **731b** against the latter the mere participation in touch and taste seems to be practically nothing, but beside absolute insensibility it seems most excellent; for it would seem a treasure to gain even this kind of knowledge rather than to lie in a state of death and non-existence.) Now it is by sense-perception that an animal differs from those organisms which have only life. But since, if it is a living animal, it must also live; therefore, when it is necessary for it to accomplish the function of that which has life, it unites and copulates, becoming like a plant, as we said before.

Testaceous animals, being intermediate between animals and plants, perform the function of neither class as belonging to both. As plants they have no sexes, and one does not generate in another; as animals they do not bear fruit from themselves like plants; but they are formed and generated from a liquid and earthy concretion. However, we must speak later of the generation of these animals.[1]

[1] III.11.

BOOK II

I

THAT the male and female are the principles of generation has been previously stated, as also what is their power and their essence. But why is it that one thing becomes and is male, another female? It is the business of our discussion as it proceeds to try and point out (1) that the sexes arise from Necessity and the first efficient cause, (2) from what sort of material they are formed. That (3) they exist because it is better and on account of the final cause, takes us back to a principle still further remote.

Now (1) some existing things are eternal and divine whilst others admit of both existence and non-existence. But (2) that which is noble and divine is always, in virtue of its own nature, the cause of the better in such things as admit of being better or worse, and what is not eternal does admit of existence and non-existence, and can partake in the better and the worse. And (3) soul is better than body, and the living, having soul, is thereby better than the lifeless which has none, and being is better than not being, living than not living. These, then, are the reasons of the generation of animals. For since it is impossible that such a class of things as animals should be of an eternal nature, therefore that which comes into being is eternal in the only way possible. Now it is impossible for it to be eternal as an individual (though of course the real essence of things is in the individual)—were it such it would be eternal—but it is possible for it as a species. **732a** This is why there is always a class of men and animals and plants. But since the male and female essences are the first principles of these, they will exist in the existing individuals for the sake of generation. Again, as the first efficient or moving cause, to which belong the definition and the form, is better and more divine in its nature than the material on which it works, it is better that the superior principle should be separated from the inferior. Therefore, wherever it is possible and so far as it is possible, the male is separated from the female. For the first principle of the movement, or efficient cause, whereby that which comes into being is male, is better and more divine than the material whereby it is female. The male, however, comes together and mingles with the female for the work of generation, because this is common to both.

A thing lives, then, in virtue of participating in the male and female principles, wherefore even plants have some kind of life; but the class of animals exists in virtue of sense-perception. The sexes are divided in nearly all of these that can move about, for the reasons already stated, and some of them, as said before,[1] emit semen in copulation, others not. The reason of this is that the higher animals are more independent in their nature, so that they have greater size, and this cannot exist without vital heat; for the greater body requires more force to move it, and heat is a motive force. Therefore, taking a general view, we may say that sanguinea are of greater size than bloodless animals, and those which move about than those which remain fixed. And these are just the animals which emit semen on account of their heat and size.

So much for the cause of the existence of the two sexes. Some animals bring to perfection and produce into the world a creature like themselves, as all those which bring their young into the world alive; others produce something undeveloped which has not yet acquired its own form; in this latter division the sanguinea lay eggs, the bloodless animals either lay an egg or give birth to a scolex. The difference between egg and scolex is this: an egg is that from a part of which the young comes into being, the rest being nutriment for it; but the whole of a scolex is developed into the whole of the young animal. Of the vivipara, which bring into the world an animal like themselves, some are internally viviparous (as men, horses, cattle, and of marine animals dolphins and the other cetacea); others first lay eggs within themselves, and only after this are **732b** externally viviparous (as the cartilaginous fishes). Among the ovipara some produce the egg in a perfect condition (as birds and all oviparous quadrupeds and footless animals, e.g. lizards and tortoises and most snakes; for the eggs of all these do not increase when once laid). The eggs of others are imperfect; such are those of fishes, crustaceans, and cephalopods, for their eggs increase after being produced.

All the vivipara are sanguineous, and the sanguinea are either viviparous or oviparous, except those which are altogether infertile. Among bloodless animals the insects pro-

[1] I. 17.

duce a scolex, alike those that are generated by copulation and those that copulate themselves though not so generated. For there are some insects of this sort, which though they come into being by spontaneous generation are yet male and female; from their union something is produced, only it is imperfect; the reason of this has been previously stated.

These classes admit of much cross-division. Not all bipeds are viviparous (for birds are oviparous), nor are they all oviparous (for man is viviparous), nor are all quadrupeds oviparous (for horses, cattle, and countless others are viviparous), nor are they all viviparous (for lizards, crocodiles, and many others lay eggs). Nor does the presence or absence of feet make the difference between them, for not only are some footless animals viviparous, as vipers and the cartilaginous fishes, while others are oviparous, as the other fishes and serpents, but also among those which have feet many are oviparous and many viviparous, as the quadrupeds above mentioned. And some which have feet, as man, and some which have not, as the whale and dolphin, are internally viviparous. By this character then it is not possible to divide them, nor is any of the locomotive organs the cause of this difference, but it is those animals which are more perfect in their nature and participate in a purer element which are viviparous, for nothing is internally viviparous unless it receive and breathe out air. But the more perfect are those which are hotter in their nature and have more moisture and are not earthy in their composition. And the measure of natural heat is the lung when it has blood in it, for generally those animals which have a lung are hotter than those which have not, and in the former class again those whose lung is not spongy nor solid nor **733a** containing only a little blood, but soft and full of blood. And as the animal is perfect but the egg and the scolex are imperfect, so the perfect is naturally produced from the more perfect. If animals are hotter as shown by their possessing a lung but drier in their nature, or are colder but have more moisture, then they either lay a perfect egg or are viviparous after laying an egg within themselves. For birds and scaly reptiles because of their heat produce a perfect egg, but because of their dryness it is only an egg; the cartilaginous fishes have less heat than these but more moisture, so that they are intermediate, for they are both oviparous and viviparous within themselves, the former because they are cold, the latter because of their moisture; for moisture is vivifying, whereas dryness is furthest removed from what has life. Since they have neither feathers nor scales such as either reptiles or other fishes have, all which are signs rather of a dry and earthy nature, the egg they produce is soft; for the earthy matter does not come to the surface in their eggs any more than in themselves. This is why they lay eggs in themselves, for if the egg were laid externally it would be destroyed, having no protection.

Animals that are cold and rather dry than moist also lay eggs, but the egg is imperfect; at the same time, because they are of an earthy nature and the egg they produce is imperfect, therefore it has a hard integument that it may be preserved by the protection of the shell-like covering. Hence fishes, because they are scaly, and crustacea, because they are of an earthy nature, lay eggs with a hard integument.

The cephalopods, having themselves bodies of a sticky nature, preserve in the same way the imperfect eggs they lay, for they deposit a quantity of sticky material about the embryo. All insects produce a scolex. Now all the insects are bloodless, wherefore all creatures that produce a scolex from themselves are so. But we cannot say simply that all bloodless animals produce a scolex, for the classes overlap one another, (1) the insects, (2) the animals that produce a scolex, (3) those that lay their egg imperfect, as the scaly fishes, the crustacea, and the cephalopoda. I say that these form a gradation, for the eggs of these latter resemble a scolex, in that they increase after oviposition, and the scolex of insects again as it develops resembles an egg; how so we shall explain later.[1]

We must observe how rightly Nature orders **733b** generation in regular gradation. The more perfect and hotter animals produce their young perfect in respect of quality (in respect of quantity this is so with no animal, for the young always increase in size after birth), and these generate living animals within themselves from the first. The second class do not generate perfect animals within themselves from the first (for they are only viviparous after first laying eggs), but still they are externally viviparous. The third class do not produce a perfect animal, but an egg, and this egg is perfect. Those whose nature is still colder than these produce an egg, but an imperfect one, which is perfected outside the body, as the class of scaly fishes, the crustacea, and the ceph-

[1] III 9.

alopods. The fifth and coldest class does not even lay an egg from itself; but so far as the young ever attain to this condition at all, it is outside the body of the parent, as has been said already.[1] For insects produce a scolex first; the scolex after developing becomes egg-like (for the so-called chrysalis or pupa is equivalent to an egg); then from this it is that a perfect animal comes into being, reaching the end of its development in the second change.

Some animals then, as said before, do not come into being from semen, but all the sanguinea do so which are generated by copulation, the male emitting semen into the female; when this has entered into her the young are formed and assume their peculiar character, some within the animals themselves when they are viviparous, others in eggs.

There is a considerable difficulty in understanding how the plant is formed out of the seed or any animal out of the semen. Everything that comes into being or is made must (1) be made out of something, (2) be made by the agency of something, and (3) must become something. Now that out of which it is made is the material; this some animals have in its first form within themselves, taking it from the female parent, as all those which are not born alive but produced as a scolex or an egg; others receive it from the mother for a long time by sucking, as the young of all those which are not only externally but also internally viviparous. Such, then, is the material out of which things come into being, but we now are inquiring not out of what the parts of an animal are made, but by what agency. Either it is something external which makes them, or else something existing in the seminal **734a** fluid and the semen; and this must either be soul or a part of soul, or something containing soul.

Now it would appear irrational to suppose that any of either the internal organs or the other parts is made by something external, since one thing cannot set up a motion in another without touching it, nor can a thing be affected in any way by another if it does not set up a motion in it. Something then of the sort we require exists in the embryo itself, being either a part of it or separate from it. To suppose that it should be something else separate from it is irrational. For after the animal has been produced does this something perish or does it remain in it? But nothing of the kind appears to be in it, nothing which is not a part of the whole plant or animal. Yet, on the other hand, it is absurd to say that it perishes after making either all the parts or only some of them. If it makes some of the parts and then perishes, what is to make the rest of them? Suppose this something makes the heart and then perishes, and the heart makes another organ, by the same argument either all the parts must perish or all must remain. Therefore it is preserved and does not perish. Therefore it is a part of the embryo itself which exists in the semen from the beginning; and if indeed there is no part of the soul which does not exist in some part of the body, it would also be a part containing soul in it from the beginning.

How, then, does it make the other parts? Either all the parts, as heart, lung, liver, eye, and all the rest, come into being together or in succession, as is said in the verse ascribed to Orpheus, for there he says that an animal comes into being in the same way as the knitting of a net. That the former is not the fact is plain even to the senses, for some of the parts are clearly visible as already existing in the embryo while others are not; that it is not because of their being too small that they are not visible is clear, for the lung is of greater size than the heart, and yet appears later than the heart in the original development. Since, then, one is earlier and another later, does the one make the other, and does the later part exist on account of the part which is next to it, or rather does the one come into being only *after* the other? I mean, for instance, that it is not the fact that the heart, having come into being first, then makes the liver, and the liver again another organ, but that the liver only comes into being *after* the heart, and not by the agency of the heart, as a man becomes a man *after* being a boy, not by his agency. An explanation of this is that, in all the productions of Nature or of art, what already exists potentially is brought into being only by what exists actually; therefore if one organ formed another the form and the character of the later organ would have to exist in the earlier, e.g. the form of the liver in the heart. And otherwise also the theory is strange and fictitious.

Yet again, if the whole animal or plant is formed from semen or seed, it is impossible that any part of it should exist ready made in the semen or seed, whether that part be able to make the other parts or no. For it is plain that, if it exists in it from the first, it was made **734b** by that which made the semen. But semen must be made first, and that is the func-

[1] The reference seems to be to 733a 31.

tion of the generating parent. So, then, it is not possible that any part should exist in it, and therefore it has not within itself that which makes the parts.

But neither can this agent be external, and yet it must needs be one or other of the two. We must try, then, to solve this difficulty, for perhaps some one of the statements made cannot be made without qualification, e.g. the statement that the parts cannot be made by what is external to the semen. For if in a certain sense they cannot, yet in another sense they can. (Now it makes no difference whether we say 'the semen' or 'that from which the semen comes', in so far as the semen has in itself the movement initiated by the other.) It is possible, then, that A should move B, and B move C; that, in fact, the case should be the same as with the automatic machines shown as curiosities. For the parts of such machines while at rest have a sort of potentiality of motion in them, and when any external force puts the first of them in motion, immediately the next is moved in actuality. As, then, in these automatic machines the external force moves the parts in a certain sense (not by touching any part at the moment, but by having touched one previously), in like manner also that from which the semen comes, or in other words that which made the semen, sets up the movement in the embryo and makes the parts of it by having first touched something though not continuing to touch it. In a way it is the innate motion that does this, as the act of building builds the house. Plainly, then, while there is something which makes the parts, this does not exist as a definite object, nor does it exist in the semen at the first as a complete part.

But how is each part formed? We must answer this by starting in the first instance from the principle that, in all products of Nature or art, a thing is made by something actually existing out of that which is potentially such as the finished product. Now the semen is of such a nature, and has in it such a principle of motion, that when the motion is ceasing each of the parts comes into being, and that as a part having life or soul. For there is no such thing as face or flesh without life or soul in it; it is only equivocally that they will be called face or flesh if the life has gone out of them, just as if they had been made of stone or wood. And the homogeneous parts and the organic come into being together. And just as we should not say that an axe or other instrument or organ was made by the fire alone, so neither shall we say that foot or hand were made by heat alone. The same applies also to flesh, for this too has a function. While, then, we may allow that hardness and softness, stickiness and brittleness, and whatever other qualities are found in the parts that have life and soul, may be caused by mere heat and cold, yet, when we come to the principle in virtue of which flesh is flesh and bone is bone, that is no longer so; what makes them is the movement set up by the male parent, who is in actuality what that out of which the offspring is made is in potentiality. This is what we find in the products of art; heat and cold may make the iron soft **735a** and hard, but what makes a sword is the movement of the tools employed, this movement containing the principle of the art. For the art is the starting-point and form of the product; only it exists in something else, whereas the movement of Nature exists in the product itself, issuing from another nature which has the form in actuality.

Has the semen soul, or not? The same argument applies here as in the question concerning the parts. As no part, if it participate not in soul, will be a part except in an equivocal sense (as the eye of a dead man is still called an 'eye'), so no soul will exist in anything except that of which it is soul; it is plain therefore that semen both has soul, and is soul, potentially.

But a thing existing potentially may be nearer or further from its realization in actuality, as e.g. a mathematician when asleep is further from his realization in actuality as engaged in mathematics than when he is awake, and when awake again but not studying mathematics he is further removed than when he is so studying. Accordingly it is not any part that is the cause of the soul's coming into being, but it is the first moving cause from outside. (For nothing generates itself, though when it has come into being it thenceforward increases itself.) Hence it is that only one part comes into being first and not all of them together. But that must first come into being which has a principle of increase (for this nutritive power exists in all alike, whether animals or plants, and this is the same as the power that enables an animal or plant to generate another like itself, that being the function of them all if naturally perfect). And this is necessary for the reason that whenever a living thing is produced it must grow. It is produced, then, by something else of the same name, as e.g. man is produced by man, but it is increased by means of itself. There is, then, something which increases it. If this is a single part, this must come into being first. Therefore if the heart is first made in some animals, and what is analogous to the heart in the others which have no heart, it is from this or its analogue that the first principle of movement would arise.

We have thus discussed the difficulties previously raised on the question what is the efficient cause of generation in each case, as the first moving and formative power.

2

The next question to be mooted concerns the nature of semen. For whereas when it issues from the animal it is thick and white, yet on cooling it becomes liquid as water, and its colour is that of water. This would appear strange, for water is not thickened by heat; yet semen is thick when it issues from within the animal's body which is hot, and becomes liquid on cooling. Again, watery fluids freeze, but semen, if exposed in frosts to the open air, does not freeze but liquefies, as if it was thickened by the opposite of cold. Yet it is unreasonable, again, to suppose that it is thickened by heat. For it is only substances having a predom-
735b inance of earth in their composition that coagulate and thicken on boiling, e.g. milk. It ought then to solidify on cooling, but as a matter of fact it does not become solid in any part but the whole of it goes like water.

This then is the difficulty. If it is water, water evidently does not thicken through heat, whereas the semen is thick and both it and the body whence it issues are hot. If it is made of earth or a mixture of earth and water, it ought not to liquefy entirely and turn to water.

Perhaps, however, we have not discriminated all the possibilities. It is not only the liquids composed of water and earthy matter that thicken, but also those composed of water and air; foam, for instance, becomes thicker and white, and the smaller and less visible the bubbles in it, the whiter and firmer does the mass appear. The same thing happens also with oil; on mixing with air it thickens, wherefore that which is whitening becomes thicker, the watery part in it being separated off by the heat and turning to air. And if oxide of lead is mixed with water or even with oil, the mass increases greatly and changes from liquid and dark to firm and white, the reason being that air is mixed in with it which increases the mass and makes the white shine through, as in foam and snow (for snow is foam). And water itself on mingling with oil becomes thick and white, because air is entangled in it by the act of pounding them together, and oil itself has much air in it (for shininess is a property of air, not of earth or water). This too is why it floats on the surface of the water, for the air contained in it as in a vessel bears it up and makes it float, being the cause of its lightness. So too oil is thickened without freezing in cold weather and frosts; it does not freeze because of its heat (for the air is hot and will not freeze), but because the air is forced together and compressed, as . . ., by the cold, the oil becomes thicker. These are the reasons why semen is firm and white when it issues from within the animal; it has a quantity of hot air in it because of the internal heat; afterwards, when the heat has evaporated and the air has cooled, it turns liquid and dark; for the water, and any small quantity of earthy matter there may be, remain in semen as it dries, as they do in phlegm.

736a Semen, then, is a compound of spirit (πνεῦμα) and water, and the former is hot air (ἀήρ); hence semen is liquid in its nature because it is made of water. What Ctesias the Cnidian has asserted of the semen of elephants is manifestly untrue; he says that it hardens so much in drying that it becomes like amber. But this does not happen, though it is true that one semen must be more earthy than another, and especially so with animals that have much earthy matter in them because of the bulk of their bodies. And it is thick and white because it is mixed with spirit, for it is also an invariable rule that it is white, and Herodotus does not report the truth when he says that the semen of the Aethiopians is black, as if everything must needs be black in those who have a black skin, and that too when he saw their teeth were white. The reason of the whiteness of semen is that it is a foam, and foam is white, especially that which is composed of the smallest parts, small in the sense that each bubble is invisible, which is what happens when water and oil are mixed and shaken together, as said before. (Even the ancients seem to have noticed that semen is of the nature of foam; at least it was from this they named the goddess who presides over union.)

This then is the explanation of the problem proposed, and it is plain too that this is why semen does not freeze; for air will not freeze.

3

The next question to raise and to answer is this. If, in the case of those animals which emit

semen into the female, that which enters makes no part of the resulting embryo, where is the material part of it diverted if (as we have seen) it acts by means of the power residing in it? It is not only necessary to decide whether what is forming in the female receives anything material, or not, from that which has entered her, but also concerning the soul in virtue of which an animal is so called (and this is in virtue of the sensitive part of the soul)—does this exist originally in the semen and in the unfertilized embryo or not, and if it does whence does it come? For nobody would put down the unfertilized embryo as soulless or in every sense bereft of life (since both the semen and the embryo of an animal have every bit as much life as a plant), and it is productive up to a certain point. That then they possess the nutritive soul is plain (and plain is it from the dis-
736b cussions elsewhere about soul why this soul must be acquired first[1]). As they develop they also acquire the sensitive soul in virtue of which an animal is an animal. For e.g. an animal does not become at the same time an animal and a man or a horse or any other particular animal. For the end is developed last, and the peculiar character of the species is the end of the generation in each individual. Hence arises a question of the greatest difficulty, which we must strive to solve to the best of our ability and as far as possible. When and how and whence is a share in reason acquired by those animals that participate in this principle? It is plain that the semen and the unfertilized embryo, while still separate from each other, must be assumed to have the nutritive soul potentially, but not actually, except that (like those unfertilized embryos that are separated from the mother) it absorbs nourishment and performs the function of the nutritive soul. For at first all such embryos seem to live the life of a plant. And it is clear that we must be guided by this in speaking of the sensitive and the rational soul. For all three kinds of soul, not only the nutritive, must be possessed potentially before they are possessed in actuality. And it is necessary either (1) that they should all come into being in the embryo without existing previously outside it, or (2) that they should all exist previously, or (3) that some should so exist and others not. Again, it is necessary that they should either (1) come into being in the material supplied by the female without entering with the semen of the male, or (2) come from the male and be imparted to the material in the female. If the latter, then either all of them, or none, or some must come into being in the male from outside.

Now that it is impossible for them all to pre-exist is clear from this consideration. Plainly those principles whose activity is bodily cannot exist without a body, e.g. walking cannot exist without feet. For the same reason also they cannot enter from outside. For neither is it possible for them to enter by themselves, being inseparable from a body, nor yet in a body, for the semen is only a secretion of the nutriment in process of change. It remains, then, for the reason alone so to enter and alone to be divine, for no bodily activity has any connexion with the activity of reason.

Now it is true that the faculty of all kinds of soul seems to have a connexion with a matter different from and more divine than the so-called elements; but as one soul differs from another in honour and dishonour, so differs also the nature of the corresponding matter. All have in their semen that which causes it to be productive; I mean what is called vital heat. This is not fire nor any such force, but it is the spiritus included in the semen and the foam-like, and the natural principle in the spiritus, being analogous to the element of the
737a stars. Hence, whereas fire generates no animal and we do not find any living thing forming in either solids or liquids under the influence of fire, the heat of the sun and that of animals does generate them. Not only is this true of the heat that works through the semen, but whatever other residuum of the animal nature there may be, this also has still a vital principle in it. From such considerations it is clear that the heat in animals neither is fire nor derives its origin from fire.

Let us return to the material of the semen, in and with which comes away from the male the spiritus conveying the principle of soul. Of this principle there are two kinds; the one is not connected with matter, and belongs to those animals in which is included something divine (to wit, what is called the reason), while the other is inseparable from matter. This material of the semen dissolves and evaporates because it has a liquid and watery nature. Therefore we ought not to expect it always to come out again from the female or to form any part of the embryo that has taken shape from it; the case resembles that of the fig-juice which curdles milk, for this too changes without becoming any part of the curdling masses.

[1] *On the Soul*, II. 4.

It has been settled, then, in what sense the embryo and the semen have soul, and in what sense they have not; they have it potentially but not actually.

Now semen is a secretion and is moved with the same movement as that in virtue of which the body increases (this increase being due to subdivision of the nutriment in its last stage). When it has entered the uterus it puts into form the corresponding secretion of the female and moves it with the same movement wherewith it is moved itself. For the female's contribution also is a secretion, and has all the parts in it potentially though none of them actually; it has in it potentially even those parts which differentiate the female from the male, for just as the young of mutilated parents are sometimes born mutilated and sometimes not, so also the young born of a female are sometimes female and sometimes male instead. For the female is, as it were, a mutilated male, and the catamenia are semen, only not pure; for there is only one thing they have not in them, the principle of soul. For this reason, whenever a wind-egg is produced by any animal, the egg so forming has in it the parts of both sexes potentially, but has not the principle in question, so that it does not develop into a living creature, for this is introduced by the semen of the male. When such a principle has ben imparted to the secretion of the female it becomes an embryo.

Liquid but corporeal substances become surrounded by some kind of covering on heating, like the solid scum which forms on boiled **737b** foods when cooling. All bodies are held together by the glutinous; this quality, as the embryo develops and increases in size, is acquired by the sinewy substance, which holds together the parts of animals, being actual sinew in some and its analogue in others. To the same class belong also skin, blood-vessels, membranes, and the like, for these differ in being more or less glutinous and generally in excess and deficiency.

4

In those animals whose nature is comparatively imperfect, when a perfect embryo (which, however, is not yet a perfect animal) has been formed, it is cast out from the mother, for reasons previously stated.[1] An embryo is then complete when it is either male or female, in the case of those animals who possess this distinction, for some (i.e. all those which are not themselves produced from a male or female parent nor from a union of the two) produce an offspring which is neither male nor female. Of the generation of these we shall speak later.

The perfect animals, those internally viviparous, keep the developing embryo within themselves and in close connexion until they give birth to a complete animal and bring it to light.

A third class is externally viviparous but first internally oviparous; they develop the egg into a perfect condition, and then in some cases the egg is set free as with creatures externally oviparous, and the animal is produced from the egg within the mother's body; in other cases, when the nutriment from the egg is consumed, development is completed by connection with the uterus, and therefore the egg is not set free from the uterus. This character marks the cartilaginous fish, of which we must speak later by themselves.[2]

Here we must make our first start from the first class; these are the perfect or viviparous animals, and of these the first is man. Now the secretion of the semen takes place in all of them just as does that of any other residual matter. For each is conveyed to its proper place without any force from the breath or compulsion of any other cause, as some assert, saying that the generative parts attract the semen like cupping-glasses, aided by the force of the breath, as if it were possible for either this secretion or the residue of the solid and liquid nutriment to go anywhere else than they do without the exertion of such a force. Their reason is that the discharge of both is attended by holding the breath, but this is a common feature of all cases when it is necessary to move **738a** anything, because strength arises through holding the breath. Why, even without this force the secretions or excretions are discharged in sleep if the parts concerned are full of them and are relaxed. One might as well say that it is by the breath that the seeds of plants are always segregated to the places where they are wont to bear fruit. No, the real cause, as has been stated already, is that there are special parts for receiving all the secretions, alike the useless (as the residues of the liquid and solid nutriment), and the blood, which has the so-called blood-vessels.

To consider now the region of the uterus in the female—the two blood-vessels, the great vessel and the aorta, divide higher up, and many fine vessels from them terminate in the

[1] Chapter I.

[2] III. 3.

uterus. These become over-filled from the nourishment they convey, nor is the female nature able to concoct it, because it is colder than man's; so the blood is excreted through very fine vessels into the uterus, these being unable on account of their narrowness to receive the excessive quantity, and the result is a sort of haemorrhage. The period is not accurately defined in women, but tends to return during the waning of the moon. This we should expect, for the bodies of animals are colder when the environment happens to become so, and the time of change from one month to another is cold because of the absence of the moon, whence also it results that this time is stormier than the middle of the month. When then the residue of the nourishment has changed into blood, the catamenia tend to occur at the above-mentioned period, but when it is not concocted a little matter at a time is always coming away, and this is why 'whites' appear in females while still small, in fact mere children. If both these discharges of the secretions are moderate, the body remains in good health, for they act as a purification of the secretions which are the causes of a morbid state of body; if they do not occur at all or if they are excessive, they are injurious, either causing illness or pulling down the patient; hence whites, if continuous and excessive, prevent girls from growing. This secretion then is necessarily discharged by females for the reasons given; for, the female nature being unable to concoct the nourishment thoroughly, there must not only be left a residue of the useless nutriment, but also there must be a residue in the blood-vessels, and this filling the channels of the finest vessels must overflow. **738b** Then Nature, aiming at the best end, uses it up in this place for the sake of generation, that another creature may come into being of the same kind as the former was going to be, for the menstrual blood is already potentially such as the body from which it is discharged.

In all females, then, there must necessarily be such a secretion, more indeed in those that have blood and of these most of all in man, but in the others also some matter must be collected in the uterine region. The reason why there is more in those that have blood and most in man has been already given, but why, if all females have such a secretion, have not all males one to correspond? For some of them do not emit semen but, just as those which do emit fashion by the movement in the semen the mass forming from the material supplied by the female, so do the animals in question bring the same to pass and exert the same formative power by the movement within themselves in that part from whence the semen is secreted. This is the region about the diaphragm in all those animals which have one, for the heart or its analogue is the first principle of a natural body, while the lower part is a mere addition for the sake of it. Now the reason why it is not all males that have a generative secretion, while all females do, is that the animal is a body with soul or life; the female always provides the material, the male that which fashions it, for this is the power that we say they each possess, and this is what is meant by calling them male and female. Thus while it is necessary for the female to provide a body and a material mass, it is not necessary for the male, because it is not within the work of art or the embryo that the tools or the maker must exist. While the body is from the female, it is the soul that is from the male, for the soul is the reality of a particular body. For this reason if animals of a different kind are crossed (and this is possible when the periods of gestation are equal and conception takes place nearly at the same season and there is no great difference in the size of the animals), the first cross has a common resemblance to both parents, as the hybrid between fox and dog, partridge and domestic fowl, but as time goes on and one generation springs from another, the final result resembles the female in form, just as foreign seeds produce plants varying in accordance with the country in which they are sown. For it is the soil that gives to the seeds the material and the body of the plant. And hence the part of the female which receives the semen is not a mere passage, but the uterus has a con-
739a siderable width, whereas the males that emit semen have only passages for this purpose, and these are bloodless.

Each of the secretions becomes such at the moment when it is in its proper place; before that there is nothing of the sort unless with much violence and contrary to nature.

We have thus stated the reason for which the generative secretions are formed in animals. But when the semen from the male (in those animals which emit semen) has entered, it puts into form the purest part of the female secretion (for the greater part of the catamenia also is useless and fluid, as is the most fluid part of the male secretion, i.e. in a single emission, the earlier discharge being in most cases apt to be infertile rather than the later, having less vital heat through want of concoction, whereas that which is concocted is thick and of a more material nature).

If there is no external discharge, either in women or other animals, on account of there not being much useless and superfluous matter in the secretion, then the quantity forming within the female altogether is as much as what is retained within those animals which have an external discharge; this is put into form by the power of the male residing in the semen secreted by him, or, as is clearly seen to happen in some insects, by the part in the female analogous to the uterus being inserted into the male.

It has been previously stated that the discharge accompanying sexual pleasure in the female contributes nothing to the embryo. The chief argument for the opposite view is that what are called bad dreams occur by night with women as with men; but this is no proof, for the same thing happens to young men also who do not yet emit semen, and to those who do emit semen but whose semen is infertile.

It is impossible to conceive without the emission of the male in union and without the secretion of the corresponding female material, whether it be discharged externally or whether there is only enough within the body. Women conceive, however, without experiencing the pleasure usual in such intercourse, if the part chance to be in heat and the uterus to have descended. But generally speaking the opposite is the case, because the os uteri is not closed when the discharge takes place which is usually accompanied by pleasure in women as well as men, and when this is so there is a readier way for the semen of the male to be drawn into the uterus.

The actual discharge does not take place within the uterus as some think, the os uteri being too narrow, but it is in the region in front of this, where the female discharges the mois-
739b ture found in some cases, that the male emits the semen. Sometimes it remains in this place; at other times, if the uterus chance to be conveniently placed and hot on account of the purgation of the catamenia, it draws it within itself. A proof of this is that pessaries, though wet when applied, are removed dry. Moreover, in all those animals which have the uterus near the hypozoma, as birds and viviparous fishes, it is impossible that the semen should be so discharged as to enter it; it must be drawn into it. This region, on account of the heat which is in it, attracts the semen. The discharge and collection of the catamenia also excite heat in this part. Hence it acts like cone-shaped vessels which, when they have been washed out with hot water, their mouth being turned downwards, draw water into themselves. And this is the way things are drawn up, but some say that nothing of the kind happens with the organic parts concerned in copulation. Precisely the opposite is the case of those who say the woman emits semen as well as the man, for if she emits it outside the uterus this must then draw it back again into itself if it is to be mixed with the semen of the male. But this is a superfluous proceeding, and Nature does nothing superfluous.

When the material secreted by the female in the uterus has been fixed by the semen of the male (this acts in the same way as rennet acts upon milk, for rennet is a kind of milk containing vital heat, which brings into one mass and fixes the similar material, and the relation of the semen to the catamenia is the same, milk and the catamenia being of the same nature)—when, I say, the more solid part comes together, the liquid is separated off from it, and as the earthy parts solidify membranes form all round it; this is both a necessary result and for a final cause, the former because the surface of a mass must solidify on heating as well as on cooling, the latter because the foetus must not be in a liquid but be separated from it. Some of these are called membranes and others choria, the difference being one of more or less, and they exist in ovipara and vivipara alike.

When the embryo is once formed, it acts like the seeds of plants. For seeds also contain the first principle of growth in themselves, and when this (which previously exists in them only potentially) has been differentiated, the shoot and the root are sent off from it, and it is
740a by the root that the plant gets nourishment; for it needs growth. So also in the embryo all the parts exist potentially in a way at the same time, but the first principle is furthest on the road to realization. Therefore the heart is first differentiated in actuality. This is clear not only to the senses (for it is so) but also on theoretical grounds. For whenever the young animal has been separated from both parents it must be able to manage itself, like a son who has set up house away from his father. Hence it must have a first principle from which comes the ordering of the body at a later stage

also, for if it is to come in from outside at a later period to dwell in it, not only may the question be asked at what time it is to do so, but also we may object that, when each of the parts is separating from the rest, it is necessary that this principle should exist first from which comes growth and movement to the other parts. (Wherefore all who say, as did Democritus, that the external parts of animals are first differentiated and the internal later, are much mistaken; it is as if they were talking of animals of stone or wood. For such as these have no principle of growth at all, but all animals have, and have it within themselves.) Therefore it is that the heart appears first distinctly marked off in all the sanguinea, for this is the first principle or origin of both homogeneous and heterogeneous parts, since from the moment that the animal or organism needs nourishment, from that moment does this deserve to be called its principle or origin. For the animal grows, and the nutriment, in its final stage, of an animal is the blood or its analogue, and of this the blood-vessels are the receptacle, wherefore the heart is the principle or origin of these also. (This is clear from the *Enquiries*[1] and the anatomical drawings.)

Since the embryo is already potentially an animal but an imperfect one, it must obtain its nourishment from elsewhere; accordingly it makes use of the uterus and the mother, as a plant does of the earth, to get nourishment, until it is perfected to the point of being now an animal potentially locomotive. So Nature has first designed the two blood-vessels from the heart, and from these smaller vessels branch off to the uterus. These are what is called the umbilicus, for this is a blood-vessel, consisting of one or more vessels in different animals. Round these is a skin-like integument, because the weakness of the vessels needs protection and shelter. The vessels join on to the uterus like the roots of plants, and through them the embryo receives its nourishment. This is why the animal remains in the uterus, not, as Democritus says, that the parts of the embryo may be moulded in conformity

740b with those of the mother. This is plain in the ovipara, for they have their parts differentiated in the egg after separation from the matrix.

Here a difficulty may be raised. If the blood is the nourishment, and if the heart, which first comes into being, already contains blood, and the nourishment comes from outside, whence did the first nourishment enter? Perhaps it is not true that *all* of it comes from outside. Just as in the seeds of plants there is something of this nature, the substance which at first appears milky, so also in the material of the animal embryo the superfluous matter of which it is formed is its nourishment from the first.

The embryo, then, grows by means of the umbilicus in the same way as a plant by its roots, or as animals themselves when separated from the nutriment within the mother, of which we must speak later at the time appropriate for discussing them. But the parts are not differentiated, as some suppose, because like is naturally carried to like. Besides many other difficulties involved in this theory, it results from it that the homogeneous parts ought to come into being each one separate from the rest, as bones and sinews by themselves, and flesh by itself, if one should accept this cause. The real cause why each of them comes into being is that the secretion of the female is potentially such as the animal is naturally, and all the parts are potentially present in it, but none actually. It is also because when the active and the passive come in contact with each other in that way in which the one is active and the other passive (I mean in the right manner, in the right place, and at the right time), straightway the one acts and the other is acted upon. The female, then, provides matter, the male the principle of motion. And as the products of art are made by means of the tools of the artist, or to put it more truly by means of their movement, and this is the activity of the art, and the art is the form of what is made in something else, so is it with the power of the nutritive soul. As later on in the case of mature animals and plants this soul causes growth from the nutriment, using heat and cold as its tools (for in these is the movement of the soul), and each thing comes into being in accordance with a certain formula, so also from the beginning does it form the product of nature. For the material by which this latter grows is the same as that from which it is constituted at first; consequently also the power which acts upon it is identical with that which originally generated it; if then this acting power is the nutritive soul, this is also the generative soul, and this is

741a the nature of every organism, existing in all animals and plants. [But the other parts of the soul exist in some animals, not in others.] In plants, then, the female is not separated from the male, but in those animals in which it

[1] *History of Animals*, III. 3.

is separated the male needs the female besides.

5

And yet the question may be raised why it is that, if indeed the female possesses the same soul and if it is the secretion of the female which is the material of the embryo, she needs the male besides instead of generating entirely from herself. The reason is that the animal differs from the plant by having sense-perception; if the sensitive soul is not present, either actually or potentially, and either with or without qualification, it is impossible for face, hand, flesh, or any other part to exist; it will be no better than a corpse or part of a corpse. If then, when the sexes are separated, it is the male that has the power of making the sensitive soul, it is impossible for the female to generate an animal from itself alone, for the process in question was seen to involve the male quality. Certainly that there is a good deal in the difficulty stated is plain in the case of the birds that lay wind-eggs, showing that the female can generate up to a certain point unaided. But this still involves a difficulty; in what way are we to say that their eggs live? It is neither possible that they should live in the same way as fertile eggs (for then they would produce a chick actually alive), nor yet can they be called eggs only in the sense in which an egg of wood or stone is so called, for the fact that these eggs go bad shows that they previously participate in some way in life. It is plain, then, that they have some soul potentially. What sort of soul will this be? It must be the lowest surely, and this is the nutritive, for this exists in all animals and plants alike. Why then does it not perfect the parts and the animal? Because they must have a sensitive soul, for the parts of animals are not like those of a plant. And so the female animal needs the help of the male, for in these animals we are speaking of the male is separate. This is exactly what we find, for the wind-eggs become fertile if the male tread the female in a certain space of time. About the cause of these things, however, we shall enter into detail later.

If there is any kind of animal which is female and has no male separate from it, it is possible that this may generate a young one from itself without copulation. No instance of this worthy of credit has been observed up to the present at any rate, but one case in the class of fishes makes us hesitate. No male of the so-called erythrinus has ever yet been seen, but females, and specimens full of roe, have been seen. Of this, however, we have as yet no proof worthy of credit. Again, some members of the class of fishes are neither male nor female,

741b as eels and a kind of mullets found in stagnant waters. But whenever the sexes are separate the female cannot generate perfectly by herself alone, for then the male would exist in vain, and Nature makes nothing in vain. Hence in such animals the male always perfects the work of generation, for he imparts the sensitive soul, either by means of the semen or without it. Now the parts of the embryo already exist potentially in the material, and so when once the principle of movement has been imparted to them they develop in a chain one after another, as the wheels are moved one by another in the automatic machines. When some of the natural philosophers say that like is brought to like, this must be understood, not in the sense that the parts are moved as changing place, but that they stay where they are and the movement is a change of quality (such as softness, hardness, colour, and the other differences of the homogeneous parts); thus they become in actuality what they previously were in potentiality. And what comes into being first is the first principle; this is the heart in the sanguinea and its analogue in the rest, as has been often said already. This is plain not only to the senses (that it is first to come into being), but also in view of its end; for life fails in the heart last of all, and it happens in all cases that what comes into being last fails first, and the first last, Nature running a double course, so to say, and turning back to the point from whence she started. For the process of becoming is from the non-existent to the existent, and that of perishing is back again from the existent to the non-existent.

6

After this, as said already, the internal parts come into being before the external. The greater become visible before the less, even if some of them do not come into being before them. First the parts above the hypozoma are differentiated and are superior in size; the part below is both smaller and less differentiated. This happens in all animals in which exists the distinction of upper and lower, except in the insects; the growth of those that produce a scolex is towards the upper part, for this is smaller in the beginning. The cephalopoda are the only locomotive animals in which the distinction of upper and lower does not exist.

What has been said applies to plants also, that the upper portion is earlier in development than the lower, for the roots push out from the seed before the shoots.

The agency by which the parts of animals are differentiated is air, not however that of the mother nor yet of the embryo itself, as some of **742a** the physicists say. This is manifest in birds, fishes, and insects. For some of these are separated from the mother and produced from an egg, within which the differentiation takes place; other animals do not breathe at all, but are produced as a scolex or an egg; those which do breathe and whose parts are differentiated within the mother's uterus yet do not breathe until the lung is perfected, and the lung and the preceding parts are differentiated before they breathe. Moreover, all polydactylous quadrupeds, as dog, lion, wolf, fox, jackal, produce their young blind, and the eyelids do not separate till after birth. Manifestly the same holds also in all the other parts; as the qualitative, so also the quantitative differentia comes into being, pre-existing potentially but being actualized later by the same causes by which the qualitative distinction is produced, and so the eyelids become two instead of one. Of course air must be present, because heat and moisture are present, the former acting and the latter being acted upon.

Some of the ancient nature-philosolphers made an attempt to state which part comes into being after which, but were not sufficiently acquainted with the facts. It is with the parts as with other things; one naturally exists prior to another. But the word 'prior' is used in more senses than one. For there is a difference between the end or final cause and that which exists for the sake of it; the latter is prior in order of development, the former is prior in reality. Again, that which exists for the sake of the end admits of division into two classes, (1) the origin of the movement, (2) that which is used by the end; I mean, for instance, (1) that which can generate, (2) that which serves as an instrument to what is generated, for the one of these, that which makes, must exist first, as the teacher before the learner, and the other later, as the pipes are later than he who learns to play upon them, for it is superfluous that men who do not know how to play should have pipes. Thus there are three things: first, the end, by which we mean that for the sake of which something else exists; secondly, the principle of movement and of generation, existing for the sake of the end (for that which can make and generate, considered simply as such, exists only in relation to what is made and generated); thirdly, the useful, that is to say what the end uses. Accordingly, there must first exist some part in which is the principle of movement (I say a part because this is from the first one part of the end and the most important part too); next after this the whole and the end; thirdly and lastly, the organic parts serving these for certain uses. Hence if there is anything of this sort which **742b** must exist in animals, containing the principle and end of all their nature, this must be the first to come into being—first, that is, considered as the moving power, but simultaneous with the whole embryo if considered as a part of the end. Therefore all the organic parts whose nature is to bring others into being must always themselves exist before them, for they are for the sake of something else, as the beginning for the sake of the end; all those parts which are for the sake of something else but are not of the nature of beginnings must come into being later. So it is not easy to distinguish which of the parts are prior, those which are for the sake of another or that for the sake of which are the former. For the parts which cause the movement, being prior to the end in order of development, come in to cause confusion, and it is not easy to distinguish these as compared with the organic parts. And yet it is in accordance with this method that we must inquire what comes into being after what; for the end is later than some parts and earlier than others. And for this reason that part which contains the first principle comes into being first, next to this the upper half of the body. This is why the parts about the head, and particularly the eyes, appear largest in the embryo at an early stage, while the parts below the umbilicus, as the legs, are small; for the lower parts are for the sake of the upper, and are neither parts of the end nor able to form it.

But they do not say well nor do they assign a necessary cause who say simply that 'it always happens so', and imagine that this is a first principle in these cases. Thus Democritus of Abdera says that 'there is no beginning of the infinite; now the cause is a beginning, and the eternal is infinite; in consequence, to ask the cause of anything of this kind is to seek for a beginning of the infinite'. Yet according to this argument, which forbids us to seek the cause, there will be no proof of any eternal truth whatever; but we see that there is a

proof of many such, whether by 'eternal' we mean what always happens or what exists eternally; it is an eternal truth that the angles of a triangle are always equal to two right angles, or that the diagonal of a square is incommensurable with the side, and nevertheless a cause and a proof can be given for these truths. While, then, it is well said that we must not take on us to seek a beginning (or first principle) of all things, yet this is not well said of all things whatever that always are or always happen, but only of those which really are first principles of the eternal things; for it is by another method, not by proof, that we acquire knowledge of the first principle. Now in that which is immovable and unchanging the first principle is simply the essence of the thing, but when we come to those things which come into being the principles are more than one, varying in kind and not all of the same kind; one of this number is the principle of movement, and therefore in all the sanguinea the heart is formed first, as was said at the beginning, and in the other animals that which
743a is analogous to the heart.

From the heart the blood-vessels extend throughout the body as in the anatomical diagrams which are represented on the wall, for the parts lie round these because they are formed out of them. The homogeneous parts are formed by heat and cold, for some are put together and solidified by the one and some by the other. The difference between these has already been discussed elsewhere, and it has been stated what kinds of things are soluble by liquid and fire, and what are not soluble by liquid and cannot be melted by fire.[1] The nutriment then oozes through the blood-vessels and the passages in each of the parts, like water in unbaked pottery, and thus is formed the flesh or its analogues, being solidified by cold, which is why it is also dissolved by fire. But all the particles given off which are too earthy, having but little moisture and heat, cool as the moisture evaporates along with the heat; so they become hard and earthy in character, as nails, horns, hoofs, and beaks, and therefore they are softened by fire but none of them is melted by it, while some of them, as egg-shells, are soluble in liquids. The sinews and bones are formed by the internal heat as the moisture dries, and hence the bones are insoluble by fire like pottery, for like it they have been as it were baked in an oven by the heat in the process of development. But it is not anything whatever that is made into flesh or bone by the heat, but only something naturally fitted for the purpose; nor is it made in any place or time whatever, but only in a place and time naturally so fitted. For neither will that which exists potentially be made except by that moving agent which possesses the actuality, nor will that which possesses the actuality make anything whatever; the carpenter would not make a box except out of wood, nor will a box be made out of the wood without the carpenter. The heat exists in the seminal secretion, and the movement and activity in it is sufficient in kind and in quantity to correspond to each of the parts. In so far as there is any deficiency or excess, the resulting product is in worse condition or physically defective, in like manner as in the case of external substances which are thickened by boiling that they may be more palatable or for any other purpose. But in the latter case it is we who apply the heat in due measure for the motion required; in the former it is the nature of the male parent that gives it, or with animals spontaneously generated it is the movement and heat imparted by the right season of the year that it is the cause.

Cooling, again, is mere deprivation of heat. Nature makes use of both; they have of necessity the power of bringing about different re-
743b sults, but in the development of the embryo we find that the one cools and the other heats for some definite purpose, and so each of the parts is formed; thus it is in one sense by necessity, in another for a final cause, that they make the flesh soft, the sinews solid and elastic, the bones solid and brittle. The skin, again, is formed by the drying of the flesh, like the scum upon boiled substances; it is so formed not only because it is on the outside, but also because what is glutinous, being unable to evaporate, remains on the surface. While in other animals the glutinous is dry, for which reason the covering of the invertebrates is testaceous or crustaceous, in the vertebrates it is rather of the nature of fat. In all of these which are not of too earthy a nature the fat is collected under the covering of the skin, a fact which points to the skin being formed out of such a glutinous substance, for fat is somewhat glutinous. As we said, all these things must be understood to be formed in one sense of necessity, but in another sense not of necessity but for a final cause.

The upper half of the body, then, is first marked out in the order of development; as

[1] *Meteorology*, IV 7–10.

time goes on the lower also reaches its full size in the sanguinea. All the parts are first marked out in their outlines and acquire later on their colour and softness or hardness, exactly as if Nature were a painter producing a work of art, for painters, too, first sketch in the animal with lines and only after that put in the colours.

Because the source of the sensations is in the heart, therefore this is the part first formed in the whole animal, and because of the heat of this organ the cold forms the brain, where the blood-vessels terminate above, corresponding to the heat of the heart. Hence the parts about the head begin to form next in order after the heart, and surpass the other parts in size, for the brain is from the first large and fluid.

There is a difficulty about what happens with the eyes of animals. Though from the beginning they appear very large in all creatures, whether they walk or swim or fly, yet they are the last of the parts to be formed completely, for in the intervening time they collapse. The reason is this. The sense-organ of the eyes is set upon certain passages, as are the other sense-organs. Whereas those of touch and taste **744a** are simply the body itself or some part of the body of animals, those of smell and hearing are passages connecting with the external air and full themselves of innate spiritus; these passages end at the small blood-vessels about the brain which run thither from the heart. But the eye is the only sense-organ that has a bodily constitution peculiar to itself. It is fluid and cold, and does not exist from the first in the place which it occupies later in the same way as the other parts do, for they exist potentially to begin with and actually come into being later, but the eye is the purest part of the liquidity about the brain drained off through the passages which are visible running from them to the membrane round the brain. A proof of this is that, apart from the brain, there is no other part in the head that is cold and fluid except the eye. Of necessity therefore this region is large at first but falls in later. For the same thing happens with the brain; at first it is liquid and large, but in course of evaporation and concoction it becomes more solid and falls in; this applies both to the brain and the eyes. The head is very large at first, on account of the brain, and the eyes appear large because of the liquid in them. They are the last organs to reach completion because the brain is formed with difficulty; for it is at a late period that it gets rid of its coldness and fluidity; this applies to all animals possessing a brain, but especially to man. For this reason the 'bregma' is the last of the bones to be formed; even after birth this bone is still soft in children. The cause of this being so with men more than with other animals is the fact that their brain is the most fluid and largest. This again is because the heat in man's heart is purest. His intellect shows how well he is tempered, for man is the wisest of animals. And children for a long time have no control over their heads on account of the heaviness of the brain; and the same applies to the parts which it is necessary to move, for it is late that the principle of motion gets control over the upper parts, and last of all over those whose motion is not connected directly with it, as that of the legs is not. Now the eyelid is such a part. But since Nature makes nothing superfluous nor in vain, it is clear also that she makes nothing too late or too soon, for if she did the result would be either in vain **744b** or superfluous. Hence it is necessary that the eyelids should be separated at the same time as the heart is able to move them. So then the eyes of animals are perfected late because of the amount of concoction required by the brain, and last of all the parts because the motion must be very strong before it can affect parts so far from the first principle of motion and so cold. And it is plain that such is the nature of the eyelids, for if the head is affected by never so little heaviness through sleepiness or drunkenness or anything else of the kind, we cannot raise the eyelids though their own weight is so small. So much for the question how the eyes come into being, and why and for what cause they are the last to be fully developed.

Each of the other parts is formed out of the nutriment, those most honourable and participating in the sovereign principle from the nutriment which is first and purest and fully concocted, those which are only necessary for the sake of the former parts from the inferior nutriment and the residues left over from the other. For Nature, like a good householder, is not in the habit of throwing away anything from which it is possible to make anything useful. Now in a household the best part of the food that comes in is set apart for the free men, the inferior and the residue of the best for the slaves, and the worst is given to the animals that live with them. Just as the intellect acts thus in the outside world with a view to the growth of the persons concerned, so in the case of the embryo itself does Nature form from the purest material the flesh and the body of the other sense-organs, and from the residues thereof bones, sinews, hair, and also nails and hoofs and the like; hence these are last to assume their form, for they have to wait till the time when Nature has some residue to spare.

The bones, then, are made in the first conformation of the parts from the seminal secretion or residue. As the animal grows the bones also grow from the natural nourishment, being the same as that of the sovereign parts, but of this they only take up the superfluous residues. For everywhere the nutriment may be divided into two kinds, the first and the second; the former is 'nutritious', being that which gives its essence both to the whole and to the parts; the latter is concerned with growth, being that which causes quantitative increase. But these must be distinguished more fully later on. The sinews are formed in the same way as the bones and out of the same materials, the seminal and nutritious residue. **745a** Nails, hair, hoofs, horns, beaks, the spurs of cocks, and any other similar parts, are on the contrary formed from the nutriment which is taken later and only concerned with growth, in other words that which is derived from the mother, or from the outer world after birth. For this reason the bones on the one hand only grow up to a certain point (for there is a limit of size in all animals, and therefore also of the growth of the bones; if these had been always able to grow, all animals that have bone or its analogue would grow as long as they lived, for these set the limit of size to animals. What is the reason of their not always increasing in size must be stated later.) Hair, on the contrary, and growths akin to hair go on growing as long as they exist at all, and increase yet more in diseases and when the body is getting old and wasting, because more residual matter is left over, as owing to old age and disease less is expended on the important parts, though when the residual matter also fails through age the hair fails with it. But the contrary is the case with the bones, for they waste away along with the body and the other parts. Hair actually goes on growing after death; it does not, however, begin growing then.

About the teeth a difficulty may be raised. They have actually the same nature as the bones, and are formed out of the bones, but nails, hair, horns, and the like are formed out of the skin, and that is why they change in colour along with it, for they become white, black, and all sorts of colours according to that of the skin. But the teeth do nothing of the sort, for they are made out of the bones in all animals that have both bones and teeth. Of all the bones they alone go on growing through life, as is plain with the teeth which grow out of the straight line so as no longer to touch each other. The reason for their growth, as a final cause, is their function, for they would soon be worn down if there were not some means of saving them; even as it is they are altogether worn down in old age in some animals which eat much and have not large teeth, their growth not being in proportion to their detrition. And so Nature has contrived well to meet the case in this also, for she causes the failure of the teeth to synchronize with old age and death. If life lasted for a thousand or ten thousand years the original teeth must have been very large indeed, and many sets of them must have been produced, for even if they had grown continuously they **745b** would still have been worn smooth and become useless for their work. The final cause of their growth has been now stated, but besides this as a matter of fact the growth of the teeth is not the same as that of the other bones. The latter all come into being in the first formation of the embryo and none of them later, but the teeth do so later. Therefore it is possible for them to grow again after the first set falls out, for though they touch the bones they are not connate with them. They are formed, however, out of the nutriment distributed to the bones, and so have the same nature, even when the bones have their own number complete.

Other animals are born in possession of teeth or their analogue (unless in cases contrary to Nature), because when they are set free from the parent they are more perfect than man; but man (also unless in cases contrary to Nature) is born without them.

The reason will be stated later why some teeth are formed and fall out but others do not fall out.[1]

It is because such parts are formed from a residue that man is the most naked in body of all animals and has the smallest nails in proportion to his size; he has the least amount of earthy residue, but that part of the blood which is not concocted is the residue, and the earthy part in the bodies of all animals is the least concocted. We have now stated how each of

[1] v. 8.

the parts is formed and what is the cause of their generation.

7

In viviparous animals, as said before, the embryo gets its growth through the umbilical cord. For since the nutritive power of the soul, as well as the others, is present in animals, it straightway sends off this cord like a root to the uterus. The cord consists of blood-vessels in a sheath, more numerous in the larger animals as cattle and the like, one in the smallest, two in those of intermediate size. Through this cord the embryo receives its nourishment in the form of blood, for the uterus is the termination of many blood-vessels. All animals with no front teeth in the upper jaw, and all those which have them in both jaws and whose uterus has not one great blood-vessel running through it but many close together instead—all these have in the uterus the so-called cotyledons (with which the umbilical cord connects and is closely united; for the vessels which pass through the cord run backwards and forwards between embryo and uterus and split up into smaller vessels all over the uterus; where they terminate, there are found the cotyledons). Their convexity is turned towards the uterus, the concavity towards the embryo. Between uterus and embryo are the chorion and **746a** the membranes. As the embryo grows and approaches perfection the cotyledons become smaller and finally disappear when it is perfected. For Nature sends the sanguineous nutriment for the embryo into this part of the uterus as she sends milk into the breasts, and because the cotyledons are gradually aggregated from many into a few the body of the cotyledon becomes like an eruption or inflammation. So long as the embryo is comparatively small, being unable to receive much nutriment, they are plain and large, but when it has increased in size they fall in together.

But most of the animals which have front teeth in both jaws and no horns have no cotyledons in the uterus, but the umbilical cord runs to meet one blood-vessel, which is large and extends throughout the uterus. Of such animals some produce one young at a time, some more than one, but the same description applies to both these classes. (This should be studied with the aid of the examples drawn in the *Anatomy* and the *Enquiries*.)[1]

[1] *History of Animals*, but where? 586b 15-23 is the only passage suitable, and that is in the seventh book, which is spurious.

For the young, if numerous, are attached each to its umbilical cord, and this to the blood-vessel of the mother; they are arranged next to one another along the stream of the blood-vessel as along a canal; and each embryo is enclosed in its membranes and chorion.

Those who say that children are nourished in the uterus by sucking some lump of flesh or other are mistaken. If so, the same would have been the case with other animals, but as it is we do not find this (and this can easily be observed by dissection). Secondly, all embryos alike, whether of creatures that fly or swim or walk, are surrounded by fine membranes separating them from the uterus and from the fluids which are formed in it; but neither in these themselves is there anything of the kind, nor is it possible for the embryo to take nourishment by means of any of them. Thirdly, it is plain that all creatures developed in eggs grow when separated from the uterus.

Natural intercourse takes place between animals of the same kind. However, those also unite whose nature is near akin and whose form is not very different, if their size is much the same and if the periods of gestation are equal. In other animals such cases are rare, but they occur with dogs and foxes and wolves; the Indian dogs also spring from the union of a dog with some wild dog-like animal. A similar **746b** thing has been seen to take place in those birds that are amative, as partridges and hens. Among birds of prey hawks of different form are thought to unite, and the same applies to some other birds. Nothing worth mentioning has been observed in the inhabitants of the sea, but the so-called 'rhinobates' especially is thought to spring from the union of the 'rhinè' and 'batus'. And the proverb about Libya, that 'Libya is always producing something new', is said to have originated from animals of different species uniting with one another in that country, for it is said that because of the want of water all meet at the few places where springs are to be found, and that even different kinds unite in consequence.

Of the animals that arise from such union all except mules are found to copulate again with each other and to be able to produce young of both sexes, but mules alone are sterile, for they do not generate by union with one another or with other animals. The problem why any individual, whether male or female, is sterile is a general one, for some men and women are sterile, and so are other animals in their several kinds, as horses and sheep. But this kind, that of mules, is universally so. The causes of sterility in other animals are several. Both men and women are sterile from birth when the parts useful for union are imperfect, so that men never grow a beard but remain like eunuchs, and women do not attain puberty; the same thing may befall others as their years advance, sometimes on account of the body being too well nourished (for men who are in too good condition and women who are too fat the seminal secretion is taken up into the body, and the former have no semen, the latter no catamenia); at other times by reason of sickness men emit the semen in a cold and liquid state, and the discharges of women are bad and full of morbid secretions. Often, too, in both sexes this state is caused by injuries in the parts and regions contributory to copulation. Some such cases are curable, others incurable, but the subjects especially remain sterile if anything of the sort has happened in the first formation of the parts in the embryo, for then are produced women of a masculine and 747a men of a feminine appearance, and in the former the catamenia do not occur, in the latter the semen is thin and cold. Hence it is with good reason that the semen of men is tested in water to find out if it is infertile, for that which is thin and cold is quickly spread out on the surface, but the fertile sinks to the bottom, for that which is well concocted is hot indeed, but that which is firm and thick is well concocted. They test women by pessaries to see if the smells thereof permeate from below upwards to the breath from the mouth, and by colours smeared upon the eyes to see if they colour the saliva. If these results do not follow it is a sign that the passages of the body, through which the catamenia are secreted, are clogged and closed. For the region about the eyes is, of all the head, that most nearly connected with the generative secretions; a proof of this is that it alone is visibly changed in sexual intercourse, and those who indulge too much in this are seen to have their eyes sunken in. The reason is that the nature of the semen is similar to that of the brain, for the material of it is watery (the heat being acquired later). And the seminal purgations are from the region of the diaphragm, for the first principle of nature is there, so that the movements from the pudenda are communicated to the chest, and the smells from the chest are perceived through the respiration.

8

In men, then, and in other kinds, as said before, such deficiency occurs sporadically, but the whole of the mule kind is sterile. The reason has not been rightly given by Empedocles and Democritus, of whom the former expresses himself obscurely, the latter more intelligibly. For they offer their demonstration in the case of all these animals alike which unite against their affinities. Democritus says that the genital passages of mules are spoilt in the mother's uterus because the animals from the first are not produced from parents of the same kind. But we find that though this is so with other animals they are none the less able to generate; yet, if this were the reason, all others that unite in this manner ought to be barren. Empedocles assigns as his reason that the mixture of the 'seeds' becomes dense, 747b each of the two seminal fluids out of which it is made being soft, for the hollows in each fit into the densities of the other, and in such cases a hard substance is formed out of soft ones, like bronze mingled with tin. Now he does not give the correct reason in the case of bronze and tin—(we have spoken of them in the *Problems*)—nor, to take general ground, does he take his principles from the intelligible. How do the 'hollows' and 'solids' fit into one another to make the mixing, e.g. in the case of wine and water? This saying is quite beyond us; for how we are to understand the 'hollows' of the wine and water is too far beyond our perception. Again, when, as a matter of fact, horse is born of horse, ass of ass, and mule of horse and ass in two ways according as the parents are stallion and she-ass or jackass and mare, why in the last case does there result something so 'dense' that the offspring is sterile, whereas the offspring of male and female horse, male and female ass, is not sterile? And yet the generative fluid of the male and female horse is soft. But both sexes of the horse cross with both sexes of the ass, and the offspring of both crosses are barren, according to Empedocles, because from both is produced something 'dense', the 'seeds' being 'soft'. If so, the offspring of stallion and mare ought also to be sterile. If one of them alone united with the ass, it might be said that the cause of the mule's being unable to generate was the unlikeness of that one to the generative fluid of the ass; but, as it is, whatever be the character of that generative fluid with which it unites in the ass, such it is also in the animal of its own kind. Then, again, the argument is intended to apply to both male and female mules alike, but the male does generate at seven years of age, it is said; it is the female alone that is entirely sterile, and even she is so only because she does not complete the development of the embryo, for a female mule has been known to conceive.

Perhaps an abstract proof might appear to be more plausible than those already given; I call it abstract because the more general it is the further is it removed from the special principles involved. It runs somewhat as follows. From male and female of the same species there are born in course of nature male and female of the same species as the parents, e.g. male and female puppies from male and female dog. From parents of different species is born a young one different in species; thus if a dog is different from a lion, the offspring of male dog and lioness or of lion and bitch will be different from both parents. If this is so, then since (1) mules are produced of both **748a** sexes and are not different in species from one another, and (2) a mule is born of horse and ass and these are different in species from mules, it is impossible that anything should be produced from mules. For (1) another kind cannot be, because the product of male and female of the same species is also of the same species, and (2) a mule cannot be, because that is the product of horse and ass which are different in form, [and it was laid down that from parents different in form is born a different animal]. Now this theory is too general and empty. For all theories not based on the special principles involved are empty; they only appear to be connected with the facts without being so really. As geometrical arguments must start from geometrical principles, so it is with the others; that which is empty may seem to be something, but is really nothing. Now the basis of this particular theory is not true, for many animals of different species are fertile with one another, as was said before. So we must not inquire into questions of natural science in this fashion any more than any other questions; we shall be more likely to find the reason by considering the facts peculiar to the two kinds concerned, horse and ass. In the first place, each of them, if mated with its own kind, bears only one young one; secondly, the females are not always able to conceive from the male (wherefore breeders put the horse to the mare again at intervals). Indeed, both the mare is deficient in catamenia, discharging less than any other quadruped, and the she-ass does not admit the impregnation, but ejects the semen with her urine, wherefore men follow flogging her after intercourse. Again the ass is an animal of cold nature, and so is not wont to be produced in wintry regions because it cannot bear cold, as in Scythia and the neighbouring country and among the Celts beyond Iberia, for this country also is cold. For this cause they do not put the jackasses to the females at the equinox, as they do with horses, but about the summer solstice, in order that the ass-foals may be born in a warm season, for the mothers bear at the same season as that in which they are impregnated, the period of gestation in both horse and ass being one year. The animal, then, being, as has been said of such a cold nature, its semen also must be cold. A proof of this is that if a horse mount a female already impregnated by an ass he does not destroy the impregnation of the ass, but if the ass be the second to mount her he does destroy that of the horse because of the coldness of his own semen. When, therefore, they unite **748b** with each other, the generative elements are preserved by the heat of the one of them, that contributed by the horse being the hotter; for in the ass both the semen of the male and the material contributed by the female are cold, and those of the horse, in both sexes, are hotter. Now when either hot is added to cold or cold to hot so as to mix, the result is that the embryo itself arising from these is preserved and thus these animals are fertile when crossed with one another, but the animal produced by them is no longer fertile but unable to produce perfect offspring.

And in general each of these animals naturally tends towards sterility. The ass has all the disadvantages already mentioned, and if it should not begin to generate after the first shedding of teeth, it no longer generates at all; so near is the constitution of the ass to being sterile. The horse is much the same; it tends naturally towards sterility, and to make it entirely so it is only necessary that its generative secretion should become colder; now this is what happens to it when mixed with the corresponding secretion of the ass. The ass in like manner comes very near generating a sterile animal when mated with its own species. Thus when the difficulty of a cross contrary to nature is added, (when too even in the other case when united with their own species they with difficulty produce a single young one), the result of the cross, being still more sterile and contrary to nature, will need nothing further to make it sterile, but will be so of necessity.

We find also that the bodies of female mules grow large because the matter which is secreted in other animals to form the catamenia is diverted to growth. But since the period of gestation in such animals is a year, the mule must not only conceive, if she is to be fertile, but must also nourish the embryo till birth, and this is impossible if there are no catamenia. But there are none in the mule; the useless part of the nutriment is discharged with the excretion from the bladder—this is why male mules do not smell to the pudenda of the females, as do the other solid-hoofed ungulates, but only to the evacuation itself—and the rest of the nutriment is used up to increase the size of the body. Hence it is sometimes possible for the female to conceive, as has been known to happen before now, but it is impossible for her to complete the process of nourishing the embryo and bringing it to birth.

The male, again, may sometimes generate, both because the male sex is naturally hotter than the female and because it does not contribute any material substance to the mixture. The result in such cases is a 'ginnus', that is to say, a dwarf mule; for 'ginni' are produced also from the crossing of horse and ass when the embryo is diseased in the uterus. The ginnus is **749a** in fact like the so-called 'metachoera' in swine, for a 'metachoerum' also is a pig injured in the uterus; this may happen to any pig. The origin of human dwarfs is similar, for these also have their parts and their whole development injured during gestation, and resemble ginni and metachoera.

BOOK III

I

We have now spoken about the sterility of mules, and about those animals which are viviparous both externally and within themselves. The generation of the oviparous sanguinea is to a certain extent similar to that of the animals that walk, and all may be embraced in the same general statement; but in other respects there are differences in them both as compared with each other and with those that walk. All alike are generated from sexual union, the male emitting semen into the female. But among the ovipara (1) birds produce a perfect hard-shelled egg, unless it be injured by disease, and the eggs of birds are all two-coloured. (2) The cartilaginous fishes, as has been often said already, are oviparous internally but produce the young alive, the egg changing previously from one part of the uterus to another; and their egg is soft-shelled and of one colour. One of this class alone does not produce the young from the egg within itself, the so-called 'frog'; the reason of which must be stated later.[1] (3) All other oviparous fishes produce an egg of one colour, but this is imperfect, for its growth is completed outside the mother's body by the same cause as are those eggs which are perfected within.

Concerning the uterus of these classes of animals, what differences there are among them and for what reasons, has been stated previously. For in some of the viviparous creatures it is high up near the hypozoma, in others low down by the pudenda; the former in the cartilaginous fishes, the latter in animals both internally and externally viviparous, such as man and horse and the rest; in the ovipara it is sometimes low, as in the oviparous fish, and sometimes high, as in birds.

Some embryos are formed in birds spontaneously, which are called wind-eggs and **749b** 'zephyria' by some; these occur in birds which are not given to flight nor rapine but which produce many young, for these birds have much residual matter, whereas in the birds of prey all such secretion is diverted to the wings and wing-feathers, while the body is small and dry and hot. (The secretion corresponding in hen-birds to catamenia, and the semen of the cock, are residues.) Since then both the wings and the semen are made from residual matter, nature cannot afford to spend much upon both. And for this same reason the birds of prey are neither given to treading much nor to laying many eggs, as are the heavy birds and those flying birds whose bodies are bulky, as the pigeon and so forth. For such residual matter is secreted largely in the heavy birds not given to flying, such as fowls, partridges, and so on, wherefore their males tread often and their females produce much material. Of such birds some lay many eggs at a time and some lay often; for instance,

[1] 754a 25–31.

the fowl, the partridge, and the Libyan ostrich lay many eggs, while the pigeon family do not lay many but lay often. For these are between the birds of prey and the heavy ones; they are flyers like the former, but have bulky bodies like the latter; hence, because they are flyers and the residue is diverted that way, they lay few eggs, but they lay often because of their having bulky bodies and their stomachs being hot and very active in concoction, and because moreover they can easily procure their food, whereas the birds of prey do so with difficulty.

Small birds also tread often and are very fertile, as are sometimes small plants, for what causes bodily growth in others turn in them to a seminal residuum. Hence the Adrianic fowls lay most eggs, for because of the smallness of their bodies the nutriment is used up in producing young. And other birds are more fertile than game-fowl, for their bodies are more fluid and bulkier, whereas those of game-fowl are leaner and drier, since a passionate spirit is found rather in such bodies as the latter. Moreover the thinness and weakness of the legs contribute to making the former class of **750a** birds naturally inclined to tread and to be fertile, as we find also in the human species; for the nourishment which otherwise goes to the legs is turned in such into a seminal secretion, what Nature takes from the one place being added at the other. Birds of prey, on the contrary, have a strong walk and their legs are thick owing to their habits, so that for all these reasons they neither tread nor lay much. The kestrel is the most fertile; for this is nearly the only bird of prey which drinks, and its moisture, both innate and acquired, along with its heat is favourable to generative products. Even this bird does not lay very many eggs, but four at the outside.

The cuckoo, though not a bird of prey, lays few eggs, because it is of a cold nature, as is shown by the cowardice of the bird, whereas a generative animal should be hot and moist. That it is cowardly is plain, for it is pursued by all the birds and lays eggs in the nests of others.

The pigeon family are in the habit of laying two for the most part, for they neither lay one (no bird does except the cuckoo, and even that sometimes lays two) nor yet many, but they frequently produce two, or three at the most, generally two, for this number lies between one and many.

It is plain from the facts that with the birds that lay many eggs the nutriment is diverted to the semen. For most trees, if they bear too much fruit, wither away after the crop when nutriment is not reserved for themselves, and this seems to be what happens to annuals, as leguminous plants, corn, and the like. For they consume all their nutriment to make seed, their kind being prolific. And some fowls after laying too much, so as even to lay two eggs in a day, have died after this. For both the birds and the plants become exhausted, and this condition is an excess of secretion of residual matter. A similar condition is the cause of the later sterility of the lioness, for at the first birth she produces five or six, then in the next year four, and again three cubs, then the next number down to one, then none at all, showing that the residue is being used up and the **750b** generative secretion is failing along with the advance of years.

We have now stated in which birds wind-eggs are found, and also what sort of birds lay many eggs or few, and for what reasons. And wind-eggs, as said before, come into being because while it is the material for generation that exists in the female of all animals, birds have no discharge of catamenia like viviparous sanguinea (for they occur in all these latter, more in some, less in others, and in some only enough in quantity just to mark the class). The same applies to fish as to birds, and so in them as in birds is found an embryonic formation without impregnation, but it is less obvious because their nature is colder. The secretion corresponding to the catamenia of vivipara is formed in birds at the appropriate season for the discharge of superfluous matter, and, because the region near the hypozoma is hot, it is perfected so far as size is concerned, but in birds and fishes alike it is imperfect for generation without the seminal fluid of the male; the cause of this has been previously given. Wind-eggs are not formed in the flying birds, for the same reason as prevents their laying many eggs; for the residual matter in birds of prey is small, and they need the male to give an impulse for the discharge of it. The wind-eggs are produced in greater numbers than the impregnated but smaller in size for one and the same reason; they are smaller in size because they are imperfect, and because they are smaller in size they are more in number. They are less pleasant for food because they are less concocted, for in all foods the concocted is more agreeable. It has been sufficiently observed, then, that neither birds' nor fishes' eggs are perfected for generation without the males. As for embryos being formed in fish also (though in a less degree) without the males, the fact has been observed especially in river fish, for some are seen to have eggs from the first, as has been written in the *Enquiries* concerning them.[1] And generally speaking in the case of birds even the impregnated eggs are not wont for the most part to attain their full growth unless the hen be trodden continually. The reason of this is that just as with women intercourse with men draws down the secretion of the ca- **751a** tamenia (for the uterus being heated attracts the moisture and the passages are opened), so this happens also with birds; the residual matter corresponding to the catamenia advances a little at a time, and is not discharged externally, because its amount is small and the uterus is high up by the hypozoma, but trickles together into the uterus itself. For as the embryo of the vivipara grows by means of the umbilical cord, so the egg grows through this matter flowing to it through the uterus. For when once the hens have been trodden, they all continue to have eggs almost without intermission, though very small ones. Hence some are wont to speak of wind-eggs as not coming into being independently but as mere relics from a previous impregnation. But this is a false view, for sufficient observations have been made of their arising without impregnation in chickens and goslings. Also the female partridges which are taken out to act as decoys, whether they have ever been impregnated or not, immediately on smelling the male and hearing his call, become filled with eggs in the latter case and lay them in the former. The reason why this happens is the same as in men and quadrupeds, for if their bodies chance to be in rut they emit semen at the mere sight of the female or at a slight touch. And such birds are of a lascivious and fertile nature, so that the impulse they need is but small when they are in this excited condition, and the secreting activity takes place quickly in them, wind-eggs forming in the unimpregnated and the eggs in those which have been impregnated growing and reaching perfection swiftly.

Among creatures that lay eggs externally birds produce their egg perfect, fish imperfect, but the eggs of the latter complete their growth outside as has been said before. The reason is that the fish kind is very fertile; now it is impossible for many eggs to reach completion within the mother and therefore they lay them outside. They are quickly discharged, for the uterus of externally oviparous fishes is near the generative passage. While the eggs of birds are two-coloured, those of all fish are one-coloured. The cause of the double colour may be seen from considering the power of each of the two parts, the white and the yolk. For the matter of the egg is secreted from the **751b** blood [no bloodless animal lays eggs], and that the blood is the material of the body has been often said already. The one part, then, of the egg is nearer the form of the animal coming into being, that is the hot part; the more earthy part gives the substance of the body and is further removed. Hence in all two-coloured eggs the animal receives the first principle of generation from the white (for the vital principle is in that which is hot), but the nutriment from the yolk. Now in animals of a hotter nature the part from which the first principle arises is separated off from the part from which comes the nutriment, the one being white and the other yellow, and the white and pure is always more than the yellow and earthy; but in the moister and less hot the yolk is more in quantity and more fluid. This is what we find in lake birds, for they are of a moister nature and are colder than the land birds, so that the so-called 'lecithus' or yolk in the eggs of such birds is large and less yellow because the white is less separated off from it. But when we come to the ovipara which are both of a cold nature and also moister (such is the fish kind) we find the white not separated at all because of the small size of the eggs and the quantity of the cold and earthy matter; therefore all fish eggs are of one colour, and white compared with yellow, yellow compared with white. Even the wind-eggs of birds have this distinction of colour, for they contain that out of which will come each of the two parts, alike that whence arises the principle of life and that whence comes the nutriment; only both these are imperfect and need the influence of the male in addition; for wind-eggs become fertile if impregnated by the male within a certain period. The difference in colour, however, is not due to any difference of sex, as if the white came from the male, the yolk from the female; both on the contrary come from the female, but the one is cold, the other hot. In all cases then where the hot part is considerable it is separated off, but where it is little it cannot be so; hence the eggs of

[1] *History of Animals*, 567a 30.

such animals, as has been said, are of one colour. The semen of the male only puts them into form; and therefore at first the egg in birds appears white and small, but as it advances it is all yellow as more of the sanguineous material is continually mixed with it; finally as the hot part is separated the white takes up a position all round it and equally distrib-
752a uted on all sides, as when a liquid boils; for the white is naturally liquid and contains in itself the vital heat; therefore it is separated off all round, but the yellow and earthy part is inside. And if we enclose many eggs together in a bladder or something of the kind and boil them over a fire so as not to make the movement of the heat quicker than the separation of the white and yolk in the eggs, then the same process takes place in the whole mass of the eggs as in a single egg, all the yellow part coming into the middle and the white surrounding it.

We have thus stated why some eggs are of one colour and others of two.

2

The principle of the male is separated off in eggs at the point where the egg is attached to the uterus, and the reason why the shape of two-coloured eggs is unsymmetrical, and not perfectly round but sharper at one end, is that the part of the white in which is contained this principle must differ from the rest. Therefore the egg is harder at this point than below, for it is necessary to shelter and protect this principle. And this is why the sharp end of the egg comes out of the hen later than the blunt end; for the part attached to the uterus comes out later, and the egg is attached at the point where is the said principle, and the principle is in the sharp end. The same is the case also in the seeds of plants; the principle of the seed is attached sometimes to the twig, sometimes to the husk, sometimes to the pericarp. This is plain in the leguminous plants, for where the two cotyledons of beans and of similar seeds are united, there is the seed attached to the parent plant, and there is the principle of the seed.

A difficulty may be raised about the growth of the egg; how is it derived from the uterus? For if animals derive their nutriment through the umbilical cord, through what do eggs derive it? They do not, like a scolex, acquire their growth by their own means. If there is anything by which they are attached to the uterus, what becomes of this when the egg is perfected? It does not come out with the egg as the cord does with animals; for when its egg is perfected the shell forms all round it. This problem is rightly raised, but it is not observed that the shell is at first only a soft membrane, and that it is only after the egg is perfected that it becomes hard and brittle; this is so nicely adjusted that it is still soft when it comes out (for otherwise it would cause pain in laying), but no sooner has it come out than it is fixed hard by cooling, the moisture quickly evaporating because there is but little of it,
752b and the earthy part remaining. Now at first a certain part of this membrane at the sharp end of eggs resembles an umbilical cord, and projects like a pipe from them while they are still small. It is plainly visible in small aborted eggs, for if the bird be drenched with water or suddenly chilled in any other way and cast out the egg too soon, it appears still sanguineous and with a small tail like an umbilical cord running through it. As the egg becomes larger this is more twisted round and becomes smaller, and when the egg is perfected this end is the sharp end. Under this is the inner membrane which separates the white and the yolk from this. When the egg is perfected, the whole of it is set free, and naturally the umbilical cord does not appear, for it is now the extreme end of the egg itself.

The egg is discharged in the opposite way from the young of vivipara; the latter are born head-first, the part where is the first principle leading, but the egg is discharged as it were feet first; the reason of this being what has been stated, that the egg is attached to the uterus at the point where is the first principle.

The young bird is produced out of the egg by the mother's incubating and aiding the concoction, the creature developing out of part of the egg, and receiving growth and completion from the remaining part. For Nature not only places the material of the creature in the egg but also the nourishment sufficient for its growth; for since the mother bird cannot perfect her young within herself she produces the nourishment in the egg along with it. Whereas the nourishment, what is called milk, is produced for the young of vivipara in another part, in the breasts, Nature does this for birds in the egg. The opposite, however, is the case to what people think and what is asserted by Alcmaeon of Crotona. For it is not the white that is the milk, but the yolk, for it is this that is the nourishment of the chick, whereas they think it is the white because of the similarity of colour.

The chick then, as has been said, comes into being by the incubation of the mother; yet if the temperature of the season is favourable, or if the place in which the eggs happen to lie is warm, the eggs are sufficiently concocted without incubation, both those of birds and those of oviparous quadrupeds. For these all lay their eggs upon the ground, where they are concocted by the heat in the earth. Such oviparous quadrupeds as do visit their eggs and incubate do so rather for the sake of protecting them than of incubation.

753a The eggs of these quadrupeds are formed in the same way as those of birds, for they are hard-shelled and two-coloured, and they are formed near the hypozoma as are those of birds, and in all other respects resemble them both internally and externally, so that the inquiry into their causes is the same for all. But whereas the eggs of quadrupeds are hatched out by the mere heat of the weather owing to their strength, those of birds are more exposed to destruction and need the mother-bird. Nature seems to wish to implant in animals a special sense of care for their young: in the inferior animals this lasts only to the moment of giving birth to the incompletely developed animal; in others it continues till they are perfect; in all that are more intelligent, during the bringing up of the young also. In those which have the greatest portion in intelligence we find familiarity and love shown also towards the young when perfected, as with men and some quadrupeds; with birds we find it till they have produced and brought up their young, and therefore if the hens do not incubate after laying they get into worse condition, as if deprived of something natural to them.

The young is perfected within the egg more quickly in sunshiny weather, the season aiding in the work, for concoction is a kind of heat. For the earth aids in the concoction by its heat, and the brooding hen does the same, for she applies the heat that is within her. And it is in the hot season, as we should expect, that the eggs are more apt to be spoilt and the so-called 'uria' or rotten eggs are produced; for just as wines turn sour in the heats from the sediment rising (for this is the cause of their being spoilt), so is it with the yolk in eggs, for the sediment and yolk are the earthy part in each case, wherefore the wine becomes turbid when the sediment mixes with it, and the like applies to the eggs that are spoiling because of the yolk. It is natural then that such should be the case with the birds that lay many eggs, for it is not easy to give the fitting amount of heat to all, but (while some have too little) others have too much and this makes them turbid, as it were by putrefaction. But this happens none the less with the birds of prey though they lay few eggs, for often one of the two becomes rotten, and the third practically always, for being of a hot nature they make the moisture in the eggs to overboil so to say. For the nature of the white is opposed to that of the yolk; the yolk congeals in frosts but

753b liquefies on heating, and therefore it liquefies on concoction in the earth or by reason of incubation, and becoming liquid serves as nutriment for the developing chick. If exposed to heat and roasted it does not become hard, because though earthy in nature it is only so in the same way as wax is; accordingly on heating too much the eggs become watery and rotten, [if they be not from a liquid residue]. The white on the contrary is not congealed by frost but rather liquefies (the reason of which has been stated before), but on exposure to heat becomes solid. Therefore being concocted in the development of the chick it is thickened. For it is from this that the young is formed (whereas the yolk turns to nutriment) and it is from this that the parts derive their growth as they are formed one after another. This is why the white and the yolk are separated by membranes, as being different in nature. The precise details of the relation of the parts to one another both at the beginning of generation and as the animals are forming, and also the details of the membranes and umbilical cords, must be learnt from what has been written in the *Enquiries;*[1] for the present investigation it is sufficient to understand this much clearly, that, when the heart has been first formed and the great blood-vessel has been marked off from it, two umbilical cords run from the vessel, the one to the membrane which encloses the yolk, the other to the membrane resembling a chorion which surrounds the whole embryo; this latter runs round on the inside of the membrane of the shell. Through the one of these the embryo receives the nutriment from the yolk, and the yolk becomes larger, for it becomes more liquid by heating. This is because the nourishment, being of a material character in its first form, must become liquid before it can be ab-

[1] *History of Animals*, VI. 3.

sorbed, just as it is with plants, and at first this embryo, whether in an egg or in the mother's uterus, lives the life of a plant, for it receives its first growth and nourishment by being attached to something else.

The second umbilical cord runs to the surrounding chorion. For we must understand that, in the case of animals developed in eggs, the chick has the same relation to the yolk as the embryo of the vivipara has to the mother so long as it is within the mother (for since the nourishment of the embryo of the ovipara is not completed within the mother, the embryo takes part of it away from her). So also the relation of the chick to the outermost membrane, the sanguineous one, is like that of the mammalian embryo to the uterus. At the same time

754a the egg-shell surrounds both the yolk and the membrane analogous to the uterus, just as if it should be put round both the embryo itself and the whole of the mother, in the vivipara. This is so because the embryo must be in the uterus and attached to the mother. Now in the vivipara the uterus is within the mother, but in the ovipara it is the other way about, as if one should say that the mother was in the uterus, for that which comes from the mother, the nutriment, is the yolk. The reason is that the process of nourishment is not completed within the mother.

As the creature grows the umbilicus running to the chorion collapses first, because it is here that the young is to come out; what is left of the yolk, and the umbilical cord running to the yolk, collapse later. For the young must have nourishment as soon as it is hatched; it is not nursed by the mother and cannot immediately procure its nourishment for itself; therefore the yolk enters within it along with its umbilicus and the flesh grows round it.

This then is the manner in which animals produced from perfect eggs are hatched in all those, whether birds or quadrupeds, which lay the egg with a hard shell. These details are plainer in the larger creatures; in the smaller they are obscure because of the smallness of the masses concerned.

3

The class of fishes is also oviparous. Those among them which have the uterus low down lay an imperfect egg for the reason previously given,[1] but the so-called 'selache' or cartilaginous fishes produce a perfect egg within themselves but are externally viviparous except one which they call the 'frog'; this alone lays a perfect egg externally. The reason is the nature of its body, for its head is many times as large as the rest of the body and is spiny and very rough. This is also why it does not receive its young again within itself nor produce them alive to begin with, for as the size and roughness of the head prevents their entering so it would prevent their exit. And while the egg of the cartilaginous fishes is soft-shelled (for they cannot harden and dry its circumference, being colder than birds), the egg of the frog-fish alone is solid and firm to protect it outside, but those of the rest are of a moist and soft nature, for they are sheltered within and by the

754b body of the mother.

The young are produced from the egg in the same way both with those externally perfected (the frog-fishes) and those internally, and the process in these eggs is partly similar to, partly different from that in birds' eggs. In the first place they have not the second umbilicus which runs to the chorion under the surrounding shell. The reason of this is that they have not the surrounding shell, for it is no use to them since the mother shelters them, and the shell is a protection to the eggs against external injury between laying and hatching out. Secondly, the process in these also begins on the surface of the egg but not where it is attached to the uterus, as in birds, for the chick is developed from the sharp end and that is where the egg was attached. The reason is that the egg of birds is separated from the uterus before it is perfected, but in most though not all cartilaginous fishes the egg is still attached to the uterus when perfect. While the young develops upon the surface the egg is consumed by it just as in birds and the other animals detached from the uterus, and at last the umbilicus of the now perfect fish is left attached to the uterus. The like is the case with all those whose eggs are detached from the uterus, for in some of them the egg is so detached when it is perfect.

The question may be asked why the development of birds and cartilaginous fishes differs in this respect. The reason is that in birds the white and yolk are separate, but fish eggs are one-coloured, the corresponding matter being completely mixed, so that there is nothing to stop the first principle being at the opposite end, for the egg is of the same nature both at the point of attachment and at the opposite end, and it is easy to draw the nourishment from the uterus by passages running from this

[1] 1, 718b 8.

principle. This is plain in the eggs which are not detached, for in some of the cartilaginous fish the egg is not detached from the uterus, but is still connected with it as it comes downwards with a view to the production of the young alive; in these the young fish when perfected is still connected by the umbilicus to the uterus when the egg has been consumed. From this it is clear that previously also, while the egg was still round the young, the passages ran to the uterus. This happens as we have said in the 'smooth hound'.

In these respects and for the reasons given the development of cartilaginous fishes differs from that of birds, but otherwise it takes place **755a** in the same way. For they have the one umbilicus in like manner as that of birds connecting with the yolk,—only in these fishes it connects with the whole egg (for it is not divided into white and yolk but all one-coloured),—and get their nourishment from this, and as it is being consumed the flesh in like manner encroaches upon and grows round it.

Such is the process of development in those fish that produce a perfect egg within themselves but are externally viviparous.

4

Most of the other fish are externally oviparous, all laying an imperfect egg except the frog-fish; the reason of this exception has been previously stated,[1] and the reason also why the others lay imperfect eggs.[2] In these also the development from the egg runs on the same lines as that of the cartilaginous and internally oviparous fishes, except that the growth is quick and from small beginnings and the outside of the egg is harder. The growth of the egg is like that of a scolex, for those animals which produce a scolex give birth to a small thing at first and this grows by itself and not through any attachment to the parent. The reason is similar to that of the growth of yeast, for yeast also grows great from a small beginning as the more solid part liquefies and the liquid is aerated. This is effected in animals by the nature of the vital heat, in yeasts by the heat of the juice commingled with them. The eggs then grow of necessity through this cause (for they have in them superfluous yeasty matter), but also for the sake of a final cause, for it is impossible for them to attain their whole growth in the uterus because these animals have so many eggs. Therefore are they very small when set free and grow quickly, small because the uterus is narrow for the multitude of the eggs, and growing quickly that the race may not perish, as it would if much of the time required for the whole development were spent in this growth; even as it is most of those laid are destroyed before hatching. Hence the class of fish is prolific, for Nature makes up for the destruction by numbers. Some fish actually burst because of the size of the eggs, as the fish called 'beloné', for its eggs are large instead of numerous, what Nature has taken away in number being added in size.

So much for the growth of such eggs and its reason.

[1] 754a 26. [2] 1, 718b 8.

5

755b A proof that these fish also are oviparous is the fact that even viviparous fish, such as the cartilaginous, are first internally oviparous, for hence it is plain that the whole class of fishes is oviparous. Where, however, both sexes exist and the eggs are produced in consequence of impregnation, the eggs do not arrive at completion unless the male sprinkle his milt upon them. Some erroneously assert that all fish are female except in the cartilaginous fishes, for they think that the females of fish differ from what are supposed to be males only in the same way as in those plants where the one bears fruit but the other is fruitless, as olive and oleaster, fig and caprifig. They think the like applies to fish except the cartilaginous, for they do not dispute the sexes in these. And yet there is no difference in the males of cartilaginous fishes and those belonging to the oviparous class in respect of the organs for the milt, and it is manifest that semen can be squeezed out of males of both classes at the right season. The female also has a uterus. But if the whole class were females and some of them unproductive (as with mules in the class of bushy-tailed animals), then not only should those which lay eggs have a uterus but also the others, only the uterus of the latter should be different from that of the former. But, as it is, some of them have organs for milt and others have a uterus, and this distinction obtains in all except two, the erythrinus and the channa, some of them having the milt organs, others a uterus. The difficulty which drives some thinkers to this conclusion is easily solved if we look at the facts. They say quite correctly that no animal which copulates produces many young, for of all those that generate from themselves perfect animals or perfect eggs none is prolific on the same scale as the ovipa-

rous fishes, for the number of eggs in these is enormous. But they had overlooked the fact that fish-eggs differ from those of birds in one circumstance. Birds and all oviparous quadrupeds, and any of the cartilaginous fish that are oviparous, produce a perfect egg, and it does not increase outside of them, whereas the eggs of fish are imperfect and do so complete their growth. Moreover the same thing applies to cephalopods also and crustacea, yet these animals are actually seen copulating, for their union lasts a long time, and it is plain in these cases that the one is male and the other has a
756a uterus. Finally, it would be strange if this distinction did not exist in the whole class, just as male and female in all the vivipara. The cause of the ignorance of those who make this statement is that the differences in the copulation and generation of various animals are of all kinds and not obvious, and so, speculating on a small induction, they think the same must hold good in all cases.

So also those who assert that conception in female fishes is caused by their swallowing the semen of the male have not observed certain points when they say this. For the males have their milt and the females their eggs at about the same time of year, and the nearer the female is to laying the more abundant and the more liquid is the milt formed in the male. And just as the increase of the milt in the male and of the roe in the female takes place at the same time, so is it also with their emission, for neither do the females lay all their eggs together, but gradually, nor do the males emit all the milt at once. All these facts are in accordance with reason. For just as the class of birds in some cases has eggs without impregnation, but few and seldom, impregnation being generally required, so we find the same thing, though to a less degree, in fish. But in both classes these spontaneous eggs are infertile unless the male, in those kinds where the male exists, shed his fluid upon them. Now in birds this must take place while the eggs are still within the mother, because they are perfect when discharged, but in fish, because the eggs are imperfect and complete their growth outside the mother in all cases, those outside are preserved by the sprinkling of the milt over them, even if they come into being by impregnation, and here it is that the milt of the males is used up. Therefore it comes down the ducts and diminishes in quantity at the same time as this happens to the eggs of the females, for the males always attend them, shedding their milt upon the eggs as they are laid. Thus then they are male and female, and all of them copulate (unless in any kind the distinction of sex does not exist), and without the semen of the male no such animal comes into being.

What helps in the deception is also the fact that the union of such fishes is brief, so that it is not observed even by many of the fishermen, for none of them ever watches anything of the sort for the sake of knowledge. Nevertheless their copulation has been seen, for fish [when
756b the tail part does not prevent it] copulate like the dolphins by throwing themselves alongside of one another. But the dolphins take longer to get free again, whereas such fishes do so quickly. Hence, not seeing this, but seeing the swallowing of the milt and the eggs, even the fishermen repeat the same simple tale, so much noised abroad, as Herodotus the story-teller,[1] as if fish were conceived by the mother's swallowing the milt,—not considering that this is impossible. For the passage which enters by way of the mouth runs to the intestines, not to the uterus, and what goes into the intestines must be turned into nutriment, for it is concocted; the uterus, however, is plainly full of eggs, and from whence did they enter it?

6

A similar story is told also of the generation of birds. For there are some who say that the raven and the ibis unite at the mouth, and among quadrupeds that the weasel brings forth its young by the mouth; so say Anaxagoras and some of the other physicists, speaking too superficially and without consideration. Concerning the birds, they are deceived by a false reasoning, because the copulation of ravens is seldom seen, but they are often seen uniting with one another with their beaks, as do all the birds of the raven family; this is plain with domesticated jackdaws. Birds of the pigeon kind do the same, but, because they also plainly copulate, therefore they have not had the same legend told of them. But the raven family is not amorous, for they are birds that produce few young, though this bird also has been seen copulating before now. It is a strange thing, however, that these theorists do not ask themselves how the semen enters the uterus through the intestine, which always concocts whatever comes into it, as the nutriment; and these birds have a uterus like others, and eggs are found in them near the hypozoma. And the weasel has a uterus in like manner to the other

[1] Herodotus, II. 93.

quadrupeds; by what passage is the embryo to get from it to the mouth? But this opinion has arisen because the young of the weasel are very small like those of the other fissipeds, of which 757a we shall speak later, and because they often carry the young about in their mouths.

Much deceived also are those who make a foolish statement about the trochus and the hyena. Many say that the hyena, and Herodorus the Heracleot says that the trochus, has two pudenda, those of the male and of the female, and that the trochus impregnates itself but the hyena mounts and is mounted in alternate years. This is untrue, for the hyena has been seen to have only one pudendum, there being no lack of opportunity for observation in some districts, but hyenas have under the tail a line like the pudendum of the female. Both male and female have such a mark, but the males are taken more frequently; this casual observation has given rise to this opinion. But enough has been said of this.

7

Touching the generation of fish, the question may be raised, why it is that in the cartilaginous fish neither the females are seen discharging their eggs nor the males their milt, whereas in the non-viviparous fishes this is seen in both sexes. The reason is that the whole cartilaginous class do not produce much semen, and further the females have their uterus near the hypozoma. For the males and females of the one class of fish differ from the males and females of the other class in like manner, for the cartilaginous are less productive of semen. But in the oviparous fish, as the females lay their eggs on account of their number, so do the males shed their milt on account of its abundance. For they have more milt than just what is required for copulation, as Nature prefers to expend the milt in helping to perfect the eggs, when the female has deposited them, rather than in forming them at first. For as has been said both further back and in our recent discussions, the eggs of birds are perfected internally but those of fish externally. The latter, indeed, resemble in a way those animals which produce a scolex, for the product discharged by them is still more imperfect than a fish's egg. It is the male that brings about the perfection of the egg both of birds and of fishes, only in the former internally, as they are perfected internally, and in the latter externally, because the egg is imperfect when deposited; but the result is the same in both cases.

757b In birds the wind-eggs become fertile, and those previously impregnated by one kind of cock change their nature to that of the later cock. And if the eggs be behindhand in growth, then, if the same cock treads the hen again after leaving off treading for a time, he causes them to increase quickly, not, however, at any period whatever of their development, but if the treading take place before the egg changes so far that the white begins to separate from the yolk. But in the eggs of fishes no such limit of time has been laid down, but the males shed their milt quickly upon them to preserve them. The reason is that these eggs are not two-coloured, and hence there is no such limit of time fixed with them as with those of birds. This fact is what we should expect, for by the time that the white and yolk are separated off from one another, the bird's egg already contains the principle that comes from the male parent . . . for the male contributes to this.

Wind-eggs, then, participate in generation so far as is possible for them. That they should be perfected into an animal is impossible, for an animal requires sense-perception; but the nutritive faculty of the soul is possessed by females as well as males, and indeed by all living things, as has been often said, wherefore the egg itself is perfect only as the embryo of a plant, but imperfect as that of an animal. If, then, there had been no male sex in the class of birds, the egg would have been produced as it is in some fishes, if indeed there is any kind of fish of such a nature as to generate without a male; but it has been said of them before that this has not yet been satisfactorily observed. But as it is both sexes exist in all birds, so that, considered as a plant, the egg is perfect, but in so far as it is not a plant it is not perfect, nor does anything else result from it; for neither has it come into being simply like a real plant nor from copulation like an animal. Eggs, however, produced from copulation but already separated into white and yolk take after the first cock; for they already contain both principles, which is why they do not change again after the second impregnation.

8

The young are produced in the same way also by the cephalopoda, e.g. sepias and the like, and by the crustacea, e.g. carabi and their kindred, for these also lay eggs in consequence of copulation, and the male has often been seen uniting with the female. Therefore those who

758a say that all fish are female and lay eggs without copulation are plainly speaking unscientifically from this point of view also. For it is a wonderful thing to suppose that the former animals lay eggs in consequence of copulation and that fish do not; if again they were unaware of this, it is a sign of ignorance. The union of all these creatures lasts a considerable time, as in insects, and naturally so, for they are bloodless and therefore of a cold nature.

In the sepias and calamaries or squids the eggs appear to be two, because the uterus is divided and appears double, but that of the poulps appears to be single. The reason is that the shape of the uterus in the poulp is round in form and spherical, the cleavage being obscure when it is filled with eggs. The uterus of the carabi is also bifid. All these animals also lay an imperfect egg for the same reason as fishes. In the carabi and their like the females produce their eggs so as to keep them attached to themselves, which is why the side-flaps of the females are larger than those of the males, to protect the eggs; the cephalopoda lay them away from themselves. The males of the cephalopoda sprinkle their milt over the females, as the male fish do over the eggs, and it becomes a sticky and glutinous mass, but in the carabi and their like nothing of the sort has been seen or can be naturally expected, for the egg is under the female and is hard-shelled. Both these eggs and those of the cephalopoda grow after deposition like those of fishes.

The sepia while developing is attached to the egg by its front part, for here alone is it possible, because this animal alone has its front and back pointing in the same direction. For the position and attitude of the young while developing you must look at the *Enquiries*.[1]

9

We have now spoken of the generation of other animals, those that walk, fly, and swim; it remains to speak of insects and testacea according to the plan laid down. Let us begin with the insects. It was observed previously that some of these are generated by copulation, others spontaneously, and besides this that they produce a scolex, and why this is so. For pretty much all creatures seem in a certain way to produce a scolex first, since the most imperfect embryo is of such a nature; and in all animals, even the viviparous and those that lay a perfect egg, the first embryo grows in size while still undifferentiated into parts; now such is the nature of the scolex. After this stage some of the ovipara produce the egg in a per-
758b fect condition, others in an imperfect, but it is perfected outside as has been often stated of fish. With animals internally viviparous the embryo becomes egg-like in a certain sense after its original formation, for the liquid is contained in a fine membrane, just as if we should take away the shell of the egg, wherefore they call the abortion of an embryo at that stage an 'efflux'.

Those insects which generate at all generate a scolex, and those which come into being spontaneously and not from copulation do so at first from a formation of this nature. I say that the former generate a scolex, for we must put down caterpillars also and the product of spiders as a sort of scolex. And yet some even of these and many of the others may be thought to resemble eggs because of their round shape, but we must not judge by shapes nor yet by softness and hardness (for what is produced by some is hard), but by the fact that the whole of them is changed into the body of the creature and the animal is not developed from a part of them. All these products that are of the nature of a scolex, after progressing and acquiring their full size, become a sort of egg, for the husk about them hardens and they are motionless during this period. This is plain in the scolex of bees and wasps and in caterpillars. The reason of this is that their nature, because of its imperfection, oviposits as it were before the right time, as if the scolex, while still growing in size, were a soft egg. Similar to this is also what happens with all other insects which come into being without copulation in wool and other such materials and in water. For all of them after the scolex-stage become immovable and their integument dries round them, and after this the latter bursts and there comes forth as from an egg an animal perfected in its second metamorphosis, most of those which are not aquatic being winged.

Another point is quite natural, which may be wondered at by many. Caterpillars at first take nourishment, but after this stage do so no longer, but what is called by some the chrysalis is motionless. The same applies to the scolex of wasps and bees, but after this comes into being the so-called nymph . . . . . . and have nothing of the kind. For an egg is also of such a nature that when it has reached

[1] *History of Animals*, v, 550a 17–26.

perfection it grows no more in size, but at first it grows and receives nourishment until it is differentiated and becomes a perfect egg. Sometimes the scolex contains in itself the material from which it is nourished and obtains **759a** such an addition to its size, e.g. in bees and wasps; sometimes it gets its nourishment from outside itself, as caterpillars and some others.

It has thus been stated why such animals go through a double development and for what reason they become immovable again after moving. And some of them come into being by copulation, like birds and vivipara and most fishes, others spontaneously, like some plants.

10

There is much difficulty about the generation of bees. If it is really true that in the case of some fishes there is such a method of generation that they produce eggs without copulation, this may well happen also with bees, to judge from appearances. For they must (1) either bring the young brood from elsewhere, as some say, and if so the young must either be spontaneously generated or produced by some other animal, or (2) they must generate them themselves, or (3) they must bring some and generate others, for this also is maintained by some, who say that they bring the young of the drones only. Again, if they generate them it must be either with or without copulation; if the former, then either (1) each kind must generate its own kind, or (2) some one kind must generate the others, or (3) one kind must unite with another for the purpose (I mean for instance (1) that bees may be generated from the union of bees, drones from that of drones, and kings from that of kings, or (2) that all the others may be generated from one, as from what are called kings and leaders, or (3) from the union of drones and bees, for some say that the former are male, the latter female, while others say that the bees are male and the drones female). But all these views are impossible if we reason first upon the facts peculiar to bees and secondly upon those which apply more generally to other animals also.

For if they do not generate the young but bring them from elsewhere, then bees ought to come into being also, if the bees did not carry them off, in the places from which the old bees carry the germs. For why, if new bees come into existence when the germs are transported, should they not do so if the germs are left there? They ought to do so just as much, whether the germs are spontaneously generated in the flowers or whether some animal generates them. And if the germs were of some other animal, then that animal ought to be produced from them instead of bees. Again, that they should collect honey is reasonable, for it is their food, but it is strange that they should collect the young if they are neither their own offspring nor food. With what object should they do so? for all animals that trouble themselves about the young labour for what **759b** appears to be their own offspring.

But, again, it is also unreasonable to suppose that the bees are female and the drones male, for Nature does not give weapons for fighting to any female, and while the drones are stingless all the bees have a sting. Nor is the opposite view reasonable, that the bees are male and the drones female, for no males are in the habit of working for their offspring, but as it is the bees do this. And generally, since the brood of the drones is found coming into being among them even if there is no mature drone present, but that of the bees is not so found without the presence of the kings (which is why some say that the young of the drones alone is brought in from outside), it is plain that they are not produced from copulation, either (1) of bee with bee or drone with drone or (2) of bees with drones. (That they should import the brood of the drones alone is impossible for the reasons already given, and besides it is unreasonable that a similar state of things should not prevail with all the three kinds if it prevails with one.) Then, again, it is also impossible that the bees themselves should be some of them male and some female, for in all kinds of animals the two sexes differ. Besides they would in that case generate their own kind, but as it is their brood is not found to come into being if the leaders are not among them, as men say. And an argument against both theories, that the young are generated by union of the bees with one another or with the drones, separately or with one another, is this: none of them has ever yet been seen copulating, whereas this would have often happened if the sexes had existed in them. It remains then, if they are generated by copulation at all, that the kings shall unite to generate them. But the drones are found to come into being even if no leaders are present, and it is not possible that the bees should either import their brood or themselves generate them by copulation. It remains then, as appears to be the case in certain fishes, that the bees should generate the drones without copulation, being indeed female in respect of generative power, but containing in themselves both sexes as plants do. Hence also they have the instrument of offence, for we ought not to call that female in which the male sex is not separated. But if this is found to be the case with drones, if they come into being without copulation, then as it is necessary that the same account should be given of the bees and the kings and that they also should be generated without copulation. Now if the brood of the bees had been found to come into being among them without the presence of the kings, it **760a** would necessarily follow that the bees also are produced from bees themselves without copulation, but as it is, since those occupied with the tendance of these creatures deny this, it remains that the kings must generate both their own kind and the bees.

As bees are a peculiar and extraordinary kind of animal so also their generation appears to be peculiar. That bees should generate without copulation is a thing which may be paralleled in other animals, but that what they generate should not be of the same kind is peculiar to them, for the erythrinus generates an erythrinus and the channa a channa. The reason is that bees themselves are not generated like flies and similar creatures, but from a kind different indeed but akin to them, for they are produced from the leaders. Hence in a sort of way their generation is analogous. For the leaders resemble the drones in size and the bees in possessing a sting; so the bees are like them in this respect, and the drones are like them in size. For there must needs be some overlapping unless the same kind is always to be produced from each; but this is impossible, for at that rate the whole class would consist of leaders. The bees, then, are assimilated to them in their power of generation, the drones in size; if the latter had had a sting also they would have been leaders, but as it is this much of the difficulty has been solved, for the leaders are like both kinds at once, like the bees in possessing a sting, like the drones in size.

But the leaders also must be generated from something. Since it is neither from the bees nor from the drones, it must be from their own kind. The grubs of the kings are produced last and are not many in number.

Thus what happens is this: the leaders generate their own kind but also another kind, that of the bees; the bees again generate another kind, the drones, but do not also generate their own kind, but this has been denied them. And since what is according to Nature is always in due order, therefore it is necessary that it should be denied to the drones even to generate another kind than themselves. This is just what we find happening, for though the drones are themselves generated, they generate nothing else, but the process reaches its limit in the third stage. And so beautifully is this arranged by Nature that the three kinds always **760b** continue in existence and none of them fails, though they do not all generate.

Another fact is also natural, that in fine seasons much honey is collected and many drones are produced but in rainy reasons a large brood of ordinary bees. For the wet causes more residual matter to be formed in the bodies of the leaders, the fine weather in that of the bees, for being smaller in size they need the fine weather more than the kings do. It is right also that the kings, being as it were made with a view to producing young, should remain within, freed from the labour of procuring necessaries, and also that they should be of a considerable size, their bodies being, as it were, constituted with a view to bearing young, and that the drones should be idle as having no weapon to fight for the food and because of the slowness of their bodies. But the bees are intermediate in size between the two other kinds, for this is useful for their work, and they are workers as having to support not only their young but also their fathers. And it agrees with our views that the bees attend upon their kings because they are their offspring (for if nothing of the sort had been the case the facts about their leadership would be unreasonable), and that, while they suffer the kings to do no work as being their parents, they punish the drones as their children, for it is nobler to punish one's children and those who have no work to perform. The fact that the leaders being few generate the bees in large numbers seems to be similar to what obtains in the generation of lions, which at first produce five, afterwards a smaller number each time, at last one and thereafter none. So the leaders at first produce a number of workers, afterwards a few of their own kind; thus the brood of the latter is smaller in number than that of the former, but where Nature has taken away from them in number she has made it up again in size.

Such appears to be the truth about the generation of bees, judging from theory and from what are believed to be the facts about them; the facts, however, have not yet been sufficiently grasped; if ever they are, then credit must be given rather to observation than to theories, and to theories only if what they affirm agrees with the observed facts.

A further indication that bees are produced without copulation is the fact that the brood appears small in the cells of the comb, whereas, whenever insects are generated by copulation, **761a** the parents remain united for a long time but produce quickly something of the nature of a scolex and of a considerable size.

Concerning the generation of animals akin to them, as hornets and wasps, the facts in all cases are similar to a certain extent, but are devoid of the extraordinary features which characterize bees; this we should expect, for they have nothing divine about them as the bees have. For the so-called 'mothers' generate the young and mould the first part of the combs, but they generate by copulation with one another, for their union has often been observed. As for all the differences of each of these kinds from one another and from bees, they must be investigated with the aid of the illustrations to the *Enquiries*.[1]

II

Having spoken of the generation of all insects, we must now speak of the testacea. Here also the facts of generation are partly like and partly unlike those in the other classes. And this is what might be expected. For compared with animals they resemble plants, compared with plants they resemble animals, so that in a sense they appear to come into being from semen, but in another sense not so, and in one way they are spontaneously generated but in another from their own kind, or some of them in the latter way, others in the former. Because their nature answers to that of plants, therefore few or no kinds of testacea come into being on land, e. g. the snails and any others, few as they are, that resemble them; but in the sea and similar waters there are many of all kinds of forms. But the class of plants has but few and one may say practically no representatives in the sea and such places, all such growing on the land. For plants and testacea are analogous; and in proportion as liquid has more quickening power than solid, water than earth, so much does the nature of testacea differ from that of plants, since the object of testacea is to be in such a relation to water as plants are to earth, as if plants were, so to say, land-oysters, oysters water-plants.

[1] *History of Animals*, IX. 41.

For such a reason also the testacea in the water vary more in form than those on the land. For the nature of liquid is more plastic than that of earth and yet not much less material, and this is especially true of the inhabitants of **761b** the sea, for fresh water, though sweet and nutritious, is cold and less material. Wherefore animals having no blood and not of a hot nature are not produced in lakes nor in the fresher among brackish waters, but only exceptionally, but it is in estuaries and at the mouths of rivers that they come into being, as testacea and cephalopoda and crustacea, all these being bloodless and of a cold nature. For they seek at the same time the warmth of the sun and food; now the sea is not only water but much more material than fresh water and hot in its nature; it has a share in all the parts of the universe, water and air and earth, so that it also has a share in all living things which are produced in connexion with each of these elements. Plants may be assigned to land, the aquatic animals to water, the land animals to air, but variations of quantity and distance make a great and wonderful difference. The fourth class must not be sought in these regions, though there certainly ought to be some animal corresponding to the element of fire, for this is counted in as the fourth of the elementary bodies. But the form which fire assumes never appears to be peculiar to it, but it always exists in some other of the elements, for that which is ignited appears to be either air or smoke or earth. Such a kind of animal must be sought in the moon, for this appears to participate in the element removed in the third degree from earth. The discussion of these things however belongs to another subject.

To return to testacea, some of them are formed spontaneously, some emit a sort of generative substance from themselves, but these also often come into being from a spontaneous formation. To understand this we must grasp the different methods of generation in plants; some of these are produced from seed, some from slips, planted out, some by budding off alongside, as the class of onions. In the last way are produced mussels, for smaller ones are always growing off alongside the original, but the whelks, the purple-fish, and those which are said to 'spawn' emit masses of a liquid slime as if originated by something of a seminal nature. We must not, however, consider that anything of the sort is real semen, but that these creatures participate in the resemblance to plants in the manner stated above. Hence when once one such creature has been produced, then **762a** is produced a number of them. For all these creatures are liable to be even spontaneously generated, and so to be formed still more plentifully in proportion if some are already existing. For it is natural that each should have some superfluous residue attached to it from the original, and from this buds off each of the creatures growing alongside of it. Again, since the nutriment and its residue possess a like power, it is likely that the product of those testacea which 'spawn' should resemble the original formation, and so it is natural that a new animal of the same kind should come into being from this also.

All those which do not bud off or 'spawn' are spontaneously generated. Now all things formed in this way, whether in earth or water, manifestly come into being in connexion with putrefaction and an admixture of rain-water. For as the sweet is separated off into the matter which is forming, the residue of the mixture takes such a form. Nothing comes into being by putrefying, but by concocting; putrefaction and the thing putrefied is only a residue of that which is concocted. For nothing comes into being out of the whole of anything, any more than in the products of art; if it did art would have nothing to do, but as it is in the one case art removes the useless material, in the other Nature does so. Animals and plants come into being in earth and in liquid because there is water in earth, and air in water, and in all air is vital heat so that in a sense all things are full of soul. Therefore living things form quickly whenever this air and vital heat are enclosed in anything. When they are so enclosed, the corporeal liquids being heated, there arises as it were a frothy bubble. Whether what is forming is to be more or less honourable in kind depends on the embracing of the psychical principle; this again depends on the medium in which the generation takes place and the material which is included. Now in the sea the earthy matter is present in large quantities, and consequently the testaceous animals are formed from a concretion of this kind, the earthy matter hardening round them and solidifying in the same manner as bones and horns (for these cannot be melted by fire), and the matter (or body) which contains the life being included within it.

The class of snails is the only class of such creatures that has been seen uniting, but it has never yet been sufficiently observed whether their generation is the result of the union or not.

It may be asked, if we wish to follow the **762b** right line of investigation, what it is in such animals the formation of which corresponds to the material principle. For in the females this is a residual secretion of the animal, potentially such as that from which it came, by imparting motion to which the principle derived from the male perfects the animal. But here what must be said to correspond to this, and whence comes or what is the moving principle which corresponds to the male? We must understand that even in animals which generate it is from the incoming nourishment that the heat in the animal makes the residue, the beginning of the conception, by secretion and concoction. The like is the case also in plants, except that in these (and also in some animals) there is no further need of the male principle, because they have it mingled with the female principle within themselves, whereas the residual secretion in most animals does need it. The nourishment again of some is earth and water, of others the more complicated combinations of these, so that what the heat in animals produces from their nutriment, this does the heat of the warm season in the environment put together and combine by concoction out of the sea-water on the earth. And the portion of the psychical principle which is either included along with it or separated off in the air makes an embryo and puts motion into it. Now in plants which are spontaneously generated the method of formation is uniform; they arise from a part of something, and while some of it is the starting-point of the plant, some is the first nourishment of the young shoots. . . . Other animals are produced in the form of a scolex, not only those bloodless animals which are not generated from parents but even some sanguinea, as a kind of mullet and some other river fishes and also the eel kind. For all of these, though they have but little blood by nature, are nevertheless sanguinea, and have a heart with blood in it as the origin of the parts; and the so-called 'entrails of earth', in which comes into being the body of the eel, have the nature of a scolex.

Hence one might suppose, in connexion with the origin of men and quadrupeds, that, if ever they were really 'earth-born' as some say, they came into being in one of two ways; that either it was by the formation of a scolex at first or else it was out of eggs. For either they must have had in themselves the nutriment for growth (and such a conception is a scolex) or they must have got it from elsewhere, and that either from the mother or from part of the conception. If then the former is impossible (I mean that nourishment should flow to them **763a** from the earth as it does in animals from the mother), then they must have got it from some part of the conception, and such generation we say is from an egg.

It is plain then that, if there really was any such beginning of the generation of all animals, it is reasonable to suppose it to have been one of these two, scolex or egg. But it is less reasonable to suppose that it was from eggs, for we do not see such generation occurring with any animal, but we do see the other both in the sanguinea above mentioned and in the bloodless animals. Such are some of the insects and such are the testacea which we are discussing; for they do not develop out of a part of something (as do animals from eggs), and they grow like a scolex. For the scolex grows towards the upper part and the first principle, since in the lower part is the nourishment for the upper. And this resembles the development of animals from eggs, except that these latter consume the whole egg, whereas in the scolex, when the upper part has grown by taking up into itself part of the substance in the lower part, the lower part is then differentiated out of the rest. The reason is that in later life also the nourishment is absorbed by all animals in the part below the hypozoma.

That the scolex grows in this way is plain in the case of bees and the like, for at first the lower part is large in them and the upper is smaller. The details of growth in the testacea are similar. This is plain in the whorls of the turbinata, for always as the animal grows the whorls become larger towards the front and what is called the head of the creature.

We have now pretty well described the manner of the development of these and the other spontaneously generated animals. That all the testacea are formed spontaneously is clear from such facts as these. They come into being on the side of boats when the frothy mud putrefies. In many places where previously nothing of the kind existed, the so-called limnostrea, a kind of oyster, have come into being when the spot turned muddy through want of water; thus when a naval armament cast anchor at Rhodes a number of clay vessels were thrown out into the sea, and after some time, when mud had collected round them, oysters used to be found in them. Here is another proof that such animals do not emit any **763b** generative substance from themselves; when certain Chians carried some live oysters over from Pyrrha in Lesbos and placed them in narrow straits of the sea where tides clash, they became no more numerous as time passed, but increased greatly in size. The so-called eggs contribute nothing to generation but are only a sign of good condition, like fat in the sanguinea, and therefore the oysters are savoury eating at these periods. A proof that this substance is not really eggs is the fact that such 'eggs' are always found in some testacea, as in pinnae, whelks, and purple-fish; only they are sometimes larger and sometimes smaller; in others as pectens, mussels, and the so-called limnostrea, they are not always present but only in the spring; as the season advances they dwindle and at last disappear altogether; the reason being that the spring is favourable to their being in good condition. In others again, as the ascidians, nothing of the sort is visible. (The details concerning these last, and the places in which they come into being, must be learnt from the *Enquiry*.)

BOOK IV

I

We have thus spoken of the generation of animals both generally and separately in all the different classes. But, since male and female are distinct in the most perfect of them, and since we say that the sexes are first principles of all living things whether animals or plants, only in some of them the sexes are separated and in others not, therefore we must speak first of the origin of the sexes in the latter. For while the animal is still imperfect in its kind the distinction is already made between male and female.

It is disputed, however, whether the embryo is male or female, as the case may be, even before the distinction is plain to our senses, and further whether it is thus differentiated within the mother or even earlier. It is said by some, as by Anaxagoras and other of the physicists, that this antithesis exists from the beginning in the germs or seeds; for the germ, they say, comes from the male while the female only provides the place in which it is to be developed, and the male is from the right, the female from the left testis, and so also that the male embryo is in the right of the uterus, the **764a** female in the left. Others, as Empedocles, say that the differentiation takes place in the uterus; for he says that if the uterus is hot or cold what enters it becomes male or female, the cause of the heat or cold being the flow of the catamenia, according as it is colder or hotter, more 'antique' or more 'recent'. Democritus of Abdera also says that the differentiation of sex takes place within the mother; that however it is not because of heat and cold that one embryo becomes female and another male, but that it depends on the question which parent it is whose semen prevails,—not the whole of the semen, but that which has come from the part by which male and female differ from one another. This is a better theory, for certainly Empedocles has made a rather light-hearted assumption in thinking that the difference between them is due only to cold and heat, when he saw that there was a great difference in the whole of the sexual parts, the difference in fact between the male pudenda and the uterus. For suppose two animals already moulded in embryo, the one having all the parts of the female, the other those of the male; suppose them then to be put into the uterus as into an oven, the former when the oven is hot, the latter when it is cold; then on the view of Empedocles that which has no uterus will be female and that which has will be male. But this is impossible. Thus the theory of Democritus would be the better of the two, at least as far as this goes, for he seeks for the origin of this difference and tries to set it forth; whether he does so well or not is another question.

Again, if heat and cold were the cause of the difference of the parts, this ought to have been stated by those who maintain the view of Empedocles; for to explain the origin of male and female is practically the same thing as to explain this, which is the manifest difference between them. And it is no small matter, starting from temperature as a principle, to collect the cause of the origin of these parts, as if it were a necessary consequence for this part which they call the uterus to be formed in the embryo under the influence of cold but not under that of heat. The same applies also to the parts which serve for intercourse, since these also differ in the way stated previously.

Moreover male and female twins are often found together in the same part of the uterus; this we have observed sufficiently by dissection in all the vivipara, both land animals and fish. Now if Empedocles had not seen this it was only natural for him to fall into error in assigning this cause of his; but if he had seen it **764b** it is strange that he should still think the heat or cold of the uterus to be the cause, since on his theory both these twins would have become either male or female, but as it is we do not see this to be the fact.

Again he says that the parts of the embryo are 'sundered', some being in the male and some in the female parent, which is why they desire intercourse with one another. If so it is necessary that the sexual parts like the rest should be separated from one another, already existing as masses of a certain size, and that they should come into being in the embryo on account of uniting with one another, not on account of cooling or heating of the semen. But perhaps it would take too long to discuss thoroughly such a cause as this which is stated by Empedocles, for its whole character seems to be fanciful. If, however, the facts about semen are such as we have actually stated, if it does not come from the whole of the body of the male parent and if the secretion of the male does not give any material at all to the embryo, then we must make a stand against both Empedocles and Democritus and any one else who argues on the same lines. For then it is not possible that the body of the embryo should exist 'sundered', part in the female parent and part in the male, as Empedocles says in the words: 'But the nature of the limbs hath been sundered, part in the man's . . .'; nor yet that a whole embryo is drawn off from each parent and the combination of the two becomes male or female according as one part prevails over another.

And, to take a more general view, though it is better to say that the one part makes the embryo female by prevailing through some superiority than to assign nothing but heat as the cause without any reflection, yet, as the form of the pudendum also varies along with the uterus from that of the father, we need an explanation of the fact that both these parts go along with each other. If it is because they are near each other, then each of the other parts also ought to go with them, for one of the prevailing parts is always near another part where the struggle is not yet decided; thus the offspring would be not only female or male but also like its mother or father respectively in all other details.

Besides, it is absurd to suppose that these parts should come into being as something isolated, without the body as a whole having changed along with them. Take first and foremost the blood-vessels, round which the whole mass of the flesh lies as round a framework. It is not reasonable that these should become of a certain quality because of the uterus, but rather that the uterus should do so on account of them. For though it is true that each is a receptacle of blood of some kind, still the system of the vessels is prior to the other; the moving principle must needs always be prior to that which it moves, and it is because it is itself of a certain quality that it is the cause of the development. The difference, then, of these parts as compared with each other in the two sexes is only a concomitant result; not this but something else must be held to be the first **765a** principle and the cause of the development of an embryo as male or female; this is so even if no semen is secreted by either male or female, but the embryo is formed in any way you please.

The same argument as that with which we meet Empedocles and Democritus will serve against those who say that the male comes from the right and the female from the left. If the male contributes no material to the embryo, there can be nothing in this view. If, as they say, he does contribute something of the sort, we must confront them in the same way as we did the theory of Empedocles, which accounts for the difference between male and female by the heat and cold of the uterus. They make the same mistake as he does, when they account for the difference by their 'right and left', though they see that the sexes differ actually by the whole of the sexual parts; for what reason then is the body of the uterus to exist in those embryos which come from the left and not in those from the right? For if an embryo have come from the left but has not acquired this part, it will be a female without a uterus, and so too there is nothing to stop another from being a male with a uterus! Besides, as has been said before, a female embryo has been observed in the right part of the uterus, a male in the left, or again both at once in the same part, and this not only once but several times.

Some again, persuaded of the truth of a view resembling that of these philosophers, say that if a man copulates with the right or left testis tied up the result is male or female offspring respectively; so at least Leophanes asserted. And some say that the same happens in the case of those who have one or other testis excised, not speaking truth but vaticinating what will happen from probabilities and jumping at the conclusion that it is so before seeing that it proves to be so. Moreover, they know not that these parts of animals contribute nothing to the production of one sex rather than the other; a proof of this is that many animals in which the distinction of sex exists, and which produce both male and female offspring, nevertheless have no testes, as the footless animals; I mean the classes of fish and of serpents.

To suppose, then, either that heat and cold are the causes of male and female, or that the different sexes come from the right and **765b** left, is not altogether unreasonable in itself; for the right of the body is hotter than the left, and the concocted semen is hotter than the unconcocted; again, the thickened is concocted, and the more thickened is more fertile. Yet to put it in this way is to seek for the cause from too remote a starting-point; we must draw near the immediate causes in so far as it is possible for us.

We have, then, previously spoken elsewhere of both the body as a whole and its parts,[1] explaining what each part is and for what reason it exists. But (1) the male and female are distinguished by a certain capacity and incapacity. (For the male is that which can concoct the blood into semen and which can form and secrete and discharge a semen carrying with it the principle of form—by 'principle' I do not mean a material principle out of which comes into being an offspring resembling the parent, but I mean the first moving cause, whether it have power to act as such in the thing itself or in something else—but the female is that which receives semen, indeed, but cannot form it for itself or secrete or discharge it.) And (2) all concoction works by means of heat. Therefore the males of animals must needs be hotter than the females. For it is by reason of cold and incapacity that the female is more abundant in blood in certain parts of her anatomy, and this abundance is an evidence of the exact opposite of what some suppose, thinking that the female is hotter than the male for this reason, i.e. the discharge of the catamenia. It is true that blood is hot, and that which has more of it is hotter than that which has less. But they

[1] In *On the Parts of Animals*, and in the first book of this treatise.

assume that this discharge occurs through excess of blood and of heat, as if it could be taken for granted that all blood is equally blood if only it be liquid and sanguineous in colour, and as if it might not become less in quantity but purer in quality in those who assimilate nourishment properly. In fact they look upon this residual discharge in the same light as that of the intestines, when they think that a greater amount of it is a sign of a hotter nature, whereas the truth is just the opposite. For consider the production of fruit; the nutriment in its first stage is abundant, but the useful product derived from it is small, indeed the final result is nothing at all compared to the quantity in the first stage. So is it with the body; the various parts receive and work up the nutriment, from the whole of which the final result is quite small. This is blood in some animals, in some its analogue. Now since (1) the one sex is able and the other is unable to reduce the residual secretion to a pure form, and (2) every capacity or power in an organism has a certain corresponding organ, whether
766a the faculty produces the desired results in a lower degree or in a higher degree, and (3) the two sexes correspond in this manner (the terms 'able' and 'unable' being used in more senses than one)—therefore it is necessary that both female and male should have organs. Accordingly the one has the uterus, the other the male organs.

Again, Nature gives both the faculty and the organ to each individual at the same time, for it is better so. Hence each region comes into being along with the secretions and the faculties, as e.g. the faculty of sight is not perfected without the eye, nor the eye without the faculty of sight; and so too the intestine and bladder come into being along with the faculty of forming the excreta. And since that from which an organ comes into being and that by which it is increased are the same (i.e. the nutriment), each of the parts will be made out of such a material and such residual matter as it is able to receive. In the second place, again, it is formed, as we say, in a certain sense, out of its opposite. Thirdly, we must understand besides this that, if it is true that when a thing perishes it becomes the opposite of what it was, it is necessary also that what is not under the sway of that which made it must change into its opposite. After these premisses it will perhaps be now clearer for what reason one embryo becomes female and another male. For when the first principle does not bear sway and cannot concoct the nourishment through lack of heat nor bring it into its proper form, but is defeated in this respect, then must needs the material which it works on change into its opposite. Now the female is opposite to the male, and that in so far as the one is female and the other male. And since it differs in its faculty, its organ also is different, so that the embryo changes into this state. And as one part of first-rate importance changes, the whole system of the animal differs greatly in form along with it. This may be seen in the case of eunuchs, who, though mutilated in one part alone, depart so much from their original appearance and approximate closely to the female form. The reason of this is that some of the parts are principles, and when a principle is moved or affected needs must many of the parts that go along with it change with it.

If then (1) the male quality or essence is a principle and a cause, and (2) the male is such in virtue of a certain capacity and the female is such in virtue of an incapacity, and (3) the essence or definition of the capacity and of the incapacity is ability or inability to concoct the nourishment in its ultimate stage, this being called blood in the sanguinea and the analogue of blood in the other animals, and (4) the cause of this capacity is in the first principle and in the part which contains the principle of natural heat—therefore a heart must be formed in the sanguinea (and the re-
766b sulting animal will be either male or female), and in the other kinds which possess the sexes must be formed that which is analogous to the heart.

This, then, is the first principle and cause of male and female, and this is the part of the body in which it resides. But the animal becomes definitely female or male by the time when it possesses also the parts by which the female differs from the male, for it is not in virtue of any part you please that it is male or female, any more than it is able to see or hear by possessing any part you please.

To recapitulate, we say that the semen, which is the foundation of the embryo, is the ultimate secretion of the nutriment. By ultimate I mean that which is carried to every part of the body, and this is also the reason why the offspring is like the parent. For it makes no difference whether we say that the semen comes from all the parts or goes to all of them, but the latter is the better. But the semen of the male differs from the corresponding secretion of the female in that it contains a principle within itself of such a kind as to set up movements also in the embryo and to concoct thoroughly the ultimate nourishment, whereas the secretion of the female contains material alone. If, then, the male element prevails it draws the female element into itself, but if it is prevailed over it changes into the opposite or is destroyed. But the female is opposite to the male, and is female because of its inability to concoct and of the coldness of the sanguineous nutriment. And Nature assigns to each of the secretions the part fitted to receive it. But the semen is a secretion, and this in the hotter animals with blood, i.e. the males, is moderate in quantity, wherefore the recipient parts of this secretion in males are only passages. But the females, owing to inability to concoct, have a great quantity of blood, for it cannot be worked up into semen. Therefore they must also have a part to receive this, and this part must be unlike the passages of the male and of a considerable size. This is why the uterus is of such a nature, this being the part by which the female differs from the male.

2

We have thus stated for what reason the one becomes female and the other male. Observed facts confirm what we have said. For more females are produced by the young and by those verging on old age than by those in the prime of life; in the former the vital heat is not yet perfect, in the latter it is failing. And those of a moister and more feminine state of body are more wont to beget females, and a liquid semen causes this more than a thicker; now all these characteristics come of deficiency in natural heat.

Again, more males are born if copulation takes place when north than when south winds are blowing. For in the latter case the animals produce more secretion, and too much secretion is harder to concoct; hence the semen **767a** of the males is more liquid, and so is the discharge of the catamenia.

Also the fact that the catamenia occur in the course of nature rather when the month is waning is due to the same causes. For this time of the month is colder and moister because of the waning and failure of the moon; as the sun makes winter and summer in the year as a whole, so does the moon in the month. This is not due to the turning of the moon, but it grows warmer as the light increases and colder as it wanes.

The shepherds also say that it not only makes a difference in the production of males and females if copulation takes place during northern or southerly winds, but even if the animals while copulating look towards the south or north; so small a thing will sometimes turn the scale and cause cold or heat, and these again influence generation.

The male and female, then, are distinguished generally, as compared with one another in connexion with the production of male and female offspring, for the causes stated. However, they also need a certain correspondence with one another to produce at all, for all things that come into being as products of art or of Nature exist in virtue of a certain ratio. Now if the hot preponderates too much it dries up the liquid; if it is very deficient it does not solidify it; for the artistic or natural product we need the due mean between the extremes. Otherwise it will be as in cooking; too much fire burns the meat, too little does not cook it, and in either case the process is a failure. So also there is need of due proportion in the mixture of the male and female elements. And for this cause it often happens to many of both sexes that they do not generate with one another, but if divorced and remarried to others do generate; and these oppositions show themselves sometimes in youth, sometimes in advanced age, alike as concerns fertility or infertility, and as concerns generation of male or female offspring.

One country also differs from another in these respects, and one water from another, for the same reasons. For the nourishment and the medical condition of the body are of such or such a kind because of the tempering of the surrounding air and of the food entering the body, especially the water; for men consume more of this than of anything else, and this enters as nourishment into all food, even solids. Hence hard waters cause infertility, and cold waters the birth of females.

3

The same causes must be held responsible for the following groups of facts. (1) Some children resemble their parents, while others do not; some being like the father and others like **767b** the mother, both in the body as a whole and in each part, male and female offspring resembling father and mother respectively rather than the other way about. (2) They resemble their parents more than remoter ancestors, and resemble those ancestors more than any chance individual. (3) Some, though resembling none of their relations, yet do at any rate resemble a human being, but others are not even like a human being but a monstrosity. For even he who does not resemble his parents is already in a certain sense a monstrosity; for in these cases Nature has in a way departed from the type. The first departure indeed is that the offspring should become female instead of male; this, however, is a natural necessity. (For the class of animals divided into sexes must be preserved, and as it is possible for the male sometimes not to prevail over the female in the mixture of the two elements, either through youth or age or some other such cause, it is necessary that animals should produce female young). And the monstrosity, though not necessary in regard of a final cause and an end, yet is necessary accidentally. As for the origin of it, we must look at it in this way. If the generative secretion in the catamenia is properly concocted, the movement imparted by the male will make the form of the embryo in the likeness of itself. (Whether we say that it is the semen or this movement that makes each of the parts grow, makes no difference; nor again whether we say that it 'makes them grow' or 'forms them from the beginning', for the formula of the movement is the same in either case.) Thus if this movement prevail, it will make the embryo male and not female, like the father and not like the mother; if it prevail not, the embryo is deficient in that faculty in which it has not prevailed. By 'each faculty' I mean this. That which generates is not only male but also a particular male, e.g. Coriscus or Socrates, and it is not only Coriscus but also a man. In this way some of the characteristics of the father are more near to him, others more remote from him considered simply as a parent and not in reference to his accidental qualities (as for instance if the parent is a scholar or the neighbour of some particular person). Now the peculiar and individual has always more force in generation than the more general and wider characteristics. Coriscus is both a man and an animal, but his manhood is nearer to his individual existence than is his animalhood. In generation both the individual and the class are operative, but the individual is the more so of the two, for this is the only true existence. And the offspring is produced indeed of a certain quality, but also as an individual, and this latter is the true existence. Therefore it is from the forces of all such existences that the efficient movements come which exist in the semen; potentially from remoter ancestors but in a higher degree and more nearly **768a** from the individual (and by the individual I mean e.g. Coriscus or Socrates). Now since everything changes not into anything haphazard but into its opposite, therefore also that which is not prevailed over in generation must change and become the opposite, in respect of that particular force in which the paternal and efficient or moving element has not prevailed. If then it has not prevailed in so far as it is male, the offspring becomes female; if in so far as it is Coriscus or Socrates, the offspring does not resemble the father but the mother. For as 'father' and 'mother' are opposed as general terms, so also the individual father is opposed to the individual mother. The like applies also to the forces that come next in order, for the offspring always changes rather into the likeness of the nearer ancestor than the more remote, both in the paternal and in the maternal line.

Some of the movements exist in the semen actually, others potentially; actually, those of the father and the general type, as man and animal; potentially those of the female and the remoter ancestors. Thus the male and efficient principle, if it lose its own nature, changes to its opposites, but the movements which form the embryo change into those nearly connected with them; for instance, if the movement of the male parent be resolved, it changes by a very slight difference into that of his father, and in the next instance into that of his grandfather; and in this way not only in the male but also in the female line the movement of the female parent changes into that of her mother, and, if not into this, then into that of her grandmother; and similarly also with the more remote ancestors.

Naturally then it is most likely that the characteristics of 'male' and of the individual father will go together, whether they prevail or are prevailed over. For the difference between them is small so that there is no difficulty in both concurring, for Socrates is an individual man with certain characters. Hence for the most part the male offspring resemble the father, and the female the mother. For in the latter case the loss of both characters takes place at once, and the change is into the two opposites; now female is opposed to male, and the individual mother to the individual father.

But if the movement coming from the male principle prevails while that coming from the individual Socrates does not, or vice versa, then the result is that male children are produced resembling the mother and female children resembling the father.

If again the movements be resolved, if the male character remain but the movement coming from the individual Socrates be resolved into that of the father of Socrates, the result will be a male child resembling its grandfather or some other of its more remote ancestors in the male line on the same principle. If the male principle be prevailed over, the child will be female and resembling most probably its mother, but, if the movement coming from the mother also be resolved, it will resemble its mother's mother or the resemblance will be to **768b** some other of its more remote ancestors in the female line on the same principle.

The same applies also to the separate parts, for often some of these take after the father, and others after the mother, and yet others after some of the remoter ancestors. For, as has been often said already, some of the movements which form the parts exist in the semen actually and others potentially. We must grasp certain fundamental general principles, not only that just mentioned (that some of the movements exist potentially and others actually), but also two others, that if a character be prevailed over it changes into its opposite, and, if it be resolved, is resolved into the movement next allied to it—if less, into that which is near, if more, into that which is further removed. Finally, the movements are so confused together that there is no resemblance to any of the family or kindred, but the only character that remains is that common to the race, i.e. it is a human being. The reason of this is that this is closely knit up with the individual characteristics; 'human being' is the general term, while Socrates, the father, and the mother, whoever she may be, are individuals.

The reason why the movements are resolved is this. The agent is itself acted upon by that on which it acts; thus that which cuts is blunted by that which is cut by it, that which heats is cooled by that which is heated by it, and in general the moving or efficient cause (except in the case of the first cause of all) does itself receive some motion in return; e.g. what pushes is itself in a way pushed again and what crushes is itself crushed again. Sometimes it is altogether more acted upon than is the thing on which it acts, so that what is heating or cooling something else is itself cooled or heated; sometimes having produced no effect, sometimes less than it has itself received. (This question has been treated in the special discussion of action and reaction, where it is laid down in what classes of things action and reaction exist.) Now that which is acted on escapes and is not mastered by the semen, either through deficiency of power in the concocting and moving agent or because what should be concocted and formed into distinct parts is too cold and in too great quantity. Thus the moving agent, mastering it in one part but not in another, makes the embryo in formation to be multiform, as happens with athletes because they eat so much. For owing to the quantity of their food their nature is not able to master it all, so as to increase and arrange their form symmetrically; therefore their limbs develop irregularly, sometimes indeed almost so much that no one of them resembles what it was before. Similar to this is also the disease known as satyrism, in which the face appears like that of a satyr owing to a quantity of unconcocted humour or wind being diverted into parts of the face.

769a We have thus discussed the cause of all these phenomena, (1) why female and male offspring are produced, (2) why some are similar to their parents, female to female and male to male, and others the other way about, females being similar to the father and males to the mother, and in general why some are like their ancestors while others are like none of them, and all this as concerns both the body as a whole and each of the parts separately. Different accounts, however, have been given of these phenomena by some of the nature-philosophers; I mean why children are like or unlike their parents. They give two versions of the reason. Some say that the child is more like that parent of the two from whom comes more semen, this applying equally both to the body as a whole and to the separate parts, on the assumption that semen comes from each part of both parents; if an equal part comes from each, then, they say, the child is like neither. But if this is false, if semen does not come off from the whole body of the parents, it is clear that the reason assigned cannot be the cause of likeness and unlikeness. Moreover, they are hard put to it to explain how it is that a female child can be like the father and a male like the mother. For (1) those who assign the same cause of sex as Empedocles or Democritus say what is on other grounds impossible, and (2) those who say that it is determined by the greater or smaller amount of semen coming from the male or female parent, and that this is why one child is male and another female, cannot show how the female is to resemble the father and the male the mother, for it is impossible that more should come from both at once. Again, for what reason is a child generally like its ancestors, even the more remote? None of the semen has come from *them* at any rate.

But those who account for the similarity in the manner which remains to be discussed, explain this point better, as well as the others. For there are some who say that the semen, though one, is as it were a common mixture (panspermia) of many elements; just as, if one should mix many juices in one liquid and then take some from it, it would be possible to take, not an equal quantity always from each juice, but sometimes more of one and sometimes more of another, sometimes some of one and none at all of another, so they say it is with the generative fluid, which is a mixture of many elements, for the offspring resembles that parent from which it has derived most. Though this theory is obscure and in many ways ficti- **769b** tious, it aims at what is better expressed by saying that what is called 'panspermia' exists potentially, not actually; it cannot exist actually, but it can do so potentially. Also, if we assign only one sort of cause, it is not easy to explain all the phenomena, (1) the distinction of sex, (2) why the female is often like the father and the male like the mother, and again (3) the resemblance to remoter ancestors, and further (4) the reason why the offspring is sometimes unlike any of these but still a human being, but sometimes, (5) proceeding further on these lines, appears finally to be not even a human being but only some kind of animal, what is called a monstrosity.

For, following what has been said, it remains to give the reason for such monsters. If the movements imparted by the semen are resolved and the material contributed by the mother is not controlled by them, at last there remains the most general substratum, that is to say the animal. Then people say that the child has the head of a ram or a bull, and so on with other animals, as that a calf has the head of a child or a sheep that of an ox. All these monsters result from the causes stated above, but they are none of the things they are said to be; there is only some similarity, such as may arise even where there is no defect of growth. Hence often jesters compare some one who is not beautiful to a 'goat breathing fire', or again to a 'ram butting', and a certain physiognomist reduced all faces to those of two or three animals, and his arguments often prevailed on people.

That, however, it is impossible for such a monstrosity to come into existence—I mean one animal in another—is shown by the great difference in the period of gestation between man, sheep, dog, and ox, it being impossible for each to be developed except in its proper time.

This is the description of some of the monsters talked about; others are such because certain parts of their form are multiplied so that they are born with many feet or many heads.

The account of the cause of monstrosities is very close and similar in a way to that of the cause of animals being born defective in any part, for monstrosity is also a kind of deficiency.

4

Democritus said that monstrosities arose because two emissions of seminal fluid met together, the one succeeding the other at an interval of time; that the later entering into the uterus reinforced the earlier so that the parts of the embryo grow together and get confused with one another. But in birds, he says, since copulation takes place quickly, both the eggs and their colour always cross one another. But if it is the fact, as it manifestly is, that sev- **770a** eral young are produced from one emission of semen and a single act of intercourse, it is better not to desert the short road to go a long way about, for in such cases it is absolutely necessary that this should occur when the semen is not separated but all enters the female at once.

If, then, we must attribute the cause to the semen of the male, this will be the way we shall have to state it, but we must rather by all means suppose that the cause lies in the material contributed by the female and in the embryo as it is forming. Hence also such monstrosities appear very rarely in animals producing only one young one, more frequently in those producing many, most of all in birds and among birds in the common fowl. For this bird produces many young, not only because it lays often like the pigeon family, but also because it has many embryos at once and copulates all the year round. Therefore it produces many double eggs, for the embryos grow together because they are near one another, as often happens with many fruits. In such double eggs, when the yolks are separated by the membrane, two separate chickens are produced with nothing abnormal about them; when the yolks are continuous, with no division between them, the chickens produced are monstrous, having one body and head but four legs and four wings; this is because the upper parts are formed earlier from the white, their nourishment being drawn from the yolk, whereas the lower part comes into being later and its nourishment is one and indivisible.

A snake has also been observed with two heads for the same reason, this class also being oviparous and producing many young. Monstrosities, however, are rarer among them owing to the shape of the uterus, for by reason of its length the numerous eggs are set in a line.

Nothing of the kind occurs with bees and wasps, because their brood is in separate cells. But in the fowl the opposite is the case, whereby it is plain that we must hold the cause of such phenomena to lie in the material. So, too, monstrosities are commoner in other animals if they produce many young. Hence they are less common in man, for he produces for the most part only one young one and that perfect; even in man monstrosities occur more often in regions where the women give birth to more than one at a time, as in Egypt. And they are commoner in sheep and goats, since they produce more young. Still more does this apply to the fissipeds, for such animals pro-
770b duce many young and imperfect, as the dog, the young of these creatures being generally blind. Why this happens and why they produce many young must be stated later,[1] but in them Nature has made an advance towards the production of monstrosities in that what they generate, being imperfect, is so far unlike the parent; now monstrosities also belong to the class of things unlike the parent. Therefore this accident also often invades animals of such a nature. So, too, it is in these that the so-called 'metachoera' are most frequent, and the condition of these also is in a way monstrous, since both deficiency and excess are monstrous. For the monstrosity belongs to the class of things contrary to Nature, not any and every kind of Nature, but Nature in her usual operations; nothing can happen contrary to Nature considered as eternal and necessary, but we speak of things being contrary to her in those cases where things generally happen in a certain way but may also happen in another way. In fact, even in the case of monstrosities, whenever things occur contrary indeed to the established order but still always in a certain way and not at random, the result seems to be less of a monstrosity because even that which is contrary to Nature is in a certain sense according to Nature, whenever, that is, the formal nature has not mastered the material nature. Therefore they do not call such things monstrosities any more than in the other cases where a phenomenon occurs habitually, as in fruits; for instance, there is a vine which some call 'capneos'; if this bear black grapes they do not judge it a monstrosity because it is in the habit of doing this very often. The reason is that it is in its nature intermediate between white and black; thus the change is not a violent one nor, so to say, contrary to Nature; at least, is it not a change into another nature. But in animals producing many young not only do the same phenomena occur, but also the numerous embryos hinder one another from becoming perfect and interfere with the generative motions imparted by the semen.

A difficulty may be raised concerning (1) the production of many young and the multiplication of the parts in a single young one, and (2) the production of few young or only one and the deficiency of the parts. Sometimes animals are born with too many toes, sometimes with one alone, and so on with the other parts, for they may be multiplied or they may be absent. Again, they may have the generative parts doubled, the one being male, the other female; this is known in men and especially in goats. For what are called 'tragaenae' are such because they have both male and female generative parts; there is a case also of a goat being born with a horn upon its leg. Changes and
771a deficiencies are found also in the internal parts, animals either not possessing some at all, or possessing them in a rudimentary condition, or too numerous or in the wrong place. No animal, indeed, has ever been born without a heart, but they are born without a spleen or with two spleens or with one kidney; there is no case again of total absence of the liver, but there are cases of its being incomplete. And all these phenomena have been seen in animals perfect and alive. Animals also which naturally have a gall-bladder are found without one; others are found to have more than one. Cases are known, too, of the organs changing places, the liver being on the left, the spleen on the right. These phenomena have been observed, as stated above, in animals whose growth is perfected; at the time of birth great confusion of every kind has been found. Those

[1] In this chapter.

which only depart a little from Nature commonly live; not so those which depart further, when the unnatural condition is in the parts which are sovereign over life.

The question then about all these cases is this. Are we to suppose that a single cause is responsible for the production of a single young one and for the deficiency of the parts, and another but still a single cause for the production of many young and the multiplication of parts, or not?

In the first place it seems only reasonable to wonder why some animals produce many young, others only one. For it is the largest animals that produce one, e. g. the elephant, camel, horse, and the other solid-hoofed ungulates; of these some are larger than all other animals, while the others are of a remarkable size. But the dog, the wolf, and practically all the fissipeds, produce many, even the small members of the class, as the mouse family. The cloven-footed animals again produce few, except the pig, which belongs to those that produce many. This certainly seems surprising, for we should expect the large animals to be able to generate more young and to secrete more semen. But precisely what we wonder at is the reason for not wondering; it is just because of their size that they do not produce many young, for the nutriment is expended in such animals upon increasing the body. But in the smaller animals Nature takes away from the size and adds the excess so gained to the seminal secretion. Moreover, more semen must needs be used in generation by the larger animal, and little by the smaller. Therefore many small ones may be produced together, but it is hard for many large ones to be so, and to those intermediate in size Nature has assigned the intermediate number. We have formerly given the reason why some animals are large, some smaller, and some between the **771b** two, and speaking generally, with regard to the number of young produced, the solid-hoofed produce one, the cloven-footed few, the many-toed many. (The reason of this is that, generally speaking, their sizes correspond to this difference.) It is not so, however, in all cases; for it is the largeness and smallness of the body that is cause of few or many young being born, not the fact that the kind of animal has one, two, or many toes. A proof of this is that the elephant is the largest of animals and yet is many-toed, and the camel, the next largest, is cloven-footed. And not only in animals that walk but also in those that fly or swim the large ones produce few, the small many, for the same reason. In like manner also it is not the largest plants that bear most fruit.

We have explained then why some animals naturally produce many young, some but few, and some only one; in the difficulty now stated we may rather be surprised with reason at those which produce many, since such animals are often seen to conceive from a single copulation. Whether the semen of the male contributes to the material of the embryo by itself becoming a part of it and mixing with the semen of the female, or whether, as *we* say, it does not act in this way but brings together and fashions the material within the female and the generative secretion as the fig-juice does the liquid substance of milk, what is the reason why it does not form a single animal of considerable size? For certainly in the parallel case the fig-juice is not separated if it has to curdle a large quantity of milk, but the more the milk and the more the fig-juice put into it, so much the greater is the curdled mass. Now it is no use to say that the several regions of the uterus attract the semen and therefore more young than one are formed, because the regions are many and the cotyledons are more than one. For two embryos are often formed in the same region of the uterus, and they may be seen lying in a row in animals that produce many, when the uterus is filled with the embryos. (This is plain from the dissections.) Rather the truth is this. As animals complete their growth there are certain limits to their size, both upwards and downwards, beyond which they cannot go, but it is in the space between these limits that they exceed or fall short of one another in size, and it is **772a** within these limits that one man (or any other animal) is larger or smaller than another. So also the generative material from which each animal is formed is not without a quantitative limit in both directions, nor can it be formed from any quantity you please. Whenever then an animal, for the cause assigned, discharges more of the female secretion than is needed for beginning the existence of a single animal, it is not possible that only one should be formed out of all this, but a number limited by the appropriate size in each case; nor will the semen of the male, or the power residing in the semen, form anything either more or less than what is according to Nature. In like manner, if the male emits more semen than is necessary, or more powers in different parts of the semen as it is divided, however much it is it will not make anything greater; on the contrary it will dry up the material of the female and destroy it. So fire also does not continue to make water hotter in proportion as it is itself increased, but there is a fixed limit to the heat of which water is capable; if that is once reached and the fire is then increased, the water no longer gets hotter but rather evaporates and at last disappears and is dried up. Now since it appears that the secretion of the female and that from the male need to stand in some proportionate relation to one another (I mean in animals of which the male emits semen), what happens in those that produce many young is this: from the very first the semen emitted by the male has power, being divided, to form several embryos, and the material contributed by the female is so much that several can be formed out of it. (The parallel of curdling milk, which we spoke of before, is no longer in point here, for what is formed by the heat of the semen is not only of a certain quantity but also of a certain quality, whereas with fig-juice and rennet quantity alone is concerned.) This then is just the reason why in such animals the embryos formed are numerous and do not all unite into one whole; it is because an embryo is not formed out of any quantity you please, but whether there is too much or too little, in either case there will be no result, for there is a limit set alike to the power of the heat which acts on the material and to the material so acted upon.

On the same principle many embryos are not formed, though the secretion is much, in the large animals which produce only one young one, for in them also both the material and that which works upon it are of a certain quantity. So then they do not secrete such material in too great quantity for the reason previously stated, and what they do secrete is naturally just enough for one embryo alone to be formed from it. If ever too much is secreted, then twins are born. Hence such cases seem to be more portentous, because they are contrary to the general and customary rule.

772b Man belongs to all three classes, for he produces one only and sometimes many or few, though naturally he almost always produces one. Because of the moisture and heat of his body he may produce many [for semen is naturally fluid and hot], but because of his size he produces few or one. On account of this it results that in man alone among animals the period of gestation is irregular; whereas the period is fixed in the rest, there are several periods in man, for children are born at seven months and at ten months and at the times between, for even those of eight months do live though less often than the rest. The reason may be gathered from what has just been said, and the question has been discussed in the *Problems*. Let this explanation suffice for these points.

The cause why the parts may be multiplied contrary to Nature is the same as the cause of the birth of twins. For the reason exists already in the embryo, whenever it aggregates more material at any point of itself than is required by the nature of the part. The result is then that either one of its parts is larger than the others, as a finger or hand or foot or any of the other extremities or limbs; or again if the embryo is cleft there may come into being more than one such part, as eddies do in rivers; as the water in these is carried along with a certain motion, if it dash against anything two systems or eddies come into being out of one, each retaining the same motion; the same thing happens also with the embryos. The abnormal parts generally are attached near those they resemble, but sometimes at a distance because of the movement taking place in the embryo, and especially because of the excess of material returning to that place whence it was taken away while retaining the form of that part whence it arose as a superfluity.

In certain cases we find a double set of generative organs [one male and the other female]. When such duplication occurs the one is always functional but not the other, because it is always insufficiently supplied with nourishment as being contrary to Nature; it is attached like a growth (for such growths also receive nourishment though they are a later development than the body proper and contrary to Nature.) If the formative power prevails, both are similar; if it is altogether vanquished, both are similar; but if it prevail here and be vanquished there, then the one is female and the other male. (For whether we consider the reason why the whole animal is male or female, or why the parts are so, makes no difference.)

When we meet with deficiency in such parts, e.g. an extremity or one of the other
773a members, we must assume the same cause as when the embryo is altogether aborted (abortion of embryos happens frequently).

Outgrowths differ from the production of many young in the manner stated before; monsters differ from these in that most of them are due to embryos growing together. Some however are also of the following kind, when the monstrosity affects greater and more sovereign parts, as for instance some monsters have two spleens or more than two kidneys. Further, the parts may migrate, the movements which form the embryo being diverted and the material changing its place. We must decide whether the monstrous animal is one or is composed of several grown together by considering the vital principle; thus, if the heart is a part of such a kind then that which has one heart will be one animal, the multiplied parts being mere outgrowths, but those which have more than one heart will be two animals grown together through their embryos having been confused.

It also often happens even in many animals that do not seem to be defective and whose growth is now complete, that some of their passages may have grown together or others may have been diverted from the normal course. Thus in some women before now the os uteri has remained closed, so that when the time for the catamenia has arrived pain has attacked them, till either the passage has burst open of its own accord or the physicians have removed the impediment; some such cases have ended in death if the rupture has been made too violently or if it has been impossible to make it at all. In some boys on the other hand the end of the penis has not coincided with the end of the passage where the urine is voided, but the passage has ended below, so that they crouch sitting to void it, and if the testes are drawn up they appear from a distance to have both male and female generative organs. The passage of the solid food also has been closed before now in sheep and some other animals; there was a cow in Perinthus which passed fine matter, as if it were sifted, through the bladder, and when the anus was cut open it quickly closed up again nor could they succeed in keeping it open.

We have now spoken of the production of few and many young, and of the outgrowth of superfluous parts or of their deficiency, and also of monstrosities.

5

Superfoetation does not occur at all in some animals but does in others; of the former some are able to bring the later formed embryo to birth, while others can only do so sometimes. The reason why it does not occur in some is
773b that they produce only one young one,
for it is not found in solid-hoofed animals and those larger than these, as owing to their size the secretion of the female is all used up for the one embryo. For all these have large bodies, and when an animal is large its foetus is large in proportion, e.g. the foetus of the elephant is as big as a calf. But superfoetation occurs in those which produce many young because the production of more than one at a birth is itself a sort of superfoetation, one being added to another. Of these all that are large, as man, bring to birth the later embryo, if the second impregnation takes place soon after the first, for such an event has been observed before now. The reason is that given above, for even in a single act of intercourse the semen discharged is more than enough for one embryo, and this being divided causes more than one child to be born, the one of which is later than the other. But when the embryo has already grown to some size and it so happens that copulation occurs again, superfoetation sometimes takes place, but rarely, since the uterus generally closes in women during the period of gestation. If this ever happens (for this also has occurred) the mother cannot bring the second embryo to perfection, but it is cast out in a state like what are called abortions. For just as, in those animals that bear only one, all the secretion of the female is converted to the first formed embryo because of its size, so it is here also; the only difference is that in the former case this happens at once, in the latter when the foetus has attained to some size, for then they are in the same state as those that bear only one. In like manner—since man naturally would produce many young, and since the size of the uterus and the quantity of the female secretion are both greater than is necessary for one embryo, only not so much so as to bring to birth a second—therefore women and mares are the only animals which admit the male during gestation, the former for the reason stated, and mares both because of the barrenness of their nature and because their uterus is of superfluous size, too large for one but too small to allow a second embryo to be brought to perfection by superfoetation. And the mare is naturally inclined to sexual intercourse because she is in the same case as the barren among women; these latter are barren because they have no monthly discharge (which corresponds to the act of intercourse in males) and mares have exceedingly little. And in all the vivipara the barren females are so inclined, because they resemble

the males when the semen has collected in the testes but is not being got rid of. For the discharge
774a of the catamenia is in females a sort of emission of semen, they being unconcocted semen as has been said before. Hence it is that those women also who are incontinent in regard to such intercourse cease from their passion for it when they have borne many children, for, the seminal secretion being then drained off, they no longer desire this intercourse. And among birds the hens are less disposed that way than the cocks, because the uterus of the hen-bird is up near the hypozoma; but with the cock-birds it is the other way, for their testes are drawn up within them so that, if any kind of such birds has much semen naturally, it is always in need of this intercourse. In females then it encourages copulation to have the uterus low down, but in males to have the testes drawn up.

It has been now stated why superfoetation is not found in some animals at all, why it is found in others which sometimes bring the later embryos to birth and sometimes not, and why some such animals are inclined to sexual intercourse while others are not.

Some of those animals in which superfoetation occurs can bring the embryos to birth even if a long time elapses between the two impregnations, if their kind is spermatic, if their body is not of a large size, and if they bear many young. For because they bear many their uterus is spacious, because they are spermatic the generative discharge is copious, and because the body is not large but the discharge is excessive and in greater measure than is required for the nourishment wanted for the embryo, therefore they can not only form animals but also bring them to birth later on. Further, the uterus in such animals does not close up during gestation because there is a quantity of the residual discharge left over. This has happened before now even in women, for in some of them the discharge continues during all the time of pregnancy. In women, however, this is contrary to Nature, so that the embryo suffers, but in such animals it is according to Nature, for their body is so formed from the beginning, as with hares. For superfoetation occurs in these animals, since they are not large and they bear many young (for they have many toes and the many-toed animals bear many), and they are spermatic. This is shown by their hairiness, for the quantity of their hair is excessive, these animals alone having hair under the feet and within the jaws. Now
774b hairiness is a sign of abundance of residual matter, wherefore among men also the hairy are given to sexual intercourse and have much semen rather than the smooth. In the hare it often happens that some of the embryos are imperfect while others of its young are produced perfect.

6

Some of the vivipara produce their young imperfect, others perfect; the one-hoofed and cloven-footed perfect, most of the many-toed imperfect. The reason of this is that the one-hoofed produce one young one, and the cloven-footed either one or two generally speaking; now it is easy to bring the few to perfection. All the many-toed animals that bear their young imperfect give birth to many. Hence, though they are able to nourish the embryos while newly formed, their bodies are unable to complete the process when the embryos have grown and acquired some size. So they produce them imperfect, like those animals which generate a scolex, for some of them when born are scarcely brought into form at all, as the fox, bear, and lion, and some of the rest in like manner; and nearly all of them are blind, as not only the animals mentioned but also the dog, wolf, and jackal. The pig alone produces both many and perfect young, and thus here alone we find any overlapping; it produces many as do the many-toed animals, but is cloven-footed or solid-hoofed (for there certainly are solid-hoofed swine). They bear, then, many young because the nutriment which would otherwise go to increase their size is diverted to the generative secretion (for considered as a solid-hoofed animal the pig is not a large one), and also it is more often cloven-hoofed, striving as it were with the nature of the solid-hoofed animals. For this reason it produces sometimes only one, sometimes two, but generally many, and brings them to perfection before birth because of the good condition of its body, being like a rich soil which has sufficient and abundant nutriment for plants.

The young of some birds also are hatched imperfect, that is to say blind; this applies to all small birds which lay many eggs, as crows and rooks, jays, sparrows, swallows, and to all those which lay few eggs without producing abundant nourishment along with the young, as ring-doves, turtle-doves, and pigeons. Hence if the eyes of swallows while still young be put out they recover their sight again, for the birds

are still developing, not yet developed, when the injury is inflicted, so that the eyes grow and sprout afresh. And in general the production of young before they are perfect is owing to inability to continue nourishing them, and they are born imperfect because they are born too soon. This is plain also with seven-months
775ª children, for since they are not perfected it often happens that even the passages, e.g. of the ears and nostrils, are not yet opened in some of them at birth, but only open later as they are growing, and many such infants survive.

In man males are more often born defective than females, but in the other animals this is not the case. The reason is that in man the male is much superior to the female in natural heat, and so the male foetus moves about more than the female, and on account of moving is more liable to injury, for what is young is easily injured since it is weak. For this same reason also the female foetus is not perfected equally with the male in man (but they are so in the other animals, for in them the female is not later in developing than the male). For while within the mother the female takes longer in developing, but after birth everything is perfected more quickly in females than in males; I mean, for instance, puberty, the prime of life, and old age. For females are weaker and colder in nature, and we must look upon the female character as being a sort of natural deficiency. Accordingly while it is within the mother it develops slowly because of its coldness (for development is concoction, and it is heat that concocts, and what is hotter is easily concocted); but after birth it quickly arrives at maturity and old age on account of its weakness, for all inferior things come sooner to their perfection or end, and as this is true of works of art so it is of what is formed by Nature. For the reason just given also twins are less likely to survive in man if one be male and one female, but this is not at all so in the other animals; for in man it is contrary to Nature that they should run an equal course, as their development does not take place in equal periods, but the male must needs be too late or the female too early; in the other animals, however, it is not contrary to Nature. A difference is also found between man and the other animals in respect of gestation, for animals are in better bodily condition most of the time, whereas in most women gestation is attended with discomfort. Their way of life is partly responsible for this, for being sedentary they are full of more residual matter; among nations where the women live a laborious life gestation is not equally conspicuous and those who are accustomed to work bear children easily both there and elsewhere; for work consumes the residual matter, but those who are sedentary have a great deal of it in them because not only is there no monthly discharge during pregnancy but also they do no work; therefore their travail is painful. But
775ᵇ work exercises them so that they can hold their breath, upon which depends the ease or difficulty of child-birth. These circumstances then, as we have said, contribute to cause the difference between women and the other animals in this state, but the most important thing is this: in some animals the discharge corresponding to the catamenia is but small, and in some not visible at all, but in women it is greater than in any other animal, so that when this discharge ceases owing to pregnancy they are troubled (for if they are not pregnant they are afflicted with ailments whenever the catamenia do not occur); and they are more troubled as a rule at the beginning of pregnancy, for the embryo is able indeed to stop the catamenia but is too small at first to consume any quantity of the secretion; later on it takes up some of it and so alleviates the mother. In the other animals, on the contrary, the residual matter is but small and so corresponds with the growth of the foetus, and as the secretions which hinder nourishment are being consumed by the foetus the mother is in better bodily condition than usual. The same holds good also with aquatic animals and birds. If it ever happens that the body of the mother is no longer in good condition when the foetus is now becoming large, the reason is that its growth needs more nourishment than the residual matter supplies. (In some few women it happens that the body is in a better state during pregnancy; these are women in whose body the residual matter is small so that it is all used up along with the nourishment that goes to the foetus.)

7

We must also speak of what is known as *mola uteri,* which occurs rarely in women but still is found sometimes during pregnancy. For they produce what is called a *mola;* it has happened before now to a woman, after she had had intercourse with her husband and supposed she had conceived, that at first the size of her belly increased and everything else happened accordingly, but yet when the time for birth came on, she neither bore a child nor was her size reduced, but she continued thus for three or four years until dysentery came on, endangering her life, and she produced a lump of flesh which is called *mola*. Moreover this condition may continue till old age and death. Such masses when expelled from the body become so hard that they can hardly be cut through even by iron. Concerning the cause of this phenomenon we have spoken in the *Problems;* the same thing happens to the embryo **776a** in the womb as to meats half cooked in roasting, and it is not due to heat, as some say, but rather to the weakness of the maternal heat. (For their nature seems to be incapable, and unable to perfect or to put the last touches to the process of generation. Hence it is that the *mola* remains in them till old age or at any rate for a long time, for in its nature it is neither perfect nor altogether a foreign body.) It is want of concoction that is the reason of its hardness, as with half-cooked meat, for this half-dressing of meat is also a sort of want of concoction.

A difficulty is raised as to why this does not occur in other animals, unless indeed it does occur and has entirely escaped observation. We must suppose the reason to be that woman alone among animals is subject to troubles of the uterus, and alone has a superfluous amount of catamenia and is unable to concoct them; when, then, the embryo has been formed of a liquid hard to concoct, then comes the so-called *mola* into being, and this happens naturally in women alone or at any rate more than in other animals.

8

Milk is formed in the females of all internally viviparous animals, becoming useful for the time of birth. For Nature has made it for the sake of the nourishment of animals after birth, so that it may neither fail at this time at all nor yet be at all superfluous; this is just what we find happening, unless anything chance contrary to Nature. In the other animals the period of gestation does not vary, and so the milk is concocted in time to suit this moment, but in man, since there are several times of birth, it must be ready at the first of these; hence in women the milk is useless before the seventh month and only then becomes useful. That it is only concocted at the last stages is what we should expect to happen also as being due to a necessary cause. For at first such residual matter when secreted is used up for the development of the embryo; now the nutritious part in all things is the sweetest and the most concocted, and thus when all such elements are removed what remains must become of necessity bitter and ill-flavoured. As the embryo is perfecting, the residual matter left over increases in quantity because the part consumed by the embryo is less; it is also sweeter since the easily concocted part is less drawn away from it. For it is no longer expended on moulding the embryo but only on slightly increasing its growth, it being now fixed because it has reached perfection (for in **776b** a sense there is a perfection even of an embryo). Therefore it comes forth from the mother and changes its mode of development, as now possessing what belongs to it; and no longer takes that which does not belong to it; and it is at this season that the milk becomes useful.

The milk collects in the upper part of the body and the breasts because of the original plan of the organism. For the part above the hypozoma is the sovereign part of the animal, while that below is concerned with nourishment and residual matter, in order that all animals which move about may contain within themselves nourishment enough to make them independent when they move from one place to another. From this upper part also is produced the generative secretion for the reason mentioned in the opening of our discussion. But both the secretion of the male and the catamenia of the female are of a sanguineous nature, and the first principle of this blood and of the blood-vessels is the heart, and the heart is in this part of the body. Therefore it is here that the change of such a secretion must first become plain. This is why the voice changes in both sexes when they begin to bear seed (for the first principle of the voice resides there, and is itself changed when its moving cause changes). At the same time the parts about the breasts are raised visibly even in males but still more in females, for the region of the breasts becomes empty and spongy in them because so much material is drained away below. This is so not only in women but also in those animals which have the mammae low down.

This change in the voice and the parts about the mammae is plain even in other creatures to those who have experience of each kind of animal, but is most remarkable in man. The reason is that in man the production of secretion is greatest in both sexes in proportion to their size as compared with other animals; I mean that of the catamenia in women and the emission of semen in men. When, therefore, the embryo no longer takes up the secretion in question but yet prevents its being discharged from the mother, it is necessary that all the residual matter should collect in all those empty parts which are set upon the same passages. And such is the position of the mammae in each kind of animals for both causes; it is so both for the sake of what is best and of necessity.

It is here, then, that the nourishment in animals is now formed and becomes thoroughly concocted. As for the cause of concoction, we may take that already given, or we may take **777a** the opposite, for it is a reasonable view also that the embryo being larger takes more nourishment, so that less is left over about this time, and the less is concocted more quickly.

That milk has the same nature as the secretion from which each animal is formed is plain, and has been stated previously. For the material which nourishes is the same as that from which Nature forms the animal in generation. Now this is the sanguineous liquid in the sanguinea, and milk is blood concocted (not corrupted; Empedocles either mistook the fact or made a bad metaphor when he composed the line: 'On the tenth day of the eighth month the milk comes into being, a white pus', for putrefaction and concoction are opposite things, and pus is a kind of putrefaction but milk is concocted). While women are suckling children the catamenia do not occur according to Nature, nor do they conceive; if they do conceive, the milk dries up. This is because the nature of the milk and of the catamenia is the same, and Nature cannot be so productive as to supply both at once; if the secretion is diverted in the one direction it must needs cease in the other, unless some violence is done contrary to the general rule. But this is as much as to say that it is contrary to Nature, for in all cases where it is not impossible for things to be otherwise than they generally are but where they may so happen, still what is the general rule is what is 'according to Nature'.

The time also at which the young animal is born has been well arranged. For when the nourishment coming through the umbilical cord is no longer sufficient for the foetus because of its size, then at the same time the milk becomes useful for the nourishment of the newly-born animal, and the blood-vessels round which the so-called umbilical cord lies as a coat collapse as the nourishment is no longer passing through it; for these reasons it is at that time also that the young animal enters into the world.

9

The natural birth of all animals is head-foremost, because the parts above the umbilical cord are larger than those below. The body then, being suspended from the cord as in a balance, inclines towards the heavy end, and the larger parts are the heavier.

10

The period of gestation is, as a matter of fact, determined generally in each animal in proportion to the length of its life. This we should expect, for it is reasonable that the development of the long-lived animals should take a longer time. Yet this is not the cause of it, but the periods only correspond accidentally for the most part; for though the larger and more **777b** perfect sanguinea do live a long time, yet the larger are not all longer-lived. Man lives a longer time than any animal of which we have any credible experience except the elephant, and yet the human kind is smaller than that of the bushy-tailed animals and many others. The real cause of long life in any animal is its being tempered in a manner resembling the environing air, along with certain other circumstances of its nature, of which we will speak later; but the cause of the time of gestation is the size of the offspring. For it is not easy for large masses to arrive at their perfection in a small time, whether they be animals or, one may say, anything else whatever. That is why horses and animals akin to them, though living a shorter time than man, yet carry their young longer; for the time in the former is a year, but in the latter ten months at the outside. For the same reason also the time is long in elephants; they carry their young two years on account of their excessive size.

We find, as we might expect, that in all animals the time of gestation and development and the length of life aims at being measured by naturally complete periods. By a natural period I mean, e.g. a day and night, a month, a year, and the greater times measured by these, and also the periods of the moon, that is to say, the full moon and her disappearance and the halves of the times between these, for it is by these that the moon's orbit fits in with that of the sun [the month being a period common to both].

The moon is a first principle because of her connexion with the sun and her participation in his light, being as it were a second smaller sun, and therefore she contributes to all generation and development. For heat and cold varying within certain limits make things to come into being and after this to perish, and it is the motions of the sun and moon that fix the limit both of the beginning and of the end of these processes. Just as we see the sea and all bodies of water settling and changing according to the movement or rest of the winds, and the air and winds again according to the course of the sun and moon, so also the things which grow out of these or are in these **778a** must needs follow suit. For it is reasonable that the periods of the less important should follow those of the more important. For in a sense a wind, too, has a life and birth and death.

As for the revolutions of the sun and moon, they may perhaps depend on other principles. It is the aim, then, of Nature to measure the coming into being and the end of animals by the measure of these higher periods, but she does not bring this to pass accurately because matter cannot be easily brought under rule and because there are many principles which hinder generation and decay from being according to Nature, and often cause things to fall out contrary to Nature.

We have now spoken of the nourishment of animals within the mother and of their birth into the world, both of each kind separately and of all in common.

BOOK V

I

We must now investigate the qualities by which the parts of animals differ. I mean such qualities of the parts as blueness and blackness in the eyes, height and depth of pitch in the voice, and differences in colour whether of the skin or of hair and feathers. Some such qualities are found to characterize the whole of a kind of animals sometimes, while in other kinds they occur at random, as is especially the case in man. Further, in connexion with the changes in the time of life, all animals are alike in some points, but are opposed in others as in the case of the voice and the colour of the hair, for some do not grow grey visibly in old age, while man is subject to this more than any other animal. And some of these affections appear immediately after birth, while others become plain as age advances or in old age.

Now we must no longer suppose that the cause of these and all such phenomena is the same. For whenever things are not the product of Nature working upon the animal kingdom as a whole, nor yet characteristic of each separate kind, then none of these things is such as it is or is so developed for any final cause. The eye for instance exists for a final cause, but it is not blue for a final cause unless this condition be characteristic of the kind of animal. In fact in some cases this condition has no connexion with the essence of the animal's being, but we must refer the causes to the ma- **778b** terial and the motive principle or efficient cause, on the view that these things come into being by Necessity. For, as was said originally in the outset of our discussion, when we are dealing with definite and ordered products of Nature, we must not say that each *is* of a certain quality because it *becomes* so, but rather that they *become* so and so because they *are* so and so, for the process of Becoming or development attends upon Being and is for the sake of Being, not *vice versa*.

The ancient Nature-philosophers however took the opposite view. The reason of this is that they did not see that the causes were numerous, but only saw the material and efficient and did not distinguish even these, while they made no inquiry at all into the formal and final causes.

Everything then exists for a final cause, and all those things which are included in the definition of each animal, or which either are means to an end or are ends in themselves, come into being both through this cause and the rest. But when we come to those things which come into being without falling under the heads just mentioned, their course must be sought in the movement or process of coming into being, on the view that the differences which mark them arise in the actual formation of the animal. An eye, for instance, the animal must have of necessity (for the fundamental idea of the animal is of such a kind), but it will have an eye of a particular kind of necessity in another sense, not the sense mentioned just above, because it is its nature to act or be acted on in this or that way.

These distinctions being drawn let us speak of what comes next in order. As soon then as the offspring of all animals are born, especially those born imperfect, they are in the habit of sleeping, because they continue sleeping also within the mother when they first acquire sensation. But there is a difficulty about the earliest period of development, whether the state of wakefulness exists in animals first, or that of sleep. Since they plainly wake up more as they grow older, it is reasonable to suppose that the opposite state, that of sleep, exists in the first stages of development. Moreover the change from not being to being must pass through the intermediate condition, and sleep seems to be in its nature such a condition, being as it were a boundary between living and not living, and the sleeper being neither altogether non-existent nor yet existent. For life most of all appertains to wakefulness, on account of sensation. But on the other hand, if it is necessary that the animal should have sensation and if it is then first an animal when it has acquired sensation, we ought to consider the original condition to be not sleep but only something resembling sleep, such a condition **779a** as we find also in plants, for indeed at this time animals do actually live the life of a plant. But it is impossible that plants should sleep, for there is no sleep which cannot be broken, and the condition in plants which is analogous to sleep cannot be broken.

It is necessary then for the embryo animal to sleep most of the time because the growth takes place in the upper part of the body, which is consequently heavier (and we have stated elsewhere that such is the cause of sleep).[1] But nevertheless they are found to wake even in the womb (this is clear in dissections and in the ovipara), and then they immediately fall into a sleep again. This is why after birth also they spend most of their time in sleep.

When awake infants do not laugh, but while asleep they both laugh and cry. For animals have sensations even while asleep, not only what are called dreams but also others besides dreams, as those persons who arise while sleeping and do many things without dreaming. For there are some who get up while sleeping and walk about seeing just like those who are awake; these have perception of what is happening, and though they are not awake, yet this perception is not like a dream. So infants presumably have sense-perception and live in their sleep owing to previous habit, being as it were without knowledge of the waking state. As time goes on and their growth is transferred to the lower part of the body, they now wake up more and spend most of their time in that condition. Children continue asleep at first more than other animals, for they are born in a more imperfect condition than other animals that are produced in anything like a perfect state, and their growth has taken place more in the upper part of the body.

The eyes of all children are bluish immediately after birth; later on they change to the colour which is to be theirs permanently. But in the case of other animals this is not visible. The reason of this is that the eyes of other animals are more apt to have only one colour for each kind of animal; e.g. cattle are dark-eyed, the eye of all sheep is pale, of others again the whole kind is blue or grey-eyed, and some are yellow (goat-eyed), as the majority of goats themselves, whereas the eyes of men happen to be of many colours, for they are blue or grey or **779b** dark in some cases and yellow in others. Hence, as the individuals in other kinds of animals do not differ from one another in the colour, so neither do they differ from themselves, for they are not of a nature to have more than one colour. Of the other animals the horse has the greatest variety of colour in the eye, for some of them are actually heteroglaucous; this phenomenon is not to be seen in any of the other animals, but man is sometimes heteroglaucous.

Why then is it that there is no visible change in the other animals if we compare their condition when newly born with their condition at a more advanced age, but that there is such a change in children? We must consider just this to be a sufficient cause, that the part concerned has only one colour in the former but several colours in the latter. And the reason why the eyes of infants are bluish and have no other colour is that the parts are weaker in the newly born and blueness is a sort of weakness.

We must also gain a general notion about the difference in eyes, for what reason some are blue, some grey, some yellow, and some dark. To suppose that the blue are fiery, as Empedocles says, while the dark have more water than fire in them, and that this is why the former, the blue, have not keen sight by day, viz. owing to deficiency of water in their composition, and the latter are in like condition by

[1] *On Sleep and Sleeplessness*, 456b 26.

night, viz. owing to deficiency of fire—this is not well said if indeed we are to assume sight to be connected with water, not fire, in all cases. Moreover it is possible to render another account of the cause of the colours, but if indeed the fact is as was stated before in the treatise on the senses, and still earlier than that in the investigations concerning soul[1]—if this sense organ is composed of water and if we were right in saying for what reason it is composed of water and not of air or fire—then we must assume the water to be the cause of the colours mentioned. For some eyes have too much liquid to be adapted to the movement, others have too little, others the due amount. Those eyes therefore in which there is much liquid are dark because much liquid is not transparent, those which have little are blue; (so we find in the sea that the transparent part of it appears light blue, the less transparent watery, and the unfathomable water is dark or deep-blue on account of its depth). When we come to the eyes between these, they differ only in degree.

We must suppose the same cause also to be responsible for the fact that blue eyes are not keen-sighted by day nor dark eyes by night. **780a** Blue eyes, because there is little liquid in them, are too much moved by the light and by visible objects in respect of their liquidity as well as their transparency, but sight is the movement of this part in so far as it is transparent, not in so far as it is liquid. Dark eyes are less moved because of the quantity of liquid in them. And so they see less well in the dusk, for the nocturnal light is weak; at the same time also liquid is in general hard to move in the night. But if the eye is to see, it must neither not be moved at all nor yet more than in so far as it is transparent, for the stronger movement drives out the weaker. Hence it is that on changing from strong colours, or on going out of the sun into the dark, men cannot see, for the motion already existing in the eye, being strong, stops that from outside, and in general neither a strong nor a weak sight can see bright things because the liquid is acted upon and moved too much.

The same thing is shown also by the morbid affections of each kind of sight. Cataract attacks the blue-eyed more, but what is called 'nyctalopia' the dark-eyed. Now cataract is a sort of dryness of the eyes and therefore it is found more in the aged, for this part also like the rest of the body gets dry towards old age; but nyctalopia is an excess of liquidity and so is found more in the younger, for their brain is more liquid.

The sight of the eye which is intermediate between too much and too little liquid is the best, for it has neither too little so as to be disturbed and hinder the movement of the colours, nor too much so as to cause difficulty of movement.

Not only the above-mentioned facts are causes of seeing keenly or the reverse, but also the nature of the skin upon what is called the pupil. This ought to be transparent, and it is necessary that the transparent should be thin and white and even, thin that the movement coming from without may pass straight through it, even that it may not cast a shade upon the liquid behind it by wrinkling (for this also is a reason why old men have not keen sight, the skin of the eye like the rest of the skin wrinkling and becoming thicker in old age), and white because black is not transparent, for that is just what is meant by 'black', what is not shone through, and that is why lanterns cannot give light if they be made of black skin. It is for these reasons then that the sight **780b** is not keen in old age nor in the diseases in question, but it is because of the small amount of liquid that the eyes of children appear blue at first.

And the reason why men especially and horses occasionally are heteroglaucous is the same as the reason why man alone grows grey and the horse is the only other animal whose hairs whiten visibly in old age. For greyness is a weakness of the fluid in the brain and an incapacity to concoct properly, and so is blueness of the eyes; excess of thinness or of thickness produces the same effect, according as this liquidity is too little or too much. Whenever then Nature cannot make the eyes correspond exactly, either by concocting or by not concocting the liquid in both, but concocts the one and not the other, then the result is heteroglaucia.

The cause of some animals being keen-sighted and others not so is not simple but double. For the word 'keen' has pretty much a double sense (and this is the case in like manner with hearing and smelling). In one sense keen sight means the power of seeing at a distance, in another it means the power of distinguishing as accurately as possible the objects seen. These two faculties are not necessarily combined in the same individual. For the same person, if he shades his eyes with his hand or look

[1] *Sense and the Sensible*, 2; *On the Soul*, III, 425a 4.

through a tube, does not distinguish the differences of colour either more or less in any way, but he will see further; in fact, men in pits or wells sometimes see the stars. Therefore if any animal's brows project far over the eye, but if the liquid in the pupil is not pure nor suited to the movement coming from external objects and if the skin over the surface is not thin, this animal will not distinguish accurately the differences of the colours but it will be able to see from a long distance (just as it can from a short one) better than those in which the liquid and the covering membrane are pure but which have no brows projecting over the eyes. For the cause of seeing keenly in the sense of distinguishing the differences is in the eye itself; as on a clean garment even small stains are visible, so also in a pure sight even small movements are plain and cause sensation. But it is the position of the eyes that is the cause of seeing things far off and of the movements in the transparent medium coming to the eyes from distant objects. A proof of this is that animals with prominent eyes do not see well at a distance, whereas those which have **781a** their eyes lying deep in the head can see things at a distance because the movement is not dispersed in space but comes straight to the eye. For it makes no difference whether we say, as some do, that seeing is caused by the sight going forth from the eye—on that view, if there is nothing projecting over the eyes, the sight must be scattered and so less of it will fall on the objects of vision and things at a distance will not be seen so well—or whether we say that seeing is due to the movement coming from the objects; for the sight also must see, in a manner resembling the movement. Things at a distance, then, would be seen best if there were, so to say, a continuous tube straight from the sight to its object, for the movement from the object would not then be dissipated; but, if that is impossible, still the further the tube extends the more accurately must distant objects be seen.

Let these, then, be given as the causes of the difference in eyes.

2

It is the same also with hearing and smell; to hear and smell accurately mean in one sense to perceive as precisely as possible all the distinctions of the objects of perception, in another sense to hear and smell far off. As with sight, so here the sense-organ is the cause of judging well the distinctions, if both that organ itself and the membrane round it be pure. For the passages of all the sense-organs, as has been said in the treatise on sensation, run to the heart, or to its analogue in creatures that have no heart. The passage of the hearing, then, since this sense-organ is of air, ends at the place where the innate spiritus causes in some animals the pulsation of the heart and in others respiration; wherefore also it is that we are able to understand what is said and repeat what we have heard, for as was the movement which entered through the sense-organ, such again is the movement which is caused by means of the voice, being as it were of one and the same stamp, so that a man can say what he has heard. And we hear less well during a yawn or expiration than during inspiration, because the starting-point of the sense-organ of hearing is set upon the part concerned with breathing and is shaken and moved as the organ moves the breath, for while setting the breath in motion it is moved itself. The same thing happens in wet weather or a damp atmosphere. . . . And the ears seemed to be filled **781b** with air because their starting-point is near the region of breathing.

Accuracy then in judging the differences of sounds and smells depends on the purity of the sense-organ and of the membrane lying upon its surface, for then all the movements become clear in such cases, as in the case of sight. Perception and non-perception at a distance also depend on the same things with hearing and smell as with sight. For those animals can perceive at a distance which have channels, so to say, running through the parts concerned and projecting far in front of the sense-organs. Therefore all animals whose nostrils are long, as the Laconian hounds, are keen-scented, for the sense-organ being above them, the movements from a distance are not dissipated but go straight to the mark, just as the movements which cause sight do with those who shadow the eyes with the hand.

Similar is the case of animals whose ears are long and project far like the eaves of a house, as in some quadrupeds, with the internal spiral passage long; these also catch the movement from afar and pass it on to the sense-organ.

In respect of sense-perception at a distance, man is, one may say, the worst of all animals in proportion to his size, but in respect of judging the differences of quality in the objects he is the best of all. The reason is that the sense-organ in man is pure and least earthy and material, and he is by nature the thinnest-skinned of all animals for his size.

The workmanship of Nature is admirable also in the seal, for though a viviparous quadruped it has no ears but only passages for hearing. This is because its life is passed in the water; now the ear is a part added to the passages to preserve the movement of the air at a distance; therefore an ear is no use to it but would even bring about the contrary result by receiving a mass of water into itself.

We have thus spoken of sight, hearing, and smell.

3

As for hair, men differ in this themselves at different ages, and also from all other kinds of animals that have hair. These are almost all which are internally viviparous, for even when the covering of such animals is spiny it must be considered as a kind of hair, as in the land **782a** hedgehog and any other such animal among the vivipara. Hairs differ in respect of hardness and softness, length and shortness, straightness and curliness, quantity and scantiness, and in addition to these qualities, in their colours, whiteness and blackness and the intermediate shades. They differ also in some of these respects according to age, as they are young or growing old. This is especially plain in man; the hair gets coarser as time goes on, and some go bald on the front of the head; children indeed do not go bald, nor do women, but men do so by the time their age is advancing. Human beings also go grey on the head as they grow old, but this is not visible in practically any other animal, though more so in the horse than others. Men go bald on the front of the head, but turn grey first on the temples; no one goes bald first on these or on the back of the head. Some such affections occur in a corresponding manner also in all animals which have not hair but something analogous to it, as the feathers of birds and scales in the class of fish.

For what purpose Nature has made hair in general for animals has been previously stated in the work dealing with the causes of the parts of animals;[1] it is the business of the present inquiry to show under what circumstances and for what necessary causes each particular kind of hair occurs. The principal cause then of thickness and thinness is the skin, for this is thick in some animals and thin in others, rare in some and dense in others. The different quality of the included moisture is also a helping cause, for in some animals this is greasy and in others watery. For generally speaking the substratum of the skin is of an earthy nature; being on the surface of the body it becomes solid and earthy as the moisture evaporates. Now the hairs or their analogue are not formed out of the flesh but out of the skin [the moisture evaporating and exhaling in them, and therefore thick hairs arise from a thick skin and thin from a thin]. If then the skin is rarer and thicker, the hairs are thick because of the quantity of earthy matter **782b** and the size of the pores, but if it is denser they are thin because of the narrowness of the pores. Further, if the moisture be watery it dries up quickly and the hairs do not gain in size, but if it be greasy the opposite happens, for the greasy is not easily dried up. Therefore the thicker-skinned animals are as a general rule thicker-haired for the causes mentioned; however, the thickest-skinned are not more so than other thick-skinned ones, as is shown by the class of swine compared to that of oxen and to the elephant and many others. And for the same reason also the hairs of the head in man are thickest, for this part of his skin is thickest and lies over most moisture and besides is very porous.

The cause of the hairs being long or short depends on the evaporating moisture not being easily dried. Of this there are two causes, quantity and quality; if the liquid is much it does not dry up easily nor if it is greasy. And for this reason the hairs of the head are longest in man, for the brain, being fluid and cold, supplies great abundance of moisture.

The hairs become straight or curly on account of the vapour arising in them. If it be smoke-like, it is hot and dry and so makes the hair curly, for it is twisted as being carried with a double motion, the earthy part tending downwards and the hot upwards. Thus, being easily bent, it is twisted owing to its weakness, and this is what is meant by curliness in hair. It is possible then that this is the cause, but it is also possible that, owing to its having but little moisture and much earthy matter in it, it is dried by the surrounding air and so coiled up together. For what is straight becomes bent, if the moisture in it is evaporated, and runs together as a hair does when burning upon the fire; curliness will then be a contraction owing to deficiency of moisture caused by the heat of the environment. A sign of this is the fact that curly hair is

[1] *On the Parts of Animals*, II, 658a 18.

harder than straight, for the dry is hard. And animals with much moisture are straight-haired; for in these hairs the moisture advances as a stream, not in drops. For this reason the Scythians on the Black Sea and the Thracians are straight-haired, for both they themselves and the environing air are moist, whereas the Aethiopians and men in hot coun-
783a tries are curly-haired, for their brains and the surrounding air are dry.

Some, however, of the thick-skinned animals are fine-haired for the cause previously stated, for the finer the pores are the finer must the hairs be. Hence the class of sheep have such hairs (for wool is only a multitude of hairs).

There are some animals whose hair is soft and yet less fine, as is the case with the class of hares compared with that of sheep; in such animals the hair is on the surface of the skin, not deeply rooted in it, and so is not long but in much the same state as the scrapings from linen, for these also are not long but are soft and do not admit of weaving.

The condition of sheep in cold climates is opposite to that of man; the hair of the Scythians is soft but that of the Sauromatic sheep is hard. The reason of this is the same as it is also in all wild animals. The cold hardens and solidifies them by drying them, for as the heat is pressed out the moisture evaporates, and both hair and skin become earthy and hard. In wild animals then the exposure to the cold is the cause of hardness in the hair, in the others the nature of the climate is the cause. A proof of this is also what happens in the sea-urchins which are used as a remedy in stranguries. For these, too, though small themselves, have large and hard spines because the sea in which they live is cold on account of its depth (for they are found in sixty fathoms and even more). The spines are large because the growth of the body is diverted to them, since having little heat in them they do not concoct their nutriment and so have much residual matter and it is from this that spines, hairs, and such things are formed; they are hard and petrified through the congealing effect of the cold. In the same way also plants are found to be harder, more earthy, and stony, if the region in which they grow looks to the north than if it looks to the south, and those in windy places than those in sheltered, for they are all more chilled and their moisture evaporates.

Hardening, then, comes of both heat and cold, for both cause the moisture to evaporate, heat *per se* and cold *per accidens* (since the moisture goes out of things along with the heat, there being no moisture without heat),
783b but whereas cold not only hardens but also condenses, heat makes a substance rarer.

For the same reason, as animals grow older, the hairs become harder in those which have hairs, and the feathers and scales in the feathered and scaly kinds. For their skins become harder and thicker as they get older, for they are dried up, and old age, as the word denotes, is earthy because the heat fails and the moisture along with it.

Men go bald visibly more than any other animal, but still such a state is something general, for among plants also some are evergreens while others are deciduous, and birds which hibernate shed their feathers. Similar to this is the condition of baldness in those human beings to whom it is incident. For leaves are shed by all plants, from one part of the plant at a time, and so are feathers and hairs by those animals that have them; it is when they are all shed together that the condition is described by the terms mentioned, for it is called 'going bald' and 'the fall of the leaf' and 'moulting'. The cause of the condition is deficiency of hot moisture, such moisture being especially the unctuous, and hence unctuous plants are more evergreen. (However we must elsewhere state the cause of this phenomena in plants, for other causes also contribute to it.) It is in winter that this happens to plants (for the change from summer to winter is more important to them than the time of life), and to those animals which hibernate (for these, too, are by nature less hot and moist than man); in the latter it is the seasons of life that correspond to summer and winter. Hence no one goes bald before the time of sexual intercourse, and at that time it is in those naturally inclined to such intercourse that baldness appears, for the brain is naturally the coldest part of the body and sexual intercourse makes men cold, being a loss of pure natural heat. Thus we should expect the brain to feel the effect of it first, for a little cause turns the scale where the thing concerned is weak and in poor condition. Thus if we reckon up these points, that the brain itself has but little heat, and further that the skin round it must needs have still less, and again that the hair must have still less than the skin inasmuch as it is furthest removed from the brain, we should reasonably expect baldness to come about this age upon those who have much semen. And it is for the same reason that the front part of the head alone goes bald **784a** in man and that he is the only animal to do so; the front part goes bald because the brain is there, and man is the only animal to go bald because his brain is much the largest and the moistest. Women do not go bald because their nature is like that of children, both alike being incapable of producing seminal secretion. Eunuchs do not become bald, because they change into the female condition. And as to the hair that comes later in life, eunuchs either do not grow it at all, or lose it if they happen to have it, with the exception of the pubic hair; for women also grow that though they have not the other, and this mutilation is a change from the male to the female condition.

The reason why the hair does not grow again in cases of baldness, although both hibernating animals recover their feathers or hair and trees that have shed their leaves grow leaves again, is this. The seasons of the year are the turning-points of their lives, rather than their age, so that when these seasons change they change with them by growing and losing feathers, hairs, or leaves respectively. But the winter and summer, spring and autumn of man are defined by his age, so that, since his ages do not return, neither do the conditions caused by them return, although the cause of the change of condition is similar in man to what it is in the animals and plants in question.

We have now spoken pretty much of all the other conditions of hair.

4

But as to their colour, it is the nature of the skin that is the cause of this in other animals (and also of their being unicoloured or varicoloured); but in man it is not the cause, except of the hair going grey through disease (not through old age), for in what is called leprosy the hairs become white; on the contrary, if the hairs are white the whiteness does not invade the skin. The reason is that the hairs grow out of skin; if, then, the skin is diseased and white the hair becomes diseased with it, and the disease of hair is greyness. But the greyness of hair which is due to age results from weakness and deficiency of heat. For as the body declines in vigour we tend to cold at every time of life, and especially in old age, this age being cold and dry. We must remember that the nutriment coming to each part of the body is concocted by the heat ap-
784b propriate to the part; if the heat is inadequate the part loses its efficiency, and destruction or disease results. (We shall speak more in detail of causes in the treatise on growth and nutrition.) Whenever, then, the hair in man has naturally little heat and too much moisture enters it, its own proper heat is unable to concoct the moisture and so it is decayed by the heat in the environing air. All decay is caused by heat, not the innate heat but external heat, as has been stated elsewhere.[1] And as there is a decay of water, of earth, and all such material bodies, so there is also of the earthy vapour, for instance what is called mould (for mould is a decay of earthy vapour). Thus also the liquid nutriment in the hair decays because it is not concocted, and what is called greyness results. It is white because mould also, practically alone among decayed things, is white. The reason of this is that it has much air in it, all earthy vapour being equivalent to thick air. For mould is, as it were, the antithesis of hoar-frost; if the ascending vapour be frozen it becomes hoar-frost, if it be decayed, mould. Hence both are on the surface of things, for vapour is superficial. And so the comic poets make a good metaphor in jest when they call grey hairs 'mould of old age' and 'hoar-frost'. For the one is generically the same as greyness, the other specifically; hoar-frost generically (for both are a vapour), mould specifically (for both are a form of decay). A proof that this is so is this: grey hairs have often grown on men in consequence of disease, and later on dark hairs instead of them after restoration to health. The reason is that in sickness the whole body is deficient in natural heat and so the parts besides, even the very small ones, participate in this weakness; and again, much residual matter is formed in the body and all its parts in illness, wherefore the incapacity in the flesh to concoct the nutriment causes the grey hairs. But when men have recovered health and strength again they change, becoming as it were young again instead of old; in consequence the states change also. Indeed, we may rightly call disease an acquired old age, old age a natural disease; at any rate, some diseases produce the same effects as old age.

Men go grey on the temples first, because the back of the head is empty of moisture ow-
785a ing to its containing no brain, and the

[1] *Meteorology*, IV, 379a 18.

'bregma' has a great deal of moisture, a large quantity not being liable to decay; the hair on the temples however has neither so little that it can concoct it nor so much that it cannot decay, for this region of the head being between the two extremes is exempt from both states. The cause of greyness in man has now been stated.

5

The reason why this change does not take place visibly on account of age in other animals is the same as that already given in the case of baldness; their brain is small and less fluid than in man, so that the heat required for concoction does not altogether fail. Among them it is most clear in horses of all animals that we know, because the bone about the brain is thinner in them than in others in proportion to their size. A sign of this is that a blow on this spot is fatal to them, wherefore Homer also has said: 'where the first hairs grow on the skull of horses, and a wound is most fatal'.[1] As then the moisture easily flows to these hairs because of the thinness of the bone, whilst the heat fails on account of age, they go grey. The reddish hairs go grey sooner than the black, redness also being a sort of weakness of hair and all weak things ageing sooner. It is said, however, that cranes become darker as they grow old. The reason of this would be, if it should prove true, that their feathers are naturally moister than others and as they grow old the moisture in the feathers is too much to decay easily.

Greyness comes about by some sort of decay, and is not, as some think, a withering. (1) A proof of the former statement is the fact that hair protected by hats or other coverings goes grey sooner (for the winds prevent decay and the protection keeps off the winds), and the fact that it is aided by anointing with a mixture of oil and water. For, though water cools things, the oil mingled with it prevents the hair from drying quickly, water being easily dried up. (2) That the process is not a withering, that the hair does not whiten as grass does by withering, is shown by the fact that some hairs grow grey from the first, whereas nothing springs up in a withered state. Many hairs also whiten at the tip, for there is least heat in the extremities and thinnest parts.

785b When the hairs of other animals are white, this is caused by nature, not by any affection. The cause of the colours in other animals is the skin; if they are white, the skin is white, if they are dark it is dark, if they are piebald in consequence of a mixture of the hairs, it is found to be white in the one part and dark in the other. But in man the skin is in no way the cause, for even white-skinned men have very dark hair. The reason is that man has the thinnest skin of all animals in proportion to his size and therefore it has not strength to change the hairs; on the contrary the skin itself changes its colour through its weakness and is darkened by sun and wind, while the hairs do not change along with it at all. But in the other animals the skin, owing to its thickness, has the influence belonging to the soil in which a thing grows, therefore the hairs change according to the skin but the skin does not change at all in consequence of the winds and the sun.

6

Of animals some are uni-coloured (I mean by this term those of which the kind as a whole has one colour, as all lions are tawny; and this condition exists also in birds, fish, and the other classes of animals alike); others though many-coloured are yet whole-coloured (I mean those whose body as a whole has the same colour, as a bull is white as a whole or dark as a whole); others are vari-coloured. This last term is used in both ways; sometimes the whole kind is vari-coloured, as leopards and peacocks, and some fish, e.g. the so-called 'thrattai'; sometimes the kind as a whole is not so, but such individuals are found in it, as with cattle and goats and, among birds, pigeons; the same applies also to other kinds of birds. The whole-coloured change much more than the uniformly coloured, both into the simple colour of another individual of the same kind (as dark changing into white and *vice versa*) and into both colours mingled. This is because it is a natural characteristic of the kind as a whole not to have one colour only, the kind being easily moved in both directions so that the colours both change more into one another and are more varied. The opposite holds with the uniformly coloured; they do not change except by an affection of the colour, and that rarely; but still they do so change, for before now white individuals have been observed among partridges, ravens, sparrows, and bears. This happens when the course of development is perverted, for what is small is easily spoilt and easily moved, and what is develop-

[1] *Iliad*, VIII. 83, 84.

786a ing is small, the beginning of all such things being on a small scale.

Change is especially found in those animals of which by nature the individual is whole-coloured but the kind many-coloured. This is owing to the water which they drink, for hot waters make the hair white, cold makes it dark, an effect found also in plants. The reason is that the hot have more air than water in them, and the air shining through causes whiteness, as also in froth. As, then, skins which are white by reason of some affection differ from those white by nature, so also in the hair the whiteness due to disease or age differs from that due to nature in that the cause is different; the latter are whitened by the natural heat, the former by the external heat. Whiteness is caused in all things by the vaporous air imprisoned in them. Hence also in all animals not uniformly coloured all the part under the belly is whiter. For practically all white animals are both hotter and better flavoured for the same reason; the concoction of their nutriment makes them well-flavoured, and heat causes the concoction. The same cause holds for those animals which are uniformly-coloured, but either dark or white; heat and cold are the causes of the nature of the skin and hair, each of the parts having its own special heat.

The tongue also varies in colour in the simply coloured as compared with the vari-coloured animals, and again in the simply coloured which differ from one another, as white and dark. The reason is that assigned before, that the skins of the vari-coloured are vari-coloured, and the skins of the white-haired and dark-haired are white and dark in each case. Now we must conceive of the tongue as one of the external parts, not taking into account the fact that it is covered by the mouth but looking on it as we do on the hand or foot; thus since the skin of the vari-coloured animals is not uniformly coloured, this is the cause of the skin on the tongue being also vari-coloured.

Some birds and some wild quadrupeds change their colour according to the seasons of the year. The reason is that, as men change according to their age, so the same thing happens to them according to the season; for this makes a greater difference to them than the change of age.

The more omnivorous animals are more vari-coloured to speak generally, and this is what might be expected; thus bees are more
786b uniformly coloured than hornets and wasps. For if the food is responsible for the change we should expect varied food to increase the variety in the movements which cause the development and so in the residual matter of the food, from which come into being hairs and feathers and skins.

So much for colours and hairs.

7

As to the voice, it is deep in some animals, high in others, in others again well-pitched and in due proportion between both extremes. Again, in some it is loud, in others small, and it differs in smoothness and roughness, flexibility and inflexibility. We must inquire then into the causes of each of these distinctions.

We must suppose then that the same cause is responsible for high and deep voices as for the change which they undergo in passing from youth to age. The voice is higher in all other animals when younger, but in cattle that of calves is deeper. We find the same thing also in the male and female sexes; in the other kinds of animals the voice of the female is higher than that of the male (this being especially plain in man, for Nature has given this faculty to him in the highest degree because he alone of animals makes use of speech and the voice is the material of speech), but in cattle the opposite obtains, for the voice of cows is deeper than that of bulls.

Now the purpose for which animals have a voice, and what is meant by 'voice' and by 'sound' generally, has been stated partly in the treatise on sensation, partly in that on the soul.[1] But since lowness of voice depends on the movement of the air being slow and its highness on its being quick, there is a difficulty in knowing whether it is that which moves or that which is moved that is the cause of the slowness or quickness. For some say that what is much is moved slowly, what is little quickly, and that the quantity of the air is the cause of some animals having a deep and others a high voice. Up to a certain point this is well said (for it seems to be rightly said in a general way that the depth depends on a certain amount of the air put in motion), but not altogether, for if this were true it would not be easy to speak both soft and deep at once, nor again both loud and high. Again, the depth seems to belong to the nobler nature, and in
787a songs the deep note is better than the high-pitched ones, the better lying in superi-

[1] *On the Soul*, II. 8; cf. *Sense and the Sensible*, 440b 27.

ority, and depth of tone being a sort of superiority. But then depth and height in the voice are different from loudness and softness, and some high-voiced animals are loud-voiced, and in like manner some soft-voiced ones are deep-voiced, and the same applies to the tones lying between these extremes. And by what else can we define these (I mean loudness and softness of voice) except by the large and small amount of the air put in motion? If then height and depth are to be decided in accordance with the distinction postulated, the result will be that the same animals will be deep- and loud-voiced, and the same will be high- and not loud-voiced; but this is false.

The reason of the difficulty is that the words 'great' and 'small', 'much' and 'little' are used sometimes absolutely, sometimes relatively to one another. Whether an animal has a great (or loud) voice depends on the air which is moved being much *absolutely,* whether it has a small voice depends on its being little *absolutely;* but whether they have a deep or high voice depends on their being thus differentiated in relation to one another. For if that which is moved surpass the strength of that which moves it, the air that is sent forth must go slowly; if the opposite, quickly. The strong, then, on account of their strength, sometimes move much air and make the movement slow, sometimes, having complete command over it, make the movement swift. On the same principle the weak either move too much air for their strength and so make the movement slow, or if they make it swift move but little because of their weakness.

These, then, are the reasons of these contrarieties, that neither are all young animals high-voiced nor all deep-voiced, nor are all the older, nor yet are the two sexes thus opposed, and again that not only the sick speak in a high voice but also those in good bodily condition, and, further, that as men verge on old age they become higher-voiced, though this age is opposite to that of youth.

Most young animals, then, and most females set but little air in motion because of their want of power, and are consequently high-voiced, for a little air is carried along quickly, and in the voice what is quick is high. But in calves and cows, in the one case because of their age, in the other because of their female nature, the part by which they set the air in motion is not strong; at the same time they set a **787b** great quantity in motion and so are deep-voiced; for that which is borne along slowly is heavy, and much air is borne along slowly. And these animals set much in movement whereas the others set but little, because the vessel through which the breath is first borne has in them a large opening and necessarily sets much air in motion, whereas in the rest the air is better dispensed. As their age advances this part which moves the air gains more strength in each animal, so that they change into the opposite condition, the high-voiced becoming deeper-voiced than they were, and the deep-voiced higher-voiced, which is why bulls have a higher voice than calves and cows. Now the strength of all animals is in their sinews, and so those in the prime of life are stronger, the young being weaker in the joints and sinews; moreover, in the young they are not yet tense, and in those now growing old the tension relaxes, wherefore both these ages are weak and powerless for movement. And bulls are particularly sinewy, even their hearts, and therefore that part by which they set the air in motion is in a tense state, like a sinewy string stretched tight. (That the heart of bulls is of such a nature is shown by the fact that a bone is actually found in some of them, and bones are naturally connected with sinew.)

All animals when castrated change to the female character, and utter a voice like that of the females because the sinewy strength in the principle of the voice is relaxed. This relaxation is just as if one should stretch a string and make it taut by hanging some weight on to it, as women do who weave at the loom, for they stretch the warp by attaching to it what are called 'laiai'. For in this way are the testes attached to the seminal passages, and these again to the blood-vessel which takes its origin in the heart near the organ which sets the voice in motion. Hence as the seminal passages change towards the age at which they are now able to secrete the semen, this part also changes along with them. As this changes, the voice again changes, more indeed in males, but the same thing happens in females too, only not so plainly, the result being what some call **788a** 'bleating' when the voice is uneven. After this it settles into the deep or high voice of the succeeding time of life. If the testes are removed the tension of the passages relaxes, as when the weight is taken off the string or the warp; as this relaxes, the organ which moves the voice is loosened in the same proportion. This, then, is the reason why the voice and the form generally changes to the female character in castrated animals; it is because the principle is relaxed upon which depends the tension of the body; not that, as some suppose, the testes are themselves a ganglion of many principles, but small changes are the causes of great ones, not *per se* but when it happens that a principle changes with them. For the principles, though small in size, are great in potency; this, indeed, is what is meant by a principle, that it is itself the cause of many things without anything else being higher than it for it to depend upon.

The heat or cold also of their habitat contributes to make some animals of such a character as to be deep-voiced, and others high-voiced. For hot breath being thick causes depth, cold breath being thin the opposite. This is clear also in pipe-playing, for if the breath of the performer is hotter, that is to say if it is expelled as by a groan, the note is deeper.

The cause of roughess and smoothness in the voice, and of all similar inequality, is that the part or organ through which the voice is conveyed is rough or smooth or generally even or uneven. This is plain when there is any moisture about the trachea or when it is roughened by any affection, for then the voice also becomes uneven.

Flexibility depends on the softness or hardness of the organ, for what is soft can be regulated and assume any form, while what is hard cannot; thus the soft organ can utter a loud or a small note, and accordingly a high or a deep one, since it easily regulates the breath, becoming itself easily great or small. But hardness cannot be regulated.

Let this be enough on all those points con-
788b cerning the voice which have not been previously discussed in the treatise on sensation and in that on the soul.

8

With regard to the teeth it has been stated previously[1] that they do not exist for a single purpose nor for the same purpose in all animals, but in some for nutrition only, in others also for fighting and for vocal speech. We must, however, consider it not alien to the discussion of generation and development to inquire into the reason why the front teeth are formed first and the grinders later, and why the latter are not shed but the former are shed and grow again.

[1] *On the Parts of Animals*, III, 661a 34 et sqq.

Democritus has spoken of these questions but not well, for he assigns the cause too generally without investigating the facts in all cases. He says that the early teeth are shed because they are formed in animals too early, for it is when animals are practically in their prime that they grow according to Nature, and suckling is the cause he assigns for their being found too early. Yet the pig also suckles but does not shed its teeth, and, further, all the animals with carnivorous dentition suckle, but some of them do not shed any teeth except the canines, e.g. lions. This mistake, then, was due to his speaking generally without examining what happens in all cases; but this is what we ought to do, for any one who makes any general statement must speak of all the particular cases.

Now we assume, basing our assumption upon what we see, that Nature never fails nor does anything in vain so far as is possible in each case. And it is necessary, if an animal is to obtain food after the time of taking milk is over, that it should have instruments for the treatment of the food. If, then, as Democritus says, this happened about the time of reaching maturity, Nature would fail in something possible for her to do. And, besides, the operation of Nature would be contrary to Nature, for what is done by violence is contrary to Nature, and it is by violence that he says the formation of the first teeth is brought about. That this view then is not true is plain from these and other similar considerations.

Now these teeth are developed before the flat teeth, in the first place because their function is earlier (for dividing comes before crushing, and the flat teeth are for crushing, the others for dividing), in the second place because the smaller is naturally developed quicker than the larger, even if both start together, and these teeth
789a are smaller in size than the grinders, because the bone of the jaw is flat in that part but narrow towards the mouth. From the greater part, therefore, must flow more nutriment to form the teeth, and from the narrower part less.

The act of sucking in itself contributes nothing to the formation of the teeth, but the heat of the milk makes them appear more quickly. A proof of this is that even in suckling animals those young which enjoy hotter milk grow their teeth quicker, heat being conducive to growth.

They are shed, after they have been formed, partly because it is better so (for what is sharp is soon blunted, so that a fresh relay is needed for the work, whereas the flat teeth cannot be blunted but are only smoothed in time by wearing down), partly from necessity because, while the roots of the grinders are fixed where the jaw is flat and the bone strong, those of the front teeth are in a thin part, so that they are weak and easily moved. They grow again because they are shed while the bone is still growing and the animal is still young enough to grow teeth. A proof of this is that even the flat teeth grow for a long time, the last of them cutting the gum at about twenty years of age; indeed in some cases the last teeth have been grown in quite old age. This is because there is much nutriment in the broad part of the bones, whereas the front part **789b** being thin soon reaches perfection and no residual matter is found in it, the nutriment being consumed in its own growth.

Democritus, however, neglecting the final cause, reduces to necessity all the operations of Nature. Now they are necessary, it is true, but yet they are for a final cause and for the sake of what is best in each case. Thus nothing prevents the teeth from being formed and being shed in this way; but it is not on account of these causes but on account of the end (or final cause); these are causes only in the sense of being the moving and efficient instruments and the material. So it is reasonable that Nature should perform most of her operations using breath as an instrument, for as some instruments serve many uses in the arts, e.g. the hammer and anvil in the smith's art, so does breath in the living things formed by Nature. But to say that necessity is the only cause is much as if we should think that the water has been drawn off from a dropsical patient on account of the lancet, not on account of health, for the sake of which the lancet made the incision.

We have thus spoken of the teeth, saying why some are shed and grow again, and others not, and generally for what cause they are formed. And we have spoken of the other affections of the parts which are found to occur not for any final end but of necessity and on account of the motive or efficient cause.

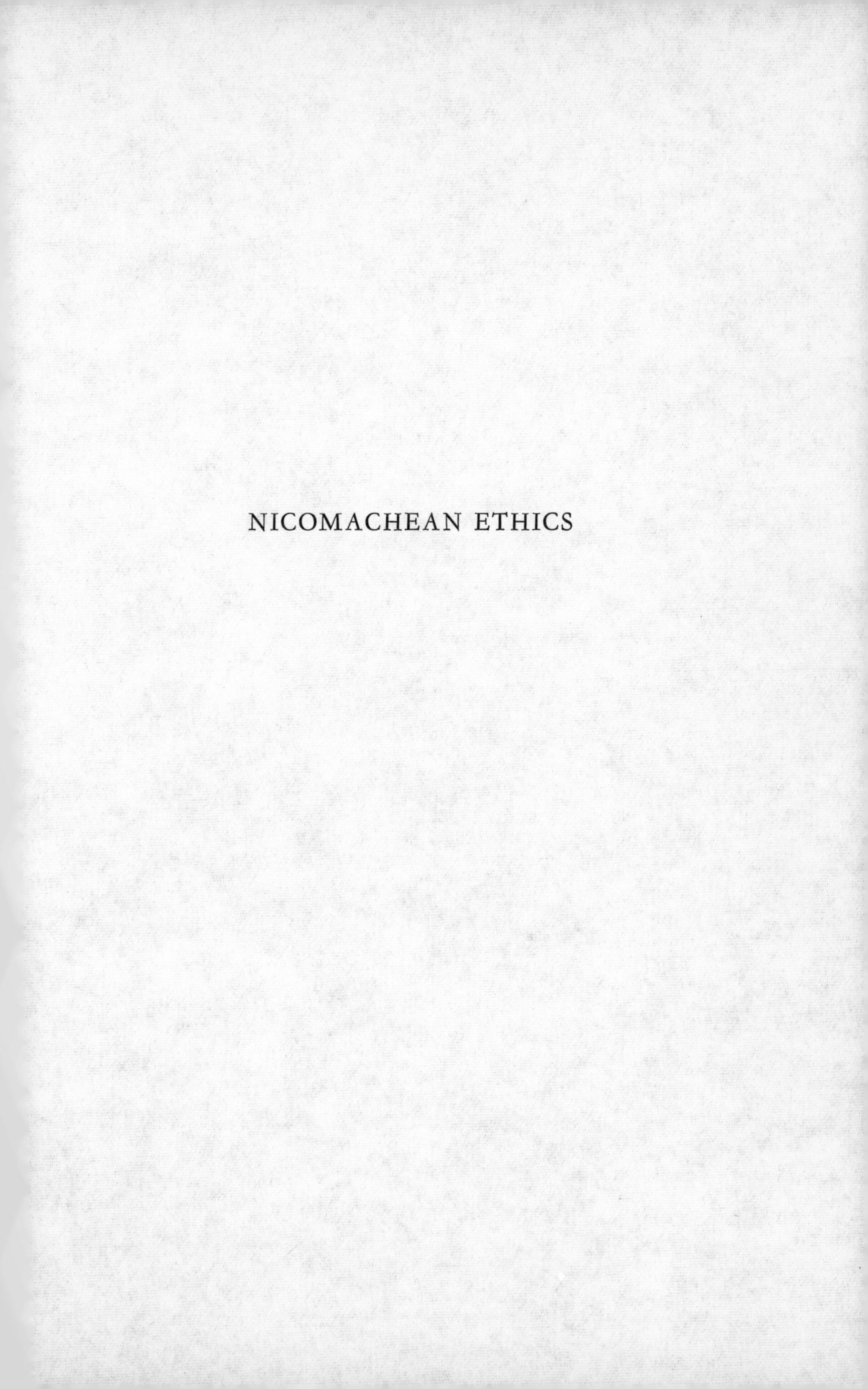

NICOMACHEAN ETHICS

CONTENTS: NICOMACHEAN ETHICS

NICOMACHEAN ETHICS

BOOK I

1

1094a EVERY art and every inquiry, and similarly every action and pursuit, is thought to aim at some good; and for this reason the good has rightly been declared to be that at which all things aim. But a certain difference is found among ends; some are activities, others are products apart from the activities that produce them. Where there are ends apart from the actions, it is the nature of the products to be better than the activities. Now, as there are many actions, arts, and sciences, their ends also are many; the end of the medical art is health, that of shipbuilding a vessel, that of strategy victory, that of economics wealth. But where such arts fall under a single capacity—as bridle-making and the other arts concerned with the equipment of horses fall under the art of riding, and this and every military action under strategy, in the same way other arts fall under yet others—in all of these the ends of the master arts are to be preferred to all the subordinate ends; for it is for the sake of the former that the latter are pursued. It makes no difference whether the activities themselves are the ends of the actions, or something else apart from the activities, as in the case of the sciences just mentioned.

2

If, then, there is some end of the things we do, which we desire for its own sake (everything else being desired for the sake of this), and if we do not choose everything for the sake of something else (for at that rate the process would go on to infinity, so that our desire would be empty and vain), clearly this must be the good and the chief good. Will not the knowledge of it, then, have a great influence on life? Shall we not, like archers who have a mark to aim at, be more likely to hit upon what is right? If so, we must try, in outline at least, to determine what it is, and of which of the sciences or capacities it is the object. It would seem to belong to the most authoritative art and that which is most truly the master art. And politics appears to be of this nature; for it is this that ordains which of the sciences should
1094b be studied in a state, and which each class of citizens should learn and up to what point they should learn them; and we see even the most highly esteemed of capacities to fall under this, e.g. strategy, economics, rhetoric; now, since politics uses the rest of the sciences, and since, again, it legislates as to what we are to do and what we are to abstain from, the end of this science must include those of the others, so that this end must be the good for man. For even if the end is the same for a single man and for a state, that of the state seems at all events something greater and more complete whether to attain or to preserve; though it is worth while to attain the end merely for one man, it is finer and more godlike to attain it for a nation or for city-states. These, then, are the ends at which our inquiry aims, since it is political science, in one sense of that term.

3

Our discussion will be adequate if it has as much clearness as the subject-matter admits of, for precision is not to be sought for alike in all discussions, any more than in all the products of the crafts. Now fine and just actions, which political science investigates, admit of much variety and fluctuation of opinion, so that they may be thought to exist only by convention, and not by nature. And goods also give rise to a similar fluctuation because they bring harm to many people; for before now men have been undone by reason of their wealth, and others by reason of their courage. We must be content, then, in speaking of such subjects and with such premisses to indicate the truth roughly and in outline, and in speaking about things which are only for the most part true and with premisses of the same kind to reach conclusions that are no better. In the same spirit, therefore, should each type of statement be *received;* for it is the mark of an educated man to look for precision in each

NOTE: The bold face numbers and letters are approximate indications of the pages and columns of the standard Berlin Greek text; the bracketed numbers of the lines in the Greek text; they are here assigned as they are assigned in the Oxford translation.

class of things just so far as the nature of the subject admits; it is evidently equally foolish to accept probable reasoning from a mathematician and to demand from a rhetorician scientific proofs.

Now each man judges well the things he knows, and of these he is a good judge. And so the man who has been educated in a subject **1095a** is a good judge of that subject, and the man who has received an all-round education is a good judge in general. Hence a young man is not a proper hearer of lectures on political science; for he is inexperienced in the actions that occur in life, but its discussions start from these and are about these; and, further, since he tends to follow his passions, his study will be vain and unprofitable, because the end aimed at is not knowledge but action. And it makes no difference whether he is young in years or youthful in character; the defect does not depend on time, but on his living, and pursuing each successive object, as passion directs. For to such persons, as to the incontinent, knowledge brings no profit; but to those who desire and act in accordance with a rational principle knowledge about such matters will be of great benefit.

These remarks about the student, the sort of treatment to be expected, and the purpose of the inquiry, may be taken as our preface.

4

Let us resume our inquiry and state, in view of the fact that all knowledge and every pursuit aims at some good, what it is that we say political science aims at and what is the highest of all goods achievable by action. Verbally there is very general agreement; for both the general run of men and people of superior refinement say that it is happiness, and identify living well and doing well with being happy; but with regard to what happiness is they differ, and the many do not give the same account as the wise. For the former think it is some plain and obvious thing, like pleasure, wealth, or honour; they differ, however, from one another—and often even the same man identifies it with different things, with health when he is ill, with wealth when he is poor; but, conscious of their ignorance, they admire those who proclaim some great ideal that is above their comprehension. Now some thought that apart from these many goods there is another which is self-subsistent and causes the goodness of all these as well. To examine all the opinions that have been held were perhaps somewhat fruitless; enough to examine those that are most prevalent or that seem to be arguable.

Let us not fail to notice, however, that there is a difference between arguments from and those to the first principles. For Plato, too, was right in raising this question and asking, as he used to do, 'are we on the way from or to the first principles?'[1] There is a difference, as there is in a race-course between the course from the judges to the turning-point and the **1095b** way back. For, while we must begin with what is known, things are objects of knowledge in two senses—some to us, some without qualification. Presumably, then, *we* must begin with things known to *us*. Hence any one who is to listen intelligently to lectures about what is noble and just, and generally, about the subjects of political science must have been brought up in good habits. For the fact is the starting-point, and if this is sufficiently plain to him, he will not at the start need the reason as well; and the man who has been well brought up has or can easily get starting-points. And as for him who neither has nor can get them, let him hear the words of Hesiod:[2]

Far best is he who knows all things himself;
Good, he that hearkens when men counsel right;
But he who neither knows, nor lays to heart
Another's wisdom, is a useless wight.

5

Let us, however, resume our discussion from the point at which we digressed.[3] To judge from the lives that men lead, most men, and men of the most vulgar type, seem (not without some ground) to identify the good, or happiness, with pleasure; which is the reason why they love the life of enjoyment. For there are, we may say, three prominent types of life—that just mentioned, the political, and thirdly the contemplative life. Now the mass of mankind are evidently quite slavish in their tastes, preferring a life suitable to beasts, but they get some ground for their view from the fact that many of those in high places share the tastes of Sardanapallus. A consideration of the prominent types of life shows that people of superior refinement and of active disposition identify happiness with honour; for this is, roughly speaking, the end of the political life. But it seems too superficial to be what we are

[1] Cf. *Republic*, 511.
[2] *Works and Days*, 293, 295-7, Rzach.
[3] a 30.

looking for, since it is thought to depend on those who bestow honour rather than on him who receives it, but the good we divine to be something proper to a man and not easily taken from him. Further, men seem to pursue honour in order that they may be assured of their goodness; at least it is by men of practical wisdom that they seek to be honoured, and among those who know them, and on the ground of their virtue; clearly, then, according to them, at any rate, virtue is better. And perhaps one might even suppose this to be, rather than honour, the end of the political life. But even this appears somewhat incomplete; for possession of virtue seems actually compatible with being asleep, or with lifelong inactivity, and, further, with the greatest suf-
1096^{a} ferings and misfortunes; but a man who was living so no one would call happy, unless he were maintaining a thesis at all costs. But enough of this; for the subject has been sufficiently treated even in the current discussions. Third comes the contemplative life, which we shall consider later.[1]

The life of money-making is one undertaken under compulsion, and wealth is evidently not the good we are seeking; for it is merely useful and for the sake of something else. And so one might rather take the afore-named objects to be ends; for they are loved for themselves. But it is evident that not even these are ends; yet many arguments have been thrown away in support of them. Let us leave this subject, then.

6

We had perhaps better consider the universal good and discuss thoroughly what is meant by it, although such an inquiry is made an uphill one by the fact that the Forms have been introduced by friends of our own. Yet it would perhaps be thought to be better, indeed to be our duty, for the sake of maintaining the truth even to destroy what touches us closely, especially as we are philosophers or lovers of wisdom; for, while both are dear, piety requires us to honour truth above our friends.

The men who introduced this doctrine did not posit Ideas of classes within which they recognized priority and posteriority (which is the reason why they did not maintain the existence of an Idea embracing all numbers); but the term 'good' is used both in the category of substance and in that of quality and in that of relation, and that which is *per se,* i.e. substance, is prior in nature to the relative (for the latter is like an offshoot and accident of being); so that there could not be a common Idea set over all these goods. Further, since 'good' has as many senses as 'being' (for it is predicated both in the category of substance, as of God and of reason, and in quality, i.e. of the virtues, and in quantity, i.e. of that which is moderate, and in relation, i.e. of the useful, and in time, i.e. of the right opportunity, and in place, i.e. of the right locality and the like), clearly it cannot be something universally present in all cases and single; for then it could not have been predicated in all the categories but in one only. Further, since of the things answering to one Idea there is one science, there would have been one science of all the goods; but as it is there are many sciences even of the things that fall under one category, e.g. of opportunity, for opportunity in war is studied by strategics and in disease by medicine, and the moderate in food is studied by medicine and in exercise by the science of gymnastics. And one might ask the question, what in the world they *mean* by 'a thing itself', if (as is the case) in 'man himself' and in a particular man the
1096^{b} account of man is one and the same. For in so far as they are man, they will in no respect differ; and if this is so, neither will 'good itself' and particular goods, in so far as they are good. But again it will not be good any the more for being eternal, since that which lasts long is no whiter than that which perishes in a day. The Pythagoreans seem to give a more plausible account of the good, when they place the one in the column of goods; and it is they that Speusippus seems to have followed.

But let us discuss these matters elsewhere;[2] an objection to what we have said, however, may be discerned in the fact that the Platonists have not been speaking about *all* goods, and that the goods that are pursued and loved for themselves are called good by reference to a single Form, while those which tend to produce or to preserve these somehow or to prevent their contraries are called so by reference to these, and in a secondary sense. Clearly, then, goods must be spoken of in two ways, and some must be good in themselves, the others by reason of these. Let us separate, then, things good in themselves from things useful, and consider whether the former are called good by reference to a single Idea. What

[1] 1177^{a} 12-1178^{a} 8, 1178^{a} 22-1179^{a} 32.

[2] Cf. *Metaphysics,* 986^{a} 22-6, 1028^{b} 21-4, 1072^{b} 30-1073^{a} 3, 1091^{a} 29-^{b} 3, ^{b} 13-1092^{a} 17.

sort of goods would one call good in themselves? Is it those that are pursued even when isolated from others, such as intelligence, sight, and certain pleasures and honours? Certainly, if we pursue these also for the sake of something else, yet one would place them among things good in themselves. Or is nothing other than the Idea of good good in itself? In that case the Form will be empty. But if the things we have named are also things good in themselves, the account of the good will have to appear as something identical in them all, as that of whiteness is identical in snow and in white lead. But of honour, wisdom, and pleasure, just in respect of their goodness, the accounts are distinct and diverse. The good, therefore, is not some common element answering to one Idea.

But what then do we mean by the good? It is surely not like the things that only chance to have the same name. Are goods one, then, by being derived from one good or by all contributing to one good, or are they rather one by analogy? Certainly as sight is in the body, so is reason in the soul, and so on in other cases. But perhaps these subjects had better be dismissed for the present; for perfect precision about them would be more appropriate to another branch of philosophy.[1] And similarly with regard to the Idea; even if there is some one good which is universally predicable of goods or is capable of separate and independent existence, clearly it could not be achieved or attained by man; but we are now seeking something attainable. Perhaps, however, some one might think it worth while to recognize this with a view to the goods that *are* attainable **1097a** and achievable; for having this as a sort of pattern we shall know better the goods that are good for us, and if we know them shall attain them. This argument has some plausibility, but seems to clash with the procedure of the sciences; for all of these, though they aim at some good and seek to supply the deficiency of it, leave on one side the knowledge of *the* good. Yet that all the exponents of the arts should be ignorant of, and should not even seek, so great an aid is not probable. It is hard, too, to see how a weaver or a carpenter will be benefited in regard to his own craft by knowing this 'good itself', or how the man who has viewed the Idea itself will be a better doctor or general thereby. For a doctor seems not even to study health in this way, but the health of man, or perhaps rather the health of a particular man; it is individuals that he is healing. But enough of these topics.

7

Let us again return to the good we are seeking, and ask what it can be. It seems different in different actions and arts; it is different in medicine, in strategy, and in the other arts likewise. What then is the good of each? Surely that for whose sake everything else is done. In medicine this is health, in strategy victory, in architecture a house, in any other sphere something else, and in every action and pursuit the end; for it is for the sake of this that all men do whatever else they do. Therefore, if there is an end for all that we do, this will be the good achievable by action, and if there are more than one, these will be the goods achievable by action.

So the argument has by a different course reached the same point; but we must try to state this even more clearly. Since there are evidently more than one end, and we choose some of these (e.g. wealth, flutes,[2] and in general instruments) for the sake of something else, clearly not all ends are final ends; but the chief good is evidently something final. Therefore, if there is only one final end, this will be what we are seeking, and if there are more than one, the most final of these will be what we are seeking. Now we call that which is in itself worthy of pursuit more final than that which is worthy of pursuit for the sake of something else, and that which is never desirable for the sake of something else more final than the things that are desirable both in themselves and for the sake of that other thing, and therefore we call final without qualification that which is always desirable in itself and never for the sake of something else.

Now such a thing happiness, above all else, is held to be; for this we choose always for **1097b** itself and never for the sake of something else, but honour, pleasure, reason, and every virtue we choose indeed for themselves (for if nothing resulted from them we should still choose each of them), but we choose them also for the sake of happiness, judging that by means of them we shall be happy. Happiness, on the other hand, no one chooses for the sake of these, nor, in general, for anything other than itself.

From the point of view of self-sufficiency the same result seems to follow; for the final good is thought to be self-sufficient. Now by self-

[1] Cf. *Metaphysics*, iv. 2.

[2] Cf. Plato, *Euthydemus*, 289.

sufficient we do not mean that which is sufficient for a man by himself, for one who lives a solitary life, but also for parents, children, wife, and in general for his friends and fellow citizens, since man is born for citizenship. But some limit must be set to this; for if we extend our requirement to ancestors and descendants and friends' friends we are in for an infinite series. Let us examine this question, however, on another occasion;[1] the self-sufficient we now define as that which when isolated makes life desirable and lacking in nothing; and such we think happiness to be; and further we think it most desirable of all things, without being counted as one good thing among others—if it were so counted it would clearly be made more desirable by the addition of even the least of goods; for that which is added becomes an excess of goods, and of goods the greater is always more desirable. Happiness, then, is something final and self-sufficient, and is the end of action.

Presumably, however, to say that happiness is the chief good seems a platitude, and a clearer account of what it is is still desired. This might perhaps be given, if we could first ascertain the function of man. For just as for a flute-player, a sculptor, or an artist, and, in general, for all things that have a function or activity, the good and the 'well' is thought to reside in the function, so would it seem to be for man, if he has a function. Have the carpenter, then, and the tanner certain functions or activities, and has man none? Is he born without a function? Or as eye, hand, foot, and in general each of the parts evidently has a function, may one lay it down that man similarly has a function apart from all these? What then can this be? Life seems to be common even to plants, but we are seeking what is peculiar to man. Let us exclude, therefore, the life of nu-
1098a trition and growth. Next there would be a life of perception, but *it* also seems to be common even to the horse, the ox, and every animal. There remains, then, an active life of the element that has a rational principle; of this, one part has such a principle in the sense of being obedient to one, the other in the sense of possessing one and exercising thought. And, as 'life of the rational element' also has two meanings, we must state that life in the sense of activity is what we mean; for this seems to be the more proper sense of the term. Now if the function of man is an activity of soul which follows or implies a rational principle, and if we say 'so-and-so- and 'a good so-and-so' have a function which is the same in kind, e.g. a lyre-player and a good lyre-player, and so without qualification in all cases, eminence in respect of goodness being added to the name of the function (for the function of a lyre-player is to play the lyre, and that of a good lyre-player is to do so well): if this is the case, [and we state the function of man to be a certain kind of life, and this to be an activity or actions of the soul implying a rational principle, and the function of a good man to be the good and noble performance of these, and if any action is well performed when it is performed in accordance with the appropriate excellence: if this is the case,] human good turns out to be activity of soul in accordance with virtue, and if there are more than one virtue, in accordance with the best and most complete.

But we must add 'in a complete life'. For one swallow does not make a summer, nor does one day; and so too one day, or a short time, does not make a man blessed and happy.

Let this serve as an outline of the good; for we must presumably first sketch it roughly, and then later fill in the details. But it would seem that any one is capable of carrying on and articulating what has once been well outlined, and that time is a good discoverer or partner in such a work; to which facts the advances of the arts are due; for any one can add what is lacking. And we must also remember what has been said before,[2] and not look for precision in all things alike, but in each class of things such precision as accords with the subject-matter, and so much as is appropriate to the inquiry. For a carpenter and a geometer investigate the right angle in different ways; the former does so in so far as the right angle is useful for his work, while the latter inquires what it is or what sort of thing it is; for he is a spectator of the truth. We must act in the same way, then, in all other matters as well, that our main task may not be subordinated to minor questions. Nor must we demand the cause in all matters
1098b alike; it is enough in some cases that the *fact* be well established, as in the case of the first principles; the fact is the primary thing or first principle. Now of first principles we see some by induction, some by perception, some by a certain habituation, and others too in other ways. But each set of principles we must try to investigate in the natural way, and we must take pains to state them definitely, since they have a great influence on what follows.

[1] I.10, 11; IX. 10.

[2] 1094b 11-27.

For the beginning is thought to be more than half of the whole, and many of the questions we ask are cleared up by it.

8

We must consider it, however, in the light not only of our conclusion and our premisses, but also of what is commonly said about it; for with a true view all the data harmonize, but with a false one the facts soon clash. Now goods have been divided into three classes,[1] and some are described as external, others as relating to soul or to body; we call those that relate to soul most properly and truly goods, and psychical actions and activities we class as relating to soul. Therefore our account must be sound, at least according to this view, which is an old one and agreed on by philosophers. It is correct also in that we identify the end with certain actions and activities; for thus it falls among goods of the soul and not among external goods. Another belief which harmonizes with our account is that the happy man lives well and does well; for we have practically defined happiness as a sort of good life and good action. The characteristics that are looked for in happiness seem also, all of them, to belong to what we have defined happiness as being. For some identify happiness with virtue, some with practical wisdom, others with a kind of philosophic wisdom, others with these, or one of these, accompanied by pleasure or not without pleasure; while others include also external prosperity. Now some of these views have been held by many men and men of old, others by a few eminent persons; and it is not probable that either of these should be entirely mistaken, but rather that they should be right in at least some one respect or even in most respects.

With those who identify happiness with virtue or some one virtue our account is in harmony; for to virtue belongs virtuous activity. But it makes, perhaps, no small difference whether we place the chief good in possession or in use, in state of mind or in activity. For the state of mind may exist without producing any **1099a** good result, as in a man who is asleep or in some other way quite inactive, but the activity cannot; for one who has the activity will of necessity be acting, and acting well. And as in the Olympic Games it is not the most beautiful and the strongest that are crowned but those who compete (for it is some of these that are victorious), so those who act win, and rightly win, the noble and good things in life.

Their life is also in itself pleasant. For pleasure is a state of *soul*, and to each man that which he is said to be a lover of is pleasant; e.g. not only is a horse pleasant to the lover of horses, and a spectacle to the lover of sights, but also in the same way just acts are pleasant to the lover of justice and in general virtuous acts to the lover of virtue. Now for most men their pleasures are in conflict with one another because these are not by nature pleasant, but the lovers of what is noble find pleasant the things that are by nature pleasant; and virtuous actions are such, so that these are pleasant for such men as well as in their own nature. Their life, therefore, has no further need of pleasure as a sort of adventitious charm, but has its pleasure in itself. For, besides what we have said, the man who does not rejoice in noble actions is not even good; since no one would call a man just who did not enjoy acting justly, nor any man liberal who did not enjoy liberal actions; and similarly in all other cases. If this is so, virtuous actions must be in themselves pleasant. But they are also *good* and *noble*, and have each of these attributes in the highest degree, since the good man judges well about these attributes; his judgement is such as we have described. Happiness then is the best, noblest, and most pleasant thing in the world, and these attributes are not severed as in the inscription at Delos—

Most noble is that which is justest, and best is health;
But pleasantest is it to win what we love.

For all these properties belong to the best activities; and these, or one—the best—of these, we identify with happiness.

Yet evidently, as we said,[2] it needs the external goods as well; for it is impossible, or not easy, to do noble acts without the proper equip- **1099b** ment. In many actions we use friends and riches and political power as instruments; and there are some things the lack of which takes the lustre from happiness, as good birth, goodly children, beauty; for the man who is very ugly in appearance or ill-born or solitary and childless is not very likely to be happy, and perhaps a man would be still less likely if he had thoroughly bad children or friends or had lost good children or friends by death. As we said, then, happiness seems to need this sort of prosperity in addition; for which reason

[1] Plato, *Euthydemus* 279; *Philebus*, 48; *Laws*, 743.

[2] 1098b 26-9.

some identify happiness with good fortune, though others identify it with virtue.

9

For this reason also the question is asked, whether happiness is to be acquired by learning or by habituation or some other sort of training, or comes in virtue of some divine providence or again by chance. Now if there is *any* gift of the gods to men, it is reasonable that happiness should be god-given, and most surely god-given of all human things inasmuch as it is the best. But this question would perhaps be more appropriate to another inquiry; happiness seems, however, even if it is not god-sent but comes as a result of virtue and some process of learning or training, to be among the most godlike things; for that which is the prize and end of virtue seems to be the best thing in the world, and something godlike and blessed.

It will also on this view be very generally shared; for all who are not maimed as regards their potentiality for virtue may win it by a certain kind of study and care. But if it is better to be happy thus than by chance, it is reasonable that the facts should be so, since everything that depends on the action of nature is by nature as good as it can be, and similarly everything that depends on art or any rational cause, and especially if it depends on the best of all causes. To entrust to chance what is greatest and most noble would be a very defective arrangement.

The answer to the question we are asking is plain also from the definition of happiness; for it has been said[1] to be a virtuous activity of soul, of a certain kind. Of the remaining goods, some must necessarily pre-exist as conditions of happiness, and others are naturally co-operative and useful as instruments. And this will be found to agree with what we said at the outset;[2] for we stated the end of political science to be the best end, and political science spends most of its pains on making the citizens to be of a certain character, viz. good and capable of noble acts.

It is natural, then, that we call neither ox nor horse nor any other of the animals happy; for none of them is capable of sharing in such **1100^a** activity. For this reason also a boy is not happy; for he is not yet capable of such acts, owing to his age; and boys who are called happy are being congratulated by reason of the hopes we have for them. For there is required, as we said,[3] not only complete virtue but also a complete life, since many changes occur in life, and all manner of chances, and the most prosperous may fall into great misfortunes in old age, as is told of Priam in the Trojan Cycle; and one who has experienced such chances and has ended wretchedly no one calls happy.

10

Must no one at all, then, be called happy while he lives; must we, as Solon says,[4] see the end? Even if we are to lay down this doctrine, is it also the case that a man *is* happy when he is *dead?* Or is not this quite absurd, especially for us who say that happiness is an activity? But if we do not call the dead man happy, and if Solon does not mean this, but that one can then safely *call* a man blessed as being at last beyond evils and misfortunes, this also affords matter for discussion; for both evil and good are thought to exist for a dead man, as much as for one who is alive but not aware of them; e.g. honours and dishonours and the good or bad fortunes of children and in general of descendants. And this also presents a problem; for though a man has lived happily up to old age and has had a death worthy of his life, many reverses may befall his descendants —some of them may be good and attain the life they deserve, while with others the opposite may be the case; and clearly too the degrees of relationship between them and their ancestors may vary indefinitely. It would be odd, then, if the dead man were to share in these changes and become at one time happy, at another wretched; while it would also be odd if the fortunes of the descendants did not for *some* time have *some* effect on the happiness of their ancestors.

But we must return to our first difficulty; for perhaps by a consideration of it our present problem might be solved. Now if we must see the end and only then call a man happy, not as being happy but as having been so before, surely this is a paradox, that when he is happy the attribute that belongs to him is not to be **1100^b** truly predicated of him because we do not wish to call living men happy, on account of the changes that may befall them, and because we have assumed happiness to be something permanent and by no means easily changed, while a single man may suffer many turns of fortune's wheel. For clearly if we were to keep pace with his fortunes, we should often call the same man happy and again

[1] 1098^a 16. [2] 1094^a 27.

[3] 1098^a 16-18. [4] Herodotus, I. 32.

wretched, making the happy man out to be a 'chameleon and insecurely based'. Or is this keeping pace with his fortunes quite wrong? Success or failure in life does not depend on these, but human life, as we said,[1] needs these as mere additions, while virtuous activities or their opposites are what constitute happiness or the reverse.

The question we have now discussed confirms our definition. For no function of man has so much permanence as virtuous activities (these are thought to be more durable even than knowledge of the sciences), and of these themselves the most valuable are more durable because those who are happy spend their life most readily and most continuously in these; for this seems to be the reason why we do not forget them. The attribute in question, then, will belong to the happy man, and he will be happy throughout his life; for always, or by preference to everything else, he will be engaged in virtuous action and contemplation, and he will bear the chances of life most nobly and altogether decorously, if he is 'truly good' and 'foursquare beyond reproach'.[2]

Now many events happen by chance, and events differing in importance; small pieces of good fortune or of its opposite clearly do not weigh down the scales of life one way or the other, but a multitude of great events if they turn out well will make life happier (for not only are they themselves such as to add beauty to life, but the way a man deals with them may be noble and good), while if they turn out ill they crush and maim happiness; for they both bring pain with them and hinder many activities. Yet even in these nobility shines through, when a man bears with resignation many great misfortunes, not through insensibility to pain but through nobility and greatness of soul.

If activities are, as we said,[3] what gives life its character, no happy man can become miserable; for he will never do the acts that are hateful and mean. For the man who is truly **1101a** good and wise, we think, bears all the chances of life becomingly and always makes the best of circumstances, as a good general makes the best military use of the army at his command and a good shoemaker makes the best shoes out of the hides that are given him; and so with all other craftsmen. And if this is the case, the happy man can never become miserable; though he will not reach *blessedness*, if he meet with fortunes like those of Priam.

[1] 1099a 31–b 7. [2] Simonides, fr. 4, Diehl. [3] l. 9.

Nor, again, is he many-coloured and changeable; for neither will he be moved from his happy state easily or by any ordinary misadventures, but only by many great ones, nor, if he has had many great misadventures, will he recover his happiness in a short time, but if at all, only in a long and complete one in which he has attained many splendid successes.

Why then should we not say that he is happy who is active in accordance with complete virtue and is sufficiently equipped with external goods, not for some chance period but throughout a complete life? Or must we add 'and who is destined to live thus and die as befits his life'? Certainly the future is obscure to us, while happiness, we claim, is an end and something in every way final. If so, we shall call happy those among living men in whom these conditions are, and are to be, fulfilled—but happy *men*. So much for these questions.

11

That the fortunes of descendants and of all a man's friends should not affect his happiness at all seems a very unfriendly doctrine, and one opposed to the opinions men hold; but since the events that happen are numerous and admit of all sorts of difference, and some come more near to us and others less so, it seems a long—nay, an infinite—task to discuss each in detail; a general outline will perhaps suffice. If, then, as some of a man's own misadventures have a certain weight and influence on life while others are, as it were, lighter, so too there are differences among the misadventures of our friends taken as a whole, and it makes a difference whether the various suffering befall the living or the dead (much more even than whether lawless and terrible deeds are presupposed in a tragedy or done on the stage), this difference also must be taken into account; or rather, perhaps, the fact that doubt is felt whether the dead share in any **1101b** good or evil. For it seems, from these considerations, that even if anything whether good or evil penetrates to them, it must be something weak and negligible, either in itself or for them, or if not, at least it must be such in degree and kind as not to make happy those who are not happy nor to take away their blessedness from those who are. The good or bad fortunes of friends, then, seem to have some effects on the dead, but effects of such a kind and degree as neither to make the happy unhappy nor to produce any other change of the kind.

12

These questions having been definitely answered, let us consider whether happiness is among the things that are praised or rather among the things that are prized; for clearly it is not to be placed among *potentialities*. Everything that is praised seems to be praised because it is of a certain kind and is related somehow to something else; for we praise the just or brave man and in general both the good man and virtue itself because of the actions and functions involved, and we praise the strong man, the good runner, and so on, because he is of a certain kind and is related in a certain way to something good and important. This is clear also from the praises of the gods; for it seems absurd that the gods should be referred to our standard, but this *is* done because praise involves a reference, as we said, to something else. But if praise is for things such as we have described, clearly what applies to the best things is not praise, but something greater and better, as is indeed obvious; for what we do to the gods and the most godlike of men is to call them blessed and happy. And so too with good *things*; no one praises happiness as he does justice, but rather calls it blessed, as being something more divine and better.

Eudoxus also seems to have been right in his method of advocating the supremacy of pleasure; he thought that the fact that, though a good, it is not praised indicated it to be better than the things that are praised, and that this is what God and the good are; for by reference to these all other things are judged. *Praise* is appropriate to virtue, for as a result of virtue men tend to do noble deeds, but *encomia* are bestowed on acts, whether of the body or of the soul. But perhaps nicety in these matters is more proper to those who have made a study of encomia; to us it is clear from
1102a what has been said that happiness is among the things that are prized and perfect. It seems to be so also from the fact that it is a first principle; for it is for the sake of this that we all do all that we do, and the first principle and cause of goods is, we claim, something prized and divine.

13

Since happiness is an activity of soul in accordance with perfect virtue, we must consider the nature of virtue; for perhaps we shall thus see better the nature of happiness. The true student of politics, too, is thought to have studied virtue above all things; for he wishes to make his fellow citizens good and obedient to the laws. As an example of this we have the lawgivers of the Cretans and the Spartans, and any others of the kind that there may have been. And if this inquiry belongs to political science, clearly the pursuit of it will be in accordance with our original plan. But clearly the virtue we must study is human virtue; for the good we were seeking was human good and the happiness human happiness. By human virtue we mean not that of the body but that of the soul; and happiness also we call an activity of soul. But if this is so, clearly the student of politics must know somehow the facts about soul, as the man who is to heal the eyes or the body as a whole must know about the eyes or the body; and all the more since politics is more prized and better than medicine; but even among doctors the best educated spend much labour on acquiring knowledge of the body. The student of politics, then, must study the soul, and must study it with these objects in view, and do so just to the extent which is sufficient for the questions we are discussing; for further precision is perhaps something more laborious than our purposes require.

Some things are said about it, adequately enough, even in the discussions outside our school, and we must use these; e. g. that one element in the soul is irrational and one has a rational principle. Whether these are separated as the parts of the body or of anything divisible are, or are distinct by definition but by nature inseparable, like convex and concave in the circumference of a circle, does not affect the present question.

Of the irrational element one division seems to be widely distributed, and vegetative in its nature, I mean that which causes nutrition and growth; for it is this kind of power of the soul
1102b that one must assign to all nurslings and to embryos, and this same power to full-grown creatures; this is more reasonable than to assign some different power to them. Now the excellence of this seems to be common to all species and not specifically human; for this part or faculty seems to function most in sleep, while goodness and badness are least manifest in sleep (whence comes the saying that the happy are not better off than the wretched for half their lives; and this happens

naturally enough, since sleep is an inactivity of the soul in that respect in which it is called good or bad), unless perhaps to a small extent some of the movements actually penetrate to the soul, and in this respect the dreams of good men are better than those of ordinary people. Enough of this subject, however; let us leave the nutritive faculty alone, since it has by its nature no share in human excellence.

There seems to be also another irrational element in the soul—one which in a sense, however, shares in a rational principle. For we praise the rational principle of the continent man and of the incontinent, and the part of their soul that has such a principle, since it urges them aright and towards the best objects; but there is found in them also another element naturally opposed to the rational principle, which fights against and resists that principle. For exactly as paralysed limbs when we intend to move them to the right turn on the contrary to the left, so is it with the soul; the impulses of incontinent people move in contrary directions. But while in the body we see that which moves astray, in the soul we do not. No doubt, however, we must none the less suppose that in the soul too there is something contrary to the rational principle, resisting and opposing it. In what sense it is distinct from the other elements does not concern us. Now even this seems to have a share in a rational principle, as we said;[1] at any rate in the continent man it obeys the rational principle—and presumably in the temperate and brave man it is still more obedient; for in him it speaks, on all matters, with the same voice as the rational principle.

Therefore the irrational element also appears to be two-fold. For the vegetative element in no way shares in a rational principle, but the appetitive and in general the desiring element in a sense shares in it, in so far as it listens to and obeys it; this is the sense in which we speak of 'taking account' of one's father or one's friends, not that in which we speak of 'accounting' for a mathematical property. That the irrational element is in some sense persuaded by a rational principle is indicated also by the giving of advice and by all reproof and **1103a** exhortation. And if this element also must be said to have a rational principle, that which has a rational principle (as well as that which has not) will be twofold, one subdivision having it in the strict sense and in itself, and the other having a tendency to obey as one does one's father.

Virtue too is distinguished into kinds in accordance with this difference; for we say that some of the virtues are intellectual and others moral, philosophic wisdom and understanding and practical wisdom being intellectual, liberality and temperance moral. For in speaking about a man's character we do not say that he is wise or has understanding but that he is good-tempered or temperate; yet we praise the wise man also with respect to his state of mind; and of states of mind we call those which merit praise virtues.

BOOK II

I

Virtue, then, being of two kinds, intellectual and moral, intellectual virtue in the main owes both its birth and its growth to teaching (for which reason it requires experience and time), while moral virtue comes about as a result of habit, whence also its name (ἠθική) is one that is formed by a slight variation from the word ἔθος (habit). From this it is also plain that none of the moral virtues arises in us by nature; for nothing that exists by nature can form a habit contrary to its nature. For instance the stone which by nature moves downwards cannot be habituated to move upwards, not even if one tries to train it by throwing it up ten thousand times; nor can fire be habituated to move downwards, nor can anything else that by nature behaves in one way be trained to behave in another. Neither by nature, then, nor contrary to nature do the virtues arise in us; rather we are adapted by nature to receive them, and are made perfect by habit.

Again, of all the things that come to us by nature we first acquire the potentiality and later exhibit the activity (this is plain in the case of the senses; for it was not by often seeing or often hearing that we got these senses, but on the contrary we had them before we used them, and did not come to have them by using them); but the virtues we get by first exercising them, as also happens in the case of the arts as well. For the things we have to learn before we can do them, we learn by doing them, e.g. men become builders by building and lyre-players by playing the lyre; so too we become

[1] I. 13.

1103b just by doing just acts, temperate by doing temperate acts, brave by doing brave acts.

This is confirmed by what happens in states; for legislators make the citizens good by forming habits in them, and this is the wish of every legislator, and those who do not effect it miss their mark, and it is in this that a good constitution differs from a bad one.

Again, it is from the same causes and by the same means that every virtue is both produced and destroyed, and similarly every art; for it is from playing the lyre that both good and bad lyre-players are produced. And the corresponding statement is true of builders and of all the rest; men will be good or bad builders as a result of building well or badly. For if this were not so, there would have been no need of a teacher, but all men would have been born good or bad at their craft. This, then, is the case with the virtues also; by doing the acts that we do in our transactions with other men we become just or unjust, and by doing the acts that we do in the presence of danger, and being habituated to feel fear or confidence, we become brave or cowardly. The same is true of appetites and feelings of anger; some men become temperate and good-tempered, others self-indulgent and irascible, by behaving in one way or the other in the appropriate circumstances. Thus, in one word, states of character arise out of like activities. This is why the activities we exhibit must be of a certain kind; it is because the states of character correspond to the differences between these. It makes no small difference, then, whether we form habits of one kind or of another from our very youth; it makes a very great difference, or rather *all* the difference.

2

Since, then, the present inquiry does not aim at theoretical knowledge like the others (for we are inquiring not in order to know what virtue is, but in order to become good, since otherwise our inquiry would have been of no use), we must examine the nature of actions, namely how we ought to do them; for these determine also the nature of the states of character that are produced, as we have said.[1] Now, that we must act according to the right rule is a common principle and must be assumed—it will be discussed later,[2] i.e. both what the right rule is, and how it is related to the other vir-
1104a tues. But this must be agreed upon beforehand, that the whole account of matters of conduct must be given in outline and not precisely, as we said at the very beginning[3] that the accounts we demand must be in accordance with the subject-matter; matters concerned with conduct and questions of what is good for us have no fixity, any more than matters of health. The general account being of this nature, the account of particular cases is yet more lacking in exactness; for they do not fall under any art or precept but the agents themselves must in each case consider what is appropriate to the occasion, as happens also in the art of medicine or of navigation.

But though our present account is of this nature we must give what help we can. First, then, let us consider this, that it is the nature of such things to be destroyed by defect and excess, as we see in the case of strength and of health (for to gain light on things imperceptible we must use the evidence of sensible things); both excessive and defective exercise destroys the strength, and similarly drink or food which is above or below a certain amount destroys the health, while that which is proportionate both produces and increases and preserves it. So too is it, then, in the case of temperance and courage and the other virtues. For the man who flies from and fears everything and does not stand his ground against anything becomes a coward, and the man who fears nothing at all but goes to meet every danger becomes rash; and similarly the man who indulges in every pleasure and abstains from none becomes self-indulgent, while the man who shuns every pleasure, as boors do, becomes in a way insensible; temperance and courage, then, are destroyed by excess and defect, and preserved by the mean.

But not only are the sources and causes of their origination and growth the same as those of their destruction, but also the sphere of their actualization will be the same; for this is also true of the things which are more evident to sense, e.g. of strength; it is produced by taking much food and undergoing much exertion, and it is the strong man that will be most able to do these things. So too is it with the virtues; by abstaining from pleasures we become temperate, and it is when we have become so that we are most able to abstain from them; and similarly too in the case of courage;
1104b for by being habituated to despise things that are terrible and to stand our ground against them we become brave, and it is when

[1] a 31–b 25.

[2] vi. 13.

[3] 1094b 11–27.

we have become so that we shall be most able to stand our ground against them.

3

We must take as a sign of states of character the pleasure or pain that ensues on acts; for the man who abstains from bodily pleasures and delights in this very fact is temperate, while the man who is annoyed at it is self-indulgent, and he who stands his ground against things that are terrible and delights in this or at least is not pained is brave, while the man who is pained is a coward. For moral excellence is concerned with pleasures and pains; it is on account of the pleasure that we do bad things, and on account of the pain that we abstain from noble ones. Hence we ought to have been brought up in a particular way from our very youth, as Plato says,[1] so as both to delight in and to be pained by the things that we ought; for this is the right education.

Again, if the virtues are concerned with actions and passions, and every passion and every action is accompanied by pleasure and pain, for this reason also virtue will be concerned with pleasures and pains. This is indicated also by the fact that punishment is inflicted by these means; for it is a kind of cure, and it is the nature of cures to be effected by contraries.

Again, as we said but lately,[2] every state of soul has a nature relative to and concerned with the kind of things by which it tends to be made worse or better; but it is by reason of pleasures and pains that men become bad, by pursuing and avoiding these—either the pleasures and pains they ought not or when they ought not or as they ought not, or by going wrong in one of the other similar ways that may be distinguished. Hence men even define the virtues as certain states of impassivity and rest; not well, however, because they speak absolutely, and do not say 'as one ought' and 'as one ought not' and 'when one ought or ought not', and the other things that may be added. We assume, then, that this kind of excellence tends to do what is best with regard to pleasures and pains, and vice does the contrary.

The following facts also may show us that virtue and vice are concerned with these same things. There being three objects of choice and three of avoidance, the noble, the advantageous, the pleasant, and their contraries, the base, the injurious, the painful, about all of these the good man tends to go right and the bad man to go wrong, and especially about pleasure; for this is common to the animals, and also it accompanies all objects of choice; for even the noble and the advantageous appear pleasant.

1105a Again, it has grown up with us all from our infancy; this is why it is difficult to rub off this passion, engrained as it is in our life. And we measure even our actions, some of us more and others less, by the rule of pleasure and pain. For this reason, then, our whole inquiry must be about these; for to feel delight and pain rightly or wrongly has no small effect on our actions.

Again, it is harder to fight with pleasure than with anger, to use Heraclitus' phrase[3], but both art and virtue are always concerned with what is harder; for even the good is better when it is harder. Therefore for this reason also the whole concern both of virtue and of political science is with pleasures and pains; for the man who uses these well will be good, he who uses them badly bad.

That virtue, then, is concerned with pleasures and pains, and that by the acts from which it arises it is both increased and, if they are done differently, destroyed, and that the acts from which it arose are those in which it actualizes itself—let this be taken as said.

4

The question might be asked, what we mean by saying that we must become just by doing just acts, and temperate by doing temperate acts; for if men do just and temperate acts, they are already just and temperate, exactly as, if they do what is in accordance with the laws of grammar and of music, they are grammarians and musicians.

Or is this not true even of the arts? It is possible to do something that is in accordance with the laws of grammar, either by chance or at the suggestion of another. A man will be a grammarian, then, only when he has both done something grammatical and done it grammatically; and this means doing it in accordance with the grammatical knowledge in himself.

Again, the case of the arts and that of the virtues are not similar; for the products of the arts have their goodness in themselves, so that it is enough that they should have a certain character, but if the acts that are in accordance with the virtues have themselves a certain character it does not follow that they are done justly or temperately. The agent also must be in a

[1] *Laws*, 653 ff.; *Republic*, 401–402.

[2] a 27–b 3.

[3] Fr. 85, Diels.

certain condition when he does them; in the first place he must have knowledge, secondly he must choose the acts, and choose them for their own sakes, and thirdly his action must proceed from a firm and unchangeable character. These are not reckoned in as conditions of
1105b the possession of the arts, except the bare knowledge; but as a condition of the possession of the virtues knowledge has little or no weight, while the other conditions count not for a little but for everything, i.e. the very conditions which result from often doing just and temperate acts.

Actions, then, are called just and temperate when they are such as the just or the temperate man would do; but it is not the man who does these that is just and temperate, but the man who also does them *as* just and temperate men do them. It is well said, then, that it is by doing just acts that the just man is produced, and by doing temperate acts the temperate man; without doing these no one would have even a prospect of becoming good.

But most people do not do these, but take refuge in theory and think they are being philosophers and will become good in this way, behaving somewhat like patients who listen attentively to their doctors, but do none of the things they are ordered to do. As the latter will not be made well in body by such a course of treatment, the former will not be made well in soul by such a course of philosophy.

5

Next we must consider what virtue is. Since things that are found in the soul are of three kinds—passions, faculties, states of character, virtue must be one of these. By passions I mean appetite, anger, fear, confidence, envy, joy, friendly feeling, hatred, longing, emulation, pity, and in general the feelings that are accompanied by pleasure or pain; by faculties the things in virtue of which we are said to be capable of feeling these, e.g. of becoming angry or being pained or feeling pity; by states of character the things in virtue of which we stand well or badly with reference to the passions, e.g. with reference to anger we stand badly if we feel it violently or too weakly, and well if we feel it moderately; and similarly with reference to the other passions.

Now neither the virtues nor the vices are *passions,* because we are not called good or bad on the ground of our passions, but are so called on the ground of our virtues and our vices, and because we are neither praised nor blamed for our passions (for the man who feels fear or anger is not praised, nor is the man who simply feels anger blamed, but the man who
1106a feels it in a certain way), but for our virtues and our vices we *are* praised or blamed.

Again, we feel anger and fear without choice, but the virtues are modes of choice or involve choice. Further, in respect of the passions we are said to be moved, but in respect of the virtues and the vices we are said not to be moved but to be disposed in a particular way.

For these reasons also they are not *faculties*; for we are neither called good nor bad, nor praised nor blamed, for the simple capacity of feeling the passions; again, we have the faculties by nature, but we are not made good or bad by nature; we have spoken of this before.[1]

If, then, the virtues are neither passions nor faculties, all that remains is that they should be *states of character.*

Thus we have stated what virtue is in respect of its genus.

6

We must, however, not only describe virtue as a state of character, but also say what sort of state it is. We may remark, then, that every virtue or excellence both brings into good condition the thing of which it is the excellence and makes the work of that thing be done well; e.g. the excellence of the eye makes both the eye and its work good; for it is by the excellence of the eye that we see well. Similarly the excellence of the horse makes a horse both good in itself and good at running and at carrying its rider and at awaiting the attack of the enemy. Therefore, if this is true in every case, the virtue of man also will be the state of character which makes a man good and which makes him do his own work well.

How this is to happen we have stated already,[2] but it will be made plain also by the following consideration of the specific nature of virtue. In everything that is continuous and divisible it is possible to take more, less, or an equal amount, and that either in terms of the thing itself or relatively to us; and the equal is an intermediate between excess and defect. By the intermediate in the object I mean that which is equidistant from each of the extremes, which is one and the same for all men; by the intermediate relatively to us that which is neither too much nor too little—and this is not one, nor the same for all. For instance, if ten is

[1] 1103a 18–b 2. [2] 1104a 11–27.

many and two is few, six is the intermediate, taken in terms of the object; for it exceeds and is exceeded by an equal amount; this is intermediate according to arithmetical proportion. But the intermediate relatively to us is not to be taken so; if ten pounds are too much for **1106b** a particular person to eat and two too little, it does not follow that the trainer will order six pounds; for this also is perhaps too much for the person who is to take it, or too little—too little for Milo, too much for the beginner in athletic exercises. The same is true of running and wrestling. Thus a master of any art avoids excess and defect, but seeks the intermediate and chooses this—the intermediate not in the object but relatively to us.

If it is thus, then, that every art does its work well—by looking to the intermediate and judging its works by this standard (so that we often say of good works of art that it is not possible either to take away or to add anything, implying that excess and defect destroy the goodness of works of art, while the mean preserves it; and good artists, as we say, look to this in their work), and if, further, virtue is more exact and better than any art, as nature also is, then virtue must have the quality of aiming at the intermediate. I mean moral virtue; for it is this that is concerned with passions and actions, and in these there is excess, defect, and the intermediate. For instance, both fear and confidence and appetite and anger and pity and in general pleasure and pain may be felt both too much and too little, and in both cases not well; but to feel them at the right times, with reference to the right objects, towards the right people, with the right motive, and in the right way, is what is both intermediate and best, and this is characteristic of virtue. Similarly with regard to actions also there is excess, defect, and the intermediate. Now virtue is concerned with passions and actions, in which excess is a form of failure, and so is defect, while the intermediate is praised and is a form of success; and being praised and being successful are both characteristics of virtue. Therefore virtue is a kind of mean, since, as we have seen, it aims at what is intermediate.

Again, it is possible to fail in many ways (for evil belongs to the class of the unlimited, as the Pythagoreans conjectured, and good to that of the limited), while to succeed is possible only in one way (for which reason also one is easy and the other difficult—to miss the mark easy, to hit it difficult); for these reasons also, then, excess and defect are characteristic of vice, and the mean of virtue;

For men are good in but one way, but bad in many.[1]

Virtue, then, is a state of character concerned **1107a** with choice, lying in a mean, i.e. the mean relative to us, this being determined by a rational principle, and by that principle by which the man of practical wisdom would determine it. Now it is a mean between two vices, that which depends on excess and that which depends on defect; and again it is a mean because the vices respectively fall short of or exceed what is right in both passions and actions, while virtue both finds and chooses that which is intermediate. Hence in respect of its substance and the definition which states its essence virtue is a mean, with regard to what is best and right an extreme.

But not every action nor every passion admits of a mean; for some have names that already imply badness, e.g. spite, shamelessness, envy, and in the case of actions adultery, theft, murder; for all of these and suchlike things imply by their names that they are themselves bad, and not the excesses or deficiencies of them. It is not possible, then, ever to be right with regard to them; one must always be wrong. Nor does goodness or badness with regard to such things depend on committing adultery with the right woman, at the right time, and in the right way, but simply to do any of them is to go wrong. It would be equally absurd, then, to expect that in unjust, cowardly, and voluptuous action there should be a mean, an excess, and a deficiency; for at that rate there would be a mean of excess and of deficiency, an excess of excess, and a deficiency of deficiency. But as there is no excess and deficiency of temperance and courage because what is intermediate is in a sense an extreme, so too of the actions we have mentioned there is no mean nor any excess and deficiency but however they are done they are wrong; for in general there is neither a mean of excess and deficiency, nor excess and deficiency of a mean.

7

We must, however, not only make this gener[al] statement, but also apply it to the individu[al] facts. For among statements about condu[ct] those which are general apply more widely, bu[t] those which are particular are more gen[uine]

[1] Fr. eleg. adesp. 16, Diehl.

ine, since conduct has to do with individual cases, and our statements must harmonize with the facts in these cases. We may take these cases from our table. With regard to feelings of fear 1107b and confidence courage is the mean; of the people who exceed, he who exceeds in fearlessness has no name (many of the states have no name), while the man who exceeds in confidence is rash, and he who exceeds in fear and falls short in confidence is a coward. With regard to pleasures and pains—not all of them, and not so much with regard to the pains—the mean is temperance, the excess self-indulgence. Persons deficient with regard to the pleasures are not often found; hence such persons also have received no name. But let us call them 'insensible'.

With regard to giving and taking of money the mean is liberality, the excess and the defect prodigality and meanness. In these actions people exceed and fall short in contrary ways; the prodigal exceeds in spending and falls short in taking, while the mean man exceeds in taking and falls short in spending. (At present we are giving a mere outline or summary, and are satisfied with this; later these states will be more exactly determined.[1]) With regard to money there are also other dispositions—a mean, magnificence (for the magnificent man differs from the liberal man; the former deals with large sums, the latter with small ones), an excess, tastelessness and vulgarity, and a deficiency, niggardliness; these differ from the states opposed to liberality, and the mode of their difference will be stated later.[2]

With regard to honour and dishonour the mean is proper pride, the excess is known as a sort of 'empty vanity', and the deficiency is undue humility; and as we said[3] liberality was related to magnificence, differing from it by dealing with small sums, so there is a state similarly related to proper pride, being concerned with small honours while that is concerned with great. For it is possible to desire honour as one ought, and more than one ought, and less, and the man who exceeds in his desires is called ambitious, the man who falls short unambitious, while the intermediate person has no name. The dispositions also are nameless, except that that of the ambitious man is called ambition. Hence the people who are at the extremes lay claim to the middle place; and we ourselves sometimes call the intermediate person ambitious and sometimes unambitious, and sometimes praise the ambitious man and sometimes the unambitious. The reason of
1108a our doing this will be stated in what follows;[4] but now let us speak of the remaining states according to the method which has been indicated.

With regard to anger also there is an excess, a deficiency, and a mean. Although they can scarcely be said to have names, yet since we call the intermediate person good-tempered let us call the mean good temper; of the persons at the extremes let the one who exceeds be called irascible, and his vice irascibility, and the man who falls short an inirascible sort of person, and the deficiency inirascibility.

There are also three other means, which have a certain likeness to one another, but differ from one another: for they are all concerned with intercourse in words and actions, but differ in that one is concerned with truth in this sphere, the other two with pleasantness; and of this one kind is exhibited in giving amusement, the other in all the circumstances of life. We must therefore speak of these too, that we may the better see that in all things the mean is praiseworthy, and the extremes neither praiseworthy nor right, but worthy of blame. Now most of these states also have no names, but we must try, as in the other cases, to invent names ourselves so that we may be clear and easy to follow. With regard to truth, then, the intermediate is a truthful sort of person and the mean may be called truthfulness, while the pretence which exaggerates is boastfulness and the person characterized by it a boaster, and that which understates is mock modesty and the person characterized by it mock-modest. With regard to pleasantness in the giving of amusement the intermediate person is ready-witted and the disposition ready wit, the excess is buffoonery and the person characterized by it a buffoon, while the man who falls short is a sort of boor and his state is boorishness. With regard to the remaining kind of pleasantness, that which is exhibited in life in general, the man who is pleasant in the right way is friendly and the mean is friendliness, while the man who exceeds is an obsequious person if he has no end in view, a flatterer if he is aiming at his own advantage, and the man who falls short and is unpleasant in all circumstances is a quarrelsome and surly sort of person.

There are also means in the passions and concerned with the passions; since shame is not a virtue, and yet praise is extended to the mod-

[1] iv. 1. [2] 1122a 20–9, b 10–18. [3] ll. 17–19.

[4] b 11–26, 1125b 14–18.

est man. For even in these matters one man is said to be intermediate, and another to exceed, as for instance the bashful man who is ashamed of everything; while he who falls short or is not ashamed of anything at all is shameless, and the intermediate person is modest. Righteous indignation is a mean between envy **1108ᵇ** and spite, and these states are concerned with the pain and pleasure that are felt at the fortunes of our neighbours; the man who is characterized by righteous indignation is pained at undeserved good fortune, the envious man, going beyond him, is pained at all good fortune, and the spiteful man falls so far short of being pained that he even rejoices. But these states there will be an opportunity of describing elsewhere;[1] with regard to justice, since it has not one simple meaning, we shall, after describing the other states, distinguish its two kinds and say how each of them is a mean; and similarly we shall treat also of the rational virtues.

8

There are three kinds of disposition, then, two of them vices, involving excess and deficiency respectively, and one a virtue, viz. the mean, and all are in a sense opposed to all; for the extreme states are contrary both to the intermediate state and to each other, and the intermediate to the extremes; as the equal is greater relatively to the less, less relatively to the greater, so the middle states are excessive relatively to the deficiencies, deficient relatively to the excesses, both in passions and in actions. For the brave man appears rash relatively to the coward, and cowardly relatively to the rash man; and similarly the temperate man appears self-indulgent relatively to the insensible man, insensible relatively to the self-indulgent, and the liberal man prodigal relatively to the mean man, mean relatively to the prodigal. Hence also the people at the extremes push the intermediate man each over to the other, and the brave man is called rash by the coward, cowardly by the rash man, and correspondingly in the other cases.

These states being thus opposed to one another, the greatest contrariety is that of the extremes to each other, rather than to the intermediate; for these are further from each other than from the intermediate, as the great is further from the small and the small from the great than both are from the equal. Again, to the intermediate some extremes show a certain likeness, as that of rashness to courage and that of prodigality to liberality; but the extremes show the greatest unlikeness to each other; now contraries are defined as the things that are furthest from each other, so that things that are further apart are more contrary.

1109ª To the mean in some cases the deficiency, in some the excess is more opposed; e.g. it is not rashness, which is an excess, but cowardice, which is a deficiency, that is more opposed to courage, and not insensibility, which is a deficiency, but self-indulgence, which is an excess, that is more opposed to temperance. This happens from two reasons, one being drawn from the thing itself; for because one extreme is nearer and liker to the intermediate, we oppose not this but rather its contrary to the intermediate. E.g. since rashness is thought liker and nearer to courage, and cowardice more unlike, we oppose rather the latter to courage; for things that are further from the intermediate are thought more contrary to it. This, then, is one cause, drawn from the thing itself; another is drawn from ourselves; for the things to which we ourselves more naturally tend seem more contrary to the intermediate. For instance, we ourselves tend more naturally to pleasures, and hence are more easily carried away towards self-indulgence than towards propriety. We describe as contrary to the mean, then, rather the directions in which we more often go to great lengths; and therefore self-indulgence, which is an excess, is the more contrary to temperance.

9

That moral virtue is a mean, then, and in what sense it is so, and that it is a mean between two vices, the one involving excess, the other deficiency, and that it is such because its character is to aim at what is intermediate in passions and in actions, has been sufficiently stated. Hence also it is no easy task to be good. For in everything it is no easy task to find the middle, e.g. to find the middle of a circle is not for every one but for him who knows; so, too, any one can get angry—that is easy—or give or spend money; but to do this to the right person, to the right extent, at the right time, with the right motive, and in the right way, *that* is not for every one, nor is it easy; where-

[1] The reference may be to the whole treatment of the moral virtues in III. 6–IV. 9, or to the discussion of shame in IV. 9, or to the discussion of these two states in *Rhetoric*, II. 6, 9, 10.

fore goodness is both rare and laudable and noble.

Hence he who aims at the intermediate must first depart from what is the more contrary to it, as Calypso advises—

Hold the ship out beyond that surf and spray.[1]

For of the extremes one is more erroneous, one less so; therefore, since to hit the mean is hard in the extreme, we must as a second best, as people say, take the least of the evils; and this will be done best in the way we describe. **1109b** But we must consider the things towards which we ourselves also are easily carried away; for some of us tend to one thing, some to another; and this will be recognizable from the pleasure and the pain we feel. We must drag ourselves away to the contrary extreme; for we shall get into the intermediate state by drawing well away from error, as people do in straightening sticks that are bent.

Now in everything the pleasant or pleasure is most to be guarded against; for we do not judge it impartially. We ought, then, to feel towards pleasure as the elders of the people felt towards Helen, and in all circumstances repeat their saying; for if we dismiss pleasure thus we are less likely to go astray. It is by doing this, then, (to sum the matter up) that we shall best be able to hit the mean.

But this is no doubt difficult, and especially in individual cases; for it is not easy to determine both how and with whom and on what provocation and how long one should be angry; for we too sometimes praise those who fall short and call them good-tempered, but sometimes we praise those who get angry and call them manly. The man, however, who deviates little from goodness is not blamed, whether he do so in the direction of the more or of the less, but only the man who deviates more widely; for *he* does not fail to be noticed. But up to what point and to what extent a man must deviate before he becomes blameworthy it is not easy to determine by reasoning, any more than anything else that is perceived by the senses; such things depend on particular facts, and the decision rests with perception. So much, then, is plain, that the intermediate state is in all things to be praised, but that we must incline sometimes towards the excess, sometimes towards the deficiency; for so shall we most easily hit the mean and what is right.

BOOK III

I

SINCE virtue is concerned with passions and actions, and on voluntary passions and actions praise and blame are bestowed, on those that are involuntary pardon, and sometimes also pity, to distinguish the voluntary and the involuntary is presumably necessary for those who are studying the nature of virtue, and useful also for legislators with a view to the assigning both of honours and of punishments. Those things, then, are thought involun- **1110a** tary, which take place under compulsion or owing to ignorance; and that is compulsory of which the moving principle is outside, being a principle in which nothing is contributed by the person who is acting or is feeling the passion, e.g. if he were to be carried somewhere by a wind, or by men who had him in their power.

But with regard to the things that are done from fear of greater evils or for some noble object (e.g. if a tyrant were to order one to do something base, having one's parents and children in his power, and if one did the action they were to be saved, but otherwise would be put to death), it may be debated whether such actions are involuntary or voluntary. Something of the sort happens also with regard to the throwing of goods overboard in a storm; for in the abstract no one throws goods away voluntarily, but on condition of its securing the safety of himself and his crew any sensible man does so. Such actions, then, are mixed, but are more like voluntary actions; for they are worthy of choice at the time when they are done, and the end of an action is relative to the occasion. Both the terms, then, 'voluntary' and 'involuntary', must be used with reference to the moment of action. Now the man acts voluntarily; for the principle that moves the instrumental parts of the body in such actions is in him, and the things of which the moving principle is in a man himself are in his power to do or not to do. Such actions, therefore, are voluntary, but in the abstract perhaps involuntary; for no one would choose any such act in itself.

For such actions men are sometimes even praised, when they endure something base or painful in return for great and noble objects

[1] *Odyssey*, XII. 219 ff. (Mackail's trans.).

gained; in the opposite case they are blamed, since to endure the greatest indignities for no noble end or for a trifling end is the mark of an inferior person. On some actions praise indeed is not bestowed, but pardon is, when one does what he ought not under pressure which overstrains human nature and which no one could withstand. But some acts, perhaps, we cannot be forced to do, but ought rather to face death after the most fearful sufferings; for the things that 'forced' Euripides' Alcmaeon to slay his mother seem absurd. It is difficult sometimes to determine what should be chosen at what cost, and what should be endured in return for what gain, and yet more difficult to abide by our decisions; for as a rule what is expected is painful, and what we are forced to do is base, whence praise and blame are bestowed on those who have been compelled or have not.

1110b What sort of acts, then, should be called compulsory? We answer that without qualification actions are so when the cause is in the external circumstances and the agent contributes nothing. But the things that in themselves are involuntary, but now and in return for these gains are worthy of choice, and whose moving principle is in the agent, are in themselves involuntary, but now and in return for these gains voluntary. They are more like voluntary acts; for actions are in the class of particulars, and the particular acts here are voluntary. What sort of things are to be chosen, and in return for what, it is not easy to state; for there are many differences in the particular cases.

But if some one were to say that pleasant and noble objects have a compelling power, forcing us from without, all acts would be for him compulsory; for it is for these objects that all men do everything they do. And those who act under compulsion and unwillingly act with pain, but those who do acts for their pleasantness and nobility do them with pleasure; it is absurd to make external circumstances responsible, and not oneself, as being easily caught by such attractions, and to make oneself responsible for noble acts but the pleasant objects responsible for base acts. The compulsory, then, seems to be that whose moving principle is outside, the person compelled contributing nothing.

Everything that is done by reason of ignorance is *not* voluntary; it is only what produces pain and repentance that is *in*voluntary. For the man who has done something owing to ignorance, and feels not the least vexation at his action, has not acted voluntarily, since he did not know what he was doing, nor yet involuntarily, since he is not pained. Of people, then, who act by reason of ignorance he who repents is thought an involuntary agent, and the man who does not repent may, since he is different, be called a not voluntary agent; for, since he differs from the other, it is better that he should have a name of his own.

Acting by reason of ignorance seems also to be different from acting *in* ignorance; for the man who is drunk or in a rage is thought to act as a result not of ignorance but of one of the causes mentioned, yet not knowingly but in ignorance.

Now every wicked man is ignorant of what he ought to do and what he ought to abstain from, and it is by reason of error of this kind that men become unjust and in general bad; but the term 'involuntary' tends to be used not if a man is ignorant of what is to his advantage—for it is not mistaken purpose that causes involuntary action (it leads rather to wickedness), nor ignorance of the universal (for *that* men are *blamed*), but ignorance of particulars, i.e. of the circumstances of the action and the objects with which it is concerned. **1111a** For it is on these that both pity and pardon depend, since the person who is ignorant of any of these acts involuntarily.

Perhaps it is just as well, therefore, to determine their nature and number. A man may be ignorant, then, of who he is, what he is doing, what or whom he is acting on, and sometimes also what (e.g. what instrument) he is doing it with, and to what end (e.g. he may think his act will conduce to some one's safety), and how he is doing it (e.g. whether gently or violently). Now of all of these no one could be ignorant unless he were mad, and evidently also he could not be ignorant of the agent; for how could he not know himself? But of what he is doing a man might be ignorant, as for instance people say 'it slipped out of their mouths as they were speaking', or 'they did not know it was a secret', as Aeschylus said of the mysteries, or a man might say he 'let it go off when he merely wanted to show its working', as the man did with the catapult. Again, one might think one's son was an enemy, as Merope did, or that a pointed spear had a button on it, or that a stone was pumice-stone; or one might give a man a draught to save him, and really kill him; or one might want to touch a man, as people do in sparring, and really wound him. The ignorance may relate, then, to any of these things, i.e. of the circumstances of the action, and the man who was ignorant of any of these is thought to have acted involuntarily, and especially if he was ignorant on the most important points; and these are thought to be the circumstances of the action and its end. Further, the doing of an act that is called involuntary in virtue of ignorance of this sort must be painful and involve repentance.

Since that which is done under compulsion or by reason of ignorance is involuntary, the voluntary would seem to be that of which the moving principle is in the agent himself, he being aware of the particular circumstances of the action. Presumably acts done by reason of anger or appetite are not rightly called involuntary. For in the first place, on that showing none of the other animals will act voluntarily, nor will children; and secondly, is it meant that we do not do voluntarily *any* of the acts that are due to appetite or anger, or that we do the noble acts voluntarily and the base acts involuntarily? Is not this absurd, when one and the same thing is the cause? But it would surely be odd to describe as involuntary the things one ought to desire; and we ought both to be angry at certain things and to have an appetite for certain things, e.g. for health and for learning. Also what is involuntary is thought to be painful, but what is in accordance with appetite is thought to be pleasant. Again, what is the difference in respect of involuntariness between errors committed upon calculation and those committed in anger? **1111b** Both are to be avoided, but the irrational passions are thought not less human than reason is, and therefore also the actions which proceed from anger or appetite are the man's actions. It would be odd, then, to treat them as involuntary.

2

Both the voluntary and the involuntary having been delimited, we must next discuss choice; for it is thought to be most closely bound up with virtue and to discriminate characters better than actions do.

Choice, then, seems to be voluntary, but not the same thing as the voluntary; the latter extends more widely. For both children and the lower animals share in voluntary action, but not in choice, and acts done on the spur of the moment we describe as voluntary, but not as chosen.

Those who say it is appetite or anger or wish or a kind of opinion do not seem to be right. For choice is not common to irrational creatures as well, but appetite and anger are. Again, the incontinent man acts with appetite, but not with choice; while the continent man on the contrary acts with choice, but not with appetite. Again, appetite is contrary to choice, but not appetite to appetite. Again, appetite relates to the pleasant and the painful, choice neither to the painful nor to the pleasant.

Still less is it anger; for acts due to anger are thought to be less than any others objects of choice.

But neither is it wish, though it seems near to it; for choice cannot relate to impossibles, and if any one said he chose them he would be thought silly; but there may be a wish even for impossibles, e.g. for immortality. And wish may relate to things that could in no way be brought about by one's own efforts, e.g. that a particular actor or athlete should win in a competition; but no one chooses such things, but only the things that he thinks could be brought about by his own efforts. Again, wish relates rather to the end, choice to the means; for instance, we wish to be healthy, but we choose the acts which will make us healthy, and we wish to be happy and say we do, but we cannot well say we choose to be so; for, in general, choice seems to relate to the things that are in our own power.

For this reason, too, it cannot be opinion; for opinion is thought to relate to all kinds of things, no less to eternal things and impossible things than to things in our own power; and it is distinguished by its falsity or truth, not by its badness or goodness, while choice is distinguished rather by these.

Now with opinion in general perhaps no one **1112a** even says it is identical. But it is not identical even with any kind of opinion; for by choosing what is good or bad we are men of a certain character, which we are not by holding certain opinions. And we choose to get or avoid something good or bad, but we have opinions about what a thing is or whom it is good for or how it is good for him; we can hardly be said to opine to get or avoid anything. And choice is praised for being related to the right object rather than for being rightly related to it, opinion for being truly related to its object. And we choose what we best know to be good, but we opine what we do not quite know; and it is not the same people that are thought to make the best choices and to have the best opinions, but some are thought to have fairly good opinions, but by reason of vice to choose what they should not. If opinion precedes choice or accompanies it, that makes no difference; for it is not this that we are considering, but whether it is *identical* with some kind of opinion.

What, then, or what kind of thing is it, since it is none of the things we have mentioned? It seems to be voluntary, but not all that is voluntary to be an object of choice. Is it, then, what has been decided on by previous deliberation? At any rate choice involves a rational principle and thought. Even the name seems to suggest that it is what is chosen before other things.

3

Do we deliberate about everything, and is everything a possible subject of deliberation, or is deliberation impossible about some things? We ought presumably to call not what a fool or a madman would deliberate about, but what a sensible man would deliberate about, a subject of deliberation. Now about eternal things no one deliberates, e.g. about the material universe or the incommensurability of the diagonal and the side of a square. But no more do we deliberate about the things that involve movement but always happen in the same way, whether of necessity or by nature or from any other cause, e.g. the solstices and the risings of the stars; nor about things that happen now in one way, now in another, e.g. droughts and rains; nor about chance events, like the finding of treasure. But we do not deliberate even about all human affairs; for instance, no Spartan deliberates about the best constitution for the Scythians. For none of these things can be brought about by our own efforts.

We deliberate about things that are in our power and can be done; and these are in fact what is left. For nature, necessity, and chance are thought to be causes, and also reason and everything that depends on man. Now every class of men deliberates about the things that can be done by their own efforts. And in the case of exact and self-contained sciences there **1112b** is no deliberation, e.g. about the letters of the alphabet (for we have no doubt how they should be written); but the things that are brought about by our own efforts, but not always in the same way, are the things about which we deliberate, e.g. questions of medical treatment or of money-making. And we do so more in the case of the art of navigation than in that of gymnastics, inasmuch as it has been less exactly worked out, and again about other things in the same ratio, and more also in the case of the arts than in that of the sciences; for we have more doubt about the former. Deliberation is concerned with things that happen in a certain way for the most part, but in which the event is obscure, and with things in which it is indeterminate. We call in others to aid us in deliberation on important questions, distrusting ourselves as not being equal to deciding.

We deliberate not about ends but about means. For a doctor does not deliberate whether he shall heal, nor an orator whether he shall persuade, nor a statesman whether he shall produce law and order, nor does any one else deliberate about his end. They assume the end and consider how and by what means it is to be attained; and if it seems to be produced by several means they consider by which it is most easily and best produced, while if it is achieved by one only they consider how it will be achieved by this and by what means *this* will be achieved, till they come to the first cause, which in the order of discovery is last. For the person who deliberates seems to investigate and analyse in the way described as though he were analysing a geometrical construction (not all investigation appears to be deliberation—for instance mathematical investigations—but all deliberation is investigation), and what is last in the order of analysis seems to be first in the order of becoming. And if we come on an impossibility, we give up the search, e.g. if we need money and this cannot be got; but if a thing appears possible we try to do it. By 'possible' things I mean things that might be brought about by our own efforts; and these in a sense include things that can be brought about by the efforts of our friends, since the moving principle is in ourselves. The subject of investigation is sometimes the instruments, sometimes the use of them; and similarly in the other cases—sometimes the means, sometimes the mode of using it or the means of bringing it about. It seems, then, as has been said, that man is a moving principle of actions; now deliberation is about the things to be done by the agent himself, and actions are for the sake of things other than themselves. For the end cannot be a subject of deliberation, but only the means; nor indeed can the particular **1113a** facts be a subject of it, as whether this is bread or has been baked as it should; for these are matters of perception. If we are to be always deliberating, we shall have to go on to infinity.

The same thing is deliberated upon and is chosen, except that the object of choice is already determinate, since it is that which has been decided upon as a result of deliberation that is the object of choice. For every one ceases to inquire how he is to act when he has brought the moving principle back to himself and to the ruling part of himself; for this is what chooses. This is plain also from the ancient constitutions, which Homer represented; for the kings announced their choices to the people. The object of choice being one of the things in our own power which is desired after deliberation, choice will be deliberate desire of things in our own power; for when we have decided as a result of deliberation, we desire in accordance with our deliberation.

We may take it, then, that we have described choice in outline, and stated the nature of its objects and the fact that it is concerned with means.

4

That *wish* is for the end has already been stated;[1] some think it is for the good, others for the apparent good. Now those who say that the good is the object of wish must admit in consequence that that which the man who does not choose aright wishes for is not an object of wish (for if it is to be so, it must also be good; but it was, if it so happened, bad); while those who say the apparent good is the object of wish must admit that there is no natural object of wish, but only what seems good to each man. Now different things appear good to different people, and, if it so happens, even contrary things.

If these consequences are unpleasing, are we to say that absolutely and in truth the good is the object of wish, but for each person the apparent good; that that which is in truth an object of wish is an object of wish to the good man, while any chance thing may be so to the bad man, as in the case of bodies also the things that are in truth wholesome are wholesome for bodies which are in good condition, while for those that are diseased other things are wholesome—or bitter or sweet or hot or heavy, and so on; since the good man judges each class of things rightly, and in each the truth appears to him? For each state of character has its own ideas of the noble and the pleasant, and perhaps the good man differs from others most by seeing the truth in each class of things, being as it were the norm and measure of them. In most things the error seems to be due to pleasure; for it appears a
1113b good when it is not. We therefore choose the pleasant as a good, and avoid pain as an evil.

5

The end, then, being what we wish for, the means what we deliberate about and choose, actions concerning means must be according to choice and voluntary. Now the exercise of the virtues is concerned with means. Therefore virtue also is in our own power, and so too vice. For where it is in our power to act it is also in our power not to act, and *vice versa*; so that, if to act, where this is noble, is in our power, not to act, which will be base, will also be in our power, and if not to act, where this is noble, is in our power, to act, which will be base, will also be in our power. Now if it is in our power to do noble or base acts, and likewise in our power not to do them, and this was what being good or bad meant, then it is in our power to be virtuous or vicious.

The saying[2] that 'no one is voluntarily wicked nor involuntarily happy' seems to be partly false and partly true; for no one is involuntarily happy, but wickedness *is* voluntary. Or else we shall have to dispute what has just been said, at any rate, and deny that man is a moving principle or begetter of his actions as of children. But if these facts are evident and we cannot refer actions to moving principles other than those in ourselves, the acts whose moving principles are in us must themselves also be in our power and voluntary.

Witness seems to be borne to this both by individuals in their private capacity and by legislators themselves; for these punish and take vengeance on those who do wicked acts (unless they have acted under compulsion or as a result of ignorance for which they are not themselves responsible), while they honour those who do noble acts, as though they meant to encourage the latter and deter the former. But no one is encouraged to do the things that are neither in our power nor voluntary; it is assumed that there is no gain in being persuaded not to be hot or in pain or hungry or the like, since we shall experience these feelings none the less. Indeed, we punish a man for his very ignorance, if he is thought responsible for the ignorance, as when penalties are doubled

[1] 1111b 26.

[2] Fr. adesp. (? Solon), Bergk, p. 1356 f.

in the case of drunkenness; for the moving principle is in the man himself, since he had the power of not getting drunk and his getting drunk was the cause of his ignorance. And we punish those who are ignorant of anything in **1114a** the laws that they ought to know and that is not difficult, and so too in the case of anything else that they are thought to be ignorant of through carelessness; we assume that it is in their power not to be ignorant, since they have the power of taking care.

But perhaps a man is the kind of man not to take care. Still they are themselves by their slack lives responsible for becoming men of that kind, and men make themselves responsible for being unjust or self-indulgent, in the one case by cheating and in the other by spending their time in drinking bouts and the like; for it is activities exercised on particular objects that make the corresponding character. This is plain from the case of people training for any contest or action; they practise the activity the whole time. Now not to know that it is from the exercise of activities on particular objects that states of character are produced is the mark of a thoroughly senseless person. Again, it is irrational to suppose that a man who acts unjustly does not wish to be unjust or a man who acts self-indulgently to be self-indulgent. But if *without* being ignorant a man does the things which will make him unjust, he will be unjust voluntarily. Yet it does not follow that if he wishes he will cease to be unjust and will be just. For neither does the man who is ill become well on those terms. We may suppose a case in which he is ill voluntarily, through living incontinently and disobeying his doctors. In that case it was *then* open to him not to be ill, but not now, when he has thrown away his chance, just as when you have let a stone go it is too late to recover it; but yet it was in your power to throw it, since the moving principle was in you. So, too, to the unjust and to the self-indulgent man it was open at the beginning not to become men of this kind, and so they are unjust and self-indulgent voluntarily; but now that they have become so it is not possible for them not to be so.

But not only are the vices of the soul voluntary, but those of the body also for some men, whom we accordingly blame; while no one blames those who are ugly by nature, we blame those who are so owing to want of exercise and care. So it is, too, with respect to weakness and infirmity; no one would reproach a man blind from birth or by disease or from a blow, but rather pity him, while every one would blame a man who was blind from drunkenness or some other form of self-indulgence. Of vices of the body, then, those in our own power are blamed, those not in our power are not. And if this be so, in the other cases also the vices that are blamed must be in our own power.

Now some one may say that all men desire the apparent good, but have no control over the appearance, but the end appears to each man in a form answering to his character. We reply **1114b** that if each man is somehow responsible for his state of mind, he will also be himself somehow responsible for the appearance; but if not, no one is responsible for his own evildoing, but every one does evil acts through ignorance of the end, thinking that by these he will get what is best, and the aiming at the end is not self-chosen but one must be born with an eye, as it were, by which to judge rightly and choose what is truly good, and he is well endowed by nature who is well endowed with this. For it is what is greatest and most noble, and what we cannot get or learn from another, but must have just such as it was when given us at birth, and to be well and nobly endowed with this will be perfect and true excellence of natural endowment. If this is true, then, how will virtue be more voluntary than vice? To both men alike, the good and the bad, the end appears and is fixed by nature or however it may be, and it is by referring everything else to this that men do whatever they do.

Whether, then, it is not by nature that the end appears to each man such as it does appear, but something also depends on him, or the end is natural but because the good man adopts the means voluntarily virtue is voluntary, vice also will be none the less voluntary; for in the case of the bad man there is equally present that which depends on himself in his actions even if not in his end. If, then, as is asserted, the virtues are voluntary (for we are ourselves somehow partly responsible for our states of character, and it is by being persons of a certain kind that we assume the end to be so and so), the vices also will be voluntary; for the same is true of them.

With regard to the virtues in *general* we have stated their genus in outline, viz. that they are means and that they are states of character, and that they tend, and by their own nature, to the doing of the acts by which they are produced, and that they are in our power and voluntary, and act as the right rule prescribes. But actions and states of character are not voluntary in the same way; for we are masters of our actions from the beginning right to the end, if we know the particular facts, but though we control the beginning of our states of char- **1115a** acter the gradual progress is not obvious any more than it is in illnesses; because it was in our power, however, to act in this way or not in this way, therefore the states are voluntary.

Let us take up the several virtues, however, and say which they are and what sort of things they are concerned with and how they are concerned with them; at the same time it will become plain how many they are. And first let us speak of courage.

6

That it is a mean with regard to feelings of fear and confidence has already been made evident;[1] and plainly the things we fear are terrible things, and these are, to speak without qualification, evils; for which reason people even define fear as expectation of evil. Now we fear all evils, e.g. disgrace, poverty, disease, friendlessness, death, but the brave man is not thought to be concerned with all; for to fear some things is even right and noble, and it is base not to fear them—e.g. disgrace; he who fears this is good and modest, and he who does not is shameless. He is, however, by some people called brave, by a transference of the word to a new meaning; for he has in him something which is like the brave man, since the brave man also is a fearless person. Poverty and disease we perhaps ought not to fear, nor in general the things that do not proceed from vice and are not due to a man himself. But not even the man who is fearless of these is brave. Yet we apply the word to him also in virtue of a similarity; for some who in the dangers of war are cowards are liberal and are confident in face of the loss of money. Nor is a man a coward if he fears insult to his wife and children or envy or anything of the kind; nor brave if he is confident when he is about to be flogged. With what sort of terrible things, then, is the brave man concerned? Surely with the greatest; for no one is more likely than he to stand his ground against what is awe-inspiring. Now death is the most terrible of all things; for it is the end, and nothing is thought to be any longer either good or bad for the dead. But the brave man would not seem to be concerned even with death in *all* circumstances, e.g. at sea or in disease. In what circumstances, then? Surely in the noblest. Now such deaths are those in battle; for these take place in the greatest and noblest danger. And these are correspondingly honoured in city-states and at the courts of monarchs. Properly, then, he will be called brave who is fearless in face of a noble death, and of all emergencies that involve death; and the emergencies of war are in the highest degree of this kind. Yet at sea also, and in disease, the **1115b** brave man is fearless, but not in the same way as the seaman; for he has given up hope of safety, and is disliking the thought of death in this shape, while they are hopeful because of their experience. At the same time, we show courage in situations where there is the opportunity of showing prowess or where death is noble; but in these forms of death neither of these conditions is fulfilled.

[1] 1107a 33–b 4.

7

What is terrible is not the same for all men; but we say there are things terrible even beyond human strength. These, then, are terrible to every one—at least to every sensible man; but the terrible things that are *not* beyond human strength differ in magnitude and degree, and so too do the things that inspire confidence. Now the brave man is as dauntless as man may be. Therefore, while he will fear even the things that are not beyond human strength, he will face them as he ought and as the rule directs, for honour's sake; for this is the end of virtue. But it is possible to fear these more, or less, and again to fear things that are not terrible as if they were. Of the faults that are committed one consists in fearing what one should not, another in fearing as we should not, another in fearing when we should not, and so on; and so too with respect to the things that inspire confidence. The man, then, who faces and who fears the right things and from the right motive, in the right way and at the right time, and who feels confidence under the corresponding conditions, is brave; for the brave man feels and acts according to the merits of the case and in whatever way the rule directs. Now the end of every activity is conformity to the corresponding state of character. This is true, therefore, of the brave man as well as of others. But courage is noble. Therefore the end also is noble; for each thing is defined by its end. Therefore it is for a noble end that the brave man endures and acts as courage directs.

Of those who go to excess he who exceeds in fearlessness has no name (we have said previously that many states of character have no names[1]), but he would be a sort of madman or insensible person if he feared nothing, neither earthquakes nor the waves, as they say the Celts do not; while the man who exceeds in confidence about what really is terrible is rash. The rash man, however, is also thought to be boastful and only a pretender to courage; at all events, as the brave man *is* with regard to what is terrible, so the rash man wishes to *appear*; and so he imitates him in situations where he can. Hence also most of them are a mixture of rashness and cowardice; for, while in these situations they display confidence, they do not hold their ground against what is really terrible. The man who exceeds in fear is a coward; for he fears both what he ought not and as he ought not, and all the similar char-
1116a acterizations attach to him. He is lacking also in confidence; but he is more conspicuous for his excess of fear in painful situations. The coward, then, is a despairing sort of person; for he fears everything. The brave man, on the other hand, has the opposite disposition; for confidence is the mark of a hopeful disposition. The coward, the rash man, and the brave man, then, are concerned with the same objects but are differently disposed towards them; for the first two exceed and fall short, while the third holds the middle, which is the right position; and rash men are precipitate, and wish for dangers beforehand but draw back when they are in them, while brave men are keen in the moment of action, but quiet beforehand.

As we have said, then, courage is a mean with respect to things that inspire confidence or fear, in the circumstances that have been stated;[2] and it chooses or endures things because it is noble to do so, or because it is base not to do so. But to die to escape from poverty or love or anything painful is not the mark of a brave man, but rather of a coward; for it is softness to fly from what is troublesome, and such a man endures death not because it is noble but to fly from evil.

8

Courage, then, is something of this sort, but the name is also applied to five other kinds. (1) First comes the courage of the citizen-soldier; for this is most like true courage. Citizen-soldiers seem to face dangers because of the penalties imposed by the laws and the reproaches they would otherwise incur, and because of the honours they win by such action; and therefore those peoples seem to be bravest among whom cowards are held in dishonour and brave men in honour. This is the kind of courage that Homer depicts, e.g. in Diomede and in Hector:

First will Polydamas be to heap reproach on me then;[3] and

For Hector one day 'mid the Trojans shall utter his vaulting harangue:
Afraid was Tydeides, and fled from my face.[4]

This kind of courage is most like to that which we described earlier,[5] because it is due to virtue; for it is due to shame and to desire of a noble object (i.e. honour) and avoidance of disgrace, which is ignoble. One might rank in the same class even those who are compelled by their rulers; but they are inferior, inasmuch as they do what they do not from shame but from fear, and to avoid not what is disgraceful but what is painful; for their masters compel them, as Hector[6] does:

But if I shall spy any dastard that cowers far from the fight,
Vainly will such an one hope to escape from the dogs.

And those who give them their posts, and beat
1116b them if they retreat,[7] do the same, and so do those who draw them up with trenches or something of the sort behind them; all of these apply compulsion. But one ought to be brave not under compulsion but because it is noble to be so.

(2) Experience with regard to particular facts is also thought to be courage; this is indeed the reason why Socrates thought courage was knowledge. Other people exhibit this quality in other dangers, and professional soldiers exhibit it in the dangers of war; for there seem to be many empty alarms in war, of which these have had the most comprehensive experience; therefore they seem brave, because the others do not know the nature of the facts. Again, their experience makes them most capable in attack and in defence, since they

[1] 1107b 2, cf. 1107b 29, 1108a 5.

[2] Chapter 6.

[3] *Iliad*, XXII. 100.

[4] *Ibid.*, VIII. 148, 149.

[5] Chapters 6, 7.

[6] Aristotle's quotation is more like *Iliad*, II. 391–3, where Agamemnon speaks, than XV. 348–51, where Hector speaks.

[7] Cf. Herodotus, VII. 223.

can use their arms and have the kind that are likely to be best both for attack and for defence; therefore they fight like armed men against unarmed or like trained athletes against amateurs; for in such contests too it is not the bravest men that fight best, but those who are strongest and have their bodies in the best condition. Professional soldiers turn cowards, however, when the danger puts too great a strain on them and they are inferior in numbers and equipment; for they are the first to fly, while citizen-forces die at their posts, as in fact happened at the temple of Hermes. For to the latter flight is disgraceful and death is preferable to safety on those terms; while the former from the very beginning faced the danger on the assumption that they were stronger, and when they know the facts they fly, fearing death more than disgrace; but the brave man is not that sort of person.

(3) Passion also is sometimes reckoned as courage; those who act from passion, like wild beasts rushing at those who have wounded them, are thought to be brave, because brave men also are passionate; for passion above all things is eager to rush on danger, and hence Homer's 'put strength into his passion'[1] and 'aroused their spirit and passion'[2] and 'hard he breathed panting'[3] and 'his blood boiled'. For all such expressions seem to indicate the stirring and onset of passion. Now brave men act for honour's sake, but passion aids them; while wild beasts act under the influence of pain; for they attack because they have been wounded or because they are afraid, since if they are in a forest they do not come near one. Thus they are not brave because, driven by pain and passion, they rush on danger without foreseeing any of the perils, since at that rate even asses would be brave when they are hungry; for blows will not drive
1117a them from their food; and lust also makes adulterers do many daring things. [Those creatures are not brave, then, which are driven on to danger by pain or passion.] The 'courage' that is due to passion seems to be the most natural, and to be courage if choice and motive be added.

Men, then, as well as beasts, suffer pain when they are angry, and are pleased when they exact their revenge; those who fight for these reasons, however, are pugnacious but not brave; for they do not act for honour's sake nor as the rule directs, but from strength of feeling; they have, however, something akin to courage.

(4) Nor are sanguine people brave; for they are confident in danger only because they have conquered often and against many foes. Yet they closely resemble brave men, because both are confident; but brave men are confident for the reasons stated earlier,[4] while these are so because they think they are the strongest and can suffer nothing. (Drunken men also behave in this way; they become sanguine). When their adventures do not succeed, however, they run away; but it was[4] the mark of a brave man to face things that are, and seem, terrible for a man, because it is noble to do so and disgraceful not to do so. Hence also it is thought the mark of a braver man to be fearless and undisturbed in sudden alarms than to be so in those that are foreseen; for it must have proceeded more from a state of character, because less from preparation; acts that are foreseen may be chosen by calculation and rule, but sudden actions must be in accordance with one's state of character.

(5) People who are ignorant of the danger also appear brave, and they are not far removed from those of a sanguine temper, but are inferior inasmuch as they have no self-reliance while these have. Hence also the sanguine hold their ground for a time; but those who have been deceived about the facts fly if they know or suspect that these are different from what they supposed, as happened to the Argives when they fell in with the Spartans and took them for Sicyonians.

We have, then, described the character both of brave men and of those who are thought to be brave.

9

Though courage is concerned with feelings of confidence and of fear, it is not concerned with both alike, but more with the things that inspire fear; for he who is undisturbed in face of these and bears himself as he should towards these is more truly brave than the man who does so towards the things that inspire confidence. It is for facing what is painful, then, as has been said,[5] that men are called brave. Hence also courage involves pain, and is justly praised; for it is harder to face what is painful than to abstain from what is pleasant.

[1] This is a conflation of *Iliad*, XI. 11 or XIV. 151 and XVI. 529.

[2] Cf. *Iliad*, V. 470; XV. 232, 594.

[3] Cf. *Odyssey*, XXIV. 318 f.

[4] 1115^b 11–24.

[5] 1115^b 7–13.

Yet the end which courage sets before it **1117b** would seem to be pleasant, but to be concealed by the attending circumstances, as happens also in athletic contests; for the end at which boxers aim is pleasant—the crown and the honours—but the blows they take are distressing to flesh and blood, and painful, and so is their whole exertion; and because the blows and the exertions are many the end, which is but small, appears to have nothing pleasant in it. And so, if the case of courage is similar, death and wounds will be painful to the brave man and against his will, but he will face them because it is noble to do so or because it is base not to do so. And the more he is possessed of virtue in its entirety and the happier he is, the more he will be pained at the thought of death; for life is best worth living for such a man, and he is knowingly losing the greatest goods, and this is painful. But he is none the less brave, and perhaps all the more so, because he chooses noble deeds of war at that cost. It is not the case, then, with all the virtues that the exercise of them is pleasant, except in so far as it reaches its end. But it is quite possible that the best soldiers may be not men of this sort but those who are less brave but have no other good; for these are ready to face danger, and they sell their life for trifling gains.

So much, then, for courage; it is not difficult to grasp its nature in outline, at any rate, from what has been said.

10

After courage let us speak of temperance; for these seem to be the virtues of the irrational parts. We have said[1] that temperance is a mean with regard to pleasures (for it is less, and not in the same way, concerned with pains); self-indulgence also is manifested in the same sphere. Now, therefore, let us determine with what sort of pleasures they are concerned. We may assume the distinction between bodily pleasures and those of the soul, such as love of honour and love of learning; for the lover of each of these delights in that of which he is a lover, the body being in no way affected, but rather the mind; but men who are concerned with such pleasures are called neither temperate nor self-indulgent. Nor, again, are those who are concerned with the other pleasures that are not bodily; for those who are fond of hearing and telling stories and who spend their days on anything that turns up are called gossips, but not self-indulgent, nor are those who are pained at the loss of money or of friends.

1118a Temperance must be concerned with bodily pleasures, but not all even of these; for those who delight in objects of vision, such as colours and shapes and painting, are called neither temperate nor self-indulgent; yet it would seem possible to delight even in these either as one should or to excess or to a deficient degree.

And so too is it with objects of hearing; no one calls those who delight extravagantly in music or acting self-indulgent, nor those who do so as they ought temperate.

Nor do we apply these names to those who delight in odour, unless it be incidentally; we do not call those self-indulgent who delight in the odour of apples or roses or incense, but rather those who delight in the odour of unguents or of dainty dishes; for self-indulgent people delight in these because these remind them of the objects of their appetite. And one may see even other people, when they are hungry, delighting in the smell of food; but to delight in this kind of thing is the mark of the self-indulgent man; for these are objects of appetite to him.

Nor is there in animals other than man any pleasure connected with these senses, except incidentally. For dogs do not delight in the scent of hares, but in the eating of them, but the scent told them the hares were there; nor does the lion delight in the lowing of the ox, but in eating it; but he perceived by the lowing that it was near, and therefore appears to delight in the lowing; and similarly he does not delight because he sees 'a stag or a wild goat',[2] but because he is going to make a meal of it. Temperance and self-indulgence, however, are concerned with the kind of pleasures that the other animals share in, which therefore appear slavish and brutish; these are touch and taste. But even of taste they appear to make little or no use; for the business of taste is the discriminating of flavours, which is done by winetasters and people who season dishes; but they hardly take pleasure in making these discriminations, or at least self-indulgent people do not, but in the actual enjoyment, which in all cases comes through touch, both in the case of food and in that of drink and in that of sexual intercourse. This is why a certain gourmand prayed that his throat might become

[1] 1107b 4–6.

[2] *Iliad*, III. 24.

longer than a crane's, implying that it was the **1118b** contact that he took pleasure in. Thus the sense with which self-indulgence is connected is the most widely shared of the senses; and self-indulgence would seem to be justly a matter of reproach, because it attaches to us not as men but as animals. To delight in such things, then, and to love them above all others, is brutish. For even of the pleasures of touch the most liberal have been eliminated, e.g. those produced in the gymnasium by rubbing and by the consequent heat; for the contact characteristic of the self-indulgent man does not affect the whole body but only certain parts.

11

Of the appetites some seem to be common, others to be peculiar to individuals and acquired; e.g. the appetite for food is natural, since every one who is without it craves for food or drink, and sometimes for both, and for love also (as Homer says)[1] if he is young and lusty; but not every one craves for this or that kind of nourishment or love, nor for the same things. Hence such craving appears to be our very own. Yet it has of course something natural about it; for different things are pleasant to different kinds of people, and some things are more pleasant to every one than chance objects. Now in the natural appetites few go wrong, and only in one direction, that of excess; for to eat or drink whatever offers itself till one is surfeited is to exceed the natural amount, since natural appetite is the replenishment of one's deficiency. Hence these people are called belly-gods, this implying that they fill their belly beyond what is right. It is people of entirely slavish character that become like this. But with regard to the pleasures peculiar to individuals many people go wrong and in many ways. For while the people who are 'fond of so and so' are so called because they delight either in the wrong things, or more than most people do, or in the wrong way, the self-indulgent exceed in all three ways; they both delight in some things that they ought not to delight in (since they are hateful), and if one ought to delight in some of the things they delight in, they do so more than one ought and than most men do.

Plainly, then, excess with regard to pleasures is self-indulgence and is culpable; with regard to pains one is not, as in the case of courage, called temperate for facing them or self-indulgent for not doing so, but the self-indulgent man is so called because he is pained more than he ought at not getting pleasant things (even his pain being caused by pleasure), and the temperate man is so called because he is not pained at the absence of what is pleasant and at his abstinence from it.

1119a The self-indulgent man, then, craves for all pleasant things or those that are most pleasant, and is led by his appetite to choose these at the cost of everything else; hence he is pained both when he fails to get them and when he is merely craving for them (for appetite involves pain); but it seems absurd to be pained for the sake of pleasure. People who fall short with regard to pleasures and delight in them less than they should are hardly found; for such insensibility is not human. Even the other animals distinguish different kinds of food and enjoy some and not others; and if there is any one who finds nothing pleasant and nothing more attractive than anything else, he must be something quite different from a man; this sort of person has not received a name because he hardly occurs. The temperate man occupies a middle position with regard to these objects. For he neither enjoys the things that the self-indulgent man enjoys most—but rather dislikes them—nor in general the things that he should not, nor anything of this sort to excess, nor does he feel pain or craving when they are absent, or does so only to a moderate degree, and not more than he should, nor when he should not, and so on; but the things that, being pleasant, make for health or for good condition, he will desire moderately and as he should, and also other pleasant things if they are not hindrances to these ends, or contrary to what is noble, or beyond his means. For he who neglects these conditions loves such pleasures more than they are worth, but the temperate man is not that sort of person, but the sort of person that the right rule prescribes.

12

Self-indulgence is more like a voluntary state than cowardice. For the former is actuated by pleasure, the latter by pain, of which the one is to be chosen and the other to be avoided; and pain upsets and destroys the nature of the person who feels it, while pleasure does nothing of the sort. Therefore self-indulgence is more voluntary. Hence also it is more a matter of reproach; for it is easier to become accustomed to its objects, since there are many

[1] *Iliad*, XXIV. 130.

things of this sort in life, and the process of habituation to them is free from danger, while with terrible objects the reverse is the case. But cowardice would seem to be voluntary in a different degree from its particular manifestations; for it is itself painless, but in these we are upset by pain, so that we even throw down our arms and disgrace ourselves in other ways; hence our acts are even thought to be done under compulsion. For the self-indulgent man, on the other hand, the particular acts are voluntary (for he does them with craving and desire), but the whole state is less so; for no one craves to be self-indulgent.

The name self-indulgence is applied also to childish faults; for they bear a certain resemblance to what we have been considering. **1119b** Which is called after which, makes no difference to our present purpose; plainly, however, the later is called after the earlier. The transference of the name seems not a bad one; for that which desires what is base and which develops quickly ought to be kept in a chastened condition, and these characteristics belong above all to appetite and to the child, since children in fact live at the beck and call of appetite, and it is in them that the desire for what is pleasant is strongest. If, then, it is not going to be obedient and subject to the ruling principle, it will go to great lengths; for in an irrational being the desire for pleasure is insatiable even if it tries every source of gratification, and the exercise of appetite increases its innate force, and if appetites are strong and violent they even expel the power of calculation. Hence they should be moderate and few, and should in no way oppose the rational principle—and this is what we call an obedient and chastened state—and as the child should live according to the direction of his tutor, so the appetitive element should live according to rational principle. Hence the appetitive element in a temperate man should harmonize with the rational principle; for the noble is the mark at which both aim, and the temperate man craves for the things he ought, as he ought, and when he ought; and this is what rational principle directs.

Here we conclude our account of temperance.

BOOK IV

I

Let us speak next of liberality. It seems to be the mean with regard to wealth; for the liberal man is praised not in respect of military matters, nor of those in respect of which the temperate man is praised, nor of judicial decisions, but with regard to the giving and taking of wealth, and especially in respect of giving. Now by 'wealth' we mean all the things whose value is measured by money. Further, prodigality and meanness are excesses and defects with regard to wealth; and meanness we always impute to those who care more than they ought for wealth, but we sometimes apply the word 'prodigality' in a complex sense; for we call those men prodigals who are incontinent and spend money on self-indulgence. Hence also they are thought the poorest characters; for they combine more vices than one. Therefore the application of the word to them is not its proper use; for a 'prodigal' means a man who has a single evil quality, that of wast- **1120a** ing his substance; since a prodigal is one who is being ruined by his own fault, and the wasting of substance is thought to be a sort of ruining of oneself, life being held to depend on possession of substance.

This, then, is the sense in which we take the word 'prodigality'. Now the things that have a use may be used either well or badly; and riches is a useful thing; and everything is used best by the man who has the virtue concerned with it; riches, therefore, will be used best by the man who has the virtue concerned with wealth; and this is the liberal man. Now spending and giving seem to be the using of wealth; taking and keeping rather the possession of it. Hence it is more the mark of the liberal man to give to the right people than to take from the right sources and not to take from the wrong. For it is more characteristic of virtue to do good than to have good done to one, and more characteristic to do what is noble than not to do what is base; and it is not hard to see that giving implies doing good and doing what is noble, and taking implies having good done to one or not acting basely. And gratitude is felt towards him who gives, not towards him who does not take, and praise also is bestowed more on him. It is easier, also, not to take than to give; for men are apter to give away their own too little than to take what is another's. Givers, too, are called liberal; but those who do not take are not praised for liberality but rather for justice; while those who take are hardly praised at all. And the liberal are almost the most loved of all virtuous characters, since they are useful; and this depends on their giving.

Now virtuous actions are noble and done for the sake of the noble. Therefore the liberal man, like other virtuous men, will give for the sake of the noble, and rightly; for he will give to the right people, the right amounts, and at the right time, with all the other qualifications that accompany right giving; and that too with pleasure or without pain; for that which is virtuous is pleasant or free from pain—least of all will it be painful. But he who gives to the wrong people or not for the sake of the noble but for some other cause, will be called not liberal but by some other name. Nor is he liberal who gives with pain; for he would prefer the wealth to the noble act, and this is not characteristic of a liberal man. But no more will the liberal man take from wrong sources; for such taking is not characteristic of the man who sets no store by wealth. Nor will he be a ready asker; for it is not characteristic of a man who confers benefits to accept them lightly. But he will take from the right sources, **1120b** e.g. from his own possessions, not as something noble but as a necessity, that he may have something to give. Nor will he neglect his own property, since he wishes by means of this to help others. And he will refrain from giving to anybody and everybody, that he may have something to give to the right people, at the right time, and where it is noble to do so. It is highly characteristic of a liberal man also to go to excess in giving, so that he leaves too little for himself; for it is the nature of a liberal man not to look to himself. The term 'liberality' is used relatively to a man's substance; for liberality resides not in the multitude of the gifts but in the state of character of the giver, and this is relative to the giver's substance. There is therefore nothing to prevent the man who gives less from being the more liberal man, if he has less to give. Those are thought to be more liberal who have not made their wealth but inherited it; for in the first place they have no experience of want, and secondly all men are fonder of their own productions, as are parents and poets. It is not easy for the liberal man to be rich, since he is not apt either at taking or at keeping, but at giving away, and does not value wealth for its own sake but as a means to giving. Hence comes the charge that is brought against fortune, that those who deserve riches most get it least. But it is not unreasonable that it should turn out so; for he cannot have wealth, any more than anything else, if he does not take pains to have it. Yet he will not give to the wrong people nor at the wrong time, and so on; for he would no longer be acting in accordance with liberality, and if he spent on these objects he would have nothing to spend on the right objects. For, as has been said, he is liberal who spends according to his substance and on the right objects; and he who exceeds is prodigal. Hence we do not call despots prodigal; for it is thought not easy for them to give and spend beyond the amount of their possessions. Liberality, then, being a mean with regard to giving and taking of wealth, the liberal man will both give and spend the right amounts and on the right objects, alike in small things and in great, and that with pleasure; he will also take the right amounts and from the right sources. For, the virtue being a mean with regard to both, he will do both as he ought; since this sort of taking accompanies proper giving, and that which is not of this sort is contrary to it, and accordingly the giving and taking that accompany each other are present together in the same man, while the contrary kinds evidently **1121a** are not. But if he happens to spend in a manner contrary to what is right and noble, he will be pained, but moderately and as he ought; for it is the mark of virtue both to be pleased and to be pained at the right objects and in the right way. Further, the liberal man is easy to deal with in money matters; for he can be got the better of, since he sets no store by money, and is more annoyed if he has not spent something that he ought than pained if he has spent something that he ought not, and does not agree with the saying of Simonides.

The prodigal errs in these respects also; for he is neither pleased nor pained at the right things or in the right way; this will be more evident as we go on. We have said[1] that prodigality and meanness are excesses and deficiencies, and in two things, in giving and in taking; for we include spending under giving. Now prodigality exceeds in giving and not taking, and falls short in taking, while meanness falls short in giving, and exceeds in taking, except in small things.

The characteristics of prodigality are not often combined; for it is not easy to give to all if you take from none; private persons soon exhaust their substance with giving, and it is to these that the name of prodigals is applied—

[1] 1119b 27.

though a man of this sort would seem to be in no small degree better than a mean man. For he is easily cured both by age and by poverty, and thus he may move towards the middle state. For he has the characteristics of the liberal man, since he both gives and refrains from taking, though he does neither of these in the right manner or well. Therefore if he were brought to do so by habituation or in some other way, he would be liberal; for he will then give to the right people, and will not take from the wrong sources. This is why he is thought to have not a bad character; it is not the mark of a wicked or ignoble man to go to excess in giving and not taking, but only of a foolish one. The man who is prodigal in this way is thought much better than the mean man both for the aforesaid reasons and because he benefits many while the other benefits no one, not even himself.

But most prodigal people, as has been said,[1] also take from the wrong sources, and are in this respect mean. They become apt to take because they wish to spend and cannot do this easily; for their possessions soon run short. Thus they are forced to provide means from some other source. At the same time, because **1121b** they care nothing for honour, they take recklessly and from any source; for they have an appetite for giving, and they do not mind how or from what source. Hence also their giving is not liberal; for it is not noble, nor does it aim at nobility, nor is it done in the right way; sometimes they make rich those who should be poor, and will give nothing to people of respectable character, and much to flatterers or those who provide them with some other pleasure. Hence also most of them are self-indulgent; for they spend lightly and waste money on their indulgences, and incline towards pleasures because they do not live with a view to what is noble.

The prodigal man, then, turns into what we have described if he is left untutored, but if he is treated with care he will arrive at the intermediate and right state. But meanness is both incurable (for old age and every disability is thought to make men mean) and more innate in men than prodigality; for most men are fonder of getting money than of giving. It also extends widely, and is multiform, since there seem to be many kinds of meanness.

For it consists in two things, deficiency in giving and excess in taking, and is not found complete in all men but is sometimes divided; some men go to excess in taking, others fall short in giving. Those who are called by such names as 'miserly', 'close', 'stingy', all fall short in giving, but do not covet the possessions of others nor wish to get them. In some this is due to a sort of honesty and avoidance of what is disgraceful (for some seem, or at least profess, to hoard their money for this reason, that they may not some day be forced to do something disgraceful; to this class belong the cheeseparer and every one of the sort; he is so called from his excess of unwillingness to give anything); while others again keep their hands off the property of others from fear, on the ground that it is not easy, if one takes the property of others oneself, to avoid having one's own taken by them; they are therefore content neither to take nor to give.

Others again exceed in respect of taking by taking anything and from any source, e.g. those who ply sordid trades, pimps and all such people, and those who lend small sums and at **1122a** high rates. For all of these take more than they ought and from wrong sources. What is common to them is evidently sordid love of gain; they all put up with a bad name for the sake of gain, and little gain at that. For those who make great gains but from wrong sources, and not the right gains, e.g. despots when they sack cities and spoil temples, we do not call mean but rather wicked, impious, and unjust. But the gamester and the footpad [and the highwayman] belong to the class of the mean, since they have a sordid love of gain. For it is for gain that both of them ply their craft and endure the disgrace of it, and the one faces the greatest dangers for the sake of the booty, while the other makes gain from his friends, to whom he ought to be giving. Both, then, since they are willing to make gain from wrong sources, are sordid lovers of gain; therefore all such forms of taking are mean.

And it is natural that meanness is described as the contrary of liberality; for not only is it a greater evil than prodigality, but men err more often in this direction than in the way of prodigality as we have described it.

So much, then, for liberality and the opposed vices.

2

It would seem proper to discuss magnificence next. For this also seems to be a virtue concerned with wealth; but it does not like liberality extend to all the actions that are con-

[1] ll. 16–19.

cerned with wealth, but only to those that involve expenditure; and in these it surpasses liberality in scale. For, as the name itself suggests, it is a fitting expenditure involving largeness of scale. But the scale is relative; for the expense of equipping a trireme is not the same as that of heading a sacred embassy. It is what is fitting, then, in relation to the agent, and to the circumstances and the object. The man who in small or middling things spends according to the merits of the case is not called magnificent (e.g. the man who can say 'many a gift I gave the wanderer'),[1] but only the man who does so in great things. For the magnificent man is liberal, but the liberal man is not necessarily magnificent. The deficiency of this state of character is called niggardliness, the excess vulgarity, lack of taste, and the like, which do not go to excess in the amount spent on right objects, but by showy expenditure in the wrong circumstances and the wrong manner; we shall speak of these vices later.[2]

The magnificent man is like an artist; for he can see what is fitting and spend large sums tastefully. For, as we said at the beginning,[3] **1122^{b}** a state of character is determined by its activities and by its objects. Now the expenses of the magnificent man are large and fitting. Such, therefore, are also his results; for thus there will be a great expenditure and one that is fitting to its result. Therefore the result should be worthy of the expense, and the expense should be worthy of the result, or should even exceed it. And the magnificent man will spend such sums for honour's sake; for this is common to the virtues. And further he will do so gladly and lavishly; for nice calculation is a niggardly thing. And he will consider how the result can be made most beautiful and most becoming rather than for how much it can be produced and how it can be produced most cheaply. It is necessary, then, that the magnificent man be also liberal. For the liberal man also will spend what he ought and as he ought; and it is in these matters that the greatness implied in the name of the magnificent man—his bigness, as it were—is manifested, since liberality is concerned with these matters; and at an equal expense he will produce a more magnificent work of art. For a possession and a work of art have not the same excellence. The most valuable possession is that which is worth most, e.g. gold, but the most valuable work of art is that which is great and beautiful (for the contemplation of such a work inspires admiration, and so does magnificence); and a work has an excellence—viz. magnificence—which involves magnitude. Magnificence is an attribute of expenditures of the kind which we call honourable, e.g. those connected with the gods—votive offerings, buildings, and sacrifices—and similarly with any form of religious worship, and all those that are proper objects of public-spirited ambition, as when people think they ought to equip a chorus or a trireme, or entertain the city, in a brilliant way. But in all cases, as has been said,[4] we have regard to the agent as well and ask who he is and what means he has; for the expenditure should be worthy of his means, and suit not only the result but also the producer. Hence a poor man cannot be magnificent, since he has not the means with which to spend large sums fittingly; and he who tries is a fool, since he spends beyond what can be expected of him and what is proper, but it is *right* expenditure that is virtuous. But great expenditure is becoming to those who have suitable means to start with, acquired by their own efforts or from ancestors or connexions, and to people of high birth or reputation, and so on; for all these things bring with them greatness and prestige. Primarily, then, the magnificent man is of this sort, and magnificence is shown in expenditures of this sort, as has been said;[5] for these are the greatest and most honourable. Of *private* occasions of expenditure the most suitable are those that take place once for all, e.g. a wedding or anything of the kind, or anything that interests **1123^{a}** the whole city or the people of position in it, and also the receiving of foreign guests and the sending of them on their way, and gifts and counter-gifts; for the magnificent man spends not on himself but on public objects, and gifts bear some resemblance to votive offerings. A magnificent man will also furnish his house suitably to his wealth (for even a house is a sort of public ornament), and will spend by preference on those works that are lasting (for these are the most beautiful), and on every class of things he will spend what is becoming; for the same things are not suitable for gods and for men, nor in a temple and in a tomb. And since each expenditure may be great of its kind, and what is most magnificent absolutely is great expenditure on a great object, but what is magnificent *here* is what is great in *these* circumstances, and greatness in

[1] *Odyssey*, XVII. 420.
[2] 1123^{a} 19–33.
[3] Cf. 1103^{b} 21–23, 1104^{a} 27–29.
[4] ^{a}24–26.
[5] ll. 19–23.

the work differs from greatness in the expense (for the most beautiful ball or bottle is magnificent as a gift to a child, but the price of it is small and mean),—therefore it is characteristic of the magnificent man, whatever kind of result he is producing, to produce it magnificently (for such a result is not easily surpassed) and to make it worthy of the expenditure.

Such, then, is the magnificent man; the man who goes to excess and is vulgar exceeds, as has been said,[1] by spending beyond what is right. For on small objects of expenditure he spends much and displays a tasteless showiness; e.g. he gives a club dinner on the scale of a wedding banquet, and when he provides the chorus for a comedy he brings them on to the stage in purple, as they do at Megara. And all such things he will do not for honour's sake but to show off his wealth, and because he thinks he is admired for these things, and where he ought to spend much he spends little and where little, much. The niggardly man on the other hand will fall short in everything, and after spending the greatest sums will spoil the beauty of the result for a trifle, and whatever he is doing he will hesitate and consider how he may spend least, and lament even that, and think he is doing everything on a bigger scale than he ought.

These states of character, then, are vices; yet they do not bring *disgrace* because they are neither harmful to one's neighbour nor very unseemly.

3

Pride seems even from its name to be concerned with great things; what sort of great things, is the first question we must try to answer. It makes no difference whether we consider the state of character or the man char-
1123b acterized by it. Now the man is thought to be proud who thinks himself worthy of great things, being worthy of them; for he who does so beyond his deserts is a fool, but no virtuous man is foolish or silly. The proud man, then, is the man we have described. For he who is worthy of little and thinks himself worthy of little is temperate, but not proud; for pride implies greatness, as beauty implies a good-sized body, and little people may be neat and well-proportioned but cannot be beautiful. On the other hand, he who thinks himself worthy of great things, being unworthy of them, is vain; though not every one who thinks himself worthy of more than he really is worthy of is vain. The man who thinks himself worthy of less than he is really worthy of is unduly humble, whether his deserts be great or moderate, or his deserts be small but his claims yet smaller. And the man whose deserts are great would seem *most* unduly humble; for what would he have done if they had been less? The proud man, then, is an extreme in respect of the greatness of his claims, but a mean in respect of the rightness of them; for he claims what is in accordance with his merits, while the others go to excess or fall short.

If, then, he deserves and claims great things, and above all the great things, he will be concerned with one thing in particular. Desert is relative to external goods; and the greatest of these, we should say, is that which we render to the gods, and which people of position most aim at, and which is the prize appointed for the noblest deeds; and this is honour; that is surely the greatest of external goods. Honours and dishonours, therefore, are the objects with respect to which the proud man is as he should be. And even apart from argument it is with honour that proud men appear to be concerned; for it is honour that they chiefly claim, but in accordance with their deserts. The unduly humble man falls short both in comparison with his own merits and in comparison with the proud man's claims. The vain man goes to excess in comparison with his own merits, but does not exceed the proud man's claims.

Now the proud man, since he deserves most, must be good in the highest degree; for the better man always deserves more, and the best man most. Therefore the truly proud man must be good. And greatness in every virtue would seem to be characteristic of a proud man. And it would be most unbecoming for a proud man to fly from danger, swinging his arms by his sides, or to wrong another; for to what end should he do disgraceful acts, he to whom nothing is great? If we consider him point by point we shall see the utter absurdity of a proud man who is not good. Nor, again, would he be worthy of honour if he were bad; for honour is the prize of virtue, and it is
1124a to the good that it is rendered. Pride, then, seems to be a sort of crown of the virtues; for it makes them greater, and it is not found without them. Therefore it is hard to be truly proud; for it is impossible without nobility and goodness of character. It is chiefly with honours and dishonours, then, that the proud man is

[1] 1122a 31–33.

concerned; and at honours that are great and conferred by good men he will be moderately pleased, thinking that he is coming by his own or even less than his own; for there can be no honour that is worthy of perfect virtue, yet he will at any rate accept it since they have nothing greater to bestow on him; but honour from casual people and on trifling grounds he will utterly despise, since it is not this that he deserves, and dishonour too, since in his case it cannot be just. In the first place, then, as has been said,[1] the proud man is concerned with honours; yet he will also bear himself with moderation towards wealth and power and all good or evil fortune, whatever may befall him, and will be neither over-joyed by good fortune nor over-pained by evil. For not even towards honour does he bear himself as if it were a very great thing. Power and wealth are desirable for the sake of honour (at least those who have them wish to get honour by means of them); and for him to whom even honour is a little thing the others must be so too. Hence proud men are thought to be disdainful.

The goods of fortune also are thought to contribute towards pride. For men who are well-born are thought worthy of honour, and so are those who enjoy power or wealth; for they are in a superior position, and everything that has a superiority in something good is held in greater honour. Hence even such things make men prouder; for they are honoured by some for having them; but in truth the good man alone is to be honoured; he, however, who has both advantages is thought the more worthy of honour. But those who without virtue have such goods are neither justified in making great claims nor entitled to the name of 'proud'; for these things imply perfect virtue. Disdainful and insolent, however, even those who have such goods become. For without virtue it is not easy to bear gracefully the goods of fortune; and, being unable to bear **1124b** them, and thinking themselves superior to others, they despise others and themselves do what they please. They imitate the proud man without being like him, and this they do where they can; so they do not act virtuously, but they do despise others. For the proud man despises justly (since he thinks truly), but the many do so at random.

He does not run into trifling dangers, nor is he fond of danger, because he honours few things; but he will face great dangers, and when he is in danger he is unsparing of his life, knowing that there are conditions on which life is not worth having. And he is the sort of man to confer benefits, but he is ashamed of receiving them; for the one is the mark of a superior, the other of an inferior. And he is apt to confer greater benefits in return; for thus the original benefactor besides being paid will incur a debt to him, and will be the gainer by the transaction. They seem also to remember any service they have done, but not those they have received (for he who receives a service is inferior to him who has done it, but the proud man wishes to be superior), and to hear of the former with pleasure, of the latter with displeasure; this, it seems, is why Thetis did not mention to Zeus the services she had done him, and why the Spartans did not recount their services to the Athenians, but those they had received. It is a mark of the proud man also to ask for nothing or scarcely anything, but to give help readily, and to be dignified towards people who enjoy high position and good fortune, but unassuming towards those of the middle class; for it is a difficult and lofty thing to be superior to the former, but easy to be so to the latter, and a lofty bearing over the former is no mark of ill-breeding, but among humble people it is as vulgar as a display of strength against the weak. Again, it is characteristic of the proud man not to aim at the things commonly held in honour, or the things in which others excel; to be sluggish and to hold back except where great honour or a great work is at stake, and to be a man of few deeds, but of great and notable ones. He must also be open in his hate and in his love (for to conceal one's feelings, i.e. to care less for truth than for what people will think, is a coward's part), and must speak and act openly; for he is free of speech because he is contemptuous, and he is given to telling the truth, except when he speaks in irony to the vulgar. He must be unable to make his life revolve round **1125a** another, unless it be a friend; for this is slavish, and for this reason all flatterers are servile and people lacking in self-respect are flatterers. Nor is he given to admiration; for nothing to him is great. Nor is he mindful of wrongs; for it is not the part of a proud man to have a long memory, especially for wrongs, but rather to overlook them. Nor is he a gossip; for he will speak neither about himself nor about another, since he cares not to be praised nor for others to be blamed; nor again is he given to praise; and for the same reason he is

[1] 1123b 15–22.

not an evil-speaker, even about his enemies, except from haughtiness. With regard to necessary or small matters he is least of all men given to lamentation or the asking of favours; for it is the part of one who takes such matters seriously to behave so with respect to them. He is one who will possess beautiful and profitless things rather than profitable and useful ones; for this is more proper to a character that suffices to itself.

Further, a slow step is thought proper to the proud man, a deep voice, and a level utterance; for the man who takes few things seriously is not likely to be hurried, nor the man who thinks nothing great to be excited, while a shrill voice and a rapid gait are the results of hurry and excitement.

Such, then, is the proud man; the man who falls short of him is unduly humble, and the man who goes beyond him is vain. Now even these are not thought to be bad (for they are not malicious), but only mistaken. For the unduly humble man, being worthy of good things, robs himself of what he deserves, and seems to have something bad about him from the fact that he does not think himself worthy of good things, and seems also not to know himself; else he would have desired the things he was worthy of, since these were good. Yet such people are not thought to be fools, but rather unduly retiring. Such a reputation, however, seems actually to make them worse; for each class of people aims at what corresponds to its worth, and these people stand back even from noble actions and undertakings, deeming themselves unworthy, and from external goods no less. Vain people, on the other hand, are fools and ignorant of themselves, and that manifestly; for, not being worthy of them, they attempt honourable undertakings, and then are found out; and they adorn themselves with clothing and outward show and such things, and wish their strokes of good fortune to be made public, and speak about them as if they would be honoured for them. But undue humility is more opposed to pride than vanity is; for it is both commoner and worse.

Pride, then, is concerned with honour on the grand scale, as has been said.[1]

4

1125^{b} There seems to be in the sphere of honour also, as was said in our first remarks on the subject,[2] a virtue which would appear to be related to pride as liberality is to magnificence. For neither of these has anything to do with the grand scale, but both dispose us as is right with regard to middling and unimportant objects; as in getting and giving of wealth there is a mean and an excess and defect, so too honour may be desired more than is right, or less, or from the right sources and in the right way. We blame both the ambitious man as aiming at honour more than is right and from wrong sources, and the unambitious man as not willing to be honoured even for noble reasons. But sometimes we praise the ambitious man as being manly and a lover of what is noble, and the unambitious man as being moderate and self-controlled, as we said in our first treatment of the subject.[3] Evidently, since 'fond of such and such an object' has more than one meaning, we do not assign the term 'ambition' or 'love of honour' always to the same thing, but when we praise the quality we think of the man who loves honour more than most people, and when we blame it we think of him who loves it more than is right. The mean being without a name, the extremes seem to dispute for its place as though that were vacant by default. But where there is excess and defect, there is also an intermediate; now men desire honour both more than they should and less; therefore it is possible also to do so as one should; at all events this is the state of character that is praised, being an unnamed mean in respect of honour. Relatively to ambition it seems to be unambitiousness, and relatively to unambitiousness it seems to be ambition, while relatively to both severally it seems in a sense to be both together. This appears to be true of the other virtues also. But in this case the extremes seem to be contradictories because the mean has not received a name.

5

Good temper is a mean with respect to anger; the middle state being unnamed, and the extremes almost without a name as well, we place good temper in the middle position, though it inclines towards the deficiency, which is without a name. The excess might be called a sort of 'irascibility'. For the passion is anger, while its causes are many and diverse.

The man who is angry at the right things and with the right people, and, further, as he ought, when he ought, and as long as he ought, is praised. This will be the good-tempered man

[1] 1107^{b} 26, 1123^{a} 34–^{b} 22.

[2] *Ibid.*, 24–27.

[3] 1107^{b} 33.

then, since good temper is praised. For the good-tempered man tends to be unperturbed and not to be led by passion, but to be angry in the manner, at the things, and for the **1126a** length of time, that the rule dictates; but he is thought to err rather in the direction of deficiency; for the good-tempered man is not revengeful, but rather tends to make allowances.

The deficiency, whether it is a sort of 'inirascibility' or whatever it is, is blamed. For those who are not angry at the things they should be angry at are thought to be fools, and so are those who are not angry in the right way, at the right time, or with the right persons; for such a man is thought not to feel things nor to be pained by them, and, since he does not get angry, he is thought unlikely to defend himself; and to endure being insulted and put up with insult to one's friends is slavish.

The excess can be manifested in all the points that have been named (for one can be angry with the wrong persons, at the wrong things, more than is right, too quickly, or too long); yet *all* are not found in the same person. Indeed they could not; for evil destroys even itself, and if it is complete becomes unbearable. Now *hot-tempered* people get angry quickly and with the wrong persons and at the wrong things and more than is right, but their anger ceases quickly—which is the best point about them. This happens to them because they do not restrain their anger but retaliate openly owing to their quickness of temper, and then their anger ceases. By reason of excess *choleric* people are quick-tempered and ready to be angry with everything and on every occasion; whence their name. *Sulky* people are hard to appease, and retain their anger long; for they repress their passion. But it ceases when they retaliate; for revenge relieves them of their anger, producing in them pleasure instead of pain. If this does not happen they retain their burden; for owing to its not being obvious no one even reasons with them, and to digest one's anger in oneself takes time. Such people are most troublesome to themselves and to their dearest friends. We call *bad-tempered* those who are angry at the wrong things, more than is right, and longer, and cannot be appeased until they inflict vengeance or punishment.

To good temper we oppose the excess rather than the defect; for not only is it commoner (since revenge is the more human), but bad-tempered people are worse to live with.

What we have said in our earlier treatment of the subject[1] is plain also from what we are now saying; viz. that it is not easy to define how, with whom, at what, and how long one should be angry, and at what point right action ceases and wrong begins. For the man who strays a little from the path, either towards the more or towards the less, is not blamed; since sometimes we praise those who exhibit **1126b** the deficiency, and call them good-tempered, and sometimes we call angry people manly, as being capable of ruling. How far, therefore, and how a man must stray before he becomes blameworthy, it is not easy to state in words; for the decision depends on the particular facts and on perception. But so much at least is plain, that the middle state is praiseworthy—that in virtue of which we are angry with the right people, at the right things, in the right way, and so on, while the excesses and defects are blameworthy—slightly so if they are present in a low degree, more if in a higher degree, and very much if in a high degree. Evidently, then, we must cling to the middle state.—Enough of the states relative to anger.

6

In gatherings of men, in social life and the interchange of words and deeds, some men are thought to be obsequious, viz. those who to give pleasure praise everything and never oppose, but think it their duty 'to give no pain to the people they meet'; while those who, on the contrary, oppose everything and care not a whit about giving pain are called churlish and contentious. That the states we have named are culpable is plain enough, and that the middle state is laudable—that in virtue of which a man will put up with, and will resent, the right things and in the right way; but no name has been assigned to it, though it most resembles friendship. For the man who corresponds to this middle state is very much what, with affection added, we call a good friend. But the state in question differs from friendship in that it implies no passion or affection for one's associates; since it is not by reason of loving or hating that such a man takes everything in the right way, but by being a man of a certain kind. For he will behave so alike towards those he knows and those he does not know, towards intimates and those who are not so, except that in each of these cases he will

[1] 1109b 14–26.

behave as is befitting; for it is not proper to have the same care for intimates and for strangers, nor again is it the same conditions that make it right to give pain to them. Now we have said generally that he will associate with people in the right way; but it is by reference to what is honourable and expedient that he will aim at not giving pain or at contributing pleasure. For he seems to be concerned with the pleasures and pains of social life; and wherever it is not honourable, or is harmful, for him to contribute pleasure, he will refuse, and will choose rather to give pain; also if his acquiescence in another's action would bring disgrace, and that in a high degree, or injury, *on that other*, while his opposition brings a little pain, he will not acquiesce but will decline. He will associate differently with people **1127a** in high station and with ordinary people, with closer and more distant acquaintances, and so too with regard to all other differences, rendering to each class what is befitting, and while for its own sake he chooses to contribute pleasure, and avoids the giving of pain, he will be guided by the consequences, if these are greater, i.e. honour and expediency. For the sake of a great future pleasure, too, he will inflict small pains.

The man who attains the mean, then, is such as we have described, but has not received a name; of those who contribute pleasure, the man who aims at being pleasant with no ulterior object is obsequious, but the man who does so in order that he may get some advantage in the direction of money or the things that money buys is a flatterer; while the man who quarrels with everything is, as has been said,[1] churlish and contentious. And the extremes seem to be contradictory to each other because the mean is without a name.

7

The mean opposed to boastfulness is found in almost the same sphere; and this also is without a name. It will be no bad plan to describe these states as well; for we shall both know the facts about character better if we go through them in detail, and we shall be convinced that the virtues are means if we see this to be so in all cases. In the field of social life those who make the giving of pleasure or pain their object in associating with others have been described;[2] let us now describe those who pursue truth or falsehood alike in words and deeds and in the claims they put forward.

[1] 1125b 14–16. [2] Chapter 6.

The boastful man, then, is thought to be apt to claim the things that bring glory, when he has not got them, or to claim more of them than he has, and the mock-modest man on the other hand to disclaim what he has or belittle it, while the man who observes the mean is one who calls a thing by its own name, being truthful both in life and in word, owning to what he has, and neither more nor less. Now each of these courses may be adopted either with or without an object. But each man speaks and acts and lives in accordance with his character, if he is *not* acting for some ulterior object. And falsehood is *in itself* mean and culpable, and truth noble and worthy of praise. Thus the truthful man is another case of a man who, being in the mean, is worthy of praise, and both forms of untruthful man are culpable, and particularly the boastful man.

Let us discuss them both, but first of all the truthful man. We are not speaking of the man who keeps faith in his agreements, i.e. in the things that pertain to justice or injustice (for this would belong to another virtue), but **1127b** the man who in the matters in which nothing of this sort is at stake is true both in word and in life because his character is such. But such a man would seem to be as a matter of fact equitable. For the man who loves truth, and is truthful where nothing is at stake, will still more be truthful where something is at stake; he will avoid falsehood as something base, seeing that he avoided it even for its own sake; and such a man is worthy of praise. He inclines rather to understate the truth; for this seems in better taste because exaggerations are wearisome.

He who claims more than he has with no ulterior object is a contemptible sort of fellow (otherwise he would not have delighted in falsehood), but seems futile rather than bad; but if he does it for an object, he who does it for the sake of reputation or honour is (for a boaster) not very much to be blamed, but he who does it for money, or the things that lead to money, is an uglier character (it is not the capacity that makes the boaster, but the purpose; for it is in virtue of his state of character and by being a man of a certain kind that he is a boaster); as one man is a liar because he enjoys the lie itself, and another because he desires reputation or gain. Now those who boast for the sake of reputation claim such qualities as win praise or congratulation, but those whose object is gain claim qualities which are of value to one's neighbours and one's lack of which is not easily detected, e.g. the powers of a seer, a sage, or a physician. For this reason it is such things as these that most people claim and boast about; for in them the above-mentioned qualities are found.

Mock-modest people, who understate things, seem more attractive in character; for they are thought to speak not for gain but to avoid parade; and here too it is qualities which bring reputation that they disclaim, as Socrates used to do. Those who disclaim trifling and obvious qualities are called humbugs and are more contemptible; and sometimes this seems to be boastfulness, like the Spartan dress; for both excess and great deficiency are boastful. But those who use understatement with moderation and understate about matters that do not very much force themselves on our notice seem attractive. And it is the boaster that seems to be opposed to the truthful man; for he is the worse character.

8

Since life includes rest as well as activity, and in this is included leisure and amusement, there seems here also to be a kind of inter-**1128a** course which is tasteful; there is such a thing as saying—and again listening to—what one should and as one should. The kind of people one is speaking or listening to will also make a difference. Evidently here also there is both an excess and a deficiency as compared with the mean. Those who carry humour to excess are thought to be vulgar buffoons, striving after humour at all costs, and aiming rather at raising a laugh than at saying what is becoming and at avoiding pain to the object of their fun; while those who can neither make a joke themselves nor put up with those who do are thought to be boorish and unpolished. But those who joke in a tasteful way are called ready-witted, which implies a sort of readiness to turn this way and that; for such sallies are thought to be movements of the character, and as bodies are discriminated by their movements, so too are characters. The ridiculous side of things is not far to seek, however, and most people delight more than they should in amusement and in jesting, and so even buffoons are called ready-witted because they are found attractive; but that they differ from the ready-witted man, and to no small extent, is clear from what has been said.

To the middle state belongs also tact; it is the mark of a tactful man to say and listen to such things as befit a good and well-bred man; for there are some things that it befits such a man to say and to hear by way of jest, and the well-bred man's jesting differs from that of a vulgar man, and the joking of an educated man from that of an uneducated. One may see this even from the old and the new comedies; to the authors of the former indecency of language was amusing, to those of the latter innuendo is more so; and these differ in no small degree in respect of propriety. Now should we define the man who jokes well by his saying what is not unbecoming to a well-bred man, or by his not giving pain, or even giving delight, to the hearer? Or is the latter definition, at any rate, itself indefinite, since different things are hateful or pleasant to different people? The kind of jokes he will listen to will be the same; for the kind he can put up with are also the kind he seems to make. There are, then, jokes he will not make; for the jest is a sort of abuse, and there are things that lawgivers forbid us to abuse; and they should, perhaps, have forbidden us even to make a jest of such. The refined and well-bred man, therefore, will be as we have described, being as it were a law to himself.

Such, then, is the man who observes the mean, whether he be called tactful or ready-witted. The buffoon, on the other hand, is the slave of his sense of humour, and spares neither himself nor others if he can raise a laugh, and says things none of which a man of refinement would say, and to some of which **1128b** he would not even listen. The boor, again, is useless for such social intercourse; for he contributes nothing and finds fault with everything. But relaxation and amusement are thought to be a necessary element in life.

The means in life that have been described, then, are three in number, and are all concerned with an interchange of words and deeds of some kind. They differ, however, in that one is concerned with truth, and the other two with pleasantness. Of those concerned with pleasure, one is displayed in jests, the other in the general social intercourse of life.

9

Shame should not be described as a virtue; for it is more like a feeling than a state of character. It is defined, at any rate, as a kind of fear of dishonour, and produces an effect similar to that produced by fear of danger; for people who feel disgraced blush, and those who fear death turn pale. Both, therefore, seem to be in a sense bodily conditions, which is thought to be characteristic of feeling rather than of a state of character.

The feeling is not becoming to every age, but only to youth. For we think young people should be prone to the feeling of shame because they live by feeling and therefore commit many errors, but are restrained by shame; and we praise young people who are prone to this feeling, but an older person no one would praise for being prone to the sense of disgrace, since we think he should not do anything that need cause this sense. For the sense of disgrace is not even characteristic of a good man, since it is consequent on bad actions (for such actions should not be done; and if some actions are disgraceful in very truth and others only according to common opinion, this makes no difference; for neither class of actions should be done, so that no disgrace should be felt); and it is a mark of a bad man even to be such as to do any disgraceful action. To be so constituted as to feel disgraced if one does such an action, and for this reason to think oneself good, is absurd; for it is for voluntary actions that shame is felt, and the good man will never voluntarily do bad actions. But shame may be said to be conditionally a good thing; *if* a good man does such actions, he will feel disgraced; but the virtues are not subject to such a qualification. And if shamelessness—not to be ashamed of doing base actions—is bad, that does not make it good to be ashamed of doing such actions. Continence too is not virtue, but a mixed sort of state; this will be shown later.[1] Now, however, let us discuss justice.

BOOK V

I

1129a WITH regard to justice and injustice we must consider (1) what kind of actions they are concerned with, (2) what sort of mean justice is, and (3) between what extremes the just act is intermediate. Our investigation shall follow the same course as the preceding discussions.

We see that all men mean by justice that kind of state of character which makes people disposed to do what is just and makes them act justly and wish for what is just; and similarly by injustice that state which makes them act unjustly and wish for what is unjust. Let us too, then, lay this down as a general basis. For the same is not true of the sciences and the faculties as of states of character. A faculty or a science which is one and the same is held to relate to contrary objects, but a state of character which is one of two contraries does *not* produce the contrary results; e.g. as a result of health we do not do what is the opposite of healthy, but only what is healthy; for we say a man walks healthily, when he walks as a healthy man would.

Now often one contrary state is recognized from its contrary, and often states are recognized from the subjects that exhibit them; for (A) if good condition is known, bad condition also becomes known, and (B) good condition is known from the things that are in good condition, and they from it. If good condition is firmness of flesh, it is necessary both that bad condition should be flabbiness of flesh and that the wholesome should be that which causes firmness in flesh. And it follows for the most part that if one contrary is ambiguous the other also will be ambiguous; e.g. if 'just' is so, that 'unjust' will be so too.

Now 'justice' and 'injustice' seem to be ambiguous, but because their different meanings approach near to one another the ambiguity escapes notice and is not obvious as it is, comparatively, when the meanings are far apart, e.g. (for here the difference in outward form is great) as the ambiguity in the use of κλεὶς for the collar-bone of an animal and for that with which we lock a door. Let us take as a starting-point, then, the various meanings of 'an unjust man'. Both the lawless man and the grasping and unfair man are thought to be unjust, so that evidently both the law-abiding and the fair man will be just. The just, then, is the lawful and the fair, the unjust the unlawful and the unfair.

1129b Since the unjust man is grasping, he must be concerned with goods—not all goods, but those with which prosperity and adversity have to do, which taken absolutely are always good, but for a particular person are not always good. Now men pray for and pursue these things; but they should not, but should pray that the things that are good absolutely may also be good for them, and should choose the things that *are* good for them. The unjust man does not always choose the greater, but also the

[1] VII. 1–10.

less—in the case of things bad absolutely; but because the lesser evil is itself thought to be in a sense good, and graspingness is directed at the good, therefore he is thought to be grasping. And he is unfair; for this contains and is common to both.

Since the lawless man was seen[1] to be unjust and the law-abiding man just, evidently all lawful acts are in a sense just acts; for the acts laid down by the legislative art are lawful, and each of these, we say, is just. Now the laws in their enactments on all subjects aim at the common advantage either of all or of the best or of those who hold power, or something of the sort; so that in one sense we call those acts just that tend to produce and preserve happiness and its components for the political society. And the law bids us do both the acts of a brave man (e.g. not to desert our post nor take to flight nor throw away our arms), and those of a temperate man (e.g. not to commit adultery nor to gratify one's lust), and those of a good-tempered man (e.g. not to strike another nor to speak evil), and similarly with regard to the other virtues and forms of wickedness, commanding some acts and forbidding others; and the rightly-framed law does this rightly, and the hastily conceived one less well. This form of justice, then, is complete virtue, but not absolutely, but in relation to our neighbour. And therefore justice is often thought to be the greatest of virtues, and 'neither evening nor morning star'[2] is so wonderful; and proverbially 'in justice is every virtue comprehended'.[3] And it is complete virtue in its fullest sense, because it is the actual exercise of complete virtue. It is complete because he who possesses it can exercise his virtue not only in himself but towards his neighbour also; for many men can exercise virtue in their own affairs, but not in their relations to **1130a** their neighbour. This is why the saying of Bias is thought to be true, that 'rule will show the man'; for a ruler is necessarily in relation to other men and a member of a society. For this same reason justice, alone of the virtues, is thought to be 'another's good',[4] because it is related to our neighbour; for it does what is advantageous to another, either a ruler or a copartner. Now the worst man is he who exercises his wickedness both towards himself and towards his friends, and the best man is not he who exercises his virtue towards himself but he who exercises it towards another; for this is a difficult task. Justice in this sense, then, is not part of virtue but virtue entire, nor is the contrary injustice a part of vice but vice entire. What the difference is between virtue and justice in this sense is plain from what we have said; they are the same but their essence is not the same; what, as a relation to one's neighbour, is justice is, as a certain kind of state without qualification, virtue.

[1] a 32–b 1.

[2] Euripides, fr. from *Melanippe* (Nauck, fr. 486).

[3] Theognis, 147. [4] Plato, *Republic* 343.

2

But at all events what we are investigating is the justice which is a *part* of virtue; for there is a justice of this kind, as we maintain. Similarly it is with injustice in the particular sense that we are concerned.

That there is such a thing is indicated by the fact that while the man who exhibits in action the other forms of wickedness acts wrongly indeed, but not graspingly (e.g. the man who throws away his shield through cowardice or speaks harshly through bad temper or fails to help a friend with money through meanness), when a man acts graspingly he often exhibits none of these vices,—no, nor all together, but certainly wickedness of some kind (for we blame him) and injustice. There is, then, another kind of injustice which is a part of injustice in the wide sense, and a use of the word 'unjust' which answers to a part of what is unjust in the wide sense of 'contrary to the law'. Again if one man commits adultery for the sake of gain and makes money by it, while another does so at the bidding of appetite though he loses money and is penalized for it, the latter would be held to be self-indulgent rather than grasping, but the former is unjust, but not self-indulgent; evidently, therefore, he is unjust by reason of his making gain by his act. Again, all other unjust acts are ascribed invariably to some particular kind of wickedness, e.g. adultery to self-indulgence, the desertion of a comrade in battle to cowardice, physical violence to anger; but if a man makes gain, his action is ascribed to no form of wickedness but injustice. Evidently, therefore, there is apart from injustice in the wide sense another, 'particular', injustice which shares the name and nature of the first, because its definition **1130b** falls within the same genus; for the significance of both consists in a relation to one's neighbour, but the one is concerned with honour or money or safety—or that which includes all these, if we had a single name for it—and its motive is the pleasure that arises from gain;

while the other is concerned with all the objects with which the good man is concerned.

It is clear, then, that there is more than one kind of justice, and that there is one which is distinct from virtue entire; we must try to grasp its genus and differentia.

The unjust has been divided into the unlawful and the unfair, and the just into the lawful and the fair. To the unlawful answers the afore-mentioned sense of injustice. But since the unfair and the unlawful are not the same, but are different as a part is from its whole (for all that is unfair is unlawful, but not all that is unlawful is unfair), the unjust and injustice in the sense of the unfair are not the same as but different from the former kind, as part from whole; for injustice in this sense is a part of injustice in the wide sense, and similarly justice in the one sense of justice in the other. Therefore we must speak also about particular justice and particular injustice, and similarly about the just and the unjust. The justice, then, which answers to the whole of virtue, and the corresponding injustice, one being the exercise of virtue as a whole, and the other that of vice as a whole, towards one's neighbour, we may leave on one side. And how the meanings of 'just' and 'unjust' which answer to these are to be distinguished is evident; for practically the majority of the acts commanded by the law are those which are prescribed from the point of view of virtue taken as a whole; for the law bids us practise every virtue and forbids us to practise any vice. And the things that tend to produce virtue taken as a whole are those of the acts prescribed by the law which have been prescribed with a view to education for the common good. But with regard to the education of the individual as such, which makes him without qualification a good *man*, we must determine later[1] whether this is the function of the political art or of another; for perhaps it is not the same to be a good man and a good citizen of any state taken at random.

Of particular justice and that which is just in the corresponding sense, (A) one kind is that which is manifested in distributions of honour or money or the other things that fall to be divided among those who have a share in the constitution (for in these it is possible for one man to have a share either unequal or equal to that of another), and (B) one is that which plays a rectifying part in transactions between **1131a** man and man. Of this there are two divisions; of transactions (1) some are voluntary and (2) others involuntary—voluntary such transactions as sale, purchase, loan for consumption, pledging, loan for use, depositing, letting (they are called voluntary because the origin of these transactions is voluntary), while of the involuntary (*a*) some are clandestine, such as theft, adultery, poisoning, procuring, enticement of slaves, assassination, false witness, and (*b*) others are violent, such as assault, imprisonment, murder, robbery with violence, mutilation, abuse, insult.

3

(A) We have shown that both the unjust man and the unjust act are unfair or unequal; now it is clear that there is also an intermediate between the two unequals involved in either case. And this is the equal; for in any kind of action in which there is a more and a less there is also what is equal. If, then, the unjust is unequal, the just is equal, as all men suppose it to be, even apart from argument. And since the equal is intermediate, the just will be an intermediate. Now equality implies at least two things. The just, then, must be both intermediate and equal and relative (i.e. for certain persons). And *qua* intermediate it must be between certain things (which are respectively greater and less); *qua* equal, it involves *two* things; *qua* just, it is for certain people. The just, therefore, involves at least four terms; for the persons for whom it is in fact just are two, and the things in which it is manifested, the objects distributed, are two. And the same equality will exist between the persons and between the things concerned; for as the latter—the things concerned—are related, so are the former; if they are not equal, they will not have what is equal, but this is the origin of quarrels and complaints—when either equals have and are awarded unequal shares, or unequals equal shares. Further, this is plain from the fact that awards should be 'according to merit' for all men agree that what is just in distribution must be according to merit in some sense though they do not all specify the same sort o merit, but democrats identify it with the statu of freeman, supporters of oligarchy wit wealth (or with noble birth), and supporters c aristocracy with excellence.

The just, then, is a species of the propo tionate (proportion being not a property onl of the kind of number which consists of al stract units, but of number in general). Fc

1 1179b 20–1181b 12. *Politics*, 1276b 16–1277b 32, 1278a 40–b5, 1288a 32–b2, 1333a 11–16, 1337a 11–14.

proportion is equality of ratios, and involves four terms at least (that discrete proportion involves four terms is plain, but so does continuous proportion, for it uses one term as two and
1131b mentions it twice; e.g. 'as the line A is to the line B, so is the line B to the line C'; the line B, then, has been mentioned twice, so that if the line B be assumed twice, the proportional terms will be four); and the just, too, involves at least four terms, and the ratio between one pair is the same as that between the other pair; for there is a similar distinction between the persons and between the things. As the term A, then, is to B, so will C be to D, and therefore, *alternando*, as A is to C, B will be to D. Therefore also the whole is in the same ratio to the whole; and this coupling the distribution effects, and, if the terms are so combined, effects justly. The conjunction, then, of the term A with C and of B with D is what is just in distribution, and this species of the just is intermediate, and the unjust is what violates the proportion; for the proportional is intermediate, and the just is proportional. (Mathematicians call this kind of proportion geometrical; for it is in geometrical proportion that it follows that the whole is to the whole as either part is to the corresponding part.) This proportion is not continuous; for we cannot get a single term standing for a person and a thing.

This, then, is what the just is—the proportional; the unjust is what violates the proportion. Hence one term becomes too great, the other too small, as indeed happens in practice; for the man who acts unjustly has too much, and the man who is unjustly treated too little, of what is good. In the case of evil the reverse is true; for the lesser evil is reckoned a good in comparison with the greater evil, since the lesser evil is rather to be chosen than the greater, and what is worthy of choice is good, and what is worthier of choice a greater good.

This, then, is one species of the just.

4

(B) The remaining one is the rectificatory, which arises in connexion with transactions both voluntary and involuntary. This form of the just has a different specific character from the former. For the justice which distributes common possessions is always in accordance with the kind of proportion mentioned above[1] (for in the case also in which the distribution is made from the common funds of a partnership it will be according to the same ratio which the funds put into the business by the partners bear to one another); and the injustice opposed to this kind of justice is that which violates the proportion. But the justice in transactions between man and man is a sort of
1132a equality indeed, and the injustice a sort of inequality; not according to that kind of proportion, however, but according to arithmetical proportion. For it makes no difference whether a good man has defrauded a bad man or a bad man a good one, nor whether it is a good or a bad man that has committed adultery; the law looks only to the distinctive character of the injury, and treats the parties as equal, if one is in the wrong and the other is being wronged, and if one inflicted injury and the other has received it. Therefore, this kind of injustice being an inequality, the judge tries to equalize it; for in the case also in which one has received and the other has inflicted a wound, or one has slain and the other been slain, the suffering and the action have been unequally distributed; but the judge tries to equalize by means of the penalty, taking away from the gain of the assailant. For the term 'gain' is applied generally to such cases, even if it be not a term appropriate to certain cases, e.g. to the person who inflicts a wound—and 'loss' to the sufferer; at all events when the suffering has been estimated, the one is called loss and the other gain. Therefore the equal is intermediate between the greater and the less, but the gain and the loss are respectively greater and less in contrary ways; more of the good and less of the evil are gain, and the contrary is loss; intermediate between them is, as we saw,[2] the equal, which we say is just; therefore corrective justice will be the intermediate between loss and gain. This is why, when people dispute, they take refuge in the judge; and to go to the judge is to go to justice; for the nature of the judge is to be a sort of animate justice; and they seek the judge as an intermediate, and in some states they call judges mediators, on the assumption that if they get what is intermediate they will get what is just. The just, then, is an intermediate, since the judge is so. Now the judge restores equality; it is as though there were a line divided into unequal parts, and he took away that by which the greater segment exceeds the half, and added it to the smaller segment. And when the whole has been equally divided, then they say they have 'their own'—i.e. when they have got what is equal. The equal is intermediate be-

[1] l. 12 f.

[2] l. 14

tween the greater and the lesser line according [30] to arithmetical proportion. It is for this reason also that it is called just (δίκαιον), because it is a division into two equal parts (δίχα), just as if one were to call it δίχαιον; and the judge (δικαστής) is one who bisects (διχαστής). For when something is subtracted from one of two equals and added to the other, the other is in excess by these two; since if what was taken from the one had not been added to the other, the latter would have been in excess **1132b** by one only. It therefore exceeds the intermediate by one, and the intermediate exceeds by one that from which something was taken. By this, then, we shall recognize both what we must subtract from that which has more, and what we must add to that which has less; we must add to the latter that by which [5] the intermediate exceeds it, and subtract from the greatest that by which it exceeds the intermediate. Let the lines AA′, BB′, CC′ be equal to one another; from the line AA′ let the segment AE have been subtracted, and to the line CC′ let the segment CD have been added, so that the whole line DCC′ exceeds the line EA′ by the segment CD and the segment CF; [9] therefore it exceeds the line BB′ by the segment CD.

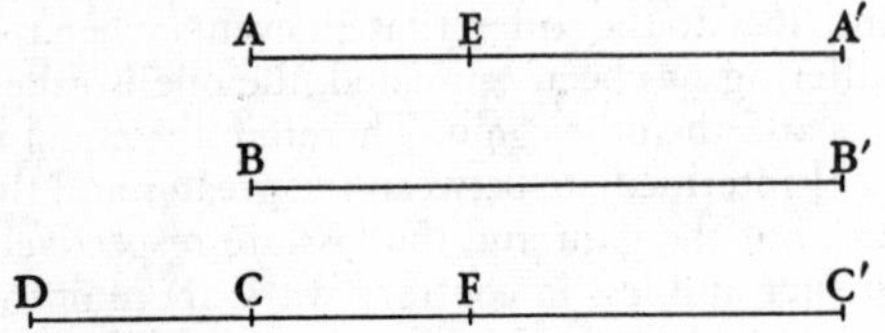

[11] These names, both loss and gain, have come from voluntary exchange; for to have more than one's own is called gaining, and to have less than one's original share is called [15] losing, e.g. in buying and selling and in all other matters in which the law has left people free to make their own terms; but when they get neither more nor less but just what belongs to themselves, they say that they have their own and that they neither lose nor gain.

Therefore the just is intermediate between a sort of gain and a sort of loss, viz. those which are involuntary; it consists in having an equal [20] amount before and after the transaction.

5

Some think that *reciprocity* is without qualification just, as the Pythagoreans said; for they defined justice without qualification as reciprocity. Now 'reciprocity' fits neither distribu- [25] tive nor rectificatory justice—yet people *want* even the justice of Rhadamanthus to mean this:

> *Should a man suffer what he did, right justice would be done*[1]

—for in many cases reciprocity and rectificatory justice are not in accord; e.g. (1) if an official has inflicted a wound, he should not be wounded in return, and if some one has wounded an official, he ought not to be [30] wounded only but punished in addition. Further (2) there is a great difference between a voluntary and an involuntary act. But in associations for exchange this sort of justice does hold men together—reciprocity in accordance with a proportion and not on the basis of precisely equal return. For it is by proportionate requital that the city holds together. Men seek to return either evil for evil—and if they cannot **1133a** not do so, think their position mere slavery—or good for good—and if they cannot do so there is no exchange, but it is by exchange that they hold together. This is why they give a prominent place to the temple of the Graces—to promote the requital of services; for this is characteristic of grace—we should serve in return one who has shown grace to us, and should another time take the initiative in showing it.

[5] Now proportionate return is secured by cross-conjunction. Let A be a builder, B a shoemaker, C a house, D a shoe. The builder, then, must get from the shoemaker the lat- [10] ter's work, and must himself give him in return his own. If, then, first there is proportionate equality of goods, and then reciprocal action takes place, the result we mention will be effected. If not, the bargain is not equal, and does not hold; for there is nothing to prevent the work of the one being better than that of the other; they must therefore be equated. (And this is true of the other arts also; for [15] they would have been destroyed if what the patient suffered had not been just what the agent did, and of the same amount and kind.) For it is not two doctors that associate for exchange, but a doctor and a farmer, or in general people who are different and unequal; but these must be equated. This is why all things that are exchanged must be somehow comparable. It is for this end that money has been introduced, and it becomes in a sense an inter- [20] mediate; for it measures all things, and therefore the excess and the defect—how many shoes are equal to a house or to a given amount

[1] Hesiod, fr. 174 Rzach.

of food. The number of shoes exchanged for a house [or for a given amount of food] must therefore correspond to the ratio of builder to shoemaker. For if this be not so, there will be no exchange and no intercourse. And this proportion will not be effected unless the goods are somehow equal. All goods must therefore be measured by some one thing, as we said before.[1] Now this unit is in truth demand, which holds all things together (for if men did not need one another's goods at all, or did not need them equally, there would be either no exchange or not the same exchange); but money has become by convention a sort of representative of demand; and this is why it has the name 'money' (*νόμισμα*)—because it exists not by nature but by law (*νόμος*) and it is in our power to change it and make it useless. There will, then, be reciprocity when the terms have been equated so that as farmer is to shoemaker, the amount of the shoemaker's work is to that of the farmer's work for which it exchanges. But we must not bring **1133b** them into a figure of proportion when they have already exchanged (otherwise one extreme will have both excesses), but when they still have their own goods. Thus they are equals and associates just because this equality can be effected in their case. Let A be a farmer, C food, B a shoemaker, D his product equated to C. If it had not been possible for reciprocity to be thus effected, there would have been no association of the parties. That demand holds things together as a single unit is shown by the fact that when men do not need one another, i.e. when neither needs the other or one does not need the other, they do not exchange, as we do when some one wants what one has oneself, e.g. when people permit the exportation of corn in exchange for wine. This equation therefore must be established. And for the future exchange—that if we do not need a thing now we shall have it if ever we do need it—money is as it were our surety; for it must be possible for us to get what we want by bringing the money. Now the same thing happens to money itself as to goods—it is not always worth the same; yet it tends to be steadier. This is why all goods must have a price set on them; for then there will always be exchange, and if so, association of man with man. Money, then, acting as a measure, makes goods commensurate and equates them; for neither would there have been association if there were not exchange, nor exchange if there were not equality, nor equality if there were not commensurability. Now in truth it is impossible that things differing so much should become commensurate, but with reference to demand they may become so sufficiently. There must, then, be a unit, and that fixed by agreement (for which reason it is called money); for it is this that makes all things commensurate, since all things are measured by money. Let A be a house, B ten minae, C a bed. A is half of B, if the house is worth five minae or equal to them; the bed, C, is a tenth of B; it is plain, then, how many beds are equal to a house, viz. five. That exchange took place thus before there was money is plain; for it makes no difference whether it is five beds that exchange for a house, or the money value of five beds.

We have now defined the unjust and the just. These having been marked off from each other, it is plain that just action is intermediate between acting unjustly and being unjustly treated; for the one is to have too much and the other to have too little. Justice is a kind of mean, but not in the same way as the other virtues, but because it relates to an intermediate amount, while injustice relates to the ex- **1134a** tremes. And justice is that in virtue of which the just man is said to be a doer, by choice, of that which is just, and one who will distribute either between himself and another or between two others not so as to give more of what is desirable to himself and less to his neighbour (and conversely with what is harmful), but so as to give what is equal in accordance with proportion; and similarly in distributing between two other persons. Injustice on the other hand is similarly related to the unjust, which is excess and defect, contrary to proportion, of the useful or hurtful. For which reason injustice is excess and defect, viz. because it is productive of excess and defect—in one's own case excess of what is in its own nature useful and defect of what is hurtful, while in the case of others it is as a whole like what it is in one's own case, but proportion may be violated in either direction. In the unjust act to have too little is to be unjustly treated; to have too much is to act unjustly.

Let this be taken as our account of the nature of justice and injustice, and similarly of the just and the unjust in general.

6

Since acting unjustly does not necessarily imply being unjust, we must ask what sort of un-

[1] l. 19.

just acts imply that the doer is unjust with respect to each type of injustice, e.g. a thief, an adulterer, or a brigand. Surely the answer does not turn on the difference between these types. For a man might even lie with a woman knowing who she was, but the origin of his act might be not deliberate choice but passion. He acts unjustly, then, but is not unjust; e.g. a man is not a thief, yet he stole, nor an adulterer, yet he committed adultery; and similarly in all other cases.

Now we have previously stated how the reciprocal is related to the just;[1] but we must not forget that what we are looking for is not only what is just without qualification but also political justice. This is found among men who share their life with a view to self-sufficiency, men who are free and either proportionately or arithmetically equal, so that between those who do not fulfil this condition there is no political justice but justice in a special sense and by analogy. For justice exists only between men whose mutual relations are governed by law; and law exists for men between whom there is injustice; for legal justice is the discrimination of the just and the unjust. And between men between whom there is injustice there is also unjust action (though there is not injustice between all between whom there is unjust action), and this is assigning too much to oneself of things good in themselves and too little of things evil in themselves. This is why we do not allow a *man* to rule, but *rational principle,* because a man behaves thus in his own interests and becomes **1134b** a tyrant. The magistrate on the other hand is the guardian of justice, and, if of justice, then of equality also. And since he is assumed to have no more than his share, if he is just (for he does not assign to himself more of what is good in itself, unless such a share is proportional to his merits—so that it is for others that he labours, and it is for this reason that men, as we stated previously,[2] say that justice is 'another's good'), therefore a reward must be given him, and this is honour and privilege; but those for whom such things are not enough become tyrants.

The justice of a master and that of a father are not the same as the justice of citizens, though they are like it; for there can be no injustice in the unqualified sense towards things that are one's own, but a man's chattel, and his child until it reaches a certain age and sets up for itself, are as it were part of himself, and no one chooses to hurt himself (for which reason there can be no injustice towards oneself). Therefore the justice or injustice of citizens is not manifested in these relations; for it was as we saw[3] according to law, and between people naturally subject to law, and these as we saw[4] are people who have an equal share in ruling and being ruled. Hence justice can more truly be manifested towards a wife than towards children and chattels, for the former is household justice; but even this is different from political justice.

7

Of political justice part is natural, part legal,—natural, that which everywhere has the same force and does not exist by people's thinking this or that; legal, that which is originally indifferent, but when it has been laid down is not indifferent, e.g. that a prisoner's ransom shall be a mina, or that a goat and not two sheep shall be sacrificed, and again all the laws that are passed for particular cases, e.g. that sacrifice shall be made in honour of Brasidas,[5] and the provisions of decrees. Now some think that all justice is of this sort, because that which is by nature is unchangeable and has everywhere the same force (as fire burns both here and in Persia), while they see change in the things recognized as just. This, however, is not true in this unqualified way, but is true in a sense; or rather, with the gods it is perhaps not true at all, while with us there is something that is just even by nature, yet all of it is changeable; but still some is by nature, some not by nature. It is evident which sort of thing, among things capable of being otherwise, is by nature, and which is not but is legal and conventional, assuming that both are equally changeable. And in all other things the same distinction will apply; by nature the right hand is stronger, yet it is possible that all men should come to be ambidextrous. The things which are just by virtue of convention **1135a** and expediency are like measures; for wine and corn measures are not everywhere equal, but larger in wholesale and smaller in retail markets. Similarly, the things which are just not by nature but by human enactment are not everywhere the same, since constitutions also are not the same, though there is but one which is everywhere by nature the best. Of things just and lawful each is related as the universal to its particulars; for the things

[1] 1132^b 21-1133^b 28. [2] 1130^a 3.

[3] ^{a} 30. [4] ^{a} 26-8. [5] Thucydides, v. 11.

that are done are many, but of *them* each is one, since it is universal.

There is a difference between the act of injustice and what is unjust, and between the act of justice and what is just; for a thing is unjust by nature or by enactment; and this very thing, when it has been done, is an act of injustice, but before it is done is not yet that but is unjust. So, too, with an act of justice (though the general term is rather 'just action', and 'act of justice' is applied to the correction of the act of injustice).

Each of these must later be examined separately with regard to the nature and number of its species and the nature of the things with which it is concerned.

8

Acts just and unjust being as we have described them, a man acts unjustly or justly whenever he does such acts voluntarily; when involuntarily, he acts neither unjustly nor justly except in an incidental way; for he does things which happen to be just or unjust. Whether an act is or is not one of injustice (or of justice) is determined by its voluntariness or involuntariness; for when it is voluntary it is blamed, and at the same time is then an act of injustice; so that there will be things that are unjust but not yet acts of injustice, if voluntariness be not present as well. By the voluntary I mean, as has been said before,[1] any of the things in a man's own power which he does with knowledge, i.e. not in ignorance either of the person acted on or of the instrument used or of the end that will be attained (e.g. whom he is striking, with what, and to what end), each such act being done not incidentally nor under compulsion (e.g. if A takes B's hand and therewith strikes C, B does not act voluntarily; for the act was not in his own power). The person struck may be the striker's father, and the striker may know that it is a man or one of the persons present, but not know that it is his father; a similar distinction may be made in the case of the end, and with regard to the whole action. Therefore that which is done in ignorance, or though not done in ignorance is not in the agent's power, or is done under compulsion, is involuntary (for many natural processes, even, we knowingly both perform and experience, **1135b** none of which is either voluntary or involuntary; e.g. growing old or dying). But in the case of unjust and just acts alike the injustice or justice may be only incidental; for a man might return a deposit unwillingly and from fear, and then he must not be said either to do what is just or to act justly, except in an incidental way. Similarly the man who under compulsion and unwillingly fails to return the deposit must be said to act unjustly, and to do what is unjust, only incidentally. Of voluntary acts we do some by choice, others not by choice; by choice those which we do after deliberation, not by choice those which we do without previous deliberation. Thus there are three kinds of injury in transactions between man and man; those done in ignorance are *mistakes* when the person acted on, the act, the instrument, or the end that will be attained is other than the agent supposed; the agent thought either that he was not hitting any one or that he was not hitting with this missile or not hitting this person or to this end, but a result followed other than that which he thought likely (e.g. he threw not with intent to wound but only to prick), or the person hit or the missile was other than he supposed. Now when (1) the injury takes place contrary to reasonable expectation, it is a *misadventure*. When (2) it is not contrary to reasonable expectation, but does not imply vice, it is a *mistake* (for a man makes a mistake when the fault originates in him, but is the victim of accident when the origin lies outside him). When (3) he acts with knowledge but not after deliberation, it is an *act of injustice*—e.g. the acts due to anger or to other passions necessary or natural to man; for when men do such harmful and mistaken acts they act unjustly, and the acts are acts of injustice, but this does not imply that the doers are unjust or wicked; for the injury is not due to vice. But when (4) a man acts from choice, he is an *unjust man* and a vicious man.

Hence acts proceeding from anger are rightly judged not to be done of malice aforethought; for it is not the man who acts in anger but he who enraged him that starts the mischief. Again, the matter in dispute is not whether the thing happened or not, but its justice; for it is apparent injustice that occasions rage. For they do not dispute about the occurrence of the act—as in commercial transactions where one of the two parties *must* be vicious—unless they do so owing to forgetfulness; but, agreeing about the fact, they dispute on which side justice lies (whereas a man who has deliberately injured another cannot

[1] 1109b35–1111a24.

help knowing that he has done so), so that the one thinks he is being treated unjustly and the other disagrees.

1136a But if a man harms another by choice, he acts unjustly; and *these* are the acts of injustice which imply that the doer is an unjust man, provided that the act violates proportion or equality. Similarly, a man *is just* when he acts justly by choice; but he *acts justly* if he merely acts voluntarily.

Of involuntary acts some are excusable, others not. For the mistakes which men make not only in ignorance but also from ignorance are excusable, while those which men do not from ignorance but (though they do them *in* ignorance) owing to a passion which is neither natural nor such as man is liable to, are not excusable.

9

Assuming that we have sufficiently defined the suffering and doing of injustice, it may be asked (1) whether the truth in expressed in Euripides' paradoxical words:

> *I slew my mother, that's my tale in brief.*
> *Were you both willing, or unwilling both?*[1]

Is it truly possible to be willingly treated unjustly, or is all suffering of injustice on the contrary involuntary, as all unjust action is voluntary? And is all suffering of injustice of the latter kind or else all of the former, or is it sometimes voluntary, sometimes involuntary? So, too, with the case of being justly treated; all just action is voluntary, so that it is reasonable that there should be a similar opposition in either case—that both being unjustly and being justly treated should be either alike voluntary or alike involuntary. But it would be thought paradoxical even in the case of being justly treated, if it were always voluntary; for some are unwillingly treated justly. (2) One might raise this question also, whether every one who has suffered what is unjust is being unjustly treated, or on the other hand it is with suffering as with acting. In action and in passivity alike it is possible to partake of justice incidentally, and similarly (it is plain) of injustice; for to do what is unjust is not the same as to act unjustly, nor to suffer what is unjust as to be treated unjustly, and similarly in the case of acting justly and being justly treated; for it is impossible to be unjustly treated if the other does not act unjustly, or justly treated unless he acts justly. Now if to act unjustly is simply to harm some one voluntarily, and 'voluntarily' means 'knowing the person acted on, the instrument, and the manner of one's acting', and the incontinent man voluntarily harms himself, not only will he voluntarily be unjustly treated but it will be possible to treat oneself unjustly. (This also is one of the questions in doubt, whether **1136b** a man can treat himself unjustly.) Again, a man may voluntarily, owing to incontinence, be harmed by another who acts voluntarily, so that it would be possible to be voluntarily treated unjustly. Or is our definition incorrect; must we to 'harming another, with knowledge both of the person acted on, of the instrument, and of the manner' add 'contrary to the wish of the person acted on'? Then a man may be voluntarily harmed and voluntarily suffer what is unjust, but no one is voluntarily treated unjustly; for no one wishes to be unjustly treated, not even the incontinent man. He acts contrary to his wish; for no one *wishes* for what he does not think to be good, but the incontinent man does *do* things that he does not think he ought to do. Again, one who gives what is his own, as Homer says Glaucus gave Diomede

> *Armour of gold for brazen, the price of a hundred beeves for nine,*[2]

is not unjustly treated; for though to give is in his power, to be unjustly treated is not, but there must be some one to treat him unjustly. It is plain, then, that being unjustly treated is not voluntary.

Of the questions we intended to discuss two still remain for discussion; (3) whether it is the man who has assigned to another more than his share that acts unjustly, or he who has the excessive share, and (4) whether it is possible to treat oneself unjustly. The questions are connected; for if the former alternative is possible and the distributor acts unjustly and not the man who has the excessive share, then if a man assigns more to another than to himself, knowingly and voluntarily, he treats himself unjustly; which is what modest people seem to do, since the virtuous man tends to take less than his share. Or does this statement too need qualification? For (*a*) he perhaps gets more than his share of some other good, e.g. of honour or of intrinsic nobility. (*b*) The question is solved by applying the distinction we applied to unjust action; for he suffers nothing contrary to his own wish, so

[1] Fr. 68 from the *Alcmeon*, Nauck.

[2] *Iliad*, VI. 236.

that he is not unjustly treated as far as this goes, but at most only suffers harm.

It is plain too that the distributor acts unjustly, but not always the man who has the excessive share; for it is not he to whom what is unjust appertains that acts unjustly, but he to whom it appertains to do the unjust act voluntarily, i.e. the person in whom lies the origin of the action, and this lies in the distributor, not in the receiver. Again, since the word 'do' is ambiguous, and there is a sense in which lifeless things, or a hand, or a servant who obeys an order, may be said to slay, he who gets an excessive share does not act unjustly, though he 'does' what is unjust.

Again, if the distributor gave his judgement in ignorance, he does not act unjustly in respect of legal justice, and his judgement is not unjust in this sense, but in a sense it *is* unjust (for legal justice and primordial justice are **1137a** different); but if with knowledge he judged unjustly, he is himself aiming at an excessive share either of gratitude or of revenge. As much, then, as if he were to share in the plunder, the man who has judged unjustly for these reasons has got too much; the fact that what he gets is different from what he distributes makes no difference, for even if he awards land with a view to sharing in the plunder he gets not land but money.

Men think that acting unjustly is in their power, and therefore that being just is easy. But it is not; to lie with one's neighbour's wife, to wound another, to deliver a bribe, is easy and in our power, but to do these things as a result of a certain state of character is neither easy nor in our power. Similarly to know what is just and what is unjust requires, men think, no great wisdom, because it is not hard to understand the matters dealt with by the laws (though these are not the things that are just, except incidentally); but how actions must be done and distributions effected in order to be just, to know *this* is a greater achievement than knowing what is good for the health; though even there, while it is easy to know that honey, wine, hellebore, cautery, and the use of the knife are so, to know how, to whom, and when these should be applied with a view to producing health, is no less an achievement than that of being a physician. Again, for this very reason men think that acting unjustly is characteristic of the just man no less than of the unjust, because he would be not less but even more capable of doing each of these unjust acts; for he could lie with a woman or wound a neighbour; and the brave man could throw away his shield and turn to flight in this direction or in that. But to play the coward or to act unjustly consists not in doing these things, except incidentally, but in doing them as the result of a certain state of character, just as to practise medicine and healing consists not in applying or not applying the knife, in using or not using medicines, but in doing so in a certain way.

Just acts occur between people who participate in things good in themselves and can have too much or too little of them; for some beings (e.g. presumably the gods) cannot have too much of them, and to others, those who are incurably bad, not even the smallest share in them is beneficial but all such goods are harmful, while to others they are beneficial up to a point; therefore justice is essentially something human.

10

Our next subject is equity and the equitable (τὸ ἐπιεικές), and their respective relations to justice and the just. For on examination they appear to be neither absolutely the same nor generically different; and while we sometimes praise what is equitable and the equitable man (so that we apply the name by way of praise even to instances of the other **1137b** virtues, instead of 'good' meaning by ἐπιεικέστερον that a thing is better), at other times, when we reason it out, it seems strange if the equitable, being something different from the just, is yet praiseworthy; for either the just or the equitable is not good, if they are different; or, if both are good, they are the same.

These, then, are pretty much the considerations that give rise to the problem about the equitable; they are all in a sense correct and not opposed to one another; for the equitable, though it is better than one kind of justice, yet is just, and it is not as being a different class of thing that it is better than the just. The same thing, then, is just and equitable, and while both are good the equitable is superior. What creates the problem is that the equitable is just, but not the legally just but a correction of legal justice. The reason is that all law is universal but about some things it is not possible to make a universal statement which shall be correct. In those cases, then, in which it is necessary to speak universally, but not possible to do so correctly, the law takes the usual case, though it is not ignorant of the possibility of error. And it is none the less correct; for the error is not in the law nor in the legislator but in the nature of the thing, since the matter of practical affairs is of this kind from the start. When the law speaks universally, then, and a case arises on it which is not covered by the universal statement, then it is right, where the legislator fails us and has erred by over-simplicity, to correct the omission—to say what the legislator himself would have said had he been present, and would have put into his law if he had known. Hence the equitable is just, and better than one kind of justice—not better than absolute justice but better than the error that arises from the absoluteness of the statement. And this is the nature of the equitable, a correction of law where it is defective owing to its universality. In fact this is the reason why all things are not determined by law, that about some things it is impossible to lay down a law, so that a decree is needed. For when the thing is indefinite the rule also is indefinite, like the leaden rule used in making the Lesbian moulding; the rule adapts itself to the shape of the stone and is not rigid, and so too the decree is adapted to the facts.

It is plain, then, what the equitable is, and that it is just and is better than one kind of justice. It is evident also from this who the equitable man is; the man who chooses and does such acts, and is no stickler for his rights in a bad sense but tends to take less than **1138a** his share though he has the law on his side, is equitable, and this state of character is equity, which is a sort of justice and not a different state of character.

11

Whether a man can treat himself unjustly or not, is evident from what has been said.[1] For (*a*) one class of just acts are those acts in accordance with any virtue which are prescribed by the law; e.g. the law does not expressly permit suicide, and what it does not expressly permit it forbids. Again, when a man in violation of the law harms another (otherwise than in retaliation) voluntarily, he acts unjustly, and a voluntary agent is one who knows both the person he is affecting by his action and the instrument he is using; and he who through anger voluntarily stabs himself does this contrary to the right rule of life, and this the law does not allow; therefore he is acting unjustly. But towards whom? Surely towards the state, not towards himself. For he suffers voluntarily, but no one is voluntarily treated unjustly. This is also the reason why the state punishes; a certain loss of civil rights attaches to the man who destroys himself, on the ground that he is treating the state unjustly.

Further (*b*) in that sense of 'acting unjustly' in which the man who 'acts unjustly' is unjust only and not bad all round, it is not possible to treat oneself unjustly (this is different from the former sense; the unjust man in one sense of the term is wicked in a particularized way just as the coward is, not in the sense of being wicked all round, so that his 'unjust act' does not manifest wickedness in general). For (i) that would imply the possibility of the same thing's having been subtracted from and added to the same thing at the same time; but this is impossible—the just and the unjust always involve more than one person. Further, (ii) unjust action is voluntary and done by choice, and *takes the initiative* (for the man who because he has suffered does the same in return is not thought to act unjustly); but if a man harms himself he suffers and does the same things *at the same time*. Further, (iii) if a man could treat himself unjustly, he could be voluntarily treated unjustly. Besides, (iv) no one acts unjustly without committing particular acts of injustice; but no one can commit adultery with his own wife or housebreaking on his own house or theft on his own property,

In general, the question 'can a man treat himself unjustly?' is solved also by the distinction we applied to the question 'can a man be voluntarily treated unjustly?'[2]

(It is evident too that both are bad, being unjustly treated and acting unjustly; for the one means having less and the other having more than the intermediate amount, which plays the part here that the healthy does in the medical art, and that good condition does in the art of bodily training. But still acting unjustly is the worse, for it involves vice and is blameworthy—involves vice which is either of the complete and unqualified kind or almost so (we must admit the latter alternative, because not all voluntary unjust action implies injustice as a state of character), while being unjustly treated does not involve vice and injustice in oneself. In itself, then, being **1138b** unjustly treated is less bad, but there is nothing to prevent its being incidentally a

[1] Cf. 1129a 32-b 1, 1136a 10-1137a 4.

[2] Cf. 1136a 31-b 5.

greater evil. But theory cares nothing for this; it calls pleurisy a more serious mischief than a stumble; yet the latter may become incidentally the more serious, if the fall due to it leads to your being taken prisoner or put to death by the enemy.)

Metaphorically and in virtue of a certain resemblance there is a justice, not indeed between a man and himself, but between certain parts of him; yet not every kind of justice but that of master and servant or that of husband and wife. For these are the ratios in which the part of the soul that has a rational principle stands to the irrational part; and it is with a view to these parts that people also think a man can be unjust to himself, viz. because these parts are liable to suffer something contrary to their respective desires; there is therefore thought to be a mutual justice between them as between ruler and ruled.

Let this be taken as our account of justice and the other, i.e. the other moral, virtues.

BOOK VI

1

SINCE we have previously said that one ought to choose that which is intermediate, not the excess nor the defect, and that the intermediate is determined by the dictates of the right rule, let us discuss the nature of these dictates. In all the states of character we have mentioned,[1] as in all other matters, there is a mark to which the man who has the rule looks, and heightens or relaxes his activity accordingly, and there is a standard which determines the mean states which we say are intermediate between excess and defect, being in accordance with the right rule. But such a statement, though true, is by no means clear; for not only here but in all other pursuits which are objects of knowledge it is indeed true to say that we must not exert ourselves nor relax our efforts too much nor too little, but to an intermediate extent and as the right rule dictates; but if a man had only this knowledge he would be none the wiser—e.g. we should not know what sort of medicines to apply to our body if some one were to say 'all those which the medical art prescribes, and which agree with the practice of one who possesses the art'. Hence it is necessary with regard to the states of the soul also not only that this true statement should be made, but also that it should be determined what is the right rule and what is the standard that fixes it.

We divided the virtues of the soul and
1139a said that some are virtues of character and others of intellect. Now we have discussed in detail the moral virtues;[1] with regard to the others let us express our view as follows, beginning with some remarks about the soul. We said before that there are two parts of the soul—that which grasps a rule or rational principle, and the irrational; let us now draw a similar distinction within the part which grasps a rational principle. And let it be assumed that there are two parts which grasp a rational principle—one by which we contemplate the kind of things whose originative causes are invariable, and one by which we contemplate variable things; for where objects differ in kind the part of the soul answering to each of the two is different in kind, since it is in virtue of a certain likeness and kinship with their objects that they have the knowledge they have. Let one of these parts be called the scientific and the other the calculative; for to deliberate and to calculate are the same thing, but no one deliberates about the invariable. Therefore the calculative is one part of the faculty which grasps a rational principle. We must, then, learn what is the best state of each of these two parts; for this is the virtue of each.

[1] In III. 6–V. 11.

2

The virtue of a thing is relative to its proper work. Now there are three things in the soul which control action and truth—sensation, reason, desire.

Of these sensation originates no action; this is plain from the fact that the lower animals have sensation but no share in action.

What affirmation and negation are in thinking, pursuit and avoidance are in desire; so that since moral virtue is a state of character concerned with choice, and choice is deliberate desire, therefore both the reasoning must be true and the desire right, if the choice is to be good, and the latter must pursue just what the former asserts. Now this kind of intellect and of truth is practical; of the intellect which is contemplative, not practical nor productive, the good and the bad state are truth and falsity respectively (for this is the work of everything intellectual); while of the part which is practical and intellectual the good state is truth in agreement with right desire.

The origin of action—its efficient, not its final cause—is choice, and that of choice is desire and reasoning with a view to an end. This is why choice cannot exist either without reason and intellect or without a moral state; for good action and its opposite cannot exist without a combination of intellect and character. Intellect itself, however, moves nothing, but only the intellect which aims at an end and is **1139b** practical; for this rules the productive intellect, as well, since every one who makes makes for an end, and that which is made is not an end in the unqualified sense (but only an end in a particular relation, and the end of a particular operation)—only that which is *done* is that; for good action is an end, and desire aims at this. Hence choice is either desiderative reason or ratiocinative desire, and such an origin of action is a man. (It is to be noted that nothing that is past is an object of choice, e.g. no one chooses to have sacked Troy; for no one *deliberates* about the past, but about what is future and capable of being otherwise, while what is past is not capable of not having taken place; hence Agathon is right in saying[1]

For this alone is lacking even to God,
To make undone things that have once been done.)

The work of both the intellectual parts, then, is truth. Therefore the states that are most strictly those in respect of which each of these parts will reach truth are the virtues of the two parts.

3

Let us begin, then, from the beginning, and discuss these states once more. Let it be assumed that the states by virtue of which the soul possesses truth by way of affirmation or denial are five in number, i.e. art, scientific knowledge, practical wisdom, philosophic wisdom, intuitive reason; we do not include judgement and opinion because in these we may be mistaken.

Now what *scientific knowledge* is, if we are to speak exactly and not follow mere similarities, is plain from what follows. We all suppose that what we know is not even capable of being otherwise; of things capable of being otherwise we do not know, when they have passed outside our observation, whether they exist or not. Therefore the object of scientific knowledge is of necessity. Therefore it is eternal; for things that are of necessity in the unqualified sense are all eternal; and things that are eternal are ungenerated and imperishable. Again, every science is thought to be capable of being taught, and its object of being learned. And all teaching starts from what is already known, as we maintain in the *Analytics*[2] also; for it proceeds sometimes through induction and sometimes by syllogism. Now induction is the starting-point which knowledge even of the universal presupposes, while syllogism proceeds *from* universals. There are therefore starting-points from which syllogism proceeds, which are not reached by syllogism; it is therefore by induction that they are acquired. Scientific knowledge is, then, a state of capacity to demonstrate, and has the other limiting characteristics which we specify in the *Analytics*,[3] for it is when a man believes in a certain way and the starting-points are known to him that he has scientific knowledge, since if they are not better known to him than the conclusion, he will have his knowledge only incidentally.

Let this, then, be taken as our account of scientific knowledge.

4

1140a In the variable are included both things made and things done; making and acting are different (for their nature we treat even the discussions outside our school as reliable); so that the reasoned state of capacity to act is different from the reasoned state of capacity to make. Hence too they are not included one in the other; for neither is acting making nor is making acting. Now since architecture is an art and is essentially a reasoned state of capacity to make, and there is neither any art that is not such a state nor any such state that is not an art, *art* is identical with a state of capacity to make, involving a true course of reasoning. All art is concerned with coming into being, i.e. with contriving and considering how something may come into being which is capable of either being or not being, and whose origin is in the maker and not in the thing made; for art is concerned neither with things that are, or come into being, by necessity, nor with things that do so in accordance with nature (since these have their origin in themselves). Making and acting being different, art must be a matter of making, not of acting. And

[1] Fr. 5, Nauck.

[2] *Posterior Analytics*, 71a 1.

[3] *Ibid.*, b 9-23.

in a sense chance and art are concerned with the same objects; as Agathon says, 'art loves chance and chance loves art'. Art, then, as has been said,[1] is a state concerned with making, involving a true course of reasoning, and lack of art on the contrary is a state concerned with making, involving a false course of reasoning; both are concerned with the variable.

5

Regarding *practical wisdom* we shall get at the truth by considering who are the persons we credit with it. Now it is thought to be the mark of a man of practical wisdom to be able to deliberate well about what is good and expedient for himself, not in some particular respect, e.g. about what sorts of thing conduce to health or to strength, but about what sorts of thing conduce to the good life in general. This is shown by the fact that we credit men with practical wisdom in some particular respect when they have calculated well with a view to some good end which is one of those that are not the object of any art. It follows that in the general sense also the man who is capable of deliberating has practical wisdom. Now no one deliberates about things that are invariable, nor about things that it is impossible for him to do. Therefore, since scientific knowledge involves demonstration, but there is no demonstration of things whose first principles are variable (for all such things might actually be otherwise), and since it is impossible to deliberate about things that are of necessity, **1140b** practical wisdom cannot be scientific knowledge nor art; not science because that which can be done is capable of being otherwise, not art because action and making are different kinds of thing. The remaining alternative, then, is that it is a true and reasoned state of capacity to act with regard to the things that are good or bad for man. For while making has an end other than itself, action cannot; for good action itself is its end. It is for this reason that we think Pericles and men like him have practical wisdom, viz. because they can see what is good for themselves and what is good for men in general; we consider that those can do this who are good at managing households or states. (This is why we call temperance (σωφροσύνη) by this name; we imply that it preserves one's practical wisdom (σῴζουσα τὴν φρόνησιν). Now what it preserves is a judgement of the kind we have described. For it is not any and every judgement that pleasant and painful objects destroy and pervert, e.g. the judgement that the triangle has or has not its angles equal to two right angles, but only judgements about what is to be done. For the originating causes of the things that are done consist in the end at which they are aimed; but the man who has been ruined by pleasure or pain forthwith fails to see any such originating cause—to see that for the sake of this or because of this he ought to choose and do whatever he chooses and does; for vice is destructive of the originating cause of action.) Practical wisdom, then, must be a reasoned and true state of capacity to act with regard to human goods. But further, while there is such a thing as excellence in art, there is no such thing as excellence in practical wisdom; and in art he who errs willingly is preferable, but in practical wisdom, as in the virtues, he is the reverse. Plainly, then, practical wisdom is a virtue and not an art. There being two parts of the soul that can follow a course of reasoning, it must be the virtue of one of the two, i.e. of that part which forms opinions; for opinion is about the variable and so is practical wisdom. But yet it is not only a reasoned state; this is shown by the fact that a state of that sort may be forgotten but practical wisdom cannot.

[1] I. 9.

6

Scientific knowledge is judgement about things that are universal and necessary, and the conclusions of demonstration, and all scientific knowledge, follow from first principles (for scientific knowledge involves apprehension of a rational ground). This being so, the first principle from which what is scientifically known follows cannot be an object of scientific knowledge, of art, or of practical wisdom; for that which can be scientifically known can be demonstrated, and art and practical wisdom **1141a** deal with things that are variable. Nor are these first principles the objects of philosophic wisdom, for it is a mark of the philosopher to have *demonstration* about some things. If, then, the states of mind by which we have truth and are never deceived about things invariable or even variable are scientific knowledge, practical wisdom, philosophic wisdom, and intuitive reason, and it cannot be any of the three (i.e. practical wisdom, scientific knowledge, or philosophic wisdom), the remaining alternative is that it is *intuitive reason* that grasps the first principles.

7

Wisdom (1) in the arts we ascribe to their most finished exponents, e.g. to Phidias as a sculptor and to Polyclitus as a maker of portrait-statues, and here we mean nothing by wisdom except excellence in art; but (2) we think that some people are wise in general, not in some particular field or in any other limited respect, as Homer says in the *Margites*,[1]

Him did the gods make neither a digger nor yet a ploughman
Nor wise in anything else.

Therefore wisdom must plainly be the most finished of the forms of knowledge. It follows that the wise man must not only know what follows from the first principles, but must also possess truth about the first principles. Therefore wisdom must be intuitive reason combined with scientific knowledge—scientific knowledge of the highest objects which has received as it were its proper completion.

Of the highest objects, we say; for it would be strange to think that the art of politics, or practical wisdom, is the best knowledge, since man is not the best thing in the world. Now if what is healthy or good is different for men and for fishes, but what is white or straight is always the same, any one would say that what is wise is the same but what is practically wise is different; for it is to that which observes well the various matters concerning itself that one ascribes practical wisdom, and it is to this that one will entrust such matters. This is why we say that some even of the lower animals have practical wisdom, viz. those which are found to have a power of foresight with regard to their own life. It is evident also that philosophic wisdom and the art of politics cannot be the same; for if the state of mind concerned with a man's own interests is to be called philosophic wisdom, there will be many philosophic wisdoms; there will not be one concerned with the good of all animals (any more than there is one art of medicine for all existing things), but a different philosophic wisdom about the good of each species.

But if the argument be that man is the best of the animals, this makes no difference; for there are other things much more divine in
1141b their nature even than man, e.g., most conspicuously, the bodies of which the heavens are framed. From what has been said it is plain, then, that philosophic wisdom is scientific knowledge, combined with intuitive reason, of the things that are highest by nature. This is why we say Anaxagoras, Thales, and men like them have philosophic but not practical wisdom, when we see them ignorant of what is to their own advantage, and why we say that they know things that are remarkable, admirable, difficult, and divine, but useless; viz. because it is not human goods that they seek.

Practical wisdom on the other hand is concerned with things human and things about which it is possible to deliberate; for we say this is above all the work of the man of practical wisdom, to deliberate well; but no one deliberates about things invariable, nor about things which have not an end, and that a good that can be brought about by action. The man who is without qualification good at deliberating is the man who is capable of aiming in accordance with calculation at the best for man of things attainable by action. Nor is practical wisdom concerned with universals only—it must also recognize the particulars; for it is practical, and practice is concerned with particulars. This is why some who do not know, and especially those who have experience, are more practical than others who know; for if a man knew that light meats are digestible and wholesome, but did not know which sorts of meat are light, he would not produce health, but the man who knows that chicken is wholesome is more likely to produce health.

Now practical wisdom is concerned with action; therefore one should have both forms of it, or the latter in preference to the former. But of practical as of philosophic wisdom there must be a controlling kind.

8

Political wisdom and practical wisdom are the same state of mind, but their essence is not the same. Of the wisdom concerned with the city, the practical wisdom which plays a controlling part is legislative wisdom, while that which is related to this as particulars to their universal is known by the general name 'political wisdom'; this has to do with action and deliberation, for a decree is a thing to be carried out in the form of an individual act. This is why the exponents of this art are alone said to 'take part in politics'; for these alone 'do things' as manual labourers 'do things'.

Practical wisdom also is identified especially with that form of it which is concerned with a man himself—with the individual; and this is known by the general name 'practical wis-

[1] Fr. 2, Allen.

dom'; of the other kinds one is called household management, another legislation, the third politics, and of the latter one part is called deliberative and the other judicial. Now knowing what is good for oneself will be one kind
1142a of knowledge, but it is very different from the other kinds; and the man who knows and concerns himself with his own interests is thought to have practical wisdom, while politicians are thought to be busybodies; hence the word of Euripides,[1]

But how could I be wise, who might at ease,
Numbered among the army's multitude,
Have had an equal share? . . .
For those who aim too high and do too much . . .

Those who think thus seek their own good, and consider that one ought to do so. From this opinion, then, has come the view that such men have practical wisdom; yet perhaps one's own good cannot exist without household management, nor without a form of government. Further, how one should order one's own affairs is not clear and needs inquiry.

What has been said is confirmed by the fact that while young men become geometricians and mathematicians and wise in matters like these, it is thought that a young man of practical wisdom cannot be found. The cause is that such wisdom is concerned not only with universals but with particulars, which become familiar from experience, but a young man has no experience, for it is length of time that gives experience; indeed one might ask this question too, why a boy may become a mathematician, but not a philosopher or a physicist. It is because the objects of mathematics exist by abstraction, while the first principles of these other subjects come from experience, and because young men have no conviction about the latter but merely use the proper language, while the essence of mathematical objects is plain enough to them?

Further, error in deliberation may be either about the universal or about the particular; we may fail to know either that all water that weighs heavy is bad, or that this particular water weighs heavy.

That practical wisdom is not scientific knowledge is evident; for it is, as has been said,[2] concerned with the ultimate particular fact, since the thing to be done is of this nature. It is opposed, then, to intuitive reason; for intuitive reason is of the limiting premisses, for which no reason can be given, while practical wisdom is concerned with the ultimate particular, which is the object not of scientific knowledge but of perception—not the perception of qualities peculiar to one sense but a perception akin to that by which we perceive that the particular figure before us is a triangle; for in that direction as well as in that of the major premiss there will be a limit. But this is rather perception than practical wisdom, though it is another kind of perception than that of the qualities peculiar to each sense.

[1] Prologue to *Philoctetes*, Fr. 787, 782. 2, Nauck.
[2] 1141b 14-22.

9

There is a difference between inquiry and deliberation; for deliberation is inquiry into a particular kind of thing. We must grasp the nature of excellence in deliberation as well—whether it is a form of scientific knowledge, or opinion, or skill in conjecture, or some other kind of thing. *Scientific knowledge* it is not; for men do not inquire about the things they
1142b know about, but good deliberation is a kind of deliberation, and he who deliberates inquires and calculates. Nor is it *skill in conjecture*; for this both involves no reasoning and is something that is quick in its operation, while men deliberate a long time, and they say that one should carry out quickly the conclusions of one's deliberation, but should deliberate slowly. Again, *readiness of mind* is different from excellence in deliberation; it is a sort of skill in conjecture. Nor again is excellence in deliberation *opinion* of any sort. But since the man who deliberates badly makes a mistake, while he who deliberates well does so correctly, excellence in deliberation is clearly a kind of correctness, but neither of knowledge nor of opinion; for there is no such thing as correctness of knowledge (since there is no such thing as error of knowledge), and correctness of opinion is truth; and at the same time everything that is an object of opinion is already determined. But again excellence in deliberation involves reasoning. The remaining alternative, then, is that it is *correctness of thinking*; for this is not yet assertion, since, while even opinion is not inquiry but has reached the stage of assertion, the man who is deliberating, whether he does so well or ill, is searching for something and calculating.

But excellence in deliberation is a certain correctness of deliberation; hence we must first inquire what deliberation is and what it is about. And, there being more than one kind of correctness, plainly excellence in deliberation is not any and every kind; for (1) the incontinent man and the bad man, if he is clever, will reach as a result of his calculation what he sets before himself, so that he will have deliberated correctly, but he will have got for himself a great evil. Now to have deliberated well is thought to be a good thing; for it is this kind of correctness of deliberation that is excellence in deliberation, viz. that which tends to attain what is good. But (2) it is possible to attain even good by a false syllogism, and to attain what one ought to do but not by the right means, the middle term being false; so that this too is not yet excellence in deliberation—this state in virtue of which one attains what one ought but not by the right means. Again (3) it is possible to attain it by long deliberation while another man attains it quickly. Therefore in the former case we have not yet got excellence in deliberation, which is rightness with regard to the expedient—rightness in respect both of the end, the manner, and the time. (4) Further it is possible to have deliberated well either in the unqualified sense or with reference to a particular end. Excellence in deliberation in the unqualified sense, then, is that which succeeds with reference to what is the end in the unqualified sense, and excellence in deliberation in a particular sense is that which succeeds relatively to a particular end. If, then, it is characteristic of men of practical wisdom to have deliberated well, excellence in deliberation will be correctness with regard to what conduces to the end of which practical wisdom is the true apprehension.

10

Understanding, also, and goodness of understanding, in virtue of which men are said to be men of understanding or of good understand-
1143a ing, are neither entirely the same as opinion or scientific knowledge (for at that rate all men would have been men of understanding), nor are they one of the particular sciences, such as medicine, the science of things connected with health, or geometry, the science of spatial magnitudes. For understanding is neither about things that are always and are unchangeable, nor about any and every one of the things that come into being, but about things which may become subjects of questioning and deliberation. Hence it is about the same objects as practical wisdom; but understanding and practical wisdom are not the same. For practical wisdom issues commands, since its end is what ought to be done or not to be done; but understanding only judges. (Understanding is identical with goodness of understanding, men of understanding with men of good understanding.) Now understanding is neither the having nor the acquiring of practical wisdom; but as learning is called understanding when it means the exercise of the faculty of knowledge, so 'understanding' is applicable to the exercise of the faculty of opinion for the purpose of judging of what some one else says about matters with which practical wisdom is concerned—and of judging soundly; for 'well' and 'soundly' are the same thing. And from this has come the use of the name 'understanding' in virtue of which men are said to be 'of good understanding', viz. from the application of the word to the grasping of scientific truth; for we often call such grasping understanding.

11

What is called judgement, in virtue of which men are said to 'be sympathetic judges' and to 'have judgement', is the right discrimination of the equitable. This is shown by the fact that we say the equitable man is above all others a man of sympathetic judgement, and identify equity with sympathetic judgement about certain facts. And sympathetic judgement is judgement which discriminates what is equitable and does so correctly; and correct judgement is that which judges what is true.

Now all the states we have considered converge, as might be expected, to the same point; for when we speak of judgement and understanding and practical wisdom and intuitive reason we credit the same people with possessing judgement and having reached years of reason and with having practical wisdom and understanding. For all these faculties deal with ultimates, i.e. with particulars; and being a man of understanding and of good or sympathetic judgement consists in being able to judge about the things with which practical wisdom is concerned; for the equities are common to all good men in relation to other men. Now all things which have to be done are included among particulars or ultimates; for not only must the man of practical wisdom know particular facts, but understanding and judgement are also concerned with things to be done, and these are ultimates. And intuitive reason is concerned with the ultimates in both directions; for both the first terms and the last are objects of intuitive reason and not of

1143b argument, and the intuitive reason which is presupposed by demonstrations grasps the unchangeable and first terms, while the intuitive reason involved in practical reasonings grasps the last and variable fact, i.e. the minor premiss. For these variable facts are the starting-points for the apprehension of the end, since the universals are reached from the particulars; of these therefore we must have perception, and this perception is intuitive reason.

This is why these states are thought to be natural endowments—why, while no one is thought to be a philosopher by nature, people are thought to have by nature judgement, understanding, and intuitive reason. This is shown by the fact that we think our powers correspond to our time of life, and that a particular age brings with it intuitive reason and judgement; this implies that nature is the cause. [Hence intuitive reason is both beginning and end; for demonstrations are from these and about these.] Therefore we ought to attend to the undemonstrated sayings and opinions of experienced and older people or of people of practical wisdom not less than to demonstrations; for because experience has given them an eye they see aright.

We have stated, then, what practical and philosophic wisdom are, and with what each of them is concerned, and we have said that each is the virtue of a different part of the soul.

12

Difficulties might be raised as to the utility of these qualities of mind. For (1) philosophic wisdom will contemplate none of the things that will make a man happy (for it is not concerned with any coming into being), and though practical wisdom has *this* merit, for what purpose do we need it? Practical wisdom is the quality of mind concerned with things just and noble and good for man, but these are the things which it is the mark of a *good* man to do, and we are none the more able to act for *knowing* them if the virtues are states of *character*, just as we are none the better able to act for knowing the things that are healthy and sound, in the sense not of producing but of issuing from the state of health; for we are none the more able to act for having the art of medicine or of gymnastics. But (2) if we are to say that a man should have practical wisdom not for the sake of knowing moral truths but for the sake of becoming good, practical wisdom will be of no use to those who *are* good; but again it is of no use to those who have *not* virtue; for it will make no difference whether they have practical wisdom themselves or obey others who have it, and it would be enough for us to do what we do in the case of health; though we wish to become healthy, yet we do not learn the art of medicine. (3) Besides this, it would be thought strange if practical wisdom, being inferior to philosophic wisdom, is to be put in authority over it, as seems to be implied by the fact that the art which produces anything rules and issues commands about that thing.

These, then, are the questions we must discuss; so far we have only stated the difficulties.

1144a (1) Now first let us say that in themselves these states must be worthy of choice because they are the virtues of the two parts of the soul respectively, even if neither of them produce anything.

(2) Secondly, they do produce something, not as the art of medicine produces health, however, but as health produces health; so does philosophic wisdom produce happiness; for, being a part of virtue entire, by being possessed and by actualizing itself it makes a man happy.

(3) Again, the work of man is achieved only in accordance with practical wisdom as well as with moral virtue; for virtue makes us aim at the right mark, and practical wisdom makes us take the right means. (Of the fourth part of the soul—the nutritive—there is no such virtue; for there is nothing which it is in its power to do or not to do.)

(4) With regard to our being none the more able to do because of our practical wisdom what is noble and just, let us begin a little further back, starting with the following principle. As we say that some people who do just acts are not necessarily just, i.e. those who do the acts ordained by the laws either unwillingly or owing to ignorance or for some other reason and not for the sake of the acts themselves (though, to be sure, they do what they should and all the things that the good man ought), so is it, it seems, that in order to be good one must be in a certain state when one does the several acts, i.e. one must do them as a result of choice and for the sake of the acts themselves. Now virtue makes the choice right, but the question of the things which should naturally be done to carry out our choice belongs not to virtue but to another faculty. We

must devote our attention to these matters and give a clearer statement about them. There is a faculty which is called cleverness; and this is such as to be able to do the things that tend towards the mark we have set before ourselves, and to hit it. Now if the mark be noble, the cleverness is laudable, but if the mark be bad, the cleverness is mere smartness; hence we call even men of practical wisdom clever or smart. Practical wisdom is not the faculty, but it does not exist without this faculty. And this eye of the soul acquires its formed state not without the aid of virtue, as has been said[1] and is plain; for the syllogisms which deal with acts to be done are things which involve a starting-point, viz. 'since the end, i.e. what is best, is of such and such a nature', whatever it may be (let it for the sake of argument be what we please); and this is not evident except to the good man; for wickedness perverts us and causes us to be deceived about the starting-points of action. Therefore it is evident that it is impossible to be practically wise without being good.

13

1144b We must therefore consider virtue also once more; for virtue too is similarly related; as practical wisdom is to cleverness—not the same, but like it—so is natural virtue to virtue in the strict sense. For all men think that each type of character belongs to its possessors in some sense by nature; for from the very moment of birth we are just or fitted for self-control or brave or have the other moral qualities; but yet we seek something else as that which is good in the strict sense—we seek for the presence of such qualities in another way. For both children and brutes have the natural dispositions to these qualities, but without reason these are evidently hurtful. Only we seem to see this much, that, while one may be led astray by them, as a strong body which moves without sight may stumble badly because of its lack of sight, still, if a man once acquires reason, that makes a difference in action; and his state, while still like what it was, will then be virtue in the strict sense. Therefore, as in the part of us which forms opinions there are two types, cleverness and practical wisdom, so too in the moral part there are two types, natural virtue and virtue in the strict sense, and of these the latter involves practical wisdom. This is why some say that all the virtues are forms of practical wisdom, and why Socrates in one respect was on the right track while in another he went astray; in thinking that all the virtues were forms of practical wisdom he was wrong, but in saying they implied practical wisdom he was right. This is confirmed by the fact that even now all men, when they define virtue, after naming the state of character and its objects add 'that (state) which is in accordance with the right rule'; now the right rule is that which is in accordance with practical wisdom. All men, then, seem somehow to divine that this kind of state is virtue, viz. that which is in accordance with practical wisdom. But we must go a little further. For it is not merely the state in accordance with the right rule, but the state that implies the *presence* of the right rule, that is virtue; and practical wisdom is a right rule about such matters. Socrates, then, thought the virtues were rules or rational principles (for he thought they were, all of them, forms of scientific knowledge), while we think they *involve* a rational principle.

It is clear, then, from what has been said, that it is not possible to be good in the strict sense without practical wisdom, nor practically wise without moral virtue. But in this way we may also refute the dialectical argument whereby it might be contended that the virtues exist in separation from each other; the same man, it might be said, is not best equipped by nature for all the virtues, so that he will have already acquired one when he has not yet acquired another. This is possible in respect of the natural virtues, but not in respect of those in respect of which a man is called without qualification
1145a good; for with the presence of the one quality, practical wisdom, will be given all the virtues. And it is plain that, even if it were of no practical value, we should have needed it because it is the virtue of the part of us in question; plain too that the choice will not be right without practical wisdom any more than without virtue; for the one determines the end and the other makes us do the things that lead to the end.

But again it is not *supreme* over philosophic wisdom, i.e. over the superior part of us, any more than the art of medicine is over health; for it does not use it but provides for its coming into being; it issues orders, then, for its sake, but not to it. Further, to maintain its supremacy would be like saying that the art of politics rules the gods because it issues orders about all the affairs of the state.

[1] ll. 6–26.

BOOK VII

1

1145a LET us now make a fresh beginning and point out that of moral states to be avoided there are three kinds—vice, incontinence, brutishness. The contraries of two of these are evident—one we call virtue, the other continence; to brutishness it would be most fitting to oppose superhuman virtue, a heroic and divine kind of virtue, as Homer has represented Priam saying of Hector that he was very good,

> *For he seemed not, he,*
> *The child of a mortal man, but as one that of God's seed came.*[1]

Therefore if, as they say, men become gods by excess of virtue, of this kind must evidently be the state opposed to the brutish state; for as a brute has no vice or virtue, so neither has a god; his state is higher than virtue, and that of a brute is a different kind of state from vice.

Now, since it is rarely that a godlike man is found—to use the epithet of the Spartans, who when they admire any one highly call him a 'godlike man'—so too the brutish type is rarely found among men; it is found chiefly among barbarians, but some brutish qualities are also produced by disease or deformity; and we also call by this evil name those men who go beyond all ordinary standards by reason of vice. Of this kind of disposition, however, we must later make some mention,[2] while we have discussed vice before;[3] we must now discuss incontinence and softness (or effeminacy), and continence and endurance; for we must **1145b** treat each of the two neither as identical with virtue or wickedness, nor as a different genus. We must, as in all other cases, set the observed facts before us and, after first discussing the difficulties, go on to prove, if possible, the truth of all the common opinions about these affections of the mind, or, failing this, of the greater number and the most authoritative; for if we both refute the objections and leave the common opinions undisturbed, we shall have proved the case sufficiently.

Now (1) both continence and endurance are thought to be included among things good and praiseworthy, and both incontinence and softness among things bad and blameworthy; and the same man is thought to be continent

[1] *Iliad*, XXIV. 258 ff. [2] Chapter 5. [3] II–IV.

and ready to abide by the result of his calculations, or incontinent and ready to abandon them. And (2) the incontinent man, knowing that what he does is bad, does it as a result of passion, while the continent man, knowing that his appetites are bad, refuses on account of his rational principle to follow them. (3) The temperate man all men call continent and disposed to endurance, while the continent man some maintain to be always temperate but others do not; and some call the self-indulgent man incontinent and the incontinent man self-indulgent indiscriminately, while others distinguish them. (4) The man of practical wisdom, they sometimes say, cannot be incontinent, while sometimes they say that some who are practically wise and clever *are* incontinent. Again (5) men are said to be incontinent even with respect to anger, honour, and gain. —These, then, are the things that are said.

2

Now we may ask (1) how a man who judges rightly can behave incontinently. That he should behave so when he has knowledge, some say is impossible; for it would be strange —so Socrates[4] thought—if when knowledge was in a man something else could master it and drag it about like a slave. For *Socrates* was entirely opposed to the view in question, holding that there is no such thing as incontinence; no one, he said, when he judges acts against what he judges best—people act so only by reason of ignorance. Now this view plainly contradicts the observed facts, and we must inquire about what happens to such a man; if he acts by reason of ignorance, what is the manner of his ignorance? For that the man who behaves incontinently does not, before he gets into this state, *think* he ought to act so, is evident. But there are *some* who concede certain of Socrates' contentions but not others; that nothing is stronger than knowledge they admit, but not that on one acts contrary to what has seemed to him the better course, and therefore they say that the incontinent man has not knowledge when he is mastered by his pleasures, but opinion. But *if* it is opinion and not knowledge, if it is not a strong conviction that resists but a weak one, as in men who hesi- **1146a** tate, we sympathize with their failure to stand by such convictions against strong ap-

[4] Plato, *Protagoras*, 352.

petites; but we do not sympathize with wickedness, nor with any of the other blameworthy states. Is it then *practical wisdom* whose resistance is mastered? That is the strongest of all states. But this is absurd; the same man will be at once practically wise and incontinent, but *no one* would say that it is the part of a practically wise man to do willingly the basest acts. Besides, it has been shown before that the man of practical wisdom is one who will *act* (for he is a man concerned with the individual facts) and who has the other virtues.

(2) Further, if continence involves having strong and bad appetites, the temperate man will not be continent nor the continent man temperate; for a temperate man will have neither excessive nor bad appetites. But the continent man *must*; for if the appetites are good, the state of character that restrains us from following them is bad, so that not all continence will be good; while if they are weak and not bad, there is nothing admirable in resisting them, and if they are weak and bad, there is nothing great in resisting these either.

(3) Further, if continence makes a man ready to stand by any and every opinion, it is bad, i.e. if it makes him stand even by a false opinion; and if incontinence makes a man apt to abandon any and every opinion, there will be a good incontinence, of which Sophocles' Neoptolemus in the *Philoctetes* will be an instance; for he is to be praised for not standing by what Odysseus persuaded him to do, because he is pained at telling a lie.

(4) Further, the sophistic argument presents a difficulty; the syllogism arising from men's wish to expose paradoxical results arising from an opponent's view, in order that they may be admired when they succeed, is one that puts us in a difficulty (for thought is bound fast when it will not rest because the conclusion does not satisfy it, and cannot advance because it cannot refute the argument). There is an argument from which it follows that folly coupled with incontinence is virtue; for a man does the opposite of what he judges, owing to incontinence, but judges what is good to be evil and something that he should not do, and in consequence he will do what is good and not what is evil.

(5) Further, he who on conviction does and pursues and chooses what is pleasant would be thought to be better than one who does so as a result not of calculation but of incontinence; for he is easier to cure since he may be persuaded to change his mind. But to the incontinent man may be applied the proverb 'when water chokes, what is one to wash it down with?' If he had been persuaded of the rightness of what he does, he would have de-
1146b sisted when he was persuaded to change his mind; but now he acts in spite of his being persuaded of something quite different.

(6) Further, if incontinence and continence are concerned with any and every kind of object, who is it that is incontinent in the unqualified sense? No one has all the forms of incontinence, but we say some people are incontinent without qualification.

3

Of some such kind are the difficulties that arise; some of these points must be refuted and the others left in possession of the field; for the solution of the difficulty is the discovery of the truth. (1) We must consider first, then, whether incontinent people act knowingly or not, and in what sense knowingly; then (2) with what sorts of object the incontinent and the continent man may be said to be concerned (i.e. whether with any and every pleasure and pain or with certain determinate kinds), and whether the continent man and the man of endurance are the same or different; and similarly with regard to the other matters germane to this inquiry. The starting-point of our investigation is (*a*) the question whether the continent man and the incontinent are differentiated by their objects or by their attitude, i.e. whether the incontinent man is incontinent simply by being concerned with such and such objects, or, instead, by his attitude, or, instead of that, by both these things; (*b*) the second question is whether incontinence and continence are concerned with any and every object or not. The man who is incontinent in the unqualified sense is neither concerned with any and every object, but with precisely those with which the self-indulgent man is concerned, nor is he characterized by being simply related to these (for then his state would be the same as self-indulgence), but by being related to them in a certain way. For the one is led on in accordance with his own choice, thinking that he ought always to pursue the present pleasure; while the other does not think so, but yet pursues it.

(1) As for the suggestion that it is true opinion and not knowledge against which we act incontinently, that makes no difference to the argument; for some people when in a

state of opinion do not hesitate, but think they know exactly. If, then, the notion is that owing to their weak conviction those who have opinion are more likely to act against their judgement than those who know, we answer that there need be no difference between knowledge and opinion in this respect; for some men are no less convinced of what they think than others of what they know; as is shown by the case of Heraclitus. But (*a*), since we use the word 'know' in two senses (for both the man who has knowledge but is not using it and he who is using it are said to know), it *will* make a difference whether, when a man does what he should not, he has the knowledge but is not exercising it, or *is* exercising it; for the latter seems strange, but not the former.

(*b*) Further, since there are two kinds of premisses, there is nothing to prevent a **1147a** man's having both premisses and acting against his knowledge, provided that he is using only the universal premiss and not the particular; for it is particular acts that have to be done. And there are also two kinds of universal term; one is predicable of the agent, the other of the object; e.g. 'dry food is good for every man', and 'I am a man', or 'such and such food is dry'; but whether 'this food is such and such', of this the incontinent man either has not or is not exercising the knowledge. There will, then, be, firstly, an enormous difference between these manners of knowing, so that to know in one way when we act incontinently would not seem anything strange, while to know in the other way would be extraordinary.

And further (*c*) the possession of knowledge in another sense than those just named is something that happens to men; for within the case of having knowledge but not using it we see a difference of state, admitting of the possibility of having knowledge in a sense and yet not having it, as in the instance of a man asleep, mad, or drunk. But now this is just the condition of men under the influence of passions; for outbursts of anger and sexual appetites and some other such passions, it is evident, actually alter our bodily condition, and in some men even produce fits of madness. It is plain, then, that incontinent people must be said to be in a similar condition to men asleep, mad, or drunk. The fact that men use the language that flows from knowledge proves nothing; for even men under the influence of these passions utter scientific proofs and verses of Empedocles, and those who have just begun to learn a science can string together its phrases, but do not yet know it; for it has to become part of themselves, and that takes time; so that we must suppose that the use of language by men in an incontinent state means no more than its utterance by actors on the stage.

(*d*) Again, we may also view the cause as follows with reference to the facts of human nature. The one opinion is universal, the other is concerned with the particular facts, and here we come to something within the sphere of perception; when a single opinion results from the two, the soul must in one type of case affirm the conclusion, while in the case of opinions concerned with production it must immediately act (e.g. if 'everything sweet ought to be tasted', and 'this is sweet', in the sense of being one of the particular sweet things, the man who can act and is not prevented must at the same time actually act accordingly). When, then, the universal opinion is present in us forbidding us to taste, and there is also the opinion that 'everything sweet is pleasant', and that 'this is sweet' (now this is the opinion that is active), and when appetite happens to be present in us, the one opinion bids us avoid the object, but appetite leads us towards it (for it can move each of our bodily parts); so that it turns out that a man behaves incontinently under the influence (in a sense) of a rule and an opinion, and of **1147b** one not contrary in itself, but only incidentally—for the appetite is contrary, not the opinion—to the right rule. It also follows that this is the reason why the lower animals are not incontinent, viz. because they have no universal judgement but only imagination and memory of particulars.

The explanation of how the ignorance is dissolved and the incontinent man regains his knowledge, is the same as in the case of the man drunk or asleep and is not peculiar to this condition; we must go to the students of natural science for it. Now, the last premiss both being an opinion about a perceptible object, and being what determines our actions, this a man either has not when he is in the state of passion, or has it in the sense in which having knowledge did not mean knowing but only talking, as a drunken man may utter the verses of Empedocles. And because the last term is not universal nor equally an object of scientific knowledge with the universal term, the position that Socrates sought to establish actually seems to result; for it is not in the presence of what is thought to be knowledge proper that the affection of incontinence arises (nor is it this that is 'dragged about' as a result of the state of passion), but in that of perceptual knowledge.

This must suffice as our answer to the question of action with and without knowledge, and how it is possible to behave incontinently with knowledge.

4

(2) We must next discuss whether there is any one who is incontinent without qualification, or all men who are incontinent are so in a particular sense, and if there is, with what sort of objects he is concerned. That both continent persons and persons of endurance, and incontinent and soft persons, are concerned with pleasures and pains, is evident.

Now of the things that produce pleasure some are necessary, while others are worthy of choice in themselves but admit of excess, the bodily causes of pleasure being necessary (by such I mean both those concerned with food and those concerned with sexual intercourse, i.e. the bodily matters with which we defined[1] self-indulgence and temperance as being concerned), while the others are not necessary but worthy of choice in themselves (e.g. victory, honour, wealth, and good and pleasant things of this sort). This being so, (*a*) those who go to excess with reference to the latter, contrary to the right rule which is in themselves, are not called incontinent simply, but incontinent with the qualification 'in respect of money, gain, honour, or anger',—not simply incontinent, on the ground that they are different from incontinent people and are called incontinent by reason of a resemblance. (Compare the case of Anthrōpos (Man), who won a contest at the Olympic games; in his case **1148a** the general definition of man differed little from the definition peculiar to *him,* but yet it *was* different.) This is shown by the fact that incontinence either without qualification or in respect of some particular bodily pleasure is blamed not only as a fault but as a kind of vice, while none of the people who are incontinent in these other respects is so blamed.

But (*b*) of the people who are incontinent with respect to bodily enjoyments, with which we say the temperate and the self-indulgent man are concerned, he who pursues the excesses of things pleasant—and shuns those of things painful, of hunger and thirst and heat and cold and all the objects of touch and taste—not by choice but contrary to his choice and his judgement, is called incontinent, not with the qualification 'in respect of this or that', e.g. of anger, but just simply. This is confirmed by the fact that men are called 'soft' with regard to these pleasures, but not with regard to any of the others. And for this reason we group together the incontinent and the self-indulgent, the continent and the temperate man—but not any of these other types—because they are concerned somehow with the same pleasures and pains; but though these are concerned with the same objects, they are not similarly related to them, but some of them make a deliberate choice while the others do not.

This is why we should describe as self-indulgent rather the man who without appetite or with but a slight appetite pursues the excesses of pleasure and avoids moderate pains, than the man who does so because of his strong appetites; for what would the former do, if he had in addition a vigorous appetite, and a violent pain at the lack of the 'necessary' objects?

Now of appetites and pleasures some belong to the class of things generically noble and good—for some pleasant things are by nature worthy of choice, while others are contrary to these, and others are intermediate, to adopt our previous distinction—e.g. wealth, gain, victory, honour. And with reference to all objects whether of this or of the intermediate kind men are not blamed for being affected by them, for desiring and loving them, but for doing so in a certain way, i.e. for going to excess. (This is why all those who contrary to the rule either are mastered by or pursue one of the objects which are naturally noble and good, e.g. those who busy themselves more than they ought about honour or about children and parents, ⟨are not wicked⟩; for these too are good, and those who busy themselves about them are praised; but yet there is an excess even in them—if like Niobe one were to fight even against the gods, or were to be as much devoted **1148b** to one's father as Satyrus nicknamed 'the filial', who was thought to be very silly on this point.) There is no wickedness, then, with regard to these objects, for the reason named, viz. because each of them is by nature a thing worthy of choice for its own sake; yet excesses in respect of them are bad and to be avoided. Similarly there is no incontinence with regard to them; for incontinence is not only to be avoided but is also a thing worthy of blame; but owing to a similarity in the state of feeling people apply the name incontinence, adding in

[1] III. 10.

each case what it is in respect of, as we may describe as a bad doctor or a bad actor one whom we should not call bad, simply. As, then, in this case we do not apply the term without qualification because each of these conditions is not badness but only analogous to it, so it is clear that in the other case also that alone must be taken to be incontinence and continence which is concerned with the same objects as temperance and self-indulgence, but we apply the term to anger by virtue of a resemblance; and this is why we say with a qualification 'incontinent in respect of anger' as we say 'incontinent in respect of honour, or of gain'.

5

(1) Some things are pleasant by nature, and of these (*a*) some are so without qualification, and (*b*) others are so with reference to particular classes either of animals or of men; while (2) others are not pleasant by nature, but (*a*) some of them become so by reason of injuries to the system, and (*b*) others by reason of acquired habits, and (*c*) others by reason of originally bad natures. This being so, it is possible with regard to each of the latter kinds to discover similar states of character to those recognized with regard to the former; I mean (A) the brutish states, as in the case of the female who, they say, rips open pregnant women and devours the infants, or of the things in which some of the tribes about the Black Sea that have gone savage are said to delight—in raw meat or in human flesh, or in lending their children to one another to feast upon—or of the story told of Phalaris.

These states are brutish, but (B) others arise as a result of disease (or, in some cases, of madness, as with the man who sacrificed and ate his mother, or with the slave who ate the liver of his fellow), and others are morbid states (C) resulting from custom, e.g. the habit of plucking out the hair or of gnawing the nails, or even coals or earth, and in addition to these paederasty; for these arise in some by nature and in others, as in those who have been the victims of lust from childhood, from habit.

Now those in whom nature is the cause of such a state no one would call incontinent, any more than one would apply the epithet to women because of the passive part they play in copulation; nor would one apply it to those who are in a morbid condition as a result of habit. To have these various types of habit is beyond the
1149ª limits of vice, as brutishness is too; for a man who has them to master or be mastered by them is not simple ⟨continence or⟩ incontinence but that which is so by analogy, as the man who is in this condition in respect of fits of anger is to be called incontinent in respect of that feeling, but not incontinent simply. For every excessive state whether of folly, of cowardice, of self-indulgence, or of bad temper, is either brutish or morbid; the man who is by nature apt to fear everything, even the squeak of a mouse, is cowardly with a brutish cowardice, while the man who feared a weasel did so in consequence of disease; and of foolish people those who by nature are thoughtless and live by their senses alone are brutish, like some races of the distant barbarians, while those who are so as a result of disease (e.g. of epilepsy) or of madness are morbid. Of these characteristics it is possible to have some only at times, and not to be mastered by them. e.g. Phalaris may have restrained a desire to eat the flesh of a child or an appetite for unnatural sexual pleasure; but it is also possible to be mastered, not merely to have the feelings. Thus, as the wickedness which is on the human level is called wickedness simply, while that which is not is called wickedness not simply but with the qualification 'brutish' or 'morbid', in the same way it is plain that some incontinence is brutish and some morbid, while only that which corresponds to *human* self-indulgence is incontinence simply.

That incontinence and continence, then, are concerned only with the same objects as self-indulgence and temperance and that what is concerned with other objects is a type distinct from incontinence, and called incontinence by a metaphor and not simply, is plain.

6

That incontinence in respect of anger is less disgraceful than that in respect of the appetites is what we will now proceed to see. (1) Anger seems to listen to argument to some extent, but to mishear it, as do hasty servants who run out before they have heard the whole of what one says, and then muddle the order, or as dogs bark if there is but a knock at the door, before looking to see if it is a friend; so anger by reason of the warmth and hastiness of its nature, though it hears, does not hear an order, and springs to take revenge. For argument or imagination informs us that we have been insulted or slighted, and anger, reasoning as it were that anything like this must be fought against, boils up straightway; while appetite, if argument or perception merely says that an object is pleasant, springs to the enjoyment **1149b** of it. Therefore anger obeys the argument in a sense, but appetite does not. It is therefore more disgraceful; for the man who is incontinent in respect of anger is in a sense conquered by argument, while the other is conquered by appetite and not by argument.

(2) Further, we pardon people more easily for following natural desires, since we pardon them more easily for following such appetites as are common to all men, and in so far as they are common; now anger and bad temper are more natural than the appetites for excess, i.e. for unnecessary objects. Take for instance the man who defended himself on the charge of striking his father by saying 'yes, but *he* struck *his* father, and *he* struck *his,* and' (pointing to his child) 'this boy will strike *me* when he is a man; it runs in the family'; or the man who when he was being dragged along by his son bade him stop at the doorway, since he himself had dragged his father only as far as that.

(3) Further, those who are more given to plotting against others are more criminal. Now a passionate man is not given to plotting, nor is anger itself—it is open; but the nature of appetite is illustrated by what the poets call Aphrodite, 'guile-weaving daughter of Cyprus', and by Homer's words about her 'embroidered girdle':

> *And the whisper of wooing is there,*
> *Whose subtlety stealeth the wits of the wise, how prudent soe'er.*[1]

Therefore if this form of incontinence is more criminal and disgraceful than that in respect of anger, it is both incontinence without qualification and in a sense vice.

(4) Further, no one commits wanton outrage with a feeling of pain, but every one who acts in anger acts with pain, while the man who commits outrage acts with pleasure. If, then, those acts at which it is most just to be angry are more criminal than others, the incontinence which is due to appetite is the more criminal; for there is no wanton outrage involved in anger.

Plainly, then, the incontinence concerned with appetite is more disgraceful than that concerned with anger, and continence and incontinence are concerned with bodily appetites and pleasures; but we must grasp the differences among the latter themselves. For, as has been said at the beginning,[2] some are human and natural both in kind and in magnitude, others are brutish, and others are due to organic injuries and diseases. Only with the first of these are temperance and self-indulgence concerned; this is why we call the lower animals neither temperate nor self-indulgent except by a metaphor, and only if some one race of animals exceeds another as a whole in wantonness, destructiveness, and omnivorous greed; these have no power of choice or calculation, but they *are* departures from the natural norm, as, among men, madmen are. **1150a** Now brutishness is a less evil than vice, though more alarming; for it is not that the better part has been perverted, as in man,—they *have* no better part. Thus it is like comparing a lifeless thing with a living in respect of badness; for the badness of that which has no originative source of movement is always less hurtful, and reason is an originative source. Thus it is like comparing injustice in the abstract with an unjust man. Each is in some sense worse; for a bad man will do ten thousand times as much evil as a brute.

7

With regard to the pleasures and pains and appetites and aversions arising through touch and taste, to which both self-indulgence and temperance were formerly narrowed down,[3] it is possible to be in such a state as to be defeated even by those of them which most people master, or to master even those by which most people are defeated; among these possibilities, those relating to pleasures are incontinence and continence, those relating to pains softness and endurance. The state of most people is intermediate, even if they lean more towards the worse states.

Now, since some pleasures are necessary while others are not, and are necessary up to a point while the excesses of them are not, nor the deficiencies, and this is equally true of appetites and pains, the man who pursues the excesses of things pleasant, or pursues to excess necessary objects, and does so by choice, for their own sake and not at all for the sake of any result distinct from them, is self-indulgent; for such a man is of necessity unlikely to repent, and therefore incurable, since a man who cannot repent cannot be cured. The man who is deficient in his pursuit of them is the

[1] *Iliad*, XIV. 214, 217.

[2] 1148b 15–31.

[3] III. 10.

opposite of self-indulgent; the man who is intermediate is temperate. Similarly, there is the man who avoids bodily pains not because he is defeated by them but by choice. (Of those who do not *choose* such acts, one kind of man is led to them as a result of the pleasure involved, another because he avoids the pain arising from the appetite, so that these types differ from one another. Now any one would think worse of a man with no appetite or with weak appetite were he to do something disgraceful, than if he did it under the influence of powerful appetite, and worse of him if he struck a blow not in anger than if he did it in anger; for what would he have done if he *had* been strongly affected? This is why the self-indulgent man is worse than the incontinent.) Of the states named, then, the latter is rather a kind of softness; the former is self-indulgence. While to the incontinent man is opposed the continent, to the soft is opposed the man of endurance; for endurance consists in resisting, while continence consists in conquering, and resisting and conquering are different, as not being beaten is different from winning; this is why continence is also more worthy of **1150b** choice than endurance. Now the man who is defective in respect of resistance to the things which most men both resist and resist successfully is soft and effeminate; for effeminacy too is a kind of softness; such a man trails his cloak to avoid the pain of lifting it, and plays the invalid without thinking himself wretched, though the man he imitates is a wretched man.

The case is similar with regard to continence and incontinence. For if a man is defeated by violent and excessive pleasures or pains, there is nothing wonderful in that; indeed we are ready to pardon him if he has resisted, as Theodectes' Philoctetes does when bitten by the snake, or Carcinus' Cercyon in the *Alope,* and as people who try to restrain their laughter burst out into a guffaw, as happened to Xenophantus. But it is surprising if a man is defeated by and cannot resist pleasures or pains which most men can hold out against, when this is not due to heredity or disease, like the softness that is hereditary with the kings of the Scythians, or that which distinguishes the female sex from the male.

The lover of amusement, too, is thought to be self-indulgent, but is really soft. For amusement is a relaxation, since it is a rest from work; and the lover of amusement is one of the people who go to excess in this.

Of incontinence one kind is impetuosity, another weakness. For some men after deliberating fail, owing to their emotion, to stand by the conclusions of their deliberation, others because they have not deliberated are led by their emotion; since some men (just as people who first tickle others are not tickled themselves), if they have first perceived and seen what is coming and have first roused themselves and their calculative faculty, are not defeated by their emotion, whether it be pleasant or painful. It is keen and excitable people that suffer especially from the impetuous form of incontinence; for the former by reason of their quickness and the latter by reason of the violence of their passions do not await the argument, because they are apt to follow their imagination.

8

The self-indulgent man, as was said,[1] is not apt to repent; for he stands by his choice; but any incontinent man is likely to repent. This is why the position is not as it was expressed in the formulation of the problem, but the self-indulgent man is incurable and the incontinent man curable; for wickedness is like a disease such as dropsy or consumption, while incontinence is like epilepsy; the former is a permanent, the latter an intermittent badness. And generally incontinence and vice are different in kind; vice is unconscious of itself, incon- **1151a** tinence is not (of incontinent men themselves, those who become temporarily beside themselves are better than those who have the rational principle but do not abide by it, since the latter are defeated by a weaker passion, and do not act without previous deliberation like the others); for the incontinent man is like the people who get drunk quickly and on little wine, i.e. on less than most people.

Evidently, then, incontinence is not vice (though perhaps it is so in a qualified sense); for incontinence is contrary to choice while vice is in accordance with choice; not but what they are similar in respect of the actions they lead to; as in the saying of Demodocus about the Milesians, 'the Milesians are not without sense, but they do the things that senseless people do', so too incontinent people are not criminal, but they will do criminal acts.

Now, since the incontinent man is apt to pursue, not on conviction, bodily pleasures that are excessive and contrary to the right rule, while the self-indulgent man is convinced be-

[1] a 21.

cause he is the sort of man to pursue them, it is on the contrary the former that is easily persuaded to change his mind, while the latter is not. For virtue and vice respectively preserve and destroy the first principle, and in actions the final cause is the first principle, as the hypotheses are in mathematics; neither in that case is it argument that teaches the first principles, nor is it so here—virtue either natural or produced by habituation is what teaches right opinion about the first principle. Such a man as this, then, is temperate; his contrary is the self-indulgent.

But there is a sort of man who is carried away as a result of passion and contrary to the right rule—a man whom passion masters so that he does not act according to the right rule, but does not master to the extent of making him ready to believe that he ought to pursue such pleasures without reserve; this is the incontinent man, who is better than the self-indulgent man, and not bad without qualification; for the best thing in him, the first principle, is preserved. And contrary to him is another kind of man, he who abides by his convictions and is not carried away, at least as a result of passion. It is evident from these considerations that the latter is a good state and the former a bad one.

9

Is the man continent who abides by any and every rule and any and every choice, or the man who abides by the right choice, and is he incontinent who abandons any and every choice and any and every rule, or he who abandons the rule that is not false and the choice that is right; this is how we put it before in our statement of the problem.[1] Or is it incidentally any and every choice but *per se* the true rule and the right choice by which the one abides and the other does not? If any one chooses or pursues this for the sake of that, *per se* he **1151b** pursues and chooses the latter, but incidentally the former. But when we speak without qualification we mean what is *per se*. Therefore in a sense the one abides by, and the other abandons, any and every opinion; but without qualification, the true opinion.

There are some who are apt to abide by their opinion, who are called strong-headed, viz. those who are hard to persuade in the first instance and are not easily persuaded to change; these have in them something like the continent man, as the prodigal is in a way like the liberal man and the rash man like the confident man; but they are different in many respects. For it is to passion and appetite that the one will not yield, since on occasion the continent man *will* be easy to persuade; but it is to argument that the others refuse to yield, for they do form appetites and many of them are led by their pleasures. Now the people who are strong-headed are the opinionated, the ignorant, and the boorish—the opinionated being influenced by pleasure and pain; for they delight in the victory they gain if they are not persuaded to change, and are pained if their decisions become null and void as decrees sometimes do; so that they are liker the incontinent than the continent man.

But there are some who fail to abide by their resolutions, not as a result of incontinence, e.g. Neoptolemus in Sophocles' *Philoctetes;* yet it was for the sake of pleasure that he did not stand fast—but a noble pleasure; for telling the truth was noble to him, but he had been persuaded by Odysseus to tell the lie. For not every one who does anything for the sake of pleasure is either self-indulgent or bad or incontinent, but he who does it for a disgraceful pleasure.

Since there is also a sort of man who takes less delight than he should in bodily things, and does not abide by the rule, he who is intermediate between him and the incontinent man is the continent man; for the incontinent man fails to abide by the rule because he delights too much in them, and this man because he delights in them too little; while the continent man abides by the rule and does not change on either account. Now if continence is good, both the contrary states must be bad, as they actually appear to be; but because the other extreme is seen in few people and seldom, as temperance is thought to be contrary only to self-indulgence, so is continence to incontinence.

Since many names are applied analogically, it is by analogy that we have come to speak of the 'continence' of the temperate man; for both the continent man and the temperate man are such as to do nothing contrary to the rule for **1152a** the sake of the bodily pleasures, but the former has and the latter has not bad appetites, and the latter is such as not to feel pleasure contrary to the rule, while the former is such as to feel pleasure but not to be led by it. And the incontinent and the self-indulgent man are also like another; they are different but both pursue bodily pleasures—the lat-

[1] 1146a 16–31.

ter, however, also thinking that he ought to do so, while the former does not think this.

10

Nor can the same man have practical wisdom and be incontinent; for it has been shown[1] that a man is at the same time practically wise, and good in respect of character. Further, a man has practical wisdom not by knowing only but by being able to act; but the incontinent man is unable to act—there is, however, nothing to prevent a *clever* man from being incontinent; this is why it is sometimes actually thought that some people have practical wisdom but are incontinent, viz. because cleverness and practical wisdom differ in the way we have described in our first discussions,[2] and are near together in respect of their reasoning, but differ in respect of their purpose—nor yet is the incontinent man like the man who knows and is contemplating a truth, but like the man who is asleep or drunk. And he acts willingly (for he acts in a sense with knowledge both of what he does and of the end to which he does it), but is not wicked, since his purpose is good; so that he is half-wicked. And he is not a criminal; for he does not act of malice aforethought; of the two types of incontinent man the one does not abide by the conclusions of his deliberation, while the excitable man does not deliberate at all. And thus the incontinent man is like a city which passes all the right decrees and has good laws, but makes no use of them, as in Anaxandrides' jesting remark,[3]

The city willed it, that cares nought for laws;

but the wicked man is like a city that uses its laws, but has wicked laws to use.

Now incontinence and continence are concerned with that which is in excess of the state characteristic of most men; for the continent man abides by his resolutions more and the incontinent man less than most men can.

Of the forms of incontinence, that of excitable people is more curable than that of those who deliberate but do not abide by their decisions, and those who are incontinent through habituation are more curable than those in whom incontinence is innate; for it is easier to change a habit than to change one's nature; even habit is hard to change just because it is like nature, as Evenus says:[4]

I say that habit's but long practice, friend,
And this becomes men's nature in the end.

We have now stated what continence, incontinence, endurance, and softness are, and how these states are related to each other.

11

1152^b The study of pleasure and pain belongs to the province of the political philosopher; for he is the architect of the end, with a view to which we call one thing bad and another good without qualification. Further, it is one of our necessary tasks to consider them; for not only did we lay it down that moral virtue and vice are concerned with pains and pleasures, but most people say that happiness involves pleasure; this is why the blessed man is called by a name derived from a word meaning enjoyment.

Now (1) some people think that no pleasure is a good, either in itself or incidentally, since the good and pleasure are not the same; (2) others think that some pleasures are good but that most are bad. (3) Again there is a third view, that even if all pleasures are good, yet the best thing in the world cannot be pleasure. (1) The reasons given for the view that pleasure is not a good at all are (*a*) that every pleasure is a perceptible process to a natural state, and that no process is of the same kind as its end, e.g. no process of building of the same kind as a house. (*b*) A temperate man avoids pleasures. (*c*) A man of practical wisdom pursues what is free from pain, not what is pleasant. (*d*) The pleasures are a hindrance to thought, and the more so the more one delights in them, e.g. in sexual pleasure; for no one could think of anything while absorbed in this. (*e*) There is no art of pleasure; but every good is the product of some art. (*f*) Children and the brutes pursue pleasures. (2) The reasons for the view that not all pleasures are good are that (*a*) there are pleasures that are actually base and objects of reproach, and (*b*) there are harmful pleasures; for some pleasant things are unhealthy. (3) The reason for the view that the best thing in the world is not pleasure is that pleasure is not an end but a process.

12

These are pretty much the things that are said. That it does not follow from these grounds that pleasure is not a good, or even the chief good, is plain from the following considerations. (A) (*a*) First, since that which is good may be so in either of two senses (one thing good simply and another good for a particular person), natural constitutions and states

[1] 1144^a 11–^{b} 32.
[2] 1144^a 23–^{b} 4.
[3] Fr. 67, Kock.
[4] Fr. 9, Diehl.

of being, and therefore also the corresponding movements and processes, will be correspondingly divisible. Of those which are thought to be bad some will be bad if taken without qualification but not bad for a particular person, but worthy of his choice, and some will not be worthy of choice even for a particular person, but only at a particular time and for a short period, though not without qualification; while others are not even pleasures, but seem to be so, viz. all those which involve pain and whose end is curative, e.g. the processes that go on in sick persons.

(*b*) Further, one kind of good being activity and another being state, the processes that restore us to our natural state are only incidentally pleasant; for that matter the activity at work in the appetites for them is the activity of so much of our state and nature as has remained unimpaired; for there are actually pleasures that involve *no* pain or appetite (e.g. **1153^{a}** those of contemplation), the nature in such a case not being defective at all. That the others are incidental is indicated by the fact that men do not enjoy the same pleasant objects when their nature is in its settled state as they do when it is being replenished, but in the former case they enjoy the things that are pleasant without qualification, in the latter the contraries of these as well; for then they enjoy even sharp and bitter things, none of which is pleasant either by nature or without qualification. The states they produce, therefore, are not pleasures naturally or without qualification; for as pleasant things differ, so do the pleasures arising from them.

(*c*) Again, it is not necessary that there should be something else better than pleasure, as some say the end is better than the process; for pleasures are not processes nor do they all involve process—they are activities and ends; nor do they arise when we are becoming something, but when we are exercising some faculty; and not all pleasures have an end different from themselves, but only the pleasures of persons who are being led to the perfecting of their nature. This is why it is not right to say that pleasure is perceptible process, but it should rather be called activity of the natural state, and instead of 'perceptible' 'unimpeded'. It is thought by *some* people to be process just because they think it is in the strict sense *good*; for they think that activity is process, which it is not.

(B) The view that pleasures are bad because some pleasant things are unhealthy is like saying that healthy things are bad because some healthy things are bad for money-making; both are bad in the respect mentioned, but they are not *bad* for *that* reason—indeed, thinking itself is sometimes injurious to health.

Neither practical wisdom nor any state of being is impeded by the pleasure arising from it; it is foreign pleasures that impede, for the pleasures arising from thinking and learning will make us think and learn all the more.

(C) The fact that no pleasure is the product of any art arises naturally enough; there is no art of any other activity either, but only of the corresponding faculty; though for that matter the arts of the perfumer and the cook *are* thought to be arts of pleasure.

(D) The arguments based on the grounds that the temperate man avoids pleasure and that the man of practical wisdom pursues the painless life, and that children and the brutes pursue pleasure, are all refuted by the same consideration. We have pointed out[1] in what sense pleasures are good without qualification and in what sense some are not good; now both the brutes and children pursue pleasures of the latter kind (and the man of practical wisdom pursues tranquil freedom from that kind), viz. those which imply appetite and pain, i.e. the bodily pleasures (for it is these that are of this nature) and the excesses of them, in respect of which the self-indulgent man is self-indulgent. This is why the temperate man avoids these pleasures; for even he *has* pleasures of his own.

13

1153^{b} But further (E) it is agreed that pain is bad and to be avoided; for some pain is without qualification bad, and other pain is bad because it is in some respect an impediment to us. Now the contrary of that which is to be avoided, *qua* something to be avoided and bad, is good. Pleasure, then, is necessarily a good. For the answer of Speusippus, that pleasure is contrary both to pain and to good, as the greater is contrary both to the less and to the equal, is not successful; since he would not say that pleasure is essentially just a species of evil.

And (F) if certain pleasures are bad, that does not prevent the chief good from being some pleasure, just as the chief good may be some form of knowledge though certain kinds of knowledge are bad. Perhaps it is even necessary, if each disposition has unimpeded activities, that, whether the activity (if unim-

[1] 1152^{b} 26–1153^{a} 7.

peded) of all our dispositions or that of some one of them is happiness, this should be the thing most worthy of our choice; and this activity is pleasure. Thus the chief good would be some pleasure, though most pleasures might perhaps be bad without qualification. And for this reason all men think that the happy life is pleasant and weave pleasure into their ideal of happiness—and reasonably too; for no activity is perfect when it is impeded, and happiness is a perfect thing; this is why the happy man needs the goods of the body and external goods, i.e. those of fortune, viz. in order that he may not be impeded in these ways. Those who say that the victim on the rack or the man who falls into great misfortunes is happy if he is good, are, whether they mean to or not, talking nonsense. Now because we need fortune as well as other things, some people think good fortune the same thing as happiness; but it is not that, for even good fortune itself when in excess is an impediment, and perhaps should then be no longer called good fortune; for its limit is fixed by reference to happiness.

And indeed the fact that all things, both brutes and men, pursue pleasure is an indication of its being somehow the chief good:

No voice is wholly lost that many peoples[1] . . .

But since no one nature or state either is or is thought the best for all, neither do all pursue the same pleasure; yet all pursue pleasure. And perhaps they actually pursue not the pleasure they think they pursue nor that which they would say they pursue, but the same pleasure; for all things have by nature something divine in them. But the bodily pleasures have appropriated the name both because we oftenest steer our course for them and because all men share in them; thus because they alone are familiar, men think there are no others.

1154a It is evident also that if pleasure, i.e. the activity of our faculties, is not a good, it will not be the case that the happy man lives a pleasant life; for to what end should he need pleasure, if it is not a good but the happy man may even live a painful life? For pain is neither an evil nor a good, if pleasure is not; why then should he avoid it? Therefore, too, the life of the good man will not be pleasanter than that of any one else, if his activities are not more pleasant.

14

(G) With regard to the bodily pleasures, those who say that *some* pleasures are very much to be chosen, viz. the noble pleasures, but not the bodily pleasures, i.e. those with which the self-indulgent man is concerned, must consider why, then, the contrary pains are bad. For the contrary of bad is good. Are the necessary pleasures good in the sense in which even that which is not bad is good? Or are they good up to a point? Is it that where you have states and processes of which there cannot be too much, there cannot be too much of the corresponding pleasure, and that where there can be too much of the one there can be too much of the other also? Now there can be too much of bodily goods, and the bad man is bad by virtue of pursuing the excess, not by virtue of pursuing the necessary pleasures (for *all* men enjoy in some way or other both dainty foods and wines and sexual intercourse, but not all men do so as they ought). The contrary is the case with pain; for he does not avoid the excess of it, he avoids it altogether; and this is peculiar to him, for the alternative to excess of pleasure is not pain, except to the man who pursues this excess.

Since we should state not only the truth, but also the cause of error—for this contributes towards producing conviction, since when a reasonable explanation is given of why the false view appears true, this tends to produce belief in the true view—therefore we must state why the bodily pleasures appear the more worthy of choice. (*a*) Firstly, then, it is because they expel pain; owing to the excesses of pain that men experience, they pursue excessive and in general bodily pleasure as being a cure for the pain. Now curative agencies produce intense feeling—which is the reason why they are pursued—because they show up against the contrary pain. (Indeed pleasure is thought not to be good for these two reasons, as has been said,[2] viz. that (*α*) some of them are activities belonging to a bad nature—either congenital, as in the case of a brute, or due to habit, i.e. those of bad men; while (*β*) others are meant to cure a defective nature, and it is better to be in a healthy state than to be getting into it, but

1154b these arise during the process of being made perfect and are therefore only incidentally good.) (*b*) Further, they are pursued because of their violence by those who cannot enjoy other pleasures. (At all events they go out of their way to manufacture thirsts somehow for themselves. When these are harmless, the practice is irreproachable; when they are hurt-

[1] Hesiod, *Works and Days*, 763.

[2] 1152b 26–33.

ful, it is bad.) For they have nothing else to enjoy, and, besides, a neutral state is painful to many people because of their nature. For the animal nature is always in travail, as the students of natural science also testify, saying that sight and hearing are painful; but we have become used to this, as they maintain. Similarly, while, in youth, people are, owing to the growth that is going on, in a situation like that of drunken men, and youth is pleasant, on the other hand people of excitable nature always need relief; for even their body is ever in torment owing to its special composition, and they are always under the influence of violent desire; but pain is driven out both by the contrary pleasure, and by any chance pleasure if it be strong; and for these reasons they become self-indulgent and bad. But the pleasures that do not involve pains do not admit of excess; and these are among the things pleasant by nature and not incidentally. By things pleasant incidentally I mean those that act as cures (for because as a result people are cured, through some action of the part that remains healthy, for this reason the process is thought pleasant); by things naturally pleasant I mean those that stimulate the action of the healthy nature.

There is no one thing that is always pleasant, because our nature is not simple but there is another element in us as well, inasmuch as we are perishable creatures, so that if the one element does something, this is unnatural to the other nature, and when the two elements are evenly balanced, what is done seems neither painful nor pleasant; for if the nature of anything were simple, the same action would always be most pleasant to it. This is why God always enjoys a single and simple pleasure; for there is not only an activity of movement but an activity of immobility, and pleasure is found more in rest than in movement. But 'change in all things is sweet', as the poet says,[2] because of some vice; for as it is the vicious man that is changeable, so the nature that needs change is vicious; for it is not simple nor good.

We have now discussed continence and incontinence, and pleasure and pain, both what each is and in what sense some of them are good and others bad; it remains to speak of friendship.

BOOK VIII

I

1155a After what we have said, a discussion of friendship would naturally follow, since it is a virtue or implies virtue, and is besides most necessary with a view to living. For without friends no one would choose to live, though he had all other goods; even rich men and those in possession of office and of dominating power are thought to need friends most of all; for what is the use of such prosperity without the opportunity of beneficence, which is exercised chiefly and in its most laudable form towards friends? Or how can prosperity be guarded and preserved without friends? The greater it is, the more exposed is it to risk. And in poverty and in other misfortunes men think friends are the only refuge. It helps the young, too, to keep from error; it aids older people by ministering to their needs and supplementing the activities that are failing from weakness; those in the prime of life it stimulates to noble actions—'two going together'[1]—for with friends men are more able both to think and to act. Again, parent seems by nature to feel it for offspring and offspring for parent, not only among men but among birds and among most animals; it is felt mutually by members of the same race, and especially by men, whence we praise lovers of their fellowmen. We may see even in our travels how near and dear every man is to every other. Friendship seems too to hold states together, and lawgivers to care more for it than for justice; for unanimity seems to be something like friendship, and this they aim at most of all, and expel faction as their worst enemy; and when men are friends they have no need of justice, while when they are just they need friendship as well, and the truest form of justice is thought to be a friendly quality.

But it is not only necessary but also noble; for we praise those who love their friends, and it is thought to be a fine thing to have many friends; and again we think it is the same people that are good men and are friends.

Not a few things about friendship are matters of debate. Some define it as a kind of likeness and say like people are friends, whence come the sayings 'like to like',[3] 'birds of a feather flock together', and so on; others on the
1155b contrary say 'two of a trade never agree'

[1] *Iliad*, x. 224.

[2] Euripides, *Orestes*, 234.

[3] *Odyssey*, xvii. 218.

On this very question they inquire for deeper and more physical causes, Euripides saying that 'parched earth loves the rain, and stately heaven when filled with rain loves to fall to earth',[1] and Heraclitus that 'it is what opposes that helps' and 'from different tones comes the fairest tune' and 'all things are produced through strife';[2] while Empedocles, as well as others, expresses the opposite view that like aims at like. The physical problems we may leave alone (for they do not belong to the present inquiry); let us examine those which are human and involve character and feeling, e.g. whether friendship can arise between any two people or people cannot be friends if they are wicked, and whether there is one species of friendship or more than one. Those who think there is only one because it admits of degrees have relied on an inadequate indication; for even things different in species admit of degree. We have discussed this matter previously.

2

The kinds of friendship may perhaps be cleared up if we first come to know the object of love. For not everything seems to be loved but only the lovable, and this is good, pleasant, or useful; but it would seem to be that by which some good or pleasure is produced that is useful, so that it is the good and the useful that are lovable as ends. Do men love, then, *the* good, or what is good for *them*? These sometimes clash. So too with regard to the pleasant. Now it is thought that each loves what is good for himself, and that the good is without qualification lovable, and what is good for each man is lovable for him; but each man loves not what is good for him but what seems good. This however will make no difference; we shall just have to say that this is 'that which seems lovable'. Now there are three grounds on which people love; of the love of lifeless objects we do not use the word 'friendship'; for it is not mutual love, nor is there a wishing of good to the other (for it would surely be ridiculous to wish wine well; if one wishes anything for it, it is that it may keep, so that one may have it oneself); but to a friend we say we ought to wish what is good for his sake. But to those who thus wish good we ascribe only goodwill, if the wish is not reciprocated; goodwill when it *is* reciprocal being friendship. Or must we add 'when it is recognized'? For many people have goodwill to those whom they have not seen but judge to be good or useful; and one of these might **1156a** return this feeling. These people seem to bear goodwill to each other; but how could one call them friends when they do not know their mutual feelings? To be friends, then, they must be mutually recognized as bearing goodwill and wishing well to each other for one of the aforesaid reasons.

[1] Fr. 898. 7–10, Nauck. [2] Fr. 8, Diels.

3

Now these reasons differ from each other in kind; so, therefore, do the corresponding forms of love and friendship. There are therefore three kinds of friendship, equal in number to the things that are lovable; for with respect to each there is a mutual and recognized love, and those who love each other wish well to each other in that respect in which they love one another. Now those who love each other for their utility do not love each other for themselves but in virtue of some good which they get from each other. So too with those who love for the sake of pleasure; it is not for their character that men love ready-witted people, but because they find them pleasant. Therefore those who love for the sake of utility love for the sake of what is good for *themselves*, and those who love for the sake of pleasure do so for the sake of what is pleasant to *themselves*, and not in so far as the other is the person loved but in so far as he is useful or pleasant. And thus these friendships are only incidental; for it is not as being the man he is that the loved person is loved, but as providing some good or pleasure. Such friendships, then, are easily dissolved, if the parties do not remain like themselves; for if the one party is no longer pleasant or useful the other ceases to love him.

Now the useful is not permanent but is always changing. Thus when the motive of the friendship is done away, the friendship is dissolved, inasmuch as it existed only for the ends in question. This kind of friendship seems to exist chiefly between old people (for at that age people pursue not the pleasant but the useful) and, of those who are in their prime or young, between those who pursue utility. And such people do not live much with each other either; for sometimes they do not even find each other pleasant; therefore they do not need such companionship unless they are useful to each other; for they are pleasant to each other only in so far as they rouse in each other hopes of something good to come. Among such friendships people also class the friendship of host and guest. On the other hand the friendship of young people seems to aim at pleasure; for they live under the guidance of emotion, and pursue above all what is pleasant to themselves and what is immediately before them; but with increasing age their pleasures become different. This is why they quickly become friends and quickly cease to be so; their friendship changes with the object that is found pleasant, and such pleasure alters quickly. **1156b** Young people are amorous too; for the greater part of the friendship of love depends on emotion and aims at pleasure; this is why they fall in love and quickly fall out of love, changing often within a single day. But these people do wish to spend their days and lives together; for it is thus that they attain the purpose of their friendship.

Perfect friendship is the friendship of men who are good, and alike in virtue; for these wish well alike to each other *qua* good, and they are good in themselves. Now those who wish well to their friends for their sake are most truly friends; for they do this by reason of their own nature and not incidentally; therefore their friendship lasts as long as they are good—and goodness is an enduring thing. And each is good without qualification and to his friend, for the good are both good without qualification and useful to each other. So too they are pleasant; for the good are pleasant both without qualification and to each other, since to each his own activities and others like them are pleasurable, and the actions of the good *are* the same or like. And such a friendship is as might be expected permanent, since there meet in it all the qualities that friends should have. For all friendship is for the sake of good or of pleasure—good or pleasure either in the abstract or such as will be enjoyed by him who has the friendly feeling—and is based on a certain resemblance; and to a friendship of good men all the qualities we have named belong in virtue of the nature of the friends themselves; for in the case of this kind of friendship the other qualities also are alike in both friends, and that which is good without qualification is also without qualification pleasant, and these are the most lovable qualities. Love and friendship therefore are found most and in their best form between such men.

But it is natural that such friendships should be infrequent; for such men are rare. Further, such friendship requires time and familiarity; as the proverb says, men cannot know each other till they have 'eaten salt together'; nor can they admit each other to friendship or be friends till each has been found lovable and been trusted by each. Those who quickly show the marks of friendship to each other wish to be friends, but are not friends unless they both are lovable and know the fact; for a wish for friendship may arise quickly, but friendship does not.

4

This kind of friendship, then, is perfect both in respect of duration and in all other respects, and in it each gets from each in all respects the same as, or something like what, he gives; which is what ought to happen between friends. Friendship for the sake of pleasure bears a resemblance to this kind; for good **1157a** people too *are* pleasant to each other. So too does friendship for the sake of utility; for the good are also useful to each other. Among men of these inferior sorts too, friendships are most permanent when the friends get the same thing from each other (e.g. pleasure), and not only that but also from the same source, as happens between ready-witted people, not as happens between lover and beloved. For these do not take pleasure in the same things, but the one in seeing the beloved and the other in receiving attentions from his lover; and when the bloom of youth is passing the friendship sometimes passes too (for the one finds no pleasure in the sight of the other, and the other gets no attentions from the first); but many lovers on the other hand are constant, if familiarity has led them to love each other's characters, these being alike. But those who exchange not pleasure but utility in their amour are both less truly friends and less constant. Those who are friends for the sake of utility part when the advantage is at an end; for they were lovers not of each other but of profit.

For the sake of pleasure or utility, then, even bad men may be friends of each other, or good men of bad, or one who is neither good nor bad may be a friend to any sort of person, but for their own sake clearly only good men can be friends; for bad men do not delight in each other unless some advantage come of the relation.

The friendship of the good too and this alone is proof against slander; for it is not easy to trust any one's talk about a man who has long been tested by oneself; and it is among good men that trust and the feeling that 'he would never wrong me' and all the other things that are demanded in true friendship are found. In the other kinds of friendship, however, there is nothing to prevent these evils arising.

For men apply the name of friends even to those whose motive is utility, in which sense states are said to be friendly (for the alliances of states seem to aim at advantage), and to those who love each other for the sake of pleasure, in which sense children are called friends. Therefore we too ought perhaps to call such people friends, and say that there are several kinds of friendship—firstly and in the proper sense that of good men *qua* good, and by analogy the other kinds; for it is in virtue of something good and something akin to what is found in true friendship that they are friends, since even the pleasant is good for the lovers of pleasure. But these two kinds of friendship are not often united, nor do the same people become friends for the sake of utility and of pleasure; for things that are only incidentally connected are not often coupled together.

1157b Friendship being divided into these kinds, bad men will be friends for the sake of pleasure or of utility, being in this respect like each other, but good men will be friends for their own sake, i.e. in virtue of their goodness. These, then, are friends without qualification; the others are friends incidentally and through a resemblance to these.

5

As in regard to the virtues some men are called good in respect of a state of character, others in respect of an activity, so too in the case of friendship; for those who live together delight in each other and confer benefits on each other, but those who are asleep or locally separated are not performing, but are disposed to perform, the activities of friendship; distance does not break off the friendship absolutely, but only the activity of it. But if the absence is lasting, it seems actually to make men forget their friendship; hence the saying 'out of sight, out of mind'. Neither old people nor sour people seem to make friends easily; for there is little that is pleasant in them, and no one can spend his days with one whose company is painful, or not pleasant, since nature seems above all to avoid the painful and to aim at the pleasant. Those, however, who approve of each other but do not live together seem to be well-disposed rather than actual friends. For there is nothing so characteristic of friends as living together (since while it is people who are in need that desire benefits, even those who are supremely happy desire to spend their days together; for solitude suits such people least of all); but people cannot live together if they are not pleasant and do not enjoy the same things, as friends who are companions seem to do.

The truest friendship, then, is that of the good, as we have frequently said;[1] for that which is without qualification good or pleasant seems to be lovable and desirable, and for each person that which is good or pleasant to him; and the good man is lovable and desirable to the good man for both these reasons. Now it looks as if love were a feeling, friendship a state of character; for love may be felt just as much towards lifeless things, but mutual love involves choice and choice springs from a state of character; and men wish well to those whom they love, for their sake, not as a result of feeling but as a result of a state of character. And in loving a friend men love what is good for themselves; for the good man in becoming a friend becomes a good to his friend. Each, then, both loves what is good for himself, and makes an equal return in goodwill and in pleasantness; for friendship is said to be equality, and both of these are found most in the friendship of the good.

6

1158a Between sour and elderly people friendship arises less readily, inasmuch as they are less good-tempered and enjoy companionship less; for these are thought to be the greatest marks of friendship and most productive of it. This is why, while young men become friends quickly, old men do not; it is because men do not become friends with those in whom they do not delight; and similarly sour people do not quickly make friends either. But such men may bear goodwill to each other; for they wish one another well and aid one another in need; but they are hardly *friends* because they do not spend their days together nor delight in each other, and these are thought the greatest marks of friendship.

One cannot be a friend to many people in the sense of having friendship of the perfect type with them, just as one cannot be in love with many people at once (for love is a sort of excess of feeling, and it is the nature of such only to be felt towards one person); and it is

[1] 1156b 7, 23, 33, 1157a 30, b 4.

not easy for many people at the same time to please the same person very greatly, or perhaps even to be good in his eyes. One must, too, acquire some experience of the other person and become familiar with him, and that is very hard. But with a view to utility or pleasure it is possible that many people should please one; for many people are useful or pleasant, and these services take little time.

Of these two kinds that which is for the sake of pleasure is the more like friendship, when both parties get the same things from each other and delight in each other or in the same things, as in the friendships of the young; for generosity is more found in such friendships. Friendship based on utility is for the commercially minded. People who are supremely happy, too, have no need of useful friends, but do need pleasant friends; for they wish to live with *some one* and, though they can endure for a short time what is painful, no one could put up with it continuously, nor even with the Good itself if it were painful to him; this is why they look out for friends who are pleasant. Perhaps they should look out for friends who, being pleasant, are also good, and good for them too; for so they will have all the characteristics that friends should have.

People in positions of authority seem to have friends who fall into distinct classes; some people are useful to them and others are pleasant, but the same people are rarely both; for they seek neither those whose pleasantness is accompanied by virtue nor those whose utility is with a view to noble objects, but in their desire for pleasure they seek for ready-witted people, and their other friends they choose as being clever at doing what they are told, and these characteristics are rarely combined. Now we have said that the *good* man *is* at the same time pleasant and useful;[1] but such a man does not become the friend of one who surpasses him in station, unless he is surpassed also in virtue; if this is not so, he does not establish equality by being proportionally exceeded in both respects. But people who surpass him in both respects are not so easy to find.

1158b However that may be, the aforesaid friendships involve equality; for the friends get the same things from one another and wish the same things for one another, or exchange one thing for another, e.g. pleasure for utility; we have said,[2] however, that they are both less truly friendships and less permanent. But it is from their likeness and their unlikeness to the same thing that they are thought both to be and not to be friendships. It is by their likeness to the friendship of virtue that they seem to be friendships (for one of them involves pleasure and the other utility, and these characteristics belong to the friendship of virtue as well); while it is because the friendship of virtue is proof against slander and permanent, while these quickly change (besides differing from the former in many other respects), that they appear *not* to be friendships; i.e. it is because of their unlikeness to the friendship of virtue.

7

But there is another kind of friendship, viz. that which involves an inequality between the parties, e.g. that of father to son and in general of elder to younger, that of man to wife and in general that of ruler to subject. And these friendships differ also from each other; for it is not the same that exists between parents and children and between rulers and subjects, nor is even that of father to son the same as that of son to father, nor that of husband to wife the same as that of wife to husband. For the virtue and the function of each of these is different, and so are the reasons for which they love; the love and the friendship are therefore different also. Each party, then, neither gets the same from the other, nor ought to seek it; but when children render to parents what they ought to render to those who brought them into the world, and parents render what they should to their children, the friendship of such persons will be abiding and excellent. In all friendships implying inequality the love also should be proportional, i.e. the better should be more loved than he loves, and so should the more useful, and similarly in each of the other cases; for when the love is in proportion to the merit of the parties, then in a sense arises equality, which is certainly held to be characteristic of friendship.

But equality does not seem to take the same form in acts of justice and in friendship; for in acts of justice what is equal in the primary sense is that which is in proportion to merit, while quantitative equality is secondary, but in friendship quantitative equality is primary and proportion to merit secondary. This becomes clear if there is a great interval in respect of virtue or vice or wealth or anything else between the parties; for then they are no longer friends, and do not even expect to

[1] 1156b 13-15, 1157a 1-3.

[2] 1156a 16-24, 1157a 20-33.

be so. And this is most manifest in the case of the gods; for they surpass us most decisively in all good things. But it is clear also in the **1159a** case of kings; for with them, too, men who are much their inferiors do not expect to be friends; nor do men of no account expect to be friends with the best or wisest men. In such cases it is not possible to define exactly up to what point friends can remain friends; for much can be taken away and friendship remain, but when one party is removed to a great distance, as God is, the possibility of friendship ceases. This is in fact the origin of the question whether friends really wish for their friends the greatest goods, e.g. that of being gods; since in that case their friends will no longer be friends to them, and therefore will not be good things for them (for friends *are* good things). The answer is that if we were right in saying that friend wishes good to friend for his sake, his friend must remain the sort of being he is, whatever that may be; therefore it is for him only so long as he remains a man that he will wish the greatest goods. But perhaps not *all* the greatest goods; for it is for himself most of all that each man wishes what is good.

8

Most people seem, owing to ambition, to wish to be loved rather than to love; which is why most men love flattery; for the flatterer is a friend in an inferior position, or pretends to be such and to love more than he is loved; and being loved seems to be akin to being honoured, and this is what most people aim at. But it seems to be not for its own sake that people choose honour, but incidentally. For most people enjoy being honoured by those in positions of authority because of their hopes (for they think that if they want anything they will get it from them; and therefore they delight in honour as a token of favour to come); while those who desire honour from good men, and men who know, are aiming at confirming their own opinion of themselves; they delight in honour, therefore, because they believe in their own goodness on the strength of the judgement of those who speak about them. In being loved, on the other hand, people delight for its own sake; whence it would seem to be better than being honoured, and friendship to be desirable in itself. But it seems to lie in loving rather than in being loved, as is indicated by the delight mothers take in loving; for some mothers hand over their children to be brought up, and so long as they know their fate they love them and do not seek to be loved in return (if they cannot have both), but seem to be satisfied if they see them prospering; and they themselves love their children even if these owing to their ignorance give them nothing of a mother's due. Now since friendship depends more on loving, and it is those who love their friends that are praised, loving seems to be the characteristic virtue of friends, so that it is only those in whom this is found in due measure that are lasting friends, and only their friendship that endures.

1159b It is in this way more than any other that even unequals can be friends; they can be equalized. Now equality and likeness are friendship, and especially the likeness of those who are like in virtue; for being steadfast in themselves they hold fast to each other, and neither ask nor give base services, but (one may say) even prevent them; for it is characteristic of good men neither to go wrong themselves nor to let their friends do so. But wicked men have no steadfastness (for they do not remain even like to themselves), but become friends for a short time because they delight in each other's wickedness. Friends who are useful or pleasant last longer; i.e. as long as they provide each other with enjoyments or advantages. Friendship for utility's sake seems to be that which most easily exists between contraries, e.g. between poor and rich, between ignorant and learned; for what a man actually lacks he aims at, and one gives something else in return. But under this head, too, might bring lover and beloved, beautiful and ugly. This is why lovers sometimes seem ridiculous, when they demand to be loved as they love; if they are equally lovable their claim can perhaps be justified, but when they have nothing lovable about them it is ridiculous. Perhaps, however, contrary does not even aim at contrary by its own nature, but only incidentally, the desire being for what is intermediate; for that is what is good, e.g. it is good for the dry not to become wet but to come to the intermediate state, and similarly with the hot and in all other cases. These subjects we may dismiss; for they are indeed somewhat foreign to our inquiry.

9

Friendship and justice seem, as we have said at the outset of our discussion,[1] to be con-

[1] 1155a 22-28.

cerned with the same objects and exhibited between the same persons. For in every community there is thought to be some form of justice, and friendship too; at least men address as friends their fellow-voyagers and fellow-soldiers, and so too those associated with them in any other kind of community. And the extent of their association is the extent of their friendship, as it is the extent to which justice exists between them. And the proverb 'what friends have is common property' expresses the truth; for friendship depends on community. Now brothers and comrades have all things in common, but the others to whom we have referred have definite things in common—some more things, others fewer; for of friendships, too, some are more and others less truly friendships. And the claims of justice differ too; the duties of parents to children **1160**[a] and those of brothers to each other are not the same, nor those of comrades and those of fellow-citizens, and so, too, with the other kinds of friendship. There is a difference, therefore, also between the acts that are unjust towards each of these classes of associates, and the injustice increases by being exhibited towards those who are friends in a fuller sense; e.g. it is a more terrible thing to defraud a comrade than a fellow-citizen, more terrible not to help a brother than a stranger, and more terrible to wound a father than any one else. And the demands of justice also seem to increase with the intensity of the friendship, which implies that friendship and justice exist between the same persons and have an equal extension.

Now all forms of community are like parts of the political community; for men journey together with a view to some particular advantage, and to provide something that they need for the purposes of life; and it is for the sake of advantage that the political community too seems both to have come together originally and to endure, for this is what legislators aim at, and they call just that which is to the common advantage. Now the other communities aim at advantage bit by bit, e.g. sailors at what is advantageous on a voyage with a view to making money or something of the kind, fellow-soldiers at what is advantageous in war, whether it is wealth or victory or the taking of a city that they seek, and members of tribes and demes act similarly [Some communities seem to arise for the sake of pleasure, viz. religious guilds and social clubs; for these exist respectively for the sake of offering sacrifice and of companionship. But all these seem to fall under the political community; for it aims not at present advantage but at what is advantageous for life as a whole], offering sacrifices and arranging gatherings for the purpose, and assigning honours to the gods, and providing pleasant relaxations for themselves. For the ancient sacrifices and gatherings seem to take place after the harvest as a sort of firstfruits, because it was at these seasons that people had most leisure. All the communities, then, seem to be parts of the political community; and the particular kinds of friendship will correspond to the particular kinds of community.

10

There are three kinds of constitution, and an equal number of deviation-forms—perversions, as it were, of them. The constitutions are monarchy, aristocracy, and thirdly that which is based on a property qualification, which it seems appropriate to call timocratic, though most people are wont to call it polity. The best of these is monarchy, the worst timocracy. The deviation from monarchy is tyran- **1160**[b] ny; for both are forms of one-man rule, but there is the greatest difference between them; the tyrant looks to his own advantage, the king to that of his subjects. For a man is not a king unless he is sufficient to himself and excels his subjects in all good things; and such a man needs nothing further; therefore he will not look to his own interests but to those of his subjects; for a king who is not like that would be a mere titular king. Now tyranny is the very contrary of this; the tyrant pursues his own good. And it is clearer in the case of tyranny that it is the worst deviation-form; but it is the contrary of the best that is worst. Monarchy passes over into tyranny; for tyranny is the evil form of one-man rule and the bad king becomes a tyrant. Aristocracy passes over into oligarchy by the badness of the rulers, who distribute contrary to equity what belongs to the city—all or most of the good things to themselves, and office always to the same people, paying most regard to wealth; thus the rulers are few and are bad men instead of the most worthy. Timocracy passes over into democracy; for these are coterminous, since it is the ideal even of timocracy to be the rule of the majority, and all who have the property qualification count as equal. Democracy is the least bad of the deviations; for in its case the form of constitution is but a slight deviation. These then are the changes to which constitutions are most subject; for these are the smallest and easiest transitions.

One may find resemblances to the constitutions and, as it were, patterns of them even in households. For the association of a father with his sons bears the form of monarchy, since the father cares for his children; and this is why Homer calls Zeus 'father';[1] it is the ideal of monarchy to be paternal rule. But among the Persians the rule of the father is tyrannical; they use their sons as slaves. Tyrannical too is the rule of a master over slaves; for it is the advantage of the master that is brought about in it. Now this seems to be a correct form of government, but the Persian type is perverted; for the modes of rule appropriate to different relations are diverse. The association of man and wife seems to be aristocratic; for the man rules in accordance with his worth, and in those matters in which a man should rule, but the matters that befit a woman he hands over to her. If the man rules in everything the relation passes over into oligarchy; for in doing so he is not acting in accordance with their respective worth, and not ruling in virtue of his superiority. Sometimes, however, wom- **1161a** en rule, because they are heiresses; so their rule is not in virtue of excellence but due to wealth and power, as in oligarchies. The association of brothers is like timocracy; for they are equal, except in so far as they differ in age; hence if they differ *much* in age, the friendship is no longer of the fraternal type. Democracy is found chiefly in masterless dwellings (for here every one is on an equality), and in those in which the ruler is weak and every one has licence to do as he pleases.

11

Each of the constitutions may be seen to involve friendship just in so far as it involves justice. The friendship between a king and his subjects depends on an excess of benefits conferred; for he confers benefits on his subjects if being a good man he cares for them with a view to their well-being, as a shepherd does for his sheep (whence Homer called Agamemnon 'shepherd of the peoples').[2] Such too is the friendship of a father, though this exceeds the other in the greatness of the benefits conferred; for he is responsible for the existence of his children, which is thought the greatest good, and for their nurture and upbringing. These things are ascribed to ancestors as well. Further, by nature a father tends to rule over his sons, ancestors over descendants, a king over his subjects. These friendships imply superiority of one party over the other, which is why ancestors are honoured. The justice therefore that exists between persons so related is not the same on both sides but is in every case proportioned to merit; for that is true of the friendship as well. The friendship of man and wife, again, is the same that is found in an aristocracy; for it is in accordance with virtue—the better gets more of what is good, and each gets what befits him; and so, too, with the justice in these relations. The friendship of brothers is like that of comrades; for they are equal and of like age, and such persons are for the most part like in their feelings and their character. Like this, too, is the friendship appropriate to timocratic government; for in such a constitution the ideal is for the citizens to be equal and fair; therefore rule is taken in turn, and on equal terms; and the friendship appropriate here will correspond.

But in the deviation-forms, as justice hardly exists, so too does friendship. It exists least in the worst form; in tyranny there is little or no friendship. For where there is nothing common to ruler and ruled, there is not friendship either, since there is not justice; e.g. between craftsman and tool, soul and body, master and slave; the latter in each case is ben- **1161b** efited by that which uses it, but there is no friendship nor justice towards lifeless things. But neither is there friendship towards a horse or an ox, nor to a slave *qua* slave. For there is nothing common to the two parties; the slave is a living tool and the tool a lifeless slave. *Qua* slave then, one cannot be friends with him. But *qua* man one can; for there seems to be some justice between any man and any other who can share in a system of law or be a party to an agreement; therefore there can also be friendship with him in so far as he is a man. Therefore while in tyrannies friendship and justice hardly exist, in democracies they exist more fully; for where the citizens are equal they have much in common.

12

Every form of friendship, then, involves association, as has been said.[3] One might, however, mark off from the rest both the friendship of kindred and that of comrades. Those of fellow-citizens, fellow-tribesmen, fellow-voyagers,

[1] e. g., *Iliad*, I. 503.

[2] e. g., *Iliad*, II. 243.

[3] 1159b 29-32.

and the like are more like mere friendships of association; for they seem to rest on a sort of compact. With them we might class the friendship of host and guest.

The friendship of kinsmen itself, while it seems to be of many kinds, appears to depend in every case on parental friendship; for parents love their children as being a part of themselves, and children their parents as being something originating from them. Now (1) parents know their offspring better than their children know that they are their children, and (2) the originator feels his offspring to be his own more than the offspring do their begetter; for the product belongs to the producer (e.g. a tooth or hair or anything else to him whose it is), but the producer does not belong to the product, or belongs in a less degree. And (3) the length of time produces the same result; parents love their children as soon as these are born, but children love their parents only after time has elapsed and they have acquired understanding or the power of discrimination by the senses. From these considerations it is also plain why mothers love more than fathers do. Parents, then, love their children as themselves (for their issue are by virtue of their separate existence a sort of other selves), while children love their parents as being born of them, and brothers love each other as being born of the same parents; for their identity with them makes them identical with each other (which is the reason why people talk of 'the same blood', 'the same stock', and so on). They are, therefore, in a sense the same thing, though in separate individuals. Two things that contribute greatly to friendship are a common upbringing and similarity of age; for 'two of an age take to each other', and people brought up together tend to be comrades; whence the friendship of brothers **1162a** is akin to that of comrades. And cousins and other kinsmen are bound up together by derivation from brothers, viz. by being derived from the same parents. They come to be closer together or farther apart by virtue of the nearness or distance of the original ancestor.

The friendship of children to parents, and of men to gods, is a relation to them as to something good and superior; for they have conferred the greatest benefits, since they are the causes of their being and of their nourishment, and of their education from their birth; and this kind of friendship possesses pleasantness and utility also, more than that of strangers, inasmuch as their life is lived more in common. The friendship of brothers has the characteristics found in that of comrades (and especially when these are good), and in general between people who are like each other, inasmuch as they belong more to each other and start with a love for each other from their very birth, and inasmuch as those born of the same parents and brought up together and similarly educated are more akin in character; and the test of time has been applied most fully and convincingly in their case.

Between other kinsmen friendly relations are found in due proportion. Between man and wife friendship seems to exist by nature; for man is naturally inclined to form couples—even more than to form cities, inasmuch as the household is earlier and more necessary than the city, and reproduction is more common to man with the animals. With the other animals the union extends only to this point, but human beings live together not only for the sake of reproduction but also for the various purposes of life; for from the start the functions are divided, and those of man and woman are different; so they help each other by throwing their peculiar gifts into the common stock. It is for these reasons that both utility and pleasure seem to be found in this kind of friendship. But this friendship may be based also on virtue, if the parties are good; for each has its own virtue and they will delight in the fact. And children seem to be a bond of union (which is the reason why childless people part more easily); for children are a good common to both and what is common holds them together.

How man and wife and in general friend and friend ought mutually to behave seems to be the same question as how it is just for them to behave; for a man does not seem to have the same duties to a friend, a stranger, a comrade, and a schoolfellow.

13

There are three kinds of friendship, as we said at the outset of our inquiry,[1] and in respect of each some are friends on an equality and others by virtue of a superiority (for not only can equally good men become friends but **1162b** a better man can make friends with a worse, and similarly in friendships of pleasure or utility the friends may be equal or unequal in the benefits they confer). This being so, equals must effect the required equalization on a basis of equality in love and in all other re-

[1] 1156a 7.

spects, while unequals must render what is in proportion to their superiority or inferiority.

Complaints and reproaches arise either only or chiefly in the friendship of utility, and this is only to be expected. For those who are friends on the ground of virtue are anxious to do well by each other (since that is a mark of virtue and of friendship), and between men who are emulating each other in this there cannot be complaints or quarrels; no one is offended by a man who loves him and does well by him—if he is a person of nice feeling he takes his revenge by doing well by the other. And the man who excels the other in the services he renders will not complain of his friend, since he gets what he aims at; for each man desires what is good. Nor do complaints arise much even in friendships of pleasure; for both get at the same time what they desire, if they enjoy spending their time together; and even a man who complained of another for *not* affording him pleasure would seem ridiculous, since it is in his power not to spend his days with him.

But the friendship of utility is full of complaints; for as they use each other for their own interests they always want to get the better of the bargain, and think they have got less than they should, and blame their partners because they do not get all they 'want and deserve'; and and those who do well by others cannot help them as much as those whom they benefit want.

Now it seems that, as justice is of two kinds, one unwritten and the other legal, one kind of friendship of utility is moral and the other legal. And so complaints arise most of all when men do not dissolve the relation in the spirit of the same type of friendship in which they contracted it. The *legal* type is that which is on fixed terms; its purely commercial variety is on the basis of immediate payment, while the more liberal variety allows time but stipulates for a definite *quid pro quo*. In this variety the debt is clear and not ambiguous, but in the postponement it contains an element of friendliness; and so some states do not allow suits arising out of such agreements, but think men who have bargained on a basis of credit ought to accept the consequences. The *moral* type is not on fixed terms; it makes a gift, or does whatever it does, as to a friend; but one expects to receive as much or more, as having not given but lent; and if a man is worse off when the relation is dissolved than he was when it was contracted he will complain. This happens because all or most men, while they wish for what is noble, choose what is advantageous; now it is noble to do well by another without a view to repayment, but it is the receiving of benefits that is advantageous. **1163b** Therefore if we can we should return the equivalent of what we have received (for we must not make a man our friend against his will; we must recognize that we were mistaken at the first and took a benefit from a person we should not have taken it from—since it was not from a friend, nor from one who did it just for the sake of acting so—and we must settle up just as if we had been benefited on fixed terms). Indeed, one would agree to repay if one could (if one could not, even the giver would not have expected one to do so); therefore if it is possible we must repay. But at the outset we must consider the man by whom we are being benefited and on what terms he is acting, in order that we may accept the benefit on these terms, or else decline it.

It is disputable whether we ought to measure a service by its utility to the receiver and make the return with a view to that, or by the benevolence of the giver. For those who have received say they have received from their benefactors what meant little to the latter and what they might have got from others—minimizing the service; while the givers, on the contrary, say it was the biggest thing they had, and what could not have been got from others, and that it was given in times of danger or similar need. Now if the friendship is one that aims at *utility*, surely the advantage to the receiver is the measure. For it is he that asks for the service, and the other man helps him on the assumption that he will receive the equivalent; so the assistance has been precisely as great as the advantage to the receiver, and therefore he must return as much as he has received, or even more (for that would be nobler). In friendships based on *virtue* on the other hand, complaints do not arise, but the purpose of the doer is a sort of measure; for in purpose lies the essential element of virtue and character.

14

Differences arise also in friendships based on superiority; for each expects to get more out of them, but when this happens the friendship is dissolved. Not only does the better man think he ought to get more, since more should be assigned to a good man, but the more useful similarly expects this; they say a useless man should not get as much as they should, since it becomes an act of public service and not a friendship if the proceeds of the friendship do not answer to the worth of the benefits conferred. For they think that, as in a commercial partnership those who put more in get more out, so it should be in friendship. But the man who is in a state of need and inferiority makes the opposite claim; they think it is the part of a good friend to help those who are in need; what, they say, is the use of being the friend of a good man or a powerful man, if one is to get nothing out of it?

1163b At all events it seems that each party is justified in his claim, and that each should get more out of the friendship than the other—not more of the same thing, however, but the superior more honour and the inferior more gain; for honour is the prize of virtue and of beneficence, while gain is the assistance required by inferiority.

It seems to be so in constitutional arrangements also; the man who contributes nothing good to the common stock is not honoured; for what belongs to the public is given to the man who benefits the public, and honour does belong to the public. It is not possible to get wealth from the common stock and at the same time honour. For no one puts up with the smaller share in *all* things; therefore to the man who loses in wealth they assign honour and to the man who is willing to be paid, wealth, since the proportion to merit equalizes the parties and preserves the friendship, as we have said.[2]

This then is also the way in which we should associate with unequals; the man who is benefited in respect of wealth or virtue must give honour in return, repaying what he can. For friendship asks a man to do what he can, not what is proportional to the merits of the case; since that cannot always be done, e.g. in honours paid to the gods or to parents; for no one could ever return to them the equivalent of what he gets, but the man who serves them to the utmost of his power is thought to be a good man.

This is why it would not seem open to a man to disown his father (though a father may disown his son); being in debt, he should repay, but there is nothing by doing which a son will have done the equivalent of what he has received, so that he is always in debt. But creditors can remit a debt; and a father can therefore do so too. At the same time it is thought that presumably no one would repudiate a son who was not far gone in wickedness; for apart from the natural friendship of father and son it is human nature not to reject a son's assistance. But the son, if he *is* wicked, will naturally avoid aiding his father, or not be zealous about it; for most people wish to get benefits, but avoid doing them, as a thing unprofitable.—So much for these questions.

BOOK IX

I

In all friendships between dissimilars it is, as we have said,[1] proportion that equalizes the parties and preserves the friendship; e.g. in the political form of friendship the shoemaker gets a return for his shoes in proportion to his **1164a** worth, and the weaver and all other craftsmen do the same. Now here a common measure has been provided in the form of money, and therefore everything is referred to this and measured by this; but in the friendship of lovers sometimes the lover complains that his excess of love is not met by love in return (though perhaps there is nothing lovable about him), while often the beloved complains that the lover who formerly promised everything now performs nothing. Such incidents happen when the lover loves the beloved for the sake of pleasure while the beloved loves the lover for the sake of utility, and they do not both possess the qualities expected of them. If these be the objects of the friendship it is dissolved when they do not get the things that formed the motives of their love; for each did not love the other person himself but the qualities he had, and these were not enduring; that is why the friendships also are transient. But the love of characters, as has been said, endures because it is self-dependent.[3] Differences arise when what they get is something different and not what they desire; for it is like getting nothing at all when we do not get what we aim at; compare the story of the person who made promises to a lyre-player, promising him the more, the better he sang, but in the morning, when the other demanded the fulfilment of his promises, said that he had given

[1] Cf. 1132b 31-33, 1158b 27, 1159a 35-b 3, 1162a 34-b 4, 1163b 11.

[2] 1162a 34-b 4, cf. 1158b 27, 1159a 35-b 3.

[3] 1156b 9-12.

pleasure for pleasure. Now if this had been what each wanted, all would have been well; but if the one wanted enjoyment but the other gain, and the one has what he wants while the other has not, the terms of the association will not have been properly fulfilled; for what each in fact wants is what he attends to, and it is for the sake of that that he will give what he has.

But who is to fix the worth of the service; he who makes the sacrifice or he who has got the advantage? At any rate the other seems to leave it to him. This is what they say Protagoras used to do; whenever he taught anything whatsoever, he bade the learner assess the value of the knowledge, and accepted the amount so fixed. But in such matters some men approve of the saying 'let a man have his fixed reward'.[1]

Those who get the money first and then do none of the things they said they would, owing to the extravagance of their promises, naturally find themselves the objects of complaint; for they do not fulfil what they agreed to. The sophists are perhaps compelled to do this because no one would give money for the things they *do* know. These people then, if they do not do what they have been paid for, are naturally made the objects of complaint.

But where there is *no* contract of service, those who give up something for the sake of the other party cannot (as we have said)[2] be complained of (for that is the nature of **1164b** the friendship of virtue), and the return to them must be made on the basis of their purpose (for it is purpose that is the characteristic thing in a friend and in virtue). And so too, it seems, should one make a return to those with whom one has studied philosophy; for their worth cannot be measured against money, and they can get no honour which will balance their services, but still it is perhaps enough, as it is with the gods and with one's parents, to give them what one can.

If the gift was not of this sort, but was made with a view to a return, it is no doubt preferable that the return made should be one that seems fair to both parties, but if this cannot be achieved, it would seem not only necessary that the person who gets the first service should fix the reward, but also just; for if the other gets in return the equivalent of the advantage the beneficiary has received, or the price he would have paid for the pleasure, he will have got what is fair as from the other.

[1] Hesiod, *Works and Days*, 370, Rzach.
[2] 1162b 6-13.

We see this happening too with things put up for sale, and in some places there are laws providing that no actions shall arise out of voluntary contracts, on the assumption that one should settle with a person to whom one has given credit, in the spirit in which one bargained with him. The law holds that it is more just that the person to whom credit was given should fix the terms than that the person who gave credit should do so. For most things are not assessed at the same value by those who have them and those who want them; each class values highly what is its own and what it is offering; yet the return is made on the terms fixed by the receiver. But no doubt the receiver should assess a thing not at what it seems worth when he has it, but at what he assessed it at before he had it.

2

A further problem is set by such questions as, whether one should in all things give the preference to one's father and obey him, or whether when one is ill one should trust a doctor, and when one has to elect a general should elect a man of military skill; and similarly whether one should render a service by preference to a friend or to a good man, and should show gratitude to a benefactor or oblige a friend, if one cannot do both.

All such questions are hard, are they not, to decide with precision? For they admit of many variations of all sorts in respect both of the magnitude of the service and of its nobility and necessity. But that we should not give the preference in all things to the same person is plain enough; and we must for the most part return benefits rather than oblige friends, as we must pay back a loan to a creditor rather than make one to a friend. But perhaps even this is not always true; e.g. should a man who has been ransomed out of the hands of brigands ransom his ransomer in return, whoever he may be (or pay him if he has not been **1165a** captured but demands payment), or should he ransom his father? It would seem that he should ransom his father in preference even to himself. As we have said,[3] then, generally the debt should be paid, but if the gift is exceedingly noble or exceedingly necessary, one should defer to these considerations. For sometimes it is not even fair to return the equivalent of what one has received, when the one man has done a service to one whom he knows

[3] 1164b 31-1165a 2.

to be good, while the other makes a return to one whom he believes to be bad. For that matter, one should sometimes not lend in return to one who has lent to oneself; for the one person lent to a good man, expecting to recover his loan, while the other has no hope of recovering from one who is believed to be bad. Therefore if the facts really are so, the demand is not fair; and if they are not, but people think they are, they would be held to be doing nothing strange in refusing. As we have often pointed out,[1] then, discussions about feelings and actions have just as much definiteness as their subject-matter.

That we should not make the same return to every one, nor give a father the preference in everything, as one does not sacrifice everything to Zeus, is plain enough; but since we ought to render different things to parents, brothers, comrades, and benefactors, we ought to render to each class what is appropriate and becoming. And this is what people seem in fact to do; to marriages they invite their kinsfolk; for these have a part in the family and therefore in the doings that affect the family; and at funerals also they think that kinsfolk, before all others, should meet, for the same reason. And it would be thought that in the matter of food we should help our parents before all others, since we owe our own nourishment to them, and it is more honourable to help in this respect the authors of our being even before ourselves; and honour too one should give to one's parents as one does to the gods, but not any and every honour; for that matter one should not give the same honour to one's father and one's mother, nor again should one give them the honour due to a philosopher or to a general, but the honour due to a father, or again to a mother. To all older persons, too, one should give honour appropriate to their age, by rising to receive them and finding seats for them and so on; while to comrades and brothers one should allow freedom of speech and common use of all things. To kinsmen, too, and fellow-tribesmen and fellow-citizens and to every other class one should always try to assign what is appropriate, and to compare the claims of each class with respect to nearness of relation and to virtue or usefulness. The comparison is easier when the persons belong to the same class, and more laborious when they are different. Yet we must not on *that* account shrink from the task, but decide the question as best we can.

[1] 1094b 11-27, 1098a 26-29, 1103b 34-1104a 5.

3

Another question that arises is whether friendships should or should not be broken off when the other party does not remain the same. Per-
1165b haps we may say that there is nothing strange in breaking off a friendship based on utility or pleasure, when our friends no longer have these attributes. For it was of these attributes that we were the friends; and when these have failed it is reasonable to love no longer. But one might complain of another if, when he loved us for our usefulness or pleasantness, he pretended to love us for our character. For, as we said at the outset,[2] most differences arise between friends when they are not friends in the spirit in which they think they are. So when a man has deceived himself and has thought he was being loved for his character, when the other person was doing nothing of the kind, he must blame himself; but when he has been deceived by the pretences of the other person, it is just that he should complain against his deceiver; he will complain with more justice than one does against people who counterfeit the currency, inasmuch as the wrongdoing is concerned with something more valuable.

But if one accepts another man as good, and he turns out badly and is seen to do so, must one still love him? Surely it is impossible, since not everything can be loved, but only what is good. What is evil neither can nor should be loved; for it is not one's duty to be a lover of evil, nor to become like what is bad; and we have said[3] that like is dear to like. Must the friendship, then, be forthwith broken off? Or is this not so in all cases, but only when one's friends are incurable in their wickedness? If they are capable of being reformed one should rather come to the assistance of their character or their property, inasmuch as this is better and more characteristic of friendship. But a man who breaks off such a friendship would seem to be doing nothing strange; for it was not to a man of this sort that he was a friend; when his friend has changed, therefore, and he is unable to save him, he gives him up.

But if one friend remained the same while the other became better and far outstripped him in virtue, should the latter treat the former as a friend? Surely he cannot. When the interval is great this becomes most plain, e.g. in the case of childish friendships; if one friend remained a child in intellect while the other

[2] 1162b 23-25. [3] 1156b 19-21, 1159b 1.

became a fully developed man, how could they be friends when they neither approved of the same things nor delighted in and were pained by the same things? For not even with regard to each other will their tastes agree, and without this (as we saw)[1] they cannot be friends; for they cannot live together. But we have discussed these matters.[2]

Should he, then, behave no otherwise towards him than he would if he had never been his friend? Surely he should keep a remembrance of their former intimacy, and as we think we ought to oblige friends rather than strangers, so to those who have been our friends we ought to make some allowance for our former friendship, when the breach has not been due to excess of wickedness.

4

1166a Friendly relations with one's neighbours, and the marks by which friendships are defined, seem to have proceeded from a man's relations to himself. For (1) we define a friend as one who wishes and does what is good, or seems so, for the sake of his friend, or (2) as one who wishes his friend to exist and live, for his sake; which mothers do to their children, and friends do who have come into conflict. And (3) others define him as one who lives with and (4) has the same tastes as another, or (5) one who grieves and rejoices with his friend; and this too is found in mothers most of all. It is by some one of these characteristics that friendship too is defined.

Now each of these is true of the good man's relation to himself (and of all other men in so far as they think themselves good; virtue and the good man seem, as has been said,[3] to be the measure of every class of things). For his opinions are harmonious, and he desires the same things with all his soul; and therefore he wishes for himself what is good and what seems so, and does it (for it is characteristic of the good man to work out the good), and does so for his own sake (for he does it for the sake of the intellectual element in him, which is thought to be the man himself); and he wishes himself to live and be preserved, and especially the element by virtue of which he thinks. For existence is good to the virtuous man, and each man wishes himself what is good, while no one chooses to possess the whole world if he has first to become some one else (for that matter, even now God possesses the good); he wishes for this only on condition of being whatever he is; and the element that thinks would seem to be the individual man, or to be so more than any other element in him. And such a man wishes to live with himself; for he does so with pleasure, since the memories of his past acts are delightful and his hopes for the future are good, and therefore pleasant. His mind is well stored too with subjects of contemplation. And he grieves and rejoices, more than any other, with himself; for the same thing is always painful, and the same thing always pleasant, and not one thing at one time and another at another; he has, so to speak, nothing to repent of.

Therefore, since each of these characteristics belongs to the good man in relation to himself, and he is related to his friend as to himself (for his friend is another self), friendship too is thought to be one of these attributes, and those who have these attributes to be friends. Whether there is or is not friendship between a man and himself is a question we may dismiss for the present; there would seem to be friendship in so far as he is two or **1166b** more, to judge from the afore-mentioned attributes of friendship, and from the fact that the extreme of friendship is likened to one's love for oneself.

But the attributes named seem to belong even to the majority of men, poor creatures though they may be. Are we to say then that in so far as they are satisfied with themselves and think they are good, they share in these attributes? Certainly no one who is thoroughly bad and impious has these attributes, or even seems to do so. They hardly belong even to inferior people; for they are at variance with themselves, and have appetites for some things and rational desires for others. This is true, for instance, of incontinent people; for they choose, instead of the things they themselves think good, things that are pleasant but hurtful; while others again, through cowardice and laziness, shrink from doing what they think best for themselves. And those who have done many terrible deeds and are hated for their wickedness even shrink from life and destroy themselves. And wicked men seek for people with whom to spend their days, and shun themselves; for they remember many a grevious deed, and anticipate others like them, when they are by themselves, but when they are with others they forget. And having nothing lovable in them they have no feeling of love to themselves. Therefore also such men

[1] 1157b 22-24. [2] *Ibid.*, 17-24, 1158b 33-35.
[3] 1113a 22-33, cf. 1099a 13.

do not rejoice or grieve with themselves; for their soul is rent by faction, and one element in it by reason of its wickedness grieves when it abstains from certain acts, while the other part is pleased, and one draws them this way and the other that, as if they were pulling them in pieces. If a man cannot at the same time be pained and pleased, at all events after a short time he is pained *because* he was pleased, and he could have wished that these things had not been pleasant to him; for bad men are laden with repentance.

Therefore the bad man does not seem to be amicably disposed even to himself, because there is nothing in him to love; so that if to be thus is the height of wretchedness, we should strain every nerve to avoid wickedness and should endeavour to be good; for so and only so can one be either friendly to oneself or a friend to another.

5

Goodwill is a friendly sort of relation, but is not *identical* with friendship; for one may have goodwill both towards people whom one does not know, and without their knowing it, but not friendship. This has indeed been said already.[1] But goodwill is not even friendly feeling. For it does not involve intensity or desire, whereas these accompany friendly feeling; and friendly feeling implies intimacy while goodwill may arise of a sudden, as it does towards competitors in a contest; we come to feel **1167a** goodwill for them and to share in their wishes, but we would not *do* anything with them; for, as we said, we feel goodwill suddenly and love them only superficially.

Goodwill seems, then, to be a beginning of friendship, as the pleasure of the eye is the beginning of love. For no one loves if he has not first been delighted by the form of the beloved, but he who delights in the form of another does not, for all that, love him, but only does so when he also longs for him when absent and craves for his presence; so too it is not possible for people to be friends if they have not come to feel goodwill for each other, but those who feel goodwill are not for all that friends; for they only *wish* well to those for whom they feel goodwill, and would not do anything with them nor take trouble for them. And so one might by an extension of the term friendship say that goodwill is inactive friendship, though when it is prolonged and reaches the point of intimacy it becomes friendship—not the friendship based on utility nor that based on pleasure; for goodwill too does not arise on those terms. The man who has received a benefit bestows goodwill in return for what has been done to him, but in doing so is only doing what is just; while he who wishes some one to prosper because he hopes for enrichment through him seems to have goodwill not to him but rather to himself, just as a man is not a friend to another if he cherishes him for the sake of some use to be made of him. In general, goodwill arises on account of some excellence and worth, when one man seems to another beautiful or brave or something of the sort, as we pointed out in the case of competitors in a contest.

6

Unanimity also seems to be a friendly relation. For this reason it is not identity of opinion; for that might occur even with people who do not know each other; nor do we say that people who have the same views on any and every subject are unanimous, e.g. those who agree about the heavenly bodies (for unanimity about these is not a friendly relation), but we do say that a city is unanimous when men have the same opinion about what is to their interest, and choose the same actions, and do what they have resolved in common. It is about things to be done, therefore, that people are said to be unanimous, and, among these, about matters of consequence and in which it is possible for both or all parties to get what they want; e.g. a city is unanimous when all its citizens think that the offices in it should be elective, or that they should form an alliance with Sparta, or that Pittacus should be their ruler—at a time when he himself was also willing to rule. But when each of two people wishes himself to have the thing in question, like the captains in the *Phoenissae,*[2] they are in a state of faction; for it is not unanimity when each of two parties thinks of the same thing, whatever that may be, but only when they think of the same thing in the same hands, e.g. when both the common people and those of the better **1167b** class wish the best men to rule; for thus and thus alone do all get what they aim at. Unanimity seems, then, to be political friendship, as indeed it is commonly said to be; for it is concerned with things that are to our interest and have an influence on our life.

Now such unanimity is found among good men; for they are unanimous both in them-

[1] 1155b 32-1156a 5.

[2] Euripides, *The Phoenician Maidens*, 588 ff.

selves and with one another, being, so to say, of one mind (for the wishes of such men are constant and not at the mercy of opposing currents like a strait of the sea), and they wish for what is just and what is advantageous, and these are the objects of their common endeavour as well. But bad men cannot be unanimous except to a small extent, any more than they can be friends, since they aim at getting more than their share of advantages, while in labour and public service they fall short of their share; and each man wishing for advantage to himself criticizes his neighbour and stands in his way; for if people do not watch it carefully the common weal is soon destroyed. The result is that they are in a state of faction, putting compulsion on each other but unwilling themselves to do what is just.

7

Benefactors are thought to love those they have benefited, more than those who have been well treated love those that have treated them well, and this is discussed as though it were paradoxical. Most people think it is because the latter are in the position of debtors and the former of creditors; and therefore as, in the case of loans, debtors wish their creditors did not exist, while creditors actually take care of the safety of their debtors, so it is thought that benefactors wish the objects of their action to exist since they will then get their gratitude, while the beneficiaries take no interest in making this return. Epicharmus would perhaps declare that they say this because they 'look at things on their bad side',[1] but it is quite like human nature; for most people are forgetful, and are more anxious to be well treated than to treat others well. But the cause would seem to be more deeply rooted in the nature of things; the case of those who have lent money is not even analogous. For they have no friendly feeling to their debtors, but only a wish that they may be kept safe with a view to what is to be got from them; while those who have done a service to others feel friendship and love for those they have served even if these are not of any use to them and never will be. This is what happens with craftsmen too; every man loves his own handiwork better than he would be loved by it if it came alive; and this
1168a happens perhaps most of all with poets; for they have an excessive love for their own poems, doting on them as if they were their children. This is what the position of benefactors is like; for that which they have treated well is their handiwork, and therefore they love this more than the handiwork does its maker. The cause of this is that existence is to all men a thing to be chosen and loved, and that we exist by virtue of activity (i.e. by living and acting), and that the handiwork *is* in a sense, the producer in activity; he loves his handiwork, therefore, because he loves existence. And this is rooted in the nature of things; for what he is in potentiality, his handiwork manifests in activity.

At the same time to the benefactor that is noble which depends on his action, so that he delights in the object of his action, whereas to the patient there is nothing noble in the agent, but at most something advantageous, and this is less pleasant and lovable. What *is* pleasant is the activity of the present, the hope of the future, the memory of the past; but most pleasant is that which depends on activity, and similarly this is most lovable. Now for a man who has made something his work remains (for the noble is lasting), but for the person acted on the utility passes away. And the memory of noble things is pleasant, but that of useful things is not likely to be pleasant, or is less so; though the reverse seems true of expectation.

Further, love is like activity, being loved like passivity; and loving and its concomitants are attributes of those who are the more active.

Again, all men love more what they have won by labour; e.g. those who have made their money love it more than those who have inherited it; and to be well treated seems to involve no labour, while to treat others well is a laborious task. These are the reasons, too, why mothers are fonder of their children than fathers; bringing them into the world costs them more pains, and they know better that the children are their own. This last point, too, would seem to apply to benefactors.

8

The question is also debated, whether a man should love himself most, or some one else. People criticize those who love themselves most, and call them self-lovers, using this as an epithet of disgrace, and a bad man seems to do everything for his own sake, and the more so the more wicked he is—and so men reproach him, for instance, with doing nothing of his own accord—while the good man acts for honour's sake, and the more so the better

[1] Fr. 146, Kaibel.

he is, and acts for his friend's sake, and sacrifices his own interest.

But the facts clash with these arguments, and this is not surprising. For men say that one **1168b** ought to love best one's best friend, and man's best friend is one who wishes well to the object of his wish for his sake, even if no one is to know of it; and these attributes are found most of all in a man's attitude towards himself, and so are all the other attributes by which a friend is defined; for, as we have said,[1] it is from this relation that all the characteristics of friendship have extended to our neighbours. All the proverbs, too, agree with this, e.g. 'a single soul',[2] and 'what friends have is common property', and 'friendship is equality', and 'charity begins at home'; for all these marks will be found most in a man's relation to himself; he is his own best friend and therefore ought to love himself best. It is therefore a reasonable question, which of the two views we should follow; for both are plausible.

Perhaps we ought to mark off such arguments from each other and determine how far and in what respects each view is right. Now if we grasp the sense in which each school uses the phrase 'lover of self', the truth may become evident. Those who use the term as one of reproach ascribe self-love to people who assign to themselves the greater share of wealth, honours, and bodily pleasures; for these are what most people desire, and busy themselves about as though they were the best of all things, which is the reason, too, why they become objects of competition. So those who are grasping with regard to these things gratify their appetites and in general their feelings and the irrational element of the soul; and most men are of this nature (which is the reason why the epithet has come to be used as it is—it takes its meaning from the prevailing type of self-love, which is a bad one); it is just, therefore, that men who are lovers of self in this way are reproached for being so. That it is those who give themselves the preference in regard to objects of this sort that most people usually call lovers of self is plain; for if a man were always anxious that he himself, above all things, should act justly, temperately, or in accordance with any other of the virtues, and in general were always to try to secure for himself the honourable course, no one will call such a man a lover of self or blame him.

But such a man would seem more than the other a lover of self; at all events he assigns to himself the things that are noblest and best, and gratifies the most authoritative element in himself and in all things obeys this; and just as a city or any other systematic whole is most properly identified with the most authoritative element in it, so is a man; and therefore the man who loves this and gratifies it is most of all a lover of self. Besides, a man is said to have or not to have self-control according as his reason has or has not the control, on the assumption that this is the man himself; and the things men have done on a rational **1169a** principle are thought most properly their own acts and voluntary acts. That this is the man himself, then, or is so more than anything else, is plain, and also that the good man loves most this part of him. Whence it follows that he is most truly a lover of self, of another type than that which is a matter of reproach, and as different from that as living according to a rational principle is from living as passion dictates, and desiring what is noble from desiring what seems advantageous. Those, then, who busy themselves in an exceptional degree with noble actions all men approve and praise; and if *all* were to strive towards what is noble and strain every nerve to do the noblest deeds, everything would be as it should be for the common weal, and every one would secure for himself the goods that are greatest, since virtue is the greatest of goods.

Therefore the good man should be a lover of self (for he will both himself profit by doing noble acts, and will benefit his fellows), but the wicked man should not; for he will hurt both himself and his neighbours, following as he does evil passions. For the wicked man, what he does clashes with what he ought to do, but what the good man ought to do he does; for reason in each of its possessors chooses what is best for itself, and the good man obeys his reason. It is true of the good man too that he does many acts for the sake of his friends and his country, and if necessary dies for them; for he will throw away both wealth and honours and in general the goods that are objects of competition, gaining for himself nobility; since he would prefer a short period of intense pleasure to a long one of mild enjoyment, a twelvemonth of noble life to many years of humdrum existence, and one great and noble action to many trivial ones. Now those who die for others doubtless attain this result; it is therefore a great prize that they choose for themselves. They will throw away wealth too on condition that their friends will

[1] Chapter 4. [2] Euripides, *Orestes*, 1046.

gain more; for while a man's friend gains wealth he himself achieves nobility; he is therefore assigning the greater good to himself. The same too is true of honour and office; all these things he will sacrifice to his friend; for this is noble and laudable for himself. Rightly then is he thought to be good, since he chooses nobility before all else. But he may even give up actions to his friend; it may be nobler to become the cause of his friend's acting than to act himself. In all the actions, therefore, that men are praised for, the good man is seen to assign to himself the greater share in what is **1169b** noble. In this sense, then, as has been said, a man should be a lover of self; but in the sense in which most men are so, he ought not.

9

It is also disputed whether the happy man will need friends or not. It is said that those who are supremely happy and self-sufficient have no need of friends; for they have the things that are good, and therefore being self-sufficient they need nothing further, while a friend, being another self, furnishes what a man cannot provide by his own effort; whence the saying 'when fortune is kind, what need of friends?'[1] But it seems strange, when one assigns all good things to the happy man, not to assign friends, who are thought the greatest of external goods. And if it is more characteristic of a friend to do well by another than to be well done by, and to confer benefits is characteristic of the good man and of virtue, and it is nobler to do well by friends than by strangers, the good man will need people to do well by. This is why the question is asked whether we need friends more in prosperity or in adversity, on the assumption that not only does a man in adversity need people to confer benefits on him, but also those who are prospering need people to do well by. Surely it is strange, too, to make the supremely happy man a solitary; for no one would choose the whole world on condition of being alone, since man is a political creature and one whose nature is to live with others. Therefore even the happy man lives with others; for he has the things that are by nature good. And plainly it is better to spend his days with friends and good men than with strangers or any chance persons. Therefore the happy man needs friends.

What then is it that the first school means, and in what respect is it right? Is it that most men identify friends with useful people? Of such friends indeed the supremely happy man will have no need, since he already has the things that are good; nor will he need those whom one makes one's friends because of their pleasantness, or he will need them only to a small extent (for his life, being pleasant, has no need of adventitious pleasure); and because he does not need *such* friends he is thought not to need friends.

But that is surely not true. For we have said at the outset[2] that happiness is an activity; and activity plainly comes into being and is not present at the start like a piece of property. If (1) happiness lies in living and being active, and the good man's activity is virtuous and pleasant in itself, as we have said at the outset,[3] and (2) a thing's being one's own is one of the attributes that make it pleasant, and (3) we can contemplate our neighbours better than ourselves and their actions better than our own, and if the actions of virtuous men who are their friends are pleasant to good **1170a** men (since these have both the attributes that are naturally pleasant),—if this be so, the supremely happy man will need friends of this sort, since his purpose is to contemplate worthy actions and actions that are his own, and the actions of a good man who is his friend have both these qualities.

Further, men think that the happy man ought to live pleasantly. Now if he were a solitary, life would be hard for him; for by oneself it is not easy to be continuously active; but with others and towards others it is easier. With others therefore his activity will be more continuous, and it is in itself pleasant, as it ought to be for the man who is supremely happy; for a good man *qua* good delights in virtuous actions and is vexed at vicious ones, as a musical man enjoys beautiful tunes but is pained at bad ones. A certain training in virtue arises also from the company of the good, as Theognis has said before us.

If we look deeper into the nature of things, a virtuous friend seems to be naturally desirable for a virtuous man. For that which is good by nature, we have said,[4] is for the virtuous man good and pleasant in itself. Now life is defined in the case of animals by the power of perception in that of man by the power of perception or thought; and a power is defined by reference to the corresponding activity, which is the essential thing; therefore life seems to be essentially the act of perceiving or

[1] Euripides, *Orestes*, 667.

[2] 1098a 16b, 31-1099a 7.

[3] 1099a 14, 21.

[4] 1099a 7-11, 1113a 25-33.

thinking. And life is among the things that are good and pleasant in themselves, since it is determinate and the determinate is of the nature of the good; and that which is good by nature is also good for the virtuous man (which is the reason why life seems pleasant to all men); but we must not apply this to a wicked and corrupt life nor to a life spent in pain; for such a life is indeterminate, as are its attributes. The nature of pain will become plainer in what follows.[1] But if life itself is good and pleasant (which it seems to be, from the very fact that all men desire it, and particularly those who are good and supremely happy; for to such men life is most desirable, and their existence is the most supremely happy) and if he who sees perceives that he sees, and he who hears, that he hears, and he who walks, that he walks, and in the case of all other activities similarly there is something which perceives that we are active, so that if we perceive, we perceive that we perceive, and if we think, that we think; and if to perceive that we perceive or think is to perceive that we exist (for existence was defined as perceiving or thinking); **1170b** and if perceiving that one lives is in itself one of the things that are pleasant (for life is by nature good, and to perceive what is good present in oneself is pleasant); and if life is desirable, and particularly so for good men, because to them existence is good and pleasant (for they are pleased at the consciousness of the presence in them of what is in itself good); and if as the virtuous man is to himself, he is to his friend also (for his friend is another self): —if all this be true, as his own being is desirable for each man, so, or almost so, is that of his friend. Now his being was seen to be desirable because he perceived his own goodness, and such perception is pleasant in itself. He needs, therefore, to be conscious of the existence of his friend as well, and this will be realized in their living together and sharing in discussion and thought; for this is what living together would seem to mean in the case of man, and not, as in the case of cattle, feeding in the same place.

If, then, being is in itself desirable for the supremely happy man (since it is by its nature good and pleasant), and that of his friend is very much the same, a friend will be one of the things that are desirable. Now that which is desirable for him he must have, or he will be deficient in this respect. The man who is to be happy will therefore need virtuous friends.

[1] x. 1-5.

10

Should we, then, make as many friends as possible, or—as in the case of hospitality it is thought to be suitable advice, that one should be 'neither a man of many guests nor a man with none'[2]—will that apply to friendship as well; should a man neither be friendless nor have an excessive number of friends?

To friends made with a view to *utility* this saying would seem thoroughly applicable; for to do services to many people in return is a laborious task and life is not long enough for its performance. Therefore friends in excess of those who are sufficient for our own life are superfluous, and hindrances to the noble life; so that we have no need of them. Of friends made with a view to *pleasure,* also, few are enough, as a little seasoning in food is enough.

But as regards *good* friends, should we have as many as possible, or is there a limit to the number of one's friends, as there is to the size of a city? You cannot make a city of ten men, and if there are a hundred thousand it is a city no longer. But the proper number is presumably not a single number, but anything that falls between certain fixed points. So for **1171a** friends too there is a fixed number—perhaps the largest number with whom one can live together (for that, we found,[3] is thought to be very characteristic of friendship); and that one cannot live with many people and divide oneself up among them is plain. Further, they too must be friends of one another, if they are all to spend their days together; and it is a hard business for this condition to be fulfilled with a large number. It is found difficult, too, to rejoice and to grieve in an intimate way with many people, for it may likely happen that one has at once to be happy with one friend and to mourn with another. Presumably, then, it is well not to seek to have as many friends as possible, but as many as are enough for the purpose of living together; for it would seem actually impossible to be a great friend to many people. This is why one cannot love several people; love is ideally a sort of excess of friendship, and that can only be felt towards one person; therefore great friendship too can only be felt towards a few people. This seems to be confirmed in practice; for we do not find many people who are friends in the comradely way of friendship,

[2] Hesiod, *Works and Days*, 750, Rzach.

[3] 1157b 19, 1158a 3, 10.

and the famous friendships of this sort are always between two people. Those who have many friends and mix intimately with them all are thought to be no one's friend, except in the way proper to fellow-citizens, and such people are also called obsequious. In the way proper to fellow-citizens, indeed, it is possible to be the friend of many and yet not be obsequious but a genuinely good man; but one cannot have with many people the friendship based on virtue and on the character of our friends themselves, and we must be content if we find even a few such.

11

Do we need friends more in good fortune or in bad? They are sought after in both; for while men in adversity need help, in prosperity they need people to live with and to make the objects of their beneficence; for they wish to do well by others. Friendship, then, is more necessary in bad fortune, and so it is useful friends that one wants in this case; but it is more noble in good fortune, and so we also seek for good men as our friends, since it is more desirable to confer benefits on these and to live with these. For the very presence of friends is pleasant both in good fortune and also in bad, since grief is lightened when friends sorrow with us. Hence one might ask whether they share as it were our burden, or—without that happening—their presence by its pleasantness, and the thought of their grieving with us, make our pain less. Whether it is for these reasons or for some other that our grief is lightened, is a question that may be dismissed; at all events what we have described appears to take place.

But their presence seems to contain a mixture of various factors. The very seeing of one's friends is pleasant, especially if one is
1171b in adversity, and becomes a safeguard against grief (for a friend tends to comfort us both by the sight of him and by his words, if he is tactful, since he knows our character and the things that please or pain us); but to see him pained at our misfortunes is painful; for every one shuns being a cause of pain to his friends. For this reason people of a manly nature guard against making their friends grieve with them, and, unless he be exceptionally insensible to pain, such a man cannot stand the pain that ensues for his friends, and in general does not admit fellow-mourners because he is not himself given to mourning; but women and womanly men enjoy sympathisers in their grief, and love them as friends and companions in sorrow. But in all things one obviously ought to imitate the better type of person.

On the other hand, the presence of friends in our *prosperity* implies both a pleasant passing of our time and the pleasant thought of their pleasure at our own good fortune. For this cause it would seem that we ought to summon our friends readily to share our good fortunes (for the beneficent character is a noble one), but summon them to our bad fortunes with hesitation; for we ought to give them as little a share as possible in our evils—whence the saying 'enough is *my* misfortune'.[1] We should summon friends to us most of all when they are likely by suffering a few inconveniences to do us a great service.

Conversely, it is fitting to go unasked and readily to the aid of those in adversity (for it is characteristic of a friend to render services, and especially to those who are in need and have not demanded them; such action is nobler and pleasanter for both persons); but when our friends are prosperous we should join readily in their activities (for they need friends for these too), but be tardy in coming forward to be the objects of their kindness; for it is not noble to be keen to receive benefits. Still, we must no doubt avoid getting the reputation of kill-joys by repulsing them; for that sometimes happens.

The presence of friends, then, seems desirable in all circumstances.

12

Does it not follow, then, that, as for lovers the sight of the beloved is the thing they love most, and they prefer this sense to the others because on it love depends most for its being and for its origin, so for friends the most desirable thing is living together? For friendship is a partnership, and as a man is to himself, so is he to his friend; now in his own case the consciousness of his being is desirable, and so therefore is the consciousness of his friend's being, and the activity of this con-
1172a sciousness is produced when they live together, so that it is natural that they aim at this. And whatever existence means for each class of men, whatever it is for whose sake they value life, in *that* they wish to occupy themselves with their friends; and so some drink together, others dice together, others join in athletic exercises and hunting, or in the

[1] Fr. adesp. 76, Nauck.

study of philosophy, each class spending their days together in whatever they love most in life; for since they wish to live with their friends, they do and share in those things which give them the sense of living together. Thus the friendship of bad men turns out an evil thing (for because of their instability they unite in bad pursuits, and besides they become evil by becoming like each other), while the friendship of good men is good, being augmented by their companionship; and they are thought to become better too by their activities and by improving each other; for from each other they take the mould of the characteristics they approve—whence the saying 'noble deeds from noble men'.[1]—So much, then, for friendship; our next task must be to discuss pleasure.

BOOK X

1

After these matters we ought perhaps next to discuss pleasure. For it is thought to be most intimately connected with our human nature, which is the reason why in educating the young we steer them by the rudders of pleasure and pain; it is thought, too, that to enjoy the things we ought and to hate the things we ought has the greatest bearing on virtue of character. For these things extend right through life, with a weight and power of their own in respect both to virtue and to the happy life, since men choose what is pleasant and avoid what is painful; and such things, it will be thought, we should least of all omit to discuss, especially since they admit of much dispute. For some say pleasure is the good, while others, on the contrary, say it is thoroughly bad—some no doubt being persuaded that the facts are so, and others thinking it has a better effect on our life to exhibit pleasure as a bad thing even if it is not; for most people (they think) incline towards it and are the slaves of their pleasures, for which reason they ought to lead them in the opposite direction, since thus they will reach the middle state. But surely this is not correct. For arguments about matters concerned with feelings and actions are less reliable than facts: and so when they clash with the facts of perception they are despised, and discredit the truth as **1172b** well; if a man who runs down pleasure is once seen to be aiming at it, his inclining towards it is thought to imply that it is all worthy of being aimed at; for most people are not good at drawing distinctions. True arguments seem, then, most useful, not only with a view to knowledge, but with a view to life also; for since they harmonize with the facts they are believed, and so they stimulate those who understand them to live according to them.—Enough of such questions; let us proceed to review the opinions that have been expressed about pleasure.

2

Eudoxus thought pleasure was the good because he saw all things, both rational and irrational, aiming at it, and because in all things that which is the object of choice is what is excellent, and that which is most the object of choice the greatest good; thus the fact that all things moved towards the same object indicated that this was for all things the chief good (for each thing, he argued, finds its own good, as it finds its own nourishment); and that which is good for all things and at which all aim was *the* good. His arguments were credited more because of the excellence of his character than for their own sake; he was thought to be remarkably self-controlled, and therefore it was thought that he was not saying what he did say as a friend of pleasure, but that the facts really were so. He believed that the same conclusion followed no less plainly from a study of the contrary of pleasure; pain was in itself an object of aversion to all things, and therefore its contrary must be similarly an object of choice. And again that is most an object of choice which we choose not because or for the sake of something else, and pleasure is admittedly of this nature; for no one asks to what end he is pleased, thus implying that pleasure is in itself an object of choice. Further, he argued that pleasure when added to any good, e.g. to just or temperate action, makes it more worthy of choice, and that it is only by itself that the good can be increased.

This argument seems to show it to be one of the goods, and no more a good than any other; for every good is more worthy of choice along with another good than taken alone. And so it is by an argument of this kind that Plato[2]

[1] Theognis, 35.

[2] *Philebus*, 60.

proves the good *not* to be pleasure; he argues that the pleasant life is more desirable with wisdom than without, and that if the mixture is better, pleasure is not the good; for the good cannot become more desirable by the addition of anything to it. Now it is clear that nothing else, any more than pleasure, can be the good if it is made more desirable by the addition of any of the things that are good in themselves. What, then, is there that satisfies this criterion, which at the same time we can participate in? It is something of this sort that we are looking for. Those who object that that at which all things aim is not necessarily good are, we may surmise, talking nonsense. For we say that **1173a** that which every one thinks really is so; and the man who attacks this belief will hardly have anything more credible to maintain instead. If it is senseless creatures that desire the things in question, there might be something in what they say; but if intelligent creatures do so as well, what sense can there be in this view? But perhaps even in inferior creatures there is some natural good stronger than themselves which aims at their proper good.

Nor does the argument about the contrary of pleasure seem to be correct. They say that if pain is an evil it does not follow that pleasure is a good; for evil is opposed to evil and at the same time both are opposed to the neutral state—which is correct enough but does not apply to the things in question. For if both pleasure and pain belonged to the class of evils they ought both to be objects of aversion, while if they belonged to the class of neutrals neither should be an object of aversion or they should both be equally so; but in fact people evidently avoid the one as evil and choose the other as good; that then must be the nature of the opposition between them.

3

Nor again, if pleasure is not a quality, does it follow that it is not a good; for the activities of virtue are not qualities either, nor is happiness. They say, however, that the good is determinate, while pleasure is indeterminate, because it admits of degrees. Now if it is from the feeling of pleasure that they judge thus, the same will be true of justice and the other virtues, in respect of which we plainly say that people of a certain character are so more or less, and act more or less in accordance with these virtues; for people may be more just or brave, and it is possible also to act justly or temperately more or less. But if their judgement is based on the various pleasures, surely they are not stating the real cause, if in fact some pleasures are unmixed and others mixed. Again, just as health admits of degrees without being indeterminate, why should not pleasure? The same proportion is not found in all things, nor a single proportion always in the same thing, but it may be relaxed and yet persist up to a point, and it may differ in degree. The case of pleasure also may therefore be of this kind.

Again, they assume[1] that the good is perfect while movements and comings into being are imperfect, and try to exhibit pleasure as being a movement and a coming into being. But they do not seem to be right even in saying that it is a movement. For speed and slowness are thought to be proper to every movement, and if a movement, e.g. that of the heavens, has not speed or slowness in itself, it has it in relation to something else; but of pleasure neither of these things is true. For while we may *become* pleased quickly as we may become angry quick- **1173b** ly, we cannot *be* pleased quickly, not even in relation to some one else, while we *can* walk, or grow, or the like, quickly. While, then, we can change quickly or slowly into a state of pleasure, we cannot quickly exhibit the activity of pleasure, i.e. be pleased. Again, how can it be a coming into being? It is not thought that any chance thing can come out of any chance thing, but that a thing is dissolved into that out of which it comes into being; and pain would be the destruction of that of which pleasure is the coming into being.

They say, too,[2] that pain is the lack of that which is according to nature, and pleasure is replenishment. But these experiences are bodily. If then pleasure is replenishment with that which is according to nature, that which feels pleasure will be that in which the replenishment takes place, i.e. the body; but that is not thought to be the case; therefore the replenishment is not pleasure, though one would be pleased when replenishment was taking place, just as one would be pained if one was being operated on. This opinion seems to be based on the pains and pleasures connected with nutrition; on the fact that when people have been short of food and have felt pain beforehand they are pleased by the replenishment. But this does not happen with all pleasures; for the pleasures of learning and, among the sensuous pleasures, those of smell, and also many sounds and sights, and memories and

[1] Plato, *Philebus*, 53-54.

[2] *Ibid.*, 31-32, 42.

hopes, do not presuppose pain. Of what then will these be the coming into being? There has not been lack of anything of which they could be the supplying anew.

In reply to those who bring forward the disgraceful pleasures one may say that these are not pleasant; if things are pleasant to people of vicious constitution, we must not suppose that they are also pleasant to others than these, just as we do not reason so about the things that are wholesome or sweet or bitter to sick people, or ascribe whiteness to the things that seem white to those suffering from a disease of the eye. Or one might answer thus—that the pleasures are desirable, but not from *these* sources, as wealth is desirable, but not as the reward of betrayal, and health, but not at the cost of eating anything and everything. Or perhaps pleasures differ in kind; for those derived from noble sources are different from those derived from base sources, and one cannot get the pleasure of the just man without being just, nor that of the musical man without being musical, and so on.

The fact, too, that a friend is different from a flatterer seems to make it plain that pleasure is not a good or that pleasures are different in kind; for the one is thought to consort with us with a view to the good, the other with a view to our pleasure, and the one is reproached for his conduct while the other is praised on the ground that he consorts with us for different
1174a ends. And no one would choose to live with the intellect of a child throughout his life, however much he were to be pleased at the things that children are pleased at, nor to get enjoyment by doing some most disgraceful deed, though he were never to feel any pain in consequence. And there are many things we should be keen about even if they brought no pleasure, e.g. seeing, remembering, knowing, possessing the virtues. If pleasures necessarily do accompany these, that makes no odds; we should choose these even if no pleasure resulted. It seems to be clear, then, that neither is pleasure the good nor is all pleasure desirable, and that some pleasures *are* desirable in themselves, differing in kind or in their sources from the others. So much for the things that are said about pleasure and pain.

4

What pleasure is, or what kind of thing it is, will become plainer if we take up the question again from the beginning. Seeing seems to be at any moment complete, for it does not lack anything which coming into being later will complete its form; and pleasure also seems to be of this nature. For it is a whole, and at no time can one find a pleasure whose form will be completed if the pleasure lasts longer. For this reason, too, it is not a movement. For every movement (e.g. that of building) takes time and is for the sake of an end, and is complete when it has made what it aims at. It is complete, therefore, only in the whole time or at that final moment. In their parts and during the time they occupy, all movements are incomplete, and are different in kind from the whole movement and from each other. For the fitting together of the stones is different from the fluting of the column, and these are both different from the making of the temple; and the making of the temple is complete (for it lacks nothing with a view to the end proposed), but the making of the base or of the triglyph is incomplete; for each is the making of only a part. They differ in kind, then, and it is not possible to find at any and every time a movement complete in form, but if at all, only in the whole time. So, too, in the case of walking and all other movements. For if locomotion is a movement from here to there, it, too, has differences in kind—flying, walking, leaping, and so on. And not only so, but in walking itself there are such differences; for the whence and whither are not the same in the whole racecourse and in a part of it, nor in one part and in another, nor
1174b is it the same thing to traverse this line and that; for one traverses not only a line but one which is in a place, and this one is in a different place from that. We have discussed movement with precision in another work,[1] but it seems that it is not complete at any and every time, but that the many movements are incomplete and different in kind, since the whence and whither give them their form. But of pleasure the form is complete at any and every time. Plainly, then, pleasure and movement must be different from each other, and pleasure must be one of the things that are whole and complete. This would seem to be the case, too, from the fact that it is not possible to move otherwise than in time, but it *is* possible to be pleased; for that which takes place in a moment is a whole.

From these considerations it is clear, too, that these thinkers are not right in saying there is a movement or a coming into being *of* pleasure. For these cannot be ascribed to all

[1] *Physics*, VI-VIII.

things, but only to those that are divisible and not wholes; there is no coming into being of seeing nor of a point nor of a unit, nor is any of these a movement or coming into being; therefore there is no movement or coming into being of pleasure either; for it is a whole.

Since every sense is active in relation to its object, and a sense which is in good condition acts perfectly in relation to the most beautiful of its objects (for perfect activity seems to be ideally of this nature; whether we say that *it* is active, or the organ in which it resides, may be assumed to be immaterial), it follows that in the case of each sense the best activity is that of the best-conditioned organ in relation to the finest of its objects. And this activity will be the most complete and pleasant. For, while there is pleasure in respect of any sense, and in respect of thought and contemplation no less, the most complete is pleasantest, and that of a well-conditioned organ in relation to the worthiest of its objects is the most complete; and the pleasure completes the activity. But the pleasure does not complete it in the same way as the combination of object and sense, both good, just as health and the doctor are not in the same way the cause of a man's being healthy. (That pleasure is produced in respect to each sense is plain; for we speak of sights and sounds as pleasant. It is also plain that it arises most of all when both the sense is at its best and it is active in reference to an object which corresponds; when both object and perceiver are of the best there will always be pleasure, since the requisite agent and patient are both present.) Pleasure completes the activity not as the corresponding permanent state does, by its immanence, but as an end which supervenes as the bloom of youth does on those in the flower of their age. So long, then, as both the intelligible or sensible object and the discriminating or contemplative faculty are as they should be, the pleasure will be involved in the activity; for when
1175a both the passive and the active factor are unchanged and are related to each other in the same way, the same result naturally follows.

How, then, is it that no one is continuously pleased? Is it that we grow weary? Certainly all human beings are incapable of continuous activity. Therefore pleasure also is not continuous; for it accompanies activity. Some things delight us when they are new, but later do so less, for the same reason; for at first the mind is in a state of stimulation and intensely active about them, as people are with respect to their vision when they look hard at a thing, but afterwards our activity is not of this kind, but has grown relaxed; for which reason the pleasure also is dulled.

One might think that all men desire pleasure because they all aim at life; life is an activity, and each man is active about those things and with those faculties that he loves most; e.g. the musician is active with his hearing in reference to tunes, the student with his mind in reference to theoretical questions, and so on in each case; now pleasure completes the activities, and therefore life, which they desire. It is with good reason, then, that they aim at pleasure too, since for every one it completes life, which is desirable. But whether we choose life for the sake of pleasure or pleasure for the sake of life is a question we may dismiss for the present. For they seem to be bound up together and not to admit of separation, since without activity pleasure does not arise, and every activity is completed by the attendant pleasure.

5

For this reason pleasures seem, too, to differ in kind. For things different in kind are, we think, completed by different things (we see this to be true both of natural objects and of things produced by art, e.g. animals, trees, a painting, a sculpture, a house, an implement); and, similarly, we think that activities differing in kind are completed by things differing in kind. Now the activities of thought differ from those of the senses, and both differ among themselves, in kind; so, therefore, do the pleasures that complete them.

This may be seen, too, from the fact that each of the pleasures is bound up with the activity it completes. For an activity is intensified by its proper pleasure, since each class of things is better judged of and brought to precision by those who engage in the activity with pleasure; e.g. it is those who enjoy geometrical thinking that become geometers and grasp the various propositions better, and, similarly, those who are fond of music or of building, and so on, make progress in their proper function by enjoying it; so the pleasures intensify the activities, and what intensifies a thing is proper to it, but things different in kind have properties different in kind.

1175b This will be even more apparent from the fact that activities are hindered by pleasures arising from other sources. For people who are fond of playing the flute are incapable of attending to arguments if they overhear some one playing the flute, since they enjoy flute-playing more than the activity in hand; so the pleasure connected with flute-playing destroys the activity concerned with argument. This happens, similarly, in all other cases, when one is active about two things at once; the more pleasant activity drives out the other, and if it is much more pleasant does so all the more, so that one even ceases from the other. This is why when we enjoy anything very much we do not throw ourselves into anything else, and do one thing only when we are not much pleased by another; e.g. in the theatre the people who eat sweets do so most when the actors are poor. Now since activities are made precise and more enduring and better by their proper pleasure, and injured by alien pleasures, evidently the two kinds of pleasure are far apart. For alien pleasures do pretty much what proper pains do, since activities are destroyed by their proper pains; e.g. if a man finds writing or doing sums unpleasant and painful, he does not write, or does not do sums, because the activity is painful. So an activity suffers contrary effects from its proper pleasures and pains, i.e. from those that supervene on it in virtue of its own nature. And alien pleasures have been stated to do much the same as pain; they destroy the activity, only not to the same degree.

Now since activities differ in respect of goodness and badness, and some are worthy to be chosen, others to be avoided, and others neutral, so, too, are the pleasures; for to each activity there is a proper pleasure. The pleasure proper to a worthy activity is good and that proper to an unworthy activity bad; just as the appetites for noble objects are laudable, those for base objects culpable. But the pleasures involved in activities are more proper to them than the desires; for the latter are separated both in time and in nature, while the former are close to the activities, and so hard to distinguish from them that it admits of dispute whether the activity is not the same as the pleasure. (Still, pleasure does not seem to *be* thought or perception—that would be strange; but because they are not found apart they appear to some people the same.) As activities are different, then, so are the corresponding pleasures. **1176a** Now sight is superior to touch in purity, and hearing and smell to taste; the pleasures, therefore, are similarly superior, and those of thought superior to these, and within each of the two kinds some are superior to others.

Each animal is thought to have a proper pleasure, as it has a proper function; viz. that which corresponds to its activity. If we survey them species by species, too, this will be evident; horse, dog, and man have different pleasures, as Heraclitus says 'asses would prefer sweepings to gold';[1] for food is pleasanter than gold to asses. So the pleasures of creatures different in kind differ in kind, and it is plausible to suppose that those of a single species do not differ. But they vary to no small extent, in the case of men at least; the same things delight some people and pain others, and are painful and odious to some, and pleasant to and liked by others. This happens, too, in the case of sweet things; the same things do not seem sweet to a man in a fever and a healthy man—nor hot to a weak man and one in good condition. The same happens in other cases. But in all such matters that which appears to the good man is thought to be really so. If this is correct, as it seems to be, and virtue and the good man as such are the measure of each thing, those also will be pleasures which appear so to him, and those things pleasant which he enjoys. If the things he finds tiresome seem pleasant to some one, that is nothing surprising; for men may be ruined and spoilt in many ways; but the things are not pleasant, but only pleasant to these people and to people in this condition. Those which are admittedly disgraceful plainly should not be said to be pleasures, except to a perverted taste; but of those that are thought to be good what kind of pleasure or what pleasure should be said to be that proper to man? Is it not plain from the corresponding activities? The pleasures follow these. Whether, then, the perfect and supremely happy man has one or more activities, the pleasures that perfect these will be said in the strict sense to be pleasures proper to man, and the rest will be so in a secondary and fractional way, as are the activities.

6

Now that we have spoken of the virtues, the forms of friendship, and the varieties of pleasure, what remains is to discuss in outline the nature of happiness, since this is what we state the end of human nature to be. Our discussion will be the more concise if we first sum up what we have said already. We said,[2] then, that it is not a disposition; for if it were it might belong to some one who was asleep throughout his life, living the life of a plant,

[1] Fr. 9, Diels. [2] 1095b 31-1096a 2, 1098b 31-1099a 7.

or, again, to some one who was suffering the greatest misfortunes. If these implications **1176^{b}** are unacceptable, and we must rather class happiness as an activity, as we have said before,[1] and if some activities are necessary, and desirable for the sake of something else, while others are so in themselves, evidently happiness must be placed among those desirable in themselves, not among those desirable for the sake of something else; for happiness does not lack anything, but is self-sufficient. Now those activities are desirable in themselves from which nothing is sought beyond the activity. And of this nature virtuous actions are thought to be; for to do noble and good deeds is a thing desirable for its own sake.

Pleasant amusements also are thought to be of this nature; we choose them not for the sake of other things; for we are injured rather than benefited by them, since we are led to neglect our bodies and our property. But most of the people who are deemed happy take refuge in such pastimes, which is the reason why those who are ready-witted at them are highly esteemed at the courts of tyrants; they make themselves pleasant companions in the tyrants' favourite pursuits, and that is the sort of man they want. Now these things are thought to be of the nature of happiness because people in despotic positions spend their leisure in them, but perhaps such people prove nothing; for virtue and reason, from which good activities flow, do not depend on despotic position; nor, if these people, who have never tasted pure and generous pleasure, take refuge in the bodily pleasures, should these for that reason be thought more desirable; for boys, too, think the things that are valued among themselves are the best. It is to be expected, then, that, as different things seem valuable to boys and to men, so they should to bad men and to good. Now, as we have often maintained,[2] those things are both valuable and pleasant which are such to the good man; and to each man the activity in accordance with his own disposition is most desirable, and, therefore, to the good man that which is in accordance with virtue. Happiness, therefore, does not lie in amusement; it would, indeed, be strange if the end were amusement, and one were to take trouble and suffer hardship all one's life in order to amuse oneself. For, in a word, everything that we choose we choose for the sake of something else—except happiness, which is an end. Now to exert oneself and work for the sake of amusement seems silly and utterly childish. But to amuse oneself in order that one may exert oneself, as Anacharsis puts it, seems right; for amusement is a sort of relaxation, and we need relaxation because we cannot work continuously. Relaxation, then, is not an end; for it is taken for the sake of activity.

1177^{a} The happy life is thought to be virtuous; now a virtuous life requires exertion, and does not consist in amusement. And we say that serious things are better than laughable things and those connected with amusement, and that the activity of the better of any two things—whether it be two elements of our being or two men—is the more serious; but the activity of the better is *ipso facto* superior and more of the nature of happiness. And any chance person—even a slave—can enjoy the bodily pleasures no less than the best man; but no one assigns to a slave a share in happiness—unless he assigns to him also a share in human life. For happiness does not lie in such occupations, but, as we have said before,[3] in virtuous activities.

7

If happiness is activity in accordance with virtue, it is reasonable that it should be in accordance with the highest virtue; and this will be that of the best thing in us. Whether it be reason or something else that is this element which is thought to be our natural ruler and guide and to take thought of things noble and divine, whether it be itself also divine or only the most divine element in us, the activity of this in accordance with its proper virtue will be perfect happiness. That this activity is contemplative we have already said.[4]

Now this would seem to be in agreement both with what we said before[5] and with the truth. For, firstly, this activity is the best (since not only is reason the best thing in us, but the objects of reason are the best of knowable objects); and secondly, it is the most continuous, since we can contemplate truth more continuously than we can *do* anything. And we think happiness has pleasure mingled with it, but the activity of philosophic wisdom is ad-

[1] 1098^{a} 5-7.

[2] 1099^{a} 13, 1113^{a} 22-33, 1166^{a} 12, 1170^{a} 14-16, 1176^{a} 15-22.

[3] 1098^{a} 16, 1176^{a} 35-^{b}9.

[4] Cf. 1095^{b} 14-1096^{a} 5, 1141^{a} 18-^{b} 3, 1143^{b} 33-1144^{a} 6, 1145^{a} 6-11.

[5] 1097^{a} 25-^{b} 21, 1099^{a} 7-21, 1173^{b} 15-19, 1174^{b} 20-23, 1175^{b} 36-1176^{a} 3.

mittedly the pleasantest of virtuous activities; at all events the pursuit of it is thought to offer pleasures marvellous for their purity and their enduringness, and it is to be expected that those who know will pass their time more pleasantly than those who inquire. And the self-sufficiency that is spoken of must belong most to the contemplative activity. For while a philosopher, as well as a just man or one possessing any other virtue, needs the necessaries of life, when they are sufficiently equipped with things of that sort the just man needs people towards whom and with whom he shall act justly, and the temperate man, the brave man, and each of the others is in the same case, but the philosopher, even when by himself, can contemplate truth, and the better the wiser he is; he can perhaps do so better if he has fellow-**1177b** workers, but still he is the most self-sufficient. And this activity alone would seem to be loved for its own sake; for nothing arises from it apart from the contemplating, while from practical activities we gain more or less apart from the action. And happiness is thought to depend on leisure; for we are busy that we may have leisure, and make war that we may live in peace. Now the activity of the practical virtues is exhibited in political or military affairs, but the actions concerned with these seem to be unleisurely. Warlike actions are completely so (for no one chooses to be at war, or provokes war, for the sake of being at war; any one would seem absolutely murderous if he were to make enemies of his friends in order to bring about battle and slaughter); but the action of the statesman is also unleisurely, and—apart from the political action itself—aims at despotic power and honours, or at all events happiness, for him and his fellow citizens—a happiness different from political action, and evidently sought as being different. So if among virtuous actions political and military actions are distinguished by nobility and greatness, and these are unleisurely and aim at an end and are not desirable for their own sake, but the activity of reason, which is contemplative, seems both to be superior in serious worth and to aim at no end beyond itself, and to have its pleasure proper to itself (and this augments the activity), and the self-sufficiency, leisureliness, unweariedness (so far as this is possible for man), and all the other attributes ascribed to the supremely happy man are evidently those connected with this activity, it follows that this will be the complete happiness of man, if it be allowed a complete term of life (for none of the attributes of happiness is *in*complete).

But such a life would be too high for man; for it is not in so far as he is man that he will live so, but in so far as something divine is present in him; and by so much as this is superior to our composite nature is its activity superior to that which is the exercise of the other kind of virtue. If reason is divine, then, in comparison with man, the life according to it is divine in comparison with human life. But we must not follow those who advise us, being men, to think of human things, and, being mortal, of mortal things, but must, so far as we can, make ourselves immortal, and strain every nerve to live in accordance with the best thing **1178a** in us; for even if it be small in bulk, much more does it in power and worth surpass everything. This would seem, too, to be each man himself, since it is the authoritative and better part of him. It would be strange, then, if he were to choose not the life of his self but that of something else. And what we said before[1] will apply now; that which is proper to each thing is by nature best and most pleasant for each thing; for man, therefore, the life according to reason is best and pleasantest, since reason more than anything else *is* man. This life therefore is also the happiest.

8

But in a secondary degree the life in accordance with the other kind of virtue is happy; for the activities in accordance with this befit our human estate. Just and brave acts, and other virtuous acts, we do in relation to each other, observing our respective duties with regard to contracts and services and all manner of actions and with regard to passions; and all of these seem to be typically human. Some of them seem even to arise from the body, and virtue of character to be in many ways bound up with the passions. Practical wisdom, too, is linked to virtue of character, and this to practical wisdom, since the principles of practical wisdom are in accordance with the moral virtues and rightness in morals is in accordance with practical wisdom. Being connected with the passions also, the moral virtues must belong to our composite nature; and the virtues of our composite nature are human; so, therefore, are the life and the happiness which correspond to these. The excellence of the reason is a thing apart; we must be content to say this much about it, for to describe it

[1] 1169b 33, 1176b 26.

precisely is a task greater than our purpose requires. It would seem, however, also to need external equipment but little, or less than moral virtue does. Grant that both need the necessaries, and do so equally, even if the statesman's work is the more concerned with the body and things of that sort; for there will be little difference there; but in what they need for the exercise of their activities there will be much difference. The liberal man will need money for the doing of his liberal deeds, and the just man too will need it for the returning of services (for wishes are hard to discern, and even people who are not just pretend to wish to act justly); and the brave man will need power if he is to accomplish any of the acts that correspond to his virtue, and the temperate man will need opportunity; for how else is either he or any of the others to be recognized? It is debated, too, whether the will or the deed is more essential to virtue, which is assumed to involve both; it is surely clear **1178b** that its perfection involves both; but for deeds many things are needed, and more, the greater and nobler the deeds are. But the man who is contemplating the truth needs no such thing, at least with a view to the exercise of his activity; indeed they are, one may say, even hindrances, at all events to his contemplation; but in so far as he is a man and lives with a number of people, he chooses to do virtuous acts; he will therefore need such aids to living a human life.

But that perfect happiness is a contemplative activity will appear from the following consideration as well. We assume the gods to be above all other beings blessed and happy; but what sort of actions must we assign to them? Acts of justice? Will not the gods seem absurd if they make contracts and return deposits, and so on? Acts of a brave man, then, confronting dangers and running risks because it is noble to do so? Or liberal acts? To whom will they give? It will be strange if they are really to have money or anything of the kind. And what would their temperate acts be? Is not such praise tasteless, since they have no bad appetites? If we were to run through them all, the circumstances of action would be found trivial and unworthy of gods. Still, every one supposes that they *live* and therefore that they are active; we cannot suppose them to sleep like Endymion. Now if you take away from a living being action, and still more production, what is left but contemplation? Therefore the activity of God, which surpasses all others in blessedness, must be contemplative; and of human activities, therefore, that which is most akin to this must be most of the nature of happiness.

This is indicated, too, by the fact that the other animals have no share in happiness, being completely deprived of such activity. For while the whole life of the gods is blessed, and that of men too in so far as some likeness of such activity belongs to them, none of the other animals is happy, since they in no way share in contemplation. Happiness extends, then, just so far as contemplation does, and those to whom contemplation more fully belongs are more truly happy, not as a mere concomitant but in virtue of the contemplation; for this is in itself precious. Happiness, therefore, must be some form of contemplation.

But, being a man, one will also need external prosperity; for our nature is not self-sufficient for the purpose of contemplation, but our body also must be healthy and must have food **1179a** and other attention. Still, we must not think that the man who is to be happy will need many things or great things, merely because he cannot be supremely happy without external goods; for self-sufficiency and action do not involve excess, and we can do noble acts without ruling earth and sea; for even with moderate advantages one can act virtuously (this is manifest enough; for private persons are thought to do worthy acts no less than despots—indeed even more); and it is enough that we should have so much as that; for the life of the man who is active in accordance with virtue will be happy. Solon, too, was perhaps sketching well the happy man when he described him[1] as moderately furnished with externals but as having done (as Solon thought) the noblest acts, and lived temperately; for one can with but moderate possessions do what one ought. Anaxagoras also seems to have supposed the happy man not to be rich nor a despot, when he said that he would not be surprised if the happy man were to seem to most people a strange person; for they judge by externals, since these are all they perceive. The opinions of the wise seem, then, to harmonize with our arguments. But while even such things carry some conviction, the truth in practical matters is discerned from the facts of life; for these are the decisive factor. We must therefore survey what we have already said, bringing it to the test of the facts of life, and if it harmonizes

[1] Herodotus, I. 30.

with the facts we must accept it, but if it clashes with them we must suppose it to be mere theory. Now he who exercises his reason and cultivates it seems to be both in the best state of mind and most dear to the gods. For if the gods have any care for human affairs, as they are thought to have, it would be reasonable both that they should delight in that which was best and most akin to them (i.e. reason) and that they should reward those who love and honour this most, as caring for the things that are dear to them and acting both rightly and nobly. And that all these attributes belong most of all to the philosopher is manifest. He, therefore, is the dearest to the gods. And he who is that will presumably be also the happiest; so that in this way too the philosopher will more than any other be happy.

9

If these matters and the virtues, and also friendship and pleasure, have been dealt with sufficiently in outline, are we to suppose that our programme has reached its end? Surely, as the saying goes, where there are things to be done the end is not to survey and recognize the
1179b various things, but rather to do them; with regard to virtue, then, it is not enough to know, but we must try to have and use it, or try any other way there may be of becoming good. Now if arguments were in themselves enough to make men good, they would justly, as Theognis says, have won very great rewards, and such rewards should have been provided; but as things are, while they seem to have power to encourage and stimulate the generous-minded among our youth, and to make a character which is gently born, and a true lover of what is noble, ready to be possessed by virtue, they are not able to encourage the many to nobility and goodness. For these do not by nature obey the sense of shame, but only fear, and do not abstain from bad acts because of their baseness but through fear of punishment; living by passion they pursue their own pleasures and the means to them, and avoid the opposite pains, and have not even a conception of what is noble and truly pleasant, since they have never tasted it. What argument would remould such people? It is hard, if not impossible, to remove by argument the traits that have long since been incorporated in the character; and perhaps we must be content if, when all the influences by which we are thought to become good are present, we get some tincture of virtue.

Now some think that we are made good by nature, others by habituation, others by teaching. Nature's part evidently does not depend on us, but as a result of some divine causes is present in those who are truly fortunate; while argument and teaching, we may suspect, are not powerful with all men, but the soul of the student must first have been cultivated by means of habits for noble joy and noble hatred, like earth which is to nourish the seed. For he who lives as passion directs will not hear argument that dissuades him, nor understand it if he does; and how can we persuade one in such a state to change his ways? And in general passion seems to yield not to argument but to force. The character, then, must somehow be there already with a kinship to virtue, loving what is noble and hating what is base.

But it is difficult to get from youth up a right training for virtue if one has not been brought up under right laws; for to live temperately and hardily is not pleasant to most people, especially when they are young. For this reason their nurture and occupations should be fixed by law; for they will not be painful when they have become customary. But it is surely
1180a not enough that when they are young they should get the right nurture and attention; since they must, even when they are grown up, practise and be habituated to them, we shall need laws for this as well, and generally speaking to cover the whole of life; for most people obey necessity rather than argument, and punishments rather than the sense of what is noble.

This is why some think that legislators ought to stimulate men to virtue and urge them forward by the motive of the noble, on the assumption that those who have been well advanced by the formation of habits will attend to such influences; and that punishments and penalties should be imposed on those who disobey and are of inferior nature, while the incurably bad should be completely banished. A good man (they think), since he lives with his mind fixed on what is noble, will submit to argument, while a bad man, whose desire is for pleasure, is corrected by pain like a beast of burden. This is, too, why they say the pains inflicted should be those that are most opposed to the pleasures such men love.

However that may be, if (as we have said)[1] the man who is to be good must be well trained and habituated, and go on to spend his

[1] 1179b 31-1180a 5.

time in worthy occupations and neither willingly nor unwillingly do bad actions, and if this can be brought about if men live in accordance with a sort of reason and right order, provided this has force,—if this be so, the paternal command indeed has not the required force or compulsive power (nor in general has the command of one man, unless he be a king or something similar), but the law *has* compulsive power, while it is at the same time a rule proceeding from a sort of practical wisdom and reason. And while people hate *men* who oppose their impulses, even if they oppose them rightly, the law in its ordaining of what is good is not burdensome.

In the Spartan state alone, or almost alone, the legislator seems to have paid attention to questions of nurture and occupations; in most states such matters have been neglected, and each man lives as he pleases, Cyclops-fashion, 'to his own wife and children dealing law'.[1] Now it is best that there should be a public and proper care for such matters; but if they are neglected by the community it would seem right for each man to help his children and friends towards virtue, and that they should have the power, or at least the will, to do this.

It would seem from what has been said that he can do this better if he makes himself capable of legislating. For public control is plainly effected by laws, and good control by good laws; whether written or unwritten would seem to make no difference, nor wheth-
1180b er they are laws providing for the education of individuals or of groups—any more than it does in the case of music or gymnastics and other such pursuits. For as in cities laws and prevailing types of character have force, so in households do the injunctions and the habits of the father, and these have even more because of the tie of blood and the benefits he confers; for the children start with a natural affection and disposition to obey. Further, private education has an advantage over public, as private medical treatment has; for while in general rest and abstinence from food are good for a man in a fever, for a particular man they may not be; and a boxer presumably does not prescribe the same style of fighting to all his pupils. It would seem, then, that the detail is worked out with more precision if the control is private; for each person is more likely to get what suits his case.

But the details can be best looked after, one by one, by a doctor or gymnastic instructor or any one else who has the general knowledge of what is good for every one or for people of a certain kind (for the sciences both are said to be, and are, concerned with what is universal); not but what some particular detail may perhaps be well looked after by an unscientific person, if he has studied accurately in the light of experience what happens in each case, just as some people seem to be their own best doctors, though they could give no help to any one else. None the less, it will perhaps be agreed that if a man does wish to become master of an art or science he must go to the universal, and come to know it as well as possible; for, as we have said, it is with this that the sciences are concerned.

And surely he who wants to make men, whether many or few, better by his care must try to become capable of legislating, if it is through laws that we can become good. For to get any one whatever—any one who is put before us—into the right condition is not for the first chance comer; if any one can do it, it is the man who knows, just as in medicine and all other matters which give scope for care and prudence.

Must we not, then, next examine whence or how one can learn how to legislate? Is it, as in all other cases, from statesmen? Certainly it was thought to be a part of statesmanship. Or is a difference apparent between statesmanship and the other sciences and arts? In the others the same people are found offering to teach the arts and practising them, e.g. doctors or painters; but while the sophists
1181a profess to teach politics, it is practised not by any of them but by the politicians, who would seem to do so by dint of a certain skill and experience rather than of thought; for they are not found either writing or speaking about such matters (though it were a nobler occupation perhaps than composing speeches for the law-courts and the assembly), nor again are they found to have made statesmen of their own sons or any other of their friends. But it was to be expected that they should if they could; for there is nothing better than such a skill that they could have left to their cities, or could prefer to have for themselves, or, therefore, for those dearest to them. Still, experience seems to contribute not a little; else they could not have become politicians by familiarity with politics; and so it seems that those who aim at knowing about the art of politics need experience as well.

[1] *Odyssey*, IX. 114 ff.

But those of the sophists who profess the art seem to be very far from teaching it. For, to put the matter generally, they do not even know what kind of thing it is nor what kinds of things it is about; otherwise they would not have classed it as identical with rhetoric or even inferior to it, nor have thought it easy to legislate by collecting the laws that are thought well of; they say it is possible to select the best laws, as though even the selection did not demand intelligence and as though right judgement were not the greatest thing, as in matters of music. For while people experienced in any department judge rightly the works produced in it, and understand by what means or how they are achieved, and what harmonizes with what, the inexperienced must be content if they do not fail to see whether the work has been well or ill made—as in the case of painting. Now laws are as it were the 'works' of the political art; how then can one learn from them to be a legislator, or judge which are best? Even medical men do not seem to be made by a study of text-books. Yet people try, at any rate, to state not only the treatments, but also how particular classes of people can be cured and should be treated—distinguishing the various habits of body; but while this seems useful to experienced people, to the inexperienced it is valueless. Surely, then, while collections of laws, and of constitutions also, may be serviceable to those who can study them and judge what is good or bad and what enactments suit what circumstances, those who go through such collections without a practised faculty will not have right judgement (unless it be as a spontaneous gift of nature), though they may perhaps become more intelligent in such matters.

Now our predecessors have left the subject of legislation to us unexamined; it is perhaps best, therefore, that we should ourselves study it, and in general study the question of the constitution, in order to complete to the best of our ability our philosophy of human nature. First, then, if anything has been said well in detail by earlier thinkers, let us try to review it; then in the light of the constitutions we have collected let us study what sorts of influence preserve and destroy states, and what sorts preserve or destroy the particular kinds of constitution, and to what causes it is due that some are well and others ill administered. When these have been studied we shall perhaps be more likely to see with a comprehensive view, which constitution is best, and how each must be ordered, and what laws and customs it must use, if it is to be at its best. Let us make a beginning of our discussion.

POLITICS

CONTENTS: POLITICS

BOOK IV (VI)

Variations of the main types of Constitutions

BOOK VIII (V)

The Ideal Education continued: Its Music and Gymnastic

POLITICS

BOOK I

1

1252a EVERY state is a community of some kind, and every community is established with a view to some good; for mankind always act in order to obtain that which they think good. But, if all communities aim at some good, the state or political community, which is the highest of all, and which embraces all the rest, aims at good in a greater degree than any other, and at the highest good.

Some people think that the qualifications of a statesman, king, householder, and master are the same, and that they differ, not in kind, but only in the number of their subjects. For example, the ruler over a few is called a master; over more, the manager of a household; over a still larger number, a statesman or king, as if there were no difference between a great household and a small state. The distinction which is made between the king and the statesman is as follows: When the government is personal, the ruler is a king; when, according to the rules of the political science, the citizens rule and are ruled in turn, then he is called a statesman.

But all this is a mistake; for governments differ in kind, as will be evident to any one who considers the matter according to the method which has hitherto guided us. As in other departments of science, so in politics, the compound should always be resolved into the simple elements or least parts of the whole. We must therefore look at the elements of which the state is composed, in order that we may see in what the different kinds of rule differ from one another, and whether any scientific result can be attained about each one of them.

2

He who thus considers things in their first growth and origin, whether a state or anything else, will obtain the clearest view of them. In the first place there must be a union of those who cannot exist without each other; namely, of male and female, that the race may continue (and this is a union which is formed, not of deliberate purpose, but because, in common with other animals and with plants, mankind have a natural desire to leave behind them an image of themselves), and of natural ruler and subject, that both may be preserved. For that which can foresee by the exercise of mind is by nature intended to be lord and master, and that which can with its body give effect to such foresight is a subject, and by nature a slave; hence master and slave have the
1252b same interest. Now nature has distinguished between the female and the slave. For she is not niggardly, like the smith who fashions the Delphian knife for many uses; she makes each thing for a single use, and every instrument is best made when intended for one and not for many uses. But among barbarians no distinction is made between women and slaves, because there is no natural ruler among them: they are a community of slaves, male and female. Wherefore the poets say,—

It is meet that Hellenes should rule over barbarians;[1]

as if they thought that the barbarian and the slave were by nature one.

Out of these two relationships between man and woman, master and slave, the first thing to arise is the family, and Hesiod is right when he says,—

First house and wife and an ox for the plough,[2]

for the ox is the poor man's slave. The family is the association established by nature for the supply of men's everyday wants, and the members of it are called by Charondas 'companions of the cupboard', and by Epimenides the Cretan, 'companions of the manger'. But when several families are united, and the association aims at something more than the supply of daily needs, the first society to be formed is the village. And the most natural form of the village appears to be that of a colony from the

NOTE: The bold face numbers and letters are approximate indications of the pages and columns of the standard Berlin Greek text; the bracketed numbers, of the lines in the Greek text; they are here assigned as they are assigned in the Oxford translation.

[1] Euripides, *Iphegenia in Aulis*, 1400.
[2] *Works and Days*, 405.

family, composed of the children and grandchildren, who are said to be 'suckled with the same milk'. And this is the reason why Hellenic states were originally governed by kings; because the Hellenes were under royal rule before they came together, as the barbarians still are. Every family is ruled by the eldest, and therefore in the colonies of the family the kingly form of government prevailed because they were of the same blood. As Homer says:[1]

Each one gives law to his children and to his wives.

For they lived dispersedly, as was the manner in ancient times. Wherefore men say that the Gods have a king, because they themselves either are or were in ancient times under the rule of a king. For they imagine, not only the forms of the Gods, but their ways of life to be like their own.

When several villages are united in a single complete community, large enough to be nearly or quite self-sufficing, the state comes into existence, originating in the bare needs of life, and continuing in existence for the sake of a good life. And therefore, if the earlier forms of society are natural, so is the state, for it is the end of them, and the nature of a thing is its end. For what each thing is when fully developed, we call its nature, whether we are speaking of a man, a horse, or a family. Besides, the final cause and end of a thing is the **1253a** best, and to be self-sufficing is the end and the best.

Hence it is evident that the state is a creation of nature, and that man is by nature a political animal. And he who by nature and not by mere accident is without a state, is either a bad man or above humanity; he is like the

Tribeless, lawless, hearthless one,

whom Homer[2] denounces—the natural outcast is forthwith a lover of war; he may be compared to an isolated piece at draughts.

Now, that man is more of a political animal than bees or any other gregarious animals is evident. Nature, as we often say, makes nothing in vain, and man is the only animal whom she has endowed with the gift of speech. And whereas mere voice is but an indication of pleasure or pain, and is therefore found in other animals (for their nature attains to the perception of pleasure and pain and the intimation of them to one another, and no further), the power of speech is intended to set forth the expedient and inexpedient, and therefore likewise the just and the unjust. And it is a characteristic of man that he alone has any sense of good and evil, of just and unjust, and the like, and the association of living beings who have this sense makes a family and a state.

Further, the state is by nature clearly prior to the family and to the individual, since the whole is of necessity prior to the part; for example, if the whole body be destroyed, there will be no foot or hand, except in an equivocal sense, as we might speak of a stone hand; for when destroyed the hand will be no better than that. But things are defined by their working and power; and we ought not to say that they are the same when they no longer have their proper quality, but only that they have the same name. The proof that the state is a creation of nature and prior to the individual is that the individual, when isolated, is not self-sufficing; and therefore he is like a part in relation to the whole. But he who is unable to live in society, or who has no need because he is sufficient for himself, must be either a beast or a god: he is no part of a state. A social instinct is implanted in all men by nature, and yet he who first founded the state was the greatest of benefactors. For man, when perfected, is the best of animals, but, when separated from law and justice, he is the worst of all; since armed injustice is the more dangerous, and he is equipped at birth with arms, meant to be used by intelligence and virtue, which he may use for the worst ends. Wherefore, if he have not virtue, he is the most unholy and the most savage of animals, and the most full of lust and gluttony. But justice is the bond of men in states, for the administration of justice, which is the determination of what is just, is the principle of order in political society.

3

Seeing then that the state is made up of households, before speaking of the state we must speak of the management of the household. The parts of household management corre- **1253b** spond to the persons who compose the household, and a complete household consists of slaves and freemen. Now we should begin by examining everything in its fewest possible elements; and the first and fewest possible parts of a family are master and slave, husband and wife, father and children. We have there-

[1] *Odyssey*, IX. 114.
[2] *Iliad*, IX. 63.

fore to consider what each of these three relations is and ought to be:—I mean the relation of master and servant, the marriage relation (the conjunction of man and wife has no name of its own), and thirdly, the procreative relation (this also has no proper name). And there is another element of a household, the so-called art of getting wealth, which, according to some, is identical with household management, according to others, a principal part of it; the nature of this art will also have to be considered by us.

Let us first speak of master and slave, looking to the needs of practical life and also seeking to attain some better theory of their relation than exists at present. For some are of opinion that the rule of a master is a science, and that the management of a household, and the mastership of slaves, and the political and royal rule, as I was saying at the outset, are all the same. Others affirm that the rule of a master over slaves is contrary to nature, and that the distinction between slave and freeman exists by law only, and not by nature; and being an interference with nature is therefore unjust.

4

Property is a part of the household, and the art of acquiring property is a part of the art of managing the household; for no man can live well, or indeed live at all, unless he be provided with necessaries. And as in the arts which have a definite sphere the workers must have their own proper instruments for the accomplishment of their work, so it is in the management of a household. Now instruments are of various sorts; some are living, others lifeless; in the rudder, the pilot of a ship has a lifeless, in the look-out man, a living instrument; for in the arts the servant is a kind of instrument. Thus, too, a possession is an instrument for maintaining life. And so, in the arrangement of the family, a slave is a living possession, and property a number of such instruments; and the servant is himself an instrument which takes precedence of all other instruments. For if every instrument could accomplish its own work, obeying or anticipating the will of others, like the statues of Daedalus, or the tripods of Hephaestus, which, says the poet,[1]

of their own accord entered the assembly of the Gods;

if, in like manner, the shuttle would weave and the plectrum touch the lyre without a hand to guide them, chief workmen would not want servants, nor masters slaves. Here, however, **1254a** another distinction must be drawn: the instruments commonly so called are instruments of production, whilst a possession is an instrument of action. The shuttle, for example, is not only of use; but something else is made by it, whereas of a garment or of a bed there is only the use. Further, as production and action are different in kind, and both require instruments, the instruments which they employ must likewise differ in kind. But life is action and not production, and therefore the slave is the minister of action. Again, a possession is spoken of as a part is spoken of; for the part is not only a part of something else, but wholly belongs to it; and this is also true of a possession. The master is only the master of the slave; he does not belong to him, whereas the slave is not only the slave of his master, but wholly belongs to him. Hence we see what is the nature and office of a slave; he who is by nature not his own but another's man, is by nature a slave; and he may be said to be another's man who, being a human being, is also a possession. And a possession may be defined as an instrument of action, separable from the possessor.

5

But is there any one thus intended by nature to be a slave, and for whom such a condition is expedient and right, or rather is not all slavery a violation of nature?

There is no difficulty in answering this question, on grounds both of reason and of fact. For that some should rule and others be ruled is a thing not only necessary, but expedient; from the hour of their birth, some are marked out for subjection, others for rule.

And there are many kinds both of rulers and subjects (and that rule is the better which is exercised over better subjects—for example, to rule over men is better than to rule over wild beasts; for the work is better which is executed by better workmen, and where one man rules and another is ruled, they may be said to have a work); for in all things which form a composite whole and which are made up of parts, whether continuous or discrete, a distinction between the ruling and the subject element comes to light. Such a duality exists in living creatures, but not in them only; it originates in the constitution of the universe; even in things which have no life there is a

[1] Homer, *Iliad*, XVIII. 376.

ruling principle, as in a musical mode. But we are wandering from the subject. We will therefore restrict ourselves to the living creature, which, in the first place, consists of soul and body: and of these two, the one is by nature the ruler, and the other the subject. But then we must look for the intentions of nature in things which retain their nature, and not in things which are corrupted. And therefore we must study the man who is in the most perfect state both of body and soul, for in him we shall see the true relation of the two; although in **1254b** bad or corrupted natures the body will often appear to rule over the soul, because they are in an evil and unnatural condition. At all events we may firstly observe in living creatures both a despotical and a constitutional rule; for the soul rules the body with a despotical rule, whereas the intellect rules the appetites with a constitutional and royal rule. And it is clear that the rule of the soul over the body, and of the mind and the rational element over the passionate, is natural and expedient; whereas the equality of the two or the rule of the inferior is always hurtful. The same holds good of animals in relation to men; for tame animals have a better nature than wild, and all tame animals are better off when they are ruled by man; for then they are preserved. Again, the male is by nature superior, and the female inferior; and the one rules, and the other is ruled; this principle, of necessity, extends to all mankind. Where then there is such a difference as that between soul and body, or between men and animals (as in the case of those whose business is to use their body, and who can do nothing better), the lower sort are by nature slaves, and it is better for them as for all inferiors that they should be under the rule of a master. For he who can be, and therefore is, another's, and he who participates in rational principle enough to apprehend, but not to have, such a principle, is a slave by nature. Whereas the lower animals cannot even apprehend a principle; they obey their instincts. And indeed the use made of slaves and of tame animals is not very different; for both with their bodies minister to the needs of life. Nature would like to distinguish between the bodies of freemen and slaves, making the one strong for servile labour, the other upright, and although useless for such services, useful for political life in the arts both of war and peace. But the opposite often happens—that some have the souls and others have the bodies of freemen. And doubtless if men differed from one another in the mere forms of their bodies as much as the statues of the Gods do from men, all would acknowledge that the inferior class should be slaves of the superior. And if this is true of the body, how much more just that a similar distinction should exist in the soul? but **1255a** the beauty of the body is seen, whereas the beauty of the soul is not seen. It is clear, then, that some men are by nature free, and others slaves, and that for these latter slavery is both expedient and right.

6

But that those who take the opposite view have in a certain way right on their side, may be easily seen. For the words slavery and slave are used in two senses. There is a slave or slavery by law as well as by nature. The law of which I speak is a sort of convention—the law by which whatever is taken in war is supposed to belong to the victors. But this right many jurists impeach, as they would an orator who brought forward an unconstitutional measure: they detest the notion that, because one man has the power of doing violence and is superior in brute strength, another shall be his slave and subject. Even among philosophers there is a difference of opinion. The origin of the dispute, and what makes the views invade each other's territory, is as follows: in some sense virtue, when furnished with means, has actually the greatest power of exercising force: and as superior power is only found where there is superior excellence of some kind, power seems to imply virtue, and the dispute to be simply one about justice (for it is due to one party identifying justice with goodwill, while the other identifies it with the mere rule of the stronger). If these views are thus set out separately, the other views have no force or plausibility against the view that the superior in virtue ought to rule, or be master. Others, clinging, as they think, simply to a principle of justice (for law and custom are a sort of justice), assume that slavery in accordance with the custom of war is justified by law, but at the same moment they deny this. For what if the cause of the war be unjust? And again, no one would ever say that he is a slave who is unworthy to be a slave. Were this the case, men of the highest rank would be slaves and the children of slaves if they or their parents chance to have been taken captive and sold. Wherefore Hellenes do not like to call Hellenes slaves, but confine the term to barbarians. Yet, in using this language, they really mean the natural slave of whom we spoke at first;[1] for it must be admitted that some are slaves everywhere, others nowhere. The same principle applies to nobility. Hellenes regard themselves as noble everywhere, and not only in their own country, but they deem the barbarians noble only when at home, thereby implying that there are two sorts of nobility and freedom, the one absolute, the other relative. The Helen of Theodectes says:[2]

Who would presume to call me servant who am on both sides sprung from the stem of the Gods?

What does this mean but that they distinguish freedom and slavery, noble and humble birth, by the two principles of good and evil? **1255b** They think that as men and animals beget men and animals, so from good men a good man springs. But this is what nature, though she may intend it, cannot always accomplish.

We see then that there is some foundation for this difference of opinion, and that all are not either slaves by nature or freemen by nature, and also that there is in some cases a marked distinction between the two classes, rendering it expedient and right for the one to be slaves and the others to be masters: the one practising obedience, the others exercising the authority and lordship which nature intended them to have. The abuse of this authority is injurious to both; for the interests of part and whole, of body and soul, are the same, and the slave is a part of the master, a living but separated part of his bodily frame. Hence, where the relation of master and slave between them is natural they are friends and have a common interest, but where it rests merely on law and force the reverse is true.

7

The previous remarks are quite enough to show that the rule of a master is not a constitutional rule, and that all the different kinds of rule are not, as some affirm, the same with each other. For there is one rule exercised over subjects who are by nature free, another over subjects who are by nature slaves. The rule of a household is a monarchy, for every house is under one head: whereas constitutional rule is a government of freemen and equals. The master is not called a master because he has science, but because he is of a certain character, and the same remark applies to the slave and the freeman. Still there may be a science for the master and a science for the slave. The science of the slave would be such as the man of Syracuse taught, who made money by instructing slaves in their ordinary duties. And such a knowledge may be carried further, so as to include cookery and similar menial arts. For some duties are of the more necessary, others of the more honourable sort; as the proverb says, 'slave before slave, master before master'.[3] But all such branches of knowledge are servile. There is likewise a science of the master, which teaches the use of slaves; for the master as such is concerned, not with the acquisition, but with the use of them. Yet this so-called science is not anything great or wonderful; for the master need only know how to order that which the slave must know how to execute. Hence those who are in a position which places them above toil have stewards who attend to their households while they occupy themselves with philosophy or with politics. But the art of acquiring slaves, I mean of justly acquiring them, differs both from the art of the master and the art of the slave, being a species of hunting or war. Enough of the distinction between master and slave.

8

1256a Let us now inquire into property generally, and into the art of getting wealth, in accordance with our usual method, for a slave has been shown[4] to be a part of property. The first question is whether the art of getting wealth is the same with the art of managing a household or a part of it, or instrumental to it; and if the last, whether in the way that the art of making shuttles is instrumental to the art of weaving, or in the way that the casting of bronze is instrumental to the art of the statuary, for they are not instrumental in the same way, but the one provides tools and the other material; and by material I mean the substratum out of which any work is made; thus wool is the material of the weaver, bronze of the statuary. Now it is easy to see that the art of household management is not identical with the art of getting wealth, for the one uses the material which the other provides. For the art which uses household stores can be no other than the art of household management.

[1] Chapter 5

[2] *Helena*, fr. 3, Nauck.

[3] Philemon, *Pancratiastes*, fr. 2, Meineke.

[4] Chapter 4.

There is, however, a doubt whether the art of getting wealth is a part of household management or a distinct art. If the getter of wealth has to consider whence wealth and property can be procured, but there are many sorts of property and riches, then are husbandry, and the care and provision of food in general, parts of the wealth-getting art or distinct arts? Again, there are many sorts of food, and therefore there are many kinds of lives both of animals and men; they must all have food, and the differences in their food have made differences in their ways of life. For of beasts, some are gregarious, others are solitary; they live in the way which is best adapted to sustain them, accordingly as they are carnivorous or herbivorous or omnivorous: and their habits are determined for them by nature in such a manner that they may obtain with greater facility the food of their choice. But, as different species have different tastes, the same things are not naturally pleasant to all of them; and therefore the lives of carnivorous or herbivorous animals further differ among themselves. In the lives of men too there is a great difference. The laziest are shepherds, who lead an idle life, and get their subsistence without trouble from tame animals; their flocks having to wander from place to place in search of pasture, they are compelled to follow them, cultivating a sort of living farm. Others support themselves by hunting, which is of different kinds. Some, for example, are brigands, others, who dwell near lakes or marshes or rivers or a sea in which there are fish, are fishermen, and others live by the pursuit of birds or wild beasts. The greater number obtain a living from the cultivated fruits of the soil. Such are the modes of subsistence which prevail among those whose industry springs up of itself, and whose food is not ac-
1256b quired by exchange and retail trade—there is the shepherd, the husbandman, the brigand, the fisherman, the hunter. Some gain a comfortable maintenance out of two employments, eking out the deficiencies of one of them by another: thus the life of a shepherd may be combined with that of a brigand, the life of a farmer with that of a hunter. Other modes of life are similarly combined in any way which the needs of men may require. Property, in the sense of a bare livelihood, seems to be given by nature herself to all, both when they are first born, and when they are grown up. For some animals bring forth, together with their offspring, so much food as will last until they are able to supply themselves; of this the vermiparous or oviparous animals are an instance; and the viviparous animals have up to a certain time a supply of food for their young in themselves, which is called milk. In like manner we may infer that, after the birth of animals, plants exist for their sake, and that the other animals exist for the sake of man, the tame for use and food, the wild, if not all, at least the greater part of them, for food, and for the provision of clothing and various instruments. Now if nature makes nothing incomplete, and nothing in vain, the inference must be that she has made all animals for the sake of man. And so, in one point of view, the art of war is a natural art of acquisition, for the art of acquisition includes hunting, an art which we ought to practise against wild beasts, and against men who, though intended by nature to be governed, will not submit; for war of such a kind is naturally just.

Of the art of acquisition then there is one kind which by nature is a part of the management of a household, in so far as the art of household management must either find ready to hand, or itself provide, such things necessary to life, and useful for the community of the family or state, as can be stored. They are the elements of true riches; for the amount of property which is needed for a good life is not unlimited, although Solon in one of his poems says that

No bound to riches has been fixed for man.[1]

But there is a boundary fixed, just as there is in the other arts; for the instruments of any art are never unlimited, either in number or size, and riches may be defined as a number of instruments to be used in a household or in a state. And so we see that there is a natural art of acquisition which is practised by managers of households and by statesmen, and what is the reason of this.

9

There is another variety of the art of acquisition which is commonly and rightly called an art of wealth-getting, and has in fact sug-
1257a gested the notion that riches and property have no limit. Being nearly connected with the preceding, it is often identified with it. But though they are not very different, neither are they the same. The kind already described is given by nature, the other is gained by experience and art.

[1] Bergk, *Poet. Lyr.*, Solon, 13. 71.

Let us begin our discussion of the question with the following considerations:

Of everything which we possess there are two uses: both belong to the thing as such, but not in the same manner, for one is the proper, and the other the improper or secondary use of it. For example, a shoe is used for wear, and is used for exchange; both are uses of the shoe. He who gives a shoe in exchange for money or food to him who wants one, does indeed use the shoe as a shoe, but this is not its proper or primary purpose, for a shoe is not made to be an object of barter. The same may be said of all possessions, for the art of exchange extends to all of them, and it arises at first from what is natural, from the circumstance that some have too little, others too much. Hence we may infer that retail trade is not a natural part of the art of getting wealth; had it been so, men would have ceased to exchange when they had enough. In the first community, indeed, which is the family, this art is obviously of no use, but it begins to be useful when the society increases. For the members of the family originally had all things in common; later, when the family divided into parts, the parts shared in many things, and different parts in different things, which they had to give in exchange for what they wanted, a kind of barter which is still practised among barbarous nations who exchange with one another the necessaries of life and nothing more; giving and receiving wine, for example, in exchange for corn, and the like. This sort of barter is not part of the wealth-getting art and is not contrary to nature, but is needed for the satisfaction of men's natural wants. The other or more complex form of exchange grew, as might have been inferred, out of the simpler. When the inhabitants of one country became more dependent on those of another, and they imported what they needed, and exported what they had too much of, money necessarily came into use. For the various necessaries of life are not easily carried about, and hence men agreed to employ in their dealings with each other something which was intrinsically useful and easily applicable to the purposes of life, for example, iron, silver, and the like. Of this the value was at first measured simply by size and weight, but in process of time they put a stamp upon it, to save the trouble of weighing and to mark the value.

1257b When the use of coin had once been discovered, out of the barter of necessary articles arose the other art of wealth-getting, namely, retail trade; which was at first probably a simple matter, but became more complicated as soon as men learned by experience whence and by what exchanges the greatest profit might be made. Originating in the use of coin, the art of getting wealth is generally thought to be chiefly concerned with it, and to be the art which produces riches and wealth; having to consider how they may be accumulated. Indeed, riches is assumed by many to be only a quantity of coin, because the arts of getting wealth and retail trade are concerned with coin. Others maintain that coined money is a mere sham, a thing not natural, but conventional only, because, if the users substitute another commodity for it, it is worthless, and because it is not useful as a means to any of the necessities of life, and, indeed, he who is rich in coin may often be in want of necessary food. But how can that be wealth of which a man may have a great abundance and yet perish with hunger, like Midas in the fable, whose insatiable prayer turned everything that was set before him into gold?

Hence men seek after a better notion of riches and of the art of getting wealth than the mere acquisition of coin, and they are right. For natural riches and the natural art of wealth-getting are a different thing; in their true form they are part of the management of a household; whereas retail trade is the art of producing wealth, not in every way, but by exchange. And it is thought to be concerned with coin; for coin is the unit of exchange and the measure or limit of it. And there is no bound to the riches which spring from this art of wealth-getting. As in the art of medicine there is no limit to the pursuit of health, and as in the other arts there is no limit to the pursuit of their several ends, for they aim at accomplishing their ends to the uttermost (but of the means there is a limit, for the end is always the limit), so, too, in this art of wealth-getting there is no limit of the end, which is riches of the spurious kind, and the acquisition of wealth. But the art of wealth-getting which consists in household management, on the other hand, has a limit; the unlimited acquisition of wealth is not its business. And, therefore, in one point of view, all riches must have a limit; nevertheless, as a matter of fact, we find the opposite to be the case; for all getters of wealth increase their hoard of coin without limit. The source of the confusion is the near connexion between the two kinds of wealth-getting; in either, the instrument is the same, although the use is different, and so they pass into one another; for each is a use of the same property, but with a difference: accumulation is the end in the one case, but there is a further end in the other. Hence some persons are led to believe that getting wealth is the object of household management, and the whole idea of their lives is that they ought either to increase their money without limit, or at any rate not to lose it. The origin of this disposition in men is that they **1258a** are intent upon living only, and not upon living well; and, as their desires are unlimited, they also desire that the means of gratifying them should be without limit. Those who do aim at a good life seek the means of obtaining bodily pleasures; and, since the enjoyment of these appears to depend on property, they are absorbed in getting wealth: and so there arises the second species of wealth-getting. For, as their enjoyment is in excess, they seek an art which produces the excess of enjoyment; and, if they are not able to supply their pleasures by the art of getting wealth, they try other arts, using in turn every faculty in a manner contrary to nature. The quality of courage, for example, is not intended to make wealth, but to inspire confidence; neither is this the aim of the general's or of the physician's art; but the one aims at victory and the other at health. Nevertheless, some men turn every quality or art into a means of getting wealth; this they conceive to be the end, and to the promotion of the end they think all things must contribute.

Thus, then, we have considered the art of wealth-getting which is unnecessary, and why men want it; and also the necessary art of wealth-getting, which we have seen to be different from the other, and to be a natural part of the art of managing a household, concerned with the provision of food, not, however, like the former kind, unlimited, but having a limit.

10

And we have found the answer to our original question, Whether the art of getting wealth is the business of the manager of a household and of the statesman or not their business?—viz. that wealth is presupposed by them. For as political science does not make men, but takes them from nature and uses them, so too nature provides them with earth or sea or the like as a source of food. At this stage begins the duty of the manager of a household, who has to order the things which nature supplies;—he may be compared to the weaver who has not to make but to use wool, and to know, too, what sort of wool is good and serviceable or bad and unserviceable. Were this otherwise, it would be difficult to see why the art of getting wealth is a part of the management of a household and the art of medicine not; for surely the members of a household must have health just as they must have life or any other necessary. The answer is that as from one point of view the master of the house and the ruler of the state have to consider about health, from another point of view not they but the physician; so in one way the art of household management, in another way the subordinate art, has to consider about wealth. But, strictly speaking, as I have already said, the means of life must be provided beforehand by nature; for the business of nature is to furnish food to that which is born, and the food of the offspring is always what remains over of that from which it is produced. Wherefore the art of getting wealth out of fruits and animals is always natural.

There are two sorts of wealth-getting, as I have said[1]; one is a part of household management, the other is retail trade: the former necessary and honourable, while that which **1258b** consists in exchange is justly censured; for it is unnatural, and a mode by which men gain from one another. The most hated sort, and with the greatest reason, is usury, which makes a gain out of money itself, and not from the natural object of it. For money was intended to be used in exchange, but not to increase at interest. And this term interest, which means the birth of money from money, is applied to the breeding of money because the offspring resembles the parent. Wherefore of all modes of getting wealth this is the most unnatural.

11

Enough has been said about the theory of wealth-getting; we will now proceed to the practical part. The discussion of such matters is not unworthy of philosophy, but to be engaged in them practically is illiberal and irksome. The useful parts of wealth-getting are, first, the knowledge of live-stock,—which are most profitable, and where, and how,—as, for example, what sort of horses or sheep or oxen or any other animals are most likely to give a

[1] 1256a 15-1258a 18.

return. A man ought to know which of these pay better than others, and which pay best in particular places, for some do better in one place and some in another. Secondly, husbandry, which may be either tillage or planting, and the keeping of bees and of fish, or fowl, or of any animals which may be useful to man. These are the divisions of the true or proper art of wealth-getting and come first. Of the other, which consists in exchange, the first and most important division is commerce (of which there are three kinds—the provision of a ship, the conveyance of goods, exposure for sale—these again differing as they are safer or more profitable), the second is usury, the third, service for hire—of this, one kind is employed in the mechanical arts, the other in unskilled and bodily labour. There is still a third sort of wealth-getting intermediate between this and the first or natural mode which is partly natural, but is also concerned with exchange, viz. the industries that make their profit from the earth, and from things growing from the earth which, although they bear no fruit, are nevertheless profitable; for example, the cutting of timber and all mining. The art of mining, by which minerals are obtained, itself has many branches, for there are various kinds of things dug out of the earth. Of the several divisions of wealth-getting I now speak generally; a minute consideration of them might be useful in practice, but it would be tiresome to dwell upon them at greater length now.

Those occupations are most truly arts in which there is the least element of chance; they are the meanest in which the body is most deteriorated, the most servile in which there is the greatest use of the body, and the most illiberal in which there is the least need of excellence.

Works have been written upon these subjects by various persons; for example, by Chares the Parian, and Apollodorus the Lemnian, who have treated of Tillage and Plant- **1259a** ing, while others have treated of other branches; any one who cares for such matters may refer to their writings. It would be well also to collect the scattered stories of the ways in which individuals have succeeded in amassing a fortune; for all this is useful to persons who value the art of getting wealth. There is the anecdote of Thales the Milesian and his financial device, which involves a principle of universal application, but is attributed to him on account of his reputation for wisdom. He was reproached for his poverty, which was supposed to show that philosophy was of no use. According to the story, he knew by his skill in the stars while it was yet winter that there would be a great harvest of olives in the coming year; so, having a little money, he gave deposits for the use of all the olive-presses in Chios and Miletus, which he hired at a low price because no one bid against him. When the harvest-time came, and many were wanted all at once and of a sudden, he let them out at any rate which he pleased, and made a quantity of money. Thus he showed the world that philosophers can easily be rich if they like, but that their ambition is of another sort. He is supposed to have given a striking proof of his wisdom, but, as I was saying, his device for getting wealth is of universal application, and is nothing but the creation of a monopoly. It is an art often practised by cities when they are in want of money; they make a monopoly of provisions.

There was a man of Sicily, who, having money deposited with him, bought up all the iron from the iron mines; afterwards, when the merchants from their various markets came to buy, he was the only seller, and without much increasing the price he gained 200 per cent. Which when Dionysius heard, he told him that he might take away his money, but that he must not remain at Syracuse, for he thought that the man had discovered a way of making money which was injurious to his own interests. He made the same discovery as Thales; they both contrived to create a monopoly for themselves. And statesmen as well ought to know these things; for a state is often as much in want of money and of such devices for obtaining it as a household, or even more so; hence some public men devote themselves entirely to finance.

12

Of household management we have seen[1] that there are three parts—one is the rule of a master over slaves, which has been discussed already,[2] another of a father, and the third of a husband. A husband and father, we saw, rules over wife and children, both free, but the rule differs, the rule over his children being a royal, over his wife a constitutional rule. For **1259b** although there may be exceptions to the order of nature, the male is by nature fitter for command than the female, just as the elder and full-grown is superior to the younger and

[1] 1253b 3-11. [2] 1253b 14-1255b 39.

more immature. But in most constitutional states the citizens rule and are ruled by turns, for the idea of a constitutional state implies that the natures of the citizens are equal, and do not differ at all. Nevertheless, when one rules and the other is ruled we endeavour to create a difference of outward forms and names and titles of respect, which may be illustrated by the saying of Amasis about his foot-pan.[1] The relation of the male to the female is of this kind, but there the inequality is permanent. The rule of a father over his children is royal, for he rules by virtue both of love and of the respect due to age, exercising a kind of royal power. And therefore Homer has appropriately called Zeus 'father of Gods and men', because he is the king of them all. For a king is the natural superior of his subjects, but he should be of the same kin or kind with them, and such is the relation of elder and younger, of father and son.

13

Thus it is clear that household management attends more to men than to the acquisition of inanimate things, and to human excellence more than to the excellence of property which we call wealth, and to the virtue of freemen more than to the virtue of slaves. A question may indeed be raised, whether there is any excellence at all in a slave beyond and higher than merely instrumental and ministerial qualities—whether he can have the virtues of temperance, courage, justice, and the like; or whether slaves possess only bodily and ministerial qualities. And, whichever way we answer the question, a difficulty arises; for, if they have virtue, in what will they differ from freemen? On the other hand, since they are men and share in rational principle, it seems absurd to say that they have no virtue. A similar question may be raised about women and children, whether they too have virtues: ought a woman to be temperate and brave and just, and is a child to be called temperate, and intemperate, or not? So in general we may ask about the natural ruler, and the natural subject, whether they have the same or different virtues. For if a noble nature is equally required in both, why should one of them always rule, and the other always be ruled? Nor can we say that this is a question of degree, for the difference between ruler and subject is a difference of kind, which the difference of more and less never is. Yet how strange is the supposition that the one ought, and that the other ought not, to have virtue! For if the ruler is intemperate and unjust, how can he rule well? if
1260a the subject, how can he obey well? If he be licentious and cowardly, he will certainly not do his duty. It is evident, therefore, that both of them must have a share of virtue, but varying as natural subjects also vary among themselves. Here the very constitution of the soul has shown us the way; in it one part naturally rules, and the other is subject, and the virtue of the ruler we maintain to be different from that of the subject;—the one being the virtue of the rational, and the other of the irrational part. Now, it is obvious that the same principle applies generally, and therefore almost all things rule and are ruled according to nature. But the kind of rule differs;—the freeman rules over the slave after another manner from that in which the male rules over the female, or the man over the child; although the parts of the soul are present in all of them, they are present in different degrees. For the slave has no deliberative faculty at all; the woman has, but it is without authority, and the child has, but it is immature. So it must necessarily be supposed to be with the moral virtues also; all should partake of them, but only in such manner and degree as is required by each for the fulfilment of his duty. Hence the ruler ought to have moral virtue in perfection, for his function, taken absolutely, demands a master artificer, and rational principle is such an artificer; the subjects, on the other hand, require only that measure of virtue which is proper to each of them. Clearly, then, moral virtue belongs to all of them; but the temperance of a man and of a woman, or the courage and justice of a man and of a woman, are not, as Socrates maintained,[2] the same; the courage of a man is shown in commanding, of a woman in obeying. And this holds of all other virtues, as will be more clearly seen if we look at them in detail, for those who say generally that virtue consists in a good disposition of the soul, or in doing rightly, or the like, only deceive themselves. Far better than such definitions is their mode of speaking, who, like Gorgias,[3] enumerate the virtues. All classes must be deemed to have their special attributes; as the poet says of women,

Silence is a woman's glory,[4]

but this is not equally the glory of man. The

[1] Herodotus, II. 172.

[2] Plato, *Meno*, 72-73.

[3] *Meno*, 71, 72.

[4] Sophocles, *Ajax*, 293.

child is imperfect, and therefore obviously his virtue is not relative to himself alone, but to the perfect man and to his teacher, and in like manner the virtue of the slave is relative to a master. Now we determined[1] that a slave is useful for the wants of life, and therefore he will obviously require only so much virtue as will prevent him from failing in his duty through cowardice or lack of self-control. Some one will ask whether, if what we are saying is true, virtue will not be required also in the artisans, for they often fail in their work through the lack of self-control? But is there not a great difference in the two cases? For the slave shares in his master's life; the artisan is less closely connected with him, and only attains excellence in proportion as he becomes a slave. **1260b** The meaner sort of mechanic has a special and separate slavery; and whereas the slave exists by nature, not so the shoemaker or other artisan. It is manifest, then, that the master ought to be the source of such excellence in the slave, and not a mere possessor of the art of mastership which trains the slave in his duties. Wherefore they are mistaken who forbid us to converse with slaves and say that we should employ command only,[2] for slaves stand even more in need of admonition than children.

So much for this subject; the relations of husband and wife, parent and child, their several virtues, what in their intercourse with one another is good, and what is evil, and how we may pursue the good and escape the evil, will have to be discussed when we speak of the different forms of government. For, inasmuch as every family is a part of a state, and these relationships are the parts of a family, and the virtue of the part must have regard to the virtue of the whole, women and children must be trained by education with an eye to the constitution, if the virtues of either of them are supposed to make any difference in the virtues of the state. And they must make a difference: for the children grow up to be citizens, and half the free persons in a state are women.[3] Of these matters, enough has been said; of what remains, let us speak at another time. Regarding, then, our present inquiry as complete, we will make a new beginning. And, first, let us examine the various theories of a perfect state.

BOOK II

1

Our purpose is to consider what form of political community is best of all for those who are most able to realize their ideal of life. We must therefore examine not only this but other constitutions, both such as actually exist in well-governed states, and any theoretical forms which are held in esteem; that what is good and useful may be brought to light. And let no one suppose that in seeking for something beyond them we are anxious to make a sophistical display at any cost; we only undertake this inquiry because all the constitutions with which we are acquainted are faulty.

We will begin with the natural beginning of the subject. Three alternatives are conceivable: The members of a state must either have (1) all things or (2) nothing in common, or (3) some things in common and some not. That they should have nothing in common is clearly impossible, for the constitution is a com- **1261a** munity, and must at any rate have a common place—one city will be in one place, and the citizens are those who share in that one city. But should a well-ordered state have all things, as far as may be, in common, or some only and not others? For the citizens might conceivably have wives and children and property in common, as Socrates proposes in the *Republic* of Plato.[4] Which is better, our present condition, or the proposed new order of society?

2

There are many difficulties in the community of women. And the principle on which Socrates rests the necessity of such an institution evidently is not established by his arguments. Further, as a means to the end which he ascribes to the state, the scheme, taken literally, is impracticable, and how we are to interpret it is nowhere precisely stated. I am speaking of the premiss from which the argument of Socrates proceeds, 'that the greater the unity of the state the better'. Is it not obvious that a state may at length attain such a degree of unity as to be no longer a state?—since the nature of a state is to be a plurality, and in tending to greater unity, from being a state, it be-

[1] 1254^b 16-39; cf. 1259^b 25 sq.

[2] Plato, *Laws*, VI. 777.

[3] Plato, *Laws*, VI. 781.

[4] *Republic*, IV. 423; V. 457; 462.

comes a family, and from being a family, an individual; for the family may be said to be more one than the state, and the individual than the family. So that we ought not to attain this greatest unity even if we could, for it would be the destruction of the state. Again, a state is not made up only of so many men, but of different kinds of men; for similars do not constitute a state. It is not like a military alliance. The usefulness of the latter depends upon its quantity even where there is no difference in quality (for mutual protection is the end aimed at), just as a greater weight of anything is more useful than a less (in like manner, a state differs from a nation, when the nation has not its population organized in villages, but lives an Arcadian sort of life); but the elements out of which a unity is to be formed differ in kind. Wherefore the principle of compensation, as I have already remarked in the *Ethics*,[1] is the salvation of states. Even among freemen and equals this is a principle which must be maintained, for they cannot all rule together, but must change at the end of a year or some other period of time or in some order of succession. The result is that upon this plan they all govern; just as if shoemakers and carpenters were to exchange their occupations, and the same persons did not always continue shoemakers and carpenters. And since it is better that this should be so in politics as well, it is clear that while there should be continuance of the same persons in power where this is possible, yet where this is
1261b not possible by reason of the natural equality of the citizens, and at the same time it is just that all should share in the government (whether to govern be a good thing or a bad), an approximation to this is that equals should in turn retire from office and should, apart from official position, be treated alike. Thus the one party rule and the others are ruled in turn, as if they were no longer the same persons. In like manner when they hold office there is a variety in the offices held. Hence it is evident that a city is not by nature one in that sense which some persons affirm; and that what is said to be the greatest good of cities is in reality their destruction; but surely the good of things must be that which preserves them. Again, in another point of view, this extreme unification of the state is clearly not good; for a family is more self-sufficing than an individual, and a city than a family, and a city only comes into being when the community is large enough to be self-sufficing. If then self-sufficiency is to be desired, the lesser degree of unity is more desirable than the greater.

[1] *Ethics*, v, 1132^b 32.

3

But, even supposing that it were best for the community to have the greatest degree of unity, this unity is by no means proved to follow from the fact 'of all men saying "mine" and "not mine" at the same instant of time', which, according to Socrates,[2] is the sign of perfect unity in a state. For the word 'all' is ambiguous. If the meaning be that every individual says 'mine' and 'not mine' at the same time, then perhaps the result at which Socrates aims may be in some degree accomplished; each man will call the same person his own son and the same person his own wife, and so of his property and of all that falls to his lot. This, however, is not the way in which people would speak who had their wives and children in common; they would say 'all' but not 'each'. In like manner their property would be described as belonging to them, not severally but collectively. There is an obvious fallacy in the term 'all': like some other words, 'both', 'odd', 'even', it is ambiguous, and even in abstract argument becomes a source of logical puzzles. That all persons call the same thing mine in the sense in which each does so may be a fine thing, but it is impracticable; or if the words are taken in the other sense, such a unity in no way conduces to harmony. And there is another objection to the proposal. For that which is common to the greatest number has the least care bestowed upon it. Every one thinks chiefly of his own, hardly at all of the common interest; and only when he is himself concerned as an individual. For besides other considerations, everybody is more inclined to neglect the duty which he expects another to fulfil; as in families many attendants are often less useful than a few. Each citizen will have a thousand sons who will not be his sons individually, but anybody will be equally
1262a the son of anybody, and will therefore be neglected by all alike. Further, upon this principle, every one will use the word 'mine' of one who is prospering or the reverse, however small a fraction he may himself be of the whole number; the same boy will be 'my son', 'so and so's son', the son of each of the thousand, or whatever be the number of the citizens; and even about this he will not be positive; for

[2] Plato, *Republic*, v. 462.

it is impossible to know who chanced to have a child, or whether, if one came into existence, it has survived. But which is better—for each to say 'mine' in this way, making a man the same relation to two thousand or ten thousand citizens, or to use the word 'mine' in the ordinary and more restricted sense? For usually the same person is called by one man his own son whom another calls his own brother or cousin or kinsman—blood relation or connexion by marriage either of himself or of some relation of his, and yet another his clansman or tribesman; and how much better is it to be the real cousin of somebody than to be a son after Plato's fashion! Nor is there any way of preventing brothers and children and fathers and mothers from sometimes recognizing one another; for children are born like their parents, and they will necessarily be finding indications of their relationship to one another. Geographers declare such to be the fact; they say that in part of Upper Libya, where the women are common, nevertheless the children who are born are assigned to their respective fathers on the ground of their likeness. And some women, like the females of other animals—for example, mares and cows—have a strong tendency to produce offspring resembling their parents, as was the case with the Pharsalian mare called Honest.

4

Other evils, against which it is not easy for the authors of such a community to guard, will be assaults and homicides, voluntary as well as involuntary, quarrels and slanders, all which are most unholy acts when committed against fathers and mothers and near relations, but not equally unholy when there is no relationship. Moreover, they are much more likely to occur if the relationship is unknown, and, when they have occurred, the customary expiations of them cannot be made. Again, how strange it is that Socrates,[1] after having made the children common, should hinder lovers from carnal intercourse only, but should permit love and familiarities between father and son or between brother and brother, than which nothing can be more unseemly, since even without them love of this sort is improper. How strange, too, to forbid intercourse for no other reason than the violence of the pleasure, as though the relationship of father and son or of brothers with one another made no difference.

[1] *Republic*, III. 403.

This community of wives and children seems better suited to the husbandmen than to the guardians, for if they have wives and chil-
1262b dren in common, they will be bound to one another by weaker ties, as a subject class should be, and they will remain obedient and not rebel. In a word, the result of such a law would be just the opposite of that which good laws ought to have, and the intention of Socrates in making these regulations about women and children would defeat itself. For friendship we believe to be the greatest good of states and the preservative of them against revolutions; neither is there anything which Socrates so greatly lauds as the unity of the state which he and all the world declare to be created by friendship. But the unity which he commends would be like that of the lovers in the *Symposium*,[2] who, as Aristophanes says, desire to grow together in the excess of their affection, and from being two to become one, in which case one or both would certainly perish. Whereas in a state having women and children common, love will be watery; and the father will certainly not say 'my son', or the son 'my father'. As a little sweet wine mingled with a great deal of water is imperceptible in the mixture, so, in this sort of community, the idea of relationship which is based upon these names will be lost; there is no reason why the so-called father should care about the son, or the son about the father, or brothers about one another. Of the two qualities which chiefly inspire regard and affection—that a thing is your own and that it is your only one—neither can exist in such a state as this.

Again, the transfer of children as soon as they are born from the rank of husbandmen or of artisans to that of guardians, and from the rank of guardians into a lower rank, will be very difficult to arrange; the givers or transferrers cannot but know whom they are giving and transferring, and to whom. And the previously mentioned[3] evils, such as assaults, unlawful loves, homicides, will happen more often amongst those who are transferred to the lower classes, or who have a place assigned to them among the guardians; for they will no longer call the members of the class they have left brothers, and children, and fathers, and mothers, and will not, therefore, be afraid of committing any crimes by reason of consanguinity. Touching the community

[2] *Symposium*, 191, 192.

[3] a 25-40.

of wives and children, let this be our conclusion.

5

Next let us consider what should be our arrangements about property: should the citizens of the perfect state have their possessions in common or not? This question may be discussed separately from the enactments about **1263a** women and children. Even supposing that the women and children belong to individuals, according to the custom which is at present universal, may there not be an advantage in having and using possessions in common? Three cases are possible: (1) the soil may be appropriated, but the produce may be thrown for consumption into the common stock; and this is the practice of some nations. Or (2), the soil may be common, and may be cultivated in common, but the produce divided among individuals for their private use; this is a form of common property which is said to exist among certain barbarians. Or (3), the soil and the produce may be alike common.

When the husbandmen are not the owners, the case will be different and easier to deal with; but when they till the ground for themselves the question of ownership will give a world of trouble. If they do not share equally in enjoyments and toils, those who labour much and get little will necessarily complain of those who labour little and receive or consume much. But indeed there is always a difficulty in men living together and having all human relations in common, but especially in their having common property. The partnerships of fellow-travellers are an example to the point; for they generally fall out over everyday matters and quarrel about any trifle which turns up. So with servants: we are most liable to take offence at those with whom we most frequently come into contact in daily life.

These are only some of the disadvantages which attend the community of property; the present arrangement, if improved as it might be by good customs and laws, would be far better, and would have the advantages of both systems. Property should be in a certain sense common, but, as a general rule, private; for, when every one has a distinct interest, men will not complain of one another, and they will make more progress, because every one will be attending to his own business. And yet by reason of goodness, and in respect of use, 'Friends', as the proverb says, 'will have all things common.' Even now there are traces of such a principle, showing that it is not impracticable, but, in well-ordered states, exists already to a certain extent and may be carried further. For, although every man has his own property, some things he will place at the disposal of his friends, while of others he shares the use with them. The Lacedaemonians, for example, use one another's slaves, and horses, and dogs, as if they were their own; and when they lack provisions on a journey, they appropriate what they find in the fields throughout the country. It is clearly better that property should be private, but the use of it common; and the special business of the legislator is to create in men this benevolent disposition. Again, how immeasurably greater is the pleasure, when a man feels a thing to be his own; for surely the love of self is a feeling implanted by nature **1263b** and not given in vain, although selfishness is rightly censured; this, however, is not the mere love of self, but the love of self in excess, like the miser's love of money; for all, or almost all, men love money and other such objects in a measure. And further, there is the greatest pleasure in doing a kindness or service to friends or guests or companions, which can only be rendered when a man has private property. These advantages are lost by excessive unification of the state. The exhibition of two virtues, besides, is visibly annihilated in such a state: first, temperance towards women (for it is an honourable action to abstain from another's wife for temperance sake); secondly, liberality in the matter of property. No one, when men have all things in common, will any longer set an example of liberality or do any liberal action; for liberality consists in the use which is made of property. Such legislation may have a specious appearance of benevolence; men readily listen to it, and are easily induced to believe that in some wonderful manner everybody will become everybody's friend, especially when some one[1] is heard denouncing the evils now existing in states, suits about contracts, convictions for perjury, flatteries of rich men and the like, which are said to arise out of the possession of private property. These evils, however, are due to a very different cause—the wickedness of human nature. Indeed, we see that there is much more quarrelling among those who have all things in common, though there are not many of them when compared with the vast numbers who have private property.

Again, we ought to reckon, not only the evils

[1] *Republic*, v. 464, 465.

from which the citizens will be saved, but also the advantages which they will lose. The life which they are to lead appears to be quite impracticable. The error of Socrates must be attributed to the false notion of unity from which he starts. Unity there should be, both of the family and of the state, but in some respects only. For there is a point at which a state may attain such a degree of unity as to be no longer a state, or at which, without actually ceasing to exist, it will become an inferior state, like harmony passing into unison, or rhythm which has been reduced to a single foot. The state, as I was saying, is a plurality, which should be united and made into a community by education; and it is strange that the author of a system of education which he thinks will make the state virtuous, should expect to improve his citizens by regulations of this sort, and not by philosophy or by customs and laws, like those which prevail at Sparta and Crete respecting common meals, whereby the
1264a legislator has made property common. Let us remember that we should not disregard the experience of ages; in the multitude of years these things, if they were good, would certainly not have been unknown; for almost everything has been found out, although sometimes they are not put together; in other cases men do not use the knowledge which they have. Great light would be thrown on this subject if we could see such a form of government in the actual process of construction; for the legislator could not form a state at all without distributing and dividing its constituents into associations for common meals, and into phratries and tribes. But all this legislation ends only in forbidding agriculture to the guardians, a prohibition which the Lacedaemonians try to enforce already.

But, indeed, Socrates has not said, nor is it easy to decide, what in such a community will be the general form of the state. The citizens who are not guardians are the majority, and about them nothing has been determined: are the husbandmen, too, to have their property in common? Or is each individual to have his own? and are their wives and children to be individual or common? If, like the guardians, they are to have all things in common, in what do they differ from them, or what will they gain by submitting to their government? Or, upon what principle would they submit, unless indeed the governing class adopt the ingenious policy of the Cretans, who give their slaves the same institutions as their own, but forbid them gymnastic exercises and the possession of arms. If, on the other hand, the inferior classes are to be like other cities in respect of marriage and property, what will be the form of the community? Must it not contain two states in one, each hostile to the other? He makes the guardians into a mere occupying garrison, while the husbandmen and artisans and the rest are the real citizens. But if so the suits and quarrels, and all the evils which Socrates affirms[1] to exist in other states, will exist equally among them. He says indeed that, having so good an education, the citizens will not need many laws, for example laws about the city or about the markets[2] but then he confines his education to the guardians. Again, he makes the husbandmen owners of the property upon condition of their paying a tribute.[3] But in that case they are likely to be much more unmanageable and conceited than the Helots, or Penestae, or slaves in general. And whether community of wives and property be necessary for the lower equally with the higher class or not, and the questions akin to this, what will be the education, form of government, laws of the lower class, Socrates has nowhere determined, neither is it easy to discover this, nor is their character of small importance if the common life of the guardians is to be maintained.
1264b Again, if Socrates makes the women common, and retains private property, the men will see to the fields, but who will see to the house? And who will do so if the agricultural class have both their property and their wives in common? Once more: it is absurd to argue, from the analogy of the animals, that men and women should follow the same pursuits, for animals have not to manage a household. The government, too, as constituted by Socrates, contains elements of danger; for he makes the same persons always rule. And if this is often a cause of disturbance among the meaner sort, how much more among high-spirited warriors? But that the persons whom he makes rulers must be the same is evident; for the gold which the God mingles in the souls of men is not at one time given to one, at another time to another, but always to the same: as he says, 'God mingles gold in some, and silver in others, from their very birth; but brass and iron in those who are meant to be artisans and husbandmen.'[4] Again, he deprives the guardians even of hap-

[1] *Republic*, v. 464, 465. [2] *Ibid.*, iv. 425.
[3] *Ibid.*, v. 464. [4] Cf. *Ibid.*, iii. 415.

piness, and says that the legislator ought to make the whole state happy.[1] But the whole cannot be happy unless most, or all, or some of its parts enjoy happiness. In this respect happiness is not like the even principle in numbers, which may exist only in the whole, but in neither of the parts; not so happiness. And if the guardians are not happy, who are? Surely not the artisans, or the common people. The Republic of which Socrates discourses has all these difficulties, and others quite as great.

6

The same, or nearly the same, objections apply to Plato's later work, the *Laws*, and therefore we had better examine briefly the constitution which is therein described. In the *Republic*, Socrates has definitely settled in all a few questions only; such as the community of women and children, the community of property, and the constitution of the state. The population is divided into two classes—one of husbandmen, and the other of warriors;[2] from this latter is taken a third class of counsellors and rulers of the state.[3] But Socrates has not determined whether the husbandmen and artisans are to have a share in the government, and whether they, too, are to carry arms and share in military service, or not. He certainly thinks[4] that the women ought to share in the education of the guardians, and to fight by their side. The remainder of the work is filled up with digressions foreign to the main subject, and with discussions about the **1265a** education of the guardians. In the *Laws* there is hardly anything but laws; not much is said about the constitution. This, which he had intended to make more of the ordinary type, he gradually brings round to the other or ideal form. For with the exception of the community of women and property, he supposes everything to be the same in both states; there is to be the same education; the citizens of both are to live free from servile occupations, and there are to be common meals in both. The only difference is that in the *Laws*, the common meals are extended to women,[5] and the warriors number 5000,[6] but in the *Republic* only 1000.[7] The discourses of Socrates are never commonplace; they always exhibit grace and originality and thought; but perfection in everything can hardly be expected. We must not overlook the fact that the number of 5000 citizens, just now mentioned, will require a territory as large as Babylon, or some other huge site, if so many persons are to be supported in idleness, together with their women and attendants, who will be a multitude many times as great. In framing an ideal we may assume what we wish, but should avoid impossibilities.

It is said that the legislator ought to have his eye directed to two points,—the people and the country. But neighbouring countries also must not be forgotten by him, firstly because the state for which he legislates is to have a political and not an isolated life. For a state must have such a military force as will be serviceable against her neighbours, and not merely useful at home. Even if the life of action is not admitted to be the best, either for individuals or states, still a city should be formidable to enemies, whether invading or retreating.

There is another point: Should not the amount of property be defined in some way which differs from this by being clearer? For Socrates says that a man should have so much property as will enable him to live temperately,[8] which is only a way of saying 'to live well'; this is too general a conception. Further, a man may live temperately and yet miserably. A better definition would be that a man must have so much property as will enable him to live not only temperately but liberally; if the two are parted, liberality will combine with luxury; temperance will be associated with toil. For liberality and temperance are the only eligible qualities which have to do with the use of property. A man cannot use property with mildness or courage, but temperately and liberally he may; and therefore the practice of these virtues is inseparable from property. There is an inconsistency, too, in equalizing the property and not regulating the number of the citizens; the population is to remain unlimited, and he thinks that it will be sufficiently equalized by a certain number of mar- **1265b** riages being unfruitful, however many are born to others, because he finds this to be the case in existing states. But greater care will be required than now; for among ourselves, whatever may be the number of citizens, the property is always distributed among them, and therefore no one is in want; but, if the property were incapable of division as in the *Laws*, the supernumeraries, whether few

[1] *Republic*, IV. 419, 420.
[2] *Ibid.*, II. 373.
[3] *Ibid.*, III. 412.
[4] *Ibid.*, V. 451.
[5] *Laws*, VI. 780.
[6] *Ibid.*, V. 737.
[7] *Republic*, IV. 423.
[8] *Laws*, V. 737.

or many, would get nothing. One would have thought that it was even more necessary to limit population than property; and that the limit should be fixed by calculating the chances of mortality in the children, and of sterility in married persons. The neglect of this subject, which in existing states is so common, is a never-failing cause of poverty among the citizens; and poverty is the parent of revolution and crime. Pheidon the Corinthian, who was one of the most ancient legislators, thought that the families and the number of citizens ought to remain the same, although originally all the lots may have been of different sizes: but in the *Laws* the opposite principle is maintained. What in our opinion is the right arrangement will have to be explained hereafter.[1]

There is another omission in the *Laws:* Socrates does not tell us how the rulers differ from their subjects; he only says that they should be related as the warp and the woof, which are made out of different wools.[2] He allows that a man's whole property may be increased fivefold,[3] but why should not his land also increase to a certain extent? Again, will the good management of a household be promoted by his arrangement of homesteads? for he assigns to each individual two homesteads in separate places,[4] and it is difficult to live in two houses.

The whole system of government tends to be neither democracy nor oligarchy, but something in a mean between them, which is usually called a polity, and is composed of the heavy-armed soldiers. Now, if he intended to frame a constitution which would suit the greatest number of states, he was very likely right, but not if he meant to say that this constitutional form came nearest to his first or ideal state; for many would prefer the Lacedaemonian, or, possibly, some other more aristocratic government. Some, indeed, say that the best constitution is a combination of all existing forms, and they praise the Lacedaemonian because it is made up of oligarchy, monarchy, and democracy, the king forming the monarchy, and the council of elders the oligarchy, while the democratic element is represented by the Ephors; for the Ephors are selected from the people. Others, however, declare the Ephoralty to be a tyranny, and find the element of democracy in the common

1266a meals and in the habits of daily life. In the *Laws*[5] it is maintained that the best constitution is made up of democracy and tyranny, which are either not constitutions at all, or are the worst of all. But they are nearer the truth who combine many forms; for the constitution is better which is made up of more numerous elements. The constitution proposed in the *Laws* has no element of monarchy at all; it is nothing but oligarchy and democracy, leaning rather to oligarchy. This is seen in the mode of appointing magistrates;[6] for although the appointment of them by lot from among those who have been already selected combines both elements, the way in which the rich are compelled by law to attend the assembly[7] and vote for magistrates or discharge other political duties, while the rest may do as they like, and the endeavour[8] to have the greater number of the magistrates appointed out of the richer classes and the highest officers selected from those who have the greatest incomes, both these are oligarchical features. The oligarchical principle prevails also in the choice of the council,[9] for all are compelled to choose, but the compulsion extends only to the choice out of the first class, and of an equal number out of the second class and out of the third class, but not in this latter case to all the voters but to those of the first three classes; and the selection of candidates out of the fourth class is only compulsory on the first and second. Then, from the persons so chosen, he says that there ought to be an equal number of each class selected. Thus a preponderance will be given to the better sort of people, who have the larger incomes, because many of the lower classes, not being compelled, will not vote. These considerations, and others which will be adduced when the time comes for examining similar polities, tend to show that states like Plato's should not be composed of democracy and monarchy. There is also a danger in electing the magistrates out of a body who are themselves elected;[10] for, if but a small number choose to combine, the elections will always go as they desire. Such is the constitution which is described in the *Laws*.

7

Other constitutions have been proposed; some by private persons, others by philosophers and

[1] Cf. VII. 1326b 26-32, 1330a 9-18, 1335b 19-26.
[2] *Laws*, V. 734, 735.
[3] *Ibid.*, V. 744.
[4] *Ibid.*, V. 745.

[5] III. 693, 701; IV. 710; VI. 756.
[6] *Ibid.*, VI. 756, 763, 765.
[7] *Ibid.*, VI. 764; and *Politics*, IV. 1294a 37, 1298b 16.
[8] *Laws*, VI. 763.
[9] *Ibid.*, VI. 756.
[10] *Ibid.*, VI. 753.

statesmen, which all come nearer to established or existing ones than either of Plato's. No one else has introduced such novelties as the community of women and children, or public tables for women: other legislators begin with what is necessary. In the opinion of some, the regulation of property is the chief point of all, that being the question upon which all revolutions turn. This danger was recognized by Phaleas of Chalcedon, who was the first to affirm that the citizens of a state ought to have equal possessions. He thought that in a **1266b** new colony the equalization might be accomplished without difficulty, not so easily when a state was already established; and that then the shortest way of compassing the desired end would be for the rich to give and not to receive marriage portions, and for the poor not to give but to receive them.

Plato in the *Laws*[1] was of opinion that, to a certain extent, accumulation should be allowed, forbidding, as I have already observed,[2] any citizen to possess more than five times the minimum qualification. But those who make such laws should remember what they are apt to forget,—that the legislator who fixes the amount of property should also fix the number of children; for, if the children are too many for the property, the law must be broken. And, besides the violation of the law, it is a bad thing that many from being rich should become poor; for men of ruined fortunes are sure to stir up revolutions. That the equalization of property exercises an influence on political society was clearly understood even by some of the old legislators. Laws were made by Solon and others prohibiting an individual from possessing as much land as he pleased; and there are other laws in states which forbid the sale of property: among the Locrians, for example, there is a law that a man is not to sell his property unless he can prove unmistakably that some misfortune has befallen him. Again, there have been laws which enjoin the preservation of the original lots. Such a law existed in the island of Leucas, and the abrogation of it made the constitution too democratic, for the rulers no longer had the prescribed qualification. Again, where there is equality of property, the amount may be either too large or too small, and the possessor may be living either in luxury or penury. Clearly, then, the legislator ought not only to aim at the equalization of properties, but at moderation in their amount. Further, if he prescribe this moderate amount equally to all, he will be no nearer the mark; for it is not the possessions but the desires of mankind which require to be equalized, and this is impossible, unless a sufficient education is provided by the laws. But Phaleas will probably reply that this is precisely what he means; and that, in his opinion, there ought to be in states, not only equal property, but equal education. Still he should tell us what will be the character of his education; there is no use in having one and the same for all, if it is of a sort that predisposes men to avarice, or ambition, or both. Moreover, civil troubles arise, not only out of the inequality of property, but out of the inequality of honour, though in opposite ways. For the common **1267a** people quarrel about the inequality of property, the higher class about the equality of honour; as the poet says,—

The bad and good alike in honour share.[3]

There are crimes of which the motive is want; and for these Phaleas expects to find a cure in the equalization of property, which will take away from a man the temptation to be a highwayman, because he is hungry or cold. But want is not the sole incentive to crime; men also wish to enjoy themselves and not to be in a state of desire—they wish to cure some desire, going beyond the necessities of life, which preys upon them; nay, this is not the only reason—they may desire superfluities in order to enjoy pleasures unaccompanied with pain, and therefore they commit crimes.

Now what is the cure of these three disorders? Of the first, moderate possessions and occupation; of the second, habits of temperance; as to the third, if any desire pleasures which depend on themselves, they will find the satisfaction of their desires nowhere but in philosophy; for all other pleasures we are dependent on others. The fact is that the greatest crimes are caused by excess and not by necessity. Men do not become tyrants in order that they may not suffer cold; and hence great is the honour bestowed, not on him who kills a thief, but on him who kills a tyrant. Thus we see that the institutions of Phaleas avail only against petty crimes.

There is another objection to them. They are chiefly designed to promote the internal welfare of the state. But the legislator should consider also its relation to neighbouring nations, and to all who are outside of it. The government must be organized with a view to

[1] v. 744.

[2] 1265b 21.

[3] *Iliad*, IX. 319.

military strength; and of this he has said not a word. And so with respect to property: there should not only be enough to supply the internal wants of the state, but also to meet dangers coming from without. The property of the state should not be so large that more powerful neighbours may be tempted by it, while the owners are unable to repel the invaders; nor yet so small that the state is unable to maintain a war even against states of equal power, and of the same character. Phaleas has not laid down any rule; but we should bear in mind that abundance of wealth is an advantage. The best limit will probably be, that a more powerful neighbour must have no inducement to go to war with you by reason of the excess of your wealth, but only such as he would have had if you had possessed less. There is a story that Eubulus, when Autophradates was going to besiege Atarneus, told him to consider how long the operation would take, and then reckon up the cost which would be incurred in the time. 'For', said he, 'I am willing for a smaller sum than that to leave Atarneus at once.' These words of Eubulus made an impression on Autophradates, and he desisted from the siege.

The equalization of property is one of the things that tend to prevent the citizens from quarrelling. Not that the gain in this direction is very great. For the nobles will be dissatisfied because they think themselves worthy of more than an equal share of honours; and this is often found to be a cause of sedition and revolution. And the avarice of mankind is insati-
1267b able; at one time two obols was pay enough; but now, when this sum has become customary, men always want more and more without end; for it is of the nature of desire not to be satisfied, and most men live only for the gratification of it. The beginning of reform is not so much to equalize property as to train the nobler sort of natures not to desire more, and to prevent the lower from getting more; that is to say, they must be kept down, but not ill-treated. Besides, the equalization proposed by Phaleas is imperfect; for he only equalizes land, whereas a man may be rich also in slaves, and cattle, and money, and in the abundance of what are called his movables. Now either all these things must be equalized, or some limit must be imposed on them, or they must all be let alone. It would appear that Phaleas is legislating for a small city only, if, as he supposes, all the artisans are to be public slaves and not to form a supplementary part of the body of citizens. But if there is a law that artisans are to be public slaves, it should only apply to those engaged on public works, as at Epidamnus, or at Athens on the plan which Diophantus once introduced.

From these observations any one may judge how far Phaleas was wrong or right in his ideas.

8

Hippodamus, the son of Euryphon, a native of Miletus, the same who invented the art of planning cities, and who also laid out the Piraeus,—a strange man, whose fondness for distinction led him into a general eccentricity of life, which made some think him affected (for he would wear flowing hair and expensive ornaments; but these were worn on a cheap but warm garment both in winter and summer); he, besides aspiring to be an adept in the knowledge of nature, was the first person not a statesman who made inquiries about the best form of government.

The city of Hippodamus was composed of 10,000 citizens divided into three parts,—one of artisans, one of husbandmen, and a third of armed defenders of the state. He also divided the land into three parts, one sacred, one public, the third private:—the first was set apart to maintain the customary worship of the gods, the second was to support the warriors, the third was the property of the husbandmen. He also divided laws into three classes, and no more, for he maintained that there are three subjects of lawsuits,—insult, injury, and homicide. He likewise instituted a single final court of appeal, to which all causes seeming to have been improperly decided might be referred; this court he formed
1268a of elders chosen for the purpose. He was further of opinion that the decisions of the courts ought not to be given by the use of a voting pebble, but that every one should have a tablet on which he might not only write a simple condemnation, or leave the tablet blank for a simple acquittal; but, if he partly acquitted and partly condemned, he was to distinguish accordingly. To the existing law he objected that it obliged the judges to be guilty of perjury, whichever way they voted. He also enacted that those who discovered anything for the good of the state should be honoured; and he provided that the children of citizens who died in battle should be maintained at the public expense, as if such an enactment had never been heard of before,

yet it actually exists at Athens and in other places. As to the magistrates, he would have them all elected by the people, that is, by the three classes already mentioned, and those who were elected were to watch over the interests of the public, of strangers, and of orphans. These are the most striking points in the constitution of Hippodamus. There is not much else.

The first of these proposals to which objection may be taken is the threefold division of the citizens. The artisans, and the husbandmen, and the warriors, all have a share in the government. But the husbandmen have no arms, and the artisans neither arms nor land, and therefore they become all but slaves of the warrior class. That they should share in all the offices is an impossibility; for generals and guardians of the citizens, and nearly all the principal magistrates, must be taken from the class of those who carry arms. Yet, if the two other classes have no share in the government, how can they be loyal citizens? It may be said that those who have arms must necessarily be masters of both the other classes, but this is not so easily accomplished unless they are numerous; and if they are, why should the other classes share in the government at all, or have power to appoint magistrates? Further, what use are farmers to the city? Artisans there must be, for these are wanted in every city, and they can live by their craft, as elsewhere; and the husbandmen, too, if they really provided the warriors with food, might fairly have a share in the government. But in the republic of Hippodamus they are supposed to have land of their own, which they cultivate for their private benefit. Again, as to this common land out of which the soldiers are maintained, if they are themselves to be the cultivators of it, the warrior class will be identical with the husbandmen, although the legislator intended to make a distinction between them. If, again, there are to be other cultivators distinct both from the husbandmen, who have land of their own, and from the warriors, they will make a fourth class, which has no place in the state and no share in anything. Or, if the same persons are to cultivate their own lands, and those of the public as well, they will have a difficulty in supplying the **1268b** quantity of produce which will maintain two households: and why, in this case, should there be any division, for they might find food themselves and give to the warriors from the same land and the same lots? There is surely a great confusion in all this.

Neither is the law to be commended which says that the judges, when a simple issue is laid before them, should distinguish in their judgement; for the judge is thus converted into an arbitrator. Now, in an arbitration, although the arbitrators are many, they confer with one another about the decision, and therefore they can distinguish; but in courts of law this is impossible, and, indeed, most legislators take pains to prevent the judges from holding any communication with one another. Again, will there not be confusion if the judge thinks that damages should be given, but not so much as the suitor demands? He asks, say, for twenty minae, and the judge allows him ten minae (or in general the suitor asks for more and the judge allows less), while another judge allows five, another four minae. In this way they will go on splitting up the damages, and some will grant the whole and others nothing: how is the final reckoning to be taken? Again, no one contends that he who votes for a simple acquittal or condemnation perjures himself, if the indictment has been laid in an unqualified form; and this is just, for the judge who acquits does not decide that the defendant owes nothing, but that he does not owe the twenty minae. He only is guilty of perjury who thinks that the defendant ought not to pay twenty minae, and yet condemns him.

To honour those who discover anything which is useful to the state is a proposal which has a specious sound, but cannot safely be enacted by law, for it may encourage informers, and perhaps even lead to political commotions. This question involves another. It has been doubted whether it is or is not expedient to make any changes in the laws of a country, even if another law be better. Now, if all changes are inexpedient, we can hardly assent to the proposal of Hippodamus; for, under pretence of doing a public service, a man may introduce measures which are really destructive to the laws or to the constitution. But, since we have touched upon this subject, perhaps we had better go a little into detail, for, as I was saying, there is a difference of opinion, and it may sometimes seem desirable to make changes. Such changes in the other arts and sciences have certainly been beneficial; medicine, for example, and gymnastic, and every other art and craft have departed from traditional usage. And, if politics be an art, change must be necessary in this as in any other art. That improvement has occurred is shown by the fact that old customs are exceedingly simple and barbarous. For the ancient Hellenes went about armed and bought their brides of each other. The remains **1269a** of ancient laws which have come down to us are quite absurd; for example, at Cumae there is a law about murder, to the effect that if the accuser produce a certain number of witnesses from among his own kinsmen, the accused shall be held guilty. Again, men in general desire the good, and not merely what their fathers had. But the primaeval inhabitants, whether they were born of the earth or were the survivors of some destruction, may be supposed to have been no better than ordinary or even foolish people among ourselves (such is certainly the tradition concerning the earth-born men); and it would be ridiculous to rest contented with their notions. Even when laws have been written down, they ought not always to remain unaltered. As in other sciences, so in politics, it is impossible that all things should be precisely set down in writing; for enactments must be universal, but actions are concerned with particulars. Hence we infer that sometimes and in certain cases laws may be changed; but when we look at the matter from another point of view, great caution would seem to be required. For the habit of lightly changing the laws is an evil, and, when the advantage is small, some errors both of lawgivers and rulers had better be left; the citizen will not gain so much by making the change as he will lose by the habit of disobedience. The analogy of the arts is false; a change in a law is a very different thing from a change in an art. For the law has no power to command obedience except that of habit, which can only be given by time, so that a readiness to change from old to new laws enfeebles the power of the law. Even if we admit that the laws are to be changed, are they all to be changed, and in every state? And are they to be changed by anybody who likes, or only by certain persons? These are very important questions; and therefore we had better reserve the discussion of them to a more suitable occasion.

9

In the governments of Lacedaemon and Crete, and indeed in all governments, two points have to be considered: first, whether any particular law is good or bad, when compared with the perfect state; secondly, whether it is or is not consistent with the idea and character which the lawgiver has set before his citizens. That in a well-ordered state the citizens should have leisure and not have to provide for their daily wants is generally acknowledged, but there is a difficulty in seeing how this leisure is to be attained. The Thessalian Penestae have often risen against their masters, and the Helots in like manner against the Lacedaemonians, for whose misfortunes they are always lying in wait. Nothing, however, of this kind has as yet happened to the Cretans; the reason probably is that the neighbouring cities, **1269b** even when at war with one another, never form an alliance with rebellious serfs, rebellions not being for their interest, since they themselves have a dependent population. Whereas all the neighbours of the Lacedaemonians, whether Argives, Messenians, or Arcadians, were their enemies. In Thessaly, again, the original revolt of the slaves occurred because the Thessalians were still at war with the neighbouring Achaeans, Perrhaebians and Magnesians. Besides, if there were no other difficulty, the treatment or management of slaves is a troublesome affair; for, if not kept in hand, they are insolent, and think that they are as good as their masters, and, if harshly treated, they hate and conspire against them. Now it is clear that when these are the results the citizens of a state have not found out the secret of managing their subject population.

Again, the licence of the Lacedaemonian women defeats the intention of the Spartan constitution, and is adverse to the happiness of the state. For, a husband and a wife being each a part of every family, the state may be considered as about equally divided into men and women; and, therefore, in those states in which the condition of the women is bad, half the city may be regarded as having no laws. And this is what has actually happened at Sparta; the legislator wanted to make the whole state hardy and temperate, and he has carried out his intention in the case of the men, but he has neglected the women, who live in every sort of intemperance and luxury. The consequence is that in such a state wealth is too highly valued, especially if the citizens fall under the dominion of their wives, after the manner of most warlike races, except the Celts and a few others who openly approve of male loves. The old mythologer would seem to have been right in uniting Ares and Aphrodite, for all warlike races are prone to the love either of men or of women. This was ex-

emplified among the Spartans in the days of their greatness; many things were managed by their women. But what difference does it make whether women rule, or the rulers are ruled by women? The result is the same. Even in regard to courage, which is of no use in daily life, and is needed only in war, the influence of the Lacedaemonian women has been most mischievous. The evil showed itself in the Theban invasion, when, unlike the women in other cities, they were utterly useless and caused more confusion than the enemy. This licence of the Lacedaemonian women existed from the earliest times, and was only
1270a what might be expected. For, during the wars of the Lacedaemonians, first against the Argives, and afterwards against the Arcadians and Messenians, the men were long away from home, and, on the return of peace, they gave themselves into the legislator's hand, already prepared by the discipline of a soldier's life (in which there are many elements of virtue), to receive his enactments. But, when Lycurgus, as tradition says, wanted to bring the women under his laws, they resisted, and he gave up the attempt. These then are the causes of what then happened, and this defect in the constitution is clearly to be attributed to them. We are not, however, considering what is or is not to be excused, but what is right or wrong, and the disorder of the women, as I have already said,[1] not only gives an air of indecorum to the constitution considered in itself, but tends in a measure to foster avarice.

The mention of avarice naturally suggests a criticism on the inequality of property. While some of the Spartan citizens have quite small properties, others have very large ones; hence the land has passed into the hands of a few. And this is due also to faulty laws; for, although the legislator rightly holds up to shame the sale or purchase of an inheritance, he allows anybody who likes to give or bequeath it. Yet both practices lead to the same result. And nearly two-fifths of the whole country are held by women; this is owing to the number of heiresses and to the large dowries which are customary. It would surely have been better to have given no dowries at all, or, if any, but small or moderate ones. As the law now stands, a man may bestow his heiress on any one whom he pleases, and, if he die intestate, the privilege of giving her away descends to his heir. Hence, although the country is able to maintain 1500 cavalry and 30,000 hoplites, the whole number of Spartan citizens fell below 1000. The result proves the faulty nature of their laws respecting property; for the city sank under a single defeat; the want of men was their ruin. There is a tradition that, in the days of their ancient kings, they were in the habit of giving the rights of citizenship to strangers, and therefore, in spite of their long wars, no lack of population was experienced by them: indeed, at one time Sparta is said to have numbered not less than 10,000 citizens. Whether this statement is true or not, it would certainly have been better to have maintained their numbers by the equalization of property. Again, the law which relates to the procreation of children is adverse to the correction of
1270b this inequality. For the legislator, wanting to have as many Spartans as he could, encouraged the citizens to have large families; and there is a law at Sparta that the father of three sons shall be exempt from military service, and he who has four from all the burdens of the state. Yet it is obvious that, if there were many children, the land being distributed as it is, many of them must necessarily fall into poverty.

The Lacedaemonian constitution is defective in another point; I mean the Ephoralty. This magistracy has authority in the highest matters, but the Ephors are chosen from the whole people, and so the office is apt to fall into the hands of very poor men, who, being badly off, are open to bribes. There have been many examples at Sparta of this evil in former times; and quite recently, in the matter of the Andrians, certain of the Ephors who were bribed did their best to ruin the state. And so great and tyrannical is their power, that even the kings have been compelled to court them, so that, in this way as well, together with the royal office the whole constitution has deteriorated, and from being an aristocracy has turned into a democracy. The Ephoralty certainly does keep the state together; for the people are contented when they have a share in the highest office, and the result, whether due to the legislator or to chance, has been advantageous. For if a constitution is to be permanent, all the parts of the state must wish that it should exist and the same arrangements be maintained. This is the case at Sparta, where the kings desire its permanence because they have due honour in their own persons; the nobles because they are repre-

[1] 1269b 12, 23.

sented in the council of elders (for the office of elder is a reward of virtue); and the people, because all are eligible to the Ephoralty. The election of Ephors out of the whole people is perfectly right, but ought not to be carried on in the present fashion, which is too childish. Again, they have the decision of great causes, although they are quite ordinary men, and therefore they should not determine them merely on their own judgement, but according to written rules, and to the laws. Their way of life, too, is not in accordance with the spirit of the constitution—they have a deal too much licence; whereas, in the case of the other citizens, the excess of strictness is so intolerable that they run away from the law into the secret indulgence of sensual pleasures.

Again, the council of elders is not free from defects. It may be said that the elders are good men and well trained in manly virtue; and that, therefore, there is an advantage to the state in having them. But that judges of important causes should hold office for life is a disputable thing, for the mind grows old as well as the body. And when men have been **1271a** educated in such a manner that even the legislator himself cannot trust them, there is real danger. Many of the elders are well known to have taken bribes and to have been guilty of partiality in public affairs. And therefore they ought not to be irresponsible; yet at Sparta they are so. But (it may be replied), 'All magistracies are accountable to the Ephors.' Yes, but this prerogative is too great for them, and we maintain that the control should be exercised in some other manner. Further, the mode in which the Spartans elect their elders is childish; and it is improper that the person to be elected should canvass for the office; the worthiest should be appointed, whether he chooses or not. And here the legislator clearly indicates the same intention which appears in other parts of his constitution; he would have his citizens ambitious, and he has reckoned upon this quality in the election of the elders; for no one would ask to be elected if he were not. Yet ambition and avarice, almost more than any other passions, are the motives of crime.

Whether kings are or are not an advantage to states, I will consider at another time[1]; they should at any rate be chosen, not as they are now, but with regard to their personal life and conduct. The legislator himself obviously did not suppose that he could make them really good men; at least he shows a great distrust of their virtue. For this reason the Spartans used to join enemies with them in the same embassy, and the quarrels between the kings were held to be conservative of the state.

Neither did the first introducer of the common meals, called 'phiditia', regulate them well. The entertainment ought to have been provided at the public cost, as in Crete; but among the Lacedaemonians every one is expected to contribute, and some of them are too poor to afford the expense; thus the intention of the legislator is frustrated. The common meals were meant to be a popular institution, but the existing manner of regulating them is the reverse of popular. For the very poor can scarcely take part in them; and, according to ancient custom, those who cannot contribute are not allowed to retain their rights of citizenship.

The law about the Spartan admirals has often been censured, and with justice; it is a source of dissension, for the kings are perpetual generals, and this office of admiral is but the setting up of another king.

1271b The charge which Plato brings, in the *Laws*,[2] against the intention of the legislator, is likewise justified; the whole constitution has regard to one part of virtue only,—the virtue of the soldier, which gives victory in war. So long as they were at war, therefore, their power was preserved, but when they had attained empire they fell, for of the arts of peace they knew nothing, and had never engaged in any employment higher than war. There is another error, equally great, into which they have fallen. Although they truly think that the goods for which men contend are to be acquired by virtue rather than by vice, they err in supposing that these goods are to be preferred to the virtue which gains them.

Once more: the revenues of the state are ill-managed; there is no money in the treasury, although they are obliged to carry on great wars, and they are unwilling to pay taxes. The greater part of the land being in the hands of the Spartans, they do not look closely into one another's contributions. The result which the legislator has produced is the reverse of beneficial; for he has made his city poor, and his citizens greedy.

Enough respecting the Spartan constitution, of which these are the principal defects.

[1] III. 14-17.

[2] *Laws*, I. 625, 630.

10

The Cretan constitution nearly resembles the Spartan, and in some few points is quite as good; but for the most part less perfect in form. The older constitutions are generally less elaborate than the later, and the Lacedaemonian is said to be, and probably is, in a very great measure, a copy of the Cretan. According to tradition, Lycurgus, when he ceased to be the guardian of King Charillus, went abroad and spent most of his time in Crete. For the two countries are nearly connected; the Lyctians are a colony of the Lacedaemonians, and the colonists, when they came to Crete, adopted the constitution which they found existing among the inhabitants. Even to this day the Perioeci, or subject population of Crete, are governed by the original laws which Minos is supposed to have enacted. The island seems to be intended by nature for dominion in Hellas, and to be well situated; it extends right across the sea, around which nearly all the Hellenes are settled; and while one end is not far from the Peloponnese, the other almost reaches to the region of Asia about Triopium and Rhodes. Hence Minos acquired the empire of the sea, subduing some of the islands and colonizing others; at last he invaded Sicily, where he died near Camicus.

The Cretan institutions resemble the Lacedaemonian. The Helots are the husbandmen of the one, the Perioeci of the other, and **1272a** both Cretans and Lacedaemonians have common meals, which were anciently called by the Lacedaemonians not 'phiditia' but 'andria'; and the Cretans have the same word, the use of which proves that the common meals originally came from Crete. Further, the two constitutions are similar; for the office of the Ephors is the same as that of the Cretan Cosmi, the only difference being that whereas the Ephors are five, the Cosmi are ten in number. The elders, too, answer to the elders in Crete, who are termed by the Cretans the council. And the kingly office once existed in Crete, but was abolished, and the Cosmi have now the duty of leading them in war. All classes share in the ecclesia, but it can only ratify the decrees of the elders and the Cosmi.

The common meals of Crete are certainly better managed than the Lacedaemonian; for in Lacedaemon every one pays so much per head, or, if he fails, the law, as I have already explained,[1] forbids him to exercise the rights of citizenship. But in Crete they are of a more popular character. There, of all the fruits of the earth and cattle raised on the public lands, and of the tribute which is paid by the Perioeci, one portion is assigned to the gods and to the service of the state, and another to the common meals, so that men, women, and children are all supported out of a common stock. The legislator has many ingenious ways of securing moderation in eating, which he conceives to be a gain; he likewise encourages the separation of men from women, lest they should have too many children, and the companionship of men with one another—whether this is a good or bad thing I shall have an opportunity of considering at another time. But that the Cretan common meals are better ordered than the Lacedaemonian there can be no doubt.

On the other hand, the Cosmi are even a worse institution than the Ephors, of which they have all the evils without the good. Like the Ephors, they are any chance persons, but in Crete this is not counterbalanced by a corresponding political advantage. At Sparta every one is eligible, and the body of the people, having a share in the highest office, want the constitution to be permanent. But in Crete the Cosmi are elected out of certain families, and not out of the whole people, and the elders out of those who have been Cosmi.

The same criticism may be made about the Cretan, which has been already made about the Lacedaemonian elders. Their irresponsibility and life tenure is too great a privilege, and their arbitrary power of acting upon their own judgement, and dispensing with written law, is dangerous. It is no proof of the goodness of the institution that the people are not discontented at being excluded from it. For there is no profit to be made out of the office as **1272b** out of the Ephoralty, since, unlike the Ephors, the Cosmi, being in an island, are removed from temptation.

The remedy by which they correct the evil of this institution is an extraordinary one, suited rather to a close oligarchy than to a constitutional state. For the Cosmi are often expelled by a conspiracy of their own colleagues, or of private individuals; and they are allowed also to resign before their term of office has expired. Surely all matters of this kind are better regulated by law than by the will of man, which is a very unsafe rule. Worst of all is the suspension of the office of Cosmi, a device to which the nobles often have recourse when

[1] 1271a 35.

they will not submit to justice. This shows that the Cretan government, although possessing some of the characteristics of a constitutional state, is really a close oligarchy.

The nobles have a habit, too, of setting up a chief; they get together a party among the common people and their own friends and then quarrel and fight with one another. What is this but the temporary destruction of the state and dissolution of society? A city is in a dangerous condition when those who are willing are also able to attack her. But, as I have already said,[1] the island of Crete is saved by her situation; distance has the same effect as the Lacedaemonian prohibition of strangers; and the Cretans have no foreign dominions. This is the reason why the Perioeci are contented in Crete, whereas the Helots are perpetually revolting. But when lately foreign invaders found their way into the island, the weakness of the Cretan constitution was revealed. Enough of the government of Crete.

11

The Carthaginians are also considered to have an excellent form of government, which differs from that of any other state in several respects, though it is in some very like the Lacedaemonian. Indeed, all three states—the Lacedaemonian, the Cretan, and the Carthaginian—nearly resemble one another, and are very different from any others. Many of the Carthaginian institutions are excellent. The superiority of their constitution is proved by the fact that the common people remains loyal to the constitution; the Carthaginians have never had any rebellion worth speaking of, and have never been under the rule of a tyrant.

Among the points in which the Carthaginian constitution resembles the Lacedaemonian are the following:—The common tables of the clubs answer to the Spartan phiditia, and their magistracy of the 104 to the Ephors; but, whereas the Ephors are any chance persons, the magistrates of the Carthaginians are elected according to merit—this is an improvement. They have also their kings and their gerusia, or council of elders, who correspond to the kings and elders of Sparta. Their kings, unlike the Spartan, are not always of the same family, nor that an ordinary one, but if there is some distinguished family they are selected out of it and not appointed by seniority—this is far better. Such officers have great power, and there-

1273a fore, if they are persons of little worth, do a great deal of harm, and they have already done harm at Lacedaemon.

Most of the defects or deviations from the perfect state, for which the Carthaginian constitution would be censured, apply equally to all the forms of government which we have mentioned. But of the deflections from aristocracy and constitutional government, some incline more to democracy and some to oligarchy. The kings and elders, if unanimous, may determine whether they will or will not bring a matter before the people, but when they are not unanimous, the people decide on such matters as well. And whatever the kings and elders bring before the people is not only heard but also determined by them, and any one who likes may oppose it; now this is not permitted in Sparta and Crete. That the magistracies of five who have under them many important matters should be co-opted, that they should choose the supreme council of 100, and should hold office longer than other magistrates (for they are virtually rulers both before and after they hold office)—these are oligarchical features; their being without salary and not elected by lot, and any similar points, such as the practice of having all suits tried by the magistrates, and not some by one class of judges or jurors and some by another, as at Lacedaemon, are characteristic of aristocracy. The Carthaginian constitution deviates from aristocracy and inclines to oligarchy, chiefly on a point where popular opinion is on their side. For men in general think that magistrates should be chosen not only for their merit, but for their wealth: a man, they say, who is poor cannot rule well,—he has not the leisure. If, then, election of magistrates for their wealth be characteristic of oligarchy, and election for merit of aristocracy, there will be a third form under which the constitution of Carthage is comprehended; for the Carthaginians choose their magistrates, and particularly the highest of them—their kings and generals—with an eye both to merit and to wealth.

But we must acknowledge that, in thus deviating from aristocracy, the legislator has committed an error. Nothing is more absolutely necessary than to provide that the highest class, not only when in office, but when out of office, should have leisure and not disgrace themselves in any way; and to this his attention should be first directed. Even if you must have regard to wealth, in order to secure leisure, yet it is surely a bad thing that the greatest offices, such as those of kings and generals,

[1] a41 sqq.

should be bought. The law which allows this abuse makes wealth of more account than virtue, and the whole state becomes avaricious. For, whenever the chiefs of the state deem anything honourable, the other citizens are sure to follow their example; and, where virtue has not the first place, there aristocracy cannot be firmly established. Those who have been at the expense of purchasing their places will be in the habit of repaying themselves; and it is absurd to suppose that a poor and honest man will be wanting to make gains, and that a lower stamp of man who has incurred a great expense will not. Wherefore they should rule who are able to rule best. And even if the legislator does not care to protect the good from poverty, he should at any rate secure leisure for them when in office.

1273b

It would seem also to be a bad principle that the same person should hold many offices, which is a favourite practice among the Carthaginians, for one business is better done by one man. The legislator should see to this and should not appoint the same person to be a flute-player and a shoemaker. Hence, where the state is large, it is more in accordance both with constitutional and with democratic principles that the offices of state should be distributed among many persons. For, as I said,[1] this arrangement is fairer to all, and any action familiarized by repetition is better and sooner performed. We have a proof in military and naval matters; the duties of command and of obedience in both these services extend to all.

The government of the Carthaginians is oligarchical, but they successfully escape the evils of oligarchy by enriching one portion of the people after another by sending them to their colonies. This is their panacea and the means by which they give stability to the state. Accident favours them, but the legislator should be able to provide against revolution without trusting to accidents. As things are, if any misfortune occurred, and the bulk of the subjects revolted, there would be no way of restoring peace by legal methods.

Such is the character of the Lacedaemonian, Cretan, and Carthaginian constitutions, which are justly celebrated.

12

Of those who have treated of governments, some have never taken any part at all in public affairs, but have passed their lives in a private station; about most of them, what was worth telling has been already told.[2] Others have been lawgivers, either in their own or in foreign cities, whose affairs they have administered; and of these some have only made laws, others have framed constitutions; for example, Lycurgus and Solon did both. Of the Lacedaemonian constitution I have already spoken.[3] As to Solon, he is thought by some to have been a good legislator, who put an end to the exclusiveness of the oligarchy, emancipated the people, established the ancient Athenian democracy, and harmonized the different elements of the state. According to their view, the council of Areopagus was an oligarchical element, the elected magistracy, aristocratical and the courts of law, democratical. The truth seems to be that the council and the elected magistracy existed before the time of Solon, and were retained by him, but that he formed the courts of law out of all the citizens, thus creating the democracy, which is the very reason why he is sometimes blamed. For in giving the supreme power to the law courts, which are elected by lot, he is thought to have destroyed the non-democratic element. When the law courts grew powerful, to please the people who were now playing the tyrant the old constitution was changed into the existing democracy. Ephialtes and Pericles curtailed the power of the Areopagus; Pericles also instituted the payment of the juries, and thus every demagogue in turn increased the power of the democracy until it became what we now see. All this is true; it seems, however, to be the result of circumstances, and not to have been intended by Solon. For the people, having been instrumental in gaining the empire of the sea in the Persian War, began to get a notion of itself, and followed worthless demagogues, whom the better class opposed. Solon, himself, appears to have given the Athenians only that power of electing to offices and calling to account the magistrates which was absolutely necessary; for without it they would have been in a state of slavery and enmity to the government. All the magistrates he appointed from the notables and the men of wealth, that is to say, from the pentacosio-medimni, or from the class called zeugitae, or from a third class of so-called knights or cavalry. The fourth class were labourers who had no share in any magistracy.

1274a

Mere legislators were Zaleucus, who gave laws to the Epizephyrian Locrians, and Charondas, who legislated for his own city of Ca-

[1] 1261b 1.

[2] Chapters 1-8.

[3] Chapter 9.

tana, and for the other Chalcidian cities in Italy and Sicily. Some people attempt to make out that Onomacritus was the first people who had any special skill in legislation, and that he, although a Locrian by birth, was trained in Crete, where he lived in the exercise of his prophetic art; that Thales was his companion, and that Lycurgus and Zaleucus were disciples of Thales, as Charondas was of Zaleucus. But their account is quite inconsistent with chronology.

There was also Philolaus, the Corinthian, who gave laws to the Thebans. This Philolaus was one of the family of the Bacchiadae, and a lover of Diocles, the Olympic victor, who left Corinth in horror of the incestuous passion which his mother Halcyone had conceived for him, and retired to Thebes, where the two friends together ended their days. The inhabitants still point out their tombs, which are in full view of one another, but one is visible from the Corinthian territory, the other not. Tradition says the two friends arranged them thus, Diocles out of horror at his misfortunes, so that the land of Corinth might not be visible from his tomb; Philolaus that it might. This is **1274b** the reason why they settled at Thebes, and so Philolaus legislated for the Thebans, and, besides some other enactments, gave them laws about the procreation of children, which they call the 'Laws of Adoption'. These laws were peculiar to him, and were intended to preserve the number of the lots.

In the legislation of Charondas there is nothing remarkable, except the suits against false witnesses. He is the first who instituted denunciation for perjury. His laws are more exact and more precisely expressed than even those of our modern legislators.

(Characteristic of Phaleas is the equalization of property; of Plato, the community of women, children, and property, the common meals of women, and the law about drinking, that the sober shall be masters of the feast; also the training of soldiers to acquire by practice equal skill with both hands, so that one should be as useful as the other.)

Draco has left laws, but he adapted them to a constitution which already existed, and there is no peculiarity in them which is worth mentioning, except the greatness and severity of the punishments.

Pittacus, too, was only a lawgiver, and not the author of a constitution; he has a law which is peculiar to him, that, if a drunken man do something wrong, he shall be more heavily punished than if he were sober; he looked not to the excuse which might be offered for the drunkard, but only to expediency, for drunken more often than sober people commit acts of violence.

Androdamas of Rhegium gave laws to the Chalcidians of Thrace. Some of them relate to homicide, and to heiresses; but there is nothing remarkable in them.

And here let us conclude our inquiry into the various constitutions which either actually exist, or have been devised by theorists.

BOOK III

I

He who would inquire into the essence and attributes of various kinds of government must first of all determine 'What is a state?' At present this is a disputed question. Some say that the state has done a certain act; others, no, not the state, but the oligarchy or the tyrant. And the legislator or statesman is concerned entirely with the state; a constitution or government being an arrangement of the inhabitants of a state. But a state is composite, like any other whole made up of many parts;—these are the citizens, who compose it. It is evident, therefore, that we must begin by **1275a** asking, Who is the citizen, and what is the meaning of the term? For here again there may be a difference of opinion. He who is a citizen in a democracy will often not be a citizen in an oligarchy. Leaving out of consideration those who have been made citizens, or who have obtained the name of citizen in any other accidental manner, we may say, first, that a citizen is not a citizen because he lives in a certain place, for resident aliens and slaves share in the place; nor is he a citizen who has no legal right except that of suing and being sued; for this right may be enjoyed under the provisions of a treaty. Nay, resident aliens in many places do not possess even such rights completely, for they are obliged to have a patron, so that they do but imperfectly participate in citizenship, and we call them citizens only in a qualified sense, as we might apply the term to children who are too young to be on the register, or to old men who have been relieved from state duties. Of these we do not say quite simply that they are citizens, but add in the one case that they are not of age, and in the other, that they are past the age, or something of that sort; the precise expression is immaterial, for our meaning is clear. Similar difficulties to those which I have mentioned may be raised and answered about deprived citizens and about exiles. But the citizen whom we are seeking to define is a citizen in the strictest sense, against whom no such exception can be taken, and his special characteristic is that he shares in the administration of justice, and in offices. Now of offices some are discontinuous, and the same persons are not allowed to hold them twice, or can only hold them after a fixed interval; others have no limit of time,—for example, the office of dicast or ecclesiast. It may, indeed, be argued that these are not magistrates at all, and that their functions give them no share in the government. But surely it is ridiculous to say that those who have the supreme power do not govern. Let us not dwell further upon this, which is a purely verbal question; what we want is a common term including both dicast and ecclesiast. Let us, for the sake of distinction, call it 'indefinite office', and we will assume that those who share in such office are citizens. This is the most comprehensive definition of a citizen, and best suits all those who are generally so called.

But we must not forget that things of which the underlying principles differ in kind, one of them being first, another second, another third, have, when regarded in this relation, nothing, or hardly anything, worth mentioning in common. Now we see that governments differ in kind, and that some of them are prior and that others are posterior; those **1275b** which are faulty or perverted are necessarily posterior to those which are perfect. (What we mean by perversion will be hereafter explained.[1]) The citizen then of necessity differs under each form of government; and our definition is best adapted to the citizen of a democracy; but not necessarily to other states. For in some states the people are not acknowledged, nor have they any regular assembly, but only extraordinary ones; and suits are distributed by sections among the magistrates. At Lacedaemon, for instance, the Ephors determine suits about contracts, which they distribute among themselves, while the elders are judges of homicide, and other causes are decided by other magistrates. A similar principle prevails at Carthage; there certain magistrates decide all causes. We may, indeed, modify our definition of the citizen so as to include these states. In them it is the holder of a definite, not of an indefinite office, who legislates and judges, and to some or all such holders of definite offices is reserved the right of deliberating or judging about some things or about all things. The conception of the citizen now begins to clear up.

He who has the power to take part in the deliberative or judicial administration of any state is said by us to be a citizen of that state; and, speaking generally, a state is a body of citizens sufficing for the purposes of life.

2

But in practice a citizen is defined to be one of whom both the parents are citizens; others insist on going further back; say to two or three or more ancestors. This is a short and practical definition; but there are some who raise the further question: How this third or fourth ancestor came to be a citizen? Gorgias of Leontini, partly because he was in a difficulty, partly in irony, said—'Mortars are what is made by the mortar-makers, and the citizens of Larissa are those who are made by the magistrates; for it is their trade to make Larissaeans'. Yet the question is really simple, for, if according to the definition just given they shared in the government, they were citizens. This is a better definition than the other. For the words, 'born of a father or mother who is a citizen', cannot possibly apply to the first inhabitants or founders of a state.

There is a greater difficulty in the case of those who have been made citizens after a revolution, as by Cleisthenes at Athens after the expulsion of the tyrants, for he enrolled in tribes many metics, both strangers and slaves. The doubt in these cases is, not who is, but **1276a** whether he who is ought to be a citizen; and there will still be a further doubt, whether he who ought not to be a citizen, is one in fact, for what ought not to be is what is false. Now, there are some who hold office, and yet ought not to hold office, whom we describe as ruling, but ruling unjustly. And the citizen was defined by the fact of his holding some kind of rule or office,—he who holds a judicial or legislative office fulfils our definition of a citizen. It is evident, therefore, that the citizens about whom the doubt has arisen must be called citizens.

[1] Cf. 1279a 19.

3

Whether they ought to be so or not is a question which is bound up with the previous inquiry.[1] For a parallel question is raised respecting the state, whether a certain act is or is not an act of the state; for example, in the transition from an oligarchy or a tyranny to a democracy. In such cases persons refuse to fulfil their contracts or any other obligations, on the ground that the tyrant, and not the state, contracted them; they argue that some constitutions are established by force, and not for the sake of the common good. But this would apply equally to democracies, for they too may be founded on violence, and then the acts of the democracy will be neither more nor less acts of the state in question than those of an oligarchy or of a tyranny. This question runs up into another:—on what principle shall we ever say that the state is the same, or different? It would be a very superficial view which considered only the place and the inhabitants (for the soil and the population may be separated, and some of the inhabitants may live in one place and some in another). This, however, is not a very serious difficulty; we need only remark that the word 'state' is ambiguous.

It is further asked: When are men, living in the same place, to be regarded as a single city—what is the limit? Certainly not the wall of the city, for you might surround all Peloponnesus with a wall. Like this, we may say, is Babylon, and every city that has the compass of a nation rather than a city; Babylon, they say, had been taken for three days before some part of the inhabitants became aware of the fact. This difficulty may, however, with advantage be deferred to another occasion; the statesman has to consider the size of the state, and whether it should consist of more than one nation or not.

Again, shall we say that while the race of inhabitants, as well as their place of abode, remain the same, the city is also the same, although the citizens are always dying and being born, as we call rivers and fountains the same, although the water is always flowing away and coming again? Or shall we say that the generations of men, like the rivers, are the same, but that the state changes? For, since the state
1276^{b} is a partnership, and is a partnership of citizens in a constitution, when the form of the government changes, and becomes different, then it may be supposed that the state is no longer the same, just as a tragic differs from a comic chorus, although the members of both may be identical. And in this manner we speak of every union or composition of elements as different when the form of their composition alters; for example, a scale containing the same sounds is said to be different, accordingly as the Dorian or the Phrygian mode is employed. And if this is true it is evident that the sameness of the state consists chiefly in the sameness of the constitution, and it may be called or not by the same name, whether the inhabitants are the same or entirely different. It is quite another question, whether a state ought or ought not to fulfil engagements when the form of government changes.

4

There is a point nearly allied to the preceding: Whether the virtue of a good man and a good citizen is the same or not. But, before entering on this discussion, we must certainly first obtain some general notion of the virtue of the citizen. Like the sailor, the citizen is a member of a community. Now, sailors have different functions, for one of them is a rower, another a pilot, and a third a look-out man, a fourth is described by some similar term; and while the precise definition of each individual's virtue applies exclusively to him, there is, at the same time, a common definition applicable to them all. For they have all of them a common object, which is safety in navigation. Similarly, one citizen differs from another, but the salvation of the community is the common business of them all. This community is the constitution; the virtue of the citizen must therefore be relative to the constitution of which he is a member. If, then, there are many forms of government, it is evident that there is not a single virtue of the good citizen which is perfect virtue. But we say that the good man is he who has one single virtue which is perfect virtue. Hence it is evident that the good citizen need not of necessity possess the virtue which makes a good man.

The same question may also be approached by another road, from a consideration of the best constitution. If the state cannot be entirely composed of good men, and yet each citizen is expected to do his own business well, and must therefore have virtue, still, inasmuch as all the citizens cannot be alike, the
1277^{a} virtue of the citizen and of the good man cannot coincide. All must have the virtue of the good citizen—thus, and thus only, can

[1] Cf. 1274^{b} 34.

the state be perfect; but they will not have the virtue of a good man, unless we assume that in the good state all the citizens must be good. Again, the state, as composed of unlikes, may be compared to the living being: as the first elements into which a living being is resolved are soul and body, as soul is made up of rational principle and appetite, the family of husband and wife, property of master and slave, so of all these, as well as other dissimilar elements, the state is composed; and, therefore, the virtue of all the citizens cannot possibly be the same, any more than the excellence of the leader of a chorus is the same as that of the performer who stands by his side. I have said enough to show why the two kinds of virtue cannot be absolutely and always the same.

But will there then be no case in which the virtue of the good citizen and the virtue of the good man coincide? To this we answer that the good *ruler* is a good and wise man, and that he who would be a statesman must be a wise man. And some persons say that even the education of the ruler should be of a special kind; for are not the children of kings instructed in riding and military exercises? As Euripides says:

No subtle arts for me, but what the state requires.[1]

As though there were a special education needed by a ruler. If then the virtue of a good ruler is the same as that of a good man, and we assume further that the subject is a citizen as well as the ruler, the virtue of the good citizen and the virtue of the good man cannot be absolutely the same, although in some cases they may; for the virtue of a ruler differs from that of a citizen. It was the sense of this difference which made Jason say that 'he felt hungry when he was not a tyrant', meaning that he could not endure to live in a private station. But, on the other hand, it may be argued that men are praised for knowing both how to rule and how to obey, and he is said to be a citizen of approved virtue who is able to do both. Now if we suppose the virtue of a good man to be that which rules, and the virtue of the citizen to include ruling and obeying, it cannot be said that they are equally worthy of praise. Since, then, it is sometimes thought that the ruler and the ruled must learn different things and not the same, but that the citizen must know and share in them both, the inference is obvious. There is, indeed, the rule of a master, which is concerned with menial offices,—the master need not know how to perform these, but may employ others in the execution of them: the other would be degrading; and by the other I mean the power actually to do menial duties, which vary much in character and are executed by various classes of slaves, such, for example, as handicraftsmen, who, as their name signifies, live by the labour of their
1277b hands:—under these the mechanic is included. Hence in ancient times, and among some nations, the working classes had no share in the government—a privilege which they only acquired under the extreme democracy. Certainly the good man and the statesman and the good citizen ought not to learn the crafts of inferiors except for their own occasional use; if they habitually practise them, there will cease to be a distinction between master and slave.

This is not the rule of which we are speaking; but there is a rule of another kind, which is exercised over freemen and equals by birth—a constitutional rule, which the ruler must learn by obeying, as he would learn the duties of general of cavalry by being under the orders of a general of cavalry, or the duties of a general of infantry by being under the orders of a general of infantry, and by having had the command of a regiment and of a company. It has been well said that 'he who has never learned to obey cannot be a good commander'. The two are not the same, but the good citizen ought to be capable of both; he should know how to govern like a freeman, and how to obey like a freeman—these are the virtues of a citizen. And, although the temperance and justice of a ruler are distinct from those of a subject, the virtue of a good man will include both; for the virtue of the good man who is free and also a subject, e.g. his justice, will not be one but will comprise distinct kinds, the one qualifying him to rule, the other to obey, and differing as the temperance and courage of men and women differ. For a man would be thought a coward if he had no more courage than a courageous woman, and a woman would be thought loquacious if she imposed no more restraint on her conversation than the good man; and indeed their part in the management of the household is different, for the duty of the one is to acquire, and of the other to preserve. Practical wisdom only is characteristic of the ruler: it would seem that all other virtues must equally belong to ruler and sub-

[1] *Aeolus*, fr. 16, Nauck.

ject. The virtue of the subject is certainly not wisdom, but only true opinion; he may be compared to the maker of the flute, while his master is like the flute-player or user of the flute.

From these considerations may be gathered the answer to the question, whether the virtue of the good man is the same as that of the good citizen, or different, and how far the same, and how far different.

5

There still remains one more question about the citizen: Is he only a true citizen who has a share of office, or is the mechanic to be included? If they who hold no office are to be deemed citizens, not every citizen can have this virtue of ruling and obeying; for this man is a citizen. And if none of the lower class are citizens, in which part of the state are they to be placed? For they are not resident aliens, and they are not foreigners. May we not reply, that **1278a** as far as this objection goes there is no more absurdity in excluding them than in excluding slaves and freedmen from any of the above-mentioned classes? It must be admitted that we cannot consider all those to be citizens who are necessary to the existence of the state; for example, children are not citizens equally with grown-up men, who are citizens absolutely, but children, not being grown up, are only citizens on a certain assumption. Nay, in ancient times, and among some nations, the artisan class *were* slaves or foreigners, and therefore the majority of them are so now. The best form of state will not admit them to citizenship; but if they are admitted, then our definition of the virtue of a citizen will not apply to every citizen, nor to every free man as such, but only to those who are freed from necessary services. The necessary people are either slaves who minister to the wants of individuals, or mechanics and labourers who are the servants of the community. These reflections carried a little further will explain their position; and indeed what has been said already[1] is of itself, when understood, explanation enough.

Since there are many forms of government there must be many varieties of citizens, and especially of citizens who are subjects; so that under some governments the mechanic and the labourer will be citizens, but not in others, as, for example, in aristocracy or the so-called government of the best (if there be such an one), in which honours are given according to virtue and merit; for no man can practise virtue who is living the life of a mechanic or labourer. In oligarchies the qualification for office is high, and therefore no labourer can ever be a citizen; but a mechanic may, for an actual majority of them are rich. At Thebes there was a law that no man could hold office who had not retired from business for ten years. But in many states the law goes to the length of admitting aliens; for in some democracies a man is a citizen though his mother only be a citizen; and a similar principle is applied to illegitimate children; the law is relaxed when there is a dearth of population. But when the number of citizens increases, first the children of a male or a female slave are excluded; then those whose mothers only are citizens; and at last the right of citizenship is confined to those whose fathers and mothers are both citizens.

Hence, as is evident, there are different kinds of citizens; and he is a citizen in the highest sense who shares in the honours of the state. Compare Homer's words 'like some dishonoured stranger';[2] he who is excluded from the honours of the state is no better than an alien. But when this exclusion is concealed, then the object is that the privileged class may deceive their fellow inhabitants.

As to the question whether the virtue of the good man is the same as that of the good **1278b** citizen, the considerations already adduced prove that in some states the good man and the good citizen are the same, and in others different. When they are the same it is not every citizen who is a good man, but only the statesman and those who have or may have, alone or in conjunction with others, the conduct of public affairs.

6

Having determined these questions, we have next to consider whether there is only one form of government or many, and if many, what they are, and how many, and what are the differences between them.

A constitution is the arrangement of magistracies in a state, especially of the highest of all. The government is everywhere sovereign in the state, and the constitution is in fact the government. For example, in democracies the people are supreme, but in oligarchies, the few; and, therefore, we say that these two forms of government also are different: and so in other cases.

First, let us consider what is the purpose

[1] 1275^a 38 sqq.

[2] *Iliad*, IX. 648; XVI. 59.

of a state, and how many forms of government there are by which human society is regulated. We have already said, in the first part of this treatise,[1] when discussing household management and the rule of a master, that man is by nature a political animal. And therefore, men, even when they do not require one another's help, desire to live together; not but that they are also brought together by their common interests in proportion as they severally attain to any measure of well-being. This is certainly the chief end, both of individuals and of states. And also for the sake of mere life (in which there is possibly some noble element so long as the evils of existence do not greatly overbalance the good) mankind meet together and maintain the political community. And we all see that men cling to life even at the cost of enduring great misfortune, seeming to find in life a natural sweetness and happiness.

There is no difficulty in distinguishing the various kinds of authority; they have been often defined already in discussions outside the school. The rule of a master, although the slave by nature and the master by nature have in reality the same interests, is nevertheless exercised primarily with a view to the interest of the master, but accidentally considers the slave, since, if the slave perish, the rule of the master perishes with him. On the other hand, the government of a wife and children and of a household, which we have called household management, is exercised in the first instance for the good of the governed or for the common good of both parties, but essentially for the good of the governed, as we **1279a** see to be the case in medicine, gymnastic, and the arts in general, which are only accidentally concerned with the good of the artists themselves. For there is no reason why the trainer may not sometimes practise gymnastics, and the helmsman is always one of the crew. The trainer or the helmsman considers the good of those committed to his care. But, when he is one of the persons taken care of, he accidentally participates in the advantage, for the helmsman is also a sailor, and the trainer becomes one of those in training. And so in politics: when the state is framed upon the principle of equality and likeness, the citizens think that they ought to hold office by turns. Formerly, as is natural, every one would take his turn of service; and then again, somebody else would look after his interest, just as he, while in office, had looked after theirs. But nowadays, for the sake of the advantage which is to be gained from the public revenues and from office, men want to be always in office. One might imagine that the rulers, being sickly, were only kept in health while they continued in office; in that case we may be sure that they would be hunting after places. The conclusion is evident: that governments which have a regard to the common interest are constituted in accordance with strict principles of justice, and are therefore true forms; but those which regard only the interest of the rulers are all defective and perverted forms, for they are despotic, whereas a state is a community of freemen.

[1] Cf. I. 1253a 2.

7

Having determined these points, we have next to consider how many forms of government there are, and what they are; and in the first place what are the true forms, for when they are determined the perversions of them will at once be apparent. The words constitution and government have the same meaning, and the government, which is the supreme authority in states, must be in the hands of one, or of a few, or of the many. The true forms of government, therefore, are those in which the one, or the few, or the many, govern with a view to the common interest; but governments which rule with a view to the private interest, whether of the one, or of the few, or of the many, are perversions. For the members of a state, if they are truly citizens, ought to participate in its advantages. Of forms of government in which one rules, we call that which regards the common interests, kingship or royalty; that in which more than one, but not many, rule, aristocracy; and it is so called, either because the rulers are the best men, or because they have at heart the best interests of the state and of the citizens. But when the citizens at large administer the state for the common interest, the government is called by the generic name,—a constitution. And there is a reason for this use of language. One man or a few may excel in virtue; but as the number increases it becomes more difficult for them **1279b** to attain perfection in every kind of virtue, though they may in military virtue, for this is found in the masses. Hence in a constitutional government the fighting-men have the supreme power, and those who possess arms are the citizens.

Of the above-mentioned forms, the perversions are as follows:—of royalty, tyranny; of aristocracy, oligarchy; of constitutional government, democracy. For tyranny is a kind of monarchy which has in view the interest of the monarch only; oligarchy has in view the interest of the wealthy; democracy, of the needy: none of them the common good of all.

8

But there are difficulties about these forms of government, and it will therefore be necessary to state a little more at length the nature of each of them. For he who would make a philosophical study of the various sciences, and does not regard practice only, ought not to overlook or omit anything, but to set forth the truth in every particular. Tyranny, as I was saying, is monarchy exercising the rule of a master over the political society; oligarchy is when men of property have the government in their hands; democracy, the opposite, when the indigent, and not the men of property, are the rulers. And here arises the first of our difficulties, and it relates to the distinction just drawn. For democracy is said to be the government of the many. But what if the many are men of property and have the power in their hands? In like manner oligarchy is said to be the government of the few; but what if the poor are fewer than the rich, and have the power in their hands because they are stronger? In these cases the distinction which we have drawn between these different forms of government would no longer hold good.

Suppose, once more, that we add wealth to the few and poverty to the many, and name the governments accordingly—an oligarchy is said to be that in which the few and the wealthy, and a democracy that in which the many and the poor are the rulers—there will still be a difficulty. For, if the only forms of government are the ones already mentioned, how shall we describe those other governments also just mentioned by us, in which the rich are the more numerous and the poor are the fewer, and both govern in their respective states. The argument seems to show that, whether in oligarchies or in democracies, the number of the governing body, whether the greater number, as in a democracy, or the smaller number, as in an oligarchy, is an accident due to the fact that the rich everywhere are few, and the poor numerous. But if so, there is a misapprehension of the causes of the difference between them. For the real difference between democracy and oligarchy is poverty and wealth. **1280a** Wherever men rule by reason of their wealth, whether they be few or many, that is an oligarchy, and where the poor rule, that is a democracy. But as a fact the rich are few and the poor many; for few are well-to-do, whereas freedom is enjoyed by all, and wealth and freedom are the grounds on which the oligarchical and democratical parties respectively claim power in the state.

9

Let us begin by considering the common definitions of oligarchy and democracy, and what is justice oligarchical and democratical. For all men cling to justice of some kind, but their conceptions are imperfect and they do not express the whole idea. For example, justice is thought by them to be, and is, equality, not, however, for all, but only for equals. And inequality is thought to be, and is, justice; neither is this for all, but only for unequals. When the persons are omitted, then men judge erroneously. The reason is that they are passing judgement on themselves, and most people are bad judges in their own case. And whereas justice implies a relation to persons as well as to things, and a just distribution, as I have already said in the *Ethics*,[1] implies the same ratio between the persons and between the things, they agree about the equality of the things, but dispute about the equality of the persons, chiefly for the reason which I have just given,—because they are bad judges in their own affairs; and secondly, because both the parties to the argument are speaking of a limited and partial justice, but imagine themselves to be speaking of absolute justice. For the one party, if they are unequal in one respect, for example wealth, consider themselves to be unequal in all; and the other party, if they are equal in one respect, for example free birth, consider themselves to be equal in all. But they leave out the capital point. For if men met and associated out of regard to wealth only, their share in the state would be proportioned to their property, and the oligarchical doctrine would then seem to carry the day. It would not be just that he who paid one mina should have the same share of a hundred minae, whether of the principal or of the profits, as he who paid the remaining ninety-nine. But a state exists for the sake of a good life, and not for the sake of life only: if life only were the object, slaves and brute animals might form a state, but they cannot, for

[1] v. 1131a 15.

they have no share in happiness or in a life of free choice. Nor does a state exist for the sake of alliance and security from injustice, nor yet for the sake of exchange and mutual intercourse; for then the Tyrrhenians and the Carthaginians, and all who have commercial treaties with one another, would be the citizens of one state. True, they have agreements about imports, and engagements that they will do no wrong to one another, and written articles of alliance. But there are no magis-
1280b tracies common to the contracting parties who will enforce their engagements; different states have each their own magistracies. Nor does one state take care that the citizens of the other are such as they ought to be, nor see that those who come under the terms of the treaty do no wrong or wickedness at all, but only that they do no injustice to one another. Whereas, those who care for good government take into consideration virtue and vice in states. Whence it may be further inferred that virtue must be the care of a state which is truly so called, and not merely enjoys the name: for without this end the community becomes a mere alliance which differs only in place from alliances of which the members live apart; and law is only a convention, 'a surety to one another of justice', as the sophist Lycophron says, and has no real power to make the citizens good and just.

This is obvious; for suppose distinct places, such as Corinth and Megara, to be brought together so that their walls touched, still they would not be one city, not even if the citizens had the right to intermarry, which is one of the rights peculiarly characteristic of states. Again, if men dwelt at a distance from one another, but not so far off as to have no intercourse, and there were laws among them that they should not wrong each other in their exchanges, neither would this be a state. Let us suppose that one man is a carpenter, another a husbandman, another a shoemaker, and so on, and that their number is ten thousand: nevertheless, if they have nothing in common but exchange, alliance, and the like, that would not constitute a state. Why is this? Surely not because they are at a distance from one another: for even supposing that such a community were to meet in one place, but that each man had a house of his own, which was in a manner his state, and that they made alliance with one another, but only against evil-doers; still an accurate thinker would not deem this to be a state, if their intercourse with one another was of the same character after as before their union. It is clear then that a state is not a mere society, having a common place, established for the prevention of mutual crime and for the sake of exchange. These are conditions without which a state cannot exist; but all of them together do not constitute a state, which is a community of families and aggregation of families in well-being, for the sake of a perfect and self-sufficing life. Such a community can only be established among those who live in the same place and intermarry. Hence arise in cities family connexions, brotherhoods, common sacrifices, amusements which draw men together. But these are created by friendship, for the will to live together is friendship. The end of the state is the good life, and these are the means towards it. And the state is the union of
1281a families and villages in a perfect and self-sufficing life, by which we mean a happy and honourable life.

Our conclusion, then, is that political society exists for the sake of noble actions, and not of mere companionship. Hence they who contribute most to such a society have a greater share in it than those who have the same or a greater freedom or nobility of birth but are inferior to them in political virtue; or than those who exceed them in wealth but are surpassed by them in virtue.

From what has been said it will be clearly seen that all the partisans of different forms of government speak of a part of justice only.

10

There is also a doubt as to what is to be the supreme power in the state:—Is it the multitude? Or the wealthy? Or the good? Or the one best man? Or a tyrant? Any of these alternatives seems to involve disagreeable consequences. If the poor, for example, because they are more in number, divide among themselves the property of the rich,—is not this unjust? No, by heaven (will be the reply), for the supreme authority justly willed it. But if this is not injustice, pray what is? Again, when in the first division all has been taken, and the majority divide anew the property of the minority, is it not evident, if this goes on, that they will ruin the state? Yet surely, virtue is not the ruin of those who possess her, nor is justice destructive of a state; and therefore this law of confiscation clearly cannot be just. If it were, all the acts of a tyrant must of necessity be just; for he only coerces other men by superior power, just as the multitude coerce the rich. But is it just then that the few and the wealthy should be the rulers? And what if they, in like manner, rob and plunder the people,—is this just? If so, the other case will likewise be just. But there can be no doubt that all these things are wrong and unjust.

Then ought the good to rule and have supreme power? But in that case everybody else, being excluded from power, will be dishonoured. For the offices of a state are posts of honour; and if one set of men always hold them, the rest must be deprived of them. Then will it be well that the one best man should rule? Nay, that is still more oligarchical, for the number of those who are dishonoured is thereby increased. Some one may say that it is bad in any case for a man, subject as he is to all the accidents of human passion, to have the supreme power, rather than the law. But what if the law itself be democratical or oligarchical, how will that help us out of our difficulties? Not at all; the same consequences will follow.

11

Most of these questions may be reserved for another occasion.[1] The principle that the multitude ought to be supreme rather than the few best is one that is maintained, and, though not free from difficulty, yet seems to contain an element of truth. For the many, of whom each **1281b** individual is but an ordinary person, when they meet together may very likely be better than the few good, if regarded not individually but collectively, just as a feast to which many contribute is better than a dinner provided out of a single purse. For each individual among the many has a share of virtue and prudence, and when they meet together, they become in a manner one man, who has many feet, and hands, and senses; that is a figure of their mind and disposition. Hence the many are better judges than a single man of music and poetry; for some understand one part, and some another, and among them they understand the whole. There is a similar combination of qualities in good men, who differ from any individual of the many, as the beautiful are said to differ from those who are not beautiful, and works of art from realities, because in them the scattered elements are combined, although, if taken separately, the eye of one person or some other feature in another person would be fairer than in the picture. Whether this principle can apply to every democracy, and to all bodies of men, is not clear. Or rather, by heaven, in some cases it is impossible of application; for the argument would equally hold about brutes; and wherein, it will be asked, do some men differ from brutes? But there may be bodies of men about whom our statement is nevertheless true. And if so, the difficulty which has been already raised,[2] and also another which is akin to it—viz. what power should be assigned to the mass of freemen and citizens, who are not rich and have no personal merit—are both solved. There is still a danger in allowing them to share the great offices of state, for their folly will lead them into error, and their dishonesty into crime. But there is a danger also in not letting them share, for a state in which many poor men are excluded from office will necessarily be full of enemies. The only way of escape is to assign to them some deliberative and judicial functions. For this reason Solon and certain other legislators give them the power of electing to offices, and of calling the magistrates to account, but they do not allow them to hold office singly. When they meet together their perceptions are quite good enough, and combined with the better class they are useful to the state (just as impure food when mixed with what is pure sometimes makes the entire mass more wholesome than a small quantity of the pure would be), but each individual, left to himself, forms an imperfect judgement. On the other hand, the popular form of government involves certain difficulties. In the first place, it might be objected that he who can judge of the healing of a sick man would be one who could himself heal his disease, and make him whole—that is, in other **1282a** words, the physician; and so in all professions and arts. As, then, the physician ought to be called to account by physicians, so ought men in general to be called to account by their peers. But physicians are of three kinds:—there is the ordinary practitioner, and there is the physician of the higher class, and thirdly the intelligent man who has studied the art: in all arts there is such a class; and we attribute the power of judging to them quite as much as to professors of the art. Secondly, does not the same principle apply to elections? For a right election can only be made by those who have knowledge; those who know geometry, for example, will choose a geometrician rightly, and those who know how to steer, a pilot;

[1] Chapters 12-17, IV, VI.

[2] Chapter 10.

and, even if there be some occupations and arts in which private persons share in the ability to choose, they certainly cannot choose better than those who know. So that, according to this argument, neither the election of magistrates, nor the calling of them to account, should be entrusted to the many. Yet possibly these objections are to a great extent met by our old answer,[1] that if the people are not utterly degraded, although individually they may be worse judges than those who have special knowledge—as a body they are as good or better. Moreover, there are some arts whose products are not judged of solely, or best, by the artists themselves, namely those arts whose products are recognized even by those who do not possess the art; for example, the knowledge of the house is not limited to the builder only; the user, or, in other words, the master, of the house will even be a better judge than the builder, just as the pilot will judge better of a rudder than the carpenter, and the guest will judge better of a feast than the cook.

This difficulty seems now to be sufficiently answered, but there is another akin to it. That inferior persons should have authority in greater matters than the good would appear to be a strange thing, yet the election and calling to account of the magistrates is the greatest of all. And these, as I was saying,[2] are functions which in some states are assigned to the people, for the assembly is supreme in all such matters. Yet persons of any age, and having but a small property qualification, sit in the assembly and deliberate and judge, although for the great officers of state, such as treasurers and generals, a high qualification is required. This difficulty may be solved in the same manner as the preceding, and the present practice of democracies may be really defensible. For the power does not reside in the dicast or senator, or ecclesiast, but in the court, and the senate, and the assembly, of which individual senators, or ecclesiasts, or dicasts, are only parts or members. And for this reason the many may claim to have a higher authority than the few; for the people, and the senate, and the courts consist of many persons, and their property collectively is greater than the property of one or of a few individuals holding great offices. But enough of this.

1282^{b} The discussion of the first question[3] shows nothing so clearly as that laws, when good, should be supreme; and that the magistrate or magistrates should regulate those matters only on which the laws are unable to speak with precision owing to the difficulty of any general principle embracing all particulars. But what are good laws has not yet been clearly explained; the old difficulty remains. The goodness or badness, justice or injustice, of laws varies of necessity with the constitutions of states. This, however, is clear, that the laws must be adapted to the constitutions. But if so, true forms of government will of necessity have just laws, and perverted forms of government will have unjust laws.

12

In all sciences and arts the end is a good, and the greatest good and in the highest degree a good in the most authoritative of all—this is the political science of which the good is justice, in other words, the common interest. All men think justice to be a sort of equality; and to a certain extent they agree in the philosophical distinctions which have been laid down by us about Ethics.[4] For they admit that justice is a thing and has a relation to persons, and that equals ought to have equality. But there still remains a question: equality or inequality of what? here is a difficulty which calls for political speculation. For very likely some persons will say that offices of state ought to be unequally distributed according to superior excellence, in whatever respect, of the citizen, although there is no other difference between him and the rest of the community; for that those who differ in any one respect have different rights and claims. But, surely, if this is true, the complexion or height of a man, or any other advantage, will be a reason for his obtaining a greater share of political rights. The error here lies upon the surface, and may be illustrated from the other arts and sciences. When a number of flute-players are equal in their art, there is no reason why those of them who are better born should have better flutes given to them; for they will not play any better on the flute, and the superior instrument should be reserved for him who is the superior artist. If what I am saying is still obscure, it will be made clearer as we proceed. For if there were a superior flute-player who was far inferior in birth and beauty, although either of these may be a greater good than the art of flute-playing, and may excel flute-playing in a greater ratio than

[1] 1281^{a} 40-^{b} 21. [2] 1281^{b} 32.
[3] Chapter 10.
[4] Cf. *Ethics*, v. 3.

he excels the others in his art, still he ought to **1283a** have the best flutes given to him, unless the advantages of wealth and birth contribute to excellence in flute-playing, which they do not. Moreover, upon this principle any good may be compared with any other. For if a given height may be measured against wealth and against freedom, height in general may be so measured. Thus if A excels in height more than B in virtue, even if virtue in general excels height still more, all goods will be commensurable; for if a certain amount is better than some other, it is clear that some other will be equal. But since no such comparison can be made, it is evident that there is good reason why in politics men do not ground their claim to office on every sort of inequality any more than in the arts. For if some be slow, and others swift, that is no reason why the one should have little and the others much; it is in gymnastic contests that such excellence is rewarded. Whereas the rival claims of candidates for office can only be based on the possession of elements which enter into the composition of a state. And therefore the noble, or freeborn, or rich, may with good reason claim office; for holders of offices must be freemen and tax-payers: a state can be no more composed entirely of poor men than entirely of slaves. But if wealth and freedom are necessary elements, justice and valour are equally so; for without the former qualities a state cannot exist at all, without the latter, not well.

13

If the existence of the state is alone to be considered, then it would seem that all or some at least, of these claims are just; but, if we take into account a good life, then, as I have already said,[1] education and virtue have superior claims. As, however, those who are equal in one thing ought not to have an equal share in all, nor those who are unequal in one thing to have an unequal share in all, it is certain that all forms of government which rest on either of these principles are perversions. All men have a claim in a certain sense, as I have already admitted,[2] but all have not an absolute claim. The rich claim because they have a greater share in the land, and land is the common element of the state; also they are generally more trustworthy in contracts. The free claim under the same title as the noble; for they are nearly akin. For the noble are citizens in a truer sense than the ignoble, and good birth is always valued in a man's own home and country. Another reason is, that those who are sprung from better ancestors are likely to be better men, for nobility is excellence of race. Virtue, too, may be truly said to have a claim, for justice has been acknowledged by us to be a social virtue, and it implies all others. Again, the many may urge their claim against the few; for, when taken collectively, and compared with the few, they are stronger and richer **1283b** and better. But, what if the good, the rich, the noble, and the other classes who make up a state, are all living together in the same city, will there, or will there not, be any doubt who shall rule?—No doubt at all in determining who ought to rule in each of the above-mentioned forms of government. For states are characterized by differences in their governing bodies—one of them has a government of the rich, another of the virtuous, and so on. But a difficulty arises when all these elements co-exist. How are we to decide? Suppose the virtuous to be very few in number: may we consider their numbers in relation to their duties, and ask whether they are enough to administer the state, or so many as will make up a state? Objections may be urged against all the aspirants to political power. For those who found their claims on wealth or family might be thought to have no basis of justice; on this principle, if any one person were richer than all the rest, it is clear that he ought to be ruler of them. In like manner he who is very distinguished by his birth ought to have the superiority over all those who claim on the ground that they are freeborn. In an aristocracy, or government of the best, a like difficulty occurs about virtue; for if one citizen be better than the other members of the government, however good they may be, he too, upon the same principle of justice, should rule over them. And if the people are to be supreme because they are stronger than the few, then if one man, or more than one, but not a majority, is stronger than the many, they ought to rule, and not the many.

All these considerations appear to show that none of the principles on which men claim to rule and to hold all other men in subjection to them are strictly right. To those who claim to be masters of the government on the ground of their virtue or their wealth, the many might fairly answer that they themselves are often better and richer than the few—I do not say individually, but collectively. And another ingenious objection which is some-

[1] Cf. 1281a 4. [2] 1280a 9 sqq.

times put forward may be met in a similar manner. Some persons doubt whether the legislator who desires to make the justest laws ought to legislate with a view to the good of the higher classes or of the many, when the case which we have mentioned occurs. Now what is just or right is to be interpreted in the sense of 'what is equal'; and that which is right in the sense of being equal is to be considered with reference to the advantage of the state, and the common good of the citizens. And a citizen is one who shares in governing **1284a** and being governed. He differs under different forms of government, but in the best state he is one who is able and willing to be governed and to govern with a view to the life of virtue.

If, however, there be some one person, or more than one, although not enough to make up the full complement of a state, whose virtue is so pre-eminent that the virtues or the political capacity of all the rest admit of no comparison with his or theirs, he or they can be no longer regarded as part of a state; for justice will not be done to the superior, if he is reckoned only as the equal of those who are so far inferior to him in virtue and in political capacity. Such an one may truly be deemed a God among men. Hence we see that legislation is necessarily concerned only with those who are equal in birth and in capacity; and that for men of pre-eminent virtue there is no law—they are themselves a law. Any one would be ridiculous who attempted to make laws for them: they would probably retort what, in the fable of Antisthenes, the lions said to the hares, when in the council of the beasts the latter began haranguing and claiming equality for all. And for this reason democratic states have instituted ostracism; equality is above all things their aim, and therefore they ostracized and banished from the city for a time those who seemed to predominate too much through their wealth, or the number of their friends, or through any other political influence. Mythology tells us that the Argonauts left Heracles behind for a similar reason; the ship Argo would not take him because she feared that he would have been too much for the rest of the crew. Wherefore those who denounce tyranny and blame the counsel which Periander gave to Thrasybulus cannot be held altogether just in their censure. The story is that Periander, when the herald was sent to ask counsel of him, said nothing, but only cut off the tallest ears of corn till he had brought the field to a level. The herald did not know the meaning of the action, but came and reported what he had seen to Thrasybulus, who understood that he was to cut off the principal men in the state; and this is a policy not only expedient for tyrants or in practice confined to them, but equally necessary in oligarchies and democracies. Ostracism is a measure of the same kind, which acts by disabling and banishing the most prominent citizens. Great powers do the same to whole cities and nations, as the Athenians did to the Samians, Chians, and Lesbians; no sooner had they obtained a firm grasp of the empire, than they humbled their allies con- **1284b** trary to treaty; and the Persian king has repeatedly crushed the Medes, Babylonians, and other nations, when their spirit has been stirred by the recollection of their former greatness.

The problem is a universal one, and equally concerns all forms of government, true as well as false; for, although perverted forms with a view to their own interests may adopt this policy, those which seek the common interest do so likewise. The same thing may be observed in the arts and sciences; for the painter will not allow the figure to have a foot which, however beautiful, is not in proportion, nor will the ship-builder allow the stern or any other part of the vessel to be unduly large, any more than the chorus-master will allow any one who sings louder or better than all the rest to sing in the choir. Monarchs, too, may practise compulsion and still live in harmony with their cities, if their own government is for the interest of the state. Hence where there is an acknowledged superiority the argument in favour of ostracism is based upon a kind of political justice. It would certainly be better that the legislator should from the first so order his state as to have no need of such a remedy. But if the need arises, the next best thing is that he should endeavour to correct the evil by this or some similar measure. The principle, however, has not been fairly applied in states; for, instead of looking to the good of their own constitution, they have used ostracism for factious purposes. It is true that under perverted forms of government, and from their special point of view, such a measure is just and expedient, but it is also clear that it is not absolutely just. In the perfect state there would be great doubts about the use of it, not when applied to excess in strength, wealth, popularity, or the like, but when used against some one who is pre-eminent in virtue,—what is to be done with him? Mankind will not say that such an one is to be expelled and exiled; on the other hand, he ought not to be a subject—that would be as if mankind should claim to rule over Zeus, dividing his offices among them. The only alternative is that all should joyfully obey such a ruler, according to what seems to be the order of nature, and that men like him should be kings in their state for life.

14

The preceding discussion, by a natural transition, leads to the consideration of royalty, which we admit to be one of the true forms of government. Let us see whether in order to be well governed a state or country should be under the rule of a king or under some other form of government; and whether monarchy, although good for some, may not be bad for others. But first we must determine whether there is one species of royalty or many. It is **1285a** easy to see that there are many, and that the manner of government is not the same in all of them.

Of royalties according to law, (1) the Lacedaemonian is thought to answer best to the true pattern; but there the royal power is not absolute, except when the kings go on an expedition, and then they take the command. Matters of religion are likewise committed to them. The kingly office is in truth a kind of generalship, irresponsible and perpetual. The king has not the power of life and death, except in a specified case, as for instance, in ancient times, he had it when upon a campaign, by right of force. This custom is described in Homer. For Agamemnon is patient when he is attacked in the assembly, but when the army goes out to battle he has the power even of life and death. Does he not say?—'When I find a man skulking apart from the battle, nothing shall save him from the dogs and vultures, for in my hands is death.'[1]

This, then, is one form of royalty—a generalship for life: and of such royalties some are hereditary and others elective.

(2) There is another sort of monarchy not uncommon among the barbarians, which nearly resembles tyranny. But this is both legal and hereditary. For barbarians, being more servile in character than Hellenes, and Asiatics than Europeans, do not rebel against a despotic government. Such royalties have the nature of tyrannies because the people are by nature slaves; but there is no danger of their being overthrown, for they are hereditary and legal. Wherefore also their guards are such as a king and not such as a tyrant would employ, that is to say, they are composed of citizens, whereas the guards of tyrants are mercenaries. For kings rule according to law over voluntary subjects, but tyrants over involuntary; and the one are guarded by their fellow-citizens, the others are guarded against them.

These are two forms of monarchy, and there was a third (3) which existed in ancient Hellas, called an Aesymnetia or dictatorship. This may be defined generally as an elective tyranny, which, like the barbarian monarchy, is legal, but differs from it in not being hereditary. Sometimes the office was held for life, sometimes for a term of years, or until certain duties had been performed. For example, the Mytilenaeans elected Pittacus leader against the exiles, who were headed by Antimenides and Alcaeus the poet. And Alcaeus himself shows in one of his banquet odes[2] that they chose Pittacus tyrant, for he reproaches his fellow-citizens for 'having made the low-born Pittacus tyrant of the spiritless and ill-**1285b** fated city, with one voice shouting his praises'.

These forms of government have always had the character of tyrannies, because they possess despotic power; but inasmuch as they are elective and acquiesced in by their subjects, they are kingly.

(4) There is a fourth species of kingly rule—that of the heroic times—which was hereditary and legal, and was exercised over willing subjects. For the first chiefs were benefactors of the people in arts or arms; they either gathered them into a community, or procured land for them; and thus they became kings of voluntary subjects, and their power was inherited by their descendants. They took the command in war and presided over the sacrifices, except those which required a priest. They also decided causes either with or without an oath; and when they swore, the form of the oath was the stretching out of their sceptre. In ancient times their power extended continuously to all things whatsoever, in city and country, as well as in foreign parts; but at a later date they relinquished several of these privileges, and others the people took from them, until in some states nothing was left to them but the sacrifices; and where they

[1] *Iliad*, II. 391-393.

[2] Fr. 37 A, Bergk.

retained more of the reality they had only the right of leadership in war beyond the border. These, then, are the four kinds of royalty. First the monarchy of the heroic ages; this was exercised over voluntary subjects, but limited to certain functions; the king was a general and a judge, and had the control of religion. The second is that of the barbarians, which is an hereditary despotic government in accordance with law. A third is the power of the so-called Aesymnete or Dictator; this is an elective tyranny. The fourth is the Lacedaemonian, which is in fact a generalship, hereditary and perpetual. These four forms differ from one another in the manner which I have described.

(5) There is a fifth form of kingly rule in which one has the disposal of all, just as each nation or each state has the disposal of public matters; this form corresponds to the control of a household. For as household management is the kingly rule of a house, so kingly rule is the household management of a city, or of a nation, or of many nations.

15

Of these forms we need only consider two, the Lacedaemonian and the absolute royalty; for most of the others lie in a region between them, having less power than the last, and more than the first. Thus the inquiry is reduced to two points: first, it is advantageous to the state that there should be a perpetual general, and if so, should the office be confined to one family, or open to the citizens in turn? **1286a** Secondly, is it well that a single man should have the supreme power in all things? The first question falls under the head of laws rather than of constitutions; for perpetual generalship might equally exist under any form of government, so that this matter may be dismissed for the present. The other kind of royalty is a sort of constitution; this we have now to consider, and briefly to run over the difficulties involved in it. We will begin by inquiring whether it is more advantageous to be ruled by the best man or by the best laws.

The advocates of royalty maintain that the laws speak only in general terms, and cannot provide for circumstances; and that for any science to abide by written rules is absurd. In Egypt the physician is allowed to alter his treatment after the fourth day, but if sooner, he takes the risk. Hence it is clear that a government acting according to written laws is plainly not the best. Yet surely the ruler cannot dispense with the general principle which exists in law, and that is a better ruler which is free from passion than that in which it is innate. Whereas the law is passionless, passion must ever sway the heart of man. Yes, it may be replied, but then on the other hand an individual will be better able to deliberate in particular cases.

The best man, then, must legislate, and laws must be passed, but these laws will have no authority when they miss the mark, though in all other cases retaining their authority. But when the law cannot determine a point at all, or not well, should the one best man or should all decide? According to our present practice assemblies meet, sit in judgement, deliberate, and decide, and their judgements all relate to individual cases. Now any member of the assembly, taken separately, is certainly inferior to the wise man. But the state is made up of many individuals. And as a feast to which all the guests contribute is better than a banquet furnished by a single man, so a multitude is a better judge of many things than any individual.

Again, the many are more incorruptible than the few; they are like the greater quantity of water which is less easily corrupted than a little. The individual is liable to be overcome by anger or by some other passion, and then his judgement is necessarily perverted; but it is hardly to be supposed that a great number of persons would all get into a passion and go wrong at the same moment. Let us assume that they are the freemen, and that they never act in violation of the law, but fill up the gaps which the law is obliged to leave. Or, if such virtue is scarcely attainable by the multitude, we need only suppose that the majority are good men and good citizens, and ask which will be the more incorruptible, the one good ruler, or the many who are all good? Will not the **1286b** many? But, you will say, there may be parties among them, whereas the one man is not divided against himself. To which we may answer that their character is as good as his. If we call the rule of many men, who are all of them good, aristocracy, and the rule of one man royalty, then aristocracy will be better for states than royalty, whether the government is supported by force or not, provided only that a number of men equal in virtue can be found.

The first governments were kingships, probably for this reason, because of old, when cities were small, men of eminent virtue were few.

Further, they were made kings because they were benefactors, and benefits can only be bestowed by good men. But when many persons equal in merit arose, no longer enduring the pre-eminence of one, they desired to have a commonwealth, and set up a constitution. The ruling class soon deteriorated and enriched themselves out of the public treasury; riches became the path to honour, and so oligarchies naturally grew up. These passed into tyrannies and tyrannies into democracies; for love of gain in the ruling classes was always tending to diminish their number, and so to strengthen the masses, who in the end set upon their masters and established democracies. Since cities have increased in size, no other form of government appears to be any longer even easy to establish.

Even supposing the principle to be maintained that kingly power is the best thing for states, how about the family of the king? Are his children to succeed him? If they are no better than anybody else, that will be mischievous. But, says the lover of royalty, the king, though he might, will not hand on his power to his children. That, however, is hardly to be expected, and is too much to ask of human nature. There is also a difficulty about the force which he is to employ; should a king have guards about him by whose aid he may be able to coerce the refractory? if not, how will he administer his kingdom? Even if he be the lawful sovereign who does nothing arbitrarily or contrary to law, still he must have some force wherewith to maintain the law. In the case of a limited monarchy there is not much difficulty in answering this question; the king must have such force as will be more than a match for one or more individuals, but not so great as that of the people. The ancients observed this principle when they gave guards to any one whom they appointed dictator or tyrant. Thus, when Dionysius asked the Syracusans to allow him guards, somebody advised that they should give him only such a number.

16

1287a At this place in the discussion there impends the inquiry respecting the king who acts solely according to his own will; he has now to be considered. The so-called limited monarchy, or kingship according to law, as I have already remarked,[1] is not a distinct form of government, for under all governments, as, for example, in a democracy or aristocracy, there may be a general holding office for life, and one person is often made supreme over the administration of a state. A magistracy of this kind exists at Epidamnus, and also at Opus, but in the latter city has a more limited power. Now, absolute monarchy, or the arbitrary rule of a sovereign over all the citizens, in a city which consists of equals, is thought by some to be quite contrary to nature; it is argued that those who are by nature equals must have the same natural right and worth, and that for unequals to have an equal share, or for equals to have an unequal share, in the offices of state, is as bad as for different bodily constitutions to have the same food and clothing. Wherefore it is thought to be just that among equals every one be ruled as well as rule, and therefore that all should have their turn. We thus arrive at law; for an order of succession implies law. And the rule of the law, it is argued, is preferable to that of any individual. On the same principle, even if it be better for certain individuals to govern, they should be made only guardians and ministers of the law. For magistrates there must be,—this is admitted; but then men say that to give authority to any one man when all are equal is unjust. Nay, there may indeed be cases which the law seems unable to determine, but in such cases can a man? Nay, it will be replied, the law trains officers for this express purpose, and appoints them to determine matters which are left undecided by it, to the best of their judgement. Further, it permits them to make any amendment of the existing laws which experience suggests. Therefore he who bids the law rule may be deemed to bid God and Reason alone rule, but he who bids man rule adds an element of the beast; for desire is a wild beast, and passion perverts the minds of rulers, even when they are the best of men. The law is reason unaffected by desire. We are told that a patient should call in a physician; he will not get better if he is doctored out of a book. But the parallel of the arts is clearly not in point; for the physician does nothing contrary to rule from motives of friendship; he only cures a patient and takes a fee; whereas magistrates do many things from spite and partiality. And, indeed, if a man suspected the physician of being in league with his enemies to destroy him for a bribe, he would rather have recourse to the book. But certainly physicians, **1287b** when they are sick, call in other physi-

[1] 1286a 2.

cians, and training-masters, when they are in training, other training-masters, as if they could not judge truly about their own case and might be influenced by their feelings. Hence it is evident that in seeking for justice men seek for the mean or neutral, for the law is the mean. Again, customary laws have more weight, and relate to more important matters, than written laws, and a man may be a safer ruler than the written law, but not safer than the customary law.

Again, it is by no means easy for one man to superintend many things; he will have to appoint a number of subordinates, and what difference does it make whether these subordinates always existed or were appointed by him because he needed them? If, as I said before,[1] the good man has a right to rule because he is better, still two good men are better than one: this is the old saying,—

two going together,[2]

and the prayer of Agamemnon,—

would that I had ten such counsellors![3]

And at this day there are magistrates, for example judges, who have authority to decide some matters which the law is unable to determine, since no one doubts that the law would command and decide in the best manner whatever it could. But some things can, and other things cannot, be comprehended under the law, and this is the origin of the vexed question whether the best law or the best man should rule. For matters of detail about which men deliberate cannot be included in legislation. Nor does any one deny that the decision of such matters must be left to man, but it is argued that there should be many judges, and not one only. For every ruler who has been trained by the law judges well; and it would surely seem strange that a person should see better with two eyes, or hear better with two ears, or act better with two hands or feet, than many with many; indeed, it is already the practice of kings to make to themselves many eyes and ears and hands and feet. For they make colleagues of those who are the friends of themselves and their governments. They must be friends of the monarch and of his government; if not his friends, they will not do what he wants; but friendship implies likeness and equality; and, therefore, if he thinks that his friends ought to rule, he must think that those who are equal to himself and like himself ought to rule equally with himself. These are the principal controversies relating to monarchy.

[1] 1283b 21, 1284b 32. [2] *Iliad*, x. 224.
[3] *Ibid.*, II. 372.

17

But may not all this be true in some cases and not in others? for there is by nature both a justice and an advantage appropriate to the rule of a master, another to kingly rule, another to constitutional rule; but there is none naturally appropriate to tyranny, or to any other perverted form of government; for these come into being contrary to nature. Now, to judge at least from what has been said, it is manifest that, where men are alike and **1288a** equal, it is neither expedient nor just that one man should be lord of all, whether there are laws, or whether there are no laws, but he himself is in the place of law. Neither should a good man be lord over good men, nor a bad man over bad; nor, even if he excels in virtue, should he have a right to rule, unless in a particular case, at which I have already hinted, and to which I will once more recur.[4] But first of all, I must determine what natures are suited for government by a king, and what for an aristocracy, and what for a constitutional government.

A people who are by nature capable of producing a race superior in the virtue needed for political rule are fitted for kingly government; and a people submitting to be ruled as freemen by men whose virtue renders them capable of political command are adapted for an aristocracy: while the people who are suited for constitutional freedom are those among whom there naturally exists a warlike multitude able to rule and to obey in turn by a law which gives office to the well-to-do according to their desert. But when a whole family, or some individual, happens to be so pre-eminent in virtue as to surpass all others, then it is just that they should be the royal family and supreme over all, or that this one citizen should be king of the whole nation. For, as I said before,[5] to give them authority is not only agreeable to that ground of right which the founders of all states, whether aristocratical, or oligarchical, or again democratical, are accustomed to put forward (for these all recognize the claim of excellence, although not the same excellence), but accords with the principle already

[4] 1284a 3, and 1288a 15.
[5] 1283b 20, 1284a 3-17, b 25.

laid down.[1] For surely it would not be right to kill, or ostracize, or exile such a person, or require that he should take his turn in being governed. The whole is naturally superior to the part, and he who has this pre-eminence is in the relation of a whole to a part. But if so, the only alternative is that he should have the supreme power, and that mankind should obey him, not in turn, but always. These are the conclusions at which we arrive respecting royalty and its various forms, and this is the answer to the question, whether it is or is not advantageous to states, and to which, and how.

18

We maintain that the true forms of government are three, and that the best must be that which is administered by the best, and in which there is one man, or a whole family, or many persons, excelling all the others together in virtue, and both rulers and subjects are fitted, the one to rule, the others to be ruled, in such a manner as to attain the most eligible life. We showed at the commencement of our inquiry[2] that the virtue of the good man is necessarily the same as the virtue of the citizen of the perfect state. Clearly then in the same manner, and by the same means through which a man becomes truly good, he will **1288b** frame a state that is to be ruled by an aristocracy or by a king, and the same education and the same habits will be found to make a good man and a man fit to be a statesman or king.

Having arrived at these conclusions, we must proceed to speak of the perfect state, and describe how it comes into being and is established.

BOOK IV

1

In all arts and sciences which embrace the whole of any subject, and do not come into being in a fragmentary way, it is the province of a single art or science to consider all that appertains to a single subject. For example, the art of gymnastic considers not only the suitableness of different modes of training to different bodies (2), but what sort is absolutely the best (1); (for the absolutely best must suit that which is by nature best and best furnished with the means of life), and also what common form of training is adapted to the great majority of men (4). And if a man does not desire the best habit of body, or the greatest skill in gymnastics, which might be attained by him, still the trainer or the teacher of gymnastic should be able to impart any lower degree of either (3). The same principle equally holds in medicine and ship-building, and the making of clothes, and in the arts generally.

Hence it is obvious that government too is the subject of a single science, which has to consider what government is best and of what sort it must be, to be most in accordance with our aspirations, if there were no external impediment, and also what kind of government is adapted to particular states. For the best is often unattainable, and therefore the true legislator and statesman ought to be acquainted, not only with (1) that which is best in the abstract, but also with (2) that which is best relatively to circumstances. We should be able further to say how a state may be constituted under any given conditions (3); both how it is originally formed and, when formed, how it may be longest preserved; the supposed state being so far from having the best constitution that it is unprovided even with the conditions necessary for the best; neither is it the best under the circumstances, but of an inferior type.

He ought, moreover, to know (4) the form of government which is best suited to states in general; for political writers, although they have excellent ideas, are often unpractical. We should consider, not only what form of government is best, but also what is possible and what is easily attainable by all. There are some who would have none but the most perfect; for this many natural advantages are required. Others, again, speak of a more attainable form, and, although they reject the constitution under which they are living, they extol some one in particular, for example the **1289a** Lacedaemonian. Any change of government which has to be introduced should be one which men, starting from their existing constitutions, will be both willing and able to adopt, since there is quite as much trouble in the reformation of an old constitution as in the establishment of a new one, just as to unlearn is as hard as to learn. And therefore, in ad-

[1] Cf. 1284b 28.

[2] Chapters 4, 5.

dition to the qualifications of the statesman already mentioned, he should be able to find remedies for the defects of existing constitutions, as has been said before.[1] This he cannot do unless he knows how many forms of government there are. It is often supposed that there is only one kind of democracy and one of oligarchy. But this is a mistake; and, in order to avoid such mistakes, we must ascertain what differences there are in the constitutions of states, and in how many ways they are combined. The same political insight will enable a man to know which laws are the best, and which are suited to different constitutions; for the laws are, and ought to be, relative to the constitution, and not the constitution to the laws. A constitution is the organization of offices in a state, and determines what is to be the governing body, and what is the end of each community. But laws are not to be confounded with the principles of the constitution; they are the rules according to which the magistrates should administer the state, and proceed against offenders. So that we must know the varieties, and the number of varieties, of each form of government, if only with a view to making laws. For the same laws cannot be equally suited to all oligarchies or to all democracies, since there is certainly more than one form both of democracy and of oligarchy.

2

In our original discussion[2] about governments we divided them into three true forms: kingly rule, aristocracy, and constitutional government, and three corresponding perversions—tyranny, oligarchy, and democracy. Of kingly rule and of aristocracy we have already spoken,[3] for the inquiry into the perfect state is the same thing with the discussion of the two forms thus named, since both imply a principle of virtue provided with external means. We have already determined in what aristocracy and kingly rule differ from one another, and when the latter should be established.[4] In what follows we have to describe the so-called constitutional government, which bears the common name of all constitutions, and the other forms, tyranny, oligarchy, and democracy.

It is obvious which of the three perversions is the worst, and which is the next in badness. That which is the perversion of the first and most divine is necessarily the worst. And **1289b** just as a royal rule, if not a mere name, must exist by virtue of some great personal superiority in the king, so tyranny, which is the worst of governments, is necessarily the farthest removed from a well-constituted form; oligarchy is little better, for it is a long way from aristocracy, and democracy is the most tolerable of the three.

A writer[5] who preceded me has already made these distinctions, but his point of view is not the same as mine. For he lays down the principle that when all the constitutions are good (the oligarchy and the rest being virtuous), democracy is the worst, but the best when all are bad. Whereas we maintain that they are in any case defective, and that one oligarchy is not to be accounted better than another, but only less bad.

Not to pursue this question further at present, let us begin by determining (1) how many varieties of constitution there are (since of democracy and oligarchy there are several); (2) what constitution is the most generally acceptable, and what is eligible in the next degree after the perfect state; and besides this what other there is which is aristocratical and well-constituted, and at the same time adapted to states in general; (3) of the other forms of government to whom each is suited. For democracy may meet the needs of some better than oligarchy, and conversely. In the next place (4) we have to consider in what manner a man ought to proceed who desires to establish some one among these various forms, whether of democracy or of oligarchy; and lastly, (5) having briefly discussed these subjects to the best of our power, we will endeavour to ascertain the modes of ruin and preservation both of constitutions generally and of each separately, and to what causes they are to be attributed.

3

The reason why there are many forms of government is that every state contains many elements. In the first place we see that all states are made up of families, and in the multitude of citizens there must be some rich and some poor, and some in a middle condition; the rich are heavy-armed, and the poor not. Of the common people, some are husbandmen, and some traders, and some artisans. There are also among the notables differences of wealth and property—for example, in the number of horses which they keep, for they cannot afford to keep them unless they are rich. And therefore in old times the cities whose strength

[1] Cf. 1288b 29. [2] III. 7. [3] III. 14-18.
[4] III. 1279a 32-37, 1286b 3-5, 1284a 3-b 34; chapter 17.

[5] Plato, *Statesman*, 302, 303.

lay in their cavalry were oligarchies, and they used cavalry in wars against their neighbours; as was the practice of the Eretrians and Chalcidians, and also of the Magnesians on the river Mæander, and of other peoples in Asia. Besides differences of wealth there are differences of rank and merit, and there are some **1290a** other elements which were mentioned by us when in treating of aristocracy we enumerated the essentials of a state. Of these elements, sometimes all, sometimes the lesser and sometimes the greater number, have a share in the government. It is evident then that there must be many forms of government, differing in kind, since the parts of which they are composed differ from each other in kind. For a constitution is an organization of offices, which all the citizens distribute among themselves, according to the power which different classes possess, for example the rich or the poor, or according to some principle of equality which includes both. There must therefore be as many forms of government as there are modes of arranging the offices, according to the superiorities and the differences of the parts of the state.

There are generally thought to be two principal forms: as men say of the winds that there are but two—north and south, and that the rest of them are only variations of these, so of governments there are said to be only two forms—democracy and oligarchy. For aristocracy is considered to be a kind of oligarchy, as being the rule of a few, and the so-called constitutional government to be really a democracy, just as among the winds we make the west a variation of the north, and the east of the south wind. Similarly of musical modes there are said to be two kinds, the Dorian and the Phrygian; the other arrangements of the scale are comprehended under one or other of these two. About forms of government this is a very favourite notion. But in either case the better and more exact way is to distinguish, as I have done, the one or two which are true forms, and to regard the others as perversions, whether of the most perfectly attempered mode or of the best form of government: we may compare the severer and more overpowering modes to the oligarchical forms, and the more relaxed and gentler ones to the democratic.

4

It must not be assumed, as some are fond of saying, that democracy is simply that form of government in which the greater number are sovereign, for in oligarchies, and indeed in every government, the majority rules; nor again is oligarchy that form of government in which a few are sovereign. Suppose the whole population of a city to be 1300, and that of these 1000 are rich, and do not allow the remaining 300 who are poor, but free, and in all other respects their equals, a share of the government—no one will say that this is a democracy. In like manner, if the poor were few and the masters of the rich who outnumber them, no one would ever call such a government, in which the rich majority have no share of office, an oligarchy. Therefore we should rather **1290b** say that democracy is the form of government in which the free are rulers, and oligarchy in which the rich; it is only an accident that the free are the many and the rich are the few. Otherwise a government in which the offices were given according to stature, as is said to be the case in Ethiopia, or according to beauty, would be an oligarchy; for the number of tall or good-looking men is small. And yet oligarchy and democracy are not sufficiently distinguished merely by these two characteristics of wealth and freedom. Both of them contain many other elements, and therefore we must carry our analysis further, and say that the government is not a democracy in which the freemen, being few in number, rule over the many who are not free, as at Apollonia, on the Ionian Gulf, and at Thera; (for in each of these states the nobles, who were also the earliest settlers, were held in chief honour, although they were but a few out of many). Neither is it a democracy when the rich have the government because they exceed in number; as was the case formerly at Colophon, where the bulk of the inhabitants were possessed of large property before the Lydian War. But the form of government is a democracy when the free, who are also poor and the majority, govern, and an oligarchy when the rich and the noble govern, they being at the same time few in number.

I have said that there are many forms of government, and have explained to what causes the variety is due. Why there are more than those already mentioned, and what they are, and whence they arise, I will now proceed to consider, starting from the principle already admitted,[1] which is that every state consists, not of one, but of many parts. If we were going to speak of the different species of ani-

[1] 1289b 27 sqq.

mals, we should first of all determine the organs which are indispensable to every animal, as for example some organs of sense and the instruments of receiving and digesting food, such as the mouth and the stomach, besides organs of locomotion. Assuming now that there are only so many kinds of organs, but that there may be differences in them—I mean different kinds of mouths, and stomachs, and perceptive and locomotive organs—the possible combinations of these differences will necessarily furnish many varieties of animals. (For animals cannot be the same which have different kinds of mouths or of ears.) And when all the combinations are exhausted, there will be as many sorts of animals as there are combinations of the necessary organs. The same, then, is true of the forms of government which have been described; states, as I have repeatedly said,[1] are composed, not of one, but of many elements. One element is the food-producing class, who are called husbandmen; **1291a** a second, the class of mechanics who practise the arts without which a city cannot exist;—of these arts some are absolutely necessary, others contribute to luxury or to the grace of life. The third class is that of traders, and by traders I mean those who are engaged in buying and selling, whether in commerce or in retail trade. A fourth class is that of the serfs or labourers. The warriors make up the fifth class, and they are as necessary as any of the others, if the country is not to be the slave of every invader. For how can a state which has any title to the name be of a slavish nature? The state is independent and self-sufficing, but a slave is the reverse of independent. Hence we see that this subject, though ingeniously, has not been satisfactorily treated in the *Republic*.[2] Socrates says that a state is made up of four sorts of people who are absolutely necessary; these are a weaver, a husbandman, a shoemaker, and a builder; afterwards, finding that they are not enough, he adds a smith, and again a herdsman, to look after the necessary animals; then a merchant, and then a retail trader. All these together form the complement of the first state, as if a state were established merely to supply the necessaries of life, rather than for the sake of the good, or stood equally in need of shoemakers and of husbandmen. But he does not admit into the state a military class until the country has increased in size, and is beginning to encroach on its neighbour's land, whereupon they go to war. Yet even amongst his four original citizens, or whatever be the number of those whom he associates in the state, there must be some one who will dispense justice and determine what is just. And as the soul may be said to be more truly part of an animal than the body, so the higher parts of states, that is to say, the warrior class, the class engaged in the administration of justice, and that engaged in deliberation, which is the special business of political common sense,—these are more essential to the state than the parts which minister to the necessaries of life. Whether their several functions are the functions of different citizens, or of the same,—for it may often happen that the same persons are both warriors and husbandmen,—is immaterial to the argument. The higher as well as the lower elements are to be equally considered parts of the state, and if so, the military element at any rate must be included. There are also the wealthy who minister to the state with their property; these form the seventh class. The eighth class is that of magistrates and of officers; for the state cannot exist without rulers. And therefore some must be able to take office and to serve the state, either always or in turn. There only remains the class of those who deliberate and who judge between disputants; we were just now distinguishing them. If presence of all these elements, and their fair and equitable organization, is necessary to **1291b** states, then there must also be persons who have the ability of statesmen. Different functions appear to be often combined in the same individual; for example, the warrior may also be a husbandman, or an artisan; or, again, the counsellor a judge. And all claim to possess political ability, and think that they are quite competent to fill most offices. But the same persons cannot be rich and poor at the same time. For this reason the rich and the poor are regarded in an especial sense as parts of a state. Again, because the rich are generally few in number, while the poor are many, they appear to be antagonistic, and as the one or the other prevails they form the government. Hence arises the common opinion that there are two kinds of government—democracy and oligarchy.

I have already explained[3] that there are many forms of constitution, and to what causes the variety is due. Let me now show that there are different forms both of democracy

[1] II. 1261a 22 sqq.; III. 1283a 14 sqq.; IV. 1289b 27-1290a 5, 1290b 23 sqq.; cf. III. 1277a 5 sqq.

[2] *Republic*, II. 369.

[3] Cf. III. 6.

and oligarchy, as will indeed be evident from what has preceded. For both in the common people and in the notables various classes are included; of the common people, one class are husbandmen, another artisans; another traders, who are employed in buying and selling; another are the seafaring class, whether engaged in war or in trade, as ferrymen or as fishermen. (In many places any one of these classes forms quite a large population; for example, fishermen at Tarentum and Byzantium, crews of triremes at Athens, merchant seamen at Aegina and Chios, ferrymen at Tenedos.) To the classes already mentioned may be added day-labourers, and those who, owing to their needy circumstances, have no leisure, or those who are not of free birth on both sides; and there may be other classes as well. The notables again may be divided according to their wealth, birth, virtue, education, and similar differences.

Of forms of democracy first comes that which is said to be based strictly on equality. In such a democracy the law says that it is just for the poor to have no more advantage than the rich; and that neither should be masters, but both equal. For if liberty and equality, as is thought by some, are chiefly to be found in democracy, they will be best attained when all persons alike share in the government to the utmost. And since the people are the majority, and the opinion of the majority is decisive, such a government must necessarily be a democracy. Here then is one sort of democracy. There is another, in which the magistrates are elected according to a certain property qualification, but a low one; he who has the required amount of property has a share in the government, but he who loses his property **1292a** loses his rights. Another kind is that in which all the citizens who are under no disqualification share in the government, but still the law is supreme. In another, everybody, if he be only a citizen, is admitted to the government, but the law is supreme as before. A fifth form of democracy, in other respects the same, is that in which, not the law, but the multitude, have the supreme power, and supersede the law by their decrees. This is a state of affairs brought about by the demagogues. For in democracies which are subject to the law the best citizens hold the first place, and there are no demagogues; but where the laws are not supreme, there demagogues spring up. For the people becomes a monarch, and is many in one; and the many have the power in their hands, not as individuals, but collectively. Homer says that 'it is not good to have a rule of many',[1] but whether he means this corporate rule, or the rule of many individuals, is uncertain. At all events this sort of democracy, which is now a monarch, and no longer under the control of law, seeks to exercise monarchical sway, and grows into a despot; the flatterer is held in honour; this sort of democracy being relatively to other democracies what tyranny is to other forms of monarchy. The spirit of both is the same, and they alike exercise a despotic rule over the better citizens. The decrees of the demos correspond to the edicts of the tyrant; and the demagogue is to the one what the flatterer is to the other. Both have great power;—the flatterer with the tyrant, the demagogue with democracies of the kind which we are describing. The demagogues make the decrees of the people override the laws, by referring all things to the popular assembly. And therefore they grow great, because the people have all things in their hands, and they hold in their hands the votes of the people, who are too ready to listen to them. Further, those who have any complaint to bring against the magistrates say, 'let the people be judges'; the people are too happy to accept the invitation; and so the authority of every office is undermined. Such a democracy is fairly open to the objection that it is not a constitution at all; for where the laws have no authority, there is no constitution. The law ought to be supreme over all, and the magistracies should judge of particulars, and only this should be considered a constitution. So that if democracy be a real form of government, the sort of system in which all things are regulated by decrees is clearly not even a democracy in the true sense of the word, for decrees relate only to particulars.

These then are the different kinds of democracy.

5

Of oligarchies, too, there are different kinds: one where the property qualification for office is such that the poor, although they form the majority, have no share in the government, yet he who acquires a qualification may obtain **1292b** a share. Another sort is when there is a qualification for office, but a high one, and the vacancies in the governing body are filled by co-optation. If the election is made out of all the qualified persons, a constitution of

[1] *Iliad*, II. 204.

this kind inclines to an aristocracy, if out of a privileged class, to an oligarchy. Another sort of oligarchy is when the son succeeds the father. There is a fourth form, likewise hereditary, in which the magistrates are supreme and not the law. Among oligarchies this is what tyranny is among monarchies, and the last-mentioned form of democracy among democracies; and in fact this sort of oligarchy receives the name of a dynasty (or rule of powerful families).

These are the different sorts of oligarchies and democracies. It should however be remembered that in many states the constitution which is established by law, although not democratic, owing to the education and habits of the people may be administered democratically, and conversely in other states the established constitution may incline to democracy, but may be administered in an oligarchical spirit. This most often happens after a revolution: for governments do not change at once; at first the dominant party are content with encroaching a little upon their opponents. The laws which existed previously continue in force, but the authors of the revolution have the power in their hands.

6

From what has been already said we may safely infer that there are so many different kinds of democracies and of oligarchies. For it is evident that either all the classes whom we mentioned[1] must share in the government, or some only and not others. When the class of husbandmen and of those who possess moderate fortunes have the supreme power, the government is administered according to law. For the citizens being compelled to live by their labour have no leisure; and so they set up the authority of the law, and attend assemblies only when necessary. They all obtain a share in the government when they have acquired the qualification which is fixed by the law—the absolute exclusion of any class would be a step towards oligarchy; hence all who have acquired the property qualification are admitted to a share in the constitution. But leisure cannot be provided for them unless there are revenues to support them. This is one sort of democracy, and these are the causes which give birth to it. Another kind is based on the distinction which naturally comes next in order; in this, every one to whose birth there is no objection is eligible, but actually shares in the government only if he can find leisure. Hence in such a democracy the supreme power is vested in the laws, because the state has no means of paying the citizens. A third kind is when all freemen have a right to share in the government, but do not actually share, for the reason which has been already given; so that in this form again the law must rule. A fourth kind of democracy is that which comes **1293a** latest in the history of states. In our own day, when cities have far outgrown their original size, and their revenues have increased, all the citizens have a place in the government, through the great preponderance of the multitude; and they all, including the poor who receive pay, and therefore have leisure to exercise their rights, share in the administration. Indeed, when they are paid, the common people have the most leisure, for they are not hindered by the care of their property, which often fetters the rich, who are thereby prevented from taking part in the assembly or in the courts, and so the state is governed by the poor, who are a majority, and not by the laws. So many kinds of democracies there are, and they grow out of these necessary causes.

Of oligarchies, one form is that in which the majority of the citizens have some property, but not very much; and this is the first form, which allows to any one who obtains the required amount the right of sharing in the government. The sharers in the government being a numerous body, it follows that the law must govern, and not individuals. For in proportion as they are further removed from a monarchical form of government, and in respect of property have neither so much as to be able to live without attending to business, nor so little as to need state support, they must admit the rule of law and not claim to rule themselves. But if the men of property in the state are fewer than in the former case, and own more property, there arises a second form of oligarchy. For the stronger they are, the more power they claim, and having this object in view, they themselves select those of the other classes who are to be admitted to the government; but, not being as yet strong enough to rule without the law, they make the law represent their wishes. When this power is intensified by a further diminution of their numbers and increase of their property, there arises a third and further stage of oligarchy, in which the governing class keep the offices in their own hands, and the law ordains that the son shall succeed the father. When, again,

[1] 1291b 17-30.

the rulers have great wealth and numerous friends, this sort of family despotism approaches a monarchy; individuals rule and not the law. This is the fourth sort of oligarchy, and is analogous to the last sort of democracy.

7

There are still two forms besides democracy and oligarchy; one of them is universally recognized and included among the four principal forms of government, which are said to be (1) monarchy, (2) oligarchy, (3) democracy, and (4) the so-called aristocracy or government of the best. But there is also a fifth, which retains the generic name of polity or constitutional government; this is not common, and therefore has not been noticed by writers who attempt to enumerate the dif-

1293b ferent kinds of government; like Plato,[1] in their books about the state, they recognize four only. The term 'aristocracy' is rightly applied to the form of government which is described in the first part of our treatise;[2] for that only can be rightly called aristocracy which is a government formed of the best men absolutely, and not merely of men who are good when tried by any given standard. In the perfect state the good man is absolutely the same as the good citizen; whereas in other states the good citizen is only good relatively to his own form of government. But there are some states differing from oligarchies and also differing from the so-called polity or constitutional government; these are termed aristocracies, and in them magistrates are certainly chosen, both according to their wealth and according to their merit. Such a form of government differs from each of the two just now mentioned, and is termed an aristocracy. For indeed in states which do not make virtue the aim of the community, men of merit and reputation for virtue may be found. And so where a government has regard to wealth, virtue, and numbers, as at Carthage, that is aristocracy; and also where it has regard only to two out of the three, as at Lacedaemon, to virtue and numbers, and the two principles of democracy and virtue temper each other. There are these two forms of aristocracy in addition to the first and perfect state, and there is a third form, viz. the constitutions which incline more than the so-called polity towards oligarchy.

[1] *Republic*, VIII, IX.

[2] III. 1279a 34, 1286b 3.

8

I have yet to speak of the so-called polity and of tyranny. I put them in this order, not because a polity or constitutional government is to be regarded as a perversion any more than the above-mentioned aristocracies. The truth is, that they all fall short of the most perfect form of government, and so they are reckoned among perversions, and the really perverted forms are perversions of these, as I said in the original discussion.[3] Last of all I will speak of tyranny, which I place last in the series because I am inquiring into the constitutions of states, and this is the very reverse of a constitution.

Having explained why I have adopted this order, I will proceed to consider constitutional government; of which the nature will be clearer now that oligarchy and democracy have been defined. For polity or constitutional government may be described generally as a fusion of oligarchy and democracy; but the term is usually applied to those forms of government which incline towards democracy, and the term aristocracy to those which incline towards oligarchy, because birth and education are commonly the accompaniments of wealth. Moreover, the rich already possess the external advantages the want of which is a temptation to crime, and hence they are called noblemen and gentlemen. And inasmuch as aristocracy seeks to give predominance to the best of the citizens, people say also of oligarchies that they are composed of noblemen

1294a and gentlemen. Now it appears to be an impossible thing that the state which is governed not by the best citizens but by the worst should be well-governed, and equally impossible that the state which is ill-governed should be governed by the best. But we must remember that good laws, if they are not obeyed, do not constitute good government. Hence there are two parts of good government; one is the actual obedience of citizens to the laws, the other part is the goodness of the laws which they obey; they may obey bad laws as well as good. And there may be a further subdivision; they may obey either the best laws which are attainable to them, or the best absolutely.

The distribution of offices according to merit is a special characteristic of aristocracy, for the principle of an aristocracy is virtue, as wealth is of an oligarchy, and freedom of a democracy. In all of them there of course exists

[3] III. 7.

the right of the majority, and whatever seems good to the majority of those who share in the government has authority. Now in most states the form called polity exists, for the fusion goes no further than the attempt to unite the freedom of the poor and the wealth of the rich, who commonly take the place of the noble. But as there are three grounds on which men claim an equal share in the government, freedom, wealth, and virtue (for the fourth or good birth is the result of the two last, being only ancient wealth and virtue), it is clear that the admixture of the two elements, that is to say, of the rich and poor, is to be called a polity or constitutional government; and the union of the three is to be called aristocracy or the government of the best, and more than any other form of government, except the true and ideal, has a right to this name. Thus far I have shown the existence of forms of states other than monarchy, democracy, and oligarchy, and what they are, and in what aristocracies differ from one another, and polities from aristocracies—that the two latter are not very unlike is obvious.

9

Next we have to consider how by the side of oligarchy and democracy the so-called polity or constitutional government springs up, and how it should be organized. The nature of it will be at once understood from a comparison of oligarchy and democracy; we must ascertain their different characteristics, and taking a portion from each, put the two together, like the parts of an indenture. Now there are three modes in which fusions of government may be effected. In the first mode we must combine the laws made by both governments, say concerning the administration of justice. In oligarchies they impose a fine on the rich if they do not serve as judges, and to the poor they give no pay; but in democracies they give pay to the poor and do not fine the rich. Now (1) the union of these two modes is a common or middle term between them, and is **1294b** therefore characteristic of a constitutional government, for it is a combination of both. This is one mode of uniting the two elements. Or (2) a mean may be taken between the enactments of the two: thus democracies require no property qualification, or only a small one, from members of the assembly, oligarchies a high one; here neither of these is the common term, but a mean between them. (3) There is a third mode, in which something is borrowed from the oligarchical and something from the democratical principle. For example, the appointment of magistrates by lot is thought to be democratical, and the election of them oligarchical; democratical again when there is no property qualification, oligarchical when there is. In the aristocratical or constitutional state, one element will be taken from each—from oligarchy the principle of electing to offices, from democracy the disregard of qualification. Such are the various modes of combination.

There is a true union of oligarchy and democracy when the same state may be termed either a democracy or an oligarchy; those who use both names evidently feel that the fusion is complete. Such a fusion there is also in the mean; for both extremes appear in it. The Lacedaemonian constitution, for example, is often described as a democracy, because it has many democratical features. In the first place the youth receive a democratical education. For the sons of the poor are brought up with the sons of the rich, who are educated in such a manner as to make it possible for the sons of the poor to be educated like them. A similar equality prevails in the following period of life, and when the citizens are grown up to manhood the same rule is observed; there is no distinction between the rich and poor. In like manner they all have the same food at their public tables, and the rich wear only such clothing as any poor man can afford. Again, the people elect to one of the two greatest offices of state, and in the other they share; for they elect the Senators and share in the Ephoralty. By others the Spartan constitution is said to be an oligarchy, because it has many oligarchical elements. That all offices are filled by election and none by lot, is one of these oligarchical characteristics; that the power of inflicting death or banishment rests with a few persons is another; and there are others. In a well attempered polity there should appear to be both elements and yet neither; also the government should rely on itself, and not on foreign aid, and on itself not through the good will of a majority—they might be equally well-disposed when there is a vicious form of government—but through the general willingness of all classes in the state to maintain the constitution.

Enough of the manner in which a constitutional government, and in which the so-called aristocracies ought to be framed.

10

1295^a Of the nature of tyranny I have still to speak, in order that it may have its place in our inquiry (since even tyranny is reckoned by us to be a form of government), although there is not much to be said about it. I have already in the former part of this treatise[1] discussed royalty or kingship according to the most usual meaning of the term, and considered whether it is or is not advantageous to states, and what kind of royalty should be established, and from what source, and how.

When speaking of royalty we also spoke[2] of two forms of tyranny, which are both according to law, and therefore easily pass into royalty. Among Barbarians there are elected monarchs who exercise a despotic power; despotic rulers were also elected in ancient Hellas, called Aesymnetes or dictators. These monarchies, when compared with one another, exhibit certain differences. And they are, as I said before,[3] royal, in so far as the monarch rules according to law over willing subjects; but they are tyrannical in so far as he is despotic and rules according to his own fancy. There is also a third kind of tyranny, which is the most typical form, and is the counterpart of the perfect monarchy. This tyranny is just that arbitrary power of an individual which is responsible to no one, and governs all alike, whether equals or betters, with a view to its own advantage, not to that of its subjects, and therefore against their will. No freeman, if he can escape from it, will endure such a government.

The kinds of tyranny are such and so many, and for the reasons which I have given.

11

We have now to inquire what is the best constitution for most states, and the best life for most men, neither assuming a standard of virtue which is above ordinary persons, nor an education which is exceptionally favoured by nature and circumstances, nor yet an ideal state which is an aspiration only, but having regard to the life in which the majority are able to share, and to the form of government which states in general can attain. As to those aristocracies, as they are called, of which we were just now speaking,[4] they either lie beyond the possibilities of the greater number of states, or they approximate to the so-called constitutional government, and therefore need no separate discussion. And in fact the conclusion at which we arrive respecting all these forms rests upon the same grounds. For if what was said in the *Ethics*[5] is true, that the happy life is the life according to virtue lived without impediment, and that virtue is a mean, then the life which is in a mean, and in a mean attainable by every one, must be the best. And the same principles of virtue and vice are characteristic of cities and of constitutions; for the con-
1295^b stitution is in a figure the life of the city.

Now in all states there are three elements: one class is very rich, another very poor, and a third in a mean. It is admitted that moderation and the mean are best, and therefore it will clearly be best to possess the gifts of fortune in moderation; for in that condition of life men are most ready to follow rational principle. But he who greatly excels in beauty, strength, birth, or wealth, or on the other hand who is very poor, or very weak, or very much disgraced, finds it difficult to follow rational principle. Of these two the one sort grow into violent and great criminals, the others into rogues and petty rascals. And two sorts of offences correspond to them, the one committed from violence, the other from roguery. Again, the middle class is least likely to shrink from rule, or to be over-ambitious for it; both of which are injuries to the state. Again, those who have too much of the goods of fortune, strength, wealth, friends, and the like, are neither willing nor able to submit to authority. The evil begins at home; for when they are boys, by reason of the luxury in which they are brought up, they never learn, even at school, the habit of obedience. On the other hand, the very poor, who are in the opposite extreme, are too degraded. So that the one class cannot obey, and can only rule despotically; the other knows not how to command and must be ruled like slaves. Thus arises a city, not of freemen, but of masters and slaves, the one despising, the other envying; and nothing can be more fatal to friendship and good fellowship in states than this: for good fellowship springs from friendship; when men are at enmity with one another, they would rather not even share the same path. But a city ought to be composed, as far as possible, of equals and similars; and these are generally the middle classes. Wherefore the city which is composed of middle-class citizens is neces-

[1] III. 14-17.
[2] III. 1285^a 16-^{b} 3.
[3] III. 1285^b 2.
[4] 1293^b 7-21, cf. 1293^b 36-1294^a 25.
[5] *Ethics*, I. 1098^a 16; VII. 1153^b 10; X. 1177^a 12.

sarily best constituted in respect of the elements of which we say the fabric of the state naturally consists. And this is the class of citizens which is most secure in a state, for they do not, like the poor, covet their neighbours' goods; nor do others covet theirs, as the poor covet the goods of the rich; and as they neither plot against others, nor are themselves plotted against, they pass through life safely. Wisely then did Phocylides pray,[1]—'Many things are best in the mean; I desire to be of a middle condition in my city.'

Thus it is manifest that the best political community is formed by citizens of the middle class, and that those states are likely to be well-administered, in which the middle class is large, and stronger if possible than both the other classes, or at any rate than either singly; for the addition of the middle class turns the scale, and prevents either of the extremes from being dominant. Great then is the good fortune of a state in which the citizens have **1296a** a moderate and sufficient property; for where some possess much, and the others nothing, there may arise an extreme democracy, or a pure oligarchy; or a tyranny may grow out of either extreme,—either out of the most rampant democracy, or out of an oligarchy; but it is not so likely to arise out of the middle constitutions and those akin to them. I will explain the reason of this hereafter, when I speak of the revolutions of states.[2] The mean condition of states is clearly best, for no other is free from faction; and where the middle class is large, there are least likely to be factions and dissensions. For a similar reason large states are less liable to faction than small ones, because in them the middle class is large; whereas in small states it is easy to divide all the citizens into two classes who are either rich or poor, and to leave nothing in the middle. And democracies are safer and more permanent than oligarchies, because they have a middle class which is more numerous and has a greater share in the government; for when there is no middle class, and the poor greatly exceed in number, troubles arise, and the state soon comes to an end. A proof of the superiority of the middle class is that the best legislators have been of a middle condition; for example, Solon, as his own verses testify; and Lycurgus, for he was not a king; and Charondas, and almost all legislators.

These considerations will help us to understand why most governments are either democratical or oligarchical. The reason is that the middle class is seldom numerous in them, and whichever party, whether the rich or the common people, transgresses the mean and predominates, draws the constitution its own way, and thus arises either oligarchy or democracy. There is another reason—the poor and the rich quarrel with one another, and whichever side gets the better, instead of establishing a just or popular government, regards political supremacy as the prize of victory, and the one party sets up a democracy and the other an oligarchy. Further, both the parties which had the supremacy in Hellas looked only to the interest of their own form of government, and established in states, the one, democracies, and the other, oligarchies; they thought of their own advantage, of the public not at all. For these reasons the middle form of government has rarely, if ever, existed, and among a very few only. One man alone of all who ever ruled in Hellas was induced to give this middle constitution to states. But it has now become a habit among the citizens of states, not even to care **1296b** about equality; all men are seeking for dominion, or, if conquered, are willing to submit.

What then is the best form of government, and what makes it the best, is evident; and of other constitutions, since we say that there are many kinds of democracy and many of oligarchy, it is not difficult to see which has the first and which the second or any other place in the order of excellence, now that we have determined which is the best. For that which is nearest to the best must of necessity be better, and that which is furthest from it worse, if we are judging absolutely and not relatively to given conditions: I say 'relatively to given conditions', since a particular government may be preferable, but another form may be better for some people.

12

We have now to consider what and what kind of government is suitable to what and what kind of men. I may begin by assuming, as a general principle common to all governments, that the portion of the state which desires the permanence of the constitution ought to be stronger than that which desires the reverse. Now every city is composed of quality and quantity. By quality I mean freedom, wealth, education, good birth, and by quantity, superiority of numbers. Quality may exist in one

[1] Fr. 12, Bergk. [2] v. 1308a 18-24.

of the classes which make up the state, and quantity in the other. For example, the meanly-born may be more in number than the well-born, or the poor than the rich, yet they may not so much exceed in quantity as they fall short in quality; and therefore there must be a comparison of quantity and quality. Where the number of the poor is more than proportioned to the wealth of the rich, there will naturally be a democracy, varying in form with the sort of people who compose it in each case. If, for example, the husbandmen exceed in number, the first form of democracy will then arise; if the artisans and labouring class, the last; and so with the intermediate forms. But where the rich and the notables exceed in quality more than they fall short in quantity, there oligarchy arises, similarly assuming various forms according to the kind of superiority possessed by the oligarchs.

The legislator should always include the middle class in his government; if he makes his laws oligarchical, to the middle class let him look; if he makes them democratical, he should equally by his laws try to attach this class to the state. There only can the government ever be stable where the middle class exceeds one or both of the others, and in that case there will be no fear that the rich will unite with the **1297a** poor against the rulers. For neither of them will ever be willing to serve the other, and if they look for some form of government more suitable to both, they will find none better than this, for the rich and the poor will never consent to rule in turn, because they mistrust one another. The arbiter is always the one trusted, and he who is in the middle is an arbiter. The more perfect the admixture of the political elements, the more lasting will be the constitution. Many even of those who desire to form aristocratical governments make a mistake, not only in giving too much power to the rich, but in attempting to overreach the people. There comes a time when out of a false good there arises a true evil, since the encroachments of the rich are more destructive to the constitution than those of the people.

13

The devices by which oligarchies deceive the people are five in number; they relate to (1) the assembly; (2) the magistracies; (3) the courts of law; (4) the use of arms; (5) gymnastic exercises. (1) The assemblies are thrown open to all, but either the rich only are fined for non-attendance, or a much larger fine is inflicted upon them. (2) As to the magistracies, those who are qualified by property cannot decline office upon oath, but the poor may. (3) In the law-courts the rich, and the rich only, are fined if they do not serve, the poor are let off with impunity, or, as in the laws of Charondas, a larger fine is inflicted on the rich, and a smaller one on the poor. In some states all citizens who have registered themselves are allowed to attend the assembly and to try causes; but if after registration they do not attend either in the assembly or at the courts, heavy fines are imposed upon them. The intention is that through fear of the fines they may avoid registering themselves, and then they cannot sit in the law-courts or in the assembly. Concerning (4) the possession of arms, and (5) gymnastic exercises, they legislate in a similar spirit. For the poor are not obliged to have arms, but the rich are fined for not having them; and in like manner no penalty is inflicted on the poor for non-attendance at the gymnasium, and consequently, having nothing to fear, they do not attend, whereas the rich are liable to a fine, and therefore they take care to attend.

These are the devices of oligarchical legislators, and in democracies they have counter devices. They pay the poor for attending the assemblies and the law-courts, and they inflict no penalty on the rich for non-attendance. It is obvious that he who would duly mix the two principles should combine the practice of both, and provide that the poor should be paid to attend, and the rich fined if they do not attend, for then all will take part; if there is no such combination, power will be in the **1297b** hands of one party only. The government should be confined to those who carry arms. As to the property qualification, no absolute rule can be laid down, but we must see what is the highest qualification sufficiently comprehensive to secure that the number of those who have the rights of citizens exceeds the number of those excluded. Even if they have no share in office, the poor, provided only that they are not outraged or deprived of their property, will be quite enough.

But to secure gentle treatment for the poor is not an easy thing, since a ruling class is not always humane. And in time of war the poor are apt to hesitate unless they are fed; when fed, they are willing enough to fight. In some states the government is vested, not only in those who are actually serving, but also in those who have served; among the Malians, for example, the governing body consisted of the latter, while the magistrates were chosen from those actually on service. And the earliest government which existed among the Hellenes, after the overthrow of the kingly power, grew up out of the warrior class, and was originally taken from the knights (for strength and superiority in war at that time depended on cavalry; indeed, without discipline, infantry are useless, and in ancient times there was no military knowledge or tactics, and therefore the strength of armies lay in their cavalry). But when cities increased and the heavy-armed grew in strength, more had a share in the government; and this is the reason why the states which we call constitutional governments have been hitherto called democracies. Ancient constitutions, as might be expected, were oligarchical and royal; their population being small they had no considerable middle class; the people were weak in numbers and organization, and were therefore more contented to be governed.

I have explained why there are various forms of government, and why there are more than is generally supposed; for democracy, as well as other constitutions, has more than one form: also what their differences are, and whence they arise, and what is the best form of government, speaking generally, and to whom the various forms of government are best suited; all this has now been explained.

14

Having thus gained an appropriate basis of discussion we will proceed to speak of the points which follow next in order. We will consider the subject not only in general but with reference to particular constitutions. All constitutions have three elements, concerning which the good lawgiver has to regard what is expedient for each constitution. When they are well-ordered, the constitution is well-ordered, and as they differ from one another, constitutions differ. There is (1) one element
1298a which deliberates about public affairs; secondly (2) that concerned with the magistracies—the questions being, what they should be, over what they should exercise authority, and what should be the mode of electing to them; and thirdly (3) that which has judicial power.

The deliberative element has authority in matters of war and peace, in making and unmaking alliances; it passes laws, inflicts death, exile, confiscation, elects magistrates and audits their accounts. These powers must be assigned either all to all the citizens or all to some of them (for example, to one or more magistracies, or different causes to different magistracies), or some of them to all, and others of them only to some. That all things should be decided by all is characteristic of democracy; this is the sort of equality which the people desire. But there are various ways in which all may share in the government; they may deliberate, not all in one body, but by turns, as in the constitution of Telecles the Milesian. There are other constitutions in which the boards of magistrates meet and deliberate, but come into office by turns, and are elected out of the tribes and the very smallest divisions of the state, until every one has obtained office in his turn. The citizens, on the other hand, are assembled only for the purposes of legislation, and to consult about the constitution, and to hear the edicts of the magistrates. In another variety of democracy the citizens form one assembly, but meet only to elect magistrates, to pass laws, to advise about war and peace, and to make scrutinies. Other matters are referred severally to special magistrates, who are elected by vote or by lot out of all the citizens. Or again, the citizens meet about election to offices and about scrutinies, and deliberate concerning war or alliances while other matters are administered by the magistrates, who, as far as is possible, are elected by vote. I am speaking of those magistracies in which special knowledge is required. A fourth form of democracy is when all the citizens meet to deliberate about everything, and the magistrates decide nothing, but only make the preliminary inquiries; and that is the way in which the last and worst form of democracy, corresponding, as we maintain, to the close family oligarchy and to tyranny, is at present administered. All these modes are democratical.

On the other hand, that some should deliberate about all is oligarchical. This again is a mode which, like the democratical, has many forms. When the deliberative class being elected out of those who have a moderate qualification are numerous and they respect and obey the prohibitions of the law without altering it, and any one who has the required qualification shares in the government, then, just because of this moderation, the oligarchy inclines towards polity. But when only selected individuals and not the whole people share in the
1298b deliberations of the state, then, al-

though, as in the former case, they observe the law, the government is a pure oligarchy. Or, again, when those who have the power of deliberation are self-elected, and son succeeds father, and they and not the laws are supreme—the government is of necessity oligarchical. Where, again, particular persons have authority in particular matters;—for example, when the whole people decide about peace and war and hold scrutinies, but the magistrates regulate everything else, and they are elected by vote—there the government is an aristocracy. And if some questions are decided by magistrates elected by vote, and others by magistrates elected by lot, either absolutely or out of select candidates, or elected partly by vote, partly by lot—these practices are partly characteristic of an aristocratical government, and partly of a pure constitutional government.

These are the various forms of the deliberative body; they correspond to the various forms of government. And the government of each state is administered according to one or other of the principles which have been laid down. Now it is for the interest of democracy, according to the most prevalent notion of it (I am speaking of that extreme form of democracy in which the people are supreme even over the laws), with a view to better deliberation to adopt the custom of oligarchies respecting courts of law. For in oligarchies the rich who are wanted to be judges are compelled to attend under pain of a fine, whereas in democracies the poor are paid to attend. And this practice of oligarchies should be adopted by democracies in their public assemblies, for they will advise better if they all deliberate together,—the people with the notables and the notables with the people. It is also a good plan that those who deliberate should be elected by vote or by lot in equal numbers out of the different classes; and that if the people greatly exceed in number those who have political training, pay should not be given to all, but only to as many as would balance the number of the notables, or that the number in excess should be eliminated by lot. But in oligarchies either certain persons should be co-opted from the mass, or a class of officers should be appointed such as exist in some states, who are termed probuli and guardians of the law; and the citizens should occupy themselves exclusively with matters on which these have previously deliberated; for so the people will have a share in the deliberations of the state, but will not be able to disturb the principles of the constitution. Again, in oligarchies either the people ought to accept the measures of the government, or not to pass anything contrary to them; or, if all are allowed to share in counsel, the decision should rest with the magistrates. The opposite of what is done in constitutional governments should be the rule in oligarchies; the veto of the majority should be final, their assent not final, but the proposal should be referred back to the magistrates. Whereas in constitutional governments they take the contrary course; the few have the negative, not the affirmative power; the af-
1299a firmation of everything rests with the multitude.

These, then, are our conclusions respecting the deliberative, that is, the supreme element in states.

15

Next we will proceed to consider the distribution of offices; this, too, being a part of politics concerning which many questions arise:—What shall their number be? Over what shall they preside, and what shall be their duration? Sometimes they last for six months, sometimes for less; sometimes they are annual, whilst in other cases offices are held for still longer periods. Shall they be for life or for a long term of years; or, if for a short term only, shall the same persons hold them over and over again, or once only? Also about the appointment to them,—from whom are they to be chosen, by whom, and how? We should first be in a position to say what are the possible varieties of them, and then we may proceed to determine which are suited to different forms of government. But what are to be included under the term 'offices'? That is a question not quite so easily answered. For a political community requires many officers; and not every one who is chosen by vote or by lot is to be regarded as a ruler. In the first place there are the priests, who must be distinguished from political officers; masters of choruses and heralds, even ambassadors, are elected by vote. Some duties of superintendence again are political, extending either to all the citizens in a single sphere of action, like the office of the general who superintends them when they are in the field, or to a section of them only, like the inspectorships of women or of youth. Other offices are concerned with household management, like that of the corn measurers who exist in many states and are elected officers. There are also menial offices which the rich have executed by their slaves. Speaking generally, those are to be called offices to which the duties are assigned of deliberating about certain measures and of judging and commanding, especially the last; for to command is the especial duty of a magistrate. But the question is not of any importance in practice; no one has ever brought into court the meaning of the word, although such problems have a speculative interest.

What kinds of offices, and how many, are necessary to the existence of a state, and which, if not necessary, yet conduce to its well-being, are much more important considerations, affecting all constitutions, but more especially small states. For in great states it is possible, and indeed necessary, that every office should have a special function; where the citizens are numerous, many may hold office. And so it happens that some offices a man holds a second time only after a long interval, and others he holds once only; and certainly every work **1299b** is better done which receives the sole, and not the divided attention of the worker. But in small states it is necessary to combine many offices in a few hands, since the small number of citizens does not admit of many holding office:—for who will there be to succeed them? And yet small states at times require the same offices and laws as large ones; the difference is that the one want them often, the others only after long intervals. Hence there is no reason why the care of many offices should not be imposed on the same person, for they will not interfere with each other. When the population is small, offices should be like the spits which also serve to hold a lamp. We must first ascertain how many magistrates are necessary in every state, and also how many are not exactly necessary, but are nevertheless useful, and then there will be no difficulty in seeing what offices can be combined in one. We should also know over which matters several local tribunals are to have jurisdiction, and in which authority should be centralized: for example, should one person keep order in the market and another in some other place, or should the same person be responsible everywhere? Again, should offices be divided according to the subjects with which they deal, or according to the persons with whom they deal: I mean to say, should one person see to good order in general, or one look after the boys, another after the women, and so on? Further, under different constitutions, should the magistrates be the same or different? For example, in democracy, oligarchy, aristocracy, monarchy, should there be the same magistrates, although they are elected, not out of equal or similar classes of citizens, but differently under different constitutions—in aristocracies, for example, they are chosen from the educated, in oligarchies from the wealthy, and in democracies from the free,—or are there certain differences in the offices answering to them as well, and may the same be suitable to some, but different offices to others? For in some states it may be convenient that the same office should have a more extensive, in other states a narrower sphere. Special offices are peculiar to certain forms of government:—for example that of probuli, which is not a democratic office, although a bule or council is. There must be some body of men whose duty is to prepare measures for the people in order that they may not be diverted from their business; when these are few in number, the state inclines to an oligarchy: or rather the probuli must always be few, and are therefore an oligarchical element. But when both institutions exist in a state, the probuli are a check on the council; for the counsellor is a democratic element, but the probuli are oligarchical. Even the power of the council disappears when de- **1300a** mocracy has taken that extreme form in which the people themselves are always meeting and deliberating about everything. This is the case when the members of the assembly receive abundant pay; for they have nothing to do and are always holding assemblies and deciding everything for themselves. A magistracy which controls the boys or the women, or any similar office, is suited to an aristocracy rather than to a democracy; for how can the magistrates prevent the wives of the poor from going out of doors? Neither is it an oligarchical office; for the wives of the oligarchs are too fine to be controlled.

Enough of these matters. I will now inquire into appointments to offices. The varieties depend on three terms, and the combinations of these give all possible modes: first, who appoints? secondly, from whom? and thirdly, how? Each of these three admits of three varieties: (A) All the citizens, or (B) only some, appoint. Either (1) the magistrates are chosen out of all or (2) out of some who are distinguished either by a property qualification, or by birth, or merit, or for some special reason, as at Megara only those were eligible who had returned from exile and fought together against the democracy. They may be appointed either (α) by vote or (β) by lot. Again, these several varieties may be coupled, I mean that (C) some officers may be elected by some, others by all, and (3) some again out of some, and others out of all, and (γ) some by vote and others by lot. Each variety of these terms admits of four modes.

For either (A 1 α) all may appoint from all by vote, or (A 1 β) all from all by lot, or (A 2 α) all from some by vote, or (A 2 β) all from some by lot (and if from all, either by sections, as, for example, by tribes, and wards, and phratries, until all the citizens have been gone through; or the citizens may be in all cases eligible indiscriminately); or again (A 1 γ, A 2 γ) to some offices in the one way, to some in the other. Again, if it is only some that appoint, they may do so either (B 1 α) from all by vote, or (B 1 β) from all by lot, or (B 2 α) from some by vote, or (B 2 β) from some by lot, or to some offices in the one way, to others in the other, i.e. (B 1 γ) from all, to some offices by vote, to some by lot, and (B 2 γ) from some, to some offices by vote, to some by lot. Thus the modes that arise, apart from two (C, 3) out of the three couplings, number twelve. Of these systems two are popular, that all should appoint from all (A 1 α) by vote or (A 1 β) by lot,— or (A 1 γ) by both. That all should not appoint at once, but should appoint from all or from some either by lot or by vote or by both, or appoint to some offices from all and to others from some ('by both' meaning to some offices by lot, to others by vote), is characteristic of a polity. And (B 1 γ) that some should appoint from all, to some offices by vote, to others by lot, is also characteristic of a polity, but more oligarchical than the former method. And (A 3 α, β, γ, B 3 α, β, γ) to appoint from both, to some offices from all, to others from some, is characteristic of a polity with a leaning towards aristocracy. **1300b** That (B 2) some should appoint from some is oligarchical,—even (B 2 β) that some should appoint from some by lot (and if this does not actually occur, it is none the less oligarchical in character), or (B 2 γ) that some should appoint from some by both. (B 1 α) that some should appoint from all, and (A 2 α) that all should appoint from some, by vote, is aristocratic.

These are the different modes of constituting magistrates, and these correspond to different forms of government:—which are proper to which, or how they ought to be established, will be evident when we determine the nature of their powers. By powers I mean such powers as a magistrate exercises over the revenue or in defence of the country; for there are various kinds of power: the power of the general, for example, is not the same with that which regulates contracts in the market.

16

Of the three parts of government, the judicial remains to be considered, and this we shall divide on the same principle. There are three points on which the varieties of law-courts depend: The persons from whom they are appointed, the matters with which they are concerned, and the manner of their appointment. I mean, (1) are the judges taken from all, or from some only? (2) how many kinds of law-courts are there? (3) are the judges chosen by vote or by lot?

First, let me determine how many kinds of law-courts there are. They are eight in number: One is the court of audits or scrutinies; a second takes cognizance of ordinary offences against the state; a third is concerned with treason against the constitution; the fourth determines disputes respecting penalties, whether raised by magistrates or by private persons; the fifth decides the more important civil cases; the sixth tries cases of homicide, which are of various kinds, (*a*) premeditated, (*b*) involuntary, (*c*) cases in which the guilt is confessed but the justice is disputed; and there may be a fourth court (*d*) in which murderers who have fled from justice are tried after their return; such as the Court of Phreatto is said to be at Athens. But cases of this sort rarely happen at all even in large cities. The different kinds of homicide may be tried either by the same or by different courts. (*7*) There are courts for strangers:—of these there are two subdivisions, (*a*) for the settlement of their disputes with one another, (*b*) for the settlement of disputes between them and the citizens. And besides all these there must be (*8*) courts for small suits about sums of a drachma up to five drachmas, or a little more, which have to be determined, but they do not require many judges.

Nothing more need be said of these small suits, nor of the courts for homicide and for strangers:—I would rather speak of political cases, which, when mismanaged, create division and disturbances in constitutions.

Now if all the citizens judge, in all the different cases which I have distinguished, they may be appointed by vote or by lot, or sometimes by lot and sometimes by vote. Or when a single class of causes are tried, the judges who decide them may be appointed, some by **1301a** vote, and some by lot. These then are the four modes of appointing judges from the whole people, and there will be likewise four modes, if they are elected from a part only; for they may be appointed from some by vote and judge in all causes; or they may be appointed from some by lot and judge in all causes; or they may be elected in some cases by vote, and in some cases taken by lot, or some courts, even when judging the same causes, may be composed of members some appointed by vote and some by lot. These modes, then, as was said, answer to those previously mentioned.

Once more, the modes of appointment may be combined; I mean, that some may be chosen out of the whole people, others out of some, some out of both; for example, the same tribunal may be composed of some who were elected out of all, and of others who were elected out of some, either by vote or by lot or by both.

In how many forms law-courts can be established has now been considered. The first form, viz. that in which the judges are taken from all the citizens, and in which all causes are tried, is democratical; the second, which is composed of a few only who try all causes, oligarchical; the third, in which some courts are taken from all classes, and some from certain classes only, aristocratical and constitutional.

BOOK V

I

THE design which we proposed to ourselves is now nearly completed. Next in order follow the causes of revolution in states, how many, and of what nature they are; what modes of destruction apply to particular states, and out of what, and into what they mostly change; also what are the modes of preservation in states generally, or in a particular state, and by what means each state may be best preserved: these questions remain to be considered.

In the first place we must assume as our starting-point that in the many forms of government which have sprung up there has always been an acknowledgement of justice and proportionate equality, although mankind fail in attaining them, as indeed I have already explained.[1] Democracy, for example, arises out of the notion that those who are equal in any respect are equal in all respects; because men are equally free, they claim to be absolutely equal. Oligarchy is based on the notion that those who are unequal in one respect are in all respects unequal; being unequal, that is, in property, they suppose themselves to be unequal absolutely. The democrats think that as they are equal they ought to be equal in all things; while the oligarchs, under the idea that they are unequal, claim too much, which is one form of inequality. All these forms of government have a kind of justice, but, tried by an absolute standard, they are faulty; and, therefore, both parties, whenever their share in the government does not accord with their preconceived ideas, stir up revolution. Those who excel in virtue have the best right of all to rebel (for they alone can with reason be **1301b** deemed absolutely unequal), but then they are of all men the least inclined to do so. There is also a superiority which is claimed by men of rank; for they are thought noble because they spring from wealthy and virtuous ancestors. Here then, so to speak, are opened the very springs and fountains of revolution; and hence arise two sorts of changes in governments; the one affecting the constitution, when men seek to change from an existing form into some other, for example, from democracy into oligarchy, and from oligarchy into democracy, or from either of them into constitutional government or aristocracy, and conversely; the other not affecting the constitution, when, without disturbing the form of government, whether oligarchy, or monarchy, or any other, they try to get the administration into their own hands. Further, there is a question of degree; an oligarchy, for example, may become more or less oligarchical, and a democracy more or less democratical; and in like manner the characteristics of the other forms of government may be more or less strictly maintained. Or the revolution may be directed against a portion of the constitution only, e.g. the establishment or overthrow of a particular office: as at Sparta it is said that Lysander attempted to overthrow the monarchy, and king Pausanias, the ephoralty. At Epidamnus, too, the change was partial. For instead of phylarchs or heads of tribes, a

[1] III. 1282b 18-30.

council was appointed; but to this day the magistrates are the only members of the ruling class who are compelled to go to the Heliaea when an election takes place, and the office of the single archon was another oligarchical feature. Everywhere inequality is a cause of revolution, but an inequality in which there is no proportion— for instance, a perpetual monarchy among equals; and always it is the desire of equality which rises in rebellion.

Now equality is of two kinds, numerical and proportional; by the first I mean sameness or equality in number or size; by the second, equality of ratios. For example, the excess of three over two is numerically equal to the excess of two over one; whereas four exceeds two in the same ratio in which two exceeds one, for two is the same part of four that one is of two, namely, the half. As I was saying before,[1] men agree that justice in the abstract is proportion, but they differ in that some think that if they are equal in any respect they are equal absolutely, others that if they are unequal in any respect they should be unequal in all. Hence there are two principal forms of government, democracy and oligarchy; for good birth **1302a** and virtue are rare, but wealth and numbers are more common. In what city shall we find a hundred persons of good birth and of virtue? whereas the rich everywhere abound. That a state should be ordered, simply and wholly, according to either kind of equality, is not a good thing; the proof is the fact that such forms of government never last. They are originally based on a mistake, and, as they begin badly, cannot fail to end badly. The inference is that both kinds of equality should be employed; numerical in some cases, and proportionate in others.

Still democracy appears to be safer and less liable to revolution than oligarchy. For in oligarchies there is the double danger of the oligarchs falling out among themselves and also with the people; but in democracies there is only the danger of a quarrel with the oligarchs. No dissension worth mentioning arises among the people themselves. And we may further remark that a government which is composed of the middle class more nearly approximates to democracy than to oligarchy, and is the safest of the imperfect forms of government.

2

In considering how dissensions and political revolutions arise, we must first of all ascertain the beginnings and causes of them which affect constitutions generally. They may be said to be three in number; and we have now to give an outline of each. We want to know (1) what is the feeling? (2) what are the motives of those who make them? (3) whence arise political disturbances and quarrels? The universal and chief cause of this revolutionary feeling has been already mentioned;[2] viz. the desire of equality, when men think that they are equal to others who have more than themselves; or, again, the desire of inequality and superiority, when conceiving themselves to be superior they think that they have not more but the same or less than their inferiors; pretensions which may and may not be just. Inferiors revolt in order that they may be equal, and equals that they may be superior. Such is the state of mind which creates revolutions. The motives for making them are the desire of gain and honour, or the fear of dishonour and loss; the authors of them want to divert punishment or dishonour from themselves or their friends. The causes and reasons of revolutions, whereby men are themselves affected in the way described, and about the things which I have mentioned, viewed in one way may be regarded as seven, and in another as more than seven. Two of them have been already noticed;[3] but they act in a different manner, for men are excited against one another by the love of gain and honour—not, as in the case which I have just supposed, **1302b** in order to obtain them for themselves, but at seeing others, justly or unjustly, engrossing them. Other causes are insolence, fear, excessive predominance, contempt, disproportionate increase in some part of the state; causes of another sort are election intrigues, carelessness, neglect about trifles, dissimilarity of elements.

3

What share insolence and avarice have in creating revolutions, and how they work, is plain enough. When the magistrates are insolent and grasping they conspire against one another and also against the constitution from which they derive their power, making their gains either at the expense of individuals or of the public. It is evident, again, what an influence honour exerts and how it is a cause of revolution. Men who are themselves dishonoured and who see others obtaining honours

[1] a26.

[2] 1301a 33 sqq., b 35 sqq.

[3] l. 32.

rise in rebellion; the honour or dishonour when undeserved is unjust; and just when awarded according to merit. Again, superiority is a cause of revolution when one or more persons have a power which is too much for the state and the power of the government; this is a condition of affairs out of which there arises a monarchy, or a family oligarchy. And therefore, in some places, as at Athens and Argos, they have recourse to ostracism. But how much better to provide from the first that there should be no such pre-eminent individuals instead of letting them come into existence and then finding a remedy.

Another cause of revolution is fear. Either men have committed wrong, and are afraid of punishment, or they are expecting to suffer wrong and are desirous of anticipating their enemy. Thus at Rhodes the notables conspired against the people through fear of the suits that were brought against them. Contempt is also a cause of insurrection and revolution; for example, in oligarchies—when those who have no share in the state are the majority, they revolt, because they think that they are the stronger. Or, again, in democracies, the rich despise the disorder and anarchy of the state; at Thebes, for example, where, after the battle of Oenophyta, the bad administration of the democracy led to its ruin. At Megara the fall of the democracy was due to a defeat occasioned by disorder and anarchy. And at Syracuse the democracy aroused contempt before the tyranny of Gelo arose; at Rhodes, before the insurrection.

Political revolutions also spring from a disproportionate increase in any part of the state. For as a body is made up of many members, and every member ought to grow in proportion, that symmetry may be preserved; but loses its nature if the foot be four cubits long and the rest of the body two spans; and, should the abnormal increase be one of quality as well as of quantity, may even take the form of another animal: even so a state has many
1303a parts, of which some one may often grow imperceptibly; for example, the number of poor in democracies and in constitutional states. And this disproportion may sometimes happen by an accident, as at Tarentum, from a defeat in which many of the notables were slain in a battle with the Iapygians just after the Persian War, the constitutional government in consequence becoming a democracy; or as was the case at Argos, where the Argives, after their army had been cut to pieces on the seventh day of the month by Cleomenes the Lacedaemonian, were compelled to admit to citizenship some of their perioeci; and at Athens, when, after frequent defeats of their infantry at the time of the Peloponnesian War, the notables were reduced in number, because the soldiers had to be taken from the roll of citizens. Revolutions arise from this cause as well, in democracies as in other forms of government, but not to so great an extent. When the rich grow numerous or properties increase, the form of government changes into an oligarchy or a government of families. Forms of government also change—sometimes even without revolution, owing to election contests, as at Heraea (where, instead of electing their magistrates, they took them by lot, because the electors were in the habit of choosing their own partisans); or owing to carelessness, when disloyal persons are allowed to find their way into the highest offices, as at Oreum, where, upon the accession of Heracleodorus to office, the oligarchy was overthrown, and changed by him into a constitutional and democratical government.

Again, the revolution may be facilitated by the slightness of the change; I mean that a great change may sometimes slip into the constitution through neglect of a small matter; at Ambracia, for instance, the qualification for office, small at first, was eventually reduced to nothing. For the Ambraciots thought that a small qualification was much the same as none at all.

Another cause of revolution is difference of races which do not at once acquire a common spirit; for a state is not the growth of a day, any more than it grows out of a multitude brought together by accident. Hence the reception of strangers in colonies, either at the time of their foundation or afterwards, has generally produced revolution; for example, the Achaeans who joined the Troezenians in the foundation of Sybaris, becoming later the more numerous, expelled them; hence the curse fell upon Sybaris. At Thurii the Sybarites quarrelled with their fellow-colonists; thinking that the land belonged to them, they wanted too much of it and were driven out. At Byzantium the new colonists were detected in a conspiracy, and were expelled by force of arms; the people of Antissa, who had received the Chian exiles, fought with them, and drove them out; and the Zancleans, after having received the Samians, were driven by them out of their own city. The citizens of Apollonia on the Euxine, after the introduction of a fresh body of colonists, had a revolution; the Syracusans, after the expulsion of their tyrants, having admitted **1303b** strangers and mercenaries to the rights of citizenship, quarrelled and came to blows; the people of Amphipolis, having received Chalcidian colonists, were nearly all expelled by them.

Now, in oligarchies the masses make revolution under the idea that they are unjustly treated, because, as I said before,[1] they are equals, and have not an equal share, and in democracies the notables revolt, because they are not equals, and yet have only an equal share.

Again, the situation of cities is a cause of revolution when the country is not naturally adapted to preserve the unity of the state. For example, the Chytians at Clazomenae did not agree with the people of the island; and the people of Colophon quarrelled with the Notians; at Athens, too, the inhabitants of the Piraeus are more democratic than those who live in the city. For just as in war the impediment of a ditch, though ever so small, may break a regiment, so every cause of difference, however slight, makes a breach in a city. The greatest opposition is confessedly that of virtue and vice; next comes that of wealth and poverty; and there are other antagonistic elements, greater or less, of which one is this difference of place.

4

In revolutions the occasions may be trifling, but great interests are at stake. Even trifles are most important when they concern the rulers, as was the case of old at Syracuse; for the Syracusan constitution was once changed by a love-quarrel of two young men, who were in the government. The story is that while one of them was away from home his beloved was gained over by his companion, and he to revenge himself seduced the other's wife. They then drew the members of the ruling class into their quarrel and so split all the people into portions. We learn from this story that we should be on our guard against the beginnings of such evils, and should put an end to the quarrels of chiefs and mighty men. The mistake lies in the beginning—as the proverb says—'Well begun is half done'; so an error at the beginning, though quite small, bears the same ratio to the errors in the other parts. In general, when the notables quarrel, the whole city is involved, as happened in Hestiaea after the Persian War. The occasion was the division of an inheritance; one of two brothers refused to give an account of their father's property and the treasure which he had found: so the poorer of the two quarrelled with him and enlisted in his cause the popular party, the other, who was very rich, the wealthy classes.

At Delphi, again, a quarrel about a marriage **1304a** was the beginning of all the troubles which followed. In this case the bridegroom, fancying some occurrence to be of evil omen, came to the bride, and went away without taking her. Whereupon her relations, thinking that they were insulted by him, put some of the sacred treasure among his offerings while he was sacrificing, and then slew him pretending that he had been robbing the temple. At Mytilene, too, a dispute about heiresses was the beginning of many misfortunes, and led to the war with the Athenians in which Paches took their city. A wealthy citizen, named Timophanes, left two daughters; Dexander, another citizen, wanted to obtain them for his sons; but he was rejected in his suit, whereupon he stirred up a revolution, and instigated the Athenians (of whom he was proxenus) to interfere. A similar quarrel about an heiress arose at Phocis between Mnaseas the father of Mnason, and Euthycrates the father of Onomarchus; this was the beginning of the Sacred War. A marriage-quarrel was also the cause of a change in the government of Epidamnus. A certain man betrothed his daughter to a person whose father, having been made a magistrate, fined the father of the girl, and the latter, stung by the insult, conspired with the unenfranchised classes to overthrow the state.

Governments also change into oligarchy or into democracy or into a constitutional government because the magistrates, or some other section of the state, increase in power or renown. Thus at Athens the reputation gained by the court of the Areopagus, in the Persian War, seemed to tighten the reins of government. On the other hand, the victory of Salamis, which was gained by the common people who served in the fleet, and won for the Athenians the empire due to command of the sea, strengthened the democracy. At Argos, the notables, having distinguished themselves against the Lacedaemonians in the battle of Mantinea, attempted to put down the democracy. At Syracuse, the people, having been the chief authors of the victory in the war

[1] 1301a 33.

with the Athenians, changed the constitutional government into democracy. At Chalcis, the people, uniting with the notables, killed Phoxus the tyrant, and then seized the government. At Ambracia, the people, in like manner, having joined with the conspirators in expelling the tyrant Periander, transferred the government to themselves. And generally, it should be remembered that those who have secured power to the state, whether private citizens, or magistrates, or tribes, or any other part or section of the state, are apt to cause revolutions. For either envy of their greatness draws others into rebellion, or they themselves, in their pride of superiority, are unwilling to remain on a level with others.

Revolutions also break out when opposite parties, e.g. the rich and the people, are equally **1304b** balanced, and there is little or no middle class; for, if either party were manifestly superior, the other would not risk an attack upon them. And, for this reason, those who are eminent in virtue usually do not stir up insurrections, always a minority. Such are the beginnings and causes of the disturbances and revolutions to which every form of government is liable.

Revolutions are effected in two ways, by force and by fraud. Force may be applied either at the time of making the revolution or afterwards. Fraud, again, is of two kinds; for (1) sometimes the citizens are deceived into acquiescing in a change of government, and afterwards they are held in subjection against their will. This was what happened in the case of the Four Hundred, who deceived the people by telling them that the king would provide money for the war against the Lacedaemonians, and, having cheated the people, still endeavoured to retain the government. (2) In other cases the people are persuaded at first, and afterwards, by a repetition of the persuasion, their goodwill and allegiance are retained. The revolutions which effect constitutions generally spring from the abovementioned causes.

5

And now, taking each constitution separately, we must see what follows from the principles already laid down.

Revolutions in democracies are generally caused by the intemperance of demagogues, who either in their private capacity lay information against rich men until they compel them to combine (for a common danger unites even the bitterest enemies), or coming forward in public stir up the people against them. The truth of this remark is proved by a variety of examples. At Cos the democracy was overthrown because wicked demagogues arose, and the notables combined. At Rhodes the demagogues not only provided pay for the multitude, but prevented them from making good to the trierarchs the sums which had been expended by them; and they, in consequence of the suits which were brought against them, were compelled to combine and put down the democracy. The democracy at Heraclea was overthrown shortly after the foundation of the colony by the injustice of the demagogues, which drove out the notables, who came back in a body and put an end to the democracy. Much in the same manner the democracy at Megara was overturned; there the demagogues drove out many of the notables in order that they might be able to confiscate their property. At length the exiles, becoming numerous, returned, and, engaging and defeating the people, established the oligarchy. The same thing happened with the **1305a** democracy of Cyme, which was overthrown by Thrasymachus. And we may observe that in most states the changes have been of this character. For sometimes the demagogues, in order to curry favour with the people, wrong the notables and so force them to combine;—either they make a division of their property, or diminish their incomes by the imposition of public services, and sometimes they bring accusations against the rich that they may have their wealth to confiscate.

Of old, the demagogue was also a general, and then democracies changed into tyrannies. Most of the ancient tyrants were originally demagogues. They are not so now, but they were then; and the reason is that they were generals and not orators, for oratory had not yet come into fashion. Whereas in our day, when the art of rhetoric has made such progress, the orators lead the people, but their ignorance of military matters prevents them from usurping power; at any rate instances to the contrary are few and slight. Tyrannies were more common formerly than now, for this reason also, that great power was placed in the hands of individuals; thus a tyranny arose at Miletus out of the office of the Prytanis, who had supreme authority in many important matters. Moreover, in those days, when cities were not large, the people dwelt in the fields, busy at their work; and their chiefs, if they possessed any military talent, seized the opportunity, and winning the confidence of the masses by professing their hatred of the wealthy, they succeeded in obtaining the tyranny. Thus at Athens Peisistratus led a faction against the men of the plain,[1] and Theagenes at Megara slaughtered the cattle of the wealthy, which he found by the river side, where they had put them to graze in land not their own. Dionysius, again, was thought worthy of the tyranny because he denounced Daphnaeus and the rich; his enmity to the notables won for him the confidence of the people. Changes also take place from the ancient to the latest form of democracy; for where there is a popular election of the magistrates and no property qualification, the aspirants for office get hold of the people, and contrive at last even to set them above the laws. A more or less complete cure for this state of things is for the separate tribes, and not the whole people, to elect the magistrates.

These are the principal causes of revolutions in democracies.

6

There are two patent causes of revolutions in oligarchies: (1) First, when the oligarchs oppress the people, for then anybody is good enough to be their champion, especially if he be himself a member of the oligarchy, as Lygdamis at Naxos, who afterwards came to be tyrant. But revolutions which commence **1305b** outside the governing class may be further subdivided. Sometimes, when the government is very exclusive, the revolution is brought about by persons of the wealthy class who are excluded, as happened at Massalia and Istros and Heraclea, and other cities. Those who had no share in the government created a disturbance, until first the elder brothers, and then the younger, were admitted; for in some places father and son, in others elder and younger brothers, do not hold office together. At Massalia the oligarchy became more like a constitutional government, but at Istros ended in a democracy, and at Heraclea was enlarged to 600. At Cnidos, again, the oligarchy underwent a considerable change. For the notables fell out among themselves, because only a few shared in the government; there existed among them the rule already mentioned, that father and son could not hold office together, and, if there were several brothers, only the eldest was admitted. The people took advantage of the quarrel, and choosing one of the notables to be their leader, attacked and conquered the oligarchs, who were divided, and division is always a source of weakness. The city of Erythrae, too, in old times was ruled, and ruled well, by the Basilidae, but the people took offence at the narrowness of the oligarchy and changed the constitution.

(2) Of internal causes of revolutions in oligarchies one is the personal rivalry of the oligarchs, which leads them to play the demagogue. Now, the oligarchical demagogue is of two sorts: either (*a*) he practises upon the oligarchs themselves (for, although the oligarchy are quite a small number, they may be a demagogue among them, as at Athens Charicles' party won power by courting the Thirty, that of Phrynichus by courting the Four Hundred); or (*b*) the oligarchs may play the demagogue with the people. This was the case at Larissa, where the guardians of the citizens endeavoured to gain over the people because they were elected by them; and such is the fate of all oligarchies in which the magistrates are elected, as at Abydos, not by the class to which they belong, but by the heavy-armed or by the people, although they may be required to have a high qualification, or to be members of a political club; or, again, where the law-courts are composed of persons outside the government, the oligarchs flatter the people in order to obtain a decision in their own favour, and so they change the constitution; this happened at Heraclea in Pontus. Again, oligarchies change whenever any attempt is made to narrow them; for then those who desire equal rights are compelled to call in the people. Changes in the oligarchy also occur when the oligarchs waste their private property by extravagant living; for then they want to innovate, and either try to make **1306a** themselves tyrants, or install some one else in the tyranny, as Hipparinus did Dionysius at Syracuse, and as at Amphipolis a man named Cleotimus introduced Chalcidian colonists, and when they arrived, stirred them up against the rich. For a like reason in Aegina the person who carried on the negotiation with Chares endeavoured to revolutionize the state. Sometimes a party among the oligarchs try directly to create a political change; sometimes they rob the treasury, and then either the thieves or, as happened at Apollonia in Pontus, those who resist them in their thieving quarrel with the rulers. But an oligarchy which is at unity with itself is not easily destroyed

[1] See Herodotus, I. 59.

from within; of this we may see an example at Pharsalus, for there, although the rulers are few in number, they govern a large city, because they have a good understanding among themselves.

Oligarchies, again, are overthrown when another oligarchy is created within the original one, that is to say, when the whole governing body is small and yet they do not all share in the highest offices. Thus at Elis the governing body was a small senate; and very few ever found their way into it, because the senators were only ninety in number, and were elected for life and out of certain families in a manner similar to the Lacedaemonian elders. Oligarchy is liable to revolutions alike in war and in peace; in war because, not being able to trust the people, the oligarchs are compelled to hire mercenaries, and the general who is in command of them often ends in becoming a tyrant, as Timophanes did at Corinth; or if there are more generals than one they make themselves into a company of tyrants. Sometimes the oligarchs, fearing this danger, give the people a share in the government because their services are necessary to them. And in time of peace, from mutual distrust, the two parties hand over the defence of the state to the army and to an arbiter between the two factions, who often ends the master of both. This happened at Larissa when Simos the Aleuad had the government, and at Abydos in the days of Iphiades and the political clubs. Revolutions also arise out of marriages or lawsuits which lead to the overthrow of one party among the oligarchs by another. Of quarrels about marriages I have already mentioned[1] some instances; another occurred at Eretria, where Diagoras overturned the oligarchy of the knights because he had been wronged about a marriage. A revolution at Heraclea, and another at Thebes, both rose out of decisions of law-courts upon a charge of adultery; in both cases the punishment was just, but executed in the spirit of party, at Heraclea upon **1306b** Eurytion, and at Thebes upon Archias; for their enemies were jealous of them and so had them pilloried in the agora. Many oligarchies have been destroyed by some members of the ruling class taking offence at their excessive despotism; for example, the oligarchy at Cnidus and at Chios.

Changes of constitutional governments, and also of oligarchies which limit the office of counsellor, judge, or other magistrate to persons having a certain money qualification, often occur by accident. The qualification may have been originally fixed according to the circumstances of the time, in such a manner as to include in an oligarchy a few only, or in a constitutional government the middle class. But after a time of prosperity, whether arising from peace or some other good fortune, the same property becomes many times as valuable, and then everybody participates in every office; this happens sometimes gradually and insensibly, and sometimes quickly. These are the causes of changes and revolutions in oligarchies.

We must remark generally, both of democracies and oligarchies, that they sometimes change, not into the opposite forms of government, but only into another variety of the same class; I mean to say, from those forms of democracy and oligarchy which are regulated by law into those which are arbitrary, and conversely.

7

In aristocracies revolutions are stirred up when a few only share in the honours of the state, a cause which has been already shown[2] to affect oligarchies; for an aristocracy is a sort of oligarchy, and, like an oligarchy, is the government of a few, although few not for the same reason; hence the two are often confounded. And revolutions will be most likely to happen, and must happen, when the mass of the people are of the high-spirited kind, and have a notion that they are as good as their rulers. Thus at Lacedaemon the so-called Partheniae, who were the sons of the Spartan peers, attempted a revolution, and, being detected, were sent away to colonize Tarentum. Again, revolutions occur when great men who are at least of equal merit are dishonoured by those higher in office, as Lysander was by the kings of Sparta; or, when a brave man is excluded from the honours of the state, like Cinadon, who conspired against the Spartans in the reign of Agesilaus; or, again, when some are very poor and others very rich, a state of society which is most often the result of war, as at Lacedaemon in the days of the Messenian War; this is proved from the poem of Tyr- **1307a** taeus, entitled 'Good Order'; for he speaks of certain citizens who were ruined by the war and wanted to have a redistribution of the land. Again, revolutions arise when an individual who is great, and might be greater,

[1] 1303b 37-1304a 17.

[2] 1305b 2 sqq.

wants to rule alone, as, at Lacedaemon, Pausanias, who was general in the Persian War, or like Hanno at Carthage.

Constitutional governments and aristocracies are commonly overthrown owing to some deviation from justice in the constitution itself; the cause of the downfall is, in the former, the ill-mingling of the two elements democracy and oligarchy; in the latter, of the three elements, democracy, oligarchy, and virtue, but especially democracy and oligarchy. For to combine these is the endeavour of constitutional governments; and most of the so-called aristocracies have a like aim, but differ from polities in the mode of combination; hence some of them are more and some less permanent. Those which incline more to oligarchy are called aristocracies, and those which incline to democracy constitutional governments. And therefore the latter are the safer of the two; for the greater the number, the greater the strength, and when men are equal they are contented. But the rich, if the constitution gives them power, are apt to be insolent and avaricious; and, in general, whichever way the constitution inclines, in that direction it changes as either party gains strength, a constitutional government becoming a democracy, an aristocracy an oligarchy. But the process may be reversed, and aristocracy may change into democracy. This happens when the poor, under the idea that they are being wronged, force the constitution to take an opposite form. In like manner constitutional governments change into oligarchies. The only stable principle of government is equality according to proportion, and for every man to enjoy his own.

What I have just mentioned actually happened at Thurii, where the qualification for office, at first high, was therefore reduced, and the magistrates increased in number. The notables had previously acquired the whole of the land contrary to law; for the government tended to oligarchy, and they were able to encroach. . . . But the people, who had been trained by war, soon got the better of the guards kept by the oligarchs, until those who had too much gave up their land.

Again, since all aristocratical governments incline to oligarchy, the notables are apt to be grasping; thus at Lacedaemon, where property tends to pass into few hands, the notables can do too much as they like, and are allowed to marry whom they please. The city of Locri was ruined by a marriage connexion with Dionysius, but such a thing could never have happened in a democracy, or in a well-balanced aristocracy.

I have already remarked that in all states
1307b revolutions are occasioned by trifles. In aristocracies, above all, they are of a gradual and imperceptible nature. The citizens begin by giving up some part of the constitution, and so with greater ease the government change something else which is a little more important, until they have undermined the whole fabric of the state. At Thurii there was a law that generals should only be re-elected after an interval of five years, and some young men who were popular with the soldiers of the guard for their military prowess, despising the magistrates and thinking that they would easily gain their purpose, wanted to abolish this law and allow their generals to hold perpetual commands; for they well knew that the people would be glad enough to elect them. Whereupon the magistrates who had charge of these matters, and who are called councillors, at first determined to resist, but they afterwards consented, thinking that, if only this one law was changed, no further inroad would be made on the constitution. But other changes soon followed which they in vain attempted to oppose; and the state passed into the hands of the revolutionists, who established a dynastic oligarchy.

All constitutions are overthrown either from within or from without; the latter, when there is some government close at hand having an opposite interest, or at a distance, but powerful. This was exemplified in the old times of the Athenians and the Lacedaemonians; the Athenians everywhere put down the oligarchies, and the Lacedaemonians the democracies.

I have now explained what are the chief causes of revolutions and dissensions in states.

8

We have next to consider what means there are of preserving constitutions in general, and in particular cases. In the first place it is evident that if we know the causes which destroy constitutions, we also know the causes which preserve them; for opposites produce opposites, and destruction is the opposite of preservation. In all well-attempered governments there is nothing which should be more jealously maintained than the spirit of obedience to law, more especially in small matters; for transgression creeps in unperceived and at last ruins the state, just as the constant recurrence of small expenses in time eats up a fortune. The expense does not take place all at once, and therefore is not observed; the mind is deceived, as in the fallacy which says that 'if each part is little, then the whole is little'. And this is true in one way, but not in another, for the whole and the all are not little, although they are made up of littles.

In the first place, then, men should guard against the beginning of change, and in the second place they should not rely upon the political devices of which I have already **1308a** spoken,[1] invented only to deceive the people, for they are proved by experience to be useless. Further, we note that oligarchies as well as aristocracies may last, not from any inherent stability in such forms of government, but because the rulers are on good terms both with the unenfranchised and with the governing classes, not maltreating any who are excluded from the government, but introducing into it the leading spirits among them. They should never wrong the ambitious in a matter of honour, or the common people in a matter of money; and they should treat one another and their fellow-citizens in a spirit of equality. The equality which the friends of democracy seek to establish for the multitude is not only just but likewise expedient among equals. Hence, if the governing class are numerous, many democratic institutions are useful; for example, the restriction of the tenure of offices to six months, that all those who are of equal rank may share in them. Indeed, equals or peers when they are numerous become a kind of democracy, and therefore demagogues are very likely to arise among them, as I have already remarked.[2] The short tenure of office prevents oligarchies and aristocracies from falling into the hands of families; it is not easy for a person to do any great harm when his tenure of office is short, whereas long possession begets tyranny in oligarchies and democracies. For the aspirants to tyranny are either the principal men of the state, who in democracies are demagogues and in oligarchies members of ruling houses, or those who hold great offices, and have a long tenure of them.

Constitutions are preserved when their destroyers are at a distance, and sometimes also because they are near, for the fear of them makes the government keep in hand the constitution. Wherefore the ruler who has a care of the constitution should invent terrors, and bring distant dangers near, in order that the citizens may be on their guard, and, like sentinels in a night-watch, never relax their attention. He should endeavour too by help of the laws to control the contentions and quarrels of the notables, and to prevent those who have not hitherto taken part in them from catching the spirit of contention. No ordinary man can discern the beginning of evil, but only the true statesman.

As to the change produced in oligarchies and constitutional governments by the alteration of the qualification, when this arises, not out of any variation in the qualification but only out of the increase of money, it is well to compare the general valuation of property with that of past years, annually in those cities in which the census is taken annually, **1308b** and in larger cities every third or fifth year. If the whole is many times greater or many times less than when the ratings recognized by the constitution were fixed, there should be power given by law to raise or lower the qualification as the amount is greater or less. Where this is not done a constitutional government passes into an oligarchy, and an oligarchy is narrowed to a rule of families; or in the opposite case constitutional government becomes democracy, and oligarchy either constitutional government or democracy.

It is a principle common to democracy, oligarchy, and every other form of government not to allow the disproportionate increase of any citizen, but to give moderate honour for a long time rather than great honour for a short time. For men are easily spoilt; not every one can bear prosperity. But if this rule is not observed, at any rate the honours which are given all at once should be taken away by degrees and not all at once. Especially should the laws provide against any one having too much power, whether derived from friends or money; if he has, he should be sent clean out of the country. And since innovations creep in through the private life of individuals also, there ought to be a magistracy which will have an eye to those whose life is not in harmony with the government, whether oligarchy or democracy or any other. And for a like reason an increase of prosperity in any part of the state should be carefully watched. The proper remedy for this evil is always to give the management of affairs and offices of state to opposite elements; such opposites are the virtuous and the many, or the rich and the poor. Another way is to combine the

[1] Cf. iv. 1297^a 13-38.

[2] 1305^b 23 sqq.

poor and the rich in one body, or to increase the middle class: thus an end will be put to the revolutions which arise from inequality.

But above all every state should be so administered and so regulated by law that its magistrates cannot possibly make money. In oligarchies special precautions should be used against this evil. For the people do not take any great offence at being kept out of the government—indeed they are rather pleased than otherwise at having leisure for their private business—but what irritates them is to think that their rulers are stealing the public money; then they are doubly annoyed; for they lose both honour and profit. If office brought no profit, then and then only could democracy and aristocracy be combined; for both notables and people might have their wishes gratified. **1309a** All would be able to hold office, which is the aim of democracy, and the notables would be magistrates, which is the aim of aristocracy. And this result may be accomplished when there is no possibility of making money out of the offices; for the poor will not want to have them when there is nothing to be gained from them—they would rather be attending to their own concerns; and the rich, who do not want money from the public treasury, will be able to take them; and so the poor will keep to their work and grow rich, and the notables will not be governed by the lower class. In order to avoid peculation of the public money, the transfer of the revenue should be made at a general assembly of the citizens, and duplicates of the accounts deposited with the different brotherhoods, companies, and tribes. And honours should be given by law to magistrates who have the reputation of being incorruptible. In democracies the rich should be spared; not only should their property not be divided, but their incomes also, which in some states are taken from them imperceptibly, should be protected. It is a good thing to prevent the wealthy citizens, even if they are willing, from undertaking expensive and useless public services, such as the giving of choruses, torch-races, and the like. In an oligarchy, on the other hand, great care should be taken of the poor, and lucrative offices should go to them; if any of the wealthy classes insult them, the offender should be punished more severely than if he had wronged one of his own class. Provision should be made that estates pass by inheritance and not by gift, and no person should have more than one inheritance; for in this way properties will be equalized, and more of the poor rise to competency. It is also expedient both in a democracy and in an oligarchy to assign to those who have less share in the government (i.e. to the rich in a democracy and to the poor in an oligarchy) an equality or preference in all but the principal offices of state. The latter should be entrusted chiefly or only to members of the governing class.

9

There are three qualifications required in those who have to fill the highest offices,—(1) first of all, loyalty to the established constitution; (2) the greatest administrative capacity; (3) virtue and justice of the kind proper to each form of government; for, if what is just is not the same in all governments, the quality of justice must also differ. There may be a doubt, however, when all these qualities do not meet in the same person, how the selection **1309b** is to be made; suppose, for example, a good general is a bad man and not a friend to the constitution, and another man is loyal and just, which should we choose? In making the election ought we not to consider two points? what qualities are common, and what are rare. Thus in the choice of a general, we should regard his skill rather than his virtue; for few have military skill, but many have virtue. In any office of trust or stewardship, on the other hand, the opposite rule should be observed; for more virtue than ordinary is required in the holder of such an office, but the necessary knowledge is of a sort which all men possess.

It may, however, be asked what a man wants with virtue if he have political ability and is loyal, since these two qualities alone will make him do what is for the public interest. But may not men have both of them and yet be deficient in self-control? If, knowing and loving their own interests, they do not always attend to them, may they not be equally negligent of the interests of the public?

Speaking generally, we may say that whatever legal enactments are held to be for the interest of various constitutions, all these preserve them. And the great preserving principle is the one which has been repeatedly mentioned,[1]—to have a care that the loyal citizens should be stronger than the disloyal. Neither should we forget the mean, which at the present day is lost sight of in perverted forms

[1] IV. 1296b 15; VI. 1320a 14; cf. II. 1270b 21 sqq.; IV. 1294b 37.

of government; for many practices which appear to be democratical are the ruin of democracies, and many which appear to be oligarchical are the ruin of oligarchies. Those who think that all virtue is to be found in their own party principles push matters to extremes; they do not consider that disproportion destroys a state. A nose which varies from the ideal of straightness to a hook or snub may still be of good shape and agreeable to the eye; but if the excess be very great, all symmetry is lost, and the nose at last ceases to be a nose at all on account of some excess in one direction or defect in the other; and this is true of every part of the human body. The same law of proportion equally holds in states. Oligarchy or democracy, although a departure from the most perfect form, may yet be a good enough government, but if any one attempts to push the principles of either to an extreme, he will begin by spoiling the government and end by having none at all. Wherefore the legislator and the statesman ought to know what democratical measures save and what destroy a democracy, and what oligarchical measures save or destroy an oligarchy. For neither the one nor the other can exist or continue to exist unless both rich and poor are included in it. If equality of property is introduced, the state must of necessity take another form; for **1310a** when by laws carried to excess one or other element in the state is ruined, the constitution is ruined.

There is an error common both to oligarchies and to democracies:—in the latter the demagogues, when the multitude are above the law, are always cutting the city in two by quarrels with the rich, whereas they should always profess to be maintaining their cause; just as in oligarchies the oligarchs should profess to maintain the cause of the people, and should take oaths the opposite of those which they now take. For there are cities in which they swear—'I will be an enemy to the people, and will devise all the harm against them which I can'; but they ought to exhibit and to entertain the very opposite feeling; in the form of their oath there should be an express declaration—'I will do no wrong to the people.'

But of all the things which I have mentioned that which most contributes to the permanence of constitutions is the adaptation of education to the form of government, and yet in our own day this principle is universally neglected. The best laws, though sanctioned by every citizen of the state, will be of no avail unless the young are trained by habit and education in the spirit of the constitution, if the laws are democratical, democratically, or oligarchically, if the laws are oligarchical. For there may be a want of self-discipline in states as well as in individuals. Now, to have been educated in the spirit of the constitution is not to perform the actions in which oligarchs or democrats delight, but those by which the existence of an oligarchy or of a democracy is made possible. Whereas among ourselves the sons of the ruling class in an oligarchy live in luxury, but the sons of the poor are hardened by exercise and toil, and hence they are both more inclined and better able to make a revolution. And in democracies of the more extreme type there has arisen a false idea of freedom which is contradictory to the true interests of the state. For two principles are characteristic of democracy, the government of the majority and freedom. Men think that what is just is equal; and that equality is the supremacy of the popular will; and that freedom means the doing what a man likes. In such democracies every one lives as he pleases, or in the words of Euripides,[1] 'according to his fancy.' But this is all wrong; men should not think it slavery to live according to the rule of the constitution; for it is their salvation.

I have now discussed generally the causes of the revolution and destruction of states, and the means of their preservation and continuance.

10

I have still to speak of monarchy, and the causes of its destruction and preservation. What I have said already respecting forms **1310b** of constitutional government applies almost equally to royal and to tyrannical rule. For royal rule is of the nature of an aristocracy, and a tyranny is a compound of oligarchy and democracy in their most extreme forms; it is therefore most injurious to its subjects, being made up of two evil forms of government, and having the perversions and errors of both. These two forms of monarchy are contrary in their very origin. The appointment of a king is the resource of the better classes against the people, and he is elected by them out of their own number, because either he himself or his family excel in virtue and virtuous actions; whereas a tyrant is chosen from the people to be their protector against the notables, and in order to prevent them from being in-

[1] Fr. 891, Nauck.

jured. History shows that almost all tyrants have been demagogues who gained the favour of the people by their accusation of the notables. At any rate this was the manner in which the tyrannies arose in the days when cities had increased in power. Others which were older originated in the ambition of kings wanting to overstep the limits of their hereditary power and become despots. Others again grew out of the class which were chosen to be chief magistrates; for in ancient times the people who elected them gave the magistrates, whether civil or religious, a long tenure. Others arose out of the custom which oligarchies had of making some individual supreme over the highest offices. In any of these ways an ambitious man had no difficulty, if he desired, in creating a tyranny, since he had the power in his hands already, either as king or as one of the officers of state. Thus Pheidon at Argos and several others were originally kings, and ended by becoming tyrants; Phalaris, on the other hand, and the Ionian tyrants, acquired the tyranny by holding great offices. Whereas Panaetius at Leontini, Cypselus at Corinth, Peisistratus at Athens, Dionysius at Syracuse, and several others who afterwards became tyrants, were at first demagogues.

And so, as I was saying,[1] royalty ranks with aristocracy, for it is based upon merit, whether of the individual or of his family, or on benefits conferred, or on these claims with power added to them. For all who have obtained this honour have benefited, or had in their power to benefit, states and nations; some, like Codrus, have prevented the state from being enslaved in war; others, like Cyrus, have given their country freedom, or have settled or gained a territory, like the Lacedaemonian, Macedonian, and Molossian kings. The **1311a** idea of a king is to be a protector of the rich against unjust treatment, of the people against insult and oppression. Whereas a tyrant, as has often been repeated,[2] has no regard to any public interest, except as conducive to his private ends; his aim is pleasure, the aim of a king, honour. Wherefore also in their desires they differ; the tyrant is desirous of riches, the king, of what brings honour. And the guards of a king are citizens, but of a tyrant mercenaries.

That tyranny has all the vices both of democracy and oligarchy is evident. As of oligarchy so of tyranny, the end is wealth; (for by wealth only can the tyrant maintain either his guard or his luxury). Both mistrust the people, and therefore deprive them of their arms. Both agree too in injuring the people and driving them out of the city and dispersing them. From democracy tyrants have borrowed the art of making war upon the notables and destroying them secretly or openly, or of exiling them because they are rivals and stand in the way of their power; and also because plots against them are contrived by men of this class, who either want to rule or to escape subjection. Hence Periander advised Thrasybulus by cutting off the tops of the tallest ears of corn, meaning that he must always put out of the way the citizens who overtop the rest. And so, as I have already intimated,[3] the beginnings of change are the same in monarchies as in forms of constitutional government; subjects attack their sovereigns out of fear or contempt, or because they have been unjustly treated by them. And of injustice, the most common form is insult, another is confiscation of property.

The ends sought by conspiracies against monarchies, whether tyrannies or royalties, are the same as the ends sought by conspiracies against other forms of government. Monarchs have great wealth and honour, which are objects of desire to all mankind. The attacks are made sometimes against their lives, sometimes against the office; where the sense of insult is the motive, against their lives. Any sort of insult (and there are many) may stir up anger, and when men are angry, they commonly act out of revenge, and not from ambition. For example, the attempt made upon the Peisistratidae arose out of the public dishonour offered to the sister of Harmodius and the insult to himself. He attacked the tyrant for his sister's sake, and Aristogeiton joined in the attack for the sake of Harmodius. A conspiracy was also formed against Periander, the **1311b** tyrant of Ambracia, because, when drinking with a favourite youth, he asked him whether by this time he was not with child by him. Philip, too, was attacked by Pausanias because he permitted him to be insulted by Attalus and his friends, and Amyntas the little, by Derdas, because he boasted of having enjoyed his youth. Evagoras of Cyprus, again, was slain by the eunuch to revenge an insult; for his wife had been carried off by Evagoras's son. Many conspiracies have originated in shameful attempts made by sovereigns on

[1] I. 2 sqq.

[2] III. 1279b 6 sqq., IV. 1295 19.

[3] 1310a 40 sqq.

the persons of their subjects. Such was the attack of Crataeas upon Archelaus; he had always hated the connexion with him, and so, when Archelaus, having promised him one of his two daughters in marriage, did not give him either of them, but broke his word and married the elder to the king of Elymeia, when he was hard pressed in a war against Sirrhas and Arrhabaeus, and the younger to his own son Amyntas, under the idea that Amyntas would then be less likely to quarrel with his son by Cleopatra—Crataeas made this slight a pretext for attacking Archelaus, though even a less reason would have sufficed, for the real cause of the estrangement was the disgust which he felt at his connexion wtih the king. And from a like motive Hellanocrates of Larissa conspired with him; for when Archelaus, who was his lover, did not fulfil his promise of restoring him to his country, he thought that the connexion between them had originated, not in affection, but in the wantonness of power. Pytho, too, and Heracleides of Aenos, slew Cotys in order to avenge their father, and Adamas revolted from Cotys in revenge for the wanton outrage which he had committed in mutilating him when a child.

Many, too, irritated at blows inflicted on the person which they deemed an insult, have either killed or attempted to kill officers of state and royal princes by whom they have been injured. Thus, at Mytilene, Megacles and his friends attacked and slew the Penthilidae, as they were going about and striking people with clubs. At a later date Smerdis, who had been beaten and torn away from his wife by Penthilus, slew him. In the conspiracy against Archelaus, Decamnichus stimulated the fury of the assassins and led the attack; he was enraged because Archelaus had delivered him to Euripides to be scourged; for the poet had been irritated at some remark made by Decamnichus on the foulness of his breath. Many other examples might be cited of murders and conspiracies which have arisen from similar causes.

Fear is another motive which, as we have said,[1] has caused conspiracies as well in monarchies as in more popular forms of government. Thus Artapanes conspired against Xerxes and slew him, fearing that he would be accused of hanging Darius against his orders,—he having been under the impression that Xerxes would forget what he had said in the middle of a meal, and that the offence would be forgiven.

Another motive is contempt, as in the case
1312a of Sardanapalus, whom some one saw carding wool with his women, if the story-tellers say truly; and the tale may be true, if not of him, of some one else. Dion attacked the younger Dionysius because he despised him, and saw that he was equally despised by his own subjects, and that he was always drunk. Even the friends of a tyrant will sometimes attack him out of contempt; for the confidence which he reposes in them breeds contempt, and they think that they will not be found out. The expectation of success is likewise a sort of contempt; the assailants are ready to strike, and think nothing of the danger, because they seem to have the power in their hands. Thus generals of armies attack monarchs; as, for example, Cyrus attacked Astyages, despising the effeminacy of his life, and believing that his power was worn out. Thus again, Seuthes the Thracian conspired against Amadocus, whose general he was.

And sometimes men are actuated by more than one motive, like Mithridates, who conspired against Ariobarzanes, partly out of contempt and partly from the love of gain.

Bold natures, placed by their sovereigns in a high military position, are most likely to make the attempt in the expectation of success; for courage is emboldened by power, and the union of the two inspires them with the hope of an easy victory.

Attempts of which the motive is ambition arise in a different way as well as in those already mentioned. There are men who will not risk their lives in the hope of gains and honours however great, but who nevertheless regard the killing of a tyrant simply as an extraordinary action which will make them famous and honourable in the world; they wish to acquire, not a kingdom, but a name. It is rare, however, to find such men; he who would kill a tyrant must be prepared to lose his life if he fail. He must have the resolution of Dion, who, when he made war upon Dionysius, took with him very few troops, saying 'that whatever measure of success he might attain would be enough for him, even if he were to die the moment he landed; such a death would be welcome to him'. But this is a temper to which few can attain.

Once more, tyrannies, like all other governments, are destroyed from without by some
1312b opposite and more powerful form of

[1] Cf. 1302b 2, 21, 1311a 25.

government. That such a government will have the will to attack them is clear; for the two are opposed in principle; and all men, if they can, do what they will. Democracy is antagonistic to tyranny, on the principle of Hesiod,[1] 'Potter hates Potter', because they are nearly akin, for the extreme form of democracy is tyranny; and royalty and aristocracy are both alike opposed to tyranny, because they are constitutions of a different type. And therefore the Lacedaemonians put down most of the tyrannies, and so did the Syracusans during the time when they were well governed.

Again, tyrannies are destroyed from within, when the reigning family are divided among themselves, as that of Gelo was, and more recently that of Dionysius; in the case of Gelo because Thrasybulus, the brother of Hiero, flattered the son of Gelo and led him into excesses in order that he might rule in his name. Whereupon the family got together a party to get rid of Thrasybulus and save the tyranny; but those of the people who conspired with them seized the opportunity and drove them all out. In the case of Dionysius, Dion, his own relative, attacked and expelled him with the assistance of the people; he afterwards perished himself.

There are two chief motives which induce men to attack tyrannies—hatred and contempt. Hatred of tyrants is inevitable, and contempt is also a frequent cause of their destruction. Thus we see that most of those who have acquired, have retained their power, but those who have inherited, have lost it, almost at once; for, living in luxurious ease, they have become contemptible, and offer many opportunities to their assailants. Anger, too, must be included under hatred, and produces the same effects. It is oftentimes even more ready to strike—the angry are more impetuous in making an attack, for they do not follow rational principle. And men are very apt to give way to their passions when they are insulted. To this cause is to be attributed the fall of the Peisistratidae and of many others. Hatred is more reasonable, for anger is accompanied by pain, which is an impediment to reason, whereas hatred is painless.

In a word, all the causes which I have mentioned[2] as destroying the last and most unmixed form of oligarchy, and the extreme form of democracy, may be assumed to affect tyranny; indeed the extreme forms of both are only tyrannies distributed among several persons. Kingly rule is little affected by external causes, and is therefore lasting; it is generally destroyed from within. And there are two ways in which the destruction may come about; **1313^{a}** (1) when the members of the royal family quarrel among themselves, and (2) when the kings attempt to administer the state too much after the fashion of a tyranny, and to extend their authority contrary to the law. Royalties do not now come into existence; where such forms of government arise, they are rather monarchies or tyrannies. For the rule of a king is over voluntary subjects, and he is supreme in all important matters; but in our own day men are more upon an equality, and no one is so immeasurably superior to others as to represent adequately the greatness and dignity of the office. Hence mankind will not, if they can help, endure it, and any one who obtains power by force or fraud is at once thought to be a tyrant. In hereditary monarchies a further cause of destruction is the fact that kings often fall into contempt, and, although possessing not tyrannical power, but only royal dignity, are apt to outrage others. Their overthrow is then readily effected; for there is an end to the king when his subjects do not want to have him, but the tyrant lasts, whether they like him or not.

The destruction of monarchies is to be attributed to these and the like causes.

11

And they are preserved, to speak generally, by the opposite causes; or, if we consider them separately, (1) royalty is preserved by the limitation of its powers. The more restricted the functions of kings, the longer their power will last unimpaired; for then they are more moderate and not so despotic in their ways; and they are less envied by their subjects. This is the reason why the kingly office has lasted so long among the Molossians. And for a similar reason it has continued among the Lacedaemonians, because there it was always divided between two, and afterwards further limited by Theopompus in various respects, more particularly by the establishment of the Ephoralty. He diminished the power of the kings, but established on a more lasting basis the kingly office, which was thus made in a certain sense not less, but greater. There is a story that when his wife once asked him

[1] *Works and Days*, 25.

[2] 1302^{b} 25-33, 1304^{b} 20-1306^{b} 21.

whether he was not ashamed to leave to his sons a royal power which was less than he had inherited from his father, 'No indeed', he replied, 'for the power which I leave to them will be more lasting.'

As to (2) tyrannies, they are preserved in two most opposite ways. One of them is the old traditional method in which most tyrants administer their government. Of such arts Periander of Corinth is said to have been the great master, and many similar devices may be gathered from the Persians in the administration of their government. There are firstly the prescriptions mentioned some distance back,[1] for the preservation of a tyranny, in so far as this is possible; viz. that the tyrant should lop off those who are too high; he must put to death men of spirit; he must not **1313b** allow common meals, clubs, education, and the like; he must be upon his guard against anything which is likely to inspire either courage or confidence among his subjects; he must prohibit literary assemblies or other meetings for discussion, and he must take every means to prevent people from knowing one another (for acquaintance begets mutual confidence). Further, he must compel all persons staying in the city to appear in public and live at his gates; then he will know what they are doing: if they are always kept under, they will learn to be humble. In short, he should practise these and the like Persian and barbaric arts, which all have the same object. A tyrant should also endeavour to know what each of his subjects says or does, and should employ spies, like the 'female detectives' at Syracuse, and the eavesdroppers whom Hiero was in the habit of sending to any place of resort or meeting; for the fear of informers prevents people from speaking their minds, and if they do, they are more easily found out. Another art of the tyrant is to sow quarrels among the citizens; friends should be embroiled with friends, the people with the notables, and the rich with one another. Also he should impoverish his subjects; he thus provides against the maintenance of a guard by the citizens, and the people, having to keep hard at work, are prevented from conspiring. The Pyramids of Egypt afford an example of this policy; also the offerings of the family of Cypselus, and the building of the temple of Olympian Zeus by the Peisistratidae, and the great Polycratean monuments at Samos; all these works were alike intended to occupy the people and keep them poor. Another practice of tyrants is to multiply taxes, after the manner of Dionysius at Syracuse, who contrived that within five years his subjects should bring into the treasury their whole property. The tyrant is also fond of making war in order that his subjects may have something to do and be always in want of a leader. And whereas the power of a king is preserved by his friends, the characteristic of a tyrant is to distrust his friends, because he knows that all men want to overthrow him, and they above all have the power.

Again, the evil practices of the last and worst form of democracy are all found in tyrannies. Such are the power given to women in their families in the hope that they will inform against their husbands, and the licence which is allowed to slaves in order that they may betray their masters; for slaves and women do not conspire against tyrants; and they are of course friendly to tyrannies and also to democracies, since under them they have a good time. For the people too would fain be a monarch, and therefore by them, as well as by the tyrant, the flatterer is held in honour; in democracies he is the demagogue; and the tyrant also has those who associate with him in a humble **1314a** spirit, which is a work of flattery.

Hence tyrants are always fond of bad men, because they love to be flattered, but no man who has the spirit of a freeman in him will lower himself by flattery; good men love others, or at any rate do not flatter them. Moreover, the bad are useful for bad purposes; 'nail knocks out nail', as the proverb says. It is characteristic of a tyrant to dislike every one who has dignity or independence; he wants to be alone in his glory, but any one who claims a like dignity or asserts his independence encroaches upon his prerogative, and is hated by him as an enemy to his power. Another mark of a tyrant is that he likes foreigners better than citizens, and lives with them and invites them to his table; for the one are enemies, but the others enter into no rivalry with him.

Such are the notes of the tyrant and the arts by which he preserves his power; there is no wickedness too great for him. All that we have said may be summed up under three heads, which answer to the three aims of the tyrant. These are, (1) the humiliation of his subjects; he knows that a mean-spirited man will not conspire against anybody: (2) the creation of mistrust among them; for a tyrant is not overthrown until men begin to

[1] 1311a 15-22.

have confidence in one another; and this is the reason why tyrants are at war with the good; they are under the idea that their power is endangered by them, not only because they will not be ruled despotically, but also because they are loyal to one another, and to other men, and do not inform against one another or against other men: (3) the tyrant desires that his subjects shall be incapable of action, for no one attempts what is impossible, and they will not attempt to overthrow a tyranny, if they are powerless. Under these three heads the whole policy of a tyrant may be summed up, and to one or other of them all his ideas may be referred: (1) he sows distrust among his subjects; (2) he takes away their power; (3) he humbles them.

This then is one of the two methods by which tyrannies are preserved; and there is another which proceeds upon an almost opposite principle of action. The nature of this latter method may be gathered from a comparison of the causes which destroy kingdoms, for as one mode of destroying kingly power is to make the office of king more tyrannical, so the salvation of a tyranny is to make it more like the rule of a king. But of one thing the tyrant must be careful; he must keep power enough to rule over his subjects, whether they like him or not, for if he once gives this up he gives up his tyranny. But though power must be retained as the foundation, in all else the tyrant should act or appear to act in the character of a king. In the first place he should **1314b** pretend a care of the public revenues, and not waste money in making presents of a sort at which the common people get excited when they see their hard-won earnings snatched from them and lavished on courtesans and strangers and artists. He should give an account of what he receives and of what he spends (a practice which has been adopted by some tyrants); for then he will seem to be a steward of the public rather than a tyrant; nor need he fear that, while he is the lord of the city, he will ever be in want of money. Such a policy is at all events much more advantageous for the tyrant when he goes from home, than to leave behind him a hoard, for then the garrison who remain in the city will be less likely to attack his power; and a tyrant, when he is absent from home, has more reason to fear the guardians of his treasure than the citizens, for the one accompany him, but the others remain behind. In the second place, he should be seen to collect taxes and to require public services only for state purposes, and that he may form a fund in case of war, and generally he ought to make himself the guardian and treasurer of them, as if they belonged, not to him, but to the public. He should appear, not harsh, but dignified, and when men meet him they should look upon him with reverence, and not with fear. Yet it is hard for him to be respected if he inspires no respect, and therefore whatever virtues he may neglect, at least he should maintain the character of a great soldier, and produce the impression that he is one. Neither he nor any of his associates should ever be guilty of the least offense against modesty towards the young of either sex who are his subjects, and the women of his family should observe a like self-control towards other women; the insolence of women has ruined many tyrannies. In the indulgence of pleasures he should be the opposite of our modern tyrants, who not only begin at dawn and pass whole days in sensuality, but want other men to see them, that they may admire their happy and blessed lot. In these things a tyrant should if possible be moderate, or at any rate should not parade his vices to the world; for a drunken and drowsy tyrant is soon despised and attacked; not so he who is temperate and wide awake. His conduct should be the very reverse of nearly everything which has been said before[1] about tyrants. He ought to adorn and improve his city, as though he were not a tyrant, but the guardian of the state. Also he should appear to be particularly earnest in the service of the Gods; for if men think that a ruler is religious **1315a** and has a reverence for the Gods, they are less afraid of suffering injustice at his hands, and they are less disposed to conspire against him, because they believe him to have the very Gods fighting on his side. At the same time his religion must not be thought foolish. And he should honour men of merit, and make them think that they would not be held in more honour by the citizens if they had a free government. The honour he should distribute himself, but the punishment should be inflicted by officers and courts of law. It is a precaution which is taken by all monarchs not to make one person great; but if one, then two or more should be raised, that they may look sharply after one another. If after all some one has to be made great, he should not be a man of bold spirit; for such dispositions

[1] 1313a 35-1314a 29.

are ever most inclined to strike. And if any one is to be deprived of his power, let it be diminished gradually, not taken from him all at once. The tyrant should abstain from all outrage; in particular from personal violence and from wanton conduct towards the young. He should be especially careful of his behaviour to men who are lovers of honour; for as the lovers of money are offended when their property is touched, so are the lovers of honour and the virtuous when their honour is affected. Therefore a tyrant ought either not to commit such acts at all; or he should be thought only to employ fatherly correction, and not to trample upon others,—and his acquaintance with youth should be supposed to arise from affection, and not from the insolence of power, and in general he should compensate the appearance of dishonour by the increase of honour.

Of those who attempt assassination they are the most dangerous, and require to be most carefully watched, who do not care to survive, if they effect their purpose. Therefore special precaution should be taken about any who think that either they or those for whom they care have been insulted; for when men are led away by passion to assault others they are regardless of themselves. As Heracleitus says, 'It is difficult to fight against anger; for a man will buy revenge with his soul.'[1]

And whereas states consist of two classes, of poor men and of rich, the tyrant should lead both to imagine that they are preserved and prevented from harming one another by his rule, and whichever of the two is stronger he should attach to his government; for, having this advantage, he has no need either to emancipate slaves or to disarm the citizens; either party added to the force which he already has, will make him stronger than his assailants.

But enough of these details;—what should be the general policy of the tyrant is obvious. He ought to show himself to his subjects in the light, not of a tyrant, but of a **1315b** steward and a king. He should not appropriate what is theirs, but should be their guardian; he should be moderate, not extravagant in his way of life; he should win the notables by companionship, and the multitude by flattery. For then his rule will of necessity be nobler and happier, because he will rule over better men whose spirits are not crushed, over men to whom he himself is not an object of hatred, and of whom he is not afraid. His power too will be more lasting. His disposition will be virtuous, or at least half virtuous; and he will not be wicked, but half wicked only.

12

Yet no forms of government are so short-lived as oligarchy and tyranny. The tyranny which lasted longest was that of Orthagoras and his sons at Sicyon; this continued for a hundred years. The reason was that they treated their subjects with moderation, and to a great extent observed the laws; and in various ways gained the favour of the people by the care which they took of them. Cleisthenes, in particular, was respected for his military ability. If report may be believed, he crowned the judge who decided against him in the games; and, as some say, the sitting statue in the Agora of Sicyon is the likeness of this person. (A similar story is told of Peisistratus, who is said on one occasion to have allowed himself to be summoned and tried before the Areopagus.)

Next in duration to the tyranny of Orthagoras was that of the Cypselidae at Corinth, which lasted seventy-three years and six months: Cypselus reigned thirty years, Periander forty and a half, and Psammetichus the son of Gorgus three. Their continuance was due to similar causes: Cypselus was a popular man, who during the whole time of his rule never had a body-guard; and Periander, although he was a tyrant, was a great soldier. Third in duration was the rule of the Peisistratidae at Athens, but it was interrupted; for Peisistratus was twice driven out, so that during three and thirty years he reigned only seventeen; and his sons reigned eighteen—altogether thirty-five years. Of other tyrannies, that of Hiero and Gelo at Syracuse was the most lasting. Even this, however, was short, not more than eighteen years in all; for Gelo continued tyrant for seven years, and died in the eighth; Hiero reigned for ten years, and Thrasybulus was driven out in the eleventh month. In fact, tyrannies generally have been of quite short duration.

I have now gone through almost all the causes by which constitutional governments **1316a** and monarchies are either destroyed or preserved.

In the *Republic* of Plato,[2] Socrates treats of revolutions, but not well, for he mentions no

[1] Fr. 85, Diels.

[2] *Republic*, VIII. 546.

cause of change which peculiarly affects the first, or perfect state. He only says that the cause is that nothing is abiding, but all things change in a certain cycle; and that the origin of the change consists in those numbers 'of which 4 and 3, married with 5, furnish two harmonies',—(he means when the number of this figure becomes solid); he conceives that nature at certain times produces bad men who will not submit to education; in which latter particular he may very likely be not far wrong, for there may well be some men who cannot be educated and made virtuous. But why is such a cause of change peculiar to his ideal state, and not rather common to all states, nay, to everything which comes into being at all? And is it by the agency of time, which, as he declares, makes all things change, that things which did not begin together, change together? For example, if something has come into being the day before the completion of the cycle, will it change with things that came into being before? Further, why should the perfect state change into the Spartan?[1] For governments more often take an opposite form than one akin to them. The same remark is applicable to the other changes; he says that the Spartan constitution changes into an oligarchy, and this into a democracy, and this again into a tyranny. And yet the contrary happens quite as often; for a democracy is even more likely to change into an oligarchy than into a monarchy. Further, he never says whether tyranny is, or is not, liable to revolutions, and if it is, what is the cause of them, or into what form it changes. And the reason is, that he could not very well have told: for there is no rule; according to him it should revert to the first and best, and then there would be a complete cycle. But in point of fact a tyranny often changes into a tyranny, as that at Sicyon changed from the tyranny of Myron into that of Cleisthenes; into oligarchy, as the tyranny of Antileon did at Chalcis; into democracy, as that of Gelo's family did at Syracuse; into aristocracy, as at Carthage, and the tyranny of Charilaus at Lacedaemon. Often an oligarchy changes into a tyranny, like most of the ancient oligarchies in Sicily; for example, the oligarchy at Leontini changed into the tyranny of Panaetius; that at Gela into the tyranny of Cleander; that at Rhegium into the tyranny of Anaxilaus; the same thing has happened in many other states. And it is absurd to suppose that the state changes into oligarchy merely because the **1316b** ruling class are lovers and makers of money,[2] and not because the very rich think it unfair that the very poor should have an equal share in the government with themselves. Moreover, in many oligarchies there are laws against making money in trade. But at Carthage, which is a democracy, there is no such prohibition; and yet to this day the Carthaginians have never had a revolution. It is absurd too for him to say that an oligarchy is two cities, one of the rich, and the other of the poor.[3] Is not this just as much the case in the Spartan constitution, or in any other in which either all do not possess equal property, or all are not equally good men? Nobody need be any poorer than he was before, and yet the oligarchy may change all the same into a democracy, if the poor form the majority; and a democracy may change into an oligarchy, if the wealthy class are stronger than the people, and the one are energetic, the other indifferent. Once more, although the causes of the change are very numerous, he mentions only one[4], which is, that the citizens become poor through dissipation and debt, as though he thought that all, or the majority of them, were originally rich. This is not true: though it is true that when any of the leaders lose their property they are ripe for revolution; but, when anybody else, it is no great matter, and an oligarchy does not even then more often pass into a democracy than into any other form of government. Again, if men are deprived of the honours of state, and are wronged, and insulted, they make revolutions, and change forms of government, even although they have not wasted their substance because they might do what they liked—of which extravagance he declares excessive freedom to be the cause.[5]

Finally, although there are many forms of oligarchies and democracies, Socrates speaks of their revolutions as though there were only one form of either of them.

[1] *Republic*, VIII. 544.

[2] *Ibid.*, 550.

[3] *Ibid.*, 551.

[4] *Ibid.*, 555.

[5] *Ibid.*, 557, 564.

BOOK VI

1

We have now considered the varieties of the deliberative or supreme power in states, and the various arrangements of law-courts and state offices, and which of them are adapted to different forms of government.[1] We have also spoken of the destruction and preservation of constitutions, how and from what causes they arise.[2]

Of democracy and all other forms of government there are many kinds; and it will be well to assign to them severally the modes of organization which are proper and advantageous to each, adding what remains to be said about them. Moreover, we ought to consider the **1317a** various combinations of these modes themselves; for such combinations make constitutions overlap one another, so that aristocracies have an oligarchical character, and constitutional governments incline to democracies.

When I speak of the combinations which remain to be considered, and thus far have not been considered by us, I mean such as these:—when the deliberative part of the government and the election of officers is constituted oligarchically, and the law-courts aristocratically, or when the courts and the deliberative part of the state are oligarchical, and the election to offices aristocratical, or when in any other way there is a want of harmony in the composition of a state.

I have shown already[3] what forms of democracy are suited to particular cities, and what of oligarchy to particular peoples, and to whom each of the other forms of government is suited. Further, we must not only show which of these governments is the best for each state, but also briefly proceed to consider how these and other forms of government are to be established.

First of all let us speak of democracy, which will also bring to light the opposite form of government commonly called oligarchy. For the purposes of this inquiry we need to ascertain all the elements and characteristics of democracy, since from the combinations of these the varieties of democratic government arise. There are several of these differing from each other, and the difference is due to two causes. One (1) has been already mentioned,[4]—differences of population; for the popular element may consist of husbandmen, or of mechanics, or of labourers, and if the first of these be added to the second, or the third to the two others, not only does the democracy become better or worse, but its very nature is changed. A second cause (2) remains to be mentioned: the various properties and characteristics of democracy, when variously combined, make a difference. For one democracy will have less and another will have more, and another will have all of these characteristics. There is an advantage in knowing them all, whether a man wishes to establish some new form of democracy, or only to remodel an existing one. Founders of states try to bring together all the elements which accord with the ideas of the several constitutions; but this is a mistake of theirs, as I have already remarked[5] when speaking of the destruction and preservation of states. We will now set forth the principles, characteristics, and aims of such states.

2

The basis of a democratic state is liberty; which, according to the common opinion of men, can only be enjoyed in such a state:—**1317b** this they affirm to be the great end of every democracy. One principle of liberty is for all to rule and be ruled in turn, and indeed democratic justice is the application of numerical not proportionate equality; whence it follows that the majority must be supreme, and that whatever the majority approve must be the end and the just. Every citizen, it is said, must have equality, and therefore in a democracy the poor have more power than the rich, because there are more of them, and the will of the majority is supreme. This, then, is one note of liberty which all democrats affirm to be the principle of their state. Another is that a man should live as he likes. This, they say, is the privilege of a freeman, since, on the other hand, not to live as a man likes is the mark of a slave. This is the second characteristic of democracy, whence has arisen the claim of men to be ruled by none, if possible, or, if this is impossible, to rule and be ruled in turns; and so it contributes to the freedom based upon equality.

[1] IV. 14-16. [2] V. [3] IV. 12.
[4] IV. 1291b 17-28, 1292b 25 sqq., 1296b 26-31.
[5] V. 1309b 18-1310a 36.

Such being our foundation and such the principle from which we start, the characteristics of democracy are as follows:—the election of officers by all out of all; and that all should rule over each, and each in his turn over all; that the appointment to all offices, or to all but those which require experience and skill, should be made by lot; that no property qualification should be required for offices, or only a very low one; that a man should not hold the same office twice, or not often, or in the case of few except military offices: that the tenure of all offices, or of as many as possible, should be brief; that all men should sit in judgement, or that judges selected out of all should judge, in all matters, or in most and in the greatest and most important,—such as the scrutiny of accounts, the constitution, and private contracts; that the assembly should be supreme over all causes, or at any rate over the most important, and the magistrates over none or only over a very few. Of all magistracies, a council is the most democratic when there is not the means of paying all the citizens, but when they are paid even this is robbed of its power; for the people then draw all cases to themselves, as I said in the previous discussion.[1] The next characteristic of democracy is payment for services; assembly, law-courts, magistrates, everybody receives pay, when it is to be had; or when it is not to be had for all, then it is given to the law-courts and to the stated assemblies, to the council and to the magistrates, or at least to any of them who are compelled to have their meals together. And whereas oligarchy is characterized by birth, wealth, and education, the notes of democracy appear to be the opposite of these,—low birth, poverty, mean employment. Another note is that no magistracy is perpetual, but **1318a** if any such have survived some ancient change in the constitution it should be stripped of its power, and the holders should be elected by lot and no longer by vote. These are the points common to all democracies; but democracy and demos in their truest form are based upon the recognized principle of democratic justice, that all should count equally; for equality implies that the poor should have no more share in the government than the rich, and should not be the only rulers, but that all should rule equally according to their numbers. And in this way men think that they will secure equality and freedom in their state.

[1] Cf. IV. 1299b 38.

3

Next comes the question, how is this equality to be obtained? Are we to assign to a thousand poor men the property qualifications of five hundred rich men? and shall we give the thousand a power equal to that of the five hundred? or, if this is not to be the mode, ought we, still retaining the same ratio, to take equal numbers from each and give them the control of the elections and of the courts?—Which, according to the democratical notion, is the juster form of the constitution,—this or one based on numbers only? Democrats say that justice is that to which the majority agree, oligarchs that to which the wealthier class; in their opinion the decision should be given according to the amount of property. In both principles there is some inequality and injustice. For if justice is the will of the few, any one person who has more wealth than all the rest of the rich put together, ought, upon the oligarchical principle, to have the sole power—but this would be tyranny; or if justice is the will of the majority, as I was before saying,[2] they will unjustly confiscate the property of the wealthy minority. To find a principle of equality in which they both agree we must inquire into their respective ideas of justice.

Now they agree in saying that whatever is decided by the majority of the citizens is to be deemed law. Granted:—but not without some reserve; since there are two classes out of which a state is composed,—the poor and the rich,—that is to be deemed law, on which both or the greater part of both agree; and if they disagree, that which is approved by the greater number, and by those who have the higher qualification. For example, suppose that there are ten rich and twenty poor, and some measure is approved by six of the rich and is disapproved by fifteen of the poor, and the remaining four of the rich join with the party of the poor, and the remaining five of the poor with that of the rich; in such a case the will of those whose qualifications, when both sides are added up, are the greatest, should prevail. If they turn out to be equal, there is no greater difficulty than at present, when, if the assembly or the courts are divided, recourse is had **1318b** to the lot, or to some similar expedient. But, although it may be difficult in theory to know what is just and equal, the practical difficulty of inducing those to forbear who can, if they like, encroach, is far greater, for the weak-

[2] Cf. III. 1281a 14.

er are always asking for equality and justice, but the stronger care for none of these things.

4

Of the four kinds of democracy, as was said in the previous discussion,[1] the best is that which comes first in order; it is also the oldest of them all. I am speaking of them according to the natural classification of their inhabitants. For the best material of democracy is an agricultural population; there is no difficulty in forming a democracy where the mass of the people live by agriculture or tending of cattle. Being poor, they have no leisure, and therefore do not often attend the assembly, and not having the necessaries of life they are always at work, and do not covet the property of others. Indeed, they find their employment pleasanter than the cares of government or office where no great gains can be made out of them, for the many are more desirous of gain than of honour. A proof is that even the ancient tyrannies were patiently endured by them, as they still endure oligarchies, if they are allowed to work and are not deprived of their property; for some of them grow quickly rich and the others are well enough off. Moreover, they have the power of electing the magistrates and calling them to account; their ambition, if they have any, is thus satisfied; and in some democracies, although they do not all share in the appointment of offices, except through representatives elected in turn out of the whole people, as at Mantinea;—yet, if they have the power of deliberating, the many are contented. Even this form of government may be regarded as a democracy, and was such at Mantinea. Hence it is both expedient and customary in the afore-mentioned[2] type of democracy that all should elect to offices, and conduct scrutinies, and sit in the law-courts, but that the great offices should be filled up by election and from persons having a qualification; the greater requiring a greater qualification, or, if there be no offices for which a qualification is required, then those who are marked out by special ability should be appointed. Under such a form of government the citizens are sure to be governed well (for the offices will always be held by the best persons; the people are willing enough to elect them and are not jealous of the good). The good and the notables will then be satisfied, for they will not be governed by men who are their inferiors, and the persons elected will rule justly, because others will call them to account. Every man should be responsible to others, nor should any one be allowed to do just as he pleases; for where absolute freedom is allowed there is nothing to restrain the evil which is inherent in every man. But **1319^a** the principle of responsibility secures that which is the greatest good in states; the right persons rule and are prevented from doing wrong, and the people have their due. It is evident that this is the best kind of democracy, and why? because the people are drawn from a certain class. Some of the ancient laws of most states were, all of them, useful with a view to making the people husbandmen. They provided either that no one should possess more than a certain quantity of land, or that, if he did, the land should not be within a certain distance from the town or the acropolis. Formerly in many states there was a law forbidding any one to sell his original allotment of land. There is a similar law attributed to Oxylus, which is to the effect that there should be a certain portion of every man's land on which he could not borrow money. A useful corrective to the evil of which I am speaking would be the law of the Aphytaeans, who, although they are numerous, and do not possess much land, are all of them husbandmen. For their properties are reckoned in the census, not entire, but only in such small portions that even the poor may have more than the amount required.

Next best to an agricultural, and in many respects similar, are a pastoral people, who live by their flocks; they are the best trained of any for war, robust in body and able to camp out. The people of whom other democracies consist are far inferior to them, for their life is inferior; there is no room for moral excellence in any of their employments, whether they be mechanics or traders or labourers. Besides, people of this class can readily come to the assembly, because they are continually moving about in the city and in the agora; whereas husbandmen are scattered over the country and do not meet, or equally feel the want of assembling together. Where the territory also happens to extend to a distance from the city, there is no difficulty in making an excellent democracy or constitutional government; for the people are compelled to settle in the country, and even if there is a town population the assembly ought not to meet, in democracies, when the country peo-

[1] iv. 1292^b 22-1293^a 10. [2] l. 6.

ple cannot come. We have thus explained how the first and best form of democracy should be constituted; it is clear that the other or in-
1319b ferior sorts will deviate in a regular order, and the population which is excluded will at each stage be of a lower kind.

The last form of democracy, that in which all share alike, is one which cannot be borne by all states, and will not last long unless well regulated by laws and customs. The more general causes which tend to destroy this or other kinds of government have been pretty fully considered.[1] In order to constitute such a democracy and strengthen the people, the leaders have been in the habit of including as many as they can, and making citizens not only of those who are legitimate, but even of the illegitimate, and of those who have only one parent a citizen, whether father or mother; for nothing of this sort comes amiss to such a democracy. This is the way in which demagogues proceed. Whereas the right thing would be to make no more additions when the number of the commonalty exceeds that of the notables and of the middle class,—beyond this not to go. When in excess of this point, the constitution becomes disorderly, and the notables grow excited and impatient of the democracy, as in the insurrection at Cyrene; for no notice is taken of a little evil, but when it increases it strikes the eye. Measures like those which Cleisthenes passed when he wanted to increase the power of the democracy at Athens, or such as were taken by the founders of popular government at Cyrene, are useful in the extreme form of democracy. Fresh tribes and brotherhoods should be established; the private rites of families should be restricted and converted into public ones; in short, every contrivance should be adopted which will mingle the citizens with one another and get rid of old connexions. Again, the measures which are taken by tyrants appear all of them to be democratic; such, for instance, as the licence permitted to slaves (which may be to a certain extent advantageous) and also that of women and children, and the allowing everybody to live as he likes. Such a government will have many supporters, for most persons would rather live in a disorderly than in a sober manner.

5

The mere establishment of a democracy is not the only or principal business of the legislator, or of those who wish to create such a state, for any state, however badly constituted, may last one, two, or three days; a far greater difficulty is the preservation of it. The legislator should therefore endeavour to have a firm foundation according to the principles already laid down concerning the preservation and destruction of states; he should guard against the destructive elements, and should
1320a make laws, whether written or unwritten, which will contain all the preservatives of states. He must not think the truly democratical or oligarchical measure to be that which will give the greatest amount of democracy or oligarchy, but that which will make them last longest. The demagogues of our own day often get property confiscated in the law-courts in order to please the people. But those who have the welfare of the state at heart should counteract them, and make a law that the property of the condemned should not be public and go into the treasury but be sacred. Thus offenders will be as much afraid, for they will be punished all the same, and the people, having nothing to gain, will not be so ready to condemn the accused. Care should also be taken that state trials are as few as possible, and heavy penalties should be inflicted on those who bring groundless accusations; for it is the practice to indict, not members of the popular party, but the notables, although the citizens ought to be all attached to the constitution as well, or at any rate should not regard their rulers as enemies.

Now, since in the last and worst form of democracy the citizens are very numerous, and can hardly be made to assemble unless they are paid, and to pay them when there are no revenues presses hardly upon the notables (for the money must be obtained by a property-tax and confiscations and corrupt practices of the courts, things which have before now overthrown many democracies); where, I say, there are no revenues, the government should hold few assemblies, and the law-courts should consist of many persons, but sit for a few days only. This system has two advantages: first, the rich do not fear the expense, even although they are unpaid themselves when the poor are paid; and secondly, causes are better tried, for wealthy persons, although they do not like to be long absent from their own affairs, do not mind going for a few days to the law-courts. Where there are revenues the demagogues should not be allowed after their manner to distribute the surplus; the poor are

[1] v. 2-7, 1311a 22-1313a 16.

always receiving and always wanting more and more, for such help is like water poured into a leaky cask. Yet the true friend of the people should see that they be not too poor, for extreme poverty lowers the character of the democracy; measures therefore should be taken which will give them lasting prosperity; and as this is equally the interest of all classes, the proceeds of the public revenues should be accumulated and distributed among its poor, if possible, in such quantities as may enable them to purchase a little farm, or, at any rate,
1320b make a beginning in trade or husbandry. And if this benevolence cannot be extended to all, money should be distributed in turn according to tribes or other divisions, and in the meantime the rich should pay the fee for the attendance of the poor at the necessary assemblies; and should in return be excused from useless public services. By administering the state in this spirit the Carthaginians retain the affections of the people; their policy is from time to time to send some of them into their dependent towns, where they grow rich. It is also worthy of a generous and sensible nobility to divide the poor amongst them, and give them the means of going to work. The example of the people of Tarentum is also well deserving of imitation, for, by sharing the use of their own property with the poor, they gain their good will. Moreover, they divide all their offices into two classes, some of them being elected by vote, the others by lot; the latter, that the people may participate in them, and the former, that the state may be better administered. A like result may be gained by dividing the same offices, so as to have two classes of magistrates, one chosen by vote, the other by lot.

Enough has been said of the manner in which democracies ought to be constituted.

6

From these considerations there will be no difficulty in seeing what should be the constitution of oligarchies. We have only to reason from opposites and compare each form of oligarchy with the corresponding form of democracy.

The first and best attempered of oligarchies is akin to a constitutional government. In this there ought to be two standards of qualification; the one high, the other low—the lower qualifying for the humbler yet indispensable offices and the higher for the superior ones. He who acquires the prescribed qualification should have the rights of citizenship. The number of those admitted should be such as will make the entire governing body stronger than those who are excluded, and the new citizen should be always taken out of the better class of the people. The principle, narrowed a little, gives another form of oligarchy; until at length we reach the most cliquish and tyrannical of them all, answering to the extreme democracy, which, being the worst, requires vigilance in proportion to its badness. For as healthy bodies and ships well provided with sailors may undergo many mishaps and survive them, whereas sickly constitutions and rotten ill-manned ships are ruined by the very least mistake, so do the worst forms of government require the greatest care. The populous-
1321a ness of democracies generally preserves them (for number is to democracy in the place of justice based on proportion); whereas the preservation of an oligarchy clearly depends on an opposite principle, viz. good order.

7

As there are four chief divisions of the common people,—husbandmen, mechanics, retail traders, labourers; so also there are four kinds of military forces,—the cavalry, the heavy infantry, the light-armed troops, the navy. When the country is adapted for cavalry, then a strong oligarchy is likely to be established. For the security of the inhabitants depends upon a force of this sort, and only rich men can afford to keep horses. The second form of oligarchy prevails when the country is adapted to heavy infantry; for this service is better suited to the rich than to the poor. But the light-armed and the naval element are wholly democratic; and nowadays, where they are numerous, if the two parties quarrel, the oligarchy are often worsted by them in the struggle. A remedy for this state of things may be found in the practice of generals who combine a proper contingent of light-armed troops with cavalry and heavy-armed. And this is the way in which the poor get the better of the rich in civil contests; being lightly armed, they fight with advantage against cavalry and heavy infantry. An oligarchy which raises such a force out of the lower classes raises a power against itself. And therefore, since the ages of the citizens vary and some are older and some younger, the fathers should have their own sons, while they are still young, taught the agile movements of light-armed troops; and these, when they have been

taken out of the ranks of the youth, should become light-armed warriors in reality. The oligarchy should also yield a share in the government to the people, either, as I said before, to those who have a property qualification, or, as in the case of Thebes, to those who have abstained for a certain number of years from mean employments, or, as at Massalia, to men of merit who are selected for their worthiness, whether previously citizens or not. The magistracies of the highest rank, which ought to be in the hands of the governing body, should have expensive duties attached to them, and then the people will not desire them and will take no offence at the privileges of their rulers when they see that they pay a heavy fine for their dignity. It is fitting also that the magistrates on entering office should offer magnificent sacrifices or erect some public edifice, and then the people who participate in the entertainments, and see the city decorated with votive offerings and buildings, will not desire an alteration in the government, and the notables will have memorials of the munificence. This, however, is anything but the fashion of our modern oligarchs, who are as covetous of gain as they are of honour; oligar-
1321b chies like theirs may be well described as petty democracies. Enough of the manner in which democracies and oligarchies should be organized.

8

Next in order follows the right distribution of offices, their number, their nature, their duties, of which indeed we have already spoken.[1] No state can exist not having the necessary offices, and no state can be well administered not having the offices which tend to preserve harmony and good order. In small states, as we have already remarked,[2] there must not be many of them, but in larger there must be a larger number, and we should carefully consider which offices may properly be united and which separated.

First among necessary offices is that which has the care of the market; a magistrate should be appointed to inspect contracts and to maintain order. For in every state there must inevitably be buyers and sellers who will supply one another's wants; this is the readiest way to make a state self-sufficing and so fulfil the purpose for which men come together into one state. A second office of a similar kind undertakes the supervision and embellishment of public and private buildings, the maintaining and repairing of houses and roads, the prevention of disputes about boundaries, and other concerns of a like nature. This is commonly called the office of City-warden, and has various departments, which, in more populous towns, are shared among different persons, one, for example, taking charge of the walls, another of the fountains, a third of harbours. There is another equally necessary office, and of a similar kind, having to do with the same matters without the walls and in the country:—the magistrates who hold this office are called Wardens of the country, or Inspectors of the woods. Besides these three there is a fourth office of receivers of taxes, who have under their charge the revenue which is distributed among the various departments; these are called Receivers or Treasurers. Another officer registers all private contracts, and decisions of the courts, all public indictments, and also all preliminary proceedings. This office again is sometimes subdivided, in which case one officer is appointed over all the rest. These officers are called Recorders or Sacred Recorders, Presidents, and the like.

Next to these comes an office of which the duties are the most necessary and also the most difficult, viz. that to which is committed the execution of punishments, or the exaction of fines from those who are posted up according
1322a to the registers; and also the custody of prisoners. The difficulty of this office arises out of the odium which is attached to it; no one will undertake it unless great profits are to be made, and any one who does is loath to execute the law. Still the office is necessary; for judicial decisions are useless if they take no effect; and if society cannot exist without them, neither can it exist without the execution of them. It is an office which, being so unpopular, should not be entrusted to one person, but divided among several taken from different courts. In like manner an effort should be made to distribute among different persons the writing up of those who are on the register of public debtors. Some sentences should be executed by the magistrates also, and in particular penalties due to the outgoing magistrates should be exacted by the incoming ones; and as regards those due to magistrates already in office, when one court has given judgement, another should exact the penalty; for example, the wardens of the city should exact the fines imposed by the wardens of the agora, and others again should exact the fines imposed by

[1] IV. 15. [2] IV. 1299a 34-b 10.

them. For penalties are more likely to be exacted when less odium attaches to the exaction of them; but a double odium is incurred when the judges who have passed also execute the sentence, and if they are always the executioners, they will be the enemies of all.

In many places, while one magistracy executes the sentence, another has the custody of the prisoners, as, for example, 'the Eleven' at Athens. It is well to separate off the jailorship also, and try by some device to render the office less unpopular. For it is quite as necessary as that of the executioners; but good men do all they can to avoid it, and worthless persons cannot safely be trusted with it; for they themselves require a guard, and are not fit to guard others. There ought not therefore to be a single or permanent officer set apart for this duty; but it should be entrusted to the young, wherever they are organized into a band or guard, and different magistrates acting in turn should take charge of it.

These are the indispensable officers, and should be ranked first:—next in order follow others, equally necessary, but of higher rank, and requiring great experience and fidelity. Such are the offices to which are committed the guard of the city, and other military functions. Not only in time of war but of peace their duty will be to defend the walls and gates, and to muster and marshal the citizens. In some states there are many such offices; in others there are a few only, while small states are content with one; these officers are called generals or commanders. Again, if a state has
1322b cavalry or light-armed troops or archers or a naval force, it will sometimes happen that each of these departments has separate officers, who are called admirals, or generals of cavalry or of light-armed troops. And there are subordinate officers called naval captains, and captains of light-armed troops and of horse; having others under them:—all these are included in the department of war. Thus much of military command.

But since many, not to say all, of these offices handle the public money, there must of necessity be another office which examines and audits them, and has no other functions. Such officers are called by various names,—Scrutineers, Auditors, Accountants, Controllers. Besides all these offices there is another which is supreme over them, and to this is often entrusted both the introduction and the ratification of measures, or at all events it presides, in a democracy, over the assembly. For there must be a body which convenes the supreme authority in the state. In some places they are called 'probuli', because they hold previous deliberations, but in a democracy more commonly 'councillors'. These are the chief political offices.

Another set of officers is concerned with the maintenance of religion; priests and guardians see to the preservation and repair of the temples of the gods and to other matters of religion. One office of this sort may be enough in small places, but in larger ones there are a great many besides the priesthood; for example superintendents of public worship, guardians of shrines, treasurers of the sacred revenues. Nearly connected with these there are also the officers appointed for the performance of the public sacrifices, except any which the law assigns to the priests; such sacrifices derive their dignity from the public hearth of the city. They are sometimes called archons, sometimes kings, and sometimes prytanes.

These, then, are the necessary offices, which may be summed up as follows: offices concerned with matters of religion, with war, with the revenue and expenditure, with the market, with the city, with the harbours, with the country; also with the courts of law, with the records of contracts, with execution of sentences, with custody of prisoners, with audits and scrutinies and accounts of magistrates; lastly, there are those which preside over the public deliberations of the state. There are likewise magistracies characteristic of states which are peaceful and prosperous, and at the same time have a regard to good order: such as the offices of guardians of women, guardians of the laws, guardians of children, and direc-
1323a tors of gymnastics; also superintendents of gymnastic and Dionysiac contests, and of other similar spectacles. Some of these are clearly not democratic offices; for example, the guardianships of women and children—the poor, not having any slaves, must employ both their women and children as servants.

Once more: there are three offices according to whose directions the highest magistrates are chosen in certain states—guardians of the law, probuli, councillors,—of these, the guardians of the law are an aristocratical, the probuli an oligarchical, the council a democratical institution. Enough of the different kinds of offices.

BOOK VII

I

He who would duly inquire about the best form of a state ought first to determine which is the most eligible life; while this remains uncertain the best form of the state must also be uncertain; for, in the natural order of things, those may be expected to lead the best life who are governed in the best manner of which their circumstances admit. We ought therefore to ascertain, first of all, which is the most generally eligible life, and then whether the same life is or is not best for the state and for individuals.

Assuming that enough has been already said in discussions outside the school concerning the best life, we will now only repeat what is contained in them. Certainly no one will dispute the propriety of that partition of goods which separates them into three classes, viz. external goods, goods of the body, and goods of the soul, or deny that the happy man must have all three. For no one would maintain that he is happy who has not in him a particle of courage or temperance or justice or prudence, who is afraid of every insect which flutters past him, and will commit any crime, however great, in order to gratify his lust of meat or drink, who will sacrifice his dearest friend for the sake of half-a-farthing, and is as feeble and false in mind as a child or a madman. These propositions are almost universally acknowledged as soon as they are uttered, but men differ about the degree or relative superiority of this or that good. Some think that a very moderate amount of virtue is enough, but set no limit to their desires of wealth, property, power, reputation, and the like. To whom we reply by an appeal to facts, which easily prove that mankind do not acquire or preserve virtue by the help of external goods, but exter- **1323b** nal goods by the help of virtue, and that happiness, whether consisting in pleasure or virtue, or both, is more often found with those who are most highly cultivated in their mind and in their character, and have only a moderate share of external goods, than among those who possess external goods to a useless extent but are deficient in higher qualities; and this is not only matter of experience, but, if reflected upon, will easily appear to be in accordance with reason. For, whereas external goods have a limit, like any other instrument, and all things useful are of such a nature that where there is too much of them they must either do harm, or at any rate be of no use, to their possessors, every good of the soul, the greater it is, is also of greater use, if the epithet useful as well as noble is appropriate to such subjects. No proof is required to show that the best state of one thing in relation to another corresponds in degree of excellence to the interval between the natures of which we say that these very states are states: so that, if the soul is more noble than our possessions or our bodies, both absolutely and in relation to us, it must be admitted that the best state of either has a similar ratio to the other. Again, it is for the sake of the soul that goods external and goods of the body are eligible at all, and all wise men ought to choose them for the sake of the soul, and not the soul for the sake of them.

Let us acknowledge then that each one has just so much of happiness as he has of virtue and wisdom, and of virtuous and wise action. God is a witness to us of this truth, for he is happy and blessed, not by reason of any external good, but in himself and by reason of his own nature. And herein of necessity lies the difference between good fortune and happiness; for external goods come of themselves, and chance is the author of them, but no one is just or temperate by or through chance. In like manner, and by a similar train of argument, the happy state may be shown to be that which is best and which acts rightly; and rightly it cannot act without doing right actions, and neither individual nor state can do right actions without virtue and wisdom. Thus the courage, justice, and wisdom of a state have the same form and nature as the qualities which give the individual who possesses them the name of just, wise, or temperate.

Thus much may suffice by way of preface: for I could not avoid touching upon these questions, neither could I go through all the arguments affecting them; these are the business of another science.

Let us assume then that the best life, both for individuals and states, is the life of virtue, when virtue has external goods enough for the **1324a** performance of good actions. If there are any who controvert our assertion, we will in this treatise pass them over, and consider their objections hereafter.

2

There remains to be discussed the question, Whether the happiness of the individual is the same as that of the state, or different? Here again there can be no doubt—no one denies that they are the same. For those who hold that the well-being of the individual consists in his wealth, also think that riches make the happiness of the whole state, and those who value most highly the life of a tyrant deem that city the happiest which rules over the greatest number; while they who approve an individual for his virtue say that the more virtuous a city is, the happier it is. Two points here present themselves for consideration: first (1), which is the more eligible life, that of a citizen who is a member of a state, or that of an alien who has no political ties; and again (2), which is the best form of constitution or the best condition of a state, either on the supposition that political privileges are desirable for all, or for a majority only? Since the good of the state and not of the individual is the proper subject of political thought and speculation, and we are engaged in a political discussion, while the first of these two points has a secondary interest for us, the latter will be the main subject of our inquiry.

Now it is evident that the form of government is best in which every man, whoever he is, can act best and live happily. But even those who agree in thinking that the life of virtue is the most eligible raise a question, whether the life of business and politics is or is not more eligible than one which is wholly independent of external goods, I mean than a contemplative life, which by some is maintained to be the only one worthy of a philosopher. For these two lives—the life of the philosopher and the life of the statesman—appear to have been preferred by those who have been most keen in the pursuit of virtue, both in our own and in other ages. Which is the better is a question of no small moment; for the wise man, like the wise state, will necessarily regulate his life according to the best end. There are some who think that while a despotic rule over others is the greatest injustice, to exercise a constitutional rule over them, even though not unjust, is a great impediment to a man's individual well-being. Others take an opposite view; they maintain that the true life of man is the practical and political, and that every virtue admits of being practised, quite as much by **1324b** statesmen and rulers as by private individuals. Others, again, are of opinion that arbitrary and tyrannical rule alone consists with happiness; indeed, in some states the entire aim both of the laws and of the constitution is to give men despotic power over their neighbours. And, therefore, although in most cities the laws may be said generally to be in a chaotic state, still, if they aim at anything, they aim at the maintenance of power: thus in Lacedaemon and Crete the system of education and the greater part of the laws are framed with a view to war. And in all nations which are able to gratify their ambition military power is held in esteem, for example among the Scythians and Persians and Thracians and Celts. In some nations there are even laws tending to stimulate the warlike virtues, as at Carthage, where we are told that men obtain the honour of wearing as many armlets as they have served campaigns. There was once a law in Macedonia that he who had not killed an enemy should wear a halter, and among the Scythians no one who had not slain his man was allowed to drink out of the cup which was handed round at a certain feast. Among the Iberians, a warlike nation, the number of enemies whom a man has slain is indicated by the number of obelisks which are fixed in the earth round his tomb; and there are numerous practices among other nations of a like kind, some of them established by law and others by custom. Yet to a reflecting mind it must appear very strange that the statesman should be always considering how he can dominate and tyrannize over others, whether they will or not. How can that which is not even lawful be the business of the statesman or the legislator? Unlawful it certainly is to rule without regard to justice, for there may be might where there is no right. The other arts and sciences offer no parallel; a physician is not expected to persuade or coerce his patients, nor a pilot the passengers in his ship. Yet most men appear to think that the art of despotic government is statesmanship, and what men affirm to be unjust and inexpedient in their own case they are not ashamed of practising towards others; they demand just rule for themselves, but where other men are concerned they care nothing about it. Such behaviour is irrational; unless the one party is, and the other is not, born to serve, in which case men have a right to command, not indeed all their fellows, but only those who are intended to be subjects; just as we ought not to hunt mankind, whether for food or sacrifice, but only the animals which may be hunted for food or sacrifice, that is to say, such wild animals as are eatable. And surely there may be a city happy in isolation, **1325a** which we will assume to be well-governed (for it is quite possible that a city thus isolated might be well-administered and have good laws); but such a city would not be constituted with any view to war or the conquest of enemies,—all that sort of thing must be excluded. Hence we see very plainly that warlike pursuits, although generally to be deemed honourable, are not the supreme end of all things, but only means. And the good lawgiver should inquire how states and races of men and communities may participate in a good life, and in the happiness which is attainable by them. His enactments will not be always the same; and where there are neighbours he will have to see what sort of studies should be practised in relation to their several characters, or how the measures appropriate in relation to each are to be adopted. The end at which the best form of government should aim may be properly made a matter of future consideration.[1]

3

Let us now address those who, while they agree that the life of virtue is the most eligible, differ about the manner of practising it. For some renounce political power, and think that the life of the freeman is different from the life of the statesman and the best of all; but others think the life of the statesman best. The argument of the latter is that he who does nothing cannot do well, and that virtuous activity is identical with happiness. To both we say: 'you are partly right and partly wrong.' The first class are right in affirming that the life of the freeman is better than the life of the despot; for there is nothing grand or noble in having the use of a slave, in so far as he is a slave; or in issuing commands about necessary things. But it is an error to suppose that every sort of rule is despotic like that of a master over slaves, for there is as great a difference between the rule over freemen and the rule over slaves as there is between slavery by nature and freedom by nature, about which I have said enough at the commencement of this treatise.[2] And it is equally a mistake to place inactivity above action, for happiness is activity, and the actions of the just and wise are the realization of much that is noble.

But perhaps some one, accepting these premisses, may still maintain that supreme power is the best of all things, because the possessors of it are able to perform the greatest number of noble actions. If so, the man who is able to rule, instead of giving up anything to his neighbour, ought rather to take away his power; and the father should make no account of his son, nor the son of his father, nor friend of friend; they should not bestow a thought on one another in comparison with this higher object, for the best is the most eligible and 'doing well' is the best. There might be some truth in such a view if we assume that robbers **1325b** and plunderers attain the chief good. But this can never be; their hypothesis is false. For the actions of a ruler cannot really be honourable, unless he is as much superior to other men as a husband is to a wife, or a father to his children, or a master to his slaves. And therefore he who violates the law can never recover by any success, however great, what he has already lost in departing from virtue. For equals the honourable and the just consist in sharing alike, as is just and equal. But that the unequal should be given to equals, and the unlike to those who are like, is contrary to nature, and nothing which is contrary to nature is good. If, therefore, there is any one superior in virtue and in the power of performing the best actions, him we ought to follow and obey, but he must have the capacity for action as well as virtue.

If we are right in our view, and happiness is assumed to be virtuous activity, the active life will be the best, both for every city collectively, and for individuals. Not that a life of action must necessarily have relation to others, as some persons think, nor are those ideas only to be regarded as practical which are pursued for the sake of practical results, but much more the thoughts and contemplations which are independent and complete in themselves; since virtuous activity, and therefore a certain kind of action, is an end, and even in the case of external actions the directing mind is most truly said to act. Neither, again, is it necessary that states which are cut off from others and choose to live alone should be inactive; for activity, as well as other things, may take place by sections; there are many ways in which the sections of a state act upon one another. The same thing is equally true of every individual. If this were otherwise, God and the universe, who have no external actions over and above their own energies, would be far enough from perfection. Hence it is evident that the

[1] 1333a 11 sqq. [2] I. 4-7.

same life is best for each individual, and for states and for mankind collectively.

4

Thus far by way of introduction. In what has preceded[1] I have discussed other forms of government; in what remains the first point to be considered is what should be the conditions of the ideal or perfect state; for the perfect state cannot exist without a due supply of the means of life. And therefore we must presuppose many purely imaginary conditions, but nothing impossible. There will be a certain number of citizens, a country in which to place them, and the like. As the weaver or shipbuilder or any other artisan must have the ma- **1326a** terial proper for his work (and in proportion as this is better prepared, so will the result of his art be nobler), so the statesman or legislator must also have the materials suited to him.

First among the materials required by the statesman is population: he will consider what should be the number and character of the citizens, and then what should be the size and character of the country. Most persons think that a state in order to be happy ought to be large; but even if they are right, they have no idea what is a large and what a small state. For they judge of the size of the city by the number of the inhabitants; whereas they ought to regard, not their number, but their power. A city too, like an individual, has a work to do; and that city which is best adapted to the fulfilment of its work is to be deemed greatest, in the same sense of the word great in which Hippocrates might be called greater, not as a man, but as a physician, than some one else who was taller. And even if we reckon greatness by numbers, we ought not to include everybody, for there must always be in cities a multitude of slaves and sojourners and foreigners; but we should include those only who are members of the state, and who form an essential part of it. The number of the latter is a proof of the greatness of a city; but a city which produces numerous artisans and comparatively few soldiers cannot be great, for a great city is not to be confounded with a populous one. Moreover, experience shows that a very populous city can rarely, if ever, be well governed; since all cities which have a reputation for good government have a limit of population. We may argue on grounds of reason, and the same result will follow. For law is order, and good law is good order; but a very great multitude cannot be orderly: to introduce order into the unlimited is the work of a divine power—of such a power as holds together the universe. Beauty is realized in number and magnitude, and the state which combines magnitude with good order must necessarily be the most beautiful. To the size of states there is a limit, as there is to other things, plants, animals, implements; for none of these retain their natural power when they are too large or too small, but they either wholly lose their nature, or are spoiled. For example, a ship which is only a span long will not be a ship at all, nor a ship a quarter of a mile long; yet there may **1326b** be a ship of a certain size, either too large or too small, which will still be a ship, but bad for sailing. In like manner a state when composed of too few is not, as a state ought to be, self-sufficing; when of too many, though self-sufficing in all mere necessaries, as a nation may be, it is not a state, being almost incapable of constitutional government. For who can be the general of such a vast multitude, or who the herald, unless he have the voice of a Stentor?

A state, then, only begins to exist when it has attained a population sufficient for a good life in the political community: it may indeed, if it somewhat exceed this number, be a greater state. But, as I was saying, there must be a limit. What should be the limit will be easily ascertained by experience. For both governors and governed have duties to perform; the special functions of a governor are to command and to judge. But if the citizens of a state are to judge and to distribute offices according to merit, then they must know each other's characters; where they do not possess this knowledge, both the election to offices and the decision of lawsuits will go wrong. When the population is very large they are manifestly settled at haphazard, which clearly ought not to be. Besides, in an over-populous state foreigners and metics will readily acquire the rights of citizens, for who will find them out? Clearly then the best limit of the population of a state is the largest number which suffices for the purposes of life, and can be taken in at a single view. Enough concerning the size of a state.

5

Much the same principle will apply to the territory of the state: every one would agree in praising the territory which is most entirely

[1] II.

self-sufficing; and that must be the territory which is all-producing, for to have all things and to want nothing is sufficiency. In size and extent it should be such as may enable the inhabitants to live at once temperately and liberally in the enjoyment of leisure. Whether we are right or wrong in laying down this limit we will inquire more precisely hereafter, when we have occasion to consider what is the right use of property and wealth: a matter which is much disputed, because men are inclined to rush into one of two extremes, some into meanness, others into luxury.

It is not difficult to determine the general character of the territory which is required (there are, however, some points on which military authorities should be heard); it should be difficult of access to the enemy, and **1327a** easy of egress to the inhabitants. Further, we require that the land as well as the inhabitants of whom we were just now speaking[1] should be taken in at a single view, for a country which is easily seen can be easily protected. As to the position of the city, if we could have what we wish, it should be well situated in regard both to sea and land. This then is one principle, that it should be a convenient centre for the protection of the whole country: the other is, that it should be suitable for receiving the fruits of the soil, and also for the bringing in of timber and any other products that are easily transported.

6

Whether a communication with the sea is beneficial to a well-ordered state or not is a question which has often been asked. It is argued that the introduction of strangers brought up under other laws, and the increase of population, will be adverse to good order; the increase arises from their using the sea and having a crowd of merchants coming and going, and is inimical to good government. Apart from these considerations, it would be undoubtedly better, both with a view to safety and to the provision of necessaries, that the city and territory should be connected with the sea; the defenders of a country, if they are to maintain themselves against an enemy, should be easily relieved both by land and by sea; and even if they are not able to attack by sea and land at once, they will have less difficulty in doing mischief to their assailants on one element, if they themselves can use both. Moreover, it is necessary that they should import from abroad what is not found in their own country, and that they should export what they have in excess; for a city ought to be a market, not indeed for others, but for herself.

Those who make themselves a market for the world only do so for the sake of revenue, and if a state ought not to desire profit of this kind it ought not to have such an emporium. Nowadays we often see in countries and cities dockyards and harbours very conveniently placed outside the city, but not too far off; and they are kept in dependence by walls and similar fortifications. Cities thus situated manifestly reap the benefit of intercourse with their ports; and any harm which is likely to accrue may be easily guarded against by the laws, which will pronounce and determine who may hold communication with one another, and who may not.

There can be no doubt that the possession of a moderate naval force is advantageous to a **1327b** city; the city should be formidable not only to its own citizens but to some of its neighbours, or, if necessary, able to assist them by sea as well as by land. The proper number or magnitude of this naval force is relative to the character of the state; for if her function is to take a leading part in politics, her naval power should be commensurate with the scale of her enterprises. The population of the state need not be much increased, since there is no necessity that the sailors should be citizens: the marines who have the control and command will be freemen, and belong also to the infantry; and wherever there is a dense population of Perioeci and husbandmen, there will always be sailors more than enough. Of this we see instances at the present day. The city of Heraclea, for example, although small in comparison with many others, can man a considerable fleet. Such are our conclusions respecting the territory of the state, its harbours, its towns, its relations to the sea, and its maritime power.

7

Having spoken of the number of the citizens,[2] we will proceed to speak of what should be their character. This is a subject which can be easily understood by any one who casts his eye on the more celebrated states of Hellas, and generally on the distribution of races in the habitable world. Those who live in a cold climate and in Europe are full of spirit, but wanting in intelligence and skill; and

[1] 1326b 22-24.

[2] 1326a 9-b 24.

therefore they retain comparative freedom, but have no political organization, and are incapable of ruling over others. Whereas the natives of Asia are intelligent and inventive, but they are wanting in spirit, and therefore they are always in a state of subjection and slavery. But the Hellenic race, which is situated between them, is likewise intermediate in character, being high-spirited and also intelligent. Hence it continues free, and is the best-governed of any nation, and, if it could be formed into one state, would be able to rule the world. There are also similar differences in the different tribes of Hellas; for some of them are of a one-sided nature, and are intelligent or courageous only, while in others there is a happy combination of both qualities. And clearly those whom the legislator will most easily lead to virtue may be expected to be both intelligent and courageous. Some[1] say that the guardians should be friendly towards those whom they know, fierce towards those whom they do not know. Now, passion is the quality of the soul which
1328a begets friendship and enables us to love; notably the spirit within us is more stirred against our friends and acquaintances than against those who are unknown to us, when we think that we are despised by them; for which reason Archilochus,[2] complaining of his friends, very naturally addresses his soul in these words,

For surely thou are plagued on account of friends.

The power of command and the love of freedom are in all men based upon this quality, for passion is commanding and invincible. Nor is it right to say that the guardians should be fierce towards those whom they do not know, for we ought not to be out of temper with any one; and a lofty spirit is not fierce by nature, but only when excited against evil-doers. And this, as I was saying before, is a feeling which men show most strongly towards their friends if they think they have received a wrong at their hands: as indeed is reasonable; for, besides the actual injury, they seem to be deprived of a benefit by those who owe them one. Hence the saying,

Cruel is the strife of brethren,[3]

and again,

They who love in excess also hate in excess.[4]

Thus we have nearly determined the number and character of the citizens of our state, and also the size and nature of their territory. I say 'nearly', for we ought not to require the same minuteness in theory as in the facts given by perception.

8

As in other natural compounds the conditions of a composite whole are not necessarily organic parts of it, so in a state or in any other combination forming a unity not everything is a part, which is a necessary condition. The members of an association have necessarily some one thing the same and common to all, in which they share equally or unequally; for example, food or land or any other thing. But where there are two things of which one is a means and the other an end, they have nothing in common except that the one receives what the other produces. Such, for example, is the relation in which workmen and tools stand to their work; the house and the builder have nothing in common, but the art of the builder is for the sake of the house. And so states require property, but property, even though living beings are included in it, is no part of a state; for a state is not a community of living beings only, but a community of equals, aiming at the best life possible. Now, whereas happiness is the highest good, being a realization and perfect practice of virtue, which some can attain, while others have little or none of it, the various qualities of men are clearly the reason why there are various kinds of states and many forms of government; for different men seek after happiness
1328b in different ways and by different means, and so make for themselves different modes of life and forms of government. We must see also how many things are indispensable to the existence of a state, for what we call the parts of a state will be found among the indispensables. Let us then enumerate the functions of a state, and we shall easily elicit what we want:

First, there must be food; secondly, arts, for life requires many instruments; thirdly, there must be arms, for the members of a community have need of them, and in their own hands, too, in order to maintain authority both against disobedient subjects and against external assailants; fourthly, there must be a certain amount of revenue, both for internal needs, and for the purposes of war; fifthly, or rather first, there must be a care of religion, which is commonly called worship; sixthly, and most necessary of all, there must be a

[1] *Republic* II. 375. [2] Fr. 67, Bergk.
[3] Euripides, fr. 975, Nauck. [4] Fr. adesp. 78, Nauck.

power of deciding what is for the public interest, and what is just in men's dealings with one another.

These are the services which every state may be said to need. For a state is not a mere aggregate of persons, but a union of them sufficing for the purposes of life; and if any of these things be wanting, it is as we maintain impossible that the community can be absolutely self-sufficing. A state then should be framed with a view to the fulfilment of these functions. There must be husbandmen to procure food, and artisans, and a warlike and a wealthy class, and priests, and judges to decide what is necessary and expedient.

9

Having determined these points, we have in the next place to consider whether all ought to share in every sort of occupation. Shall every man be at once husbandman, artisan, councillor, judge, or shall we suppose the several occupations just mentioned assigned to different persons? or, thirdly, shall some employments be assigned to individuals and others common to all? The same arrangement, however, does not occur in every constitution; as we were saying, all may be shared by all, or not all by all, but only some by some; and hence arise the differences of constitutions, for in democracies all share in all, in oligarchies the opposite practice prevails. Now, since we are here speaking of the best form of government, i.e. that under which the state will be most happy (and happiness, as has been already said, cannot exist without virtue), it clearly follows that in the state which is best governed and possesses men who are just absolutely, and not merely relatively to the principle of the constitution, the citizens must not lead the life of mechanics or tradesmen, for such a life is ignoble and inimical to virtue. Neither must they be husband-
1329a men, since leisure is necessary both for the development of virtue and the performance of political duties.

Again, there is in a state a class of warriors, and another of councillors, who advise about the expedient and determine matters of law, and these seem in an especial manner parts of a state. Now, should these two classes be distinguished, or are both functions to be assigned to the same persons? Here again there is no difficulty in seeing that both functions will in one way belong to the same, in another, to different persons. To different persons in so far as these employments are suited to different primes of life, for the one requires wisdom and the other strength. But on the other hand, since it is an impossible thing that those who are able to use or to resist force should be willing to remain always in subjection, from this point of view the persons are the same; for those who carry arms can always determine the fate of the constitution. It remains therefore that both functions should be entrusted by the ideal constitution to the same persons, not, however, at the same time, but in the order prescribed by nature, who has given to young men strength and to older men wisdom. Such a distribution of duties will be expedient and also just, and is founded upon a principle of conformity to merit. Besides, the ruling class should be the owners of property, for they are citizens, and the citizens of a state should be in good circumstances; whereas mechanics or any other class which is not a producer of virtue have no share in the state. This follows from our first principle, for happiness cannot exist without virtue, and a city is not to be termed happy in regard to a portion of the citizens, but in regard to them all. And clearly property should be in their hands, since the husbandmen will of necessity be slaves or barbarian Perioeci.

Of the classes enumerated there remain only the priests, and the manner in which their office is to be regulated is obvious. No husbandman or mechanic should be appointed to it; for the Gods should receive honour from the citizens only. Now since the body of the citizens is divided into two classes, the warriors and the councillors, and it is beseeming that the worship of the Gods should be duly performed, and also a rest provided in their service for those who from age have given up active life, to the old men of these two classes should be assigned the duties of the priesthood.

We have shown what are the necessary conditions, and what the parts of a state: husbandmen, craftsmen, and labourers of all kinds are necessary to the existence of states, but the parts of the state are the warriors and councillors. And these are distinguished severally from one another, the distinction being in some cases permanent, in others not.

10

It is no new or recent discovery of political
1329b philosophers that the state ought to be

divided into classes, and that the warriors should be separated from the husbandmen. The system has continued in Egypt and in Crete to this day, and was established, as tradition says, by a law of Sesostris in Egypt and of Minos in Crete. The institution of common tables also appears to be of ancient date, being in Crete as old as the reign of Minos, and in Italy far older. The Italian historians say that there was a certain Italus king of Oenotria, from whom the Oenotrians were called Italians, and who gave the name of Italy to the promontory of Europe lying within the Scylletic and Lametic Gulfs, which are distant from one another only half a day's journey. They say that this Italus converted the Oenotrians from shepherds into husbandmen, and besides other laws which he gave them, was the founder of their common meals; even in our day some who are derived from him retain this institution and certain other laws of his. On the side of Italy towards Tyrrhenia dwelt the Opici, who are now, as of old, called Ausones; and on the side towards Iapygia and the Ionian Gulf, in the district called Siritis, the Chones, who are likewise of Oenotrian race. From this part of the world originally came the institution of common tables; the separation into castes from Egypt, for the reign of Sesostris is of far greater antiquity than that of Minos. It is true indeed that these and many other things have been invented several times over in the course of ages, or rather times without number; for necessity may be supposed to have taught men the inventions which were absolutely required, and when these were provided, it was natural that other things which would adorn and enrich life should grow up by degrees. And we may infer that in political institutions the same rule holds. Egypt witnesses to the antiquity of all these things, for the Egyptians appear to be of all people the most ancient; and they have laws and a regular constitution existing from time immemorial. We should therefore make the best use of what has been already discovered, and try to supply defects.

I have already remarked that the land ought to belong to those who possess arms and have a share in the government, and that the husbandmen ought to be a class distinct from them; and I have determined what should be the extent and nature of the territory. Let me proceed to discuss the distribution of the land, and the character of the agricultural class; for I do not think that property ought to be **1330a** common, as some maintain, but only that by friendly consent there should be a common use of it; and that no citizen should be in want of subsistence.

As to common meals, there is a general agreement that a well-ordered city should have them; and we will hereafter explain what are our own reasons for taking this view. They ought, however, to be open to all the citizens. And yet it is not easy for the poor to contribute the requisite sum out of their private means, and to provide also for their household. The expense of religious worship should likewise be a public charge. The land must therefore be divided into two parts, one public and the other private, and each part should be subdivided, part of the public land being appropriated to the service of the Gods, and the other part used to defray the cost of the common meals; while of the private land, part should be near the border, and the other near the city, so that, each citizen having two lots, they may all of them have land in both places; there is justice and fairness in such a division, and it tends to inspire unanimity among the people in their border wars. Where there is not this arrangement, some of them are too ready to come to blows with their neighbours, while others are so cautious that they quite lose the sense of honour. Wherefore there is a law in some places which forbids those who dwell near the border to take part in public deliberations about wars with neighbours, on the ground that their interests will pervert their judgement. For the reasons already mentioned, then, the land should be divided in the manner described. The very best thing of all would be that the husbandmen should be slaves taken from among men who are not all of the same race and not spirited, for if they have no spirit they will be better suited for their work, and there will be no danger of their making a revolution. The next best thing would be that they should be perioeci of foreign race, and of a like inferior nature; some of them should be the slaves of individuals, and employed on the private estates of men of property, the remainder should be the property of the state and employed on the common land. I will hereafter explain what is the proper treatment of slaves, and why it is expedient that liberty should be always held out to them as the reward of their services.

11

We have already said that the city should be open to the land and to the sea,[1] and to the whole country as far as possible. In respect of the place itself our wish would be that its situation should be fortunate in four things. The first, health—this is a necessity: cities which lie towards the east, and are blown upon by winds coming from the east, are the healthiest; next in healthfulness are those which are sheltered from the north wind, for they have a milder winter. The site of the city **1330b** should likewise be convenient both for political administration and for war. With a view to the latter it should afford easy egress to the citizens, and at the same time be inaccessible and difficult of capture to enemies. There should be a natural abundance of springs and fountains in the town, or, if there is a deficiency of them, great reservoirs may be established for the collection of rain-water, such as will not fail when the inhabitants are cut off from the country by war. Special care should be taken of the health of the inhabitants, which will depend chiefly on the healthiness of the locality and of the quarter to which they are exposed, and secondly, on the use of pure water; this latter point is by no means a secondary consideration. For the elements which we use most and oftenest for the support of the body contribute most to health, and among these are water and air. Wherefore, in all wise states, if there is a want of pure water, and the supply is not all equally good, the drinking water ought to be separated from that which is used for other purposes.

As to strongholds, what is suitable to different forms of government varies: thus an acropolis is suited to an oligarchy or a monarchy, but a plain to a democracy; neither to an aristocracy, but rather a number of strong places. The arrangement of private houses is considered to be more agreeable and generally more convenient, if the streets are regularly laid out after the modern fashion which Hippodamus introduced, but for security in war the antiquated mode of building, which made it difficult for strangers to get out of a town and for assailants to find their way in, is preferable. A city should therefore adopt both plans of building: it is possible to arrange the houses irregularly, as husbandmen plant their vines in what are called 'clumps'. The whole town should not be laid out in straight lines, but only certain quarters and regions; thus security and beauty will be combined.

As to walls, those who say that cities making any pretension to military virtue should not have them, are quite out of date in their notions; and they may see the cities which prided themselves on this fancy confuted by facts. True, there is little courage shown in seeking for safety behind a rampart when an enemy is similar in character and not much superior in number; but the superiority of the besiegers may be and often is too much both for ordinary human valour and for that which is found only in a few; and if they are to be saved and to escape defeat and outrage, the **1331a** strongest wall will be the truest soldierly precaution, more especially now that missiles and siege engines have been brought to such perfection. To have no walls would be as foolish as to choose a site for a town in an exposed country, and to level the heights; or as if an individual were to leave his house unwalled, lest the inmates should become cowards. Nor must we forget that those who have their cities surrounded by walls may either take advantage of them or not, but cities which are unwalled have no choice.

If our conclusions are just, not only should cities have walls, but care should be taken to make them ornamental, as well as useful for warlike purposes, and adapted to resist modern inventions. For as the assailants of a city do all they can to gain an advantage, so the defenders should make use of any means of defence which have been already discovered, and should devise and invent others, for when men are well prepared no enemy even thinks of attacking them.

12

As the walls are to be divided by guard-houses and towers built at suitable intervals, and the body of citizens must be distributed at common tables, the idea will naturally occur that we should establish some of the common tables in the guard-houses. These might be arranged as has been suggested; while the principal common tables of the magistrates will occupy a suitable place, and there also will be the buildings appropriated to religious worship except in the case of those rites which the law or the Pythian oracle has restricted to a special locality. The site should be a spot seen far and wide, which gives due elevation to virtue and towers over the neighbourhood. Below this spot should be established an agora, such

[1] 1327a 4-40.

as that which the Thessalians call the 'freemen's agora'; from this all trade should be excluded, and no mechanic, husbandman, or any such person allowed to enter, unless he be summoned by the magistrates. It would be a charming use of the place, if the gymnastic exercises of the elder men were performed there. For in this noble practice different ages should be separated, and some of the magistrates should stay with the boys, while the grown-up men remain with the magistrates; for the presence of the magistrates is the best mode of inspiring true modesty and ingenuous fear. **1331b** There should also be a traders' agora, distinct and apart from the other, in a situation which is convenient for the reception of goods both by sea and land.

But in speaking of the magistrates we must not forget another section of the citizens, viz. the priests, for whom public tables should likewise be provided in their proper place near the temples. The magistrates who deal with contracts, indictments, summonses, and the like, and those who have the care of the agora and of the city respectively, ought to be established near an agora and some public place of meeting; the neighbourhood of the traders' agora will be a suitable spot; the upper agora we devote to the life of leisure, the other is intended for the necessities of trade.

The same order should prevail in the country, for there too the magistrates, called by some 'Inspectors of Forests' and by others 'Wardens of the Country', must have guardhouses and common tables while they are on duty; temples should also be scattered throughout the country, dedicated, some to Gods, and some to heroes.

But it would be a waste of time for us to linger over details like these. The difficulty is not in imagining but in carrying them out. We may talk about them as much as we like, but the execution of them will depend upon fortune. Wherefore let us say no more about these matters for the present.

13

Returning to the constitution itself, let us seek to determine out of what and what sort of elements the state which is to be happy and well-governed should be composed. There are two things in which all well-being consists: one of them is the choice of a right end and aim of action, and the other the discovery of the actions which are means towards it; for the means and the end may agree or disagree. Sometimes the right end is set before men, but in practice they fail to attain it; in other cases they are successful in all the means, but they propose to themselves a bad end; and sometimes they fail in both. Take, for example, the art of medicine; physicians do not always understand the nature of health, and also the means which they use may not effect the desired end. In all arts and sciences both the end and the means should be equally within our control.

The happiness and well-being which all men manifestly desire, some have the power of attaining, but to others, from some accident or defect of nature, the attainment of them is not granted; for a good life requires a supply of external **1332a** goods, in a less degree when men are in a good state, in a greater degree when they are in a lower state. Others again, who possess the conditions of happiness, go utterly wrong from the first in the pursuit of it. But since our object is to discover the best form of government, that, namely, under which a city will be best governed, and since the city is best governed which has the greatest opportunity of obtaining happiness, it is evident that we must clearly ascertain the nature of happiness.

We maintain, and have said in the *Ethics*,[1] if the arguments there adduced are of any value, that happiness is the realization and perfect exercise of virtue, and this not conditional, but absolute. And I used the term 'conditional' to express that which is indispensable, and 'absolute' to express that which is good in itself. Take the case of just actions; just punishments and chastisements do indeed spring from a good principle, but they are good only because we cannot do without them—it would be better that neither individuals nor states should need anything of the sort—but actions which aim at honour and advantage are absolutely the best. The conditional action is only the choice of a lesser evil; whereas these are the foundation and creation of good. A good man may make the best even of poverty and disease, and the other ills of life; but he can only attain happiness under the opposite conditions (for this also has been determined in accordance with ethical arguments, that the good man is he for whom, because he is virtuous, the things that are absolutely good are good; it is also plain that his use of these goods must be virtuous and in the absolute sense good). This makes men fancy that external goods are

[1] *Ethics*, I. 1098a 16; X. 1176b 4.

the cause of happiness, yet we might as well say that a brilliant performance on the lyre was to be attributed to the instrument and not to the skill of the performer.

It follows then from what has been said that some things the legislator must find ready to his hand in a state, others he must provide. And therefore we can only say: May our state be constituted in such a manner as to be blessed with the goods of which fortune disposes (for we acknowledge her power): whereas virtue and goodness in the state are not a matter of chance but the result of knowledge and purpose. A city can be virtuous only when the citizens who have a share in the government are virtuous, and in our state all the citizens share in the government; let us then inquire how a man becomes virtuous. For even if we could suppose the citizen body to be virtuous, without each of them being so, yet the latter would be better, for in the virtue of each the virtue of all is involved.

There are three things which make men good and virtuous; these are nature, habit, rational principle. In the first place, every one must be born a man and not some other animal; so, too, he must have a certain character, both of body and soul. But some qualities
1332b there is no use in having at birth, for they are altered by habit, and there are some gifts which by nature are made to be turned by habit to good or bad. Animals lead for the most part a life of nature, although in lesser particulars some are influenced by habit as well. Man has rational principle, in addition, and man only. Wherefore nature, habit, rational principle must be in harmony with one another; for they do not always agree; men do many things against habit and nature, if rational principle persuades them that they ought. We have already determined what natures are likely to be most easily moulded by the hands of the legislator. All else is the work of education; we learn some things by habit and some by instruction.

14

Since every political society is composed of rulers and subjects, let us consider whether the relations of one to the other should interchange or be permanent. For the education of the citizens will necessarily vary with the answer given to this question. Now, if some men excelled others in the same degree in which gods and heroes are supposed to excel mankind in general (having in the first place a great advantage even in their bodies, and secondly in their minds), so that the superiority of the governors was undisputed and patent to their subjects, it would clearly be better that once for all the one class should rule and the others serve. But since this is unattainable, and kings have no marked superiority over their subjects, such as Scylax affirms to be found among the Indians, it is obviously necessary on many grounds that all the citizens alike should take their turn of governing and being governed. Equality consists in the same treatment of similar persons, and no government can stand which is not founded upon justice. For if the government be unjust every one in the country unites with the governed in the desire to have a revolution, and it is an impossibility that the members of the government can be so numerous as to be stronger than all their enemies put together. Yet that governors should excel their subjects is undeniable. How all this is to be effected, and in what way they will respectively share in the government, the legislator has to consider. The subject has been already mentioned.[1] Nature herself has provided the distinction when she made a difference between old and young within the same species of whom she fitted the one to govern and the other to be governed. No one takes offence at being governed when he is young, nor does he think himself better than this governors, especially if he will enjoy the same privilege when he reaches the required age.

We conclude that from one point of view governors and governed are identical, and from another different. And therefore their ed-
1333a ucation must be the same and also different. For he who would learn to command well must, as men say, first of all learn to obey. As I observed in the first part of this treatise, there is one rule which is for the sake of the rulers and another rule which is for the sake of the ruled; the former is a despotic, the latter a free government. Some commands differ not in the thing commanded, but in the intention with which they are imposed. Wherefore, many apparently menial offices are an honour to the free youth by whom they are performed; for actions do not differ as honourable or dishonourable in themselves so much as in the end and intention of them. But since we say that the virtue of the citizen and ruler is the same as that of the good man, and that the same person must first be a subject and then a ruler, the legislator has to see that they become

[1] 1329a 2-17.

good men, and by what means this may be accomplished, and what is the end of the perfect life.

Now the soul of man is divided into two parts, one of which has a rational principle in itself, and the other, not having a rational principle in itself, is able to obey such a principle. And we call a man in any way good because he has the virtues of these two parts. In which of them the end is more likely to be found is no matter of doubt to those who adopt our division; for in the world both of nature and of art the inferior always exists for the sake of the better or superior, and the better or superior is that which has a rational principle. This principle, too, in our ordinary way of speaking, is divided into two kinds, for there is a practical and a speculative principle. This part, then, must evidently be similarly divided. And there must be a corresponding division of actions; the actions of the naturally better part are to be preferred by those who have it in their power to attain to two out of the three or to all, for that is always to every one the most eligible which is the highest attainable by him. The whole of life is further divided into two parts, business and leisure, war and peace, and of actions some aim at what is necessary and useful, and some at what is honourable. And the preference given to one or the other class of actions must necessarily be like the preference given to one or other part of the soul and its actions over the other; there must be war for the sake of peace, business for the sake of leisure, things useful and necessary for the sake of things honourable. All these points the statesman should keep in view when he frames his laws; he should consider the parts of the soul and their functions, and above all the better and the end; he should also remember the diversities of human lives and actions. For men must be able to engage in business **1333b** and go to war, but leisure and peace are better; they must do what is necessary and indeed what is useful, but what is honourable is better. On such principles children and persons of every age which requires education should be trained. Whereas even the Hellenes of the present day who are reputed to be best governed, and the legislators who gave them their constitutions, do not appear to have framed their governments with a regard to the best end, or to have given them laws and education with a view to all the virtues, but in a vulgar spirit have fallen back on those which promised to be more useful and profitable. Many modern writers have taken a similar view: they commend the Lacedaemonian constitution, and praise the legislator for making conquest and war his sole aim, a doctrine which may be refuted by argument and has long ago been refuted by facts. For most men desire empire in the hope of accumulating the goods of fortune; and on this ground Thibron and all those who have written about the Lacedaemonian constitution have praised their legislator, because the Lacedaemonians, by being trained to meet dangers, gained great power. But surely they are not a happy people now that their empire has passed away, nor was their legislator right. How ridiculous is the result, if, while they are continuing in the observance of his laws and no one interferes with them, they have lost the better part of life! These writers further err about the sort of government which the legislator should approve, for the government of freemen is nobler and implies more virtue than despotic government. Neither is a city to be deemed happy or a legislator to be praised because he trains his citizens to conquer and obtain dominion over their neighbours, for there is great evil in this. On a similar principle any citizen who could, should obviously try to obtain the power in his own state,—the crime which the Lacedaemonians accuse king Pausanias of attempting, although he had so great honour already. No such principle and no law having this object is either statesmanlike or useful or right. For the same things are best both for individuals and for states, and these are the things which the legislator ought to implant in the minds of his citizens. Neither should men study war with a view to the enslavement of those who do not deserve to be enslaved; but first of all they should provide against their own enslavement, and in the second place obtain empire for the good of the governed, and not for the sake **1334a** of exercising a general despotism, and in the third place they should seek to be masters only over those who deserve to be slaves. Facts, as well as arguments, prove that the legislator should direct all his military and other measures to the provision of leisure and the establishment of peace. For most of these military states are safe only while they are at war, but fall when they have acquired their empire; like unused iron they lose their temper in time of peace. And for this the legislator is to blame, he never having taught them how to lead the life of peace.

15

Since the end of individuals and of states is the same, the end of the best man and of the best constitution must also be the same; it is therefore evident that there ought to exist in both of them the virtues of leisure; for peace, as has been often repeated,[1] is the end of war, and leisure of toil. But leisure and cultivation may be promoted, not only by those virtues which are practised in leisure, but also by some of those which are useful to business. For many necessaries of life have to be supplied before we can have leisure. Therefore a city must be temperate and brave, and able to endure: for truly, as the proverb says, 'There is no leisure for slaves,' and those who cannot face danger like men are the slaves of any invader. Courage and endurance are required for business and philosophy for leisure, temperance and justice for both, and more especially in times of peace and leisure, for war compels men to be just and temperate, whereas the enjoyment of good fortune and the leisure which comes with peace tend to make them insolent. Those then who seem to be the best-off and to be in the possession of every good, have special need of justice and temperance,—for example, those (if such there be, as the poets say) who dwell in the Islands of the Blest; they above all will need philosophy and temperance and justice, and all the more the more leisure they have, living in the midst of abundance. There is no difficulty in seeing why the state that would be happy and good ought to have these virtues. If it be disgraceful in men not to be able to use the goods of life, it is peculiarly disgraceful not to be able to use them in time of leisure,—to show excellent qualities in action and war, and when they have peace and leisure to be no better than slaves. Wherefore we should not practise virtue after the manner of the Lacedaemonians. For they, while agreeing with other men in their **1334b** conception of the highest goods, differ from the rest of mankind in thinking that they are to be obtained by the practice of a single virtue. And since ⟨they think⟩ these goods and the enjoyment of them greater than the enjoyment derived from the virtues . . . and that ⟨it should be practised⟩ for its own sake, is evident from what has been said; we must now consider how and by what means it is to be attained.

We have already determined that nature and habit and rational principle are required,[2] and, of these, the proper *nature* of the citizens has also been defined by us.[3] But we have still to consider whether the training of early life is to be that of rational principle or habit, for these two must accord, and when in accord they will then form the best of harmonies. The rational principle may be mistaken and fail in attaining the highest ideal of life, and there may be a like evil influence of habit. Thus much is clear in the first place, that, as in all other things, birth implies an antecedent beginning, and that there are beginnings whose end is relative to a further end. Now, in men rational principle and mind are the end towards which nature strives, so that the birth and moral discipline of the citizens ought to be ordered with a view to them. In the second place, as the soul and body are two, we see also that there are two parts of the soul, the rational and the irrational, and two corresponding states—reason and appetite. And as the body is prior in order of generation to the soul, so the irrational is prior to the rational. The proof is that anger and wishing and desire are implanted in children from their very birth, but reason and understanding are developed as they grow older. Wherefore, the care of the body ought to precede that of the soul, and the training of the appetitive part should follow: none the less our care of it must be for the sake of the reason, and our care of the body for the sake of the soul.

16

Since the legislator should begin by considering how the frames of the children whom he is rearing may be as good as possible, his first care will be about marriage—at what age should his citizens marry, and who are fit to marry? In legislating on this subject he ought to consider the persons and the length of their life, that their procreative life may terminate at the same period, and that they may not differ in their bodily powers, as will be the case if the man is still able to beget children while the woman is unable to bear them, or the woman able to bear while the man is unable to beget, for from these causes arise quarrels and differences between married persons. Secondly, he must consider the time at which the children will succeed to their parents; there ought not to be too great an interval of age, for then the parents will be too old to derive any pleasure from their affection, or to be of any

[1] 1333^a 35, 1334^a 2.

[2] 1332^a 39 sqq.

[3] Chapter 7.

1335a use to them. Nor ought they to be too nearly of an age; to youthful marriages there are many objections—the children will be wanting in respect to the parents, who will seem to be their contemporaries, and disputes will arise in the management of the household. Thirdly, and this is the point from which we digressed,[1] the legislator must mould to his will the frames of newly-born children. Almost all these objects may be secured by attention to one point. Since the time of generation is commonly limited within the age of seventy years in the case of a man, and of fifty in the case of a woman, the commencement of the union should conform to these periods. The union of male and female when too young is bad for the procreation of children; in all other animals the offspring of the young are small and ill-developed, and with a tendency to produce female children, and therefore also in man, as is proved by the fact that in those cities in which men and women are accustomed to marry young, the people are small and weak; in childbirth also younger women suffer more, and more of them die; some persons say that this was the meaning of the response once given to the Troezenians—the oracle really meant that many died because they married too young; it had nothing to do with the ingathering of the harvest. It also conduces to temperance not to marry too soon; for women who marry early are apt to be wanton; and in men too the bodily frame is stunted if they marry while the seed is growing (for there is a time when the growth of the seed, also, ceases, or continues to but a slight extent). Women should marry when they are about eighteen years of age, and men at seven and thirty; then they are in the prime of life, and the decline in the powers of both will coincide. Further, the children, if their birth takes place soon, as may reasonably be expected, will succeed in the beginning of their prime, when the fathers are already in the decline of life, and have nearly reached their term of three-score years and ten.

Thus much of the age proper for marriage: the season of the year should also be considered; according to our present custom, people generally limit marriage to the season of winter, and they are right. The precepts of physicians and natural philosophers about generation should also be studied by the parents themselves; the physicians give good advice about the favourable conditions of the

1335b body, and the natural philosophers about the winds; of which they prefer the north to the south.

What constitution in the parent is most advantageous to the offspring is a subject which we will consider more carefully when we speak of the education of children, and we will only make a few general remarks at present. The constitution of an athlete is not suited to the life of a citizen, or to health, or to the procreation of children, any more than the valetudinarian or exhausted constitution, but one which is in a mean between them. A man's constitution should be inured to labour, but not to labour which is excessive or of one sort only, such as is practised by athletes; he should be capable of all the actions of a freeman. These remarks apply equally to both parents.

Women who are with child should be careful of themselves; they should take exercise and have a nourishing diet. The first of these prescriptions the legislator will easily carry into effect by requiring that they shall take a walk daily to some temple, where they can worship the gods who preside over birth. Their minds, however, unlike their bodies, they ought to keep quiet, for the offspring derive their natures from their mothers as plants do from the earth.

As to the exposure and rearing of children, let there be a law that no *deformed* child shall live, but that on the ground of an *excess* in the number of children, if the established customs of the state forbid this (for in our state population has a limit), no child is to be exposed, but when couples have children in excess, let abortion be procured before sense and life have begun; what may or may not be lawfully done in these cases depends on the question of life and sensation.

And now, having determined at what ages men and women are to begin their union, let us also determine how long they shall continue to beget and bear offspring for the state; men who are too old, like men who are too young, produce children who are defective in body and mind; the children of very old men are weakly. The limit, then, should be the age which is the prime of their intelligence, and this in most persons, according to the notion of some poets who measure life by periods of seven years, is about fifty; at four or five years later, they should cease from having families; and from that time forward only cohabit with one another for the sake of health, or for some similar reason.

[1] 1334b 29 sqq.

As to adultery, let it be held disgraceful, in general, for any man or woman to be found in any way unfaithful when they are **1336a** married, and called husband and wife. If during the time of bearing children anything of the sort occur, let the guilty person be punished with a loss of privileges in proportion to the offence.

17

After the children have been born, the manner of rearing them may be supposed to have a great effect on their bodily strength. It would appear from the example of animals, and of those nations who desire to create the military habit, that the food which has most milk in it is best suited to human beings; but the less wine the better, if they would escape diseases. Also all the motions to which children can be subjected at their early age are very useful. But in order to preserve their tender limbs from distortion, some nations have had recourse to mechanical appliances which straighten their bodies. To accustom children to the cold from their earliest years is also an excellent practice, which greatly conduces to health, and hardens them for military service. Hence many barbarians have a custom of plunging their children at birth into a cold stream; others, like the Celts, clothe them in a light wrapper only. For human nature should be early habituated to endure all which by habit it can be made to endure; but the process must be gradual. And children, from their natural warmth, may be easily trained to bear cold. Such care should attend them in the first stage of life.

The next period lasts to the age of five; during this no demand should be made upon the child for study or labour, lest its growth be impeded; and there should be sufficient motion to prevent the limbs from being inactive. This can be secured, among other ways, by amusement, but the amusement should not be vulgar or tiring or effeminate. The Directors of Education, as they are termed, should be careful what tales or stories the children hear,[1] for all such things are designed to prepare the way for the business of later life, and should be for the most part imitations of the occupations which they will hereafter pursue in earnest.[2] Those are wrong who in their laws attempt to check the loud crying and screaming of children, for these contribute towards their growth, and, in a manner, exercise their bodies.[3] Straining the voice has a strengthening effect similar to that produced by the retention of the breath in violent exertions. The Directors of Education should have an eye to their bringing up, and in particular should take care that they are left as little as **1336b** possible with slaves. For until they are seven years old they must live at home; and therefore, even at this early age, it is to be expected that they should acquire a taint of meanness from what they hear and see. Indeed, there is nothing which the legislator should be more careful to drive away than indecency of speech; for the light utterance of shameful words leads soon to shameful actions. The young especially should never be allowed to repeat or hear anything of the sort. A freeman who is found saying or doing what is forbidden, if he be too young as yet to have the privilege of reclining at the public tables, should be disgraced and beaten, and an elder person degraded as his slavish conduct deserves. And since we do not allow improper language, clearly we should also banish pictures or speeches from the stage which are indecent. Let the rulers take care that there be no image or picture representing unseemly actions, except in the temples of those Gods at whose festivals the law permits even ribaldry, and whom the law also permits to be worshipped by persons of mature age on behalf of themselves, their children, and their wives. But the legislator should not allow youth to be spectators of iambi or of comedy until they are of an age to sit at the public tables and to drink strong wine; by that time education will have armed them against the evil influences of such representations.

We have made these remarks in a cursory manner,—they are enough for the present occasion; but hereafter we will return to the subject and after a fuller discussion determine whether such liberty should or should not be granted, and in what way granted, if at all. Theodorus, the tragic actor, was quite right in saying that he would not allow any other actor, not even if he were quite second-rate, to enter before himself, because the spectators grew fond of the voices which they first heard. And the same principle applies universally to association with things as well as with persons, for we always like best whatever comes first. And therefore youth should be kept strangers to all that is bad, and especially to things which suggest vice or hate. When

[1] Plato, *Republic*, II. 377 ff.

[2] Plato, *Laws*, I. 643.

[3] Plato, *Ibid.*, VII. 792.

the five years have passed away, during the two following years they must look on at the pursuits which they are hereafter to learn. There are two periods of life with reference to which education has to be divided, from seven to the age of puberty, and onwards to the age of one and twenty. The poets who divide ages by sevens are in the main right; but we **1337a** should observe the divisions actually made by nature; for the deficiences of nature are what art and education seek to fill up.

Let us then first inquire if any regulations are to be laid down about children, and secondly, whether the care of them should be the concern of the state or of private individuals, which latter is in our own day the common custom, and in the third place, what these regulations should be.

BOOK VIII

1

No one will doubt that the legislator should direct his attention above all to the education of youth; for the neglect of education does harm to the constitution. The citizen should be moulded to suit the form of government under which he lives. For each government has a peculiar character which originally formed and which continues to preserve it. The character of democracy creates democracy, and the character of oligarchy creates oligarchy; and always the better the character, the better the government.

Again, for the exercise of any faculty or art a previous training and habituation are required; clearly therefore for the practice of virtue. And since the whole city has one end, it is manifest that education should be one and the same for all, and that it should be public, and not private,—not as at present, when every one looks after his own children separately, and gives them separate instruction of the sort which he thinks best; the training in things which are of common interest should be the same for all. Neither must we suppose that any one of the citizens belongs to himself, for they all belong to the state, and are each of them a part of the state, and the care of each part is inseparable from the care of the whole. In this particular as in some others the Lacedaemonians are to be praised, for they take the greatest pains about their children, and make education the business of the state.

2

That education should be regulated by law and should be an affair of state is not to be denied, but what should be the character of this public education, and how young persons should be educated, are questions which remain to be considered. As things are, there is disagreement about the subjects. For mankind are by no means agreed about the things to be taught, whether we look to virtue or the best life. Neither is it clear whether education is more concerned with intellectual or with moral virtue. The existing practice is perplexing; no one knows on what principle we should proceed—should the useful in life, or should virtue, or should the higher knowledge, be the aim of our training; all three opinions **1337b** have been entertained. Again, about the means there is no agreement; for different persons, starting with different ideas about the nature of virtue, naturally disagree about the practice of it. There can be no doubt that children should be taught those useful things which are really necessary, but not all useful things; for occupations are divided into liberal and illiberal; and to young children should be imparted only such kinds of knowledge as will be useful to them without vulgarizing them. And any occupation, art, or science, which makes the body or soul or mind of the freeman less fit for the practice or exercise of virtue, is vulgar; wherefore we call those arts vulgar which tend to deform the body, and likewise all paid employments, for they absorb and degrade the mind. There are also some liberal arts quite proper for a freeman to acquire, but only in a certain degree, and if he attend to them too closely, in order to attain perfection in them, the same evil effects will follow. The object also which a man sets before him makes a great difference; if he does or learns anything for his own sake or for the sake of his friends, or with a view to excellence, the action will not appear illiberal; but if done for the sake of others, the very same action will be thought menial and servile. The received subjects of instruction, as I have already remarked,[1] are partly of a liberal and partly of an illiberal character.

3

The customary branches of education are in number four; they are—(1) reading and writ-

[1] a 39-b 3.

ing, (2) gymnastic exercises, (3) music, to which is sometimes added (4) drawing. Of these, reading and writing and drawing are regarded as useful for the purposes of life in a variety of ways, and gymnastic exercises are thought to infuse courage. Concerning music a doubt may be raised—in our own day most men cultivate it for the sake of pleasure, but originally it was included in education, because nature herself, as has been often said,[1] requires that we should be able, not only to work well, but to use leisure well; for, as I must repeat once again, the first principle of all action is leisure. Both are required, but leisure is better than occupation and is its end; and therefore the question must be asked, what ought we to do when at leisure? Clearly we ought not to be amusing ourselves, for then amusement would be the end of life. But if this is inconceivable, and amusement is needed more amid serious occupations than at other times (for he who is hard at work has need of relaxation, and amusement gives relaxation, whereas occupation is always accompanied with exertion and effort), we should introduce amusements only at suitable times, and they should be our medicines, for the emotion which they create in the soul is a relaxation, **1338a** and from the pleasure we obtain rest. But leisure of itself gives pleasure and happiness and enjoyment of life, which are experienced, not by the busy man, but by those who have leisure. For he who is occupied has in view some end which he has not attained; but happiness is an end, since all men deem it to be accompanied with pleasure and not with pain. This pleasure, however, is regarded differently by different persons, and varies according to the habit of individuals; the pleasure of the best man is the best, and springs from the noblest sources. It is clear then that there are branches of learning and education which we must study merely with a view to leisure spent in intellectual activity, and these are to be valued for their own sake; whereas those kinds of knowledge which are useful in business are to be deemed necessary, and exist for the sake of other things. And therefore our fathers admitted music into education, not on the ground either of its necessity or utility, for it is not necessary, nor indeed useful in the same manner as reading and writing, which are useful in money-making, in the management of a household, in the acquisition of knowledge and in political life, nor like drawing, useful for a more correct judgement of the works of artists, nor again like gymnastic, which gives health and strength; for neither of these is to be gained from music. There remains, then, the use of music for intellectual enjoyment in leisure; which is in fact evidently the reason of its introduction, this being one of the ways in which it is thought that a freeman should pass his leisure; as Homer says—

But he who alone should be called to the pleasant feast,

and afterwards he speaks of others whom he describes as inviting

The bard who would delight them all.[2]

And in another place Odysseus says there is no better way of passing life than when men's hearts are merry and

The banqueters in the hall, sitting in order, hear the voice of the minstrel.[3]

It is evident, then, that there is a sort of education in which parents should train their sons, not as being useful or necessary, but because it is liberal or noble. Whether this is of one kind only, or of more than one, and if so, what they are, and how they are to be imparted, must hereafter be determined. Thus much we are now in a position to say, that the ancients witness to us; for their opinion may be gathered from the fact that music is one of the received and traditional branches of education. Further, it is clear that children should be instructed in some useful things,—for example, in reading and writing,—not only for their usefulness, but also because many other sorts of knowledge are acquired through them. With a like view they may be taught drawing, not to prevent their making mistakes in their own purchases, or in order that they may not be imposed upon in the **1338b** buying or selling of articles, but perhaps rather because it makes them judges of the beauty of the human form. To be always seeking after the useful does not become free and exalted souls. Now it is clear that in education practice must be used before theory, and the body be trained before the mind; and therefore boys should be handed over to the trainer, who creates in them the proper habit of body, and to the wrestling-master, who teaches them their exercises.

[1] II. 1271a 41 sqq.; VII. 1333a 16-1334b 3; *Ethics*, x. 6.

[2] *Odyssey*, XVII. 385.

[3] *Odyssey*, IX. 7.

4

Of those states which in our own day seem to take the greatest care of children, some aim at producing in them an athletic habit, but they only injure their forms and stunt their growth. Although the Lacedaemonians have not fallen into this mistake, yet they brutalize their children by laborious exercises which they think will make them courageous. But in truth, as we have often repeated,[1] education should not be exclusively, or principally, directed to this end. And even if we suppose the Lacedaemonians to be right in their end, they do not attain it. For among barbarians and among animals courage is found associated, not with the greatest ferocity, but with a gentle and lion-like temper. There are many races who are ready enough to kill and eat men, such as the Achaeans and Heniochi, who both live about the Black Sea; and there are other mainland tribes, as bad or worse, who all live by plunder, but have no courage. It is notorious that the Lacedaemonians themselves, while they alone were assiduous in their laborious drill, were superior to others, but now they are beaten both in war and gymnastic exercises. For their ancient superiority did not depend on their mode of training their youth, but only on the circumstance that they trained them when their only rivals did not. Hence we may infer that what is noble, not what is brutal, should have the first place; no wolf or other wild animal will face a really noble danger; such dangers are for the brave man. And parents who devote their children to gymnastics while they neglect their necessary education, in reality vulgarize them; for they make them useful to the art of statesmanship in one quality only, and even in this the argument proves them to be inferior to others. We should judge the Lacedaemonians not from what they have been, but from what they are; for now they have rivals who compete with their education; formerly they had none.

It is an admitted principle, that gymnastic exercises should be employed in education, and that for children they should be of a lighter kind, avoiding severe diet or painful toil, lest the growth of the body be impaired. The evil of excessive training in early years is strik-
1339a ingly proved by the example of the Olympic victors; for not more than two or three of them have gained a prize both as boys and as men; their early training and severe gymnastic exercises exhausted their constitutions. When boyhood is over, three years should be spent in other studies; the period of life which follows may then be devoted to hard exercise and strict diet. Men ought not to labour at the same time with their minds and with their bodies; for the two kinds of labour are opposed to one another; the labour of the body impedes the mind, and the labour of the mind the body.

5

Concerning music there are some questions which we have already raised;[2] these we may now resume and carry further; and our remarks will serve as a prelude to this or any other discussion of the subject. It is not easy to determine the nature of music, or why any one should have a knowledge of it. Shall we say, for the sake of amusement and relaxation, like sleep or drinking, which are not good in themselves, but are pleasant, and at the same time 'make care to cease', as Euripides[3] says? And for this end men also appoint music, and make use of all three alike,—sleep, drinking, music,—to which some add dancing. Or shall we argue that music conduces to virtue, on the ground that it can form our minds and habituate us to true pleasures as our bodies are made by gymnastic to be of a certain character? Or shall we say that it contributes to the enjoyment of leisure and mental cultivation, which is a third alternative? Now obviously youths are not to be instructed with a view to their amusement, for learning is no amusement, but is accompanied with pain. Neither is intellectual enjoyment suitable to boys of that age, for it is the end, and that which is imperfect cannot attain the perfect or end. But perhaps it may be said that boys learn music for the sake of the amusement which they will have when they are grown up. If so, why should they learn themselves, and not, like the Persian and Median kings, enjoy the pleasure and instruction which is derived from hearing others? (for surely persons who have made music the business and profession of their lives will be better performers than those who practise only long enough to learn). If they must learn music, on the same principle they should learn cookery, which is absurd. And even granting that music may form the character, the objection still holds: why should we learn ourselves? Why cannot

[1] II. 1271a 41-b 10; VII. 1333b 5 sqq., 1334a 40 sqq.

[2] 1337b 27-1338a 30.

[3] *Bacchantes*, 381.

1339b we attain true pleasure and form a correct judgement from hearing others, like the Lacedaemonians?—for they, without learning music, nevertheless can correctly judge, as they say, of good and bad melodies. Or again, if music should be used to promote cheerfulness and refined intellectual enjoyment, the objection still remains—why should we learn ourselves instead of enjoying the performances of others? We may illustrate what we are saying by our conception of the Gods; for in the poets Zeus does not himself sing or play on the lyre. Nay, we call professional performers vulgar; no freeman would play or sing unless he were intoxicated or in jest. But these matters may be left for the present.

The first question is whether music is or is not to be a part of education. Of the three things mentioned in our discussion, which does it produce?—education or amusement or intellectual enjoyment, for it may be reckoned under all three, and seems to share in the nature of all of them. Amusement is for the sake of relaxation, and relaxation is of necessity sweet, for it is the remedy of pain caused by toil; and intellectual enjoyment is universally acknowledged to contain an element not only of the noble but of the pleasant, for happiness is made up of both. All men agree that music is one of the pleasantest things, whether with or without song; as Musaeus says,

Song is to mortals of all things the sweetest.

Hence and with good reason it is introduced into social gatherings and entertainments, because it makes the hearts of men glad: so that on this ground alone we may assume that the young ought to be trained in it. For innocent pleasures are not only in harmony with the perfect end of life, but they also provide relaxation. And whereas men rarely attain the end, but often rest by the way and amuse themselves, not only with a view to a further end, but also for the pleasure's sake, it may be well at times to let them find a refreshment in music. It sometimes happens that men make amusement the end, for the end probably contains some element of pleasure, though not any ordinary or lower pleasure; but they mistake the lower for the higher, and in seeking for the one find the other, since every pleasure has a likeness to the end of action. For the end is not eligible for the sake of any future good, nor do the pleasures which we have described exist for the sake of any future good but of the past, that is to say, they are the alleviation of past toils and pains. And we may infer this to be the reason why men seek happiness from these pleasures. But music is pursued, not only as an alleviation of past toil, but also as providing recreation. And who can say whether, having this use, it may not also have a no-
1340a bler one? In addition to this common pleasure, felt and shared in by all (for the pleasure given by music is natural, and therefore adapted to all ages and characters), may it not have also some influence over the character and the soul? It must have such an influence if characters are affected by it. And that they are so affected is proved in many ways, and not least by the power which the songs of Olympus exercise; for beyond question they inspire enthusiasm, and enthusiasm is an emotion of the ethical part of the soul. Besides, when men hear imitations, even apart from the rhythms and tunes themselves, their feelings move in sympathy. Since then music is a pleasure, and virtue consists in rejoicing and loving and hating aright, there is clearly nothing which we are so much concerned to acquire and to cultivate as the power of forming right judgements, and of taking delight in good dispositions and noble actions. Rhythm and melody supply imitations of anger and gentleness, and also of courage and temperance, and of all the qualities contrary to these, and of the other qualities of character, which hardly fall short of the actual affections, as we know from our own experience, for in listening to such strains our souls undergo a change. The habit of feeling pleasure or pain at mere representations is not far removed from the same feeling about realities; for example, if any one delights in the sight of a statue for its beauty only, it necessarily follows that the sight of the original will be pleasant to him. The objects of no other sense, such as taste or touch, have any resemblance to moral qualities; in visible objects there is only a little, for there are figures which are of a moral character, but only to a slight extent, and all do not participate in the feeling about them. Again, figures and colours are not imitations, but signs, of moral habits, indications which the body gives of states of feeling. The connexion of them with morals is slight, but in so far as there is any, young men should be taught to look, not at the works of Pauson, but at those of Polygnotus, or any other painter or sculptor who expresses moral ideas. On the other hand, even in mere melo-

dies there is an imitation of character, for the musical modes differ essentially from one another, and those who hear them are differently affected by each. Some of them make **1340b** men sad and grave, like the so-called Mixolydian, others enfeeble the mind, like the relaxed modes, another, again, produces a moderate and settled temper, which appears to be the peculiar effect of the Dorian; the Phrygian inspires enthusiasm. The whole subject has been well treated by philosophical writers on this branch of education, and they confirm their arguments by facts. The same principles apply to rhythms; some have a character of rest, others of motion, and of these latter again, some have a more vulgar, others a nobler movement. Enough has been said to show that music has a power of forming the character, and should therefore be introduced into the education of the young. The study is suited to the stage of youth, for young persons will not, if they can help, endure anything which is not sweetened by pleasure, and music has a natural sweetness. There seems to be in us a sort of affinity to musical modes and rhythms, which makes some philosophers say that the soul is a tuning, others, that it possesses tuning.

6

And now we have to determine the question which has been already raised,[1] whether children should be themselves taught to sing and play or not. Clearly there is a considerable difference made in the character by the actual practice of the art. It is difficult, if not impossible, for those who do not perform to be good judges of the performances of others. Besides, children should have something to do, and the rattle of Archytas, which people give to their children in order to amuse them and prevent them from breaking anything in the house, was a capital invention, for a young thing cannot be quiet. The rattle is a toy suited to the infant mind, and education is a rattle or a toy for children of a larger growth. We conclude then that they should be taught music in such a way as to become not only critics but performers.

The question what is or is not suitable for different ages may be easily answered; nor is there any difficulty in meeting the objection of those who say that the study of music is vulgar. We reply (1) in the first place, that they who are to be judges must also be performers, and that they should begin to practise early, although when they are older they may be spared the execution; they must have learned to appreciate what is good and to delight in it, thanks to the knowledge which they acquired in their youth. As to (2) the vulgarizing effect which music is supposed to exercise, this is a question which we shall have no difficulty in determining, when we have considered to what extent freemen who are being trained to political virtue should pursue the art, what **1341a** melodies and what rhythms they should be allowed to use, and what instruments should be employed in teaching them to play; for even the instrument makes a difference. The answer to the objection turns upon these distinctions; for it is quite possible that certain methods of teaching and learning music do really have a degrading effect. It is evident then that the learning of music ought not to impede the business of riper years, or to degrade the body or render it unfit for civil or military training, whether for bodily exercises at the time or for later studies.

The right measure will be attained if students of music stop short of the arts which are practised in professional contests, and do not seek to acquire those fantastic marvels of execution which are now the fashion in such contests, and from these have passed into education. Let the young practise even such music as we have prescribed, only until they are able to feel delight in noble melodies and rhythms, and not merely in that common part of music in which every slave or child and even some animals find pleasure.

From these principles we may also infer what instruments should be used. The flute, or any other instrument which requires great skill, as for example the harp, ought not to be admitted into education, but only such as will make intelligent students of music or of the other parts of education. Besides, the flute is not an instrument which is expressive of moral character; it is too exciting. The proper time for using it is when the performance aims not at instruction, but at the relief of the passions. And there is a further objection; the impediment which the flute presents to the use of the voice detracts from its educational value. The ancients therefore were right in forbidding the flute to youths and freemen, although they had once allowed it. For when their wealth gave them a greater inclination to leisure, and they had loftier notions of excellence, being also elated with their success, both

[1] $1339^a\ 33$-$^b\ 10$.

before and after the Persian War, with more zeal than discernment they pursued every kind of knowledge, and so they introduced the flute into education. At Lacedaemon there was a choragus who led the chorus with a flute, and at Athens the instrument became so popular that most freemen could play upon it. The popularity is shown by the tablet which Thrasippus dedicated when he furnished the chorus to Ecphantides. Later experience enabled men to judge what was or was not really conducive to virtue, and they rejected both the flute and several other old-fashioned instruments, such as the Lydian harp, the many-stringed lyre, the 'heptagon', 'triangle', 'sambuca', and the like—which are intended only **1341^b** to give pleasure to the hearer, and require extraordinary skill of hand. There is a meaning also in the myth of the ancients, which tells how Athene invented the flute and then threw it away. It was not a bad idea of theirs, that the Goddess disliked the instrument because it made the face ugly; but with still more reason may we say that she rejected it because the acquirement of flute-playing contributes nothing to the mind, since to Athene we ascribe both knowledge and art.

Thus then we reject the professional instruments and also the professional mode of education in music (and by professional we mean that which is adopted in contests), for in this the performer practises the art, not for the sake of his own improvement, but in order to give pleasure, and that of a vulgar sort, to his hearers. For this reason the execution of such music is not the part of a freeman but of a paid performer, and the result is that the performers are vulgarized, for the end at which they aim is bad. The vulgarity of the spectator tends to lower the character of the music and therefore of the performers; they look to him —he makes them what they are, and fashions even their bodies by the movements which he expects them to exhibit.

7

We have also to consider rhythms and modes, and their use in education. Shall we use them all or make a distinction? and shall the same distinction be made for those who practise music with a view to education, or shall it be some other? Now we see that music is produced by melody and rhythm, and we ought to know what influence these have respectively on education, and whether we should prefer excellence in melody or excellence in rhythm. But as the subject has been very well treated by many musicians of the present day, and also by philosophers who have had considerable experience of musical education, to these we would refer the more exact student of the subject; we shall only speak of it now after the manner of the legislator, stating the general principles.

We accept the division of melodies proposed by certain philosophers into ethical melodies, melodies of action, and passionate or inspiring melodies, each having, as they say, a mode corresponding to it. But we maintain further that music should be studied, not for the sake of one, but of many benefits, that is to say, with a view to (1) education, (2) purgation (the word 'purgation' we use at present without explanation, but when hereafter we speak of poetry,[1] we will treat the subject with more precision); music may also serve (3) for intellectual enjoyment, for relaxation and for recreation after exertion. It is clear, therefore, that **1342^a** all the modes must be employed by us, but not all of them in the same manner. In education the most ethical modes are to be preferred, but in listening to the performances of others we may admit the modes of action and passion also. For feelings such as pity and fear, or, again, enthusiasm, exist very strongly in some souls, and have more or less influence over all. Some persons fall into a religious frenzy, whom we see as a result of the sacred melodies—when they have used the melodies that excite the soul to mystic frenzy—restored as though they had found healing and purgation. Those who are influenced by pity or fear, and every emotional nature, must have a like experience, and others in so far as each is susceptible to such emotions, and all are in a manner purged and their souls lightened and delighted. The purgative melodies likewise give an innocent pleasure to mankind. Such are the modes and the melodies in which those who perform music at the theatre should be invited to compete. But since the spectators are of two kinds—the one free and educated, and the other a vulgar crowd composed of mechanics, labourers, and the like—there ought to be contests and exhibitions instituted for the relaxation of the second class also. And the music will correspond to their minds; for as their minds are perverted from the natural state, so there are perverted modes and highly strung and unnaturally coloured melodies. A man receives pleasure

[1] Cf. *Poetics*, 1449^b 27.

from what is natural to him, and therefore professional musicians may be allowed to practise this lower sort of music before an audience of a lower type. But, for the purposes of education, as I have already said,[1] those modes and melodies should be employed which are ethical, such as the Dorian, as we said before;[2] though we may include any others which are approved by philosophers who have had a musical education. The Socrates of the *Republic*[3] is wrong in retaining only the Phrygian mode along with the Dorian, and the more so **1342b** because he rejects the flute; for the Phrygian is to the modes what the flute is to musical instruments—both of them are exciting and emotional. Poetry proves this, for Bacchic frenzy and all similar emotions are most suitably expressed by the flute, and are better set to the Phrygian than to any other mode. The dithyramb, for example, is acknowledged to be Phrygian, a fact of which the connoisseurs of music offer many proofs, saying, among other things, that Philoxenus, having attempted to compose his *Mysians* as a dithyramb in the Dorian mode, found it impossible, and fell back by the very nature of things into the more appropriate Phrygian. All men agree that the Dorian music is the gravest and manliest. And whereas we say that the extremes should be avoided and the mean followed, and whereas the Dorian is a mean between the other modes, it is evident that our youth should be taught the Dorian music.

Two principles have to be kept in view, what is possible, what is becoming: at these every man ought to aim. But even these are relative to age; the old, who have lost their powers, cannot very well sing the high-strung modes, and nature herself seems to suggest that their songs should be of the more relaxed kind. Wherefore the musicians likewise blame Socrates, and with justice, for rejecting the relaxed modes in education under the idea that they are intoxicating, not in the ordinary sense of intoxication (for wine rather tends to excite men), but because they have no strength in them. And so, with a view also to the time of life when men begin to grow old, they ought to practise the gentler modes and melodies as well as the others, and, further, any mode, such as the Lydian above all others appears to be, which is suited to children of tender age, and possesses the elements both of order and of education. Thus it is clear that education should be based upon three principles—the mean, the possible, the becoming, these three.

[1] 1342a 2. [2] 1340b 3 sqq.
[3] Plato, *Republic*, III. 399.

THE ATHENIAN CONSTITUTION

CONTENTS: THE ATHENIAN CONSTITUTION

I. Sketch of Athenian History

THE ATHENIAN CONSTITUTION

1

... [They[1] were tried] by a court empanelled from among the noble families, and sworn upon the sacrifices. The part of accuser was taken by Myron. They were found guilty of the sacrilege, and their bodies were cast out of their graves and their race banished for evermore. In view of this expiation, Epimenides the Cretan performed a purification of the city.

2

After this event there was contention for a long [2] time between the upper classes and the populace. Not only was the constitution at this time oligarchical in every respect, but the poorer classes, men, women, and children, were the serfs of the rich. They were known as Pelătae and also as Hectēmŏri, because they cultivated the lands of the rich at the rent thus indicated. The whole country was in the hands of a few persons, and if the tenants failed to pay their rent they were liable to be haled into slavery, and their children with them. All loans were secured upon the debtor's person, a custom which prevailed until the time of Solon, who was the first to appear as the champion of the [3] people. But the hardest and bitterest part of the constitution in the eyes of the masses was their state of serfdom. Not but what they were also discontented with every other feature of their lot; for, to speak generally, they had no part nor share in anything.

3

Now the ancient constitution, as it existed before the time of Draco, was organized as follows. The magistrates were elected according to qualifications of birth and wealth. At first they governed for life, but subsequently for [2] terms of ten years. The first magistrates, both in date and in importance, were the King, the Polemarch, and the Archon. The earliest of these offices was that of the King, which existed from ancestral antiquity. To this was added, secondly, the office of Polemarch, on account of some of the kings proving feeble in war; for it was on this account that Ion was invited to accept the post on an occasion of pressing need. [3] The last of the three offices was that of the Archon, which most authorities state to have come into existence in the time of Medon. Others assign it to the time of Acastus, and adduce as proof the fact that the nine Archons swear to execute their oaths 'as in the days of Acastus,' which seems to suggest that it was in his time that the descendants of Codrus retired from the kingship in return for the prerogatives conferred upon the Archon. Whichever way it may be, the difference in date is small; but that it was the last of these magistracies to be created is shown by the fact that the Archon has no part in the ancestral sacrifices, as the King and the Polemarch have, but exclusively in those of later origin. So it is only at a comparatively late date that the office of Archon has become of great importance, through the dignity conferred by these later [4] additions. The Thesmothĕtae[2] were appointed many years afterwards, when these offices had already become annual, with the object that they might publicly record all legal decisions, and act as guardians of them with a view to determining the issues between litigants. Accordingly their office, alone of those which have been mentioned, was never of more than annual duration.

[5] Such, then, is the relative chronological precedence of these offices. At that time the

[1] The narrative opens with the trial of the Alcmeonidae for sacrilege. Cylon, a young noble, had attempted to seize despotic power by force; but his attempt failed, and his adherents fled to sanctuary, which they were only induced to leave under a safe conduct. This was violated by the archon Megacles, one of the great house of the Alcmeonidae, who caused them all to be put to death; a sacrilege which was supposed to be the cause of the misfortunes which subsequently befell Athens, until the Alcmeonidae submitted themselves to trial. The date of Cylon's attempt to set himself up as tyrant is shown by this treatise to have been before the time of Draco; and, as Cylon was an Olympic victor in 640 B.C., and was apparently still a young man at the time of his attempt, the latter (which took place in an Olympic year) may be assigned to 632 B.C. The expulsion of the Alcmeonidae did not take place till many years afterwards; the visit of Epimenides probably took place about 596 B.C., shortly before the legislation of Solon. Aristotle is here carrying down the story of Cylon's attempt to its conclusion, and he subsequently goes back to the reforms of Draco.

NOTE: The bracketed numbers, assigned as they are in the Oxford translation, indicate the paragraphs of the Oxford Greek text.

[2] The six junior Archons.

nine Archons did not all live together. The King occupied the building now known as the Bucolium, near the Prytanēum, as may be seen from the fact that even to the present day the marriage of the King's wife to Dionysus[1] takes place there. The Archon lived in the Prytaneum, the Polemarch in the Epilycēum. The latter building was formerly called the Polemarchēum, but after Epilycus, during his term of office as Polemarch, had rebuilt it and fitted it up, it was called the Epilyceum. The Thesmothetae occupied the Thesmothetēum. In the time of Solon, however, they all came together into the Thesmotheteum. They had power to decide cases finally on their own authority, not, as now, merely to hold a preliminary hearing. Such then was the arrangement [6] of the magistracies. The Council of Areopagus had as its constitutionally assigned duty the protection of the laws; but in point of fact it administered the greater and most important part of the government of the state, and inflicted personal punishments and fines summarily upon all who misbehaved themselves. This was the natural consequence of the facts that the Archons were elected under qualifications of birth and wealth, and that the Areopagus was composed of those who had served as Archons; for which latter reason the membership of the Areopagus is the only office which has continued to be a life-magistracy to the present day.

4

Such was, in outline, the first constitution, but not very long after the events above recorded, in the archonship of Aristaichmus,[2] Draco enacted his ordinances. Now his constitution had the following form. The franchise was given to all who could furnish themselves with a [2] military equipment. The nine Archons and the Treasurers were elected by this body from persons possessing an unencumbered property of not less than ten minas, the less important officials from those who could furnish themselves with a military equipment, and the generals [Stratēgi] and commanders of the cavalry [Hipparchi] from those who could show an unencumbered property of not less than a hundred minas, and had children born in lawful wedlock over ten years of age. These officers were required to hold to bail the Prytănes, the Strategi, and the Hipparchi of the preceding year until their accounts had been audited, taking four securities of the same class as that to which the Strategi and the Hipparchi [3] belonged. There was also to be a Council, consisting of four hundred and one members, elected by lot from among those who possessed the franchise. Both for this and for the other magistracies the lot was cast among those who were over thirty years of age; and no one might hold office twice until every one else had had his turn, after which they were to cast the lot afresh. If any member of the Council failed to attend when there was a sitting of the Council or of the Assembly, he paid a fine, to the amount of three drachmas if he was a Pentacosiomedimnus,[3] two if he was a Knight, and [4] one if he was a Zeugites. The Council of Areopagus was guardian of the laws, and kept watch over the magistrates to see that they executed their offices in accordance with the laws. Any person who felt himself wronged might lay an information before the Council of Areopagus, on declaring what law was broken by [5] the wrong done to him. But, as has been said before,[4] loans were secured upon the persons of the debtors, and the land was in the hands of a few.

5

Since such, then, was the organization of the constitution, and the many were in slavery to the few, the people rose against the upper class. [2] The strife was keen, and for a long time the two parties were ranged in hostile camps against one another, till at last,[5] by common consent, they appointed Solon to be mediator and Archon, and committed the whole constitution to his hands. The immediate occasion of his appointment was his poem, which begins with the words:

I behold, and within my heart deep sadness has claimed its place,
As I mark the oldest home of the ancient Ionian race
Slain by the sword.

In this poem he fights and disputes on behalf of each party in turn against the other, and finally he advises them to come to terms and put an end to the quarrel existing between [3] them. By birth and reputation Solon was one of the foremost men of the day, but in

[1] The wife of the King-archon every year went through the ceremony of marriage to the god Dionysus, at the feast of the Anthesteria.

[2] The name of this Archon is not otherwise known, but the traditional date of Draco is 621 B.C.

[3] See chapter 7. 4.

[4] Chapter 2. 2.

[5] The traditional date for Solon's legislation is 594 B.C.

wealth and position he was of the middle class, as is generally agreed, and is, indeed, established by his own evidence in these poems, where he exhorts the wealthy not to be grasp-

But ye who have store of good, who are sated and overflow,
Restrain your swelling soul, and still it and keep it low:
Let the heart that is great within you be trained a lowlier way;
Ye shall not have all at your will, and we will not for ever obey.

ing. Indeed, he constantly fastens the blame of the conflict on the rich; and accordingly at the beginning of the poem he says that he fears 'the love of wealth and an overweening mind', evidently meaning that it was through these that the quarrel arose.

6

As soon as he was at the head of affairs, Solon liberated the people once and for all, by prohibiting all loans on the security of the debtor's person: and in addition he made laws by which he cancelled all debts, public and private. This measure is commonly called the Seisachtheia [= removal of burdens], since thereby the people had their loads removed from them. In
[2] connexion with it some persons try to traduce the character of Solon. It so happened that, when he was about to enact the Seisachtheia, he communicated his intention to some members of the upper class, whereupon, as the partisans of the popular party say, his friends stole a march on him; while those who wish to attack his character maintain that he too had a share in the fraud himself. For these persons borrowed money and bought up a large amount of land, and so when, a short time afterwards, all debts were cancelled, they became wealthy; and this, they say, was the origin of the families which were afterwards looked on as having been wealthy from primeval times. However,
[3] the story of the popular party is by far the most probable. A man who was so moderate and public-spirited in all his other actions, that when it was within his power to put his fellow-citizens beneath his feet and establish himself as tyrant, he preferred instead to incur the hostility of both parties by placing his honour and the general welfare above his personal aggrandisement, is not likely to have consented to defile his hands by such a petty and palpable
[4] fraud. That he had this absolute power is, in the first place, indicated by the desperate condition of the country; moreover, he mentions it himself repeatedly in his poems, and it is universally admitted. We are therefore bound to consider this accusation to be false.

7

Next Solon drew up a constitution and enacted new laws; and the ordinances of Draco ceased to be used, with the exception of those relating to murder. The laws were inscribed on the wooden stands, and set up in the King's Porch, and all swore to obey them; and the nine Archons made oath upon the stone,[1] declaring that they would dedicate a golden statue if they should transgress any of them. This is the origin of the oath to that effect which they take
[2] to the present day. Solon ratified his laws for a hundred years; and the following was the fashion in which he organized the constitu-
[3] tion. He divided the population according to property into four classes, just as it had been divided before, namely, Pentacosiomedimni, Knights, Zeugitae, and Thetes.[2] The various magistracies, namely, the nine Archons, the Treasurers, the Commissioners for Public Contracts (Polētae), the Eleven,[3] and the Exchequer Clerks (Colacrĕtae),[4] he assigned to the Pentacosiomedimni, the Knights, and the Zeugitae, giving offices to each class in proportion to the value of their rateable property. To those who ranked among the Thetes he gave nothing but a place in the Assembly and in the
[4] juries. A man had to rank as a Pentacosiomedimnus if he made, from his own land, five hundred measures, whether liquid or solid. Those ranked as Knights who made three hundred measures, or, as some say, those who were able to maintain a horse. In support of the latter definition they adduce the name of the class, which may be supposed to be derived from this fact, and also some votive offerings of early times; for in the Acropolis there is a votive offering, a statue of Diphilus, bearing this inscription:

[1] See chapter 55. 5.

[2] The name Pentacosiomedimnus means one who possesses 500 measures, as explained in the text below; that of Knight, or Horseman, implies ability to keep a horse; that of Zeugites, ability to keep a yoke of oxen; while the Thetes were originally serfs attached to the soil.

[3] The superintendents of the state prison; see chapter 52. 1.

[4] These officers, whose original function was said to have been to 'collect the pieces after a sacrifice', were the Treasury officials in early times, who received the taxes and handed them over to be kept by the Treasurers. In later times the Colacretae seem to have ceased to exist, and they are not mentioned in Aristotle's enumeration of the officials in his own day.

The son of Diphilus, Anthemion hight,
Raised from the Thetes and become a knight,
Did to the gods this sculptured charger bring,
For his promotion a thank-offering.

And a horse stands in evidence beside the man, implying that this was what was meant by belonging to the rank of Knight. At the same time it seems reasonable to suppose that this class, like the Pentacosiomedimni, was defined by the possession of an income of a certain number of measures. Those ranked as Zeugitae who made two hundred measures, liquid or solid; and the rest ranked as Thetes, and were not eligible for any office. Hence it is that even at the present day, when a candidate for any office is asked to what class he belongs, no one would think of saying that he belonged to the Thetes.

8

The elections to the various offices Solon enacted should be by lot, out of candidates selected by each of the tribes. Each tribe selected ten candidates for the nine archonships, and among these the lot was cast. Hence it is still the custom for each tribe to choose ten candidates by lot, and then the lot is again cast among these. A proof that Solon regulated the elections to office according to the property classes may be found in the law still in force with regard to the Treasurers, which enacts that they shall be [2] chosen from the Pentacosiomedimni.[1] Such was Solon's legislation with respect to the nine Archons; whereas in early times the Council of Areopagus[2] summoned suitable persons according to its own judgement and appointed them for the year to the several offices. There [3] were four tribes, as before, and four tribe-kings. Each tribe was divided into three Trittyes [= Thirds], with twelve Naucraries[3] in each; and the Naucraries had officers of their own, called Naucrāri, whose duty it was to superintend the current receipts and expenditure. Hence, among the laws of Solon now obsolete, it is repeatedly written that the Naucrari are to receive and to spend out of the Naucraric fund. [4] Solon also appointed a Council of four hundred, a hundred from each tribe; but he assigned to the Council of the Areopagus the duty of superintending the laws, acting as before as the guardian of the constitution in general. It kept watch over the affairs of the state in most of the more important matters, and corrected offenders, with full powers to inflict either fines or personal punishment. The money received in fines it brought up into the Acropolis, without assigning the reason for the mulct. It also tried those who conspired for the overthrow of the state, Solon having enacted a process of impeachment to deal with such of-[5] fenders. Further, since he saw the state often engaged in internal disputes, while many of the citizens from sheer indifference accepted whatever might turn up, he made a law with express reference to such persons, enacting that any one who, in a time of civil factions, did not take up arms with either party, should lose his rights as a citizen and cease to have any part in the state.

9

Such, then, was his legislation concerning the magistracies. There are three points in the constitution of Solon which appear to be its most democratic features: first and most important, the prohibition of loans on the security of the debtor's person; secondly, the right of every person who so willed to claim redress on behalf of any one to whom wrong was being done; thirdly, the institution of the appeal to the jury-courts; and it is to this last, they say, that the masses have owed their strength most of all, since, when the democracy is master of the voting-power, it is master of the constitution. [2] Moreover, since the laws were not drawn up in simple and explicit terms (but like the one concerning inheritances and wards of state), disputes inevitably occurred, and the courts had to decide in every matter, whether public or private. Some persons in fact believe that Solon deliberately made the laws indefinite, in order that the final decision might be in the hands of the people. This, however, is not probable, and the reason no doubt was that it is impossible to attain ideal perfection when framing a law in general terms; for we must judge of his intentions, not from the actual results in the present day, but from the general tenor of the rest of his legislation.

10

These seem to be the democratic features of his laws; but in addition, before the period of his legislation, he carried through his abolition of debts, and after it his increase in the standards

[1] See chapter 47. 1.

[2] The elections by the Areopagus, which may have begun as early as the first successors of Codrus, apparently lasted till the reforms of Draco, by which the franchise was conferred on all who could furnish a military equipment, and the magistrates were presumably thenceforward elected in the general Ecclesia or Assembly.

[3] See chapter 21. 5; and cf. Herodotus, v. 71.

of weights and measures, and of the currency. [2] During his administration the measures were made larger than those of Pheidon, and the mina, which previously had a standard of seventy drachmas, was raised to the full hundred. The standard coin in earlier times was the two-drachma piece. He also made weights corresponding with the coinage, sixty-three minas going to the talent; and the odd three minas were distributed among the staters and the other values.

11

When he had completed his organization of the constitution in the manner that has been described, he found himself beset by people coming to him and harassing him concerning his laws, criticizing here and questioning there, till, as he wished neither to alter what he had decided on nor yet to be an object of ill will to every one by remaining in Athens, he set off on a journey to Egypt, with the combined objects of trade and travel, giving out that he should not return for ten years. He considered that there was no call for him to expound the laws personally, but that every one should obey [2] them just as they were written. Moreover, his position at this time was unpleasant. Many members of the upper class had been estranged from him on account of his abolition of debts, and both parties were alienated through their disappointment at the condition of things which he had created. The mass of the people had expected him to make a complete redistribution of all property, and the upper class hoped he would restore everything to its former position, or, at any rate, make but a small change. Solon, however, had resisted both classes. He might have made himself a despot by attaching himself to whichever party he chose, but he preferred, though at the cost of incurring the enmity of both, to be the saviour of his country and the ideal lawgiver.

12

The truth of this view of Solon's policy is established alike by common consent, and by the mention he has himself made of the matter in his poems. Thus:

I gave to the mass of the people such rank as befitted their need,
I took not away their honour, and I granted naught to their greed;
While those who were rich in power, who in wealth were glorious and great,
I bethought me that naught should befall them unworthy their splendour and state;
So I stood with my shield outstretched, and both were safe in its sight,
And I would not that either should triumph, when the triumph was not with right.

[2] Again he declares how the mass of the people ought to be treated:

But thus will the people best the voice of their leaders obey,
When neither too slack is the rein, nor violence holdeth the sway;
For indulgence breedeth a child, the presumption that spurns control,
When riches too great are poured upon men of unbalanced soul.

[3] And again elsewhere he speaks about the persons who wished to redistribute the land:

So they came in search of plunder, and their cravings knew no bound,
Every one among them deeming endless wealth would here be found.
And that I with glozing smoothness hid a cruel mind within.
Fondly then and vainly dreamt they; now they raise an angry din,
And they glare askance in anger, and the light within their eyes
Burns with hostile flames upon me. Yet therein no justice lies.
All I promised, fully wrought I with the gods at hand to cheer,
Naught beyond in folly ventured. Never to my soul was dear
With a tyrant's force to govern, nor to see the good and base
Side by side in equal portion share the rich home of our race.

[4] Once more he speaks of the abolition of debts and of those who before were in servitude, but were released owing to the Seisachtheia:

Of all the aims for which I summoned forth
The people, was there one I compassed not?
Thou, when slow time brings justice in its train,
O mighty mother of the Olympian gods,
Dark Earth, thou best canst witness, from whose breast
I swept the pillars broadcast planted there,
And made thee free, who hadst been slave of yore.
And many a man whom fraud or law had sold
For from his god-built land, an outcast slave,
I brought again to Athens; yea, and some,
Exiles from home through debt's oppressive load,
Speaking no more the dear Athenian tongue,
But wandering far and wide, I brought again;
And those that here in vilest slavery

Crouched 'neath a master's frown, I set them free.
Thus might and right were yoked in harmony,
Since by the force of law I won my ends
And kept my promise. Equal laws I gave
To evil and to good, with even hand
Drawing straight justice for the lot of each.
But had another held the goad as I,
One in whose heart was guile and greediness,
He had not kept the people back from strife.
For had I granted, now what pleased the one,
Then what their foes devised in counterpoise,
Of many a man this state had been bereft.
Therefore I showed my might on every side,
Turning at bay like wolf among the hounds.

[5] And again he reviles both parties for their grumblings in the times that followed:

Nay, if one must lay blame where blame is due,
Wer't not for me, the people ne'er had set
Their eyes upon these blessings e'en in dreams:—
While greater men, the men of wealthier life,
Should praise me and should court me as their friend.

For had any other man, he says, received this exalted post,

He had not kept the people back, nor ceased
Til he had robbed the richness of the milk.
But I stood forth a landmark in the midst,
And barred the foes from battle.

13

Such then, were Solon's reasons for his departure from the country. After his retirement the city was still torn by divisions. For four years, indeed, they lived in peace; but in the fifth year after Solon's government they were unable to elect an Archon on account of their dissensions, and again four years later they elected no Archon for the same reason. Subse-
[2] quently, after a similar period had elapsed, Damasias was elected Archon;[1] and he governed for two years and two months, until he was forcibly expelled from his office. After this it was agreed, as a compromise, to elect ten Archons, five from the Eupatridae, three from the Agroeci, and two from the Demiurgi,[2] and they ruled for the year following Damasias. It is clear from this that the Archon was at the time the magistrate who possessed the greatest power, since it is always in connexion with this
[3] office that conflicts are seen to arise. But altogether they were in a continual state of internal disorder. Some found the cause and justification of their discontent in the abolition of debts, because thereby they had been reduced to poverty; others were dissatisfied with the political constitution, because it had undergone a revolutionary change; while with others the motive was found in personal rivalries among
[4] themselves. The parties at this time were three in number. First there was the party of the Shore, led by Megacles the son of Alcmeon, which was considered to aim at a moderate form of government; then there were the men of the Plain, who desired an oligarchy and were led by Lycurgus; and thirdly there were the men of the Highlands, at the head of whom was Pisistratus, who was looked on as an ex-
[5] treme democrat. This latter party was reinforced by those who had been deprived of the debts due to them, from motives of poverty, and by those who were not of pure descent, from motives of personal apprehension. A proof of this is seen in the fact that after the tyranny was overthrown a revision was made of the citizen-roll, on the ground that many persons were partaking in the franchise without having a right to it. The names given to the respective parties were derived from the districts in which they held their lands.

14

Pisistratus had the reputation of being an extreme democrat, and he also had distinguished himself greatly in the war with Megara. Taking advantage of this, he wounded himself, and by representing that his injuries had been inflicted on him by his political rivals, he persuaded the people, through a motion proposed by Aristion, to grant him a bodyguard. After he had got these 'club-bearers', as they were called, he made an attack with them on the people and seized the Acropolis. This happened in the archonship of Comeas, thirty-one years after the legislation of Solon. It is related
[2] that, when Pisistratus asked for his bodyguard, Solon opposed the request, and declared that in so doing he proved himself wiser than half the people and braver than the rest,—wiser than those who did not see that Pisistratus designed to make himself tyrant, and braver than those who saw it and kept silence. But when all his words availed nothing he carried forth his armour and set it up in front of his house, saying that he had helped his country so far as lay in his power (he was already a very old man), and that he called on all others to do the
[3] same. Solon's exhortations, however, proved fruitless, and Pisistratus assumed the

[1] Probably in 582 B.C.

[2] Eupatridae = the aristocrats; Agroeci = the country, or agricultural, party; Demiurgi = the handworkers, or labour party.

sovereignty. His administration was more like a constitutional government than the rule of a tyrant; but before his power was firmly established, the adherents of Megacles and Lycurgus made a coalition and drove him out. This took place in the archonship of Hegesias, five [4] years after the first establishment of his rule. Eleven years later Megacles, being in difficulties in a party struggle, again opened negotiations with Pisistratus, proposing that the latter should marry his daughter; and on these terms he brought him back to Athens, by a very primitive and simple-minded device. He first spread abroad a rumour that Athena was bringing back Pisistratus, and then, having found a woman of great stature and beauty, named Phyë (according to Herodotus, of the deme of Paeānia, but as others say a Thracian flower-seller of the deme of Collytus), he dressed her in a garb resembling that of the goddess and brought her into the city with Pisistratus. The latter drove in on a chariot with the woman beside him, and the inhabitants of the city, struck with awe, received him with adoration.

15

In this manner did his first return take place. He did not, however, hold his power long, for about six years after his return he was again expelled. He refused to treat the daughter of Megacles as his wife, and being afraid, in consequence, of a combination of the two opposing parties, he retired from the country. First [2] he led a colony to a place called Rhaicēlus, in the region of the Thermaic gulf; and thence he passed to the country in the neighbourhood of Mt. Pangaeus. Here he acquired wealth and hired mercenaries; and not till ten years had elapsed did he return to Eretria and make an attempt to recover the government by force. In this he had the assistance of many allies, notably the Thebans and Lygdămis of Naxos, and also the Knights who held the supreme power in the constitution of Eretria. After his victory [3] in the battle at Pallēnē he captured Athens, and when he had disarmed the people he at last had his tyranny securely established, and was [4] able to take Naxos and set up Lygdamis as ruler there. He effected the disarmament of the people in the following manner. He ordered a parade in full armour in the Thesēum, and began to make a speech to the people. He spoke for a short time, until the people called out that they could not hear him, whereupon he bade them come up to the entrance of the Acropolis, in order that his voice might be better heard. Then, while he continued to speak to them at great length, men whom he had appointed for the purpose collected the arms and locked them up in the chambers of the Theseum hard by, and came and made a signal to him that it was [5] done. Pisistratus accordingly, when he had finished the rest of what he had to say, told the people also what had happened to their arms; adding that they were not to be surprised or alarmed, but go home and attend to their private affairs, while he would himself for the future manage all the business of the state.

16

Such was the origin and such the vicissitudes [2] of the tyranny of Pisistratus. His administration was temperate, as has been said before, and more like constitutional government than a tyranny. Not only was he in every respect humane and mild and ready to forgive those who offended, but, in addition, he advanced money to the poorer people to help them in their labours, so that they might make their living by [3] agriculture. In this he had two objects, first that they might not spend their time in the city but might be scattered over all the face of the country, and secondly that, being moderately well off and occupied with their own business, they might have neither the wish nor the time [4] to attend to public affairs. At the same time his revenues were increased by the thorough cultivation of the country, since he imposed a tax of one tenth on all the produce. For the [5] same reasons he instituted the local justices,[1] and often made expeditions in person into the country to inspect it and to settle disputes between individuals, that they might not come into the city and neglect their farms. It [6] was in one of these progresses that, as the story goes, Pisistratus had his adventure with the man of Hymettus, who was cultivating the spot afterwards known as 'Tax-free Farm'. He saw a man digging and working at a very stony piece of ground, and being surprised he sent his attendant to ask what he got out of this plot of land. 'Aches and pains', said the man; 'and that's what Pisistratus ought to have his tenth of'. The man spoke without knowing who his questioner was; but Pisistratus was so pleased with his frank speech and his industry [7] that he granted him exemption from all taxes. And so in matters in general he burdened the people as little as possible with his government, but always cultivated peace and kept them in all quietness. Hence the tyranny

[1] See chapter 53. 1.

of Pisistratus was often spoken of proverbially as 'the age of gold'; for when his sons succeeded him the government became much harsher.
[*8*] But most important of all in this respect was his popular and kindly disposition. In all things he was accustomed to observe the laws, without giving himself any exceptional privileges. Once he was summoned on a charge of homicide before the Areopagus, and he appeared in person to make his defence; but the prosecutor was afraid to present himself and abandoned the
[*9*] case. For these reasons he held power long, and whenever he was expelled he regained his position easily. The majority alike of the upper class and of the people were in his favour; the former he won by his social intercourse with them, the latter by the assistance which he gave to their private purses, and his nature fitted him to win the hearts of both. Moreover, the
[*10*] laws in reference to tyrants at that time in force at Athens were very mild, especially the one which applies more particularly to the establishment of a tyranny. The law ran as follows: 'These are the ancestral statutes of the Athenians; if any persons shall make an attempt to establish a tyranny, or if any person shall join in setting up a tyranny, he shall lose his civic rights, both himself and his whole house.'

17

Thus did Pisistratus grow old in the possession of power, and he died a natural death in the archonship of Philoneos,[1] three and thirty years from the time at which he first established himself as tyrant, during nineteen of
[*2*] which he was in possession of power; the rest he spent in exile. It is evident from this that the story is mere gossip which states that Pisistratus was the youthful favourite of Solon and commanded in the war against Megara for the recovery of Salamis. It will not harmonize with their respective ages, as any one may see who will reckon up the years of the life of
[*3*] each of them, and the dates at which they died. After the death of Pisistratus his sons took up the government, and conducted it on the same system. He had two sons by his first and legitimate[2] wife, Hippias and Hipparchus, and two by his Argive consort, Iophon and Hegesistrătus, who was surnamed Thessalus.
[*4*] For Pisistratus took a wife from Argos, Timonassa, the daughter of a man of Argos, named Gorgīlus; she had previously been the wife of Archīnus of Ambracia, one of the descendants of Cypsĕlus. This was the origin of his friendship with the Argives, on account of which a thousand of them were brought over by Hegesistratus and fought on his side in the battle at Pallene. Some authorities say that this marriage took place after his first expulsion from Athens, others while he was in possession of the government.

18

Hippias and Hipparchus assumed the control of affairs on grounds alike of standing and of age; but Hippias, as being also naturally of a statesmanlike and shrewd disposition, was really the head of the government. Hipparchus was youthful in disposition, amorous, and fond of literature (it was he who invited to Athens Anacreon, Simonides, and the other poets),
[*2*] while Thessalus was much junior in age, and was violent and headstrong in his behaviour. It was from his character that all the evils arose which befell the house.[3] He became enamoured of Harmodius, and, since he failed to win his affection, he lost all restraint upon his passion, and in addition to other exhibitions of rage he finally prevented the sister of Harmodius from taking the part of a basket-bearer in the Panathenaic procession, alleging as his reason that Harmodius was a person of loose life. Thereupon, in a frenzy of wrath, Harmodius and Aristogeiton did their celebrated deed, in conjunction with a number of confederates.[4] But while they were lying in
[*3*] wait for Hippias in the Acropolis at the time of the Panathenaea (Hippias, at this moment, was awaiting the arrival of the procession, while Hipparchus was organizing its dispatch) they saw one of the persons privy to the plot talking familiarly with him. Thinking that he was betraying them, and desiring to do something before they were arrested, they rushed down and made their attempt without waiting for the rest of their confederates. They succeeded in killing Hipparchus near the Leocorēum while he was engaged in arranging the procession, but ruined the design as a whole;
[*4*] of the two leaders, Harmodius was killed on the spot by the guards, while Aristogeiton was arrested, and perished later after suffering long tortures. While under the torture he accused many persons who belonged by birth to the most distinguished families and were also personal friends of the tyrants. At first the gov-

[1] 527 B.C.
[2] Pisistratus's second wife was a foreigner, and therefore not legitimate according to strict Athenian law.
[3] Cf. Thucydides, VI. 54.
[4] Cf. *Ibid.*, VI. 56.

ernment could find no clue to the conspiracy; for the current story,[1] that Hippias made all who were taking part in the procession leave their arms, and then detected those who were carrying secret daggers, cannot be true, since at that time they did not bear arms in the processions, this being a custom instituted at a later period by the democracy. According to the [5] story of the popular party, Aristogeiton accused the friends of the tyrants with the deliberate intention that the latter might commit an impious act, and at the same time weaken themselves, by putting to death innocent men who were their own friends; others say that he [6] told no falsehood, but was betraying the actual accomplices. At last, when for all his efforts he could not obtain release by death, he promised to give further information against a number of other persons; and, having induced Hippias to give him his hand to confirm his word, as soon as he had hold of it he reviled him for giving his hand to the murderer of his brother, till Hippias, in a frenzy of rage, lost control of himself and snatched out his dagger and dispatched him.

19

After this event the tyranny became much harsher. In consequence of his vengeance for his brother, and of the execution and banishment of a large number of persons, Hippias became a distrusted and an embittered man. [2] About three years after the death of Hipparchus, finding his position in the city insecure, he set about fortifying Munichia, with the intention of establishing himself there. While he was still engaged on this work, however, he was expelled by Cleomenes, king of Lacedaemon, in consequence of the Spartans being continually incited by oracles to overthrow the tyranny. These oracles were obtained in the [3] following way. The Athenian exiles, headed by the Alcmeonidae, could not by their own power effect their return, but failed continually in their attempts. Among their other failures, they fortified a post in Attica, Lipsydrium, above Mt. Parnes, and were there joined by some partisans from the city; but they were besieged by the tyrants and reduced to surrender. After this disaster the following became a popular drinking song:

Ah! Lipsydrium, faithless friend!
Lo, what heroes to death didst send,
Nobly born and great in deed!
Well did they prove themselves at need
Of noble sires a noble seed.

[4] Having failed, then, in very other method, they took the contract for rebuilding the temple at Delphi,[2] thereby obtaining ample funds, which they employed to secure the help of the Lacedaemonians. All this time the Pythia kept continually enjoining on the Lacedaemonians who came to consult the oracle, that they must free Athens; till finally she succeeded in impelling the Spartans to that step, although the house of Pisistratus was connected with them by ties of hospitality. The resolution of the Lacedaemonians was, however, at least equally due to the friendship which had been formed between the house of Pisistratus [5] and Argos. Accordingly they first sent Anchimolus by sea at the head of an army; but he was defeated and killed, through the arrival of Cineas of Thessaly to support the sons of Pisistratus with a force of a thousand horsemen. Then, being roused to anger by this disaster, they sent their king, Cleomenes, by land at the head of a larger force; and he, after defeating the Thessalian cavalry when they attempted to intercept his march into Attica, shut up Hippias within what was known as the Pelargic wall and blockaded him there with the assistance of the Athenians. While he [6] was sitting down before the place, it so happened that the sons of the Pisistratidae were captured in an attempt to slip out; upon which the tyrants capitulated on condition of the safety of their children, and surrendered the Acropolis to the Athenians, five days being first allowed them to remove their effects. This took place in the archonship of Harpactides,[3] after they had held the tyranny for about seventeen years since their father's death, or in all, including the period of their father's rule, for nine-and-forty years.

20

After the overthrow of the tyranny, the rival leaders in the state were Isagoras son of Tisander, a partisan of the tyrants, and Cleisthenes, who belonged to the family of the Alcmeonidae. Cleisthenes, being beaten in the political clubs, called in the people by giving the franchise to the masses. Thereupon Isagoras, find- [2] ing himself left inferior in power, invited Cleomenes, who was united to him by ties of hospitality, to return to Athens, and persuaded him to 'drive out the pollution', a plea derived

[1] Cf. Thucydides, vi. 58.

[2] Cf. Herodotus, ii. 180.

[3] Apparently the spring of 510 B.C.

from the fact that the Alcmeonidae were supposed to be under the curse of pollution. On
[3] this Cleisthenes retired from the country, and Cleomenes, entering Attica with a small force, expelled, as polluted, seven hundred Athenian families. Having effected this, he next attempted to dissolve the Council, and to set up Isagoras and three hundred of his partisans as the supreme power in the state. The Council, however, resisted, the populace flocked together, and Cleomenes and Isagoras, with their adherents, took refuge in the Acropolis. Here the people sat down and besieged them for two days; and on the third they agreed to let Cleomenes and all his followers depart, while they summoned Cleisthenes and
[4] the other exiles back to Athens. When the people had thus obtained the command of affairs, Cleisthenes was their chief and popular leader. And this was natural; for the Alcmeonidae were perhaps the chief cause of the expulsion of the tyrants, and for the greater part of their rule were at perpetual war with them.
[5] But even earlier than the attempts of the Alcmeonidae, one Cedon made an attack on the tyrants; when there came another popular drinking song, addressed to him:

Pour a health yet again, boy, to Cedon; forget not this duty to do,
If a health is an honour befitting the name of a good man and true.

21

The people, therefore, had good reason to place confidence in Cleisthenes. Accordingly, now that he was the popular leader, three years after the expulsion of the tyrants, in the archon-
[2] ship of Isagoras,[1] his first step was to distribute the whole population into ten tribes in place of the existing four, with the object of intermixing the members of the different tribes, and so securing that more persons might have a share in the franchise. From this arose the saying 'Do not look at the tribes', addressed to those who wished to scrutinize the lists of the
[3] old families. Next he made the Council to consist of five hundred members instead of four hundred, each tribe now contributing fifty, whereas formerly each had sent a hundred. The reason why he did not organize the people into twelve tribes was that he might not have to use the existing division into trittyes; for the four tribes had twelve trittyes, so that he would not have achieved his object of redistributing the population in fresh combinations. Further,
[4] he divided the country into thirty groups of demes, ten from the districts about the city, ten from the coast, and ten from the interior. These he called trittyes; and he assigned three of them by lot to each tribe, in such a way that each should have one portion in each of these three localities. All who lived in any given deme he declared fellow-demesmen, to the end that the new citizens might not be exposd by the habitual use of family names, but that men might be officially described by the names of their demes; and accordingly it is by the names of their demes that the Athenians speak of one
[5] another. He also instituted Demarchs, who had the same duties as the previously existing Naucrari,—the demes being made to take the place of the naucraries. He gave names to the demes, some from the localities to which they belonged, some from the persons who founded them, since some of the areas no longer corresponded to localities possessing names. On the
[6] other hand he allowed every one to retain his family and clan and religious rites according to ancestral custom. The names given to the tribes were the ten which the Pythia appointed out of the hundred selected national heroes.

[1] 508 B.C.

22

By these reforms the constitution became much more democratic than that of Solon. The laws of Solon had been obliterated by disuse during the period of the tyranny, while Cleisthenes substituted new ones with the object of securing the goodwill of the masses. Among these
[2] was the law concerning ostracism. Four years[2] after the establishment of this system, in the archonship of Hermocreon, they first imposed upon the Council of Five Hundred the oath which they take to the present day. Next they began to elect the generals by tribes, one from each tribe, while the Polemarch was the
[3] commander of the whole army. Then, eleven years later, in the archonship of Phaenippus they won the battle of Marathon; and two years after this victory, when the people had now gained self-confidence, they for the first time made use of the law of ostracism.

[2] This, if correct, would place this event in 504 B.C. But, in the first place, that year belongs to another Archon; and secondly, it is inconsistent with the statement below, that the battle of Marathon occurred eleven years later. Marathon was fought in 490 B.C., therefore the archonship of Hermocreon should be assigned to 501 B.C., for which year no name occurs in the extant lists of Archons. Whether the mistake in the present passage is due to the author or a copyist it is impossible to say.

This had originally been passed as a precaution against men in high office, because Pisistratus took advantage of his position as a [4] popular leader and general to make himself tyrant; and the first person ostracized was one of his relatives, Hipparchus son of Charmus, of the deme of Collytus, the very person on whose account especially Cleisthenes had enacted the law, as he wished to get rid of him. Hitherto, however, he had escaped; for the Athenians, with the usual leniency of the democracy, allowed all the partisans of the tyrants, who had not joined in their evil deeds in the time of the troubles to remain in the city; and the chief and leader of these was [5] Hipparchus. Then in the very next year, in the archonship of Telesinus,[1] they for the first time since the tyranny elected, tribe by tribe, the nine Archons by lot out of the five hundred[2] candidates selected by the demes, all the earlier ones having been elected by vote; and in the same year Megacles son of Hippocrates, of the deme of Alopĕcē, was ostracized. Thus for [6] three years they continued to ostracize the friends of the tyrants, on whose account the law had been passed; but in the following year they began to remove others as well, including any one who seemed to be more powerful than was expedient. The first person unconnected with the tyrants who was ostracized was [7] Xanthippus son of Ariphron. Two years later, in the archonship of Nicodemus, the mines of Maroneia were discovered, and the state made a profit of a hundred talents from the working of them. Some persons advised the people to make a distribution of the money among themselves, but this was prevented by Themistocles. He refused to say on what he proposed to spend the money, but he bade them lend it to the hundred richest men in Athens, one talent to each, and then, if the manner in which it was employed pleased the people, the expenditure should be charged to the state, but otherwise the state should receive the sum back from those to whom it was lent. On these terms he received the money and with it he had a hundred triremes built, each of the hundred individuals building one; and it was with these ships that they fought the battle of Salamis against the barbarians. About this time [8] Aristides the son of Lysimachus was ostracized. Three years later, however, in the archonship of Hypsichides, all the ostracized persons were recalled, on account of the advance of the army of Xerxes; and it was laid down for the future that persons under sentence of ostracism must live between Geraestus and Scyllaeum, on pain of losing their civic rights irrevocably.

23

So far, then, had the city progressed by this time, growing gradually with the growth of the democracy; but after the Persian wars the Council of Areopagus once more developed strength and assumed the control of the state. It did not acquire this supremacy by virtue of any formal decree, but because it had been the cause of the battle of Salamis being fought. When the generals were utterly at a loss how to meet the crisis and made proclamation that every one should see to his own safety, the Areopagus provided a donation of money, distributing eight drachmas to each member of the ships' crews, and so prevailed on them to [2] go on board. On these grounds people bowed to its prestige; and during this period Athens was well administered. At this time they devoted themselves to the prosecution of the war and were in high repute among the Greeks, so that the command by sea was conferred upon them, in spite of the opposition of [3] the Lacedaemonians. The leaders of the people during this period were Aristides, son of Lysimachus, and Themistocles, son of Neocles, of whom the latter appeared to devote himself to the conduct of war, while the former had the reputation of being a clever statesman and the most upright man of his time. Accordingly the one was usually employed as general, the other as political adviser. The [4] rebuilding of the fortifications they conducted in combination, although they were political opponents; but it was Aristides who, seizing the opportunity afforded by the discredit brought upon the Lacedaemonians by Pausanias, guided the public policy in the matter of the defection of the Ionian states from [5] the alliance with Sparta. It follows that it was he who made the first assessment of tribute from the various allied states, two years after the battle of Salamis, in the archonship of Timosthenes;[3] and it was he who took the oath of offensive and defensive alliance with the Ionians, on which occasion they cast the masses of iron into the sea.[4]

24

After this, seeing the state growing in confidence and much wealth accumulated, he ad-

[1] 487 B.C. Cf. Herodotus, VI. 109.
[2] Cf. chapter 8. 1.

[3] 478 B.C. [4] Cf. Herodotus, I. 165.

vised the people to lay hold of the leadership of the league, and to quit the country districts and settle in the city. He pointed out to them that all would be able to gain a living there, some by service in the army, others in the garrisons, others by taking a part in public affairs; and in this way they would secure the leader-
[2] ship. This advice was taken; and when the people had assumed the supreme control they proceeded to treat their allies in a more imperious fashion, with the exception of the Chians, Lesbians, and Samians. These they maintained to protect their empire, leaving their constitutions untouched, and allowing them to retain whatever dominion they then
[3] possessed. They also secured an ample maintenance for the mass of the population in the way which Aristides had pointed out to them. Out of the proceeds of the tributes and the taxes and the contributions of the allies more than twenty thousand persons were maintained. There were 6,000 jurymen, 1,600 bowmen, 1,200 Knights, 500 members of the Council, 500 guards of the dockyards, besides fifty guards in the Acropolis. There were some 700 magistrates at home, and some 700 abroad. Further, when they subsequently went to war, there were in addition 2,500 heavy-armed troops, twenty guard-ships, and other ships which collected the tributes, with crews amounting to 2,000 men, selected by lot; and besides these there were the persons maintained at the Prytanēum, and orphans, and gaolers, since all these were supported by the state.

25

Such was the way in which the people earned their livelihood. The supremacy of the Areopagus lasted for about seventeen years after the Persian wars, although gradually declining. But as the strength of the masses increased, Ephialtes, son of Sophonides, a man with a reputation for incorruptibility and public virtue, who had become the leader of the people, made an attack upon that Council. First of all
[2] he ruined many of its members by bringing actions against them with reference to their administration. Then, in the archonship of Conon,[1] he stripped the Council of all the acquired prerogatives from which it derived its guardianship of the constitution, and assigned some of them to the Council of Five
[3] Hundred, and others to the Assembly and the law-courts. In this revolution he was assisted by Themistocles,[2] who was himself a member of the Areopagus, but was expecting to be tried before it on a charge of treasonable dealings with Persia. This made him anxious that it should be overthrown, and accordingly he warned Ephialtes that the Council intended to arrest him, while at the same time he informed the Areopagites that he would reveal to them certain persons who were conspiring to subvert the constitution. He then conducted the representatives delegated by the Council to the residence of Ephialtes, promising to show them the conspirators who assembled there, and proceeded to converse with them in an earnest manner. Ephialtes, seeing this, was seized with alarm and took refuge in suppliant
[4] guise at the altar. Every one was astounded at the occurrence, and presently, when the Council of Five Hundred met, Ephialtes and Themistocles together proceeded to denounce the Areopagus to them. This they repeated in similar fashion in the Assembly, until they succeeded in depriving it of its power. Not long afterwards, however, Ephialtes was assassinated by Aristodĭcus of Tanagra. In this way was the Council of Areopagus deprived of its guardianship of the state.

26

After this revolution the administration of the state became more and more lax, in consequence of the eager rivalry of candidates for popular favour. During this period the moderate party, as it happened, had no real chief, their leader being Cimon son of Miltiades, who was a comparatively young man, and had been late in entering public life; and at the same time the general populace suffered great losses by war. The soldiers for active service were selected at that time from the roll of citizens, and as the generals were men of no military experience, who owed their position solely to their family standing, it continually happened that some two or three thousand of the troops perished on an expedition; and in this way the best men alike of the lower and the upper classes were exhausted. Consequently in most
[2] matters of administration less heed was paid to the laws than had formerly been the case. No alteration, however, was made in the method of election of the nine Archons, except that five years after the death of Ephialtes it was decided that the candidates to be submitted to the lot for that office might be selected from the Zeugitae as well as from the higher classes.[3] The first Archon from that

[1] 462 B.C. [2] Cf. Thucydides, I. 137.

[3] See chapter 7. 4.

lass was Mnesitheides.[1] Up to this time all he Archons had been taken from the Pentaosiomedimni and Knights, while the Zeugiae were confined to the ordinary magistracies, ave where an evasion of the law was over-
3] looked. Four years later, in the archonship f Lysicrates,[2] the thirty 'local justices',[3] as they vere called, were re-established; and two years
4] afterwards, in the archonship of Antilotus,[4] in consequence of the great increase in he number of citizens, it was resolved, on the notion of Pericles, that no one should be adnitted to the franchise who was not of citizen irth by both parents.

27

Ifter this Pericles came forward as popular eader, having first distinguished himself while till a young man by prosecuting Cimon on the udit of his official accounts as general. Under is auspices the constitution became still more lemocratic. He took away some of the privleges of the Areopagus, and, above all, he urned the policy of the state in the direction of ea power, which caused the masses to acquire onfidence in themselves and consequently to ake the conduct of affairs more and more into
2] their own hands. Moreover, forty-eight ears after the battle of Salamis, in the archnship of Pythodōrus,[5] the Peloponnesian war roke out, during which the populace was hut up in the city and became accustomed to ain its livelihood by military service, and so, artly voluntarily and partly involuntarily, determined to assume the administration of the
3] state itself. Pericles was also the first to nstitute pay for service in the law-courts, as a id for popular favour to counterbalance the vealth of Cimon. The latter, having private ossessions on a regal scale, not only performed he regular public services magnificently, but lso maintained a large number of his fellowlemesmen. Any member of the deme of Lacădae could go every day to Cimon's house and here receive a reasonable provision; while his state was guarded by no fences, so that any ne who liked might help himself to the fruit
4] from it. Pericles' private property was uite unequal to this magnificence and acordingly he took the advice of Damonides of)ia (who was commonly supposed to be the erson who prompted Pericles in most of his neasures, and was therefore subsequently ostracized), which was that, as he was beaten in the matter of private possessions, he should make gifts to the people from their own property; and accordingly he instituted pay for the members of the juries. Some critics accuse him of thereby causing a deterioration in the character of the juries, since it was always the common people who put themselves forward for selection as jurors, rather than the men of bet-
[5] ter position. Moreover, bribery came into existence after this, the first person to introduce it being Anytus, after his command at Pylos.[6] He was prosecuted by certain individuals on account of his loss of Pylos, but escaped by bribing the jury.

28

So long, however, as Pericles was leader of the people, things went tolerably well with the state; but when he was dead there was a great change for the worse. Then for the first time did the people choose a leader who was of no reputation among men of good standing, whereas up to this time such men had always been found as leaders of the democracy. The
[2] first leader of the people, in the very beginning of things, was Solon, and the second was Pisistratus, both of them men of birth and position. After the overthrow of the tyrants there was Cleisthenes, a member of the house of the Alcmeonidae; and he had no rival opposed to him after the expulsion of the party of Isagoras. After this Xanthippus was the leader of the people, and Miltiades of the upper class. Then came Themistocles and Aristides,[7] and after them Ephialtes as leader of the people, and Cimon son of Miltiades of the wealthier class. Pericles followed as leader of the people, and Thucydides, who was connected by marriage with Cimon, of the opposition. After the
[3] death of Pericles, Nicias, who subsequently fell in Sicily, appeared as leader of the aristocracy, and Cleon son of Cleaenetus of the people. The latter seems, more than any one else, to have been the cause of the corruption of the democracy by his wild undertakings; and he was the first to use unseemly shouting and coarse abuse on the Bema, and to harangue the people with his cloak girt up short about him, whereas all his predecessors had spoken decently and in order. These were succeeded by Ther-

[1] 457 B.C. [2] 453 B.C.
[3] See chapters 16. 5, and 53. 1. [4] 451 B.C.
[5] Spring of 431 B.C. See Thucydides, II. 2.

[6] Pylos was recaptured by the Spartans, owing to the neglect of Anytus to relieve it, in 411 B.C. Anytus was one of the leaders of the moderate aristocratic party (chapter 34. 3), and one of the prosecutors of Socrates.
[7] See chapter 23. 3.

amenes son of Hagnon as leader of the one party, and the lyre-maker Cleophon of the people. It was Cleophon who first granted the two-obol donation for the theatrical performances, and for some time it continued to be given; but then Callicrates of Paeania ousted him by promising to add a third obol to the sum. Both of these persons were subsequently condemned to death; for the people, even if they are deceived for a time, in the end generally come to detest those who have beguiled them into [4] any unworthy action. After Cleophon the popular leadership was occupied successively by the men who chose to talk the biggest and pander the most to the tastes of the majority, with their eyes fixed only on the interests of [5] the moment. The best statesmen at Athens, after those of early times, seem to have been Nicias, Thucydides, and Theramenes. As to Nicias and Thucydides, nearly every one agrees that they were not merely men of birth and character, but also statesmen, and that they ruled the state with paternal care. On the merits of Theramenes opinion is divided, because it so happened that in his time public affairs were in a very stormy state. But those who give their opinion deliberately find him, not, as his critics falsely assert, overthrowing every kind of constitution, but supporting every kind so long as it did not transgress the laws; thus showing that he was able, as every good citizen should be, to live under any form of constitution, while he refused to countenance illegality and was its constant enemy.

29

So long as the fortune of the war continued even, the Athenians preserved the democracy; but after the disaster in Sicily, when the Lacedaemonians had gained the upper hand through their alliance with the king of Persia, they were compelled to abolish the democracy and establish in its place the constitution of the Four Hundred. The speech recommending this course before the vote was made by Melobius, and the motion was proposed by Pythodorus of Anaphlystus; but the real argument which persuaded the majority was the belief that the king of Persia was more likely to form an alliance with them if the constitution were on an oligarchical basis. The motion of Pytho- [2] dorus was to the following effect. The popular Assembly was to elect twenty persons, over forty years of age, who, in conjunction with the existing ten members of the Committee of Public Safety, after taking an oath that they would frame such measures as they thought best for the state, should then prepare proposals for the public safety. In addition any other person might make proposals, so that of all the schemes before them the people [3] might choose the best. Cleitophon concurred with the motion of Pythodorus, but moved that the committee should also investigate the ancient laws enacted by Cleisthenes when he created the democracy, in order that they might have these too before them and so be in a position to decide wisely; his suggestion being that the constitution of Cleisthenes [4] was not really democratic, but closely akin to that of Solon. When the committee was elected, their first proposal was that the Prytanes[1] should be compelled to put to the vote any motion that was offered on behalf of the public safety. Next they abolished all indictments for illegal proposals, all impeachments and pubic prosecutions, in order that every Athenian should be free to give his counsel on the situation, if he chose; and they decreed that if any person imposed a fine on any other for his acts in this respect, or prosecuted him or summoned him before the courts, he should, on an information being laid against him, be summarily arrested and brought before the generals, who should deliver him to the Eleven [5] to be put to death. After these preliminary measures, they drew up the constitution in the following manner. The revenues of the state were not to be spent on any purpose except the war. All magistrates should serve without remuneration for the period of the war, except the nine Archons and the Prytanes for the time being, who should each receive three obols a day. The whole of the rest of the administration was to be committed, for the period of the war, to those Athenians who were most capable of serving the state personally or pecuniarily, to the number of not less than five thousand. This body was to have full powers, to the extent even of making treaties with whomsoever they willed; and ten representatives, over forty years of age, were to be elected from each tribe to draw up the list of the Five Thousand, after taking an oath on a full and perfect sacrifice.

30

These were the recommendations of the committee; and when they had been ratified the Five Thousand[3] elected from their own num

[1] See chapter 43. 4. [2] See chapter 52. 1.

[3] See chapter 32. 3, and Thucydides, VIII. 92.

ber a hundred commissioners to draw up the constitution. They, on their appointment, drew [2] up and produced the following recommendations. There should be a Council, holding office for a year, consisting of men over thirty years of age, serving without pay. To this body should belong the Generals, the nine Archons, the Amphictyonic Registrar (*Hieromnemon*),[1] the Taxiarchs, the Hipparchs, the Phylarchs,[2] the commanders of garrisons, the Treasurers of Athena and the other gods, ten in number, the Hellenic Treasurers (*Hellenotamiae*),[3] the Treasurers of the other non-sacred moneys, to the number of twenty, the ten Commissioners of Sacrifices (*Hieropoei*), and the ten Superintendents of the mysteries. All these were to be appointed by the Council from a larger number of selected candidates, chosen from its members for the time being. The other offices were all to be filled by lot, and not from the members of the Council. The Hellenic Treasurers who actually administered the funds [3] should not sit with the Council. As regards the future, four Councils were to be created, of men of the age already mentioned, and one of these was to be chosen by lot to take office at once, while the others were to receive it in turn, in the order decided by the lot. For this purpose the hundred commissioners were to distribute themselves and all the rest as equally as possible into four parts, and cast lots for precedence, and [4] the selected body should hold office for a year. They were to administer that office as seemed to them best, both with reference to the safe custody and due expenditure of the finances, and generally with regard to all other matters to the best of their ability. If they desired to take a larger number of persons into counsel, each member might call in one assistant of his own choice, subject to the same qualification of age. The Council was to sit once every five days, unless there was any special need for more frequent sittings. The casting of the lot for the Council was to be held by the nine Archons; votes on divisions were to be counted by five tellers chosen by lot from the members of the Council, and of these one was to be [5] selected by lot every day to act as president. These five persons were to cast lots for precedence between the parties wishing to appear before the Council, giving the first place to sacred matters, the second to heralds, the third to embassies, and the fourth to all other subjects; but matters concerning the war might be dealt with, on the motion of the generals, whenever there was need, without balloting. Any mem- [6] ber of the Council who did not enter the Council-house at the time named should be fined a drachma for each day, unless he was away on leave of absence from the Council.

[1] This is the title of one of the two members sent by each Amphictyonic state to the general councils. He served as secretary, while the other, the Pylagoras, was the actual representative of his state.

[2] Chapter 61. 3-6.

[3] These were the officers appointed to receive the contribution of the allied states of the Confederacy of Delos, or, as these states subsequently became, the subject-allies of the Athenian empire. After the loss of the empire by the result of the Poloponnesian war these officers were no longer required, and consequently ceased to exist.

31

Such was the constitution which they drew up for the time to come, but for the immediate present they devised the following scheme. There should be a Council of Four Hundred, as in the ancient constitution, forty from each tribe, chosen out of candidates of more than thirty years of age, selected by the members of the tribes. This Council should appoint the magistrates and draw up the form of oath which they were to take; and in all that concerned the laws, in the examination of official accounts, and in other matters generally, they [2] might act according to their discretion. They must, however, observe the laws that might be enacted with reference to the constitution of the state, and had no power to alter them nor to pass others. The generals should be provisionally elected from the whole body of the Five Thousand, but so soon as the Council came into existence it was to hold an examination of military equipments, and thereon elect ten persons, together with a secretary, and the persons thus elected should hold office during the coming year with full powers, and should have the right, whenever they desired [3] it, of joining in the deliberations of the Council. The Five Thousand was also to elect a single Hipparch and ten Phylarchs; but for the future the Council was to elect these officers according to the regulations above laid down. No office, except those of member of the Council and of general, might be held more than once, either by the first occupants or by their successors. With reference to the future distribution of the Four Hundred into the four successive sections, the hundred commissioners must divide them whenever the time comes for the citizens to join in the Council along with the rest.

32

The hundred commissioners appointed by the Five Thousand drew up the constitution as just stated; and after it had been ratified by the people, under the presidency of Aristomachus, the existing Council, that of the year of Callias,[1] was dissolved before it had completed its term of office. It was dissolved on the fourteenth day of the month Thargelion, and the Four Hundred entered into office on the twenty-first; whereas the regular Council, elected by lot, ought to have entered into office on the
[2] fourteenth of Scirophorion.[2] Thus was the oligarchy established, in the archonship of Callias, just about a hundred years after the expulsion of the tyrants. The chief promoters of the revolution were Pisander, Antiphon, and Theramenes, all of them men of good birth and with high reputations for ability and judge-
[3] ment. When, however, this constitution had been established, the Five Thousand were only nominally selected, and the Four Hundred, together with the ten officers on whom full powers had been conferred,[3] occupied the Council-house and really administered the government. They began by sending ambassadors to the Lacedaemonians proposing a cessation of the war on the basis of the existing position; but as the Lacedaemonians refused to listen to them unless they would also abandon the command of the sea, they broke off the negotiations.

33

For about four months the constitution of the Four Hundred lasted, and Mnasilochus held office as Archon of their nomination for two months of the year of Theopompus, who was Archon for the remaining ten. On the loss of the naval battle of Eretria, however, and the revolt of the whole of Euboea except Orĕum, the indignation of the people was greater than at any of the earlier disasters, since they drew far more supplies at this time from Euboea than from Attica itself. Accordingly they deposed the Four Hundred and committed the management of affairs to the Five Thousand, consisting of persons possessing a military equipment. At the same time they voted that pay should
[2] not be given for any public office. The persons chiefly responsible for the revolution were Aristocrates and Theramenes, who disapproved of the action of the Four Hundred in retaining the direction of affairs entirely in their own hands, and referring nothing to the Five Thousand. During this period the constitution of the state seems to have been admirable, since it was a time of war and the franchise was in the hands of those who possessed a military equipment.[4]

34

The people, however, in a very short time deprived the Five Thousand of their monopoly of the government.[5] Then, six years after the overthrow of the Four Hundred, in the archonship of Callias of Angĕlē,[6] the battle of Arginusae took place, of which the results were, first, that the ten generals who had gained the victory were all condemned by a single decision, owing to the people being led astray by persons who aroused their indignation; though, as a matter of fact, some of the generals had actually taken no part in the battle, and others were themselves picked up by other vessels. Secondly, when the Lacedaemonians proposed to evacuate Decelēa and make peace on the basis of the existing position, although some of the Athenians supported this proposal, the majority refused to listen to them. In this they were led astray by Cleophon, who appeared in the Assembly drunk and wearing his breastplate, and prevented peace being made, declaring that he would never accept peace unless the Lacedaemonians abandoned
[2] their claims on all the cities allied with them. They mismanaged their opportunity then, and in a very short time they learnt their mistake. The next year, in the archonship of Alexias, they suffered the disaster of Aegospotami, the consequence of which was that Lysander became master of the city, and set up the Thirty as its governors. He did so in the
[3] following manner. One of the terms of peace stipulated that the state should be governed according to 'the ancient constitution'. Accordingly the popular party tried to preserve the democracy, while that part of the upper class which belonged to the political clubs, together with the exiles who had returned since the peace, aimed at an oligarchy, and those who

[1] Callias' year of office began in 412 B.C., and was now within two months of its end. The date of the entry of the Four Hundred into office is consequently in May, 411 B.C.

[2] Roughly equivalent to June.

[3] See chapter 31. 2.

[4] Cf. Thucydides VIII. 97.

[5] Probably after the battle of Cyzicus, in 410 B.C., when the fleet, which was democratic in its sympathies, returned to Athens.

[6] 406 B.C.

were not members of any club, though in other respects they considered themselves as good as any other citizens, were anxious to restore the ancient constitution. The latter class included Archīnus, Anytus, Cleitophon, Phormisius, and many others, but their most prominent leader was Theramenes. Lysander, however, threw his influence on the side of the oligarchical party, and the popular Assembly was compelled by sheer intimidation to pass a vote establishing the oligarchy. The motion to this effect was proposed by Dracontides of Aphidna.

35

In this way were the Thirty established in power, in the archonship of Pythodorus.[1] As soon, however, as they were masters of the city, they ignored all the resolutions which had been passed relating to the organization of the constitution, but after appointing a Council of Five Hundred and the other magistrates out of a thousand selected candidates, and associating with themselves ten Archons in Piraeus, eleven superintendents of the prison, and three hundred 'lash-bearers' as attendants, with the help
[2] of these they kept the city under their own control. At first, indeed, they behaved with moderation towards the citizens and pretended to administer the state according to the ancient constitution. In pursuance of this policy they took down from the hill of Areopagus the laws of Ephialtes and Archestratus relating to the Areopagite Council; they also repealed such of the statutes of Solon as were obscure,[2] and abolished the supreme power of the law-courts. In this they claimed to be restoring the constitution and freeing it from obscurities; as, for instance, by making the testator free once for all to leave his property as he pleased, and abolishing the existing limitations in cases of insanity, old age, and undue female influence, in order that no opening might be left for professional accusers. In other matters also their conduct
[3] was similar. At first, then, they acted on these lines, and they destroyed the professional accusers and those mischievous and evil-minded persons who, to the great detriment of the democracy, had attached themselves to it in order to curry favour with it. With all of this the city was much pleased, and thought that the
[4] Thirty were doing it with the best of motives. But so soon as they had got a firmer hold on the city, they spared no class of citizens, but put to death any persons who were eminent for wealth or birth or character. Herein they aimed at removing all whom they had reason to fear, while they also wished to lay hands on their possessions; and in a short time they put to death not less than fifteen hundred persons.

[1] The year 404-403 B.C. [2] See chapter 9. 2.

36

Theramenes, however, seeing the city thus falling into ruin, was displeased with their proceedings, and counselled them to cease such unprincipled conduct and let the better classes have a share in the government. At first they resisted his advice, but when his proposals came to be known abroad, and the masses began to associate themselves with him, they were seized with alarm lest he should make himself the leader of the people and destroy their despotic power. Accordingly they drew up a list of three thousand citizens, to whom they announced that they would give a share in
[2] the constitution. Theramenes, however, criticized this scheme also, first on the ground that, while proposing to give all respectable citizens a share in the constitution, they were actually giving it only to three thousand persons, as though all merit were confined within that number; and secondly because they were doing two inconsistent things, since they made the government rest on the basis of force, and yet made the governors inferior in strength to the governed. However, they took no notice of his criticisms, and for a long time put off the publication of the list of the Three Thousand and kept to themselves the names of those who had been placed upon it; and every time they did decide to publish it they proceeded to strike out some of those who had been included in it, and insert others who had been omitted.

37

Now when winter had set in, Thrasybūlus and the exiles occupied Phylē, and the force which the Thirty led out to attack them met with a reverse. Thereupon the Thirty decided to disarm the bulk of the population and to get rid of Theramenes; which they did in the following way. They introduced two laws into the Council, which they commanded it to pass; the first of them gave the Thirty absolute power to put to death any citizen who was not included in the list of the Three Thousand, while the second disqualified all persons from participation in the franchise who should have assisted in the demolition of the fort of Eëtioneia, or have acted in any way against the Four Hundred who had organized the previous oligarchy. Theramenes had done both, and accordingly, when these laws were ratified, he became excluded from the franchise and the [2] Thirty had full power to put him to death. Theramenes having been thus removed, they disarmed all the people except the Three Thousand, and in every respect showed a great advance in cruelty and crime. They also sent ambassadors to Lacedaemon to blacken the character of Theramenes and to ask for help; and the Lacedaemonians, in answer to their appeal, sent Callibius as military governor with about seven hundred troops, who came and occupied the Acropolis.

38

These events were followed by the occupation of Munichia by the exiles from Phyle, and their victory over the Thirty and their partisans. After the fight the party of the city retreated, and next day they held a meeting in the marketplace and deposed the Thirty, and elected ten citizens with full powers to bring the war to a termination. When, however, the Ten had taken over the government they did nothing towards the object for which they were elected, but sent envoys to Lacedaemon to ask for help and to borrow money. Further, finding that [2] the citizens who possessed the franchise were displeased at their proceedings, they were afraid lest they should be deposed, and consequently, in order to strike terror into them (in which design they succeeded), they arrested Demarĕtus, one of the most eminent citizens, and put him to death. This gave them a firm hold on the government, and they also had the support of Callibius and his Peloponnesians, together with several of the Knights; for some of the members of this class were the most zealous among the citizens to prevent the re- [3] turn of the exiles from Phyle. When, however, the party in Piraeus and Munichia began to gain the upper hand in the war, through the defection of the whole populace to them, the party in the city deposed the original Ten, and elected another Ten, consisting of men of the highest repute. Under their administration, and with their active and zealous co-operation, the treaty of reconciliation was made and the populace returned to the city. The most prominent members of this board were Rhinon of Paeania and Phayllus of Acherdus, who, even before the arrival of Pausanias, opened negotiations with the party in Piraeus, and after his arrival seconded his efforts to bring about the [4] return of the exiles. For it was Pausanias, the king of the Lacedaemonians, who brought the peace and reconciliation to a fulfilment, in conjunction with the ten commissioners of arbitration who arrived later from Lacedaemon, at his own earnest request. Rhinon and his colleagues received a vote of thanks for the goodwill shown by them to the people, and though they received their charge under an oligarchy and handed in their accounts under a democracy, no one, either of the party that had stayed in the city or of the exiles that had returned from the Piraeus, brought any complaint against them. On the contrary, Rhinon was immediately elected general on account of his conduct in this office.

39

This reconciliation was effected in the archonship of Eucleides,[1] on the following terms. All persons who, having remained in the city during the troubles, were now anxious to leave it, were to be free to settle at Eleusis, retaining their civil rights and possessing full and independent powers of self-government, and with the free enjoyment of their own personal prop- [2] erty. The temple at Eleusis should be common ground for both parties, and should be under the superintendence of the Cerȳces and the Eumolpidae,[2] according to primitive custom. The settlers at Eleusis should not be allowed to enter Athens, nor the people of Athens to enter Eleusis, except at the season of the mysteries, when both parties should be free from these restrictions. The secessionists should pay their share to the fund for the common defence out of their revenues, just like all the other Atheni- [3] ans. If any of the seceding party wished to take a house in Eleusis, the people would help them to obtain the consent of the owner; but if they could not come to terms, they should appoint three valuers on either side, and the owner should receive whatever price they should appoint. Of the inhabitants of Eleusis, those whom the secessionists wished to remain should be allowed to do so. The list of those who de- [4] sired to secede should be made up within ten days after the taking of the oaths in the case of persons already in the country, and their actual departure should take place within twenty days; persons at present out of the country should have the same terms allowed to them [5] after their return. No one who settled at Eleusis should be capable of holding any office

[1] i.e. late in the summer of 403 B.C.

[2] Two ancient Athenian families, who from the earliest times had retained the duty of superintending the Eleusinian mysteries. See chapter 57. 1.

in Athens until he should again register himself on the roll as a resident in the city. Trials
for homicide, including all cases in which one
party had either killed or wounded another,
[6] should be conducted according to ancestral
practice. There should be a general amnesty
concerning past events towards all persons except the Thirty, the Ten, the Eleven, and the
magistrates in Piraeus; and these too should be
included if they should submit their accounts
in the usual way. Such accounts should be giv-
en by the magistrates in Piraeus before a court
of citizens rated in Piraeus, and by the magistrates in the city before a court of those rated
in the city. On these terms those who wished
to do so might secede. Each party was to repay
separately the money which it had borrowed
for the war.

40

When the reconciliation had taken place on
these terms, those who had fought on the side
of the Thirty felt considerable apprehensions,
and a large number intended to secede. But as
they put off entering their names till the last
moment, as people will do, Archīnus, observing their numbers, and being anxious to retain them as citizens, cut off the remaining
days during which the list should have remained open; and in this way many persons
were compelled to remain, though they did so
very unwillingly until they recovered confi-
[2] dence. This is one point in which Archinus
appears to have acted in a most statesmanlike
manner, and another was his subsequent prosecution of Thrasybulus on the charge of illegality, for a motion by which he proposed to confer the franchise on all who had taken part in
the return from Piraeus, although some of
them were notoriously slaves. And yet a third
such action was when one of the returned exiles began to violate the amnesty, whereupon
Archinus haled him to the Council and persuaded them to execute him without trial, telling them that now they would have to show
whether they wished to preserve the democracy and abide by the oaths they had taken; for
if they let this man escape they would encourage others to imitate him, while if they executed him they would make an example for all
to learn by. And this was exactly what happened; for after this man had been put to death
[3] no one ever again broke the amnesty. On
the contrary, the Athenians seem, both in public and in private, to have behaved in the most
unprecedentedly admirable and public-spirited
way with reference to the preceding troubles.
Not only did they blot out all memory of former offences, but they even repaid to the Lacedaemonians out of the public purse the money
which the Thirty had borrowed for the war,
although the treaty required each party, the
party of the city and the party of Piraeus, to
pay its own debts separately. This they did because they thought it was a necessary first step
in the direction of restoring harmony; but in
other states, so far from the democratic parties
making advances from their own possessions,
they are rather in the habit of making a general redistribution of the land. A final recon-
[4] ciliation was made with the secessionists at
Eleusis two years after the secession, in the
archonship of Xenaenĕtus.[1]

41

This, however, took place at a later date; at the
time of which we are speaking the people, having secured the control of the state, established
the constitution which exists at the present day.
Pythodōrus was Archon at the time, but the
democracy seems to have assumed the supreme
power with perfect justice, since it had effected
its own return by its own exertions. This was
[2] the eleventh change which had taken place
in the constitution of Athens. The first modification of the primaeval condition of things was
when Ion and his companions brought the people together into a community, for then the
people was first divided into the four tribes,
and the tribe-kings were created. Next, and
first after this, having now some semblance of
a constitution, was that which took place in
the reign of Theseus, consisting in a slight deviation from absolute monarchy. After this came
the constitution formed under Draco, when the
first code of laws was drawn up. The third was
that which followed the civil war, in the time
of Solon; from this the democracy took its rise.
The fourth was the tyranny of Pisistratus; the
fifth the constitution of Cleisthenes, after the
overthrow of the tyrants, of a more democratic
character than that of Solon. The sixth was that
which followed on the Persian wars, when the
Council of Areopagus had the direction of the
state. The seventh, succeeding this, was the
constitution which Aristides sketched out, and
which Ephialtes brought to completion by overthrowing the Areopagite Council; under this
the nation, misled by the demagogues, made
the most serious mistakes in the interest of its
maritime empire. The eighth was the estab-

[1] 401 B.C.

lishment of the Four Hundred, followed by the ninth, the restored democracy. The tenth was the tyranny of the Thirty and the Ten. The eleventh was that which followed the return from Phyle and Piraeus; and this has continued from that day to this, with continual accretions of power to the masses. The democracy has made itself master of everything and administers everything by its votes in the Assembly and by the law-courts, in which it holds the supreme power. Even the jurisdiction of the Council has passed into the hands of the people at large; and this appears to be a judicious change, since small bodies are more open to corruption, whether by actual money or influ-
[3] ence, than large ones. At first they refused to allow payment for attendance at the Assembly; but the result was that people did not attend. Consequently, after the Prytanes had tried many devices in vain in order to induce the populace to come and ratify the votes, Agyrrhius, in the first instance, made a provision of one obol a day, which Heracleides of Clazomenae, nicknamed 'the king', increased to two obols, and Agyrrhius again to three.

42

The present state of the constitution is as follows. The franchise is open to all who are of citizen birth by both parents. They are enrolled among the demesmen at the age of eighteen. On the occasion of their enrolment the demesmen give their votes on oath, first whether the candidates appear to be of the age prescribed by the law (if not, they are dismissed back into the ranks of the boys), and secondly whether the candidate is free born and of such parentage as the laws require. Then if they decide that he is not a free man, he appeals to the law-courts, and the demesmen appoint five of their own number to act as accusers; if the court decides that he has no right to be enrolled, he is sold by the state as a slave, but if he wins his case he has a right to be enrolled among the demesmen without further ques-
[2] tion. After this the Council examines those who have been enrolled, and if it comes to the conclusion that any of them is less than eighteen years of age, it fines the demesmen who enrolled him. When the youths (*Ephēbi*) have passed this examination, their fathers meet by their tribes, and appoint on oath three of their fellow tribesmen, over forty years of age, who, in their opinion, are the best and most suitable persons to have charge of the youths; and of these the Assembly elects one from each tribe as guardian, together with a director, chosen from the general body of Athenians, to control
[3] the while. Under the charge of these persons the youths first of all make the circuit of the temples; then they proceed to Piraeus, and some of them garrison Munichia and some the south shore. The Assembly also elects two trainers, with subordinate instructors, who teach them to fight in heavy armour, to use the bow and javelin, and to discharge a catapult. The guardians receive from the state a drachma apiece for their keep, and the youths four obols apiece. Each guardian receives the allowance for all the members of his tribe and buys the necessary provisions for the common stock (they mess together by tribes), and generally superintends everything. In this way they
[4] spend the first year. The next year, after giving a public display of their military evolutions, on the occasion when the Assembly meets in the theatre, they receive a shield and spear from the state; after which they patrol
[5] the country and spend their time in the forts. For these two years they are on garrison duty, and wear the military cloak, and during this time they are exempt from all taxes. They also can neither bring an action at law, nor have one brought against them, in order that they may have no excuse for requiring leave of absence; though exception is made in cases of actions concerning inheritances and wards of state, or of any sacrificial ceremony connected with the family. When the two years have elapsed they thereupon take their position among the other citizens. Such is the manner of the enrolment of the citizens and the training of the youths.

43

All the magistrates that are concerned with the ordinary routine of administration are elected by lot, except the Military Treasurer, the Commissioners of the Theoric fund, and the Superintendent of Springs. These are elected by vote, and hold office from one Panathenaic festival to the next. All military officers are also elected by vote.
[2] The Council of Five Hundred is elected by lot, fifty from each tribe. Each tribe holds the office of Prytanes in turn, the order being determined by lot; the first four serve for thirty-six days each, the last six for thirty-five, since
[3] the reckoning is by lunar years.[1] The Pry-

[1] The ordinary Attic year was of 354 days, divided into twelve lunar months of thirty and twenty-nine days al-

tanes for the time being, in the first place, mess together in the Tholus, and receive a sum of money from the state for their maintenance; and, secondly, they convene the meetings of the Council and the Assembly. The Council they convene every day, unless it is a holiday, the Assembly four times in each prytany. It is also their duty to draw up the programme of the business of the Council and to decide what subjects are to be dealt with on each particular day, and where the sitting is to be held. They [4] also draw up the programme for the meetings of the Assembly. One of these in each prytany is called the 'sovereign' Assembly; in this the people have to ratify the continuance of the magistrates in office, if they are performing their duties properly, and to consider the supply of corn and the defence of the country. On this day, too, impeachments are introduced by those who wish to do so, the lists of property confiscated by the state are read, and also applications for inheritances and wards of state, so that nothing may pass unclaimed without [5] the cognizance of any person concerned. In the sixth prytany, in addition to the business already stated, the question is put to the vote whether it is desirable to hold a vote of ostracism or not; and complaints against professional accusers, whether Athenian or aliens domiciled in Athens, are received, to the number of not more than three of either class, together with cases in which an individual has made some promise to the people and has not [6] performed it. Another Assembly in each prytany is assigned to the hearing of petitions, and at this meeting any one is free, on depositing the petitioner's olive-branch, to speak to the people concerning any matter, public or private. The two remaining meetings are devoted to all other subjects, and the laws require them to deal with three questions connected with religion, three connected with heralds and embassies, and three on secular subjects. Sometimes questions are brought forward without a preliminary vote of the Assembly to take them into consideration.

Heralds and envoys appear first before the Prytanes, and the bearers of dispatches also deliver them to the same officials.

---

ternately. The deficiency was made up by inserting intercalary months, at first every alternate year, then three in eight years, and subsequently seven in nineteen. In an intercalary year the duration of the prytanies was thirty-nine and thirty-eight days, in place of thirty-six and thirty-five.

44

There is a single President of the Prytanes, elected by lot, who presides for a night and a day; he may not hold the office for more than that time, nor may the same individual hold it twice. He keeps the keys of the sanctuaries in which the treasures and public records of the state are preserved, and also the public seal; and he is bound to remain in the Tholus, together with one-third of the Prytanes, named [2] by himself. Whenever the Prytanes convene a meeting of the Council or Assembly, he appoints by lot nine Proedri, one from each tribe except that which holds the office of Prytanes for the time being; and out of these nine he similarly appoints one as President, [3] and hands over the programme for the meeting to them. They take it and see to the preservation of order, put forward the various subjects which are to be considered, decide the results of the votings, and direct the proceedings generally. They also have power to dismiss the meeting. No one may act as President more than once in the year, but he may be a Proedrus once in each prytany.

[4] Elections to the offices of General and Hipparch and all other military commands are held in the Assembly, in such manner as the people decide; they are held after the sixth prytany by the first board of Prytanes in whose term of office the omens are favourable. There has, however, to be a preliminary consideration by the Council in this case also.[1]

45

In former times the Council had full powers to inflict fines and imprisonment and death; but when it had consigned Lysimachus to the executioner, and he was sitting in the immediate expectation of death, Eumelides of Alopĕcē rescued him from its hands, maintaining that no citizen ought to be put to death except on the decision of a court of law. Accordingly a trial was held in a law-court, and Lysimachus was acquitted, receiving henceforth the nickname of 'the man from the drum-head'; and the people deprived the Council thenceforward of the power to inflict death or imprisonment or fine, passing a law that if the Council condemn any person for an offence or inflict a fine, the Thesmothetae shall bring the sentence or fine before the law-court, and the decision of the jurors shall be the final judgement in the matter.

[1] See chapter 45. 4.

[2] The Council passes judgement on nearly all magistrates, especially those who have the control of money; its judgement, however, is not final, but is subject to an appeal to the law-courts. Private individuals, also, may lay an information against any magistrate they please for not obeying the laws, but here too there is an appeal to the law-courts if the Council de-
[3] clare the charge proved. The Council also examines those who are to be its members for the ensuing year, and likewise the nine Archons.[1] Formerly the Council had full power to reject candidates for office as unsuitable, but now they have an appeal to the law-courts. In
[4] all these matters, therefore, the Council has no final jurisdiction. It takes, however, preliminary cognizance of all matters brought before the Assembly, and the Assembly cannot vote on any question unless it has first been considered by the Council and placed on the programme by the Prytanes; since a person who carries a motion in the Assembly is liable to an action for illegal proposal on these grounds.

46

The Council also superintends the triremes that are already in existence, with their tackle and sheds, and builds new triremes or quadriremes, whichever the Assembly votes, with tackle and sheds to match. The Assembly appoints master-builders for the ships by vote; and if they do not hand them over completed to the next Council, the old Council cannot receive the customary donation—that being normally given to it during its successor's term of office. For the building of the triremes it ap-
[2] points ten commissioners, chosen from its own members. The Council also inspects all public buildings, and if it is of opinion that the state is being defrauded, it reports the culprit to the Assembly, and on condemnation hands him over to the law-courts.

47

The Council also co-operates with other magistrates in most of their duties. First there are the treasurers of Athena, ten in number, elected by lot, one from each tribe. According to the law of Solon—which is still in force—they must be Pentacosiomedimni, but in point of fact the person on whom the lot falls holds the office even though he be quite a poor man. These officers take over charge of the statue of Athena, the figures of Victory, and all the other ornaments of the temple, together with the money, in the presence of the Council. Then
[2] there are the Commissioners for Public Contracts (*Polētae*), ten in number, one chosen by lot from each tribe, who farm out the public contracts. They lease the mines and taxes, in conjunction with the Military Treasurer and the Commissioners of the Theoric fund, in the presence of the Council, and grant, to the persons indicated by the vote of the Council, the mines which are let out by the state, including both the workable ones, which are let for three years, and those which are let under special agreements for [ten?] years. They also sell, in the presence of the Council, the property of those who have gone into exile from the court of the Areopagus, and of others whose goods have been confiscated, and the nine Archons ratify the contracts. They also hand over to the Council lists of the taxes which are farmed out
[3] for the year, entering on whitened tablets the name of the lessee and the amount paid. They make separate lists, first of those who have to pay their instalments in each prytany, on ten several tablets, next of those who pay thrice in the year, with a separate tablet for each instalment, and finally of those who pay in the ninth prytany. They also draw up a list of farms and dwellings which have been confiscated and sold by order of the courts; for these too come within their province. In the case of dwellings the value must be paid up in five years, and in that of farms, in ten. The in-
[4] stalments are paid in the ninth prytany. Further, the King-archon brings before the Council the leases of the sacred enclosures, written on whitened tablets. These too are leased for ten years, and the instalments are paid in the [ninth] prytany; consequently it is in this prytany that the greatest amount of money is collected. The tablets containing the
[5] lists of the instalments are carried into the Council, and the public clerk takes charge of them. Whenever a payment of instalments is to be made he takes from the pigeon-holes the precise list of the sums which are to be paid and struck off on that day, and delivers it to the Receivers-General. The rest are kept apart, in order that no sum may be struck off before it is paid.

48

There are ten Receivers-General (*Apodectae*), elected by lot, one from each tribe. These officers receive the tablets, and strike off the instalments as they are paid, in the presence of the

[1] See chapter 55. 2.

Council in the Council-chamber, and give the tablets back to the public clerk. If any one fails to pay his instalment, a note is made of it on the tablet; and he is bound to pay double the amount of the deficiency, or, in default, to be imprisoned. The Council has full power by the laws to exact these payments and to inflict this [2] imprisonment. They receive all the instalments, therefore, on one day, and portion the money out among the magistrates; and on the next day they bring up the report of the apportionment, written on a wooden notice-board, and read it out in the Council-chamber, after which they ask publicly in the Council whether any one knows of any malpractice in reference to the apportionment, on the part of either a magistrate or a private individual, and if any one is charged with malpractice they take a vote on it.

[3] The Council also elects ten Auditors (*Logistae*) by lot from its own members, to audit the accounts of the magistrates for each pry- [4] tany. They also elect one Examiner of Accounts (*Euthūnus*) by lot from each tribe, with two assessors (*Paredri*) for each examiner, whose duty it is to sit at the ordinary market hours, each opposite the statue of the eponymous hero of his tribe; and if any one wishes to prefer a charge, on either public or private grounds, against any magistrate who has passed his audit before the law-courts, within three days of his having so passed, he enters on a whitened tablet his own name and that of the magistrate prosecuted, together with the malpractice that is alleged against him. He also appends his claim for a penalty of such amount as seems to him fitting, and gives in the record [5] to the Examiner. The latter takes it, and if after reading it he considers it proved he hands it over, if a private case, to the local justices who introduce cases for the tribe concerned, while if it is a public case he enters it on the register of the Thesmothetae. Then, if the Thesmothetae accept it, they bring the accounts of this magistrate once more before the law-court, and the decision of the jury stands as the final judgement.

49

The Council also inspects the horses belonging to the state. If a man who has a good horse is found to keep it in bad condition, he is mulcted in his allowance of corn; while those which cannot keep up or which shy and will not stand steady, it brands with a wheel on the jaw, and the horse so marked is disqualified for service. It also inspects those who appear to be fit for service as scouts, and any one whom it rejects is deprived of his horse. It also examines the infantry who serve among the cavalry, and [2] any one whom it rejects ceases to receive his pay. The roll of the cavalry is drawn up by the Commissioners of Enrolment (*Catalŏgeis*), ten in number, elected by the Assembly by open vote. They hand over to the Hipparchs and Phylarchs the list of those whom they have enrolled, and these officers take it and bring it up before the Council, and there open the sealed tablet containing the names of the cavalry. If any of those who have been on the roll previously make affidavit that they are physically incapable of cavalry service, they strike them out; then they call up the persons newly enrolled, and if any one makes affidavit that he is either physically or pecuniarily incapable of cavalry service they dismiss him, but if no such affidavit is made the Council vote whether the individual in question is suitable for the purpose or not. If they vote in the affirmative his name is entered on the tablet; if not, he is dismissed with the others.

[3] Formerly the Council used to decide on the plans for public buildings and the contract for making the robe of Athena;[1] but now this work is done by a jury in the law-courts appointed by lot, since the Council was considered to have shown favouritism in its decisions. The Council also shares with the Military Treasurer the superintendence of the manufacture of the images of Victory and the prizes at the Panathenaic festival.

[4] The Council also examines infirm paupers; for there is a law which provides that persons possessing less than three minas, who are so crippled as to be unable to do any work, are, after examination by the Council, to receive two obols a day from the state for their support. A treasurer is appointed by lot to attend to them.

[5] The Council also, speaking broadly, cooperates in most of the duties of all the other magistrates; and this ends the list of the functions of that body.

50

There are ten Commissioners for Repairs of Temples, elected by lot, who receive a sum of

[1] This was the robe which was carried in procession at the great Panathenaic festival. It was embroidered with mythological subjects, and was woven on each occasion by a number of girls, under the superintendence of two of superior family.

thirty minas from the Receivers-General, and therewith carry out the most necessary repairs in the temples.

[2] There are also ten City Commissioners (*Astynŏmi*), of whom five hold office in Piraeus and five in the city. Their duty is to see that female flute- and harp- and lute-players are not hired at more than two drachmas, and if more than one person is anxious to hire the same girl, they cast lots and hire her out to the person to whom the lot falls. They also provide that no collector of sewage shall shoot any of his sewage within ten stradia of the walls; they prevent people from blocking up the streets by building, or stretching barriers across them, or making drain-pipes in mid-air with a discharge into the street, or having doors which open outwards; they also remove the corpses of those who die in the streets, for which purpose they have a body of state slaves assigned to them.

51

Market Commissioners (*Agoranŏmi*) are elected by lot, five for Piraeus, five for the city. Their statutory duty is to see that all articles offered for sale in the market are pure and unadulterated.

[2] Commissioners of Weights and Measures (*Metronŏmi*) are elected by lot, five for the city, and five for Piraeus. They see that sellers use fair weights and measures.

[3] Formerly there were ten Corn Commissioners (*Sitophylăces*), elected by lot, five for Piraeus, and five for the city; but now there are twenty for the city and fifteen for Piraeus. Their duties are, first, to see that the unprepared corn in the market is offered for sale at reasonable prices, and secondly, to see that the millers sell barley meal at a price proportionate to that of barley, and that the bakers sell their loaves at a price proportionate to that of wheat, and of such weight as the Commissioners may appoint; for the law requires them to fix the standard weight.

[4] There are ten Superintendents of the Mart, elected by lot, whose duty is to superintend the Mart, and to compel merchants to bring up into the city two-thirds of the corn which is brought by sea to the Corn Mart.

52

The Eleven also are appointed by lot to take care of the prisoners in the state gaol. Thieves, kidnappers, and pickpockets are brought to them, and if they plead guilty they are executed, but if they deny the charge the Eleven bring the case before the law-courts; if the prisoners are acquitted, they release them, but if not, they then execute them. They also bring up before the law-courts the list of farms and houses claimed as state-property; and if it is decided that they are so, they deliver them to the Commissioners for Public Contracts. The Eleven also bring up informations laid against magistrates alleged to be disqualified; this function comes within their province, but some such cases are brought up by the Thesmothetae.

[2] There are also five Introducers of Cases (*Eisagōgeis*), elected by lot, one for each pair of tribes, who bring up the 'monthly' cases[1] to the law-courts. 'Monthly' cases are these: refusal to pay up a dowry where a party is bound to do so, refusal to pay interest on money borrowed at 12 per cent.[2], or where a man desirous of setting up business in the market has borrowed from another man capital to start with; also cases of slander, cases arising out of friendly loans or partnerships, and cases concerned with slaves, cattle, and the office of trierarch, [3] or with banks. These are brought up as 'monthly' cases and are introduced by these officers; but the Receivers-General perform the same function in cases for or against the farmers of taxes. Those in which the sum concerned is not more than ten drachmas they can decide summarily, but all above that amount they bring into the law-courts as 'monthly' cases.

53

The Forty[3] are also elected by lot, four from each tribe, before whom suitors bring all other cases. Formerly they were thirty in number, and they went on circuit through the demes to hear causes; but after the oligarchy of the [2] Thirty they were increased to forty. They have full powers to decide cases in which the amount at issue does not exceed ten drachmas, but anything beyond that value they hand over to the Arbitrators. The Arbitrators take up the case, and, if they cannot bring the parties to an agreement, they give a decision. If their decision satisfies both parties, and they abide by it, the case is at an end; but if either of the parties appeals to the law-courts, the Arbitrators en-

[1] i.e. cases which have to be decided within a month, as being considered to be of a pressing nature.

[2] If the rate of interest was higher, the creditor could not make use of this procedure.

[3] See chapters 16. 5, and 26. 3.

close the evidence, the pleadings, and the laws quoted in the case in two urns, those of the plaintiff in the one, and those of the defendant [3] in the other. These they seal up and, having attached to them the decision of the arbitrator, written out on a tablet, place them in the custody of the four justices whose function it is to introduce cases on behalf of the tribe of the defendant. These officers take them and bring up the case before the law-court, to a jury of two hundred and one members in cases up to the value of a thousand drachmas, or to one of four hundred and one in cases above that value. No laws or pleadings or evidence may be used except those which were adduced before the Arbitrator, and have been enclosed in the urns.

[4] The Arbitrators are persons in the sixtieth year of their age; this appears from the schedule of the Archons and the Eponymi. There are two classes of Eponymi, the ten who give their names to the tribes, and the forty-two of the years of service. The youths, on being enrolled among the citizens, were formerly registered upon whitened tablets, and the names were appended of the Archon in whose year they were enrolled, and of the Eponymus who had been in course in the preceding year; at the present day they are written on a bronze pillar, which stands in front of the Council-chamber, near [5] the Eponymi of the tribes. Then the Forty take the last of the Eponymi of the years of service, and assign the arbitrations to the persons belonging to that year, casting lots to determine which arbitrations each shall undertake; and every one is compelled to carry through the arbitrations which the lot assigns to him. The law enacts that any one who does not serve as Arbitrator when he has arrived at the necessary age shall lose his civil rights, unless he happens to be holding some other office during that year, or to be out of the country. These are the only persons who escape the [6] duty. Any one who suffers injustice at the hands of the Arbitrator may appeal to the whole board of Arbitrators, and if they find the magistrate guilty, the law enacts that he shall lose his civil rights. The persons thus con[7] demned have, however, in their turn an appeal. The Eponymi are also used in reference to military expeditions; when the men of military age are despatched on service, a notice is put up stating that the men from such-and-such an Archon and Eponymus to such-and-such another Archon and Eponymus are to go on the expedition.

54

The following magistrates also are elected by lot: Five Commissioners of Roads (*Hodopoei*), who, with an assigned body of public slaves, are required to keep the roads in order: and ten [2] Auditors, with ten assistants, to whom all persons who have held any office must give in their accounts. These are the only officers who audit the accounts of those who are subject to examination, and who bring them up for examination before the law-courts. If they detect any magistrate in embezzlement, the jury condemn him for theft, and he is obliged to repay tenfold the sum he is declared to have misappropriated. If they charge a magistrate with accepting bribes and the jury convict him, they fine him for corruption, and this sum too is repaid tenfold. Or if they convict him of unfair dealing, he is fined on that charge, and the sum assessed is paid without increase, if payment is made before the ninth prytany, but otherwise it is doubled. A tenfold fine is not doubled.

[3] The Clerk of the Prytany, as he is called, is also elected by lot. He has the charge of all public documents, and keeps the resolutions which are passed by the Assembly, and checks the transcripts of all other official papers and attends at the sessions of the Council. Formerly he was elected by open vote, and the most distinguished and trustworthy persons were elected to the post, as is known from the fact that the name of this officer is appended on the pillars recording treaties of alliance and grants of consulship and citizenship. Now, however, he [4] is elected by lot. There is, in addition, a Clerk of the Laws, elected by lot, who attends at the sessions of the Council; and he too checks [5] the transcript of all the laws. The Assembly also elects by open vote a clerk to read documents to it and to the Council; but he has no other duty except that of reading aloud.

[6] The Assembly also elects by lot the Commissioners of Public Worship (*Hieropoei*) known as the Commissioners for Sacrifices, who offer the sacrifices appointed by oracle, and, in conjunction with the seers, take the aus[7] pices whenever there is occasion. It also elects by lot ten others, known as Annual Commissioners, who offer certain sacrifices and administer all the quadrennial festivals except the Panathenaea. There are the following quadrennial festivals: first that of Delos (where there is also a sexennial festival), secondly the Brauronia, thirdly the Heracleia, fourthly the Eleusinia, and fifthly the Panathenaea; and no two of

these are celebrated in the same place. To these the Hephaestia has now been added, in the archonship of Cephisophon.

[8] An Archon is also elected by lot for Salamis, and a Demarch for Piraeus. These officers celebrate the Dionysia in these two places, and appoint Chorēgi. In Salamis, moreover, the name of the Archon is publicly recorded.

55

All the foregoing magistrates are elected by lot, and their powers are those which have been stated. To pass on to the nine Archons, as they are called, the manner of their appointment from the earliest times has been described already. At the present day six Thesmothetae are elected by lot, together with their clerk, and in addition to these an Archon, a King, and a Polemarch. One is elected from each tribe. [2] They are examined first of all by the Council of Five Hundred, with the exception of the clerk. The latter is examined only in the law-court, like other magistrates (for all magistrates, whether elected by lot or by open vote, are examined before entering on their offices); but the nine Archons are examined both in the Council and again in the law-court. Formerly no one could hold the office if the Council rejected him, but now there is an appeal to the law-court, which is the final authority in the [3] matter of the examination. When they are examined, they are asked, first, 'Who is your father, and of what deme? who is your father's father? who is your mother? who is your mother's father, and of what deme?' Then the candidate is asked whether he possesses an ancestral Apollo and a household Zeus, and where their sanctuaries are; next if he possesses a family tomb, and where; then if he treats his parents well, and pays his taxes, and has served on the required military expeditions. When the examiner has put these questions, he proceeds, 'Call the witnesses to these facts'; and when the candidate [4] has produced his witnesses, he next asks, 'Does any one wish to make any accusation against this man?' If an accuser appears, he gives the parties an opportunity of making their accusation and defence, and then puts it to the Council to pass the candidate or not, and to the law-court to give the final vote. If no one wishes to make an accusation, he proceeds at once to the vote. Formerly a single individual gave the vote, but now all the members are obliged to vote on the candidates, so that if any unprincipled candidate has managed to get rid of his accusers, it may still be possible for him [5] to be disqualified before the law-court. When the examination has been thus completed, they proceed to the stone on which are the pieces of the victims, and on which the Arbitrators take oath before declaring their decisions, and witnesses swear to their testimony. On this stone the Archons stand, and swear to execute their office uprightly and according to the laws, and not to receive presents in respect of the performance of their duties, or, if they do, to dedicate a golden statue. When they have taken this oath they proceed to the Acropolis, and there they repeat it; after this they enter upon their office.

56

The Archon, the King, and the Polemarch have each two assessors, nominated by themselves. These officers are examined in the law-court before they begin to act, and give in accounts on each occasion of their acting.

[2] As soon as the Archon enters office, he begins by issuing a proclamation that whatever any one possessed before he entered into office, that he shall possess and hold until the end of [3] his term. Next he assigns Chorēgi to the tragic poets, choosing three of the richest persons out of the whole body of Athenians. Formerly he used also to assign five Chorēgi to the comic poets, but now the tribes provide the Chorēgi for them. Then he receives the Chorēgi who have been appointed by the tribes for the men's and boys' choruses and the comic poets at the Dionysia, and for the men's and boys' choruses at the Thargelia (at the Dionysia there is a chorus for each tribe, but at the Thargelia one between two tribes, each tribe bearing its share in providing it); he transacts the exchanges of properties for them, and reports any excuses that are tendered, if any one says that he has already borne this burden, or that he is exempt because he has borne a similar burden and the period of his exemption has not yet expired, or that he is not of the required age; since the Chorēgus of a boys' chorus must [4] be over forty years of age. He also appoints Chorēgi for the festival at Delos, and a chief of the mission for the thirty-oar boat which conveys the youths thither. He also superintends sacred processions, both that in honour of Asclepius, when the initiated keep house, and that of the great Dionysia—the latter in conjunction with the Superintendents of that festival. These officers, ten in number, were formerly elected by open vote in the Assembly,

and used to provide for the expenses of the procession out of their private means; but now one is elected by lot from each tribe, and the state contributes a hundred minas for the ex-
[5] penses. The Archon also superintends the procession at the Thargelia, and that in honour of Zeus the Saviour. He also manages the contests at the Dionysia and the Thargelia.

These, then, are the festivals which he super-
[6] intends. The suits and indictments which come before him, and which he, after a preliminary inquiry, brings up before the law-courts, are as follows. Injury to parents (for bringing these actions the prosecutor cannot suffer any penalty); injury to orphans (these actions lie against their guardians); injury to a ward of state (these lie against their guardians or their husbands),[1] injury to an orphan's estate (these too lie against the guardians); mental derangement, where a party charges another with destroying his own property through unsoundness of mind; for appointment of liquidators, where a party refuses to divide property in which others have a share; for constituting a wardship; for determining between rival claims to a wardship; for granting inspection of property to which another party lays claim; for appointing oneself as guardian; and for de-
[7] termining disputes as to inheritances and wards of state. The Archon also has the care of orphans and wards of state, and of women who, on the death of their husbands, declare themselves to be with child; and he has power to inflict a fine on those who offend against the persons under his charge, or to bring the case before the law-courts. He also leases the houses of orphans and wards of state until they reach the age of fourteen, and takes mortgages on them; and if the guardians fail to provide the necessary food for the children under their charge, he exacts it from them. Such are the duties of the Archon.

57

The King in the first place superintends the mysteries, in conjunction with the Superintendents of Mysteries. The latter are elected in the Assembly by open vote, two from the general body of Athenians, one from the Eumolpidae, and one from the Cerȳces. Next, he superintends the Lenaean Dionysia, which consists of a procession and a contest. The procession is ordered by the King and the Superintendents in conjunction; but the contest is managed by the King alone. He also manages all the contests of the torch-race; and to speak broadly, he administers all the ancestral sacri-
[2] fices. Indictments for impiety come before him, or any disputes between parties concerning priestly rites; and he also determines all controversies concerning sacred rites for the ancient families and the priests. All actions for homicide come before him, and it is he that makes the proclamation requiring polluted persons to keep away from sacred ceremonies.
[3] Actions for homicide and wounding are heard, if the homicide or wounding be wilful, in the Areopagus; so also in cases of killing by poison, and of arson. These are the only cases heard by that Council. Cases of unintentional homicide, or of intent to kill, or of killing a slave or a resident alien or a foreigner, are heard by the court of Palladium. When the homicide is acknowledged, but legal justification is pleaded, as when a man takes an adulterer in the act, or kills another by mistake in battle, or in an athletic contest, the prisoner is tried in the court of Delphinium. If a man who is in banishment for a homicide which admits of reconciliation[2] incurs a further charge of killing or wounding, he is tried in Phreatto, and he makes his defence from a boat moored
[4] near the shore. All these cases, except those which are heard in the Areopagus, are tried by the Ephetae on whom the lot falls. The King introduces them, and the hearing is held within sacred precincts and in the open air. Whenever the King hears a case he takes off his crown. The person who is charged with homicide is at all other times excluded from the temples, nor is it even lawful for him to enter the market-place; but on the occasion of his trial he enters the temple and makes his defence. If the actual offender is unknown, the writ runs against 'the doer of the deed'. The King and the tribe-kings also hear the cases in which the guilt rests on inanimate objects and the lower animals.[3]

58

The Polemarch performs the sacrifices to Artemis the huntress and to Enyalius, and arranges

[1] The state still continued its protection of heiresses even after they were married. Its care only ceased when they had children capable of inheriting the property.

[2] A person who committed an involuntary homicide had to give pecuniary satisfaction to the relatives of the deceased, and he was compelled to go into exile for a year unless they gave him leave to return earlier.

[3] This is a relic of a very primitive custom, by which any object that had caused a man's death was put upon its trial. In later times it may have served the purpose of a coroner's inquest.

the contest at the funeral of those who have fallen in war, and makes offerings to the memory of Harmodius and Aristogeiton. Only private
[2] actions come before him, namely those in which resident aliens, both ordinary and privileged, and agents of foreign states are concerned. It is his duty to receive these cases and divide them into ten groups, and assign to each tribe the group which comes to it by lot; after which the magistrates who introduce cases for the tribe hand them over to the Arbitrators.
[3] The Polemarch, however, brings up in person cases in which an alien is charged with deserting his patron or neglecting to provide himself with one, and also of inheritances and wards of state where aliens are concerned; and in fact, generally, whatever the Archon does for citizens, the Polemarch does for aliens.

59

The Thesmothetae in the first place have the power of prescribing on what days the law-courts are to sit, and next of assigning them to the several magistrates; for the latter must follow the arrangement which the Thesmothetae assign. Moreover they introduce impeachments
[2] before the Assembly, and bring up all votes for removal from office, challenges of a magistrate's conduct before the Assembly, indictments for illegal proposals, or for proposing a law which is contrary to the interests of the state, complaints against Proedri or their president for their conduct in office, and the ac-
[3] counts presented by the generals. All indictments also come before them in which a deposit has to be made by the prosecutor, namely, indictments for concealment of foreign origin, for corrupt evasion of foreign origin (when a man escapes the disqualification by bribery), for blackmailing accusations, bribery, false entry of another as a state debtor, false testimony to the service of a summons, conspiracy to enter a man as a state debtor, corrupt removal from the list of debtors, and adul-
[4] tery. They also bring up the examinations of all magistrates, and the rejections by the
[5] demes and the condemnations by the Council. Moreover they bring up certain private suits in cases of merchandise and mines, or where a slave has slandered a free man. It is they also who cast lots to assign the courts to the various magistrates, whether for private or
[6] public cases. They ratify commercial treaties, and bring up the cases which arise out of such treaties; and they also bring up cases of
[7] perjury from the Areopagus. The casting of lots for the jurors is conducted by all the nine Archons, with the clerk to the Thesmothetae as the tenth, each performing the duty for his own tribe. Such are the duties of the nine Archons.

60

There are also ten Commissioners of Games (Athlothĕtae), elected by lot, one from each tribe. These officers, after passing an examination, serve for four years; and they manage the Panathenaic procession, the contest in music and that in gymnastic, and the horse-race; they also provide the robe of Athena and, in conjunction with the Council, the vases,[1] and they present the oil to the athletes. This oil is col-
[2] lected from the sacred olives. The Archon requisitions it from the owners of the farms on which the sacred olives grow, at the rate of three-quarters of a pint from each plant. Formerly the state used to sell the fruit itself, and if any one dug up or broke down one of the sacred olives, he was tried by the Council of Areopagus, and if he was condemned, the penalty was death. Since, however, the oil has been paid by the owner of the farm, the procedure has lapsed, though the law remains; and the oil is a state charge upon the property instead of being taken from the individual plants. When,
[3] then, the Archon has collected the oil for his year of office, he hands it over to the Treasurers to preserve in the Acropolis, and he may not take his seat in the Areopagus until he has paid over to the Treasurers the full amount. The Treasurers keep it in the Acropolis until the Panathenaea, when they measure it out to the Commissioners of Games, and they again to the victorious competitors. The prizes for the victors in the musical contest consist of silver and gold, for the victors in manly vigour, of shields, and for the victors in the gymnastic contest and the horse-race, of oil.

61

All officers connected with military service are elected by open vote. In the first place, ten Generals (Stratēgi), who were formerly elected one from each tribe, but now are chosen from the whole mass of citizens. Their duties are assigned to them by open vote; one is appointed to command the heavy infantry, and leads them if they go out to war; one to the defence of the country, who remains on the defensive,

[1] The vases given as prizes at the Panathenaea.

and fights if there is war within the borders of
the country; two to Piraeus, one of whom is assigned to Munichia, and one to the south shore,
and these have charge of the defence of the
Piraeus; and one to superintend the symmo-
ries,[1] who nominates the trierarchs[2] and arranges exchanges of properties for them, and
brings up actions to decide on rival claims in
connexion with them. The rest are dispatched
to whatever business may be on hand at the
[2] moment. The appointment of these officers
is submitted for confirmation in each prytany,
when the question is put whether they are considered to be doing their duty. If any officer is
rejected on this vote, he is tried in the law-
court, and if he is found guilty the people decide what punishment or fine shall be inflicted
on him; but if he is acquitted he resumes his
office. The Generals have full power, when on
active service, to arrest any one for insubordi-
nation, or to cashier him publicly, or to inflict
a fine; the latter is, however, unusual.
[3] There are also ten Taxiarchs, one from
each tribe, elected by open vote; and each commands his own tribesmen and appoints cap-
[4] tains of companies (Lochāgi). There are
also two Hipparchs, elected by open vote from
the whole mass of the citizens, who command
the cavalry, each taking five tribes. They have
the same powers as the Generals have in respect of the infantry, and their appointments
are also subject to confirmation. There are also
[5] ten Phylarchs, elected by open vote, one
from each tribe, to command the cavalry, as the
[6] Taxiarchs do the infantry. There is also a
Hipparch for Lemnos, elected by open vote,
who has charge of the cavalry in Lemnos.
[7] There is also a treasurer of the Paralus, and
another of the Ammonias, similarly elected.[3]

62

Of the magistrates elected by lot, in former times some including the nine Archons, were elected out of the tribe as a whole, while others, namely those who are now elected in the Theseum, were apportioned among the demes; but since the demes used to sell the elections, these magistrates too are now elected from the whole tribe, except the members of the Council and the guards of the dockyards, who are still left to the demes.

[2] Pay is received for the following services.
First the members of the Assembly receive a
drachma for the ordinary meetings, and nine
obols for the 'sovereign' meeting. Then the
jurors at the law-courts receive three obols; and
the members of the Council five obols. They
Prytanes receive an allowance of an obol for
their maintenance. The nine Archons receive
four obols apiece for maintenance, and also
keep a herald and a flute-player; and the Archon for Salamis receives a drachma a day. The
Commissioners for Games dine in the Prytanēum during the month of Hecatombaeon in
which the Panathenaic festival takes place,
from the fourteenth day onwards. The Amphictyonic deputies to Delos receive a drachma
a day from the exchequer of Delos. Also all
magistrates sent to Samos, Scyros, Lemnos, or
Imbros receive an allowance for their maintenance. The military offices may be held any
[3] number of times, but none of the others
more than once, except the membership of the
Council, which may be held twice.

63

The juries for the law-courts are chosen by
lot by the nine Archons, each for their own
tribe, and by the clerk to the Thesmothetae for
[2] the tenth. There are ten entrances into the
courts, one for each tribe; twenty rooms in
which the lots are drawn, two for each tribe; a
hundred chests, ten for each tribe; other chests,
in which are placed the tickets of the jurors on
whom the lot falls; and two vases. Further,
staves, equal in number to the jurors required,
are placed by the side of each entrance; and
counters are put into one vase, equal in number to the staves. These are inscribed with letters of the alphabet beginning with the eleventh (*lambda*), equal in number to the courts
which require to be filled. All persons above
[3] thirty years of age are qualified to serve as
jurors, provided they are not debtors to the
state and have not lost their civil rights. If any
unqualified person serves as juror, an information is laid against him, and he is brought before the court; and, if he is convicted, the jurors assess the punishment or fine which they
consider him to deserve. If he is condemned to
a money fine, he must be imprisoned until he
has paid up both the original debt, on account

[1] The companies into which the richer members of the community were formed (first in 377 B.C.) for the payment of the extraordinary charges in war-time.

[2] The trierarchs were the persons (chosen from the richest men in the community) who were required to undertake the equipment of a trireme at their own expense.

[3] These are the two triremes, usually known as 'sacred,' which were used for special state services.

of which the information was laid against him,
and also the fine which the court has imposed
[4] upon him. Each juror has his ticket of box-
wood, on which is inscribed his name, with the
name of his father and his deme, and one of
the letters of the alphabet up to *kappa*; for the
jurors in their several tribes are divided into
ten sections, with approximately an equal num-
[5] ber in each letter. When the Thesmothetes
has decided by lot which letters are required to
attend at the courts, the servant puts up above
each court the letter which has been assigned
to it by the lot.

64

The ten chests above mentioned are placed in
front of the entrance used by each tribe, and
are inscribed with the letters of the alphabet
from *alpha* to *kappa*. The jurors cast in their
tickets, each into the chest on which is inscribed the letter which is on his ticket; then
the servant shakes them all up, and the Archon
[2] draws one ticket from each chest. The individual so selected is called the Ticket-hanger
(*Empēctes*), and his function is to hang up the
tickets out of his chest on the bar which bears
the same letter as that on the chest. He is chos-
en by lot, lest, if the Ticket-hanger were always
the same person, he might tamper with the results. There are five of these bars in each of the
[3] rooms assigned for the lot-drawing. Then
the Archon casts in the dice and thereby chooses the jurors from each tribe, room by room.
The dice are made of brass, coloured black or
white; and according to the number of jurors
required, so many white dice are put in, one
for each five tickets, while the remainder are
black, in the same proportion. As the Archon
draws out the dice, the crier calls out the names
of the individuals chosen. The Ticket-hanger
[4] is included among those selected. Each
juror, as he is chosen and answers to his name,
draws a counter from the vase, and holding it
out with the letter uppermost shows it first to
the presiding Archon; and he, when he has
seen it, throws the ticket of the juror into the
chest on which is inscribed the letter which is
on the counter, so that the juror must go into
the court assigned to him by lot, and not into
one chosen by himself, and that it may be impossible for any one to collect the jurors of his
[5] choice into any particular court. For this
purpose chests are placed near the Archon, as
many in number as there are courts to be filled
that day, bearing the letters of the courts on
which the lot has fallen.

65

The juror thereupon, after showing his counter again to the attendant, passes through the
barrier into the court. The attendant gives him
a staff of the same colour as the court bearing
the letter which is on his counter, so as to ensure his going into the court assigned to him by
lot; since, if he were to go into any other, he
would be betrayed by the colour of his staff.
[2] Each court has a certain colour painted on
the lintel of the entrance. Accordingly the jur-
or, bearing his staff, enters the court which has
the same colour as his staff, and the same letter
as his counter. As he enters, he receives a
voucher from the official to whom this duty has
[3] been assigned by lot. So with their counters
and their staves the selected jurors take their
seats in the court, having thus completed the
process of admission. The unsuccessful candidates receive back their tickets from the Ticket-
[4] hangers. The public servants carry the
chests from each tribe, one to each court, containing the names of the members of the tribe
who are in that court, and hand them over to
the officials assigned to the duty of giving back
their tickets to the jurors in each court, so that
these officials may call them up by name and
pay them their fee.

66

When all the courts are full, two ballot boxes
are placed in the first court, and a number of
brazen dice, bearing the colours of the several
courts, and other dice inscribed with the names
of the presiding magistrates. Then two of the
Thesmothetae, selected by lot, severally throw
the dice with the colours into one box, and
those with the magistrates' names into the other. The magistrate whose name is first drawn
is thereupon proclaimed by the crier as assigned for duty in the court which is first
drawn, and the second in the second, and similarly with the rest. The object of this procedure is that no one may know which court he
will have, but that each may take the court assigned to him by lot.
[2] When the jurors have come in, and have
been assigned to their respective courts, the
presiding magistrate in each court draws one
ticket out of each chest (making ten in all, one
out of each tribe), and throws them into another empty chest. He then draws out five of
them, and assigns one to the superintendence
of the water-clock, and the other four to the
telling of the votes. This is to prevent any tam-

pering beforehand with either the superintendent of the clock or the tellers of the votes, and to secure that there is no malpractice in these [3] respects. The five who have not been selected for these duties receive from them a statement of the order in which the jurors shall receive their fees, and of the places where the several tribes shall respectively gather in the court for this purpose when their duties are completed; the object being that the jurors may be broken up into small groups for the reception of their pay, and not all crowd together and impede one another.

67

These preliminaries being concluded, the cases are called on. If it is a day for private cases, the private litigants are called. Four cases are taken in each of the categories defined in the law, and the litigants swear to confine their speeches to the point at issue. If it is a day for public causes, the public litigants are called, and only [2] one case is tried. Water-clocks are provided, having small supply-tubes, into which the water is poured by which the length of the pleadings is regulated. Ten gallons are allowed for a case in which an amount of more than five thousand drachmas is involved, and three for the second speech on each side. When the amount is between one and five thousand drachmas, seven gallons are allowed for the first speech and two for the second; when it is less than one thousand, five and two. Six gallons are allowed for arbitrations between rival claimants, in which there is no second speech. [3] The official chosen by lot to superintend the water-clock places his hand on the supply-tube whenever the clerk is about to read a resolution or law or affidavit or treaty. When, however, a case is conducted according to a set measurement of the day, he does not stop the [4] supply, but each party receives an equal allowance of water. The standard of measurement is the length of the days in the month [5] Poseideon[1]. . . . The measured day is employed in cases when imprisonment, death, exile, loss of civil rights, or confiscation of goods is assigned as the penalty.

68

Most of the courts consist of 500 members . . . ; and when it is necessary to bring public cases before a jury of 1,000 members, two courts combine for the purpose, [while the most important cases of all are brought before] 1500 [2] jurors, or three courts. The ballot balls are made of brass with stems running through the centre, half of them having the stem pierced and the other half solid. When the speeches are concluded, the officials assigned to the taking of the votes give each juror two ballot balls, one pierced and one solid. This is done in full view of the rival litigants, to secure that no one shall receive two pierced or two solid balls. Then the official designated for the purpose takes away the jurors' staves, in return for which each one as he records his vote receives a brass voucher market with the numeral 3 (because he gets three obols when he gives it up). This is to ensure that all shall vote; since no one can get a [3] voucher unless he votes. Two urns, one of brass and the other of wood, stand in the court, in distinct spots so that no one may surreptitiously insert ballot balls; in these the jurors record their votes. The brazen urn is for effective votes,[2] the wooden for unused votes; and the brazen urn has a lid pierced so as to take only one ballot ball, in order that no one may put in two at a time.

[4] When the jurors are about to vote, the crier demands first whether the litigants enter a protest against any of the evidence; for no protest can be received after the voting has begun. Then he proclaims again, 'The pierced ballot for the plaintiff, the solid for the defendant'; and the juror, taking his two ballot balls from the stand, with his hand closed over the stem so as not to show either the pierced or the solid ballot to the litigants, casts the one which is to count into the brazen urn, and the other into the wooden urn.

69

When all the jurors have voted, the attendants take the urn containing the effective votes and discharge them on to a reckoning board having as many cavities as there are ballot balls, so that the effective votes, whether pierced or solid, may be plainly displayed and easily counted. Then the officials assigned to the taking of the votes tell them off on the board, the solid in one place and the pierced in another, and the crier announces the numbers of the votes, the pierced ballots being for the prosecutor and the solid for the defendant. Whichever has the majority is victorious; but if the votes are equal the verdict is for the defendant.

[1] December to January.

[2] Each juror receives two ballots, and uses one to record his vote, and throws the other away.

[2] Then, if damages have to be awarded, they vote again in the same way, first returning their pay-vouchers and receiving back their staves. Half a gallon of water is allowed to each party for the discussion of the damages. Finally, when all has been completed in accordance with the law, the jurors receive their pay in the order assigned by the lot.

RHETORIC

CONTENTS: RHETORIC

BOOK I

BOOK II

RHETORIC

BOOK I

I

1354ª Rhetoric is the counterpart of Dialectic. Both alike are concerned with such things as come, more or less, within the general ken of all men and belong to no definite science. Accordingly all men make use, more or less, of both; for to a certain extent all men attempt to discuss statements and to maintain them, to defend themselves and to attack others. Ordinary people do this either at random or through practice and from acquired habit. Both ways being possible, the subject can plainly be handled systematically, for it is possible to inquire the reason why some speakers succeed through practice and others spontaneously; and every one will at once agree that such an inquiry is the function of an art.

Now, the framers of the current treatises on rhetoric have constructed but a small portion of that art. The modes of persuasion are the only true constituents of the art: everything else is merely accessory. These writers, however, say nothing about enthymemes, which are the substance of rhetorical persuasion, but deal mainly with non-essentials. The arousing of prejudice, pity, anger, and similar emotions has nothing to do with the essential facts, but is merely a personal appeal to the man who is judging the case. Consequently if the rules for trials which are now laid down in some states—especially in well-governed states—were applied everywhere, such people would have nothing to say. All men, no doubt, *think* that the laws should prescribe such rules, but some, as in the court of Areopagus, give practical effect to their thoughts and forbid talk about non-essentials. This is sound law and custom. It is not right to pervert the judge by moving him to anger or envy or pity—one might as well warp a carpenter's rule before using it. Again, a litigant has clearly nothing to do but to show that the alleged fact is so or is not so, that it has or has not happened. As to whether a thing is important or unimportant, just or unjust, the judge must surely refuse to take his instructions from the litigants: he must decide for himself all such points as the law-giver has not already defined for him.

Now, it is of great moment that well-drawn laws should themselves define all the points they possibly can and leave as few as may be to the decision of the judges; and this for several reasons. First, to find one man, or a few **1354ᵇ** men, who are sensible persons and capable of legislating and administering justice is easier than to find a large number. Next, laws are made after long consideration, whereas decisions in the courts are given at short notice, which makes it hard for those who try the case to satisfy the claims of justice and expediency. The weightiest reason of all is that the decision of the lawgiver is not particular but prospective and general, whereas members of the assembly and the jury find it *their* duty to decide on definite cases brought before them. They will often have allowed themselves to be so much influenced by feelings of friendship or hatred or self-interest that they lose any clear vision of the truth and have their judgement obscured by considerations of personal pleasure or pain. In general, then, the judge should, we say, be allowed to decide as few things as possible. But questions as to whether something has happened or has not happened, will be or will not be, is or is not, must of necessity be left to the judge, since the lawgiver cannot foresee them. If this is so, it is evident that any one who lays down rules about other matters, such as what must be the contents of the 'introduction' or the 'narration' or any of the other divisions of a speech, is theorizing about non-essentials as if they belonged to the art. The only question with which these writers here deal is how to put the judge into a given frame of mind. About the orator's proper modes of persuasion they have nothing to tell us; nothing, that is, about how to gain skill in enthymemes.

Hence it comes that, although the same systematic principles apply to political as to for-

Note: The bold face numbers and letters are approximate indications of the pages and columns of the standard Berlin Greek text; the bracketed numbers, of the lines in the Greek text; they are here assigned as they are assigned in the Oxford translation.

ensic oratory, and although the former is a nobler business, and fitter for a citizen, than that which concerns the relations of private individuals, these authors say nothing about political oratory, but try, one and all, to write treatises on the way to plead in court. The reason for this is that in political oratory there is less inducement to talk about nonessentials. Political oratory is less given to unscrupulous practices than forensic, because it treats of wider issues. In a political debate the man who is forming a judgement is making a decision about his own vital interests. There is no need, therefore, to prove anything except that the facts are what the supporter of a measure maintains they are. In forensic oratory this is not enough; to conciliate the listener is what pays here. It is other people's affairs that are to be decided, so that the judges, intent on their own satisfaction and listening with partiality, surrender themselves to the **1355a** disputants instead of judging between them. Hence in many places, as we have said already,[1] irrelevant speaking is forbidden in the law-courts: in the public assembly those who have to form a judgement are themselves well able to guard against that.

It is clear, then, that rhetorical study, in its strict sense, is concerned with the modes of persuasion. Persuasion is clearly a sort of demonstration, since we are most fully persuaded when we consider a thing to have been demonstrated. The orator's demonstration is an enthymeme, and this is, in general, the most effective of the modes of persuasion. The enthymeme is a sort of syllogism, and the consideration of syllogisms of all kinds, without distinction, is the business of dialectic, either of dialectic as a whole or of one of its branches. It follows plainly, therefore, that he who is best able to see how and from what elements a syllogism is produced will also be best skilled in the enthymeme, when he has further learnt what its subject-matter is and in what respects it differs from the syllogism of strict logic. The true and the approximately true are apprehended by the same faculty; it may also be noted that men have a sufficient natural instinct for what is true, and usually do arrive at the truth. Hence the man who makes a good guess at truth is likely to make a good guess at probabilities.

It has now been shown that the ordinary writers on rhetoric treat of non-essentials; it has also been shown why they have inclined more towards the forensic branch of oratory.

Rhetoric is useful (1) because things that are true and things that are just have a natural tendency to prevail over their opposites, so that if the decisions of judges are not what they ought to be, the defeat must be due to the speakers themselves, and they must be blamed accordingly. Moreover, (2) before some audiences not even the possession of the exactest knowledge will make it easy for what we say to produce conviction. For argument based on knowledge implies instruction, and there are people whom one cannot instruct. Here, then, we must use, as our modes of persuasion and argument, notions possessed by everybody, as we observed in the *Topics*[2] when dealing with the way to handle a popular audience. Further, (3) we must be able to employ persuasion, just as strict reasoning can be employed, on opposite sides of a question, not in order that we may in practice employ it in both ways (for we must not make people believe what is wrong), but in order that we may see clearly what the facts are, and that, if another man argues unfairly, we on our part may be able to confute him. No other of the arts draws opposite conclusions: dialectic and rhetoric alone do this. Both these arts draw opposite conclusions impartially. Nevertheless, the underlying facts do not lend themselves equally well to the contrary views. No; things that are true and things that are better are, by their nature, practically always easier to prove and easier to believe in. Again, (4) it **1355b** is absurd to hold that a man ought to be ashamed of being unable to defend himself with his limbs, but not of being unable to defend himself with speech and reason, when the use of rational speech is more distinctive of a human being than the use of his limbs. And if it be objected that one who uses such power of speech unjustly might do great harm, *that* is a charge which may be made in common against all good things except virtue, and above all against the things that are most useful, as strength, health, wealth, generalship. A man can confer the greatest of benefits by a right use of these, and inflict the greatest of injuries by using them wrongly.

It is clear, then, that rhetoric is not bound up with a single definite class of subjects, but is as universal as dialectic; it is clear, also, that it is useful. It is clear, further, that its function is not simply to succeed in persuad-

[1] 1354a 22.

[2] *Topics*, I. 2(101a 30-4).

ing, but rather to discover the means of coming as near such success as the circumstances of each particular case allow. In this it resembles all other arts. For example, it is not the function of medicine simply to make a man quite healthy, but to put him as far as may be on the road to health; it is possible to give excellent treatment even to those who can never enjoy sound health. Furthermore, it is plain that it is the function of one and the same art to discern the real and the apparent means of persuasion, just as it is the function of dialectic to discern the real and the apparent syllogism. What makes a man a 'sophist' is not his faculty, but his moral purpose. In rhetoric, however, the term 'rhetorician' may describe either the speaker's knowledge of the art, or his moral purpose. In dialectic it is different: a man is a 'sophist' because he has a certain kind of moral purpose, a 'dialectician' in respect, not of his moral purpose, but of his faculty.

Let us now try to give some account of the systematic principles of Rhetoric itself—of the right method and means of succeeding in the object we set before us. We must make as it were a fresh start, and before going further define what rhetoric is.

2

Rhetoric may be defined as the faculty of observing in any given case the available means of persuasion. This is not a function of any other art. Every other art can instruct or persuade about its own particular subject-matter; for instance, medicine about what is healthy and unhealthy, geometry about the properties of magnitudes, arithmetic about numbers, and the same is true of the other arts and sciences. But rhetoric we look upon as the power of observing the means of persuasion on almost any subject presented to us; and that is why we say that, in its technical character, it is not concerned with any special or definite class of subjects.

Of the modes of persuasion some belong strictly to the art of rhetoric and some do not. By the latter I mean such things as are not supplied by the speaker but are there at the outset—witnesses, evidence given under torture, written contracts, and so on. By the former I mean such as we can ourselves construct by means of the principles of rhetoric. The one kind has merely to be used, the other has to be invented.

1356a Of the modes of persuasion furnished by the spoken word there are three kinds. The first kind depends on the personal character of the speaker; the second on putting the audience into a certain frame of mind; the third on the proof, or apparent proof, provided by the words of the speech itself. Persuasion is achieved by the speaker's personal character when the speech is so spoken as to make us think him credible. We believe good men more fully and more readily than others: this is true generally whatever the question is, and absolutely true where exact certainty is impossible and opinions are divided. This kind of persuasion, like the others, should be achieved by what the speaker says, not by what people think of his character before he begins to speak. It is not true, as some writers assume in their treatises on rhetoric, that the personal goodness revealed by the speaker contributes nothing to his power of persuasion; on the contrary, his character may almost be called the most effective means of persuasion he possesses. Secondly, persuasion may come through the hearers, when the speech stirs their emotions. Our judgements when we are pleased and friendly are not the same as when we are pained and hostile. It is towards producing these effects, as we maintain, that present-day writers on rhetoric direct the whole of their efforts. This subject shall be treated in detail when we come to speak of the emotions.[1] Thirdly, persuasion is effected through the speech itself when we have proved a truth or an apparent truth by means of the persuasive arguments suitable to the case in question.

There are, then, these three means of effecting persuasion. The man who is to be in command of them must, it is clear, be able (1) to reason logically, (2) to understand human character and goodness in their various forms, and (3) to understand the emotions—that is, to name them and describe them, to know their causes and the way in which they are excited. It thus appears that rhetoric is an offshoot of dialectic and also of ethical studies. Ethical studies may fairly be called political; and for this reason rhetoric masquerades as political science, and the professors of it as political experts—sometimes from want of education, sometimes from ostentation, sometimes owing to other human failings. As a matter of fact, it is a branch of dialectic and similar to it, as we said at the outset.[2] Neither rhetoric nor dialectic is the scientific study of any one separate subject: both are faculties for provid-

[1] II. 2-11. [2] I. 1(1354a 1).

ing arguments. This is perhaps a sufficient account of their scope and of how they are related to each other.

With regard to the persuasion achieved by **1356b** proof or apparent proof: just as in dialectic there is induction on the one hand and syllogism or apparent syllogism on the other, so it is in rhetoric. The example is an induction, the enthymeme is a syllogism, and the apparent enthymeme is an apparent syllogism. I call the enthymeme a rhetorical syllogism, and the example a rhetorical induction. Every one who effects persuasion through proof does in fact use either enthymemes or examples: there is no other way. And since every one who proves anything at all is bound to use either syllogisms or inductions (and this is clear to us from the *Analytics*[1]), it must follow that enthymemes are syllogisms and examples are inductions. The difference between example and enthymeme is made plain by the passages in the *Topics*[2] where induction and syllogism have already been discussed. When we base the proof of a proposition on a number of similar cases, this is induction in dialectic, example in rhetoric; when it is shown that, certain propositions being true, a further and quite distinct proposition must also be true in consequence, whether invariably or usually, this is called syllogism in dialectic, enthymeme in rhetoric. It is plain also that each of these types of oratory has its advantages. Types of oratory, I say: for what has been said in the *Methodics* applies equally well here; in some oratorical styles examples prevail, in others enthymemes; and in like manner, some orators are better at the former and some at the latter. Speeches that rely on examples are as persuasive as the other kind, but those which rely on enthymemes excite the louder applause. The sources of examples and enthymemes, and their proper uses, we will discuss later.[3] Our next step is to define the processes themselves more clearly.

A statement is persuasive and credible either because it is directly self-evident or because it appears to be proved from other statements that are so. In either case it is persuasive because there is somebody whom it persuades. But none of the arts theorize about individual cases. Medicine, for instance, does not theorize about what will help to cure Socrates or Callias, but only about what will help to cure any or all of a given class of patients: this alone is its business: individual cases are so infinitely various that no systematic knowledge of them is possible. In the same way the theory of rhetoric is concerned not with what seems probable to a given individual like Socrates or Hippias, but with what seems probable to men of a given type; and this is true of dialectic also. Dialectic does not construct its syllogisms out of any haphazard materials, such as the fancies of crazy people, but out of materials that call for discussion; and rhetoric, too, draws upon the regular subjects of debate. The duty **1357a** of rhetoric is to deal with such matters as we deliberate upon without arts or systems to guide us, in the hearing of persons who cannot take in at a glance a complicated argument, or follow a long chain of reasoning. The subjects of our deliberation are such as seem to present us with alternative possibilities: about things that could not have been, and cannot now or in the future be, other than they are, nobody who takes them to be of this nature wastes his time in deliberation.

It is possible to form syllogisms and draw conclusions from the results of previous syllogisms; or, on the other hand, from premisses which have not been thus proved, and at the same time are so little accepted that they call for proof. Reasonings of the former kind will necessarily be hard to follow owing to their length, for we assume an audience of untrained thinkers; those of the latter kind will fail to win assent, because they are based on premisses that are not generally admitted or believed.

The enthymeme and the example must, then, deal with what is in the main contingent, the example being an induction, and the enthymeme a syllogism, about such matters. The enthymeme must consist of few propositions, fewer often than those which make up the normal syllogism. For if any of these propositions is a familiar fact, there is no need even to mention it; the hearer adds it himself. Thus, to show that Dorieus has been victor in a contest for which the prize is a crown, it is enough to say 'For he has been victor in the Olympic games', without adding 'And in the Olympic games the prize is a crown', a fact which everybody knows.

There are few facts of the 'necessary' type that can form the basis of rhetorical syllogisms. Most of the things about which we make decisions, and into which therefore we inquire, present us with alternative possibilities. For it is about our actions that we deliberate and inquire, and all our actions have a contin-

[1] *Prior Analytics*, II. 23, 24; *Posterior Analytics*, I. 1.

[2] *Topics*, I. 1, 12.

[3] II. 20-4.

gent character; hardly any of them are determined by necessity. Again, conclusions that state what is merely usual or possible must be drawn from premisses that do the same, just as 'necessary' conclusions must be drawn from 'necessary' premisses; this too is clear to us from the *Analytics*.[1] It is evident, therefore, that the propositions forming the basis of enthymemes, though some of them may be 'necessary', will most of them be only usually true. Now the materials of enthymemes are Probabilities and Signs, which we can see must correspond respectively with the propositions that are generally and those that are necessarily true. A Probability is a thing that usually happens; not, however, as some definitions would suggest, anything whatever that usually happens, but only if it belongs to the class of the 'contingent' or 'variable'. It bears the same relation to that in respect of which it is probable as the universal bears to the particular. Of
1357b Signs, one kind bears the same relation to the statement it supports as the particular bears to the universal, the other the same as the universal bears to the particular. The infallible kind is a 'complete proof' (τεκμήριον); the fallible kind has no specific name. By infallible signs I mean those on which syllogisms proper may be based: and this shows us why this kind of Sign is called 'complete proof': when people think that what they have said cannot be refuted, they then think that they are bringing forward a 'complete proof', meaning that the matter has now been demonstrated and completed (πεπερασμένον); for the word πέρας has the same meaning (of 'end' or 'boundary') as the word τέκμαρ in the ancient tongue. Now the one kind of Sign (that which bears to the proposition it supports the relation of particular to universal) may be illustrated thus. Suppose it were said, 'The fact that Socrates was wise and just is a sign that the wise are just'. Here we certainly have a Sign; but even though the proposition be true, the argument is refutable, since it does not form a syllogism. Suppose, on the other hand, it were said, 'The fact that he has a fever is a sign that he is ill', or, 'The fact that she is giving milk is a sign that she has lately borne a child'. Here we have the infallible kind of Sign, the only kind that constitutes a complete proof, since it is the only kind that, if the particular statement is true, is irrefutable. The other kind of Sign, that which bears to the proposition it supports the relation of universal to particular, might be illustrated by saying, 'The fact that he breathes fast is a sign that he has a fever'. This argument also is refutable, even if the statement about the fast breathing be true, since a man may breathe hard without having a fever.

It has, then, been stated above what is the nature of a Probability, of a Sign, and of a complete proof, and what are the differences between them. In the *Analytics*[2] a more explicit description has been given of these points; it is there shown why some of these reasonings can be put into syllogisms and some cannot.

The 'example' has already been described as one kind of induction; and the special nature of the subject-matter that distinguishes it from the other kinds has also been stated above. Its relation to the proposition it supports is not that of part to whole, nor whole to part, nor whole to whole, but of part to part, or like to like. When two statements are of the same order, but one is more familiar than the other, the former is an 'example'. The argument may, for instance, be that Dionysius, in asking as he does for a bodyguard, is scheming to make himself a despot. For in the past Peisistratus kept asking for a bodyguard in order to carry out such a scheme, and did make himself a despot as soon as he got it; and so did Theagenes at Megara; and in the same way all other instances known to the speaker are made into examples, in order to show what is not yet known, that Dionysius has the same purpose in making the same request: all these being instances of the one general principle, that a man who asks for a bodyguard is scheming
1358a to make himself a despot. We have now described the sources of those means of persuasion which are popularly supposed to be demonstrative.

There is an important distinction between two sorts of enthymemes that has been wholly overlooked by almost everybody—one that also subsists between the syllogisms treated of in dialectic. One sort of enthymeme really belongs to rhetoric, as one sort of syllogism really belongs to dialectic; but the other sort really belongs to other arts and faculties, whether to those we already exercise or to those we have not yet acquired. Missing this distinction, people fail to notice that the more correctly they handle their particular subject the further they are getting away from pure rhetoric or dialectic. This statement will be clearer if expressed more fully. I mean that the

[1] *Prior Analytics*, I. 8, 12-14, 27.

[2] *Ibid.*, II. 27.

proper subjects of dialectical and rhetorical syllogisms are the things with which we say the regular or universal Lines of Argument are concerned, that is to say those lines of argument that apply equally to questions of right conduct, natural science, politics, and many other things that have nothing to do with one another. Take, for instance, the line of argument concerned with 'the more or less'. On this line of argument it is equally easy to base a syllogism or enthymeme about any of what nevertheless are essentially disconnected subjects—right conduct, natural science, or anything else whatever. But there are also those special Lines of Argument which are based on such propositions as apply only to particular groups or classes of things. Thus there are propositions about natural science on which it is impossible to base any enthymeme or syllogism about ethics, and other propositions about ethics on which nothing can be based about natural science. The same principle applies throughout. The general Lines of Argument have no special subject-matter, and therefore will not increase our understanding of any particular class of things. On the other hand, the better the selection one makes of propositions suitable for special Lines of Argument, the nearer one comes, unconsciously, to setting up a science that is distinct from dialectic and rhetoric. One may succeed in stating the required principles, but one's science will be no longer dialectic or rhetoric, but the science to which the principles thus discovered belong. Most enthymemes are in fact based upon these particular or special Lines of Argument; comparatively few on the common or general kind. As in the *Topics*,[1] therefore, so in this work, we must distinguish, in dealing with enthymemes, the special and the general Lines of Argument on which they are to be founded. By special Lines of Argument I mean the propositions peculiar to each several class of things, by general those common to all classes alike. We may begin with the special Lines of Argument. But, first of all, let us classify rhetoric into its varieties. Having distinguished these we may deal with them one by one, and try to discover the elements of which each is composed, and the propositions each must employ.

3

Rhetoric falls into three divisions, determined by the three classes of listeners to speeches. For of the three elements in speech-making—speaker, subject, and person addressed—it is the last one, the hearer, that determines the
1358b speech's end and object. The hearer must be either a judge, with a decision to make about things past or future, or an observer. A member of the assembly decides about future events, a juryman about past events: while those who merely decide on the orator's skill are observers. From this it follows that there are three divisions of oratory—(1) political, (2) forensic, and (3) the ceremonial oratory of display.

Political speaking urges us either to do or not to do something: one of these two courses is always taken by private counsellors, as well as by men who address public assemblies. Forensic speaking either attacks or defends somebody: one or other of these two things must always be done by the parties in a case. The ceremonial oratory of display either praises or censures somebody. These three kinds of rhetoric refer to three different kinds of time. The political orator is concerned with the future: it is about things to be done hereafter that he advises, for or against. The party in a case at law is concerned with the past; one man accuses the other, and the other defends himself, with reference to things already done. The ceremonial orator is, properly speaking, concerned with the present, since all men praise or blame in view of the state of things existing at the time, though they often find it useful also to recall the past and to make guesses at the future.

Rhetoric has three distinct ends in view, one for each of its three kinds. The political orator aims at establishing the expediency or the harmfulness of a proposed course of action; if he urges its acceptance, he does so on the ground that it will do good; if he urges its rejection, he does so on the ground that it will do harm; and all other points, such as whether the proposal is just or unjust, honourable or dishonourable, he brings in as subsidiary and relative to this main consideration. Parties in a law-case aim at establishing the justice or injustice of some action, and they too bring in all other points as subsidiary and relative to this one. Those who praise or attack a man aim at proving him worthy of honour or the reverse, and they too treat all other considerations with reference to this one.

That the three kinds of rhetoric do aim respectively at the three ends we have mentioned is shown by the fact that speakers will

[1] Cp. *Topics*, I. 10, 14; III. 5.

sometimes not try to establish anything else. Thus, the litigant will sometimes not deny that a thing has happened or that he has done harm. But that he is guilty of injustice he will never admit; otherwise there would be no need of a trial. So too, political orators often make any concession short of admitting that they are recommending their hearers to take an inexpedient course or not to take an expedient one. The question whether it is not *unjust* for a city to enslave its innocent neighbours often does not trouble them at all. In like manner those who praise or censure a man do not con-
1359a sider whether his acts have been expedient or not, but often make it a ground of actual praise that he has neglected his own interest to do what was honourable. Thus, they praise Achilles because he championed his fallen friend Patroclus, though he knew that this meant death, and that otherwise he need not die: yet while to die thus was the nobler thing for him to do, the expedient thing was to live on.

It is evident from what has been said that it is these three subjects, more than any others, about which the orator must be able to have propositions at his command. Now the propositions of Rhetoric are Complete Proofs, Probabilities, and Signs. Every kind of syllogism is composed of propositions, and the enthymeme is a particular kind of syllogism composed of the aforesaid propositions.

Since only possible actions, and not impossible ones, can ever have been done in the past or the present, and since things which have not occurred, or will not occur, also cannot have been done or be going to be done, it is necessary for the political, the forensic, and the ceremonial speaker alike to be able to have at their command propositions about the possible and the impossible, and about whether a thing has or has not occurred, will or will not occur. Further, all men, in giving praise or blame, in urging us to accept or reject proposals for action, in accusing others or defending themselves, attempt not only to prove the points mentioned but also to show that the good or the harm, the honour or disgrace, the justice or injustice, is great or small, either absolutely or relatively; and therefore it is plain that we must also have at our command propositions about greatness or smallness and the greater or the lesser—propositions both universal and particular. Thus, we must be able to say which is the greater or lesser good, the greater or lesser act of justice or injustice; and so on.

Such, then, are the subjects regarding which we are inevitably bound to master the propositions relevant to them. We must now discuss each particular class of these subjects in turn, namely those dealt with in political, in ceremonial, and lastly in legal, oratory.

4

First, then, we must ascertain what are the kinds of things, good or bad, about which the political orator offers counsel. For he does not deal with all things, but only with such as may or may not take place. Concerning things which exist or will exist inevitably, or which cannot possibly exist or take place, no counsel can be given. Nor, again, can counsel be given about the whole class of things which may or may not take place; for this class includes some good things that occur naturally, and some that occur by accident; and about these it is useless to offer counsel. Clearly counsel can only be given on matters about which people deliberate; matters, namely, that ultimately depend on ourselves, and which we have it in our power to set going. For we turn a thing over in our mind until we have reached the point of seeing whether we can do it or not.

1359b Now to enumerate and classify accurately the usual subjects of public business, and further to frame, as far as possible, true definitions of them, is a task which we must not attempt on the present occasion. For it does not belong to the art of rhetoric, but to a more instructive art and a more real branch of knowledge; and as it is, rhetoric has been given a far wider subject-matter than strictly belongs to it. The truth is, as indeed we have said already,[1] that rhetoric is a combination of the science of logic and of the ethical branch of politics; and it is partly like dialectic, partly like sophistical reasoning. But the more we try to make either dialectic or rhetoric not, what they really are, practical faculties, but sciences, the more we shall inadvertently be destroying their true nature; for we shall be re-fashioning them and shall be passing into the region of sciences dealing with definite subjects rather than simply with words and forms of reasoning. Even here, however, we will mention those points which it is of practical importance to distinguish, their fuller treatment falling naturally to political science.

The main matters on which all men deliberate and on which political speakers make

[1] I. 2(1356a 25 ff).

speeches are some five in number: ways and means, war and peace, national defence, imports and exports, and legislation.

As to Ways and Means, then, the intending speaker will need to know the number and extent of the country's sources of revenue, so that, if any is being overlooked, it may be added, and, if any is defective, it may be increased. Further, he should know all the expenditure of the country, in order that, if any part of it is superfluous, it may be abolished, or, if any is too large, it may be reduced. For men become richer not only by increasing their existing wealth but also by reducing their expenditure. A comprehensive view of these questions cannot be gained solely from experience in home affairs; in order to advise on such matters a man must be keenly interested in the methods worked out in other lands.

As to Peace and War, he must know the extent of the military strength of his country, both actual and potential, and also the nature of that actual and potential strength; and further, what wars his country has waged, and how it has waged them. He must know these facts not only about his own country, but also about neighbouring countries; and also about countries with which war is likely, in order that peace may be maintained with those stronger than his own, and that his own may have power to make war or not against those **1360a** that are weaker. He should know, too, whether the military power of another country is like or unlike that of his own; for this is a matter that may affect their relative strength. With the same end in view he must, besides, have studied the wars of other countries as well as those of his own, and the way they ended; similar causes are likely to have similar results.

With regard to National Defence: he ought to know all about the methods of defence in actual use, such as the strength and character of the defensive force and the positions of the forts—this last means that he must be well acquainted with the lie of the country—in order that a garrison may be increased if it is too small or removed if it is not wanted, and that the strategic points may be guarded with special care.

With regard to the Food Supply: he must know what outlay will meet the needs of his country; what kinds of food are produced at home and what imported; and what articles must be exported or imported. This last he must know in order that agreements and commercial treaties may be made with the countries concerned. There are, indeed, two sorts of state to which he must see that his countrymen give no cause for offence, states stronger than his own, and states with which it is advantageous to trade.

But while he must, for security's sake, be able to take all this into account, he must before all things understand the subject of legislation; for it is on a country's laws that its whole welfare depends. He must, therefore, know how many different forms of constitution there are; under what conditions each of these will prosper and by what internal developments or external attacks each of them tends to be destroyed. When I speak of destruction through internal developments I refer to the fact that all constitutions, except the best one of all, are destroyed both by not being pushed far enough and by being pushed too far. Thus, democracy loses its vigour, and finally passes into oligarchy, not only when it is not pushed far enough, but also when it is pushed a great deal too far; just as the aquiline and the snub nose not only turn into normal noses by not being aquiline or snub enough, but also by being too violently aquiline or snub arrive at a condition in which they no longer look like noses at all. It is useful, in framing laws, not only to study the past history of one's own country, in order to understand which constitution is desirable for it now, but also to have a knowledge of the constitutions of other nations, and so to learn for what kinds of nation the various kinds of constitution are suited. From this we can see that books of travel are useful aids to legislation, since from these we may learn the laws and customs of different races. The political speaker will also find the researches of historians useful. But all this is the business of political science and not of rhetoric.

These, then, are the most important kinds of **1360b** information which the political speaker must possess. Let us now go back and state the premisses from which he will have to argue in favour of adopting or rejecting measures regarding these and other matters.

5

It may be said that every individual man and all men in common aim at a certain end which determines what they choose and what they avoid. This end, to sum it up briefly, is happiness and its constituents. Let us, then, by way of illustration only, ascertain what is in general the nature of happiness, and what are the elements of its constituent parts. For all advice to do things or not to do them is concerned with happiness and with the things that make for or against it; whatever creates or increases happiness or some part of happiness, we ought to do; whatever destroys or hampers happiness, or gives rise to its opposite, we ought not to do.

We may define happiness as prosperity combined with virtue; or as independence of life; or as the secure enjoyment of the maximum of pleasure; or as a good condition of property and body, together with the power of guarding one's property and body and making use of them. That happiness is one or more of these things, pretty well everybody agrees.

From this definition of happiness it follows that its constituent parts are:—good birth, plenty of friends, good friends, wealth, good children, plenty of children, a happy old age, also such bodily excellences as health, beauty, strength, large stature, athletic powers, together with fame, honour, good luck, and virtue. A man cannot fail to be completely independent if he possesses these internal and these external goods; for besides these there are no others to have. (Goods of the soul and of the body are internal. Good birth, friends, money, and honour are external.) Further, we think that he should possess resources and luck, in order to make his life really secure. As we have already ascertained what happiness in general is, so now let us try to ascertain what each of these parts of it is.

Now good birth in a race or a state means that its members are indigenous or ancient: that its earliest leaders were distinguished men, and that from them have sprung many who were distinguished for qualities that we admire.

The good birth of an individual, which may come either from the male or the female side, implies that both parents are free citizens, and that, as in the case of the state, the founders of the line have been notable for virtue or wealth or something else which is highly prized, and that many distinguished persons belong to the family, men and women, young and old.

The phrases 'possession of good children' and 'of many children' bear a quite clear meaning. Applied to a community, they mean that its young men are numerous and of good
1361ª quality: good in regard to bodily excellences, such as stature, beauty, strength, athletic powers; and also in regard to the excellences of the soul, which in a young man are temperance and courage. Applied to an individual, they mean that his own children are numerous and have the good qualities we have described. Both male and female are here included; the excellences of the latter are, in body, beauty and stature; in soul, self-command and an industry that is not sordid. Communities as well as individuals should lack none of these perfections, in their women as well as in their men. Where, as among the Lacedaemonians, the state of women is bad, almost half of human life is spoilt.

The constituents of wealth are: plenty of coined money and territory; the ownership of numerous, large, and beautiful estates; also the ownership of numerous and beautiful implements, live stock, and slaves. All these kinds of property are our own, are secure, gentlemanly, and useful. The useful kinds are those that are productive, the gentlemanly kinds are those that provide enjoyment. By 'productive' I mean those from which we get our income; by 'enjoyable', those from which we get nothing worth mentioning except the use of them. The criterion of 'security' is the ownership of property in such places and under such conditions that the use of it is in our power; and it is 'our own' if it is in our own power to dispose of it or keep it. By 'disposing of it' I mean giving it away or selling it. Wealth as a whole consists in using things rather than in owning them; it is really the activity—that is, the use—of property that constitutes wealth.

Fame means being respected by everybody, or having some quality that is desired by all men, or by most, or by the good, or by the wise.

Honour is the token of a man's being famous for doing good. It is chiefly and most properly paid to those who have already done good; but also to the man who can do good in future. Doing good refers either to the preservation of life and the means of life, or to wealth, or to some other of the good things which it is hard to get either always or at that particular place or time—for many gain honour for things which seem small, but the place and the occasion account for it. The constituents of honour are: sacrifices; commemoration, in verse or prose; privileges; grants of land; front seats at civic celebrations; state burial; statues; public maintenance; among foreigners, obeisances and giving place; and such presents as are among various bodies of men regarded as marks of honour. For a present is not only the bestowal of a piece of property, but also a token of honour; which explains why honour-loving as well as money-loving persons desire it. The present brings to **1361b** both what they want; it is a piece of property, which is what the lovers of money desire; and it brings honour, which is what the lovers of honour desire.

The excellence of the body is health; that is, a condition which allows us, while keeping free from disease, to have the use of our bodies; for many people are 'healthy' as we are told Herodicus was; and these no one can congratulate on their 'health', for they have to abstain from everything or nearly everything that men do.—Beauty varies with the time of life. In a young man beauty is the possession of a body fit to endure the exertion of running and of contests of strength; which means that he is pleasant to look at; and therefore all-round athletes are the most beautiful, being naturally adapted both for contests of strength and for speed also. For a man in his prime, beauty is fitness for the exertion of warfare, together with a pleasant but at the same time formidable appearance. For an old man, it is to be strong enough for such exertion as is necessary, and to be free from all those deformities of old age which cause pain to others. Strength is the power of moving some one else at will; to do this, you must either pull, push, lift, pin, or grip him; thus you must be strong in all of those ways or at least in some. Excellence in size is to surpass ordinary people in height, thickness, and breadth by just as much as will not make one's movements slower in consequence. Athletic excellence of the body consists in size, strength, and swiftness; swiftness implying strength. He who can fling forward his legs in a certain way, and move them fast and far, is good at running; he who can grip and hold down is good at wrestling; he who can drive an adversary from his ground with the right blow is a good boxer: he who can do both the last is a good pancratiast, while he who can do all is an 'all-round' athlete.

Happiness in old age is the coming of old age slowly and painlessly; for a man has not this happiness if he grows old either quickly, or tardily but painfully. It arises both from the excellences of the body and from good luck. If a man is not free from disease, or if he is not strong, he will not be free from suffering; nor can he continue to live a long and painless life unless he has good luck. There is, indeed, a capacity for long life that is quite independent of health or strength; for many people live long who lack the excellences of the body; but for our present purpose there is no use in going into the details of this.

The terms 'possession of many friends' and 'possession of good friends' need no explanation; for we define a 'friend' as one who will always try, for your sake, to do what he takes to be good for you. The man towards whom many feel thus has many friends; if these are worthy men, he has good friends.

'Good luck' means the acquisition or possession of all or most, or the most important, of those good things which are due to luck. **1362a** Some of the things that are due to luck may also be due to artificial contrivance; but many are independent of art, as for example those which are due to nature—though, to be sure, things due to luck may actually be contrary to nature. Thus health may be due to artificial contrivance, but beauty and stature are due to nature. All such good things as excite envy are, as a class, the outcome of good luck. Luck is also the cause of good things that happen contrary to reasonable expectation: as when, for instance, all your brothers are ugly, but you are handsome yourself; or when you find a treasure that everybody else has overlooked; or when a missile hits the next man and misses you; or when you are the only man not to go to a place you have gone to regularly, while the others go there for the first time and are killed. All such things are reckoned pieces of good luck.

As to virtue, it is most closely connected with the subject of Eulogy, and therefore we will wait to define it until we come to discuss that subject.[1]

6

It is now plain what our aims, future or actual, should be in urging, and what in depreciating, a proposal; the latter being the opposite of the former. Now the political or deliberative orator's aim is utility: deliberation seeks to determine not ends but the means to ends, i.e. what it is most useful to do. Further, utility is a good thing. We ought therefore to assure ourselves of the main facts about Goodness and Utility in general.

We may define a good thing as that which ought to be chosen for its own sake; or as that for the sake of which we choose something

[1] I. 9.

else; or as that which is sought after by all things, or by all things that have sensation or reason, or which will be sought after by any things that acquire reason; or as that which must be prescribed for a given individual by reason generally, or is prescribed for him by his individual reason, this being his individual good; or as that whose presence brings anything into a satisfactory and self-sufficing condition; or as self-sufficiency; or as what produces, maintains, or entails characteristics of this kind, while preventing and destroying their opposites. One thing may entail another in either of two ways—(1) simultaneously, (2) subsequently. Thus learning entails knowledge subsequently, health entails life simultaneously. Things are productive of other things in three senses: first as being healthy produces health; secondly, as food produces health; and thirdly, as exercise does—i.e. it does so usually. All this being settled, we now see that both the acquisition of good things and the removal of bad things must be good; the latter entails freedom from the evil things simultaneously, while the former entails possession of the good things subsequently. The acquisition of a greater in place of a lesser good, or of a lesser in place of a greater evil, is also good, for in proportion as the greater ex-
1362b ceeds the lesser there is acquisition of good or removal of evil. The virtues, too, must be something good; for it is by possessing these that we are in a good condition, and they tend to produce good works and good actions. They must be severally named and described elsewhere.[1] Pleasure, again, must be a good thing, since it is the nature of all animals to aim at it. Consequently both pleasant and beautiful things must be good things, since the former are productive of pleasure, while of the beautiful things some are pleasant and some desirable in and for themselves.

The following is a more detailed list of things that must be good. Happiness, as being desirable in itself and sufficient by itself, and as being that for whose sake we choose many other things. Also justice, courage, temperance, magnanimity, magnificence, and all such qualities, as being excellences of the soul. Further, health, beauty, and the like, as being bodily excellences and productive of many other good things: for instance, health is productive both of pleasure and of life, and therefore is thought the greatest of goods, since these two things which it causes, pleasure and life, are two of the things most highly prized by ordinary people. Wealth, again: for it is the excellence of possession, and also productive of many other good things. Friends and friendship: for a friend is desirable in himself and also productive of many other good things. So, too, honour and reputation, as being pleasant, and productive of many other good things, and usually accompanied by the presence of the good things that cause them to be bestowed. The faculty of speech and action; since all such qualities are productive of what is good. Further—good parts, strong memory, receptiveness, quickness of intuition, and the like, for all such faculties are productive of what is good. Similarly, all the sciences and arts. And life: since, even if no other good were the result of life, it is desirable in itself. And justice, as the cause of good to the community.

The above are pretty well all the things admittedly good. In dealing with things whose goodness is disputed, we may argue in the following ways:—That is good of which the contrary is bad. That is good the contrary of which is to the advantage of our enemies; for example, if it is to the particular advantage of our enemies that we should be cowards, clearly courage is of particular value to our countrymen. And generally, the contrary of that which our enemies desire, or of that at which they rejoice, is evidently valuable. Hence the passage beginning:

Surely would Priam exult.[2]

This principle usually holds good, but not always, since it may well be that our interest is sometimes the same as that of our enemies. Hence it is said that 'evils draw men together';
1363a that is, when the same thing is hurtful to them both.

Further: that which is not in excess is good, and that which is greater than it should be is bad. That also is good on which much labour or money has been spent; the mere fact of this makes it seem good, and such a good is assumed to be an end—an end reached through a long chain of means; and any end is a good. Hence the lines beginning:

And for Priam ⟨and Troy-town's folk⟩ should they leave behind them a boast;[3]

and

Oh, it were shame
To have tarried so long and return empty-handed as erst we came;[4]

[1] Chapter 9.

[2] *Iliad*, I. 255. [3] *Ibid.*, II. 160. [4] *Ibid.*, II. 298.

and there is also the proverb about 'breaking the pitcher at the door'.

That which most people seek after, and which is obviously an object of contention, is also a good; for, as has been shown,[1] that is good which is sought after by everybody, and 'most people' is taken to be equivalent to 'everybody'. That which is praised is good, since no one praises what is not good. So, again, that which is praised by our enemies [or by the worthless]; for when even those who have a grievance think a thing good, it is at once felt that every one must agree with them; our enemies can admit the fact only because it is evident, just as those must be worthless whom their friends censure and their enemies do not. (For this reason the Corinthians conceived themselves to be insulted by Simonides when he wrote:

Against the Corinthians hath Ilium no complaint.[2])

Again, that is good which has been distinguished by the favour of a discerning or virtuous man or woman, as Odysseus was distinguished by Athena, Helen by Theseus, Paris by the goddesses, and Achilles by Homer. And, generally speaking, all things are good which men deliberately choose to do; this will include the things already mentioned, and also whatever may be bad for their enemies or good for their friends, and at the same time practicable. Things are 'practicable' in two senses: (1) it is possible to do them, (2) it is easy to do them. Things are done 'easily' when they are done either without pain or quickly: the 'difficulty' of an act lies either in its painfulness or in the long time it takes. Again, a thing is good if it is as men wish; and they wish to have either no evil at all or at least a balance of good over evil. This last will happen where the penalty is either imperceptible or slight. Good, too, are things that are a man's very own, possessed by no one else, exceptional; for this increases the credit of having them. So are things which befit the possessors, such as whatever is appropriate to their birth or capacity, and whatever they feel they ought to have but lack—such things may indeed be trifling, but none the less men deliberately make them the goal of their action. And things easily effected; for these are practicable (in the sense of being easy); such things are those in which every one, or most people, or one's equals, or one's inferiors have succeeded. Good also are the things by which we shall gratify our friends or annoy our enemies; and the things chosen by those whom we admire: and the things for which we are fitted by nature or experience, since we think we shall succeed more easily in these: and those in which no worthless man can succeed, for such things bring greater praise: and those which we do in fact desire, for what we desire is taken to be not only pleasant but also better. Further, a
1363b man of a given disposition makes chiefly for the corresponding things: lovers of victory make for victory, lovers of honour for honour, money-loving men for money, and so with the rest. These, then, are the sources from which we must derive our means of persuasion about Good and Utility.

7

Since, however, it often happens that people agree that two things are both useful but do not agree about which is the more so, the next step will be to treat of relative goodness and relative utility.

A thing which surpasses another may be regarded as being that other thing plus something more, and that other thing which is surpassed as being what is contained in the first thing. Now to call a thing 'greater' or 'more' always implies a comparison of it with one that is 'smaller' or 'less', while 'great' and 'small', 'much' and 'little', are terms used in comparison with normal magnitude. The 'great' is that which surpasses the normal, the 'small' is that which is surpassed by the normal; and so with 'many' and 'few'.

Now we are applying the term 'good' to what is desirable for its own sake and not for the sake of something else; to that at which all things aim; to what they would choose if they could acquire understanding and practical wisdom; and to that which tends to produce or preserve such goods, or is always accompanied by them. Moreover, that for the sake of which things are done is the end (an end being that for the sake of which all else is done), and for each individual that thing is a good which fulfils these conditions in regard to himself. It follows, then, that a greater number of goods is a greater good than one or than a smaller number, if that one or that smaller number is included in the count; for then the larger number surpasses the smaller, and the smaller quantity is surpassed as being contained in the larger.

[1] 1362a 23.
[2] Simonides, fr. 50, Bergk.

Again, if the largest member of one class surpasses the largest member of another, then the one class surpasses the other; and if one class surpasses another, then the largest member of the one surpasses the largest member of the other. Thus, if the tallest man is taller than the tallest woman, then men in general are taller than women. Conversely, if men in general are taller than women, then the tallest man is taller than the tallest woman. For the superiority of class over class is proportionate to the superiority possessed by their largest specimens. Again, where one good is always accompanied by another, but does not always accompany it, it is greater than the other, for the use of the second thing is implied in the use of the first. A thing may be accompanied by another in three ways, either simultaneously, subsequently, or potentially. Life accompanies health simultaneously (but not health life), knowledge accompanies the act of learning subsequently, cheating accompanies sacrilege potentially, since a man who has committed sacrilege is always capable of cheating. Again, when two things each surpass a third, that which does so by the greater amount is the greater of the two; for it must surpass the greater as well as the less of the other two. A thing productive of a greater good than another is productive of is itself a greater good than that other. For this conception of 'productive of a greater' has been implied in our argument. Likewise, that which is produced by a greater good is itself a greater good; thus, if what is wholesome is more desirable and a greater good than what gives pleasure, health too must be a greater good

1364a than pleasure. Again, a thing which is desirable in itself is a greater good than a thing which is not desirable in itself, as for example bodily strength than what is wholesome, since the latter is not pursued for its own sake, whereas the former is; and this was our definition of the good. Again, if one of two things is an end, and the other is not, the former is the greater good, as being chosen for its own sake and not for the sake of something else; as, for example, exercise is chosen for the sake of physical well-being. And of two things that which stands less in need of the other, or of other things, is the greater good, since it is more self-sufficing. (That which stands 'less' in need of others is that which needs either *fewer* or *easier* things.) So when one thing does not exist or cannot come into existence without a second, while the second can exist without the first, the second is the better. That which does not need something else is more self-sufficing than that which does, and presents itself as a greater good for that reason. Again, that which is a beginning of other things is a greater good than that which is not, and that which is a cause is a greater good than that which is not; the reason being the same in each case, namely that without a cause and a beginning nothing can exist or come into existence. Again, where there are two sets of consequences arising from two different beginnings or causes, the consequences of the more important beginning or cause are themselves the more important; and conversely, that beginning or cause is itself the more important which has the more important consequences. Now it is plain, from all that has been said, that one thing may be shown to be more important than another from two opposite points of view: it may appear the more important (1) because it is a beginning and the other thing is not, and also (2) because it is not a beginning and the other thing is—on the ground that the end is more important and is not a beginning. So Leodamas, when accusing Callistratus, said that the man who prompted the deed was more guilty than the doer, since it would not have been done if he had not planned it. On the other hand, when accusing Chabrias he said that the doer was worse than the prompter, since there would have been no deed without some one to do it; men, said he, plot a thing only in order to carry it out.

Further, what is rare is a greater good than what is plentiful. Thus, gold is a better thing than iron, though less useful: it is harder to get, and therefore better worth getting. Reversely, it may be argued that the plentiful is a better thing than the rare, because we can make more use of it. For what is often useful surpasses what is seldom useful, whence the saying

The best of things is water.[1]

More generally: the hard thing is better than the easy, because it is rarer: and reversely, the easy thing is better than the hard, for it is as we wish it to be. That is the greater good whose contrary is the greater evil, and whose loss affects us more. Positive goodness and badness are more important than the mere *absence* of goodness and badness: for positive goodness and badness are ends, which the mere

[1] Pindar, *Olympians*, I. I.

absence of them cannot be. Further, in proportion as the functions of things are noble or base, the things themselves are good or bad: conversely, in proportion as the things themselves are good or bad, their functions also are good or bad; for the nature of results corresponds with that of their causes and beginnings, and conversely the nature of causes and beginnings corresponds with that of their results. Moreover, those things are greater goods, superiority in which is more desirable or more honourable. Thus, keenness of sight is more desirable than keenness of smell, sight generally being more desirable than smell gen-
1364b erally; and similarly, unusually great love of friends being more honourable than unusually great love of money, ordinary love of friends is more honourable than ordinary love of money. Conversely, if one of two normal things is better or nobler than the other, an unusual degree of that thing is better or nobler than an unusual degree of the other. Again, one thing is more honourable or better than another if it is more honourable or better to desire it; the importance of the object of a given instinct corresponds to the importance of the instinct itself; and for the same reason, if one thing is more honourable or better than another, it is more honourable and better to desire it. Again, if one science is more honourable and valuable than another, the activity with which it deals is also more honourable and valuable; as is the science, so is the reality that is its object, each science being authoritative in its own sphere. So, also, the more valuable and honourable the object of a science, the more valuable and honourable the science itself is in consequence. Again, that which would be judged, or which has been judged, a good thing, or a better thing than something else, by all or most people of understanding, or by the majority of men, or by the ablest, must be so; either without qualification, or in so far as they use their understanding to form their judgement. This is indeed a general principle, applicable to all other judgements also; not only the goodness of things, but their essence, magnitude, and general nature are in fact just what knowledge and understanding will declare them to be. Here the principle is applied to judgements of goodness, since one definition of 'good' was 'what beings that acquire understanding will choose in any given case': from which it clearly follows that that thing is *better* which understanding declares to be so. That, again, is a better thing which attaches to better men, either absolutely, or in virtue of their being better; as courage is better than strength. And that is a greater good which would be chosen by a better man, either absolutely, or in virtue of his being better: for instance, to suffer wrong rather than to do wrong, for that would be the choice of the juster man. Again, the pleasanter of two things is the better, since *all* things pursue pleasure, and things instinctively desire pleasurable sensation *for its own sake;* and these are two of the characteristics by which the 'good' and the 'end' have been defined. One pleasure is greater than another if it is more unmixed with pain, or more lasting. Again, the nobler thing is better than the less noble, since the noble is either what is pleasant or what is desirable in itself. And those things also are greater goods which men desire more earnestly to bring about for themselves or for their friends, whereas those things which they least desire to bring about are greater evils. And those things which are more lasting are better than those which are more fleeting, and the more secure than the less; the enjoyment of the lasting has the advantage of being longer, and that of the secure has the advantage of suiting our wishes, being there for us whenever we like. Further, in accordance with the rule of co-ordinate terms and inflexions of the same stem, what is true of one such related word is true of all. Thus if the action qualified by the term 'brave' is more noble and desirable than the action qualified by the term 'temperate', then 'bravery' is more desirable than 'temperance' and 'being brave' than 'being temperate'. That, again, which is chosen by all is a greater good than that which is not, and that chosen by the majority than
1365a that chosen by the minority. For that which *all* desire is good, as we have said;[1] and so, the more a thing is desired, the better it is. Further, that is the better thing which is considered so by competitors or enemies, or, again, by authorized judges or those whom they select to represent them. In the first two cases the decision is virtually that of every one, in the last two that of authorities and experts. And sometimes it may be argued that what all share is the better thing, since it is a dishonour not to share in it; at other times, that what none or few share is better, since it is rarer. The more praiseworthy things are, the nobler and therefore the better they are. So with the things that earn greater honours than

[1] 1363b 14.

others—honour is, as it were, a measure of value; and the things whose absence involves comparatively heavy penalties; and the things that are better than others admitted or believed to be good. Moreover, things look better merely by being divided into their parts, since they then seem to surpass a greater number of things than before. Hence Homer says that Meleager was roused to battle by the thought of

All horrors that light on a folk whose city is ta'en of their foes,
When they slaughter the men, when the burg is wasted with ravening flame,
When strangers are haling young children to thraldom, ⟨fair women to shame.⟩[1]

The same effect is produced by piling up facts in a climax after the manner of Epicharmus. The reason is partly the same as in the case of division (for combination too makes the impression of great superiority), and partly that the original thing appears to be the cause and origin of important results. And since a thing is better when it is harder or rarer than other things, its superiority may be due to seasons, ages, places, times, or one's natural powers. When a man accomplishes something beyond his natural power, or beyond his years, or beyond the measure of people like him, or in a special way, or at a special place or time, his deed will have a high degree of nobleness, goodness, and justice, or of their opposites. Hence the epigram on the victor at the Olympic games:

In time past, bearing a yoke on my shoulders, of wood unshaven,
I carried my loads of fish from Argos to Tegea town.[2]

So Iphicrates used to extol himself by describing the low estate from which he had risen. Again, what is natural is better than what is acquired, since it is harder to come by. Hence the words of Homer:

I have learnt from none but myself.[3]

And the best part of a good thing is particularly good; as when Pericles in his funeral oration said that the country's loss of its young men in battle was 'as if the spring were taken out of the year'. So with those things which are of service when the need is pressing; for example, in old age and times of sickness. And of two things that which leads more directly to the end in view is the better. So too is that which is better for people generally as well as for a particular individual. Again, what *can* be got is better than what cannot, for it is good in a given case and the other thing is not. And what is at the end of life is better than what is not, since those things are ends in a greater degree which are nearer the end. What aims at reality is better than **1365b** what aims at appearance. We may define what aims at appearance as what a man will not choose if nobody is to know of his having it. This would seem to show that to receive benefits is more desirable than to confer them, since a man will choose the former even if nobody is to know of it, but it is not the general view that he will choose the latter if nobody knows of it. What a man wants to *be* is better than what a man wants to *seem,* for in aiming at that he is aiming more at reality. Hence men say that justice is of small value, since it is more desirable to seem just than to be just, whereas with health it is not so. That is better than other things which is more useful than they are for a number of different purposes; for example, that which promotes life, good life, pleasure, and noble conduct. For this reason wealth and health are commonly thought to be of the highest value, as possessing all these advantages. Again, that is better than other things which is accompanied both with less pain and with actual pleasure; for here there is more than one advantage; and so here we have the good of feeling pleasure and also the good of not feeling pain. And of two good things that is the better whose addition to a third thing makes a better whole than the addition of the other to the same thing will make. Again, those things which we are seen to possess are better than those which we are not seen to possess, since the former have the air of reality. Hence wealth may be regarded as a greater good if its existence is known to others. That which is dearly prized is better than what is not—the sort of thing that some people have only one of, though others have more like it. Accordingly, blinding a one-eyed man inflicts worse injury than half-blinding a man with two eyes; for the one-eyed man has been robbed of what he dearly prized.

The grounds on which we must base our arguments, when we are speaking for or against a proposal, have now been set forth more or less completely.

[1] *Iliad*, IX. 592-4.
[2] Simonides, fr. 163, Bergk.
[3] *Odyssey*, XXII. 347.

8

The most important and effective qualification for success in persuading audiences and speaking well on public affairs is to understand all the forms of government and to discriminate their respective customs, institutions, and interests. For all men are persuaded by considerations of their interest, and their interest lies in the maintenance of the established order. Further, it rests with the supreme authority to give authoritative decisions, and this varies with each form of government; there are as many different supreme authorities as there are different forms of government. The forms of government are four—democracy, oligarchy, aristocracy, monarchy. The supreme right to judge and decide always rests, therefore, with either a part or the whole of one or other of these governing powers.

A Democracy is a form of government under which the citizens distribute the offices of state among themselves by lot, whereas under oligarchy there is a property qualification, under aristocracy one of education. By education I mean that education which is laid down by the law; for it is those who have been loyal to the national institutions that hold office under an aristocracy. These are bound to be looked upon as 'the best men', and it is from this fact that this form of government has derived its name ('the rule of the best'). Monarchy, as the word implies, is the constitution in which one man has authority over all. There are two forms of monarchy: kingship, which is limited by prescribed conditions, and 'tyranny', which is not limited by anything.

We must also notice the ends which the various forms of government pursue, since people choose in practice such actions as will lead to the realization of their ends. The end of democracy is freedom; of oligarchy, wealth; of aristocracy, the maintenance of education and national institutions; of tyranny, the protection of the tyrant. It is clear, then, that we must distinguish those particular customs, institutions, and interests which tend to realize the ideal of each constitution, since men choose their means with reference to their ends. But rhetorical persuasion is effected not only by demonstrative but by ethical argument; it helps a speaker to convince us, if we believe that he has certain qualities himself, namely, goodness, or goodwill towards us, or both together. Similarly, we should know the moral qualities characteristic of each form of government, for the special moral character of each is bound to provide us with our most effective means of persuasion in dealing with it. We shall learn the qualities of governments in the same way as we learn the qualities of individuals, since they are revealed in their deliberate acts of choice; and these are determined by the end that inspires them.

We have now considered the objects, immediate or distant, at which we are to aim when urging any proposal, and the grounds on which we are to base our arguments in favour of its utility. We have also briefly considered the means and methods by which we shall gain a good knowledge of the moral qualities and institutions peculiar to the various forms of government—only, however, to the extent demanded by the present occasion; a detailed account of the subject has been given in the *Politics*.[1]

9

We have now to consider Virtue and Vice, the Noble and the Base, since these are the objects of praise and blame. In doing so, we shall at the same time be finding out how to make our hearers take the required view of our own characters—our second method of persuasion. The ways in which to make them trust the goodness of other people are also the ways in which to make them trust our own. Praise, again, may be serious or frivolous; nor is it always of a human or divine being but often of inanimate things, or of the humblest of the lower animals. Here too we must know on what grounds to argue, and must, therefore, now discuss the subject, though by way of illustration only.

The Noble is that which is both desirable for its own sake and also worthy of praise; or that which is both good and also pleasant because good. If this is a true definition of the Noble, it follows that virtue must be noble, since it is both a good thing and also praiseworthy. Virtue is, according to the usual view, a faculty of providing and preserving good things; or a faculty of conferring many great benefits, and benefits of all kinds on all occasions. The forms of Virtue are justice, courage, temperance, magnificence, magnanimity, liberality, gentleness, prudence, wisdom. If virtue is a faculty of beneficence, the highest kinds of it must be those which are most useful to others, and for this reason men honour most the

[1] *Politics*, III and IV.

just and the courageous, since courage is useful to others in war, justice both in war and in peace. Next comes liberality; liberal people let their money go instead of fighting for it, whereas other people care more for money than for anything else. Justice is the virtue through which everybody enjoys his own possessions in accordance with the law; its opposite is injustice, through which men enjoy the possessions of others in defiance of the law. Courage is the virtue that disposes men to do noble deeds in situations of danger, in accordance with the law and in obedience to its commands; cowardice is the opposite. Temperance is the virtue that disposes us to obey the law where physical pleasures are concerned; incontinence is the opposite. Liberality disposes us to spend money for others' good; illiberality is the opposite. Magnanimity is the virtue that disposes us to do good to others on a large scale; [its opposite is meanness of spirit]. Magnificence is a virtue productive of greatness in matters involving the spending of money. The opposites of these two are smallness of spirit and meanness respectively. Prudence is that virtue of the understanding which enables men to come to wise decisions about the relation to happiness of the goods and evils that have been previously mentioned.[1]

The above is a sufficient account, for our present purpose, of virtue and vice in general, and of their various forms. As to further aspects of the subject, it is not difficult to discern the facts; it is evident that things productive of virtue are noble, as tending towards virtue; and also the effects of virtue, that is, the signs of its presence and the acts to which it leads. And since the signs of virtue, and such acts as it is the mark of a virtuous man to do or have done to him, are noble, it follows that all deeds or signs of courage, and everything done courageously, must be noble things; and so with what is just and actions done justly. (Not, however, actions justly done to us; here justice is unlike the other virtues; 'justly' does not always mean 'nobly'; when a man is punished, it is more shameful that this should be justly than unjustly done to him). The same is true of the other virtues. Again, those actions are noble for which the reward is simply honour, or honour more than money. So are those in which a man aims at something desirable for some one else's sake; actions good absolutely, such as those a man does for his country without thinking of himself; actions good in their own nature; actions that are not good simply for the individual, since individual in-
1367ᵃ terests are selfish. Noble also are those actions whose advantage may be enjoyed after death, as opposed to those whose advantage is enjoyed during one's lifetime: for the latter are more likely to be for one's own sake only. Also, all actions done for the sake of others, since less than other actions are done for one's own sake; and all successes which benefit others and not oneself; and services done to one's benefactors, for this is just; and good deeds generally, since they are not directed to one's own profit. And the opposites of those things of which men feel ashamed, for men are ashamed of saying, doing, or intending to do shameful things. So when Alcaeus said

Something I fain would say to thee,
Only shame restraineth me,[2]

Sappho wrote

If for things good and noble thou wert yearning,
If to speak baseness were thy tongue not burning,
No load of shame would on thine eyelids weigh;
What thou with honour wishest thou wouldst say.[3]

Those things, also, are noble for which men strive anxiously, without feeling fear; for they feel thus about the good things which lead to fair fame. Again, one quality or action is nobler than another if it is that of a naturally finer being: thus a man's will be nobler than a woman's. And those qualities are noble which give more pleasure to other people than to their possessors; hence the nobleness of justice and just actions. It is noble to avenge oneself on one's enemies and not to come to terms with them; for requital is just, and the just is noble; and not to surrender is a sign of courage. Victory, too, and honour belong to the class of noble things, since they are desirable even when they yield no fruits, and they prove our superiority in good qualities. Things that deserve to be remembered are noble, and the more they deserve this, the nobler they are. So are the things that continue even after death; those which are always attended by honour; those which are exceptional; and those which are possessed by one person alone—these last are more readily remembered than others. So again are possessions that bring no

[1] Cf. 1362ᵇ 10-28.

[2] Alcaeus, fr. 55, Bergk.

[3] Sappho, fr. 28, Bergk.

profit, since they are more fitting than others for a gentleman. So are the distinctive qualities of a particular people, and the symbols of what it specially admires, like long hair in Sparta, where this is a mark of a free man, as it is not easy to perform any menial task when one's hair is long. Again, it is noble not to practise any sordid craft, since it is the mark of a free man not to live at another's beck and call. We are also to assume, when we wish either to praise a man or blame him, that qualities closely allied to those which he actually has are identical with them; for instance, that the cautious man is cold-blooded and treacherous, and that the stupid man is an honest fellow or the thick-skinned man a good-tempered one. We can always idealize any given man by drawing on the virtues akin to his actual qualities; thus we may say that the passionate and excitable man is 'outspoken'; or that the arrogant man is 'superb' or 'impressive'. Those who run to extremes will be said to possess the corresponding good qualities; rashness will be called courage, and extravagance generosity. That will be what most people think; and at the same time this method enables an advocate to draw a misleading inference from the motive, arguing that if a man runs into danger needlessly, much more will he do so in a noble cause; and if a man is open-handed to any one and every one, he will be so to his friends also, since it is the extreme form of goodness to be good to everybody.

We must also take into account the nature of our particular audience when making a speech of praise; for, as Socrates used to say, it is not difficult to praise the Athenians to an Athenian audience.[1] If the audience esteems a given quality, we must say that our hero has that quality, no matter whether we are addressing Scythians or Spartans or philosophers. Everything, in fact, that is esteemed we are to represent as noble. After all, people regard the two things as much the same.

All actions are noble that are appropriate to the man who does them: if, for instance, they are worthy of his ancestors or of his own past career. For it makes for happiness, and is a noble thing, that he should add to the honour he already has. Even inappropriate actions are noble if they are better and nobler than the appropriate ones would be; for instance, if one who was just an average person when all went well becomes a hero in adversity, or if he becomes better and easier to get on with the higher he rises. Compare the saying of Iphicrates, 'Think what I was and what I am'; and the epigram on the victor at the Olympic games,

In time past, bearing a yoke on my shoulders, of wood unshaven,[2]

and the encomium of Simonides,

A woman whose father, whose husband, whose brethren were princes all.[3]

Since we praise a man for what he has actually done, and fine actions are distinguished from others by being intentionally good, we must try to prove that our hero's noble acts are intentional. This is all the easier if we can make out that he has often acted so before, and therefore we must assert coincidences and accidents to have been intended. Produce a number of good actions, all of the same kind, and people will think that they must have been intended, and that they prove the good qualities of the man who did them.

Praise is the expression in words of the eminence of a man's good qualities, and therefore we must display his actions as the product of such qualities. Encomium refers to what he has actually done; the mention of accessories, such as good birth and education, merely helps to make our story credible—good fathers are likely to have good sons, and good training is likely to produce good character. Hence it is only when a man has already done something that we bestow *encomiums* upon him. Yet the actual deeds are evidence of the doer's character: even if a man has not actually done a given good thing, we shall bestow *praise* on him, if we are sure that he is the sort of man who *would* do it. To call any one blest is, it may be added, the same thing as to call him happy; but these are not the same thing as to bestow praise and encomium upon him; the two latter are a part of 'calling happy', just as goodness is a part of happiness.

To praise a man is in one respect akin to urging a course of action. The suggestions which would be made in the latter case become encomiums when differently expressed. When we know what action or character is required, then, in order to express these facts as suggestions for action, we have to change and reverse our form of words. Thus the statement 'A man should be proud not of what he owes

[1] Cp. Plato, *Menexenus*, 235 D.

[2] Cf. I. 7(1365a 24-8), for this and the previous quotation.

[3] Simonides, fr. III, Bergk.

to fortune but of what he owes to himself', if put like this, amounts to a suggestion; to make it into praise we must put it thus, 'Since he is proud not of what he owes to fortune but of what he owes to himself.' Consequently, whenever you want to praise any one, think what you would urge people to do; and when you want to urge the doing of anything, think what you would praise a man for having done. Since suggestion may or may not forbid an action, the praise into which we convert it must have one or other of two opposite forms of expression accordingly.

There are, also, many useful ways of heightening the effect of praise. We must, for instance, point out that a man is the only one, or the first, or almost the only one who has done something, or that he has done it better than any one else; all these distinctions are honourable. And we must, further, make much of the particular season and occasion of an action, arguing that we could hardly have looked for it just then. If a man has often achieved the same success, we must mention this; that is a strong point; he himself, and not luck, will then be given the credit. So, too, if it is on his account that observances have been devised and instituted to encourage or honour such achievements as his own: thus we may praise Hippolochus because the first encomium ever made was for him, or Harmodius and Aristogeiton because their statues were the first to be put up in the market-place. And we may censure bad men for the opposite reason.

Again, if you cannot find enough to say of a man himself, you may pit him against others, which is what Isocrates used to do owing to his want of familiarity with forensic pleading. The comparison should be with famous men; that will strengthen your case; it is a noble thing to surpass men who are themselves great. It is only natural that methods of 'heightening the effect' should be attached particularly to speeches of praise; they aim at proving superiority over others, and any such superiority is a form of nobleness. Hence if you cannot compare your hero with famous men, you should at least compare him with other people generally, since any superiority is held to reveal excellence. And, in general, of the lines of argument which are common to all speeches, this 'heightening of effect' is most suitable for declamations, where we take our hero's actions as admitted facts, and our business is simply to invest these with dignity and nobility. 'Examples' are most suitable to deliberative speeches; for we judge of future events by divination from past events. Enthymemes are most suitable to forensic speeches; it is our doubts about past events that most admit of arguments showing why a thing must have happened or proving that it did happen.

The above are the general lines on which all, or nearly all, speeches of praise or blame are constructed. We have seen the sort of thing we must bear in mind in making such speeches, and the materials out of which encomiums and censures are made. No special treatment of censure and vituperation is needed. Knowing the above facts, we know their contraries; and it is out of these that speeches of censure are made.

10

1368b We have next to treat of Accusation and Defence, and to enumerate and describe the ingredients of the syllogisms used therein. There are three things we must ascertain—first, the nature and number of the incentives to wrong-doing; second, the state of mind of wrongdoers; third, the kind of persons who are wronged, and their condition. We will deal with these questions in order. But before that let us define the act of 'wrong-doing'.

We may describe 'wrong-doing' as injury voluntarily inflicted contrary to law. 'Law' is either special or general. By special law I mean that written law which regulates the life of a particular community; by general law, all those unwritten principles which are supposed to be acknowledged everywhere. We do things 'voluntarily' when we do them consciously and without constraint. (Not all voluntary acts are deliberate, but all deliberate acts are conscious—no one is ignorant of what he deliberately intends.) The causes of our deliberately intending harmful and wicked acts contrary to law are (1) vice, (2) lack of self-control. For the wrongs a man does to others will correspond to the bad quality or qualities that he himself possesses. Thus it is the mean man who will wrong others about money, the profligate in matters of physical pleasure, the effeminate in matters of comfort, and the coward where danger is concerned—his terror makes him abandon those who are involved in the same danger. The ambitious man does wrong for the sake of honour, the quick-tempered from anger, the lover of victory for the sake of victory, the embittered man for the sake of revenge, the stupid man because he has misguided notions of right and wrong, the shameless man because he does not mind what people think of him; and so with the rest—any wrong that any one does to others corresponds to his particular faults of character.

However, this subject has already been cleared up in part in our discussion of the virtues[1] and will be further explained later when we treat of the emotions.[2] We have now to consider the motives and states of mind of wrongdoers, and to whom they do wrong.

Let us first decide what sort of things people are trying to get or avoid when they set about doing wrong to others. For it is plain that the prosecutor must consider, out of all the aims that can ever induce us to do wrong to our neighbours, how many, and which, affect his adversary; while the defendant must consider how many, and which, do *not* affect him. Now every action of every person either is or is not due to that person himself. Of those not due to himself some are due to chance, the others to necessity; of these latter, again, some are due to compulsion, the others to nature. Consequently all actions that are not due to a man himself are due either to chance or to na-
1369[a] ture or to compulsion. All actions that *are* due to a man himself and caused by himself are due either to habit or to rational or irrational craving. Rational craving is a craving for good, i.e. a *wish*—nobody wishes for anything unless he thinks it good. Irrational craving is twofold, viz. anger and appetite.

Thus every action must be due to one or other of seven causes: chance, nature, compulsion, habit, reasoning, anger, or appetite. It is superfluous further to distinguish actions according to the doers' ages, moral states, or the like; it is of course true that, for instance, young men do have hot tempers and strong appetites; still, it is not through youth that they act accordingly, but through anger or appetite. Nor, again, is action due to wealth or poverty; it is of course true that poor men, being short of money, do have an appetite for it, and that rich men, being able to command needless pleasures, do have an appetite for such pleasures: but here, again, their actions will be *due* not to wealth or poverty but to appetite. Similarly, with just men, and unjust men, and all others who are said to act in accordance with their moral qualities, their actions will really be due to one of the causes mentioned—either reasoning or emotion: due, indeed, sometimes to good dispositions and good emotions, and sometimes to bad; but that good qualities should be followed by good emotions, and bad by bad, is merely an accessory fact—it is no doubt true that the temperate man, for instance, because he is temperate, *is* always and at once attended by healthy opinions and appetites in regard to pleasant things, and the intemperate man by unhealthy ones. So we must ignore such distinctions. Still we must consider what kinds of actions and of people usually go together; for while there are no definite kinds of action associated with the fact that a man is fair or dark, tall or short, it does make a difference if he is young or old, just or unjust. And, generally speaking, all those accessory qualities that cause distinctions of human character are important: e.g. the sense of wealth or poverty, of being lucky or unlucky. This shall be dealt with later[3]—let us now deal first with the rest of the subject before us.

The things that happen by chance are all those whose cause cannot be determined, that have no purpose, and that happen neither always nor usually nor in any fixed way. The definition of chance shows just what they are. Those things happen by nature which have a fixed and internal cause; they take place
1369[b] uniformly, either always or usually. There is no need to discuss in exact detail the things that happen contrary to nature, nor to ask whether they happen in some sense naturally or from some other cause; it would seem that chance is at least partly the cause of such events. Those things happen through compulsion which take place contrary to the desire or reason of the doer, yet through his own agency. Acts are done from habit which men do because they have often done them before. Actions are due to reasoning when, in view of any of the goods already mentioned,[4] they appear useful either as ends or as means to an end, and are performed for that reason: 'for that reason,' since even licentious persons perform a certain number of useful actions, but because they are pleasant and not because they are useful. To passion and anger are due all acts of revenge. Revenge and punishment are different things. Punishment is inflicted for the sake of the person punished; revenge for that of the punisher, to satisfy his feelings. (What anger is will be made clear when we come to discuss the emotions.[5]) Appetite is the cause of all actions that appear pleasant. Habit, whether acquired by mere familiarity or by effort, belongs to the class of pleasant things,

[1] I. 9. [2] II. I-II.

[3] II. 12-17. [4] I. 6. [5] II. 2.

for there are many actions not naturally pleasant which men perform with pleasure, once they have become used to them. To sum up then, all actions due to ourselves either are or seem to be either good or pleasant. Moreover, as all actions due to ourselves are done voluntarily and actions not due to ourselves are done involuntarily, it follows that all voluntary actions must either be or seem to be either good or pleasant; for I reckon among goods escape from evils or apparent evils and the exchange of a greater evil for a less (since these things are in a sense positively desirable), and likewise I count among pleasures escape from painful or apparently painful things and the exchange of a greater pain for a less. We must ascertain, then, the number and nature of the things that are useful and pleasant. The useful has been previously examined in connexion with political oratory;[1] let us now proceed to examine the pleasant. Our various definitions must be regarded as adequate, even if they are not exact, provided they are clear.

11

We may lay it down that Pleasure is a movement, a movement by which the soul as a whole is consciously brought into its normal state of being; and that Pain is the opposite. If
1370a this is what pleasure is, it is clear that the pleasant is what tends to produce this condition, while that which tends to destroy it, or to cause the soul to be brought into the opposite state, is painful. It must therefore be pleasant as a rule to move towards a natural state of being, particularly when a natural process has achieved the complete recovery of that natural state. Habits also are pleasant; for as soon as a thing has become habitual, it is virtually natural; habit is a thing not unlike nature; what happens often is akin to what happens always, natural events happening always, habitual events often. Again, that is pleasant which is not forced on us; for force is unnatural, and that is why what is compulsory is painful, and it has been rightly said

All that is done on compulsion is bitterness unto the soul.[2]

So all acts of concentration, strong effort, and strain are necessarily painful; they all involve compulsion and force, unless we are accustomed to them, in which case it is custom that makes them pleasant. The opposites to these are pleasant; and hence ease, freedom from toil, relaxation, amusement, rest, and sleep belong to the class of pleasant things; for these are all free from any element of compulsion. Everything, too, is pleasant for which we have the desire within us, since desire is the craving for pleasure. Of the desires some are irrational, some associated with reason. By irrational I mean those which do not arise from any opinion held by the mind. Of this kind are those known as 'natural'; for instance, those originating in the body, such as the desire for nourishment, namely hunger and thirst, and a separate kind of desire answering to each kind of nourishment; and the desires connected with taste and sex and sensations of touch in general; and those of smell, hearing, and vision. Rational desires are those which we are induced to have; there are many things we desire to see or get because we have been told of them and induced to believe them good. Further, pleasure is the consciousness through the senses of a certain kind of emotion; but imagination is a feeble sort of sensation, and there will always be in the mind of a man who remembers or expects something an image or picture of what he remembers or expects. If this is so, it is clear that memory and expectation also, being accompanied by sensation, may be accompanied by pleasure. It follows that anything pleasant is either present and perceived, past and remembered, or future and expected, since we perceive present pleasures, remember past ones, and expect future ones. Now the things that are pleasant to re-
1370b member are not only those that, when actually perceived as present, *were* pleasant, but also some things that were not, provided that their results have subsequently proved noble and good. Hence the words

Sweet 'tis when rescued to remember pain,[3]

and

Even his griefs are a joy long after to one that remembers
All that he wrought and endured.[4]

The reason of this is that it is pleasant even to be merely free from evil. The things it is pleasant to expect are those that when present are felt to afford us either great delight or great but not painful benefit. And in general, all the things that delight us when they are present also do so, as a rule, when we merely remember or expect them. Hence even being an-

[1] I. 6.
[2] Evenus, fr. 8, Bergk.
[3] Euripides, *Andromeda*, fr. 133 Nauck.
[4] Cf. *Odyssey*, XV. 400, 401.

gry is pleasant—Homer said of wrath that

Sweeter it is by far than the honeycomb dripping with sweetness[1]—

for no one grows angry with a person on whom there is no prospect of taking vengeance, and we feel comparatively little anger, or none at all, with those who are much our superiors in power. Some pleasant feeling is associated with most of our appetites we are enjoying either the memory of a past pleasure or the expectation of a future one, just as persons down with fever, during their attacks of thirst, enjoy remembering the drinks they have had and looking forward to having more. So also a lover enjoys talking or writing about his loved one, or doing any little thing connected with him; all these things recall him to memory and make him actually present to the eye of imagination. Indeed, it is always the first sign of love, that besides enjoying some one's presence, we remember him when he is gone, and feel pain as well as pleasure, because he is there no longer. Similarly there is an element of pleasure even in mourning and lamentation for the departed. There is grief, indeed, at his loss, but pleasure in remembering him and as it were seeing him before us in his deeds and in his life. We can well believe the poet when he says

He spake, and in each man's heart he awakened the love of lament.[2]

Revenge, too, is pleasant; it is pleasant to get anything that it is painful to fail to get, and angry people suffer extreme pain when they fail to get their revenge; but they enjoy the prospect of getting it. Victory also is pleasant, and not merely to 'bad losers', but to every one; the winner sees himself in the light of a champion, and everybody has a more or less keen appetite for being that. The pleasantness of victory implies of course that combative **1371a** sports and intellectual contests are pleasant (since in these it often happens that some one wins) and also games like knuckle-bones, ball, dice, and draughts. And similarly with the serious sports; some of these become pleasant when one is accustomed to them; while others are pleasant from the first, like hunting with hounds, or indeed any kind of hunting. For where there is competition, there is victory. That is why forensic pleading and debating contests are pleasant to those who are accustomed to them and have the capacity for them. Honour and good repute are among the most pleasant things of all; they make a man see himself in the character of a fine fellow, especially when he is credited with it by people whom he thinks good judges. His neighbours are better judges than people at a distance; his associates and fellow-countrymen better than strangers; his contemporaries better than posterity; sensible persons better than foolish ones; a large number of people better than a small number: those of the former class, in each case, are the more likely to be good judges of him. Honour and credit bestowed by those whom you think much inferior to yourself—e.g. children or animals—you do not value: not for its own sake, anyhow: if you do value it, it is for some other reason. Friends belong to the class of pleasant things; it is pleasant to love—if you love wine, you certainly find it delightful: and it is pleasant to be loved, for this too makes a man see himself as the possessor of goodness, a thing that every being that has a feeling for it desires to possess: to be loved means to be valued for one's own personal qualities. To be admired is also pleasant, simply because of the honour implied. Flattery and flatterers are pleasant: the flatterer is a man who, you believe, admires and likes you. To do the same thing often is pleasant, since, as we saw, anything habitual is pleasant. And to change is also pleasant: change means an approach to nature, whereas invariable repetition of anything causes the excessive prolongation of a settled condition: therefore, says the poet,

Change is in all things sweet.[3]

That is why what comes to us only at long intervals is pleasant, whether it be a person or a thing; for it is a change from what we had before, and, besides, what comes only at long intervals has the value of rarity. Learning things and wondering at things are also pleasant as a rule; wondering implies the desire of learning, so that the object of wonder is an object of desire; while in learning one is brought into one's natural condition. Conferring and receiving benefits belong to the class of pleasant things; to receive a benefit is to get what one desires; to confer a benefit implies both posses- **1371b** sion and superiority, both of which are things we try to attain. It is because beneficent acts are pleasant that people find it pleasant to put their neighbours straight again and to sup-

[1] *Iliad*, XVIII. 109.

[2] *Ibid.*, XXIII. 108; *Odyssey*, IV. 183.

[3] Euripides, *Orestes*, 234.

ply what they lack. Again, since learning and wondering are pleasant, it follows that such things as acts of imitation must be pleasant—for instance, painting, sculpture, poetry—and every product of skilful imitation; this latter, even if the object imitated is not itself pleasant; for it is not the object itself which here gives delight; the spectator draws inferences ('That is a so-and-so') and thus learns something fresh. Dramatic turns of fortune and hairbreadth escapes from perils are pleasant, because we feel all such things are wonderful.

And since what is natural is pleasant, and things akin to each other seem natural to each other, therefore all kindred and similar things are usually pleasant to each other; for instance, one man, horse, or young person is pleasant to another man, horse, or young person. Hence the proverbs 'mate delights mate', 'like to like',[1] 'beast knows beast', 'jackdaw to jackdaw', and the rest of them. But since everything like and akin to oneself is pleasant, and since every man is himself more like and akin to himself than any one else is, it follows that all of us must be more or less fond of ourselves. For all this resemblance and kinship is present particularly in the relation of an individual to himself. And because we are all fond of ourselves, it follows that what is our own is pleasant to all of us, as for instance our own deeds and words. That is why we are usually fond of our flatterers, [our lovers,] and honour; also of our children, for our children are our own work. It is also pleasant to complete what is defective, for the whole thing thereupon becomes our own work. And since power over others is very pleasant, it is pleasant to be thought wise, for practical wisdom secures us power over others. (Scientific wisdom is also pleasant, because it is the knowledge of many wonderful things.) Again, since most of us are ambitious, it must be pleasant to disparage our neighbours as well as to have power over them. It is pleasant for a man to spend his time over what he feels he can do best; just as the poet says,

To that he bends himself,
To that each day allots most time, wherein
He is indeed the best part of himself.[2]

Similarly, since amusement and every kind of relaxation and laughter too belong to the class of pleasant things, it follows that ludicrous things are pleasant, whether men, words, or

1372a deeds. We have discussed the ludicrous separately in the treatise on the *Art of Poetry*.

So much for the subject of pleasant things: by considering their opposites we can easily see what things are unpleasant.

12

The above are the motives that make men do wrong to others; we are next to consider the states of mind in which they do it, and the persons to whom they do it.

They must themselves suppose that the thing can be done, and done by them: either that they can do it without being found out, or that if they are found out they can escape being punished, or that if they are punished the disadvantage will be less than the gain for themselves or those they care for. The general subject of apparent possibility and impossibility will be handled later on,[3] since it is relevant not only to forensic but to all kinds of speaking. But it may here be said that people think that they can themselves most easily do wrong to others without being punished for it if they possess eloquence, or practical ability, or much legal experience, or a large body of friends, or a great deal of money. Their confidence is greatest if they personally possess the advantages mentioned: but even without them they are satisfied if they have friends or supporters or partners who do possess them: they can thus both commit their crimes and escape being found out and punished for committing them. They are also safe, they think, if they are on good terms with their victims or with the judges who try them. Their victims will in that case not be on their guard against being wronged, and will make some arrangement with them instead of prosecuting; while their judges will favour them because they like them, either letting them off altogether or imposing light sentences. They are not likely to be found out if their appearance contradicts the charges that might be brought against them: for instance, a weakling is unlikely to be charged with violent assault, or a poor and ugly man with adultery. Public and open injuries are the easiest to do, because nobody could at all suppose them possible, and therefore no precautions are taken. The same is true of crimes so great and terrible that no man living could be suspected of them: here too no precautions are taken. For all men guard against ordinary offences, just as they guard against ordinary diseases; but no one

[1] *Odyssey*, XVII. 218. [2] Euripides, fr. 183 N².

[3] II. 19.

takes precautions against a disease that nobody has ever had. You feel safe, too, if you have either no enemies or a great many; if you have none, you expect not to be watched and therefore not to be detected; if you have a great many, you will be watched, and therefore people will think you can never risk an attempt on them, and you can defend your innocence by pointing out that you could never have taken such a risk. You may also trust to hide your crime by the way you do it or the place you do it in, or by some convenient means of disposal.

You may feel that even if you are found out you can stave off a trial, or have it postponed, or corrupt your judges: or that even if you are sentenced you can avoid paying damages, or can at least postpone doing so for a long time: or that you are so badly off that you will have nothing to lose. You may feel that the gain to be got by wrong-doing is great or certain or immediate, and that the penalty is small **1372b** or uncertain or distant. It may be that the advantage to be gained is greater than any possible retribution: as in the case of despotic power, according to the popular view. You may consider your crimes as bringing you solid profit, while their punishment is nothing more than being called bad names. Or the opposite argument may appeal to you: your crimes may bring you some credit (thus you may, incidentally, be avenging your father or mother, like Zeno), whereas the punishment may amount to a fine, or banishment, or something of that sort. People may be led on to wrong others by either of these motives or feelings; but no man by both—they will affect people of quite opposite characters. You may be encouraged by having often escaped detection or punishment already; or by having often tried and failed; for in crime, as in war, there are men who will always refuse to give up the struggle. You may get your pleasure on the spot and the pain later, or the gain on the spot and the loss later. That is what appeals to weak-willed persons—and weakness of will may be shown with regard to all the objects of desire. It may on the contrary appeal to you—as it does appeal to self-controlled and sensible people—that the pain and loss are immediate, while the pleasure and profit come later and last longer. You may feel able to make it appear that your crime was due to chance, or to necessity, or to natural causes, or to habit: in fact, to put it generally, as if you had failed to do right rather than actually done wrong. You may be able to trust other people to judge you equitably. You may be stimulated by being in want: which may mean that you want necessaries, as poor people do, or that you want luxuries, as rich people do. You may be encouraged by having a particularly good reputation, because that will save you from being suspected: or by having a particularly bad one, because nothing you are likely to do will make it worse.

The above, then, are the various states of mind in which a man sets about doing wrong to others. The kind of people to whom he does wrong, and the ways in which he does it, must be considered next. The people to whom he does it are those who have what he wants himself, whether this means necessities or luxuries and materials for enjoyment. His victims may be far off or near at hand. If they are near, he gets his profit quickly; if they are far off, vengeance is slow, as those think who plunder the Carthaginians. They may be those who are trustful instead of being cautious and watchful, since all such people are easy to elude. Or those who are too easy-going to have enough energy to prosecute an offender. Or sensitive people, who are not apt to show fight over questions of money. Or those who have been wronged already by many people, and yet have not prosecuted; such men must surely be the proverbial 'Mysian prey'. Or those who have either never or often been wronged before; in neither case will they take precautions; if they have never been wronged they think they never will, and if they have often been wronged they feel that surely it cannot happen again. Or those whose character has been attacked in the past, or is exposed to attack in the future: they will be too much frightened of the judges to make up their minds to prosecute, nor can they win their case if they do: **1373a** this is true of those who are hated or unpopular. Another likely class of victim is those who their injurer can pretend have, themselves or through their ancestors or friends, treated badly, or intended to treat badly, the man himself, or his ancestors, or those he cares for; as the proverb says, 'wickedness needs but a pretext'. A man may wrong his enemies, because that is pleasant: he may equally wrong his friends, because that is easy. Then there are those who have no friends, and those who lack eloquence and practical capacity; these will either not attempt to prosecute, or they will come to terms, or failing that they will lose their case. There are those whom it does not pay to waste time in waiting for trial or damages, such as foreigners and small farmers; they will settle for a trifle, and always be ready to leave off. Also those who have themselves wronged others, either often, or in the same way as they are now being wronged themselves—for it is felt that next to no wrong is done to people when it is the same wrong as they have often themselves done to others: if, for instance, you assault a man who has been accustomed to behave with violence to others. So too with those who have done wrong to others, or have meant to, or mean to, or are likely to do so; there is something fine and pleasant in wronging such persons, it seems as though almost no wrong were done. Also those by doing wrong to whom we shall be gratifying our friends, or those we admire or love, or our masters, or in general the people by reference to whom we mould our lives. Also those whom we may wrong and yet be sure of equitable treatment. Also those against whom we have had any grievance, or any previous differences with them, as Callippus had when he behaved as he did to Dion: here too it seems as if almost no wrong were being done. Also those who are on the point of being wronged by others if we fail to wrong them ourselves, since here we feel we have no time left for thinking the matter over. So Aenesidemus is said to have sent the 'cottabus' prize to Gelon, who had just reduced a town to slavery, because Gelon had got there first and forestalled his own attempt. Also those by wronging whom we shall be able to do many righteous acts; for we feel that we can then easily cure the harm done. Thus Jason the Thessalian said that it is a duty to do some unjust acts in order to be able to do many just ones.

Among the kinds of wrong done to others are those that are done universally, or at least commonly: one expects to be forgiven for doing these. Also those that can easily be kept dark, as where things that can rapidly be consumed like eatables are concerned, or things that can easily be changed in shape, colour, or combination, or things that can easily be stowed away almost anywhere—portable objects that you can stow away in small corners, or things so like others of which you have plenty already that nobody can tell the difference. There are also wrongs of a kind that shame prevents the victim speaking about, such as outrages done to the women in his household or to himself or to his sons. Also those for which you would be thought very litigious to prosecute any one—trifling wrongs, or wrongs for which people are usually excused.

The above is a fairly complete account of the circumstances under which men do wrong to others, of the sort of wrongs they do, of the sort of persons to whom they do them, and of their reasons for doing them.

13

1373b It will now be well to make a complete classification of just and unjust actions. We may begin by observing that they have been defined relatively to two kinds of law, and also relatively to two classes of persons. By the two kinds of law I mean particular law and universal law. Particular law is that which each community lays down and applies to its own members: this is partly written and partly unwritten. Universal law is the law of Nature. For there really is, as every one to some extent divines, a natural justice and injustice that is binding on all men, even on those who have no association or covenant with each other. It is this that Sophocles' Antigone clearly means when she says that the burial of Polyneices was a just act in spite of the prohibition: she means that it was just by nature.

Not of to-day or yesterday it is,
But lives eternal: none can date its birth.[1]

And so Empedocles, when he bids us kill no living creature, says that doing this is not just for some people while unjust for others,

Nay, but, an all-embracing law, through the realms of the sky
Unbroken it stretcheth, and over the earth's immensity.[2]

And as Alcidamas says in his Messeniac Oration. . . .

The actions that we ought to do or not to do have also been divided into two classes as affecting either the whole community or some one of its members. From this point of view we can perform just or unjust acts in either of two ways—towards one definite person, or towards the community. The man who is guilty of adultery or assault is doing wrong to some definite person; the man who avoids service in the army is doing wrong to the community.

Thus the whole class of unjust actions may be divided into two classes, those affecting the community, and those affecting one or

[1] Sophocles, *Antigone*, 456, 7.

[2] Empedocles, 380.

more other persons. We will next, before going further, remind ourselves of what 'being wronged' means. Since it has already[1] been settled that 'doing a wrong' must be intentional, 'being wronged' must consist in having an injury done to you by some one who *intends* to do it. In order to be wronged, a man must (1) suffer actual harm, (2) suffer it against his will. The various possible forms of harm are clearly explained by our previous[2] separate discussion of goods and evils. We have also seen that a voluntary action is one where the doer knows what he is doing.[3] We now see that every accusation must be of an action affecting either the community or some individual. The doer of the action must either understand and intend the action, or not understand and intend it. In the former case, he must be acting either from deliberate choice or from passion. (Anger will be discussed when we speak of the passions[4], the motives for crime and the state of mind of the criminal have already[5] been discussed.) Now it often happens that a **1374a** man will admit an act, but will not admit the prosecutor's label for the act nor the facts which that label implies. He will admit that he took a thing but not that he 'stole' it; that he struck some one first, but not that he committed 'outrage'; that he had intercourse with a woman, but not that he committed 'adultery'; that he is guilty of theft, but not that he is guilty of 'sacrilege', the object stolen not being consecrated; that he has encroached, but not that he has 'encroached on State lands'; that he has been in communication with the enemy, but not that he has been guilty of 'treason'. Here therefore we must be able to distinguish what is theft, outrage, or adultery, from what is not, if we are to be able to make the justice of our case clear, no matter whether our aim is to establish a man's guilt or to establish his innocence. Wherever such charges are brought against a man, the question is whether he is or is not guilty of a criminal offence. It is deliberate purpose that constitutes wickedness and criminal guilt, and such names as 'outrage' or 'theft' imply deliberate purpose as well as the mere action. A blow does not always amount to 'outrage', but only if it is struck with some such purpose as to insult the man struck or gratify the striker himself. Nor does taking a thing without the owner's knowledge always amount to 'theft', but only if it is taken with the intention of keeping it and injuring the owner. And as with these charges, so with all the others.

[1] I. 10. [2] I. 6. [3] I. 10. [4] II. 2.
[5] I, 11 and 12.

We saw that there are two kinds of right and wrong conduct towards others, one provided for by written ordinances, the other by unwritten. We have now discussed the kind about which the laws have something to say. The other kind has itself two varieties. First, there is the conduct that springs from exceptional goodness or badness, and is visited accordingly with censure and loss of honour, or with praise and increase of honour and decorations: for instance, gratitude to, or requital of, our benefactors, readiness to help our friends, and the like. The second kind makes up for the defects of a community's written code of law. This is what we call equity; people regard it as just; it is, in fact, the sort of justice which goes beyond the written law. Its existence partly is and partly is not intended by legislators; not intended, where they have noticed no defect in the law; intended, where they find themselves unable to define things exactly, and are obliged to legislate as if that held good always which in fact only holds good usually; or where it is not easy to be complete owing to the endless possible cases presented, such as the kinds and sizes of weapons that may be used to inflict wounds—a lifetime would be too short to make out a complete list of these. If, then, a precise statement is impossible and yet legislation is necessary, the law must be expressed in wide terms; and so, if a man has no more than a finger-ring on his hand when he lifts it to strike or actually strikes another man, he is guilty of a criminal act according to the unwritten words of the **1374b** law; but he is innocent really, and it is equity that declares him to be so. From this definition of equity it is plain what sort of actions, and what sort of persons, are equitable or the reverse. Equity must be applied to forgivable actions; and it must make us distinguish between criminal acts on the one hand, and errors of judgement, or misfortunes, on the other. (A 'misfortune' is an act, not due to moral badness, that has unexpected results: an 'error of judgement' is an act, also not due to moral badness, that has results that might have been expected: a 'criminal act' has results that might have been expected, but *is* due to moral badness, for that is the source of all actions inspired by our appetites.) Equity bids us be merciful to the weakness of human nature; to think less about the laws than about the man who framed them, and less about what he said than about what he meant; not to consider the actions of the accused so much as his intentions, nor this or that detail so much as the whole story; to ask not what a man is now but what he has always or usually been. It bids us remember benefits rather than injuries, and benefits received rather than benefits conferred; to be patient when we are wronged; to settle a dispute by negotiation and not by force; to prefer arbitration to litigation—for an arbitrator goes by the equity of a case, a judge by the strict law, and arbitration was invented with the express purpose of securing full power for equity.

The above may be taken as a sufficient account of the nature of equity.

14

The worse of two acts of wrong done to others is that which is prompted by the worse disposition. Hence the most trifling acts may be the worst ones; as when Callistratus charged Melanopus with having cheated the temple-builders of three consecrated half-obols. The converse is true of just acts. This is because the greater is here potentially contained in the less: there is no crime that a man who has stolen three consecrated half-obols would shrink from committing. Sometimes, however, the worse act is reckoned not in this way but by the greater harm that it does. Or it may be because no punishment for it is severe enough to be adequate; or the harm done may be incurable —a difficult and even hopeless crime to defend; or the sufferer may not be able to get his injurer legally punished, a fact that makes the harm incurable, since legal punishment and chastisement are the proper cure. Or again, the man who has suffered wrong may have inflicted some fearful punishment on himself; then the doer of the wrong ought in justice to receive a still more fearful punishment. Thus Sophocles, when pleading for retribution to Euctemon, who had cut his own throat because of the outrage done to him, said he **1375a** would not fix a penalty less than the victim had fixed for himself. Again, a man's crime is worse if he has been the first man, or the only man, or almost the only man, to commit it: or if it is by no means the first time he has gone seriously wrong in the same way: or if his crime has led to the thinking-out and invention of measures to prevent and punish similar crimes—thus in Argos a penalty is inflicted on a man on whose account a law is passed, and also on those on whose account the prison was built: or if a crime is specially brutal, or specially deliberate: or if the report of it awakes more terror than pity. There are also such rhetorically effective ways of putting it as the following: That the accused has disregarded and broken not one but many solemn obligations like oaths, promises, pledges, or rights of intermarriage between states—here the crime is worse because it consists of many crimes; and that the crime was committed in the very place where criminals are punished, as for example perjurers do—it is argued that a man who will commit a crime in a law-court would commit it anywhere. Further, the worse deed is that which involves the doer in special shame; that whereby a man wrongs his benefactors—for he does more than one wrong, by not merely doing them harm but failing to do them good; that which breaks the unwritten laws of justice—the better sort of man will be just without being forced to be so, and the written laws depend on force while the unwritten ones do not. It may however be argued otherwise, that the crime is worse which breaks the written laws: for the man who commits crimes for which terrible penalties are provided will not hesitate over crimes for which no penalty is provided at all.—So much, then, for the comparative badness of criminal actions.

15

There are also the so-called 'non-technical' means of persuasion; and we must now take a cursory view of these, since they are specially characteristic of forensic oratory. They are five in number: laws, witnesses, contracts, tortures, oaths.

First, then, let us take laws and see how they are to be used in persuasion and dissuasion, in accusation and defence. If the written law tells against our case, clearly we must appeal to the universal law, and insist on its greater equity and justice. We must argue that the juror's oath 'I will give my verdict according to my honest opinion' means that one will not simply follow the letter of the written law. We must urge that the principles of equity are permanent and changeless, and that the universal law does not change either, for it is the law of nature, whereas written laws often do change. This is the bearing the lines in Sophocles' *Antigone*, where Antigone pleads that in burying her brother she had broken Creon's law, but not the unwritten law:

1375b

Not of to-day or yesterday they are,
But live eternal: ⟨none can date their birth.⟩
Not I would fear the wrath of any man
⟨And brave God's vengeance⟩ for defying these.[1]

We shall argue that justice indeed is true and profitable, but that sham justice is not, and that consequently the written law is not, because it does not fulfil the true purpose of law. Or that justice is like silver, and must be assayed by the judges, if the genuine is to be distinguished from the counterfeit. Or that the better a man is, the more he will follow and abide by the unwritten law in preference to the written. Or perhaps that the law in question contradicts some other highly-esteemed law, or even contradicts itself. Thus it may be that one law will enact that all contracts must be held binding, while another forbids us ever to make illegal contracts. Or if a law is ambiguous, we shall turn it about and consider which construction best fits the interests of justice or utility, and then follow that way of looking at it. Or if, though the law still exists, the situation to meet which it was passed exists no longer, we must do our best to prove this and to combat the law thereby. If however the written law supports our case, we must urge that the oath 'to give my verdict according to my honest opinion' is not meant to make the judges give a verdict that is contrary to the law, but to save them from the guilt of perjury if they misunderstand what the law really means. Or that no one chooses what is absolutely good, but every one what is good for himself. Or that not to use the laws is as bad as to have no laws at all. Or that, as in the other arts, it does not pay to try to be cleverer than the doctor: for less harm comes from the doctor's mistakes than from the growing habit of disobeying authority. Or that trying to be cleverer than the laws is just what is forbidden by those codes of law that are accounted best.—So far as the laws are concerned, the above discussion is probably sufficient.

As to witnesses, they are of two kinds, the ancient and the recent; and these latter, again, either do or do not share in the risks of the trial. By 'ancient' witnesses I mean the poets and all other notable persons whose judgements are known to all. Thus the Athenians appealed to Homer[2] as a witness about Salamis; and the men of Tenedos not long ago appealed to Periander of Corinth in their dispute with the people of Sigeum; and Cleophon supported his accusation of Critias by quoting the elegiac verse of Solon, maintaining that discipline had long been slack in the family of Critias, or Solon would never have written,

Pray thee, bid the red-haired Critias do what his father commands him.[3]

These witnesses are concerned with past events. As to future events we shall also appeal
1376a to soothsayers: thus Themistocles quoted the oracle about 'the wooden wall' as a reason for engaging the enemy's fleet. Further, proverbs are, as has been said, one form of evidence. Thus if you are urging somebody not to make a friend of an old man, you will appeal to the proverb,

Never show an old man kindness.[4]

Or if you are urging that he who has made away with fathers should also make away with their sons, quote,

Fool, who slayeth the father and leaveth his sons to avenge him.[5]

'Recent' witnesses are well-known people who have expressed their opinions about some disputed matter: such opinions will be useful support for subsequent disputants on the same points: thus Eubulus used in the law-courts against the reply Plato had made to Archibius, 'It has become the regular custom in this country to admit that one is a scoundrel'. There are also those witnesses who share the risk of punishment if their evidence is pronounced false. These are valid witnesses to the fact that an action was or was not done, that something is or is not the case; they are not valid witnesses to the quality of an action, to its being just or unjust, useful or harmful. On such questions of *quality* the opinion of detached persons is highly trustworthy. Most trustworthy of all are the 'ancient' witnesses, since they cannot be corrupted.

In dealing with the evidence of witnesses, the following are useful arguments. If you have no witnesses on your side, you will argue that the judges must decide from what is probable; that this is meant by 'giving a verdict in accordance with one's honest opinion'; that probabilities cannot be bribed to mislead the court; and that probabilities are never convicted of perjury. If you *have* witnesses, and the other man has not, you will argue that proba-

[1] Sophocles, *Antigone*, 456. [2] *Iliad*, II. 557.

[3] Solon, fr. 22, Bergk.

[4] Diogenianus, VI. 61, III. 89. [5] Stasinus, *Cypria*, fr. 22.

bilities cannot be put on their trial, and that we could do without the evidence of witnesses altogether if we need do no more than balance the pleas advanced on either side.

The evidence of witnesses may refer either to ourselves or to our opponent; and either to questions of fact or to questions of personal character: so, clearly, we need never be at a loss for useful evidence. For if we have no evidence of fact supporting our own case or telling against that of our opponent, at least we can always find evidence to prove our own worth or our opponent's worthlessness. Other arguments about a witness—that he is a friend or an enemy or neutral, or has a good, bad, or indifferent reputation, and any other such distinctions—we must construct upon the same general lines as we use for the regular rhetorical proofs.

Concerning contracts argument can be so far employed as to increase or diminish their importance and their credibility; we shall try **1376b** to increase both if they tell in our favour, and to diminish both if they tell in favour of our opponent. Now for confirming or upsetting the credibility of contracts the procedure is just the same as for dealing with witnesses, for the credit to be attached to contracts depends upon the character of those who have signed them or have the custody of them. The contract being once admitted genuine, we must insist on its importance, if it supports our case. We may argue that a contract is a law, though of a special and limited kind; and that, while contracts do not of course make the law binding, the law does make any lawful contract binding, and that the law itself as a whole is a sort of contract, so that any one who disregards or repudiates any contract is repudiating the law itself. Further, most business relations—those, namely, that are voluntary—are regulated by contracts, and if these lose their binding force, human intercourse ceases to exist. We need not go very deep to discover the other appropriate arguments of this kind. If, however, the contract tells against us and for our opponents, in the first place those arguments are suitable which we can use to fight a law that tells against us. We do not regard ourselves as bound to observe a bad law which it was a mistake ever to pass: and it is ridiculous to suppose that we are bound to observe a bad and mistaken contract. Again, we may argue that the duty of the judge as umpire is to decide what is just, and therefore he must ask where justice lies, and not what this or that document means. And that it is impossible to pervert justice by fraud or by force, since it is founded on nature, but a party to a contract may be the victim of either fraud or force. Moreover, we must see if the contract contravenes either universal law or any written law of our own or another country; and also if it contradicts any other previous or subsequent contract; arguing that the subsequent is the binding contract, or else that the previous one was right and the subsequent one fraudulent —whichever way suits us. Further, we must consider the question of utility, noting whether the contract is against the interest of the judges or not; and so on—these arguments are as obvious as the others.

Examination by torture is one form of evidence, to which great weight is often attached because it is in a sense compulsory. Here again it is not hard to point out the available grounds for magnifying its value, if it happens to tell in our favour, and arguing that it is the only form of evidence that is infallible; or, on the other hand, for refuting it if it tells against us and **1377a** for our opponent, when we may say what is true of torture of every kind alike, that people under its compulsion tell lies quite as often as they tell the truth, sometimes persistently refusing to tell the truth, sometimes recklessly making a false charge in order to be let off sooner. We ought to be able to quote cases, familiar to the judges, in which this sort of thing has actually happened. [We must say that evidence under torture is not trustworthy, the fact being that many men whether thick-witted, tough-skinned, or stout of heart endure their ordeal nobly, while cowards and timid men are full of boldness till they see the ordeal of these others: so that no trust can be placed in evidence under torture.]

In regard to oaths, a fourfold division can be made. A man may either both offer and accept an oath, or neither, or one without the other—that is, he may offer an oath but not accept one, or accept an oath but not offer one. There is also the situation that arises when an oath has already been sworn either by himself or by his opponent.

If you refuse to offer an oath, you may argue that men do not hesitate to perjure themselves; and that if your opponent does swear, you lose your money, whereas, if he does not, you think the judges will decide against him; and that the risk of an unfavourable verdict is preferable, since you trust the judges and do not trust him.

If you refuse to accept an oath, you may argue that an oath is always paid for; that you would of course have taken it if you had been a rascal, since if you *are* a rascal you had better make something by it, and you would in that case have to swear in order to succeed. Thus your refusal, you argue, must be due to high principle, not to fear of perjury: and you may aptly quote the saying of Xenophanes,

'Tis not fair that he who fears not God
should challenge him who doth.[1]

It is as if a strong man were to challenge a weakling to strike, or be struck by, him.

If you agree to accept an oath, you may argue that you trust yourself but not your opponent; and that (to invert the remark of Xenophanes) the fair thing is for the impious man to offer the oath and for the pious man to accept it; and that it would be monstrous if you yourself were unwilling to accept an oath in a case where you demand that the judges should do so before giving their verdict. If you wish to offer an oath, you may argue that piety disposes you to commit the issue to the gods; and that your opponent ought not to want other judges than himself, since you leave the decision with him; and that it is outrageous for your opponents to refuse to swear about this question, when they insist that others should do so.

Now that we see how we are to argue in each case separately, we see also how we are to argue when they occur in pairs, namely, when you are willing to accept the oath but not to offer it; to offer it but not to accept it; both to accept and to offer it; or to do neither. These **1377b** are of course combinations of the cases already mentioned, and so your arguments also must be combinations of the arguments already mentioned.

If you have already sworn an oath that contradicts your present one, you must argue that it is not perjury, since perjury is a crime, and a crime must be a voluntary action, whereas actions due to the force or fraud of others are involuntary. You must further reason from this that perjury depends on the intention and not on the spoken words. But if it is your opponent who has already sworn an oath that contradicts his present one, you must say that if he does not abide by his oaths he is the enemy of society, and that this is the reason why men take an oath before administering the laws. 'My opponents insist that you, the judges, must abide by the oath you have sworn, and yet they are not abiding by their own oaths.' And there are other arguments which may be used to magnify the importance of the oath.—[So much, then, for the 'non-technical' modes of persuasion.]

BOOK II

I

We have now considered the materials to be used in supporting or opposing a political measure, in pronouncing eulogies or censures, and for prosecution and defence in the law courts. We have considered the received opinions on which we may best base our arguments so as to convince our hearers—those opinions with which our enthymemes deal, and out of which they are built, in each of the three kinds of oratory, according to what may be called the special needs of each.

But since rhetoric exists to affect the giving of decisions—the hearers decide between one political speaker and another, and a legal verdict *is* a decision—the orator must not only try to make the argument of his speech demonstrative and worthy of belief; he must also make his own character look right and put his hearers, who are to decide, into the right frame of mind. Particularly in political oratory, but also in lawsuits, it adds much to an orator's influence that his own character should look right and that he should be thought to entertain the right feelings towards his hearers; and also that his hearers themselves should be in just the right frame of mind. That the orator's own character should look right is particularly important in political speaking: that the audience should be in the right frame of mind, in lawsuits. When people are feeling friendly and placable, they think one sort of thing; when they are feeling angry or hostile, they think either something totally different **1378a** or the same thing with a different intensity: when they feel friendly to the man who comes before them for judgement, they regard him as having done little wrong, if any; when they feel hostile, they take the opposite view. Again, if they are eager for, and have good hopes of, a thing that will be pleasant if it happens, they think that it certainly will hap-

[1] Diels, *Vors.*, I. 44.

pen and be good for them: whereas if they are indifferent or annoyed, they do not think so.

There are three things which inspire confidence in the orator's own character—the three, namely, that induce us to believe a thing apart from any proof of it: good sense, good moral character, and goodwill. False statements and bad advice are due to one or more of the following three causes. Men either form a false opinion through want of good sense; or they form a true opinion, but because of their moral badness do not say what they really think; or finally, they are both sensible and upright, but not well disposed to their hearers, and may fail in consequence to recommend what they know to be the best course. These are the only possible cases. It follows that any one who is thought to have all three of these good qualities will inspire trust in his audience. The way to make ourselves thought to be sensible and morally good must be gathered from the analysis of goodness already given:[1] the way to establish your own goodness is the same as the way to establish that of others. Good will and friendliness of disposition will form part of our discussion of the emotions,[2] to which we must now turn.

The Emotions are all those feelings that so change men as to affect their judgements, and that are also attended by pain or pleasure. Such are anger, pity, fear and the like, with their opposites. We must arrange what we have to say about each of them under three heads. Take, for instance, the emotion of anger: here we must discover (1) what the state of mind of angry people is, (2) who the people are with whom they usually get angry, and (3) on what grounds they get angry with them. It is not enough to know one or even two of these points; unless we know all three, we shall be unable to arouse anger in any one. The same is true of the other emotions. So just as earlier in this work we drew up a list of useful propositions for the orator, let us now proceed in the same way to analyse the subject before us.

2

Anger may be defined as an impulse, accompanied by pain, to a conspicuous revenge for a conspicuous slight directed without justification towards what concerns oneself or towards what concerns one's friends. If this is a proper definition of anger, it must always be felt towards some particular individual, e.g. Cleon, and not 'man' in general. It must be felt because the other has done or intended to do **1378b** something to him or one of his friends. It must always be attended by a certain pleasure—that which arises from the expectation of revenge. For since nobody aims at what he thinks he cannot attain, the angry man is aiming at what he can attain, and the belief that you will attain your aim is pleasant. Hence it has been well said about wrath,

Sweeter it is by far than the honeycomb dripping with sweetness,
And spreads through the hearts of men.[3]

It is also attended by a certain pleasure because the thoughts dwell upon the act of vengeance, and the images then called up cause pleasure, like the images called up in dreams.

Now slighting is the actively entertained opinion of something as obviously of no importance. We think bad things, as well as good ones, have serious importance; and we think the same of anything that tends to produce such things, while those which have little or no such tendency we consider unimportant. There are three kinds of slighting—contempt, spite, and insolence. (1) Contempt is one kind of slighting: you feel contempt for what you consider unimportant, and it is just such things that you slight. (2) Spite is another kind; it is a thwarting another man's wishes, not to get something yourself but to prevent his getting it. The slight arises just from the fact that you do not aim at something for yourself: clearly you do not think that he can do you harm, for then you would be afraid of him instead of slighting him, nor yet that he can do you any good worth mentioning, for then you would be anxious to make friends with him. (3) Insolence is also a form of slighting, since it consists in doing and saying things that cause shame to the victim, not in order that anything may happen to yourself, or because anything has happened to yourself, but simply for the pleasure involved. (Retaliation is not 'insolence', but vengeance.) The cause of the pleasure thus enjoyed by the insolent man is that he thinks himself greatly superior to others when ill-treating them. That is why youths and rich men are insolent; they think themselves superior when they show insolence. One sort of insolence is to rob people of the honour due to them; you certainly slight them thus; for it is the unimportant, for

[1] I. 9. [2] II. 4.

[3] *Iliad*, XVIII. 109.

good or evil, that has no honour paid to it. So Achilles says in anger:

He hath taken my prize for himself and hath done me dishonour,[1]

and

Like an alien honoured by none,[2]

meaning that this is why he is angry. A man expects to be specially respected by his inferiors in birth, in capacity, in goodness, and generally in anything in which he is much their
1379ᵃ superior: as where money is concerned a wealthy man looks for respect from a poor man; where speaking is concerned, the man with a turn for oratory looks for respect from one who cannot speak; the ruler demands the respect of the ruled, and the man who thinks he ought to be a ruler demands the respect of the man whom he thinks he ought to be ruling. Hence it has been said

Great is the wrath of kings, whose father is Zeus almighty,[3]

and

Yea, but his rancour abideth long afterward also,[4]

their great resentment being due to their great superiority. Then again a man looks for respect from those who he thinks owe him good treatment, and these are the people whom he has treated or is treating well, or means or has meant to treat well, either himself, or through his friends, or through others at his request.

It will be plain by now, from what has been said, (1) in what frame of mind, (2) with what persons, and (3) on what grounds people grow angry. (1) The frame of mind is that in which any pain is being felt. In that condition, a man is always aiming at something. Whether, then, another man opposes him either directly in any way, as by preventing him from drinking when he is thirsty, or indirectly, the act appears to him just the same; whether some one works against him, or fails to work with him, or otherwise vexes him while he is in this mood, he is equally angry in all these cases. Hence people who are afflicted by sickness or poverty or love or thirst or any other unsatisfied desires are prone to anger and easily roused: especially against those who slight their present distress. Thus a sick man is angered by disregard of his illness, a poor man by disregard of his poverty, a man waging war by disregard of the war he is waging, a lover by disregard of his love, and so throughout, any other sort of slight being enough if special slights are wanting. Each man is predisposed, by the emotion now controlling him, to his own particular anger. Further, we are angered if we happen to be expecting a contrary result: for a quite unexpected evil is specially painful, just as the quite unexpected fulfilment of our wishes is specially pleasant. Hence it is plain what seasons, times, conditions, and periods of life tend to stir men easily to anger, and where and when this will happen; and it is plain that the more we are under these conditions the more easily we are stirred.

These, then, are the frames of mind in which men are easily stirred to anger. The persons with whom we get angry are those who laugh, mock, or jeer at us, for such conduct is insolent. Also those who inflict injuries upon us that are marks of insolence. These injuries must be such as are neither retaliatory nor profitable to the doers: for only then will they be felt to be due to insolence. Also those who speak ill of us, and show contempt for us, in connexion with the things we ourselves most care about: thus those who are eager to win fame as philosophers get angry with those who show contempt for their philosophy; those who pride themselves upon their appearance get angry with those who show contempt for their appearance and so on in other cases. We feel particularly angry on this account if we suspect that we are in fact, or that people think we are, lacking completely or to any effective extent in
1379ᵇ the qualities in question. For when we are convinced that we excel in the qualities for which we are jeered at, we can ignore the jeering. Again, we are angrier with our friends than with other people, since we feel that our friends ought to treat us well and not badly. We are angry with those who have usually treated us with honour or regard, if a change comes and they behave to us otherwise: for we think that they feel contempt for us, or they would still be behaving as they did before. And with those who do not return our kindnesses or fail to return them adequately, and with those who oppose us though they are our inferiors: for all such persons seem to feel contempt for us; those who oppose us seem to think us inferior to themselves, and those who do not return our kindnesses seem to think

[1] *Iliad*, I. 356. [2] *Ibid.*, IX. 648.
[3] *Ibid.*, II. 196. [4] *Ibid.*, I. 82.

that those kindnesses were conferred by inferiors. And we feel particularly angry with men of no account at all, if they slight us. For, by our hypothesis, the anger caused by the slight is felt towards people who are not justified in slighting us, and our inferiors are not thus justified. Again, we feel angry with friends if they do not speak well of us or treat us well; and still more, if they do the contrary; or if they do not perceive our needs, which is why Plexippus is angry with Meleager in Antiphon's play; for this want of perception shows that they are slighting us—we do not fail to perceive the needs of those for whom we care. Again we are angry with those who rejoice at our misfortunes or simply keep cheerful in the midst of our misfortunes, since this shows that they either hate us or are slighting us. Also with those who are indifferent to the pain they give us: this is why we get angry with bringers of bad news. And with those who listen to stories about us or keep on looking at our weaknesses; this seems like either slighting us or hating us; for those who love us share in all our distresses and it must distress any one to keep on looking at his own weaknesses. Further, with those who slight us before five classes of people: namely, (1) our rivals, (2) those whom we admire, (3) those whom we wish to admire us, (4) those for whom we feel reverence, (5) those who feel reverence for us: if any one slights us before such persons, we feel particularly angry. Again, we feel angry with those who slight us in connexion with what we are as honourable men bound to champion—our parents, children, wives, or subjects. And with those who do not return a favour, since such a slight is unjustifiable. Also with those who reply with humorous levity when we are speaking seriously, for such behaviour indicates contempt. And with those who treat us less well than they treat everybody else; it is another mark of contempt that they should think we do not deserve what every one else deserves. Forgetfulness, too, causes anger, as when our own names are forgotten, trifling as this may be; since forgetfulness is felt to be another sign that we are being slighted; it is due to negligence, and to neglect us is to slight us.

The persons with whom we feel anger, the frame of mind in which we feel it, and the **1380a** reasons why we feel it, have now all been set forth. Clearly the orator will have to speak so as to bring his hearers into a frame of mind that will dispose them to anger, and to represent his adversaries as open to such charges and possessed of such qualities as do make people angry.

3

Since growing calm is the opposite of growing angry, and calmness the opposite of anger, we must ascertain in what frames of mind men are calm, towards whom they feel calm, and by what means they are made so. Growing calm may be defined as a settling down or quieting of anger. Now we get angry with those who slight us; and since slighting is a voluntary act, it is plain that we feel calm towards those who do nothing of the kind, or who do or seem to do it involuntarily. Also towards those who intended to do the opposite of what they did do. Also towards those who treat themselves as they have treated us: since no one can be supposed to slight himself. Also towards those who admit their fault and are sorry: since we accept their grief at what they have done as satisfaction, and cease to be angry. The punishment of servants shows this: those who contradict us and deny their offence we punish all the more, but we cease to be incensed against those who agree that they deserved their punishment. The reason is that it is shameless to deny what is obvious, and those who are shameless towards us slight us and show contempt for us: anyhow, we do not feel shame before those of whom we are thoroughly contemptuous. Also we feel calm towards those who humble themselves before us and do not gainsay us; we feel that they thus admit themselves our inferiors, and inferiors feel fear, and nobody can slight any one so long as he feels afraid of him. That our anger ceases towards those who humble themselves before us is shown even by dogs, who do not bite people when they sit down. We also feel calm towards those who are serious when we are serious, because then we feel that we are treated seriously and not contemptuously. Also towards those who have done us more kindnesses than we have done them. Also towards those who pray to us and beg for mercy, since they humble themselves by doing so. Also towards those who do not insult or mock at or slight any one at all, or not any worthy person or any one like ourselves. In general, the things that make us calm may be inferred by seeing what the opposites are of those that make us angry. We are not angry with people we fear or respect, as long as we fear or respect them; you cannot be afraid of a person and also at the same time angry with him. Again, we feel no anger, or comparatively little, with those who have done what they did through anger: we do not feel that they have done it from a wish to slight us, for no one slights people when angry with them, since slighting **1380b** is painless, and anger is painful. Nor do we grow angry with those who reverence us.

As to the frame of mind that makes people calm, it is plainly the opposite to that which makes them angry, as when they are amusing themselves or laughing or feasting; when they are feeling prosperous or successful or satisfied; when, in fine, they are enjoying freedom from pain, or inoffensive pleasure, or justifiable hope. Also when time has passed and their anger is no longer fresh, for time puts an end to anger. And vengeance previously taken on one person puts an end to even greater anger felt against another person. Hence Philocrates, being asked by some one, at a time when the public was angry with him, 'Why don't you defend yourself?' did right to reply, 'The time is not yet.' 'Why, when *is* the time?' 'When I see some one else calumniated.' For men become calm when they have spent their anger on somebody else. This happened in the case of Ergophilus: though the people were more irritated against him than against Callisthenes, they acquitted him because they had condemned Callisthenes to death the day before. Again, men become calm if they have convicted the offender; or if he has already suffered worse things than they in their anger would have themselves inflicted upon him; for they feel as if they were already avenged. Or if they feel that they themselves are in the wrong and are suffering justly (for anger is not excited by what is just), since men no longer think then that they are suffering without justification; and anger, as we have seen,[1] means this. Hence we ought always to inflict a preliminary punishment in words: if that is done, even slaves are less aggrieved by the actual punishment. We also feel calm if we think that the offender will not see that he is punished on our account and because of the way he has treated us. For anger has to do with individuals. This is plain from the definition. Hence the poet has well written:

Say that it was Odysseus, sacker of cities,[2]

implying that Odysseus would not have considered himself avenged unless the Cyclops perceived both by whom and for what he had been blinded. Consequently we do not get angry with any one who cannot be aware of our anger, and in particular we cease to be angry with people once they are dead, for we feel that the worst has been done to them, and that they will neither feel pain nor anything else that we in our anger aim at making them feel. And therefore the poet has well made Apollo say, in order to put a stop to the anger of Achilles against the dead Hector,

For behold in his fury he doeth despite to the senseless clay.[3]

It is now plain that when you wish to calm others you must draw upon these lines of argument; you must put your hearers into the corresponding frame of mind, and represent those with whom they are angry as formidable, or as worthy of reverence, or as benefactors, or as involuntary agents, or as much distressed at what they have done.

4

Let us now turn to Friendship and Enmity, and ask towards whom these feelings are entertained, and why. We will begin by defining friendship and friendly feeling. We may describe friendly feeling towards any one as wishing for him what you believe to be good things, not for your own sake but for his, and **1381a** being inclined, so far as you can, to bring these things about. A friend is one who feels thus and excites these feelings in return: those who think they feel thus towards each other think themselves friends. This being assumed, it follows that your friend is the sort of man who shares your pleasure in what is good and your pain in what is unpleasant, for your sake and for no other reason. This pleasure and pain of his will be the token of his good wishes for you, since we all feel glad at getting what we wish for, and pained at getting what we do not. Those, then, are friends to whom the same things are good and evil; and those who are, moreover, friendly or unfriendly to the same people; for in that case they must have the same wishes, and thus by wishing for each other what they wish for themselves, they show themselves each other's friends. Again, we feel friendly to those who have treated us well, either ourselves or those we care for, whether on a large scale, or readily, or at some particular crisis; provided it was for our own sake. And also to those who

[1] II. 2, beginning. [2] *Odyssey*, IX. 504.

[3] *Iliad*, XXIV. 54.

we think *wish* to treat us well. And also to our friends' friends, and to those who like, or are liked by, those whom we like ourselves. And also to those who are enemies to those whose enemies we are, and dislike, or are disliked by, those whom we dislike. For all such persons think the things good which we think good, so that they wish what is good for us; and this, as we saw,[1] is what friends must do. And also to those who are willing to treat us well where money or our personal safety is concerned: and therefore we value those who are liberal, brave, or just. The just we consider to be those who do not live on others; which means those who work for their living, especially farmers and others who work with their own hands. We also like temperate men, because they are not unjust to others; and, for the same reason, those who mind their own business. And also those whose friends we wish to be, if it is plain that they wish to be our friends: such are the morally good, and those well thought of by every one, by the best men, or by those whom we admire or who admire us. And also those with whom it is pleasant to live and spend our days: such are the good-tempered, and those who are not too ready to show us our mistakes, and those who are not cantankerous or quarrelsome—such people are always wanting to fight us, and those who fight us we feel wish for the opposite of what we wish for ourselves—and those who have the tact to make and take a joke; here both parties have the same object in view, when they can stand being made fun of as well as do it prettily themselves. And we also feel friendly towards those who praise such good qualities as we possess, and especially if they praise the good qualities that we **1381b** are not too sure we *do* possess. And towards those who are cleanly in their person, their dress, and all their way of life. And towards those who do not reproach us with what we have done amiss to them or they have done to help us, for both actions show a tendency to criticize us. And towards those who do not nurse grudges or store up grievances, but are always ready to make friends again; for we take it that they will behave to us just as we find them behaving to every one else. And towards those who are not evil speakers and who are aware of neither their neighbours' bad points nor our own, but of our good ones only, as a good man always will be. And towards those who do not try to thwart us when we are angry or in earnest, which would mean being ready to fight us. And towards those who have some serious feeling towards us, such as admiration for us, or belief in our goodness, or pleasure in our company; especially if they feel like this about qualities in us for which we especially wish to be admired, esteemed, or liked. And towards those who are like ourselves in character and occupation, provided they do not get in our way or gain their living from the same source as we do—for then it will be a case of 'potter against potter':

> *Potter to potter and builder to builder begrudge their reward.*[2]

And those who desire the same things as we desire, if it is possible for us both to share them together; otherwise the same trouble arises here too. And towards those with whom we are on such terms that, while we respect their opinions, we need not blush before them for doing what is conventionally wrong: as well as towards those before whom we should be ashamed to do anything really wrong. Again, our rivals, and those whom we should like to envy us—though without ill-feeling—either we like these people or at least we wish them to like us. And we feel friendly towards those whom we help to secure good for themselves, provided we are not likely to suffer heavily by it ourselves. And those who feel as friendly to us when we are not with them as when we are—which is why all men feel friendly towards those who are faithful to their dead friends. And, speaking generally, towards those who are really fond of their friends and do not desert them in trouble; of all good men, we feel most friendly to those who show their goodness as friends. Also towards those who are honest with us, including those who will tell us of their own weak points: it has just been said that with our friends we are not ashamed of what is conventionally wrong, and if we do have this feeling, we do not love them; if therefore we do not have it, it looks as if we *did* love them. We also like those with whom we do not feel frightened or uncomfortable—nobody can like a man of whom he feels frightened. Friendship has various forms—comradeship, intimacy, kinship, and so on.

Things that cause friendship are: doing kindnesses; doing them unasked; and not proclaiming the fact when they are done, which shows that they were done for our own sake and not for some other reason.

[1] II. 4. beginning.

[2] Hesiod, *Works and Days*, 25.

1382^a Enmity and Hatred should clearly be studied by reference to their opposites. Enmity may be produced by anger or spite or calumny. Now whereas anger arises from offences against oneself, enmity may arise even without that; we may hate people merely because of what we take to be their character. Anger is always concerned with individuals—a Callias or a Socrates—whereas hatred is directed also against classes: we all hate any thief and any informer. Moreover, anger can be cured by time; but hatred cannot. The one aims at giving pain to its object, the other at doing him harm; the angry man wants his victims to feel; the hater does not mind whether they feel or not. All painful things are felt; but the greatest evils, injustice and folly, are the least felt, since their presence causes no pain. And anger is accompanied by pain, hatred is not; the angry man feels pain, but the hater does not. Much may happen to make the angry man pity those who offend him, but the hater under no circumstances wishes to pity a man whom he has once hated: for the one would have the offenders suffer for what they have done; the other would have them cease to exist.

It is plain from all this that we can prove people to be friends or enemies; if they are not, we can make them out to be so; if they claim to be so, we can refute their claim; and if it is disputed whether an action was due to anger or to hatred, we can attribute it to whichever of these we prefer.

5

To turn next to Fear, what follows will show the things and persons of which, and the states of mind in which, we feel afraid. Fear may be defined as a pain or disturbance due to a mental picture of some destructive or painful evil in the future. Of destructive or painful evils only; for there are some evils, e.g. wickedness or stupidity, the prospect of which does not frighten us: I mean only such as amount to great pains or losses. And even these only if they appear not remote but so near as to be imminent: we do not fear things that are a very long way off: for instance, we all know we shall die, but we are not troubled thereby, because death is not close at hand. From this definition it will follow that fear is caused by whatever we feel has great power of destroying us, or of harming us in ways that tend to cause us great pain. Hence the very indications of such things are terrible, making us feel that the terrible thing itself is close at hand; the approach of what is terrible is just what we mean by 'danger'. Such indications are the enmity and anger of people who have power to do something to us; for it is plain that they have the will to do it, and so they are on the point of doing it. Also injustice in possession of power; for it is the unjust man's will to do evil that makes him unjust. Also outraged virtue in possession of power; **1382^b** for it is plain that, when outraged, it always has the will to retaliate, and now it has the power to do so. Also fear felt by those who have the power to do something to us, since such persons are sure to be ready to do it. And since most men tend to be bad—slaves to greed, and cowards in danger—it is, as a rule, a terrible thing to be at another man's mercy; and therefore, if we have done anything horrible, those in the secret terrify us with the thought that they may betray or desert us. And those who can do us wrong are terrible to us when we are liable to be wronged; for as a rule men do wrong to others whenever they have the power to do it. And those who have been wronged, or believe themselves to be wronged, are terrible; for they are always looking out for their opportunity. Also those who have done people wrong, if they possess power, since they stand in fear of retaliation: we have already[1] said that wickedness possessing power is terrible. Again, our rivals for a thing cause us fear when we cannot both have it at once; for we are always at war with such men. We also fear those who are to be feared by stronger people than ourselves: if they can hurt those stronger people, still more can they hurt us; and, for the same reason, we fear those whom those stronger people are actually afraid of. Also those who have destroyed people stronger than we are. Also those who are attacking people weaker than we are: either they are already formidable, or they will be so when they have thus grown stronger. Of those we have wronged, and of our enemies or rivals, it is not the passionate and outspoken whom we have to fear, but the quiet, dissembling, unscrupulous; since we never know when they are upon us, we can never be sure they are at a safe distance. All terrible things are more terrible if they give us no chance of retrieving a blunder—either no chance at all, or only one that depends on our enemies and not ourselves. Those things are also worse which we cannot, or

[1] 1382^a 34.

cannot easily, help. Speaking generally, anything causes us to feel fear that when it happens to, or threatens, others cause us to feel pity.

The above are, roughly, the chief things that are terrible and are feared. Let us now describe the conditions under which we ourselves feel fear. If fear is associated with the expectation that something destructive will happen to us, plainly nobody will be afraid who believes nothing can happen to him; we shall not fear things that we believe cannot happen to us, nor people who we believe cannot inflict them upon us; nor shall we be afraid at times when we think ourselves safe from them. It follows therefore that fear is felt by those who believe something to be likely to happen to them, at the hands of particular persons, in a particular form, and at a particular time. People do not believe this when they are, or think they **1383a** are, in the midst of great prosperity, and are in consequence insolent, contemptuous, and reckless—the kind of character produced by wealth, physical strength, abundance of friends, power: nor yet when they feel they have experienced every kind of horror already and have grown callous about the future, like men who are being flogged and are already nearly dead—if they are to feel the anguish of uncertainty, there must be some faint expectation of escape. This appears from the fact that fear sets us thinking what can be done, which of course nobody does when things are hopeless. Consequently, when it is advisable that the audience should be frightened, the orator must make them feel that they really are in danger of something, pointing out that it has happened to others who were stronger than they are, and is happening, or has happened, to people like themselves, at the hands of unexpected people, in an unexpected form, and at an unexpected time.

Having now seen the nature of fear, and of the things that cause it, and the various states of mind in which it is felt, we can also see what Confidence is, about what things we feel it, and under what conditions. It is the opposite of fear, and what causes it is the opposite of what causes fear; it is, therefore, the expectation associated with a mental picture of the nearness of what keeps us safe and the absence or remoteness of what is terrible: it may be due either to the near presence of what inspires confidence or to the absence of what causes alarm. We feel it if we can take steps—many, or important, or both—to cure or prevent trouble; if we have neither wronged others nor been wronged by them; if we have either no rivals at all or no strong ones; if our rivals who are strong are our friends or have treated us well or been treated well by us; or if those whose interest is the same as ours are the more numerous party, or the stronger, or both.

As for our own state of mind, we feel confidence if we believe we have often succeeded and never suffered reverses, or have often met danger and escaped it safely. For there are two reasons why human beings face danger calmly: they may have no experience of it, or they may have means to deal with it: thus when in danger at sea people may feel confident about what will happen either because they have no experience of bad weather, or because their experience gives them the means of dealing with it. We also feel confident whenever there is nothing to terrify other people like ourselves, or people weaker than ourselves, or people than whom we believe ourselves to be stronger—and we believe this if we have conquered them, or conquered others who are as strong as they are, or stronger. Also if we believe ourselves superior to our rivals in the number and importance of the **1383b** advantages that make men formidable—wealth, physical strength, strong bodies of supporters, extensive territory, and the possession of all, or the most important, appliances of war. Also if we have wronged no one, or not many, or not those of whom we are afraid; and generally, if our relations with the gods are satisfactory, as will be shown especially by signs and oracles. The fact is that anger makes us confident—that anger is excited by our knowledge that we are not the wrongers but the wronged, and that the divine power is always supposed to be on the side of the wronged. Also when, at the outset of an enterprise, we believe that we cannot and shall not fail, or that we shall succeed completely.—So much for the causes of fear and confidence.

6

We now turn to Shame and Shamelessness; what follows will explain the things that cause these feelings, and the persons before whom, and the states of mind under which, they are felt. Shame may be defined as pain or disturbance in regard to bad things, whether present, past, or future, which seem likely to involve us in discredit; and shamelessness as contempt or indifference in regard to these same bad things. If this definition be granted, it follows that we feel shame at such bad things as we think are disgraceful to ourselves or to those we care for. These evils are, in the first place, those due to moral badness. Such are throwing away one's shield or taking to flight; for these bad things are due to cowardice. Also, withholding a deposit or otherwise wronging people about money; for these acts are due to injustice. Also, having carnal intercourse with forbidden persons, at wrong times, or in wrong places; for these things are due to licentiousness. Also, making profit in petty or disgraceful ways, or out of helpless persons, e.g. the poor, or the dead—whence the proverb 'He would pick a corpse's pocket'; for all this is due to low greed and meanness. Also, in money matters, giving less help than you might, or none at all, or accepting help from those worse off than yourself; so also borrowing when it will seem like begging; begging when it will seem like asking the return of a favour; asking such a return when it will seem like begging; praising a man *in order that* it may seem like begging; and going on begging in spite of failure: all such actions are tokens of meanness. Also, praising people to their face, and praising extravagantly a man's good points and glozing over his weaknesses, and showing extravagant sympathy with his grief when you are in his presence, and all that sort of thing; all this shows the disposition of a flatterer. Also, refusing to endure hardships that are endured **1384a** by people who are older, more delicately brought up, of higher rank, or generally less capable of endurance than ourselves: for all this shows effeminacy. Also, accepting benefits, especially accepting them often, from another man, and then abusing him for conferring them: all this shows a mean, ignoble disposition. Also, talking incessantly about yourself, making loud professions, and appropriating the merits of others; for this is due to boastfulness. The same is true of the actions due to any of the other forms of badness of moral character, of the tokens of such badness, &c.: they are all disgraceful and shameless. Another sort of bad thing at which we feel shame is, lacking a share in the honourable things shared by every one else, or by all or nearly all who are like ourselves. By 'those like ourselves' I mean those of our own race or country or age or family, and generally those who are on our own level. Once we are on a level with others, it is a disgrace to be, say, less well educated than they are; and so with other advantages: all the more so, in each case, if it is seen to be our own fault: wherever we are ourselves to blame for our present, past, or future circumstances, it follows at once that this is to a greater extent due to our moral badness. We are moreover ashamed of having done to us, having had done, or being about to have done to us acts that involve us in dishonour and reproach; as when we surrender our persons, or lend ourselves to vile deeds, e.g. when we submit to outrage. And acts of yielding to the lust of others are shameful whether willing or unwilling (yielding to force being an instance of unwillingness), since unresisting submission to them is due to unmanliness or cowardice.

These things, and others like them, are what cause the feeling of shame. Now since shame is a mental picture of disgrace, in which we shrink from the disgrace itself and not from its consequences, and we only care what opinion is held of us because of the people who form that opinion, it follows that the people before whom we feel shame are those whose opinion of us matters to us. Such persons are: those who admire us, those whom we admire, those by whom we wish to be admired, those with whom we are competing, and those whose opinion of us we respect. We admire those, and wish those to admire us, who possess any good thing that is highly esteemed; or from whom we are very anxious to get something that they are able to give us—as a lover feels. We compete with our equals. We respect, as true, the views of sensible people, such as our elders and those who have been well educated. And we feel more shame about a thing if it is done openly, before all men's eyes. Hence the proverb, 'shame dwells in the eyes'. For this reason we feel most shame before those who will always be with us and those who notice what we do, since in both cases eyes are **1384b** upon us. We also feel it before those not open to the same imputation as ourselves: for it is plain that their opinions about it are the opposite of ours. Also before those who are hard on any one whose conduct they think wrong; for what a man does himself, he is said not to resent when his neighbours do it: so that of course he does resent their doing what he does not do himself. And before those who are likely to tell everybody about you; not telling others is as good as not believing you wrong. People are likely to tell others about you if you have wronged them, since they are on the look out to harm you; or if they speak evil of everybody, for those who attack the innocent will be still more ready to attack the guilty. And before those whose main occupation is with their neighbours' failings—people like satirists and writers of comedy; these are really a kind of evil-speakers and tell-tales. And before those who have never yet known us come to grief, since their attitude to us has amounted to admiration so far: that is why we feel ashamed to refuse those a favour who ask one for the first time—we have not as yet lost credit with them. Such are those who are just beginning to wish to be our friends; for they have seen our best side only (hence the appropriateness of Euripides' reply to the Syracusans): and such also are those among our old acquaintances who know nothing to our discredit. And we are ashamed not merely of the actual shameful conduct mentioned, but also of the evidences of it: not merely, for example, of actual sexual intercourse, but also of its evidences; and not merely of disgraceful acts but also of disgraceful talk. Similarly we feel shame not merely in presence of the persons mentioned but also of those who will tell them what we have done, such as their servants or friends. And, generally, we feel no shame before those upon whose opinions we quite look down as untrustworthy (no one feels shame before small children or animals); nor are we ashamed of the same things before intimates as before strangers, but before the former of what seem genuine faults, before the latter of what seem conventional ones.

The conditions under which we shall feel shame are these: first, having people related to us like those before whom, as has been said,[1] we feel shame. These are, as was stated, persons whom we admire, or who admire us, or by whom we wish to be admired, or from whom we desire some service that we shall not obtain if we forfeit their good opinion. These persons may be actually looking on (as Cydias represented them in his speech on land assignments in Samos, when he told the Athenians to imagine the Greeks to be standing all around them, actually seeing the way they voted and not merely going to hear about it afterwards): or again they may be near at hand, or may be likely to find out about what we do. This is why in misfortune we do not wish to be seen by those who once wished themselves like us; for such a feeling implies admiration. And men feel shame when they **1385a** have acts or exploits to their credit on which they are bringing dishonour, whether these are their own, or those of their ancestors, or those of other persons with whom they have some close connexion. Generally, we feel shame before those for whose own misconduct we should also feel it—those already mentioned; those who take us as their models; those whose teachers or advisers we have been; or other people, it may be, like ourselves, whose rivals we are. For there are many things that shame before such people makes us do or leave undone. And we feel more shame when we are likely to be continually seen by, and go about under the eyes of, those who know of our disgrace. Hence, when Antiphon the poet was to be cudgelled to death by order of Dionysius, and saw those who were to perish with him covering their faces as they went through the gates, he said, 'Why do you cover your faces? Is it lest some of these spectators should see you *to-morrow?*'

So much for Shame; to understand Shamelessness, we need only consider the converse cases, and plainly we shall have all we need.

7

To take Kindness next: the definition of it will show us towards whom it is felt, why, and in what frames of mind. Kindness—under the influence of which a man is said to 'be kind'—may be defined as helpfulness towards some one in need, not in return for anything, nor for the advantage of the helper himself, but for that of the person helped. Kindness is great if shown to one who is in great need, or who needs what is important and hard to get, or who needs it at an important and difficult crisis; or if the helper is the only, the first, or the chief person to give the help. Natural cravings constitute such needs; and in particular cravings, accompanied by pain, for what is not being attained. The appetites are cravings of this kind: sexual desire, for instance, and those which arise during bodily injuries and in dangers; for appetite is active both in danger and in pain. Hence those who stand by us in poverty or in banishment, even if they do not help us much, are yet really kind to us, because our need is great and the occasion pressing; for instance, the man who gave the mat in the Lyceum. The helpfulness must

[1] 1384a 27.

therefere meet, preferably, just this kind of need; and failing just this kind, some other kind as great or greater. We now see to whom, why, and under what conditions kindness is shown; and these facts must form the basis of our arguments. We must show that the persons helped are, or have been, in such pain and need as has been described, and that their helpers gave, or are giving, the kind of help described, in the kind of need described. We can also see how to eliminate the idea of kindness and make our opponents ap- **1385b** pear unkind: we may maintain that they are being or have been helpful simply to promote their own interest—this, as has been stated,[1] is not kindness; or that their action was accidental, or was forced upon them; or that they were not doing a favour, but merely returning one, whether they know this or not—in either case the action *is* a mere return, and is therefore not a kindness even if the doer does *not* know how the case stands. In considering this subject we must look at all the 'categories': an act may be an act of kindness because (1) it is a particular thing, (2) it has a particular magnitude or (3) quality, or (4) is done at a particular time or (5) place. As evidence of the want of kindness, we may point out that a smaller service had been refused to the man in need; or that the same service, or an equal or greater one, has been given to his enemies; these facts show that the service in question was not done for the sake of the person helped. Or we may point out that the thing desired was worthless and that the helper knew it: no one will admit that he is in need of what is worthless.

8

So much for Kindness and Unkindness. Let us now consider Pity, asking ourselves what things excite pity, and for what persons, and in what states of our mind pity is felt. Pity may be defined as a feeling of pain caused by the sight of some evil, destructive or painful, which befalls one who does not deserve it, and which we might expect to befall ourselves or some friend of ours, and moreover to befall us soon. In order to feel pity, we must obviously be capable of supposing that some evil may happen to us or some friend of ours, and moreover some such evil as is stated in our definition or is more or less of that kind. It is therefore not felt by those completely ruined, who suppose that no further evil can befall them, since the worst has befallen them already; nor by those who imagine themselves immensely fortunate—their feeling is rather presumptuous insolence, for when they think they possess all the good things of life, it is clear that the impossibility of evil befalling them will be included, this being one of the good things in question. Those who think evil *may* befall them are such as have already had it befall them and have safely escaped from it; elderly men, owing to their good sense and their experience; weak men, especially men inclined to cowardice; and also educated people, since these can take long views. Also those who have parents living, or children, or wives; for these are our own, and the evils mentioned above may easily befall them. And those who are neither moved by any courageous emotion such as anger or confidence (these emotions take no account of the future), nor by a disposition to presumptuous insolence (insolent men, too, take no account of the possibility that something evil will happen to them), nor yet by great fear (panic-stricken people do not feel pity, because they are taken up with what is happening to themselves); only those feel pity who are between these two extremes. In order to feel pity we must also believe in the goodness of at least some people; if you think nobody good, you will be- **1386a** lieve that everybody deserves evil fortune. And, generally, we feel pity whenever we are in the condition of remembering that similar misfortunes have happened to us or ours, or expecting them to happen in future.

So much for the mental conditions under which we feel pity. What we pity is stated clearly in the definition. All unpleasant and painful things excite pity if they tend to destroy and annihilate; and all such evils as are due to chance, if they are serious. The painful and destructive evils are: death in its various forms, bodily injuries and afflictions, old age, diseases, lack of food. The evils due to chance are: friendlessness, scarcity of friends (it is a pitiful thing to be torn away from friends and companions), deformity, weakness, mutilation; evil coming from a source from which good ought to have come; and the frequent repetition of such misfortunes. Also the coming of good when the worst has happened: e.g. the arrival of the Great King's gifts for Diopeithes after his death. Also that either no good should have befallen a man at all, or that he should not be able to enjoy it when it has.

[1] 1385a 18.

The grounds, then, on which we feel pity are these or like these. The people we pity are: those whom we know, if only they are not very closely related to us—in that case we feel about them as if we were in danger ourselves. For this reason Amasis did not weep, they say, at the sight of his son being led to death, but did weep when he saw his friend begging: the latter sight was pitiful, the former terrible, and the terrible is different from the pitiful; it tends to cast out pity, and often helps to produce the opposite of pity. Again, we feel pity when the danger is near ourselves. Also we pity those who are like us in age, character, disposition, social standing, or birth; for in all these cases it appears more likely that the same misfortune may befall us also. Here too we have to remember the general principle that what we fear for ourselves excites our pity when it happens to others. Further, since it is when the sufferings of others are close to us that they excite our pity (we cannot remember what disasters happened a hundred centuries ago, nor look forward to what will happen a hundred centuries hereafter, and therefore feel little pity, if any, for such things): it follows that those who heighten the effect of their words with suitable gestures, tones, dress, and dramatic action generally, are especially successful in exciting pity: they thus put the disasters before our eyes, and make them seem close to us, just coming or just past. Anything that has just happened, or is going to happen soon, is particularly piteous: so too therefore are the tokens and the actions of sufferers—the garments and the like of those who have already suffered; the words and the like of those actually suffering—of those, for instance, who are on the point of death. Most piteous of all is it when, in such times of trial, the victims are persons of noble character: whenever they are so, our pity is especially excited, because their innocence, as well as the setting of their misfortunes before our eyes, makes their misfortunes seem close to ourselves.

9

Most directly opposed to pity is the feeling called Indignation. Pain at unmerited good fortune is, in one sense, opposite to pain at unmerited bad fortune, and is due to the same moral qualities. Both feelings are associated with good moral character; it is our duty both to feel sympathy and pity for unmerited distress, and to feel indignation at unmerited prosperity; for whatever is undeserved is unjust, and that is why we ascribe indignation even to the gods. It might indeed be thought that envy is similarly opposed to pity, on the ground that envy it closely akin to indignation, or even the same thing. But it is not the same. It is true that it also is a disturbing pain excited by the prosperity of others. But it is excited not by the prosperity of the undeserving but by that of people who are like us or equal with us. The two feelings have this in common, that they must be due not to some untoward thing being likely to befall ourselves, but only to what is happening to our neighbour. The feeling ceases to be envy in the one case and indignation in the other, and becomes fear, if the pain and disturbance are due to the prospect of something bad for ourselves as the result of the other man's good fortune. The feelings of pity and indignation will obviously be attended by the converse feelings of satisfaction. If you are pained by the unmerited distress of others, you will be pleased, or at least not pained, by their merited distress. Thus no good man can be pained by the punishment of parricides or murderers. These are things we are bound to rejoice at, as we must at the prosperity of the deserving; both these things are just, and both give pleasure to any honest man, since he cannot help expecting that what has happened to a man like him will happen to him too. All these feelings are associated with the same type of moral character. And their contraries are associated with the contrary type; the man who is delighted by others' misfortunes is identical with the man who envies others' prosperity. For any one who is pained by the occurrence or existence of a given thing must be pleased by that thing's non-existence or destruction. We can now see that all these feelings tend to prevent pity (though they differ among themselves, for the reasons given), so that all are equally useful for neutralizing an appeal to pity.

We will first consider Indignation—reserving the other emotions for subsequent discussion—and ask with whom, on what grounds, and in what states of mind we may be indignant. These questions are really answered by what has been said already. Indignation is pain caused by the sight of undeserved good fortune. It is, then, plain to begin with that there are some forms of good the sight of which cannot cause it. Thus a man may be just or brave, or acquire moral goodness: but we shall not be indignant with him for that reason, any more than we shall pity him for the contrary reason. Indignation is roused by the sight of wealth, power, and the like—by all those things, roughly speaking, which are deserved by good men and by those who possess the goods of nature—noble birth, beauty, and so on. Again, what is long established seems akin to what exists by nature; and therefore we feel more indignation at those possessing a given good if they have as a matter of fact only just got it and the prosperity it brings with it. The newly rich give more offence than those whose wealth is of long standing and inherited. The same is true of those who have office or power, plenty of friends, a fine family, &c. We feel the same when these advantages of theirs secure them others. For here again, the newly rich give us more offence by obtaining office through their riches than do those whose wealth is of long standing; and so in all other cases. The reason is that what the latter have is felt to be really their own, but what the others have is not; what appears to have been always what it is is regarded as real, and so the possessions of the newly rich do not seem to be really their own. Further, it is not any and every man that deserves any given kind of good; there is a certain correspondence and appropriateness in such things; thus it is appropriate for brave men, not for just men, to have fine weapons, and for men of family, not for parvenus, to make distinguished marriages. Indignation may therefore properly be felt when any one gets what is not appropriate for him, though he may be a good man enough. It may also be felt when any one sets himself up against his superior, especially against his superior in some particular respect—whence the lines

Only from battle he shrank with Aias Telamon's son;
Zeus had been angered with him, had he fought with a mightier one;[1]

1387b but also, even apart from that, when the inferior in any sense contends with his superior; a musician, for instance, with a just man, for justice is a finer thing than music.

Enough has been said to make clear the grounds on which, and the persons against whom, Indignation is felt—they are those mentioned, and others like him. As for the people who feel it; we feel it if we do ourselves deserve the greatest possible goods and moreover have them, for it is an injustice that those who are not our equals should have been held to deserve as much as we have. Or, secondly, we feel it if we are really good and honest people; our judgement is then sound, and we loathe any kind of injustice. Also if we are ambitious and eager to gain particular ends, especially if we are ambitious for what others are getting without deserving to get it. And, generally, if we think that we ourselves deserve a thing and that others do not, we are disposed to be indignant with those others so far as that thing is concerned. Hence servile, worthless, unambitious persons are not inclined to Indignation, since there is nothing they can believe themselves to deserve.

From all this it is plain what sort of men those are at whose misfortunes, distresses, or failures we ought to feel pleased, or at least not pained: by considering the facts described we see at once what their contraries are. If therefore our speech puts the judges in such a frame of mind as that indicated and shows that those who claim pity on certain definite grounds do not deserve to secure pity but do deserve not to secure it, it will be impossible for the judges to feel pity.

10

To take Envy next: we can see on what grounds, against what persons, and in what states of mind we feel it. Envy is pain at the sight of such good fortune as consists of the good things already mentioned; we feel it towards our equals; not with the idea of getting something for ourselves, but because the other people have it. We shall feel it if we have, or think we have, equals; and by 'equals' I mean equals in birth, relationship, age, disposition, distinction, or wealth. We feel envy also if we fall but a little short of having everything; which is why people in high place and prosperity feel it—they think every one else is taking what belongs to themselves. Also if we are exceptionally distinguished for some particular thing, and especially if that thing is wisdom or good fortune. Ambitious men are more envious than those who are not. So also those who profess wisdom; they are ambitious—to be thought wise. Indeed, generally, those who aim at a reputation for anything are envious on this particular point. And small-minded men are envious, for everything seems great to them. The good things which excite envy have al- **1388a** ready been mentioned. The deeds or possessions which arouse the love of reputa-

[1] *Iliad*, xi. 542.

tion and honour and the desire for fame, and the various gifts of fortune, are almost all subject to envy; and particularly if we desire the thing ourselves, or think we are entitled to it, or if having it puts us a little above others, or not having it a little below them. It is clear also what kind of people we envy; that was included in what has been said already: we envy those who are near us in time, place, age, or reputation. Hence the line:

Ay, kin can even be jealous of their kin.[1]

Also our fellow-competitors, who are indeed the people just mentioned—we do not compete with men who lived a hundred centuries ago, or those not yet born, or the dead, or those who dwell near the Pillars of Hercules, or those whom, in our opinion or that of others, we take to be far below us or far above us. So too we compete with those who follow the same ends as ourselves: we compete with our rivals in sport or in love, and generally with those who are after the same things; and it is therefore these whom we are bound to envy beyond all others. Hence the saying:

Potter against potter.[2]

We also envy those whose possession of or success in a thing is a reproach to us: these are our neighbours and equals; for it is clear that it is our own fault we have missed the good thing in question; this annoys us, and excites envy in us. We also envy those who have what we ought to have, or have got what we did have once. Hence old men envy younger men, and those who have spent much envy those who have spent little on the same thing. And men who have not got a thing, or not got it yet, envy those who have got it quickly. We can also see what things and what persons give pleasure to envious people, and in what states of mind they feel it: the states of mind in which they feel pain are those under which they will feel pleasure in the contrary things. If therefore we ourselves with whom the decision rests are put into an envious state of mind, and those for whom our pity, or the award of something desirable, is claimed are such as have been described, it is obvious that they will win no pity from us.

11

We will next consider Emulation, showing in what follows its causes and objects, and the state of mind in which it is felt. Emulation is pain caused by seeing the presence, in persons whose nature is like our own, of good things that are highly valued and are possible for ourselves to acquire; but it is felt not because others have these goods, but because we have not got them ourselves. It is therefore a good feeling felt by good persons, whereas envy is a bad feeling felt by bad persons. Emulation makes us take steps to secure the good things in question, envy makes us take steps to stop our neighbour having them. Emulation must therefore tend to be felt by persons who believe themselves to deserve certain good **1388b** things that they have not got, it being understood that no one aspires to things which appear impossible. It is accordingly felt by the young and by persons of lofty disposition. Also by those who possess such good things as are deserved by men held in honour—these are wealth, abundance of friends, public office, and the like; on the assumption that they ought to be good men, they are emulous to gain such goods because they ought, in their belief, to belong to men whose state of mind is good. Also by those whom all others think deserving. We also feel it about anything for which our ancestors, relatives, personal friends, race, or country are specially honoured, looking upon that thing as really our own, and therefore feeling that we deserve to have it. Further, since all good things that are highly honoured are objects of emulation, moral goodness in its various forms must be such an object, and also all those good things that are useful and serviceable to others: for men honour those who are morally good, and also those who do them service. So with those good things our possession of which can give enjoyment to our neighbours—wealth and beauty rather than health. We can see, too, what persons are the objects of the feeling. They are those who have these and similar things—those already mentioned, as courage, wisdom, public office. Holders of public office—generals, orators, and all who possess such powers—can do many people a good turn. Also those whom many people wish to be like; those who have many acquaintances or friends; those whom many admire, or whom we ourselves admire; and those who have been praised and eulogized by poets or prose-writers. Persons of the contrary sort are objects of contempt: for the feeling and notion of contempt are opposite to those of emulation. Those who are such as to emulate or be emulated by others are in-

[1] Aeschylus, fr. 305, Nauck.
[2] Hesiod, *Works and Days*, 25.

evitably disposed to be contemptuous of all such persons as are subject to those bad things which are contrary to the good things that are the objects of emulation: despising them for just that reason. Hence we often despise the fortunate, when luck comes to them without their having those good things which are held in honour.

This completes our discussion of the means by which the several emotions may be produced or dissipated, and upon which depend the persuasive arguments connected with the emotions.

12

Let us now consider the various types of human character, in relation to the emotions and moral qualities, showing how they correspond to our various ages and fortunes. By emotions I mean anger, desire, and the like; these we have discussed already.[1] By moral qualities I mean virtues and vices; these also have been discussed already,[2] as well as the various things that various types of men tend to will and to do.[3] By ages I mean youth, the prime of life, and old age. By fortune **1389a** I mean birth, wealth, power, and their opposites—in fact, good fortune and ill fortune.

To begin with the Youthful type of character. Young men have strong passions, and tend to gratify them indiscriminately. Of the bodily desires, it is the sexual by which they are most swayed and in which they show absence of self-control. They are changeable and fickle in their desires, which are violent while they last, but quickly over: their impulses are keen but not deep-rooted, and are like sick people's attacks of hunger and thirst. They are hot-tempered, and quick-tempered, and apt to give way to their anger; bad temper often gets the better of them, for owing to their love of honour they cannot bear being slighted, and are indignant if they imagine themselves unfairly treated. While they love honour, they love victory still more; for youth is eager for superiority over others, and victory is one form of this. They love both more than they love money, which indeed they love very little, not having yet learnt what it means to be without it—this is the point of Pittacus' remark about Amphiaraus. They look at the good side rather than the bad, not having yet witnessed many instances of wickedness. They trust others readily, because they have not yet often been cheated. They are sanguine; nature warms their blood as though with excess of wine; and besides that, they have as yet met with few disappointments. Their lives are mainly spent not in memory but in expectation; for expectation refers to the future, memory to the past, and youth has a long future before it and a short past behind it: on the first day of one's life one has nothing at all to remember, and can only look forward. They are easily cheated, owing to the sanguine disposition just mentioned. Their hot tempers and hopeful dispositions make them more courageous than older men are; the hot temper prevents fear, and the hopeful disposition creates confidence; we cannot feel fear so long as we are feeling angry, and any expectation of good makes us confident. They are shy, accepting the rules of society in which they have been trained, and not yet believing in any other standard of honour. They have exalted notions, because they have not yet been humbled by life or learnt its necessary limitations; moreover, their hopeful disposition makes them think themselves equal to great things—and that means having exalted notions. They would always rather do noble deeds than useful ones: their lives are regulated more by moral feeling than by reasoning; and whereas reasoning leads us to choose what is useful, moral goodness leads us to choose what is noble. They are fonder of their friends, intimates, and companions than older **1389b** men are, because they like spending their days in the company of others, and have not yet come to value either their friends or anything else by their usefulness to themselves. All their mistakes are in the direction of doing things excessively and vehemently. They disobey Chilon's precept by overdoing everything; they love too much and hate too much, and the same thing with everything else. They think they know everything, and are always quite sure about it; this, in fact, is why they overdo everything. If they do wrong to others, it is because they mean to insult them, not to do them actual harm. They are ready to pity others, because they think every one an honest man, or anyhow better than he is: they judge their neighbour by their own harmless natures, and so cannot think he deserves to be treated in that way. They are fond of fun and therefore witty, wit being well-bred insolence.

[1] II. 1. ff [2] I. 9. [3] I. 6(1363a 19).

13

Such, then is the character of the Young. The character of Elderly Men—men who are past their prime—may be said to be formed for the most part of elements that are the contrary of all these. They have lived many years; they have often been taken in, and often made mistakes; and life on the whole is a bad business. The result is that they are sure about nothing and *under-do* everything. They 'think', but they never 'know'; and because of their hesitation they always add a 'possibly' or a 'perhaps', putting everything this way and nothing positively. They are cynical; that is, they tend to put the worse construction on everything. Further, their experience makes them distrustful and therefore suspicious of evil. Consequently they neither love warmly nor hate bitterly, but following the hint of Bias they love as though they will some day hate and hate as though they will some day love. They are small-minded, because they have been humbled by life: their desires are set upon nothing more exalted or unusual than what will help them to keep alive. They are not generous, because money is one of the things they must have, and at the same time their experience has taught them how hard it is to get and how easy to lose. They are cowardly, and are always anticipating danger; unlike that of the young, who are warm-blooded, their temperament is chilly; old age has paved the way for cowardice; fear is, in fact, a form of chill. They love life; and all the more when their last day has come, because the object of all desire is something we have not got, and also because we desire most strongly that which we need most urgently. They are too fond of themselves; this is one form that small-mindedness takes. Because of this, they guide their lives too much by considerations of what is useful and too little by what is noble—for
1390a the useful is what is good for oneself, and the noble what is good absolutely. They are not shy, but shameless rather; caring less for what is noble than for what is useful, they feel contempt for what people may think of them. They lack confidence in the future; partly through experience—for most things go wrong, or anyhow turn out worse than one expects; and partly because of their cowardice. They live by memory rather than by hope; for what is left to them of life is but little as compared with the long past; and hope is of the future, memory of the past. This, again, is the cause of their loquacity; they are continually talking of the past, because they enjoy remembering it. Their fits of anger are sudden but feeble. Their sensual passions have either altogether gone or have lost their vigour: consequently they do not feel their passions much, and their actions are inspired less by what they do feel than by the love of gain. Hence men at this time of life are often supposed to have a self-controlled character; the fact is that their passions have slackened, and they are slaves to the love of gain. They guide their lives by reasoning more than by moral feeling; reasoning being directed to utility and moral feeling to moral goodness. If they wrong others, they mean to injure them, not to insult them. Old men may feel pity, as well as young men, but not for the same reason. Young men feel it out of kindness; old men out of weakness, imagining that anything that befalls any one else might easily happen to them, which, as we saw,[1] is a thought that excites pity. Hence they are querulous, and not disposed to jesting or laughter—the love of laughter being the very opposite of querulousness.

Such are the characters of Young Men and Elderly Men. People always think well of speeches adapted to, and reflecting, their own character: and we can now see how to compose our speeches so as to adapt both them and ourselves to our audiences.

14

As for Men in their Prime, clearly we shall find that they have a character between that of the young and that of the old, free from the extremes of either. They have neither that excess of confidence which amounts to rashness, nor too much timidity, but the right amount of each. They neither trust everybody nor distrust everybody, but judge people correctly. Their lives will be guided not by the
1390b sole consideration either of what is noble or of what is useful, but by both; neither by parsimony nor by prodigality, but by what is fit and proper. So, too, in regard to anger and desire; they will be brave as well as temperate, and temperate as well as brave; these virtues are divided between the young and the old; the young are brave but intemperate, the old temperate but cowardly. To put it generally, all the valuable qualities that youth and

[1] II. 8 (1386a 24 and 29.)

age divide between them are united in the prime of life, while all their excesses or defects are replaced by moderation and fitness. The body is in its prime from thirty to five-and-thirty; the mind about forty-nine.

15

So much for the types of character that distinguish youth, old age, and the prime of life. We will now turn to those Gifts of Fortune by which human character is affected. First let us consider Good Birth. Its effect on character is to make those who have it more ambitious; it is the way of all men who have something to start with to add to the pile, and good birth implies ancestral distinction. The well-born man will look down even on those who are as good as his own ancestors, because any far-off distinction is greater than the same thing close to us, and better to boast about. Being well-born, which means coming of a fine stock, must be distinguished from nobility, which means being true to the family nature—a quality not usually found in the well-born, most of whom are poor creatures. In the generations of men as in the fruits of the earth, there is a varying yield; now and then, where the stock is good, exceptional men are produced for a while, and then decadence sets in. A clever stock will degenerate towards the insane type of character, like the descendants of Alcibiades or of the elder Dionysius; a steady stock towards the fatuous and torpid type, like the descendants of Cimon, Pericles, and Socrates.

16

The type of character produced by Wealth lies on the surface for all to see. Wealthy men are insolent and arrogant; their possession of wealth affects their understanding; they feel as if they had every good thing that exists; wealth becomes a sort of standard of value for
1391a everything else, and therefore they imagine there is nothing it cannot buy. They are luxurious and ostentatious; luxurious, because of the luxury in which they live and the prosperity which they display; ostentatious and vulgar, because, like other people's, their minds are regularly occupied with the object of their love and admiration, and also because they think that other people's idea of happiness is the same as their own. It is indeed quite natural that they should be affected thus; for if you have money, there are always plenty of people who come begging from you. Hence the saying of Simonides about wise men and rich men, in answer to Hiero's wife, who asked him whether it was better to grow rich or wise. 'Why, rich,' he said; 'for I see the wise men spending their days at the rich men's doors.' Rich men also consider themselves worthy to hold public office; for they consider they already have the things that give a claim to office. In a word, the type of character produced by wealth is that of a prosperous fool. There is indeed one difference between the type of the newly-enriched and those who have long been rich: the newly-enriched have all the bad qualities mentioned in an exaggerated and worse form—to be newly-enriched means, so to speak, *no education in riches*. The wrongs they do others are not meant to injure their victims, but spring from insolence or self-indulgence, e.g. those that end in assault or in adultery.

17

As to Power: here too it may fairly be said that the type of character it produces is mostly obvious enough. Some elements in this type it shares with the wealthy type, others are better. Those in power are more ambitious and more manly in character than the wealthy, because they aspire to do the great deeds that their power permits them to do. Responsibility makes them more serious: they have to keep paying attention to the duties their position involves. They are dignified rather than arrogant, for the respect in which they are held inspires them with dignity and therefore with moderation—dignity being a mild and becoming form of arrogance. If they wrong others, they wrong them not on a small but on a great scale.

Good fortune in certain of its branches produces the types of character belonging to the conditions just described, since these conditions are in fact more or less the kinds of good fortune that are regarded as most important. It may be added that good fortune leads us to gain all we can in the way of family happiness and bodily advantages. It does
1391b indeed make men more supercilious and more reckless; but there is one excellent quality that goes with it—piety, and respect for the divine power, in which they believe because of events which are really the result of chance.

This account of the types of character that correspond to differences of age or fortune may end here; for to arrive at the opposite types to those described, namely, those of the poor, the unfortunate, and the powerless, we have only to ask what the opposite qualities are.

18

The use of persuasive speech is to lead to decisions. (When we know a thing, and have decided about it, there is no further use in speaking about it.) This is so even if one is addressing a single person and urging him to do or not to do something, as when we scold a man for his conduct or try to change his views: the single person is as much your 'judge' as if he were one of many; we may say, without qualification, that any one is your judge whom you have to persuade. Nor does it matter whether we are arguing against an actual opponent or against a mere proposition; in the latter case we still have to use speech and overthrow the opposing arguments, and we attack these as we should attack an actual opponent. Our principle holds good of ceremonial speeches also; the 'onlookers' for whom such a speech is put together are treated as the judges of it. Broadly speaking, however, the only sort of person who can strictly be called a judge is the man who decides the issue in some matter of public controversy; that is, in law suits and in political debates, in both of which there are issues to be decided. In the section on political oratory an account has already been given of the types of character that mark the different constitutions.[1]

The manner and means of investing speeches with moral character may now be regarded as fully set forth.

Each of the main divisions of oratory has, we have seen,[2] its own distinct purpose. With regard to each division, we have noted the accepted views and propositions upon which we may base our arguments—for political, for ceremonial, and for forensic speaking. We have further determined completely by what means speeches may be invested with the required moral character. We are now to proceed to discuss the arguments common to *all* oratory. All orators, besides their special lines of argument, are bound to use, for instance, the topic of the Possible and Impossible; and to try to show that a thing has happened, or will happen in future. Again, the topic of Size is common to all oratory; all of us have to argue that things are bigger or smaller than they seem, whether we are making political speeches, speeches of eulogy or attack, or prosecuting **1392a** or defending in the law-courts. Having analysed these subjects, we will try to say what we can about the general principles of arguing by 'enthymeme' and 'example', by the addition of which we may hope to complete the project with which we set out. Of the above-mentioned general lines of argument, that concerned with Amplification is—as has been already said[3]—most appropriate to ceremonial speeches; that concerned with the Past, to forensic speeches, where the required decision is always about the past; that concerned with Possibility and the Future, to political speeches.

19

Let us first speak of the Possible and Impossible. It may plausibly be argued: That if it is possible for one of a pair of contraries to be or happen, then it is possible for the other: e.g. if a man can be cured, he can also fall ill; for any two contraries are equally possible, in so far as they are contraries. That if of two similar things one is possible, so is the other. That if the harder of two things is possible, so is the easier. That if a thing can come into existence in a good and beautiful form, then it can come into existence generally; thus a house can exist more easily than a beautiful house. That if the beginning of a thing can occur, so can the end; for nothing impossible occurs or begins to occur; thus the commensurability of the diagonal of a square with its side neither occurs nor can begin to occur. That if the end is possible, so is the beginning; for all things that occur have a beginning. That if that which is posterior in essence or in order of generation can come into being, so can that which is prior: thus if a man can come into being, so can a boy, since the boy comes first in order of generation; and if a boy can, so can a man, for the man also is first. That those things are possible of which the love or desire is natural; for no one, as a rule, loves or desires impossibilities. That things which are the object of any kind of science or art are possible and exist or come into existence. That anything is possible the first step in whose production depends on men or things which we can compel or persuade to produce it, by our greater strength, our control of them, or our friendship with them. That where the parts are possible, the whole is possible; and where the whole is possible, the parts are usually

[1] I. 8.

[2] I. 3.

[3] I. 9.

possible. For if the slit in front, the toe-piece, and the upper leather can be made, then shoes can be made; and if shoes, then also the front **1392b** slit and toe-piece. That if a whole genus is a thing that can occur, so can the species; and if the species can occur, so can the genus: thus, if a sailing vessel can be made, so also can a trireme; and if a trireme, then a sailing vessel also. That if one of two things whose existence depends on each other is possible, so is the other; for instance, if 'double', then 'half', and if 'half', then 'double'. That if a thing can be produced without art or preparation, it can be produced still more certainly by the careful application of art to it. Hence Agathon has said:

To some things we by art must needs attain,
Others by destiny or luck we gain.[1]

That if anything is possible to inferior, weaker, and stupider people, it is more so for their opposites; thus Isocrates said that it would be a strange thing if he could not discover a thing that Euthynus had found out. As for Impossibility, we can clearly get what we want by taking the contraries of the arguments stated above.

Questions of Past Fact may be looked at in the following ways: First, that if the less likely of two things has occurred, the more likely must have occurred also. That if one thing that usually follows another has happened, then that other thing has happened; that, for instance, if a man has forgotten a thing, he has also once learnt it. That if a man had the power and the wish to do a thing, he has done it; for every one does do whatever he intends to do whenever he can do it, there being nothing to stop him. That, further, he has done the thing in question either if he intended it and nothing external prevented him; or if he had the power to do it and was angry at the time; or if he had the power to do it and his heart was set upon it—for people as a rule do what they long to do, if they can; bad people through lack of self-control; good people, because their hearts are set upon good things. Again, that if a thing was 'going to happen', it has happened; if a man was 'going to do something', he has done it, for it is likely that the intention was carried out. That if one thing has happened which naturally happens before another or with a view to it, the other has happened; for instance, if it has lightened, it has also thundered; and if an action has been attempted, it has been done. That if one thing has happened which naturally happens after another, or with a view to which that other happens, then that other (that which happens first, or happens with a view to this thing) has also happened; thus, if it has thundered it has also lightened, and if an action has been done it has been attempted. Of all these sequences some are inevitable and some merely usual. The arguments for the *non*-occurrence of anything can obviously be found by considering the opposites of those that have been mentioned.

1393a How questions of Future Fact should be argued is clear from the same considerations: That a thing will be done if there is both the power and the wish to do it; or if along with the power to do it there is a craving for the result, or anger, or calculation, prompting it. That the thing will be done, in these cases, if the man is actually setting about it, or even if he means to do it later—for usually what we mean to do happens rather than what we do not mean to do. That a thing will happen if another thing which naturally happens before it has already happened; thus, if it is clouding over, it is likely to rain. That if the means to an end have occurred, then the end is likely to occur; thus, if there is a foundation, there will be a house.

For arguments about the Greatness and Smallness of things, the greater and the lesser, and generally great things and small, what we have already said will show the line to take. In discussing deliberative oratory we have spoken about the relative greatness of various goods, and about the greater and lesser in general.[2] Since therefore in each type of oratory the object under discussion is some kind of good—whether it is utility, nobleness, or justice—it is clear that every orator must obtain the materials of amplification through these channels. To go further than this, and try to establish abstract laws of greatness and superiority, is to argue without an object; in practical life, particular facts count more than generalizations.

Enough has now been said about these questions of possibility and the reverse, of past or future fact, and of the relative greatness or smallness of things.

20

The special forms of oratorical argument having now been discussed, we have next to treat

[1] Agathon, fr. 8, Nauck.

[2] I. 7.

of those which are common to all kinds of oratory. These are of two main kinds, 'Example' and 'Enthymeme'; for the 'Maxim' is part of an enthymeme.

We will first treat of argument by Example, for it has the nature of induction, which is the foundation of reasoning. This form of argument has two varieties; one consisting in the mention of actual past facts, the other in the invention of facts by the speaker. Of the latter, again, there are two varieties, the illustrative parallel and the fable (e.g. the fables of Aesop, or those from Libya). As an instance of the mention of actual facts, take the following. The speaker may argue thus: 'We must prepare for war against the king of Persia and not let him subdue Egypt. For Darius of old did **1393b** not cross the Aegean until he had seized Egypt; but once he had seized it, he did cross. And Xerxes, again, did not attack us until he had seized Egypt; but once he had seized it, he did cross. If therefore the present king seizes Egypt, he also will cross, and therefore we must not let him.'

The illustrative parallel is the sort of argument Socrates used: e.g. 'Public officials ought not to be selected by lot. That is like using the lot to select athletes, instead of choosing those who are fit for the contest; or using the lot to select a steersman from among a ship's crew, as if we ought to take the man on whom the lot falls, and not the man who knows most about it.'

Instances of the fable are that of Stesichorus about Phalaris, and that of Aesop in defence of the popular leader. When the people of Himera had made Phalaris military dictator, and were going to give him a bodyguard, Stesichorus wound up a long talk by telling them the fable of the horse who had a field all to himself. Presently there came a stag and began to spoil his pasturage. The horse, wishing to revenge himself on the stag, asked a man if he could help him to do so. The man said, 'Yes, if you will let me bridle you and get on to your back with javelins in my hand'. The horse agreed, and the man mounted; but instead of getting his revenge on the stag, the horse found himself the slave of the man. 'You too', said Stesichorus, 'take care lest, in your desire for revenge on your enemies, you meet the same fate as the horse. By making Phalaris military dictator, you have already let yourselves be bridled. If you let him get on to your backs by giving him a bodyguard, from that moment you will be his slaves.'

Aesop, defending before the assembly at Samos a poular leader who was being tried for his life, told this story: A fox, in crossing a river, was swept into a hole in the rocks; and, not being able to get out, suffered miseries for a long time through the swarms of fleas that fastened on her. A hedgehog, while roaming around, noticed the fox; and feeling sorry for her asked if he might remove the fleas. But the fox declined the offer; and when the hedgehog asked why, she replied, 'These fleas are by this time full of me and not sucking much blood; if you take them away, others will come with fresh appetites and drink up all the blood I have left.' 'So, men of Samos', said Aesop, 'my client will do you no further harm; he is wealthy already. But if you put him to death, others will come along who are not rich, **1394a** and their peculations will empty your treasury completely.'

Fables are suitable for addresses to popular assemblies; and they have one advantage—they are comparatively easy to invent, whereas it is hard to find parallels among actual past events. You will in fact frame them just as you frame illustrative parallels: all you require is the power of thinking out your analogy, a power developed by intellectual training. But while it is easier to supply parallels by inventing fables, it is more valuable for the political speaker to supply them by quoting what has actually happened, since in most respects the future will be like what the past has been.

Where we are unable to argue by Enthymeme, we must try to demonstrate our point by this method of Example, and to convince our hearers thereby. If we *can* argue by Enthymeme, we should use our Examples as subsequent supplementary evidence. They should not precede the Enthymemes: that will give the argument an inductive air, which only rarely suits the conditions of speech-making. If they follow the enthymemes, they have the effect of witnesses giving evidence, and this always tells. For the same reason, if you put your examples first you must give a large number of them; if you put them last, a single one is sufficient; even a single witness will serve if he is a good one. It has now been stated how many varieties of argument by Example there are, and how and when they are to be employed.

21

We now turn to the use of Maxims, in order to see upon what subjects and occasions, and for what kind of speaker, they will appropriately form part of a speech. This will appear most clearly when we have defined a maxim. It is a statement; not a particular fact, such as the character of Iphicrates, but of a general kind; nor is it about any and every subject—e.g. 'straight is the contrary of curved' is not a maxim—but only about questions of practical conduct, courses of conduct to be chosen or avoided. Now an Enthymeme is a syllogism dealing with such practical subjects. It is therefore roughly true that the premisses or conclusions of Enthymemes, considered apart from the rest of the argument, are Maxims: e.g.

Never should any man whose wits are sound
Have his sons taught more wisdom than their fellows.[1]

Here we have a Maxim; add the reason or explanation, and the whole thing is an Enthymeme; thus—

It makes them idle; and therewith they earn
Ill-will and jealousy throughout the city.[2]

1394b Again,

There is no man in all things prosperous,[3]

and

There is no man among us all is free,

are maxims; but the latter, taken with what follows it, is an Enthymeme—

For all are slaves of money or of chance.[4]

From this definition of a maxim it follows that there are four kinds of maxims. In the first place, the maxim may or may not have a supplement. Proof is needed where the statement is paradoxical or disputable; no supplement is wanted where the statement contains nothing paradoxical, either because the view expressed is already a known truth, e.g.

Chiefest of blessings is health for a man, as it seemeth to me,[5]

this being the general opinion: or because, as soon as the view is stated, it is clear at a glance, e.g.

No love is true save that which loves for ever.[6]

Of the Maxims that do have a supplement attached, some are part of an Enthymeme, e.g.

Never should any man whose wits are sound, &c.[7]

Others have the essential character of Enthymemes, but are not stated as parts of Enthymemes; these latter are reckoned the best; they are those in which the reason for the view expressed is simply implied, e.g.

O mortal man, nurse not immortal wrath.[8]

To say 'it is not right to nurse immortal wrath' is a maxim; the added words 'O mortal man' give the reason. Similarly, with the words

Mortal creatures ought to cherish mortal, not immortal thoughts.[9]

What has been said has shown us how many kinds of Maxims there are, and to what subjects the various kinds are appropriate. They must not be given without supplement if they express disputed or paradoxical views: we must, in that case, either put the supplement first and make a maxim of the conclusion, e.g. you might say, 'For my part, since both unpopularity and idleness are undesirable, I hold that it is better not to be educated'; or you may say this first, and then add the previous clause. Where a statement, without being paradoxical, is not obviously true, the reason should be added as concisely as possible. In such cases both laconic and enigmatic sayings are suitable: thus one might say what **1395a** Stesichorus said to the Locrians, 'Insolence is better avoided, lest the cicalas chirp on the ground'.

The use of Maxims is appropriate only to elderly men, and in handling subjects in which the speaker is experienced. For a young man to use them is—like telling stories—unbecoming; to use them in handling things in which one has no experience is silly and ill-bred: a fact sufficiently proved by the special fondness of country fellows for striking out maxims, and their readiness to air them.

To declare a thing to be universally true when it is not is most appropriate when working up feelings of horror and indignation in our hearers; especially by way of preface, or after the facts have been proved. Even hackneyed and commonplace maxims are to be used, if they suit one's purpose: just because they are commonplace, every one seems to agree with them, and therefore they are taken for truth. Thus, any one who is calling on his

[1] Euripides, *Medea*, 295. [2] *Ibid.*, 297.
[3] Euripides, fr. 661, Nauck. [4] Euripides, *Hecuba*, 864 ff.
[5] Possibly a fragment of Epicharmus.
[6] Euripides, *Troades*, 1051.

[7] Euripides, *Medea*, 295. [8] Fr. Adesp. 79, Nauck.
[9] Epicharmus?

men to risk an engagement without obtaining favourable omens may quote

One omen of all is best, that we fight for our fatherland.[1]

Or, if he is calling on them to attack a stronger force—

The War-God showeth no favour.[2]

Or, if he is urging people to destroy the innocent children of their enemies—

Fool, who slayeth the father and leaveth his sons to avenge him.[3]

Some proverbs are also maxims, e.g. the proverb 'An Attic neighbour'. You are not to avoid uttering maxims that contradict such sayings as have become public property (I mean such sayings as 'know thyself' and 'nothing in excess') if doing so will raise your hearers' opinion of your character, or convey an effect of strong emotion—e.g. an angry speaker might well say, 'It is not true that we ought to know ourselves: anyhow, if this man had known himself, he would never have thought himself fit for an army command.' It will raise people's opinion of our character to say, for instance, 'We ought not to follow the saying that bids us treat our friends as future enemies: much better to treat our enemies as future friends.' The moral purpose should be implied partly by the very wording of our maxim. Failing this, we should add our reason: e.g. having said 'We should treat our friends, not as the saying advises, but as if they were going to be our friends always', we should add 'for the other behaviour is that of a traitor': or we might put it, 'I disapprove of that saying. A true friend will treat his friend as if he were going to be his friend for ever'; and again, 'Nor do I approve of the saying "nothing in excess": we are bound to hate bad men excessively.'

1395b One great advantage of Maxims to a speaker is due to the want of intelligence in his hearers, who love to hear him succeed in expressing as a universal truth the opinions which they hold themselves about particular cases. I will explain what I mean by this, indicating at the same time how we are to hunt down the maxims required. The maxim, as has been already said,[4] is a general statement and people love to hear stated in general terms what they already believe in some particular connexion: e.g. if a man happens to have bad neighbours or bad children, he will agree with any one who tells him, 'Nothing is more annoying than having neighbours', or, 'Nothing is more foolish than to be the parent of children.' The orator has therefore to guess the subjects on which his hearers really hold views already, and what those views are, and then must express, as general truths, these same views on these same subjects. This is one advantage of using maxims. There is another which is more important—it invests a speech with moral character. There is moral character in every speech in which the moral purpose is conspicuous: and maxims always produce this effect, because the utterance of them amounts to a general declaration of moral principles: so that, if the maxims are sound, they display the speaker as a man of sound moral character. So much for the Maxim—its nature, varieties, proper use, and advantages.

22

We now come to the Enthymemes, and will begin the subject with some general consideration of the proper way of looking for them, and then proceed to what is a distinct question, the lines of argument to be embodied in them. It has already[5] been pointed out that the Enthymeme is a syllogism, and in what sense it is so. We have also noted the differences between it and the syllogism of dialectic. Thus we must not carry its reasoning too far back, or the length of our argument will cause obscurity: nor must we put in all the steps that lead to our conclusion, or we shall waste words in saying what is manifest. It is this simplicity that makes the uneducated more effective than the educated when addressing popular audiences—makes them, as the poets[6] tell us, 'charm the crowd's ears more finely'. Educated men lay down broad general principles; uneducated men argue from common knowledge and draw obvious conclusions. We must not, therefore, start from any and every accepted opinion, but only from those we have defined—those accepted by our judges or by those whose **1396a** authority they recognize: and there must, moreover, be no doubt in the minds of most, if not all, of our judges that the opinions put forward really are of this sort. We should also base our arguments upon probabilities as well as upon certainties.

1 *Iliad*, XII. 243.
2 *Ibid.*, XVIII. 309.
3 Cf. I. 15(1376a 7).
4 1394a 23.

5 I. 2(1356b 3, 1357a 16).
6 Cf. Euripides, *Hippolytus*, 989.

The first thing we have to remember is this. Whether our argument concerns public affairs or some other subject, we must know some, if not all, of the facts about the subject on which we are to speak and argue. Otherwise we can have no materials out of which to construct arguments. I mean, for instance, how could we advise the Athenians whether they should go to war or not, if we did not know their strength, whether it was naval or military or both, and how great it is; what their revenues amount to; who their friends and enemies are; what wars, too, they have waged, and with what success; and so on? Or how could we eulogize them if we knew nothing about the sea-fight at Salamis, or the battle of Marathon, or what they did for the Heracleidae, or any other facts like that? All eulogy is based upon the noble deeds—real or imaginary—that stand to the credit of those eulogized. On the same principle, invectives are based on facts of the opposite kind: the orator looks to see what base deeds—real or imaginary—stand to the discredit of those he is attacking, such as treachery to the cause of Hellenic freedom, or the enslavement of their gallant allies against the barbarians (Aegina, Potidaea, &c.), or any other misdeeds of this kind that are recorded against them. So, too, in a court of law: whether we are prosecuting or defending, we must pay attention to the existing facts of the case. It makes no difference whether the subject is the Lacedaemonians or the Athenians, a man or a god; we must do the same thing. Suppose it to be Achilles whom we are to advise, to praise or blame, to accuse or defend; here too we must take the facts, real or imaginary; these must be our material, whether we are to praise or blame him for the noble or base deeds he has done, to accuse or defend him for his just or unjust treatment of others, or to advise him about what is or is not to his interest. The same thing applies to any subject whatever. Thus, in handling the question whether justice is or is not a good, we must start with the real facts about justice and goodness. We see, then, that this is the only way in which any one ever proves anything, **1396b** whether his arguments are strictly cogent or not: not all facts can form his basis, but only those that bear on the matter in hand: nor, plainly, can proof be effected otherwise by means of the speech. Consequently, as appears in the *Topics,*[1] we must first of all have by us a selection of arguments about questions that may arise and are suitable for us to handle; and then we must try to think out arguments of the same type for special needs as they emerge; not vaguely and indefinitely, but by keeping our eyes on the actual facts of the subject we have to speak on, and gathering in as many of them as we can that bear closely upon it: for the more actual facts we have at our command, the more easily we prove our case; and the more closely they bear on the subject, the more they will seem to belong to that speech only instead of being commonplaces. By 'commonplaces' I mean, for example, eulogy of Achilles because he is a human being or a demi-god, or because he joined the expedition against Troy: these things are true of many others, so that this kind of eulogy applies no better to Achilles than to Diomede. The special facts here needed are those that are true of Achilles alone; such facts as that he slew Hector, the bravest of the Trojans, and Cycnus the invulnerable, who prevented all the Greeks from landing, and again that he was the youngest man who joined the expedition, and was not bound by oath to join it, and so on.

Here, again, we have our first principle of selection of Enthymemes—that which refers to the lines of argument selected. We will now consider the various elementary classes of enthymemes. (By an 'elementary class' of enthymeme I mean the same thing as a 'line of argument'.) We will begin, as we must begin, by observing that there are two kinds of enthymemes. One kind proves some affirmative or negative proposition; the other kind disproves one. The difference between the two kinds is the same as that between syllogistic proof and disproof in dialectic. The demonstrative enthymeme is formed by the conjunction of compatible propositions; the refutative, by the conjunction of incompatible propositions.

We may now be said to have in our hands the lines of argument for the various *special* subjects that it is useful or necessary to handle, having selected the propositions suitable in various cases. We have, in fact, already ascertained the lines of argument applicable to enthymemes about good and evil, the noble and the base, justice and injustice, and also to those about types of character, emotions, and moral qualities.[2] Let us now lay hold of certain facts **1397a** about the whole subject, considered from a different and more general point of view. In the course of our discussion we will

[1] Cf. *Topics,* I. 14.

[2] I. 4-14; II. 11-18.

take note of the distinction between lines of proof and lines of disproof:[1] and also of those lines of argument used in what seems to be enthymemes, but are not, since they do not represent valid syllogisms.[2] Having made all this clear, we will proceed to classify Objections and Refutations, showing how they can be brought to bear upon enthymemes.[3]

23

1. One line of positive proof is based upon consideration of the opposite of the thing in question. Observe whether that opposite has the opposite quality. If it has not, you refute the original proposition; if it has, you establish it. E.g. 'Temperance is beneficial; for licentiousness is hurtful'. Or, as in the Messenian speech, 'If war is the cause of our present troubles, peace is what we need to put things right again'.[4] Or—

For if not even evil-doers should
Anger us if they meant not what they did,
Then can we owe no gratitude to such
As were constrained to do the good they did us.[5]

Or—

Since in this world liars may win belief,
Be sure of the opposite likewise—that this world
Hears many a true word and believes it not.[6]

2. Another line of proof is got by considering some modification of the key-word, and arguing that what can or cannot be said of the one, can or cannot be said of the other: e.g. 'just' does not always mean 'beneficial', or 'justly' would always mean 'beneficially', whereas it is *not* desirable to be justly put to death.

3. Another line of proof is based upon correlative ideas. If it is true that one man *gave* noble or just treatment to another, you argue that the other must have *received* noble or just treatment; or that where it is right to command obedience, it must have been right to obey the command. Thus Diomedon, the tax-farmer, said of the taxes: 'If it is no disgrace for you to sell them, it is no disgrace for us to buy them'. Further, if 'well' or 'justly' is true of the person to whom a thing is done, you argue that it is true of the doer. But it is possible to draw a false conclusion here. It may be just that A should be treated in a certain way, and yet *not* just that he should be so treated by B. Hence you must ask yourself two distinct questions: (1) Is it right that A should be thus
1397b treated? (2) Is it right that B should thus treat him? and apply your results properly, according as your answers are Yes or No. Sometimes in such a case the two answers differ: you may quite easily have a position like that in the *Alcmaeon* of Theodectes:

And was there none to loathe thy mother's crime?[7]

to which question Alcmaeon in reply says,

Why, there are two things to examine here.

And when Alphesiboea asks what he means, he rejoins:

They judged her fit to die, not me to slay her.

Again there is the lawsuit about Demosthenes and the men who killed Nicanor; as they were judged to have killed him justly, it was thought that he was killed justly. And in the case of the man who was killed at Thebes, the judges were requested to decide whether it was unjust that he should be killed, since if it was not, it was argued that it could not have been unjust to kill him.

4. Another line of proof is the *a fortiori*. Thus it may be argued that if even the gods are not omniscient, certainly human beings are not. The principle here is that, if a quality does not in fact exist where it is *more* likely to exist, it clearly does not exist where it is *less* likely. Again, the argument that a man who strikes his father also strikes his neighbours follows from the principle that, if the less likely thing is true, the more likely thing is true also; for a man is less likely to strike his father than to strike his neighbours. The argument, then, may run thus. Or it may be urged that, if a thing is not true where it is more likely, it is not true where it is less likely; or that, if it is true where it is less likely, it is true where it is more likely: according as we have to show that a thing *is* or is *not* true. This argument might also be used in a case of parity, as in the lines:

Thou hast pity for thy sire, who has lost his sons:
Hast none for Oeneus, whose brave son is dead?[8]

And, again, 'if Theseus did no wrong, neither

[1] II. 23. [2] II. 24. [3] II. 25.

[4] Cf. Baiter-Sauppe, *Or. Att.*, Pt., II, p. 154 (Alcid., *Messen.*, fr. 2).

[5] Fr. Adesp. 80, Nauck.

[6] Euripides, *Thyestes*, fr. 396, N.[2]

[7] Theodectes, *Alcmaeon*, Nauck, p. 801.

[8] Fr. Adesp. 81, Nauck.

did Paris'; or 'if the sons of Tyndareus did no wrong, neither did Paris'; or 'if Hector did well to slay Patroclus, Paris did well to slay Achilles'.[1] And 'if other followers of an art are not bad men, neither are philosophers'.[2] And 'if generals are not bad men because it often happens that they are condemned to death, neither are sophists'. And the remark that 'if each individual among you ought to think of his own city's reputation, you ought all to think of the reputation of Greece as a whole'.

5. Another line of argument is based on considerations of time. Thus Iphicrates, in the case against Harmodius, said, 'if before doing the deed I had bargained that, if I did it, I should have a statue, you would have given me one. Will you not give me one now that I *have* done the deed? You must not make promises when you are expecting a thing to be done for you, and refuse to fulfil them when the thing has been done.'[3] And, again, to induce the Thebans to let Philip pass through their territory into Attica, it was argued that 'if

1398a he had insisted on this before he helped them against the Phocians, they would have promised to do it. It is monstrous, therefore, that just because he threw away his advantage then, and trusted their honour, they should not let him pass through now'.

6. Another line is to apply to the other speaker what he has said against yourself. It is an excellent turn to give to a debate, as may be seen in the *Teucer*.[4] It was employed by Iphicrates in his reply to Aristophon. 'Would *you*', he asked, 'take a bribe to betray the fleet?' 'No', said Aristophon; and Iphicrates replied, 'Very good: if you, who are Aristophon, would not betray the fleet, would I, who am Iphicrates?'[5] Only, it must be recognized beforehand that the other man is more likely than you are to commit the crime in question. Otherwise you will make yourself ridiculous; if it is Aristeides who is prosecuting, you cannot say that sort of thing to him. The purpose is to discredit the prosecutor, who as a rule would have it appear that his character is better than that of the defendant, a pretension which it is desirable to upset. But the use of such an argument is in all cases ridiculous if you are attacking others for what you do or would do yourself, or are urging others to do what you neither do nor would do yourself.

7. Another line of proof is secured by defining your terms. Thus, 'What is the supernatural? Surely it is either a god or the work of a god. Well, any one who believes that the work of a god exists, cannot help also believing that gods exist'.[6] Or take the argument of Iphicrates, 'Goodness is true nobility; neither Harmodius nor Aristogeiton had any nobility before they did a noble deed'. He also argued that he himself was more akin to Harmodius and Aristogeiton than his opponent was. 'At any rate, my deeds are more akin to those of Harmodius and Aristogeiton than yours are'.[7] Another example may be found in the *Alexander*.[8] 'Every one will agree that by incontinent people we mean those who are not satisfied with the enjoyment of one love.' A further example is to be found in the reason given by Socrates for not going to the court of Archelaus. He said that 'one is *insulted* by being unable to requite benefits, as well as by being unable to requite injuries'.[9] All the persons mentioned define their term and get at its essential meaning, and then use the result when reasoning on the point at issue.

8. Another line of argument is founded upon the various senses of a word. Such a word is 'rightly', as has been explained in the *Topics*.

9. Another line is based upon logical division. Thus, 'All men do wrong from one of three motives, A, B, or C: in my case A and B are out of the question, and even the accusers do not allege C'.

10. Another line is based upon induction. Thus from the case of the woman of Peparethus it might be argued that women everywhere can settle correctly the facts about their

1398b children. Another example of this occurred at Athens in the case between the orator Mantias and his son, when the boy's mother revealed the true facts: and yet another at Thebes, in the case between Ismenias and Stilbon, when Dodonis proved that it was Ismenias who was the father of her son Thettaliscus, and he was in consequence always regarded as being so. A further instance of induction may be taken from the *Law* of Theodectes:[10] 'If

[1] Baiter-Sauppe, *Or. Att.*, Pt. II. p, 223; Polycrates, Or. IX, fragm. I.

[2] Cf. Isocrates, *Antidosis*, § 209.

[3] Baiter-Sauppe, p. 179; Lysias, Or. XVIII, fragm. I.

[4] Of Sophocles.

[5] Baiter-Sauppe, *op. cit.*, p. 191; Lysias, Or. LXV, fragm. I.

[6] Cf. Plato, *Apology*, 27.

[7] Baiter-Sauppe, *op. cit.*, p. 179; Lysias, Or. XVIII, fr. 2.

[8] *Ibid.*, p. 223; Polycrates, Or. IX, fr. 2.

[9] Cf. Xenophon, *Apol. Socr.* 17; Laertius, *Vit. Socr.* II. 5, 25.

[10] Cf. Baiter-Sauppe, *Or. Att.*, Pt. II, p. 247 (Theodectes, Νόμος, fr. I).

we do not hand over our horses to the care of men who have mishandled other people's horses, nor ships to those who have wrecked other people's ships, and if this is true of everything else alike, then men who have failed to secure other people's safety are not to be employed to secure our own.' Another instance is the argument of Alcidamas:[1] "Every one honours the wise. Thus the Parians have honoured Archilochus, in spite of his bitter tongue; the Chians Homer, though he was not their countryman; the Mytilenaeans Sappho, though she was a woman; the Lacedaemonians actually made Chilon a member of their senate, though they are the least literary of men; the Italian Greeks honoured Pythagoras; the inhabitants of Lampsacus gave public burial to Anaxagoras, though he was an alien, and honour him even to this day. ⟨It may be argued that peoples for whom philosophers legislate are always prosperous⟩ on the ground that the Athenians became prosperous under Solon's laws and the Lacedaemonians under those of Lycurgus, while at Thebes no sooner did the leading men become philosophers than the country began to prosper.

11. Another line of argument is founded upon some decision already pronounced, whether on the same subject or on one like it or contrary to it. Such a proof is most effective if every one has always decided thus; but if not every one, then at any rate most people; or if all, or most, wise or good men have thus decided, or the actual judges of the present question, or those whose authority they accept, or any one whose decision they cannot gainsay because he has complete control over them, or those whom it is not seemly to gainsay, as the gods, or one's father, or one's teachers. Thus Autocles said, when attacking Mixidemides, that it was a strange thing that the Dread Goddesses could without loss of dignity submit to the judgement of the Areopagus, and yet Mixidemides could not. Or as Sappho said, 'Death is an evil thing; the gods have so judged it, or they would die'.[2] Or again as Aristippus said in reply to Plato when he spoke somewhat too dogmatically, as Aristippus thought: 'Well, anyhow, our *friend*', meaning Socrates, 'never spoke like that'. And Hegesippus, having previously consulted Zeus at Olympia, asked Apollo at Delphi 'whether his opinion was the same as his **1399a** father's', implying that it would be shameful for him to contradict his father. Thus too Isocrates argued that Helen must have been a good woman, because Theseus decided that she was; and Paris a good man, because the goddesses chose him before all others; and Evagoras also, says Isocrates, was good, since when Conon met with his misfortune he betook himself to Evagoras without trying any one else on the way.

12. Another line of argument consists in taking separately the parts of a subject. Such is that given in the *Topics*:[3] 'What *sort* of motion is the soul? for it must be this or that.' The *Socrates* of Theodectes provides an example: 'What temple has he profaned? What gods recognized by the state has he not honoured?'[4]

13. Since it happens that any given thing usually has both good and bad consequences, another line of argument consists in using those consequences as a reason for urging that a thing should or should not be done, for prosecuting or defending any one, for eulogy or censure. E.g. education leads both to unpopularity, which is bad, and to wisdom, which is good. Hence you either argue, 'It is therefore not well to be educated, since it is not well to be unpopular': or you answer, 'No, it is well to be educated, since it is well to be wise'. The *Art of Rhetoric* of Callippus is made up of this line of argument, with the addition of those of Possibility and the others of that kind already described.[5]

14. Another line of argument is used when we have to urge or discourage a course of action that may be done in either of two opposite ways, and have to apply the method just mentioned to both. The difference between this one and the last is that, whereas in the last any two things are contrasted, here the things contrasted are opposites. For instance, the priestess enjoined upon her son not to take to public speaking: 'For', she said, 'if you say what is right, men will hate you; if you say what is wrong, the gods will hate you.' The reply might be, 'On the contrary, you *ought* to take to public speaking: for if you say what is right, the gods will love you; if you say what is wrong, men will love you.' This amounts to the proverbial 'buying the marsh with the salt'. It is just this situation, viz. when each of two opposites has both a good and a bad consequence opposite respectively to

[1] *Ibid.*, p. 155; Alcidamas, Μουσεῖον, fr. 2.

[2] Sappho, fr. 137, Bergk.

[3] Cf. *Topics*, II. 4; IV. 1.

[4] Baiter-Sauppe, *Or. Att.*, Pt. II, p. 247; Theodectes, Σωκράτους Ἀπολογία, fragm. 1.

[5] II. 19 above.

each other, that has been termed *divarication*.

15. Another line of argument is this: The things people approve of openly are not those which they approve of secretly: openly, their chief praise is given to justice and nobleness; but in their hearts they prefer their own advantage. Try, in face of this, to establish the point of view which your opponent has not adopted. This is the most effective of the forms of argument that contradict common opinion.

16. Another line is that of rational correspondence. E.g. Iphicrates, when they were trying to compel his son, a youth under the prescribed age, to perform one of the state duties because he was tall, said 'If you count tall boys men, you will next be voting short men boys'.[1] And Theodectes in his *Law* **1399b** said, 'You make citizens of such mercenaries as Strabax and Charidemus, as a reward of their merits; will you not make exiles of such citizens as those who have done irreparable harm among the mercenaries?'

17. Another line is the argument that if two results are the same their antecedents are also the same. For instance, it was a saying of Xenophanes that to assert that the gods had birth is as impious as to say that they die; the consequence of both statements is that there is a time when the gods do not exist. This line of proof assumes generally that the result of any given thing is always the same: e.g. 'you are going to decide not about Isocrates, but about the value of the whole profession of philosophy.' Or, 'to give earth and water' means slavery; or, 'to share in the Common Peace' means obeying orders. We are to make either such assumptions or their opposite, as suits us best.

18. Another line of argument is based on the fact that men do not always make the same choice on a later as on an earlier occasion, but reverse their previous choice. E.g. the following enthymeme: 'When we were exiles, we fought in order to return; now we have returned, it would be strange to choose exile in order not to have to fight.'[2] On one occasion, that is, they chose to be true to their homes at the cost of fighting, and on the other to avoid fighing at the cost of deserting their homes.

19. Another line of argument is the assertion that some *possible* motive for an event or state of things is the *real* one: e.g. that a gift was given in order to cause pain by its withdrawal. This notion underlies the lines:

God gives to many great prosperity,
Not of good will towards them, but to make
The ruin of them more conspicuous.[3]

Or take the passage from the *Meleager* of Antiphon:

To slay no boar, but to be witnesses
Of Meleager's prowess unto Greece.[4]

Or the argument in the *Ajax* of Theodectes, that Diomede chose out Odysseus not to do him honour, but in order that his companion might be a lesser man than himself—such a motive for doing so is quite possible.

20. Another line of argument is common to forensic and deliberative oratory, namely, to consider inducements and deterrents, and the motives people have for doing or avoiding the actions in question. These are the conditions which make us bound to act if they are for us, and to refrain from action if they are against us: that is, we are bound to act if the action is possible, easy, and useful to ourselves or our friends or hurtful to our enemies; this is true even if the action entails loss, provided the loss is outweighed by the solid advantage. A speaker will urge action by pointing to such conditions, and discourage it by pointing to the **1400a** opposite. These same arguments also form the materials for accusation or defence —the deterrents being pointed out by the defence, and the inducements by the prosecution. As for the defence, . . . This topic forms the whole *Art of Rhetoric* both of Pamphilus and of Callippus.

21. Another line of argument refers to things which are supposed to happen and yet seem incredible. We may argue that people could not have believed them, if they had not been true or nearly true: even that they are the more likely to be true because they are incredible. For the things which men believe are either facts or probabilities: if, therefore, a thing that *is* believed is improbable and even incredible, it must be true, since it is certainly not believed because it is at all probable or credible. An example is what Androcles of the deme Pitthus said in his well-known arraignment of the law. The audience tried to shout him down when he observed that the laws required a law to set them right. 'Why', he went on, 'fish need salt, improbable and incredible as this might seem for creatures reared in salt water; and olive-cakes need oil, incredible as it is that what produces oil should need it.'[5]

[1] Cf. Baiter-Sauppe, *Or. Att.*, Pt. II, p. 219.
[2] Cf. Lysias, Or. XXXIV, § 11.
[3] Fr. Adesp. 82, N.
[4] Antiphon, fr. 2, N., p. 792.
[5] Baiter-Sauppe, *Or. Att.*, Pt. II, pp. 153-4, Androcles.

22. Another line of argument is to refute our opponent's case by noting any contrasts or contradictions of dates, acts, or words that it anywhere displays; and this in any of the three following connexions. (1) Referring to our opponent's conduct, e.g. 'He says he is devoted to you, yet he conspired with the Thirty.' (2) Referring to our own conduct, e.g. 'He says I am litigious, and yet he cannot prove that I have been engaged in a single lawsuit.' (3) Referring to both of us together, e.g. '*He* has never even *lent* any one a penny, but *I* have *ransomed* quite a number of you.'

23. Another line that is useful for men and causes that have been really or seemingly slandered, is to show why the facts are not as supposed; pointing out that there is a reason for the false impression given. Thus a woman, who had palmed off her son on another woman, was thought to be the lad's mistress because she embraced him; but when her action was explained the charge was shown to be groundless. Another example is from the *Ajax* of Theodectes, where Odysseus tells Ajax the reason why, though he is really braver than Ajax, he is not thought so.

24. Another line of argument is to show that if the *cause* is present, the *effect* is present, and if absent, absent. For by proving the cause you at once prove the effect, and conversely nothing can exist without its cause. Thus Thrasybulus accused Leodamas of having had his name recorded as a criminal on the slab in the Acropolis, and of erasing the record in the time of the Thirty Tyrants: to which Leodamas replied, 'Impossible: for the Thirty would have trusted me all the more if my quarrel with the commons had been inscribed on the slab.'[1]

25. Another line is to consider whether the accused person can take or could have taken a better course than that which he is recommending or taking, or has taken. If he has *not* taken **1400b** this better course, it is clear that he is not guilty, since no one deliberately and consciously chooses what is bad. This argument is, however, fallacious, for it often becomes clear after the event how the action could have been done better, though before the event this was far from clear.

26. Another line is, when a contemplated action is inconsistent with any past action, to examine them both together. Thus, when the people of Elea asked Xenophanes if they should or should not sacrifice to Leucothea and mourn for her, he advised them not to mourn for her if they thought her a goddess, and not to sacrifice to her if they thought her a mortal woman.

27. Another line is to make previous mistakes the grounds of accusation or defence. Thus, in the *Medea* of Carcinus the accusers allege that Medea has slain her children; 'at all events', they say, 'they are not to be seen'—Medea having made the mistake of sending her children away. In defence she argues that it is not her children, but Jason, whom she would have slain; for it would have been a mistake on her part not to do this if she *had* done the other. This special line of argument for enthymeme forms the whole of the *Art of Rhetoric* in use before Theodorus.

28. Another line is to draw meanings from names. Sophocles, for instance, says,

O steel in heart as thou art steel in name.[2]

This line of argument is common in praises of the gods. Thus, too, Conon called Thrasybulus *rash in counsel.* And Herodicus said of Thrasymachus, 'You are always *bold in battle*'; of Polus, 'you are always *a colt*'; and of the legislator Draco that his laws were those not of a human being but of *a dragon,* so savage were they. And, in Euripides, Hecuba says of Aphrodite,

Her name and Folly's (ἀφροσύνης) *rightly begin alike,*[3]

and Chaeremon writes

Pentheus—a name foreshadowing grief (πένθος) *to come.*[4]

The Refutative Enthymeme has a greater reputation than the Demonstrative, because within a small space it works out two opposing arguments, and arguments put side by side are clearer to the audience. But of all syllogisms, whether refutative or demonstrative, those are most applauded of which we foresee the conclusions from the beginning, so long as they are not obvious at first sight—for part of the pleasure we feel is at our own intelligent anticipation; or those which we follow well enough to see the point of them as soon as the last word has been uttered.

24

Besides genuine syllogisms, there may be syllogisms that look genuine but are not;

[1] Baiter-Sauppe, *Or. Att.*, Pt. II, pp. 216-17.

[2] Sophocles, fr. 597, N. [3] Euripides, *Troades*, 990.

[4] Chaeremon, fr. 4, N., p. 783.

and since an enthymeme is merely a syllogism of a particular kind, it follows that, besides genuine enthymemes, there may be those that look genuine but are not.

1. Among the lines of argument that form **1401a** the Spurious Enthymeme the first is that which arises from the particular words employed.

(*a*) One variety of this is when—as in dialectic, without having gone through any reasoning process, we make a final statement as if it were the conclusion of such a process, 'Therefore so-and-so is not true', 'Therefore also so-and-so must be true'—so too in rhetoric a compact and antithetical utterance passes for an enthymeme, such language being the proper province of enthymeme, so that it is seemingly the form of wording here that causes the illusion mentioned. In order to produce the effect of genuine reasoning by our form of wording it is useful to summarize the results of a number of previous reasonings: as 'some he saved—others he avenged—the Greeks he freed'.[1] Each of these statements has been previously proved from other facts; but the mere collocation of them gives the impression of establishing some fresh conclusion.

(*b*) Another variety is based on the use of similar words for different things; e.g. the argument that the mouse must be a noble creature, since it gives its name to the most august of all religious rites—for such the Mysteries are. Or one may introduce, into a eulogy of the dog, the dog-star; or Pan, because Pindar said:

> *O thou blessed one!*
> *Thou whom they of Olympus call*
> *The hound of manifold shape*
> *That follows the Mother of Heaven:*[2]

or we may argue that, because there is much disgrace in there *not* being a dog about, there is honour in *being* a dog. Or that Hermes is readier than any other god to go shares, since we never say 'shares all round' except of him. Or that speech is a very excellent thing, since good men are not said to be worth money but to be worthy of esteem—the phrase 'worthy of esteem' also having the meaning of 'worth speech'.

2. Another line is to assert of the whole what is true of the parts, or of the parts what is true of the whole. A whole and its parts are supposed to be identical, though often they are not. You have therefore to adopt whichever of these two lines better suits your purpose. That is how Euthydemus argues: e.g. that any one knows that there is a trireme in the Peiraeus, since he knows the separate details that make up this statement. There is also the argument that one who knows the letters knows the whole word, since the word is the same thing as the letters which compose it; or that, if a double portion of a certain thing is harmful to health, then a single portion must not be called wholesome, since it is absurd that two good things should make one bad thing. Put thus, the enthymeme is refutative; put as follows, demonstrative: 'For one good thing cannot be made up of two bad things.' The whole line of argument is fallacious. Again, there is Polycrates' saying that Thrasybulus put down thirty tyrants, where the speaker adds them up one by one. Or the argument in the *Orestes* of Theodectes, where the argument is from part to whole:

> *'Tis right that she who slays her lord should die.*[3]

'It is right, too, that the son should avenge his **1401b** father. Very good: these two things are what Orestes has done.' Still, perhaps the two things, once they are put together, do not form a right act. The fallacy might also be said to be due to omission, since the speaker fails to say by whose hand a husband-slayer should die.

3. Another line is the use of indignant language, whether to support your own case or to overthrow your opponent's. We do this when we paint a highly-coloured picture of the situation without having proved the facts of it: if the defendant does so, he produces an impression of his innocence; and if the prosecutor goes into a passion, he produces an impression of the defendant's guilt. Here there is no genuine enthymeme: the hearer infers guilt or innocence, but no proof is given, and the inference is fallacious accordingly.

4. Another line is to use a 'Sign', or single instance, as certain evidence; which, again, yields no valid proof. Thus, it might be said that lovers are useful to their countries, since the love of Harmodius and Aristogeiton caused the downfall of the tyrant Hipparchus. Or, again, that Dionysius is a thief, since he is a vicious man—there is, of course, no valid proof here; not every vicious man is a thief, though every thief is a vicious man.

5. Another line represents the accidental as

[1] Isocrates, *Evagoras*, 65-9.
[2] Pindar, fr. 96, Bergk.
[3] Theodectes, fr. 5, Nauck, p. 803.

essential. An instance is what Polycrates says of the mice, that they 'came to the rescue' because they gnawed through the bowstrings.[1] Or it might be maintained that an invitation to dinner is a great honour, for it was because he was *not* invited that Achilles was 'angered' with the Greeks at Tenedos.[2] As a fact, what angered him was the *insult* involved; it was a mere accident that this was the particular form that the insult took.

6. Another is the argument from consequence. In the *Alexander,* for instance, it is argued that Paris must have had a lofty disposition, since he despised society and lived by himself on Mount Ida: because lofty people do this kind of thing, therefore Paris too, we are to suppose, had a lofty soul. Or, if a man dresses fashionably and roams around at night, he is a rake, since that is the way rakes behave. Another similar argument points out that beggars sing and dance in temples, and that exiles can live wherever they please, and that such privileges are at the disposal of those we account happy and therefore every one might be regarded as happy if only he has those privileges. What matters, however, is the *circumstances* under which the privileges are enjoyed. Hence this line too falls under the head of fallacies by omission.

7. Another line consists in representing as causes things which are not causes, on the ground that they happened along with or before the event in question. They assume that, because B happens *after* A, it happens *because* of A. Politicians are especially fond of taking this line. Thus Demades said that the policy of Demosthenes was the cause of all the mischief, 'for after it the war occurred'.[3]

8. Another line consists in leaving out any mention of time and circumstances. E.g. the argument that Paris was justified in taking Helen, since her father left her free to choose: here the freedom was presumably not perpetual; it could only refer to her first choice, beyond which her father's authority could not **1402a** go. Or again, one might say that to strike a free man is an act of wanton outrage; but it is not so in every case—only when it is unprovoked.

9. Again, a spurious syllogism may, as in 'eristical' discussions, be based on the confusion of the absolute with that which is not absolute but particular. As, in dialectic, for instance, it may be argued that what-is-not *is,* on the ground that what-is-not *is* what-is-not; or that the unknown can be known, on the ground that it can be known to *be* unknown: so also in rhetoric a spurious enthymeme may be based on the confusion of some particular probability with absolute probability. Now no particular probability is universally probable: as Agathon says,

One might perchance say that was probable—
That things improbable oft will hap to men.[4]

For what is improbable does happen, and therefore it is probable that improbable things *will* happen. Granted this, one might argue that 'what is improbable is probable'. But this is not true absolutely. As, in eristic, the imposture comes from not adding any clause specifying relationship or reference or manner; so here it arises because the probability in question is not general but specific. It is of this line of argument that Corax's *Art of Rhetoric* is composed. If the accused is not open to the charge—for instance if a weakling be tried for violent assault—the defence is that he was not likely to do such a thing. But if he *is* open to the charge—i.e. if he is a *strong* man—the defence is still that he was not likely to do such a thing, since he could be sure that people would think he *was* likely to do it. And so with any other charge: the accused must be either open or not open to it: there is in either case an appearance of probable innocence, but whereas in the latter case the probability is genuine, in the former it can only be asserted in the special sense mentioned. This sort of argument illustrates what is meant by making the worse argument seem the better. Hence people were right in objecting to the training Protagoras undertook to give them. It was a fraud; the probability it handled was not genuine but spurious, and has a place in no art except Rhetoric and Eristic.

25

Enthymemes, genuine and apparent, have now been described; the next subject is their Refutation.

An argument may be refuted either by a counter-syllogism or by bringing an objection. It is clear that counter-syllogisms can be built up from the same lines of arguments as the

[1] Baiter-Sauppe, *Or. Att.*, Pt. II, pp. 221, 222 (Polycrates).
[2] Sophocles, Ἀχαιῶν σύλλογος, Nauck, p. 161.
[3] Baiter-Sauppe, p. 315 (Demades).
[4] Agathon, fr. 9, Nauck, p. 765.

original syllogisms: for the materials of syllogisms are the ordinary opinions of men, and such opinions often contradict each other. Objections, as appears in the *Topics*,[1] may be raised in four ways—either by directly attacking your opponent's own statement, or by putting forward another statement like it, or by putting forward a statement contrary to it, or by quoting previous decisions.

1. By 'attacking your opponent's own statement' I mean, for instance, this: if his enthymeme should assert that love is always good, **1402b** the objection can be brought in two ways, either by making the general statement that 'all want is an evil', or by making the particular one that there would be no talk of 'Caunian love' if there were not evil loves as well as good ones.

2. An objection 'from a contrary statement' is raised when, for instance, the opponent's enthymeme having concluded that a good man does good to all his friends, you object, 'That proves nothing, for a bad man does not do evil to all his friends'.

3. An example of an objection 'from a like statement' is, the enthymeme having shown that ill-used men always hate their ill-users, to reply, 'That proves nothing, for well-used men do not always love those who used them well'.

4. The 'decisions' mentioned are those proceeding from well-known men; for instance, if the enthymeme employed has concluded that 'Some allowance ought to be made for drunken offenders, since they did not know what they were doing', the objection will be, 'Pittacus, then, deserves no approval, or he would not have prescribed specially severe penalties for offences due to drunkenness'.

Enthymemes are based upon one or other of four kinds of alleged fact: (1) Probabilities, (2) Examples, (3) Infallible Signs, (4) Ordinary Signs. (1) Enthymemes based upon Probabilities are those which argue from what is, or is supposed to be, usually true. (2) Enthymemes based upon Example are those which proceed by induction from one or more similar cases, arrive at a general proposition, and then argue deductively to a particular inference. (3) Enthymemes based upon Infallible Signs are those which argue from the inevitable and invariable. (4) Enthymemes based upon ordinary Signs are those which argue from some universal or particular proposition, true or false.

[1] Cf. *Topics*, VIII. 10.

Now (1) as a Probability is that which happens usually but not always, Enthymemes founded upon Probabilities can, it is clear, always be refuted by raising some objection. The refutation is not always genuine: it may be spurious: for it consists in showing not that your opponent's premiss is not probable, but only in showing that it is not inevitably true. Hence it is always in defence rather than in accusation that it is possible to gain an advantage by using this fallacy. For the accuser uses probabilities to prove his case: and to refute a conclusion as improbable is not the same thing as to refute it as not inevitable. Any argument based upon what usually happens is always open to objection: otherwise it would not be a probability but an invariable and necessary truth. But the judges think, if the refutation takes this form, either that the accuser's case is not probable or that they must not decide it; which, as we said, is a false piece of reasoning. For they ought to decide by considering not merely what *must* be true but also what is *likely* to be true: this is, indeed, the meaning of 'giving a verdict in accordance with one's honest opinion'. Therefore it is not enough for the defendant to refute the accusation by proving that the charge is not *bound* to be true: he must do so by showing that it is not *likely* to be true. For this purpose his objection must state what is more usually true than the statement attacked. It may do so in either of two ways: either in respect of frequency or in respect of exactness. It will be most convincing if it does so in both respects; for if the thing in question *both* happens **1403a** *oftener* as we represent it *and* happens more *as* we represent it, the probability is particularly great.

(2) Fallible Signs, and Enthymemes based upon them, can be refuted even if the facts are correct, as was said at the outset. For we have shown in the *Analytics*[2] that no Fallible Sign can form part of a valid logical proof.

(3) Enthymemes depending on examples may be refuted in the same way as probabilities. If we have a negative instance, the argument is refuted, in so far as it is proved not inevitable, even though the positive examples are more similar and more frequent. And if the positive examples *are* more numerous and more frequent, we must contend that the present case is dissimilar, or that its conditions are dissimilar, or that it is different in some way or other.

[2] *Prior Analytics*, II. 27.

(4) It will be impossible to refute Infallible Signs, and Enthymemes resting on them, by showing in any way that they do not form a valid logical proof: this, too, we see from the *Analytics*.[1] All we can do is to show that the fact alleged does not exist. If there is no doubt that it does, and that it is an Infallible Sign, refutation now becomes impossible: for this is equivalent to a demonstration which is clear in every respect.

26

Amplification and Depreciation are not an element of enthymeme. By 'an element of enthymeme' I mean the same thing as a line of enthymematic argument'—a general class embracing a large number of particular kinds of enthymeme. Amplification and Depreciation are one kind of enthymeme, viz. the kind used to show that a thing is great or small; just as there are other kinds used to show that a thing is good or bad, just or unjust, and anything else of the sort. All these things are the *subject-matter* of syllogisms and enthymemes; none of these is the line of argument of an enthymeme; no more, therefore, are Amplification and Depreciation. Nor are Refutative Enthymemes a different species from Constructive. For it is clear that refutation consists either in offering positive proof or in raising an objection. In the first case we prove the opposite of our adversary's statements. Thus, if he shows that a thing has happened, we show that it has not; if he shows that it has not happened, we show that it has. This, then, could not be the distinction if there were one, since the same means are employed by both parties, enthymemes being adduced to show that the fact is or is not so-and-so. An objection, on the other hand, is not an enthymeme at all, as was said in the *Topics*,[2] it consists in stating some accepted opinion from which it will be clear that our opponent has not reasoned correctly or has made a false assumption.

Three points must be studied in making a speech; and we have now completed the account of (1) Examples, Maxims, Enthymemes, and in general the *thought*-element—**1403b** the way to invent and refute arguments. We have next to discuss (2) Style, and (3) Arrangement.

BOOK III

I

In making a speech one must study three points: first, the means of producing persuasion; second, the style, or language, to be used; third, the proper arrangement of the various parts of the speech. We have already specified the sources of persuasion. We have shown that these are three in number; what they are; and why there are only these three: for we have shown that persuasion must in every case be effected either (1) by working on the emotions of the judges themselves, (2) by giving them the right impression of the speakers' character, or (3) by proving the truth of the statements made.

Enthymemes also have been described, and the sources from which they should be derived; there being both special and general lines of argument for enthymemes.

Our next subject will be the style of expression. For it is not enough to know *what* we ought to say; we must also say it *as* we ought; much help is thus afforded towards producing the right impression of a speech. The first question to receive attention was naturally the one that comes first naturally—how persuasion can be produced from the facts themselves. The second is how to set these facts out in language. A third would be the proper method of delivery; this is a thing that affects the success of a speech greatly; but hitherto the subject has been neglected. Indeed, it was long before it found a way into the arts of tragic drama and epic recitation: at first poets acted their tragedies themselves. It is plain that delivery has just as much to do with oratory as with poetry. (In connexion with poetry, it has been studied by Glaucon of Teos among others.) It is, essentially, a matter of the right management of the voice to express the various emotions—of speaking loudly, softly, or between the two; of high, low, or intermediate pitch; of the various rhythms that suit various subjects. These are the three things—volume of sound, modulation of pitch, and rhythm—that a speaker bears in mind. It is those who *do* bear them in mind who usually win prizes in the dramatic contests; and just as in drama the actors now count for more than the poets, so it is in the contests of public life, owing to the defects of our political in-

[1] *Ibid.*, II. 27.

[2] Cf. *Topics*, VIII. 10.

stitutions. No systematic treatise upon the rules of delivery has yet been composed; indeed, even the study of language made no progress till late in the day. Besides, delivery is—very properly—not regarded as an ele-
1404a vated subject of inquiry. Still, the whole business of rhetoric being concerned with appearances, we must pay attention to the subject of delivery, unworthy though it is, because we cannot do without it. The right thing in speaking really is that we should be satisfied not to annoy our hearers, without trying to delight them: we ought in fairness to fight our case with no help beyond the bare facts: nothing, therefore, should matter except the proof of those facts. Still, as has been already said, other things affect the result considerably, owing to the defects of our hearers. The arts of language cannot help having a small but real importance, whatever it is we have to expound to others: the way in which a thing is said does affect its intelligibility. Not, however, so much importance as people think. All such arts are fanciful and meant to charm the hearer. Nobody uses fine language when teaching geometry.

When the principles of delivery have been worked out, they will produce the same effect as on the stage. But only very slight attempts to deal with them have been made and by a few people, as by Thrasymachus in his 'Appeals to Pity'. Dramatic ability is a natural gift, and can hardly be systematically taught. The principles of good diction can be so taught, and therefore we have men of ability in this direction too, who win prizes in their turn, as well as those speakers who excel in delivery—speeches of the written or literary kind owe more of their effect to their direction than to their thought.

It was naturally the poets who first set the movement going; for words represent things, and they had also the human voice at their disposal, which of all our organs can best represent other things. Thus the arts of recitation and acting were formed, and others as well. Now it was because poets seemed to win fame through their fine language when their thoughts were simple enough, that the language of oratorical prose at first took a poetical colour, e.g. that of Gorgias. Even now most uneducated people think that poetical language makes the finest discourses. That is not true: the language of prose is distinct from that of poetry. This is shown by the state of things to-day, when even the language of tragedy has altered its character. Just as iambics were adopted, instead of tetrameters, because they are the most prose-like of all metres, so tragedy has given up all those words, not used in ordinary talk, which decorated the early drama and are still used by the writers of hexameter poems. It is therefore ridiculous to imitate a poetical manner which the poets themselves have dropped; and it is now plain that we have not to treat in detail the whole question of style, but may confine ourselves to that part of it which concerns our present subject, rhetoric. The other—the poetical—part of it has been discussed in the treatise on the *Art of Poetry*.[1]

2

1404b We may, then, start from the observations there made, including the definition of style. Style to be good must be clear, as is proved by the fact that speech which fails to convey a plain meaning will fail to do just what speech has to do. It must also be appropriate, avoiding both meanness and undue elevation; poetical language is certainly free from meanness, but it is not appropriate to prose. Clearness is secured by using the words (nouns and verbs alike) that are current and ordinary. Freedom from meanness, and positive adornment too, are secured by using the other words mentioned in the *Art of Poetry*.[2] Such variation from what is usual makes the language appear more stately. People do not feel towards strangers as they do towards their own countrymen, and the same thing is true of their feeling for language. It is therefore well to give to everyday speech an unfamiliar air: people like what strikes them, and are struck by what is out of the way. In verse such effects are common, and there they are fitting: the persons and things there spoken of are comparatively remote from ordinary life. In prose passages they are far less often fitting because the subject-matter is less exalted. Even in poetry, it is not quite appropriate that fine language should be used by a slave or a very young man, or about very trivial subjects: even in poetry the style, to be appropriate, must sometimes be toned down, though at other times heightened. We can now see that a writer must disguise his art and give the impression of speaking naturally and not artificially. Naturalness is persuasive, artificiality is the contrary; for our hearers are prejudiced and think we have some design

[1] *Poetics*, 20-2. [2] *Ibid.*, 21, 22.

against them, as if we were mixing their wines for them. It is like the difference between the quality of Theodorus' voice and the voices of all other actors: his really seems to be that of the character who is speaking, theirs do not. We can hide our purpose successfully by taking the single words of our composition from the speech of ordinary life. This is done in poetry by Euripides, who was the first to show the way to his successors.

Language is composed of nouns and verbs. Nouns are of the various kinds considered in the treatise on Poetry.[1] Strange words, compound words, and invented words must be used sparingly and on few occasions: on *what* occasions we shall state later.[2] The reason for this restriction has been already indicated: they depart from what is suitable, in the direction of excess. In the language of prose, besides the regular and proper terms for things, metaphorical terms only can be used with advantage. This we gather from the fact that these two classes of terms, the proper or regular and the metaphorical—these and no others—are used by everybody in conversation. We can now see that a good writer can produce a style that is distinguished without being obtrusive, and is at the same time clear, thus satisfying our definition of good oratorical prose. Words of ambiguous meaning are chiefly useful to enable the sophist to mislead his hearers. Synonyms are useful to the poet, by which I mean words whose ordinary
1405a meaning is the same, e.g. πορεύεσθαι (*advancing*) and βαδίζειν (*proceeding*); these two are ordinary words and have the same meaning.

In the *Art of Poetry*,[3] as we have already said, will be found definitions of these kinds of words; a classification of Metaphors; and mention of the fact that metaphor is of great value both in poetry and in prose. Prose-writers must, however, pay specially careful attention to metaphor, because their other resources are scantier than those of poets. Metaphor, moreover, gives style clearness, charm, and distinction as nothing else can: and it is not a thing whose use can be taught by one man to another. Metaphors, like epithets, must be fitting, which means that they must fairly correspond to the thing signified: failing this, their inappropriateness will be conspicuous: the want of harmony between two things is emphasized by their being placed side by side. It is like having to ask ourselves what dress will suit an old man; certainly not the crimson cloak that suits a young man. And if you wish to pay a compliment, you must take your metaphor from something better in the same line; if to disparage, from something worse. To illustrate my meaning: since opposites are in the same class, you do what I have suggested if you say that a man who begs 'prays', and a man who prays 'begs'; for praying and begging are both varieties of asking. So Iphicrates called Callias a 'mendicant priest' instead of a 'torch-bearer', and Callias replied that Iphicrates must be uninitiated or he would have called him not a 'mendicant priest' but a 'torch-bearer'. Both are religious titles, but one is honourable and the other is not. Again, somebody calls actors 'hangers-on of Dionysus', but they call themselves 'artists': each of these terms is a metaphor, the one intended to throw dirt at the actor, the other to dignify him. And pirates now call themselves 'purveyors'. We can thus call a crime a mistake, or a mistake a crime. We can say that a thief 'took' a thing, or that he 'plundered' his victim. An expression like that of Euripides' Telephus,

King of the oar, on Mysia's coast he landed,[4]

is inappropriate; the word 'king' goes beyond the dignity of the subject, and so the art is *not* concealed. A metaphor may be amiss because the very syllables of the words conveying it fail to indicate sweetness of vocal utterance. Thus Dionysius the Brazen in his elegies calls poetry 'Calliope's screech'.[5] Poetry and screeching are both, to be sure, vocal utterances. But the metaphor is bad, because the sounds of 'screeching', unlike those of poetry, are discordant and unmeaning. Further, in using metaphors to give names to nameless things, we must draw them not from remote but from kindred and similar things, so that the kinship is clearly perceived as soon as the words are said. Thus in the celebrated riddle
1405b

I marked how a man glued bronze with
fire to another man's body,[6]

the process is nameless; but both it and gluing are a kind of application, and that is why the application of the cupping-glass is here called a 'gluing'. Good riddles do, in general, provide

[1] *Ibid.*, 21. [2] III. 3, 7.
[3] Cf. *Poetics*, 21, 22.

[4] Euripides, *Telephus*, Nauck, p. 583.
[5] Dionysius Chalcus, fr. 7, Bergk, vol. II, p. 264.
[6] Cleobulina, fr. 1, Bergk, vol. II, p. 62.

us with satisfactory metaphors: for metaphors imply riddles, and therefore a good riddle can furnish a good metaphor. Further, the materials of metaphors must be beautiful; and the beauty, like the ugliness, of all words may, as Licymnius says, lie in their sound or in their meaning. Further, there is a third consideration—one that upsets the fallacious argument of the sophist Bryson, that there is no such thing as foul language, because in whatever words you put a given thing your meaning is the same. This is untrue. One term may describe a thing more truly than another, may be more like it, and set it more intimately before our eyes. Besides, two different words will represent a thing in two different lights; so on this ground also one term must be held fairer or fouler than another. For both of two terms will indicate what *is* fair, or what *is* foul, but not simply their fairness or their foulness, or if so, at any rate not in an equal degree. The materials of metaphor must be beautiful to the ear, to the understanding, to the eye or some other physical sense. It is better, for instance, to say 'rosy-fingered morn',[1] than 'crimson-fingered' or, worse still, 'red-fingered morn'. The epithets that we apply, too, may have a bad and ugly aspect, as when Orestes is called a 'mother-slayer'; or a better one, as when he is called his 'father's avenger'.[2] Simonides, when the victor in the mule-race offered him a small fee, refused to write him an ode, because, he said, it was so unpleasant to write odes to half-asses: but on receiving an adequate fee, he wrote

Hail to you, daughters of storm-footed steeds,[3]

though of course they were daughters of asses too. The same effect is attained by the use of diminutives, which make a bad thing less bad and a good thing less good. Take, for instance, the banter of Aristophanes in the *Babylonians* where he uses 'goldlet' for 'gold', 'cloaklet' for 'cloak', 'scofflet' for 'scoff', and 'plaguelet'. But alike in using epithets and in using diminutives we must be wary and must observe the mean.

3

Bad taste in language may take any of four forms:—

(1) The misuse of compound words. Lycophron, for instance, talks of the '*many-visaged* heaven' above the '*giant-crested* earth', and again the '*strait-pathed* shore';[4] and Gor-
1406a gias of the '*pauper-poet* flatterer' and 'oath-breaking and *over-oath-keeping*'.[5] Alcidamas uses such expressions as 'the soul filling with rage and face becoming *flame-flushed*', and 'he thought their enthusiasm would be *issue-fraught*' and '*issue-fraught* he made the persuasion of his words', and '*sombre-hued* is the floor of the sea'.[6] The way all these words are compounded makes them, we feel, fit for verse only. This, then, is one form in which bad taste is shown.

(2) Another is the employment of strange words. For instance, Lycophron talks of 'the *prodigious* Xerxes' and '*spoliative* Sciron';[7] Alcidamas of 'a *toy* for poetry' and 'the *witlessness* of nature', and says '*whetted* with the *unmitigated* temper of his spirit'.[8]

(3) A third form is the use of long, unseasonable, or frequent epithets. It is appropriate enough for a poet to talk of 'white milk',[9] but in prose such epithets are sometimes lacking in appropriateness or, when spread too thickly, plainly reveal the author turning his prose into poetry. Of course we must use some epithets, since they lift our style above the usual level and give it an air of distinction. But we must aim at the due mean, or the result will be worse than if we took no trouble at all; we shall get something actually bad instead of something merely not good. That is why the epithets of Alcidamas seem so tasteless; he does not use them as the seasoning of the meat, but as the meat itself, so numerous and swollen and aggressive are they. For instance, he does not say 'sweat', but 'the *moist* sweat'; not 'to the Isthmian games', but 'to the *world-concourse* of the Isthmian games'; not 'laws', but 'the laws *that are monarchs of states*'; not 'at a run', but '*his heart impelling him to speed of foot*'; not 'a school of the Muses', but '*Nature's* school of the Muses had he inherited'; and so '*frowning* care of heart', and 'achiever' not of 'popularity' but of '*universal* popularity', and '*dispenser* of pleasure to his audience', and 'he concealed it' not 'with boughs' but 'with boughs *of the forest trees*', and 'he clothed' not 'his body' but '*his body's nakedness*', and 'his soul's desire was *counter-imitative*' (this is at one and the same time

[1] *Iliad*, I. 477, &c.
[2] Euripides, *Orestes*, 1587, 1588.
[3] Simonides, fr. 7, Bergk, vol. III, p. 390.
[4] Cf. Blass, *Att. Bereds.*, II, p. 364.
[5] Baiter-Sauppe, *op. cit.*, p. 131; Gorgias, fr. VII. 2.
[6] *Ibid.*, p. 156; Alcidamas.
[7] Blass, *loc. cit.*
[8] Baiter-Sauppe, *op. cit.*, p. 156; Alcidamas.
[9] e. g. *Iliad*, IV. 434.

a compound and an epithet, so that it seems a poet's effort), and 'so *extravagant* the excess of his wickedness'.[1] We thus see how the inappropriateness of such poetical language imports absurdity and tastelessness into speeches, as well as the obscurity that comes from all this verbosity—for when the sense is plain, you only obscure and spoil its clearness by piling up words.

The ordinary use of compound words is where there is no term for a thing and some compound can be easily formed, like 'pastime' (χρονοτριβεῖν); but if this is much done, the **1406b** prose character disappears entirely. We now see why the language of compounds is just the thing for writers of dithyrambs, who love sonorous noises; strange words for writers of epic poetry, which is a proud and stately affair; and metaphor for iambic verse, the metre which (as has been already[2] said) is widely used to-day.

(4) There remains the fourth region in which bad taste may be shown, metaphor. Metaphors like other things may be inappropriate. Some are so because they are ridiculous; they are indeed used by comic as well as tragic poets. Others are too grand and theatrical; and these, if they are far-fetched, may also be obscure. For instance, Gorgias talks of 'events that are green and full of sap', and says 'foul was the deed you sowed and evil the harvest you reaped'.[3] That is too much like poetry. Alcidamas, again, called philosophy 'a fortress that threatens the power of law', and the *Odyssey* 'a goodly looking-glass of human life',[4] and talked about 'offering no such toy to poetry': all these expressions fail, for the reasons given, to carry the hearer with them. The address of Gorgias to the swallow, when she had let her droppings fall on him as she flew overhead, is in the best tragic manner. He said, 'Nay, shame, O Philomela'. Considering her as a bird, you could not call her act shameful; considering her as a girl, you could; and so it was a good gibe to address her as what she was once and not as what she is.

4

The Simile also is a metaphor; the difference is but slight. When the poet says of Achilles that he

Leapt on the foe as a lion,[5]

this is a simile; when he says of him 'the lion leapt', it is a metaphor—here, since both are courageous, he has transferred to Achilles the name of 'lion'. Similes are useful in prose as well as in verse; but not often, since they are of the nature of poetry. They are to be employed just as metaphors are employed, since they are really the same thing except for the difference mentioned.

The following are examples of similes. Androtion said of Idrieus that he was like a terrier let off the chain, that flies at you and bites you—Idrieus too was savage now that he was let out of *his* chains. Theodamas compared Archidamus to an Euxenus who could not do geometry—a proportional simile, implying that Euxenus is an Archidamus who *can* do geometry. In Plato's *Republic* those who strip the dead are compared to curs which bite the stones thrown at them but do not touch the thrower,[6] and there is the simile about the Athenian people, who are compared to a ship's captain who is strong but a little deaf;[7] and the one about poets' verses, which are likened to persons who lack beauty but possess youthful freshness—when the freshness has faded the charm perishes, and so with verses **1407a** when broken up into prose.[8] Pericles compared the Samians to children who take their pap but go on crying; and the Boeotians to holm-oaks, because they were ruining one another by civil wars just as one oak causes another oak's fall. Demosthenes said that the Athenian people were like sea-sick men on board ship. Again, Demosthenes compared the political orators to nurses who swallow the bit of food themselves and then smear the children's lips with the spittle. Antisthenes compared the lean Cephisodotus to frankincense, because it was his consumption that gave one pleasure. All these ideas may be expressed either as similes or as metaphors; those which succeed as metaphors will obviously do well also as similes, and similes, with the explanation omitted, will appear as metaphors. But the proportional metaphor must always apply reciprocally to either of its co-ordinate terms. For instance, if a drinking-bowl is the shield of Dionysus, a shield may fittingly be called the drinking-bowl of Ares.

5

Such, then, are the ingredients of which speech is composed. The foundation of good style is

[1] Baiter-Sauppe, *op. cit.*, p. 156; Alcidamas.
[2] III. 1 (1404a 13).
[3] Baiter-Sauppe, *op. cit.*, p. 131; Gorgias.
[4] *Ibid.*, p. 156; Alcidamas.
[5] Cf. *Iliad*, XX. 164.
[6] Plato, *Republic*, V. 469.
[7] *Ibid.*, VI. 488.
[8] Cf. *Ibid.*, X. 601.

correctness of language, which falls under five heads. (1) First, the proper use of connecting words, and the arrangement of them in the natural sequence which some of them require. For instance, the connective *μέν* (e.g. *ἐγὼ μέν*) requires the correlative *δέ* (e.g. *ὁ δέ*). The answering word must be brought in before the first has been forgotten, and not be widely separated from it; nor, except in the few cases where this is appropriate, is another connective to be introduced before the one required. Consider the sentence, 'But I, as soon as he told me (for Cleon had come begging and praying), took them along and set out.' In this sentence many connecting words are inserted in front of the one required to complete the sense; and if there is a long interval before 'set out', the result is obscurity. One merit, then, of good style lies in the right use of connecting words. (2) The second lies in calling things by their own special names and not by vague general ones. (3) The third is to avoid ambiguities; unless, indeed, you definitely desire to be ambiguous, as those do who have nothing to say but are pretending to mean something. Such people are apt to put that sort of thing into verse. Empedocles, for instance, by his long circumlocutions imposes on his hearers; these are affected in the same way as most people are when they listen to diviners, whose ambiguous utterances are received with nods of acquiescence—

Croesus by crossing the Halys will ruin a mighty realm.[1]

1407b Diviners use these vague generalities about the matter in hand because their predictions are thus, as a rule, less likely to be falsified. We are more likely to be right, in the game of 'odd and even', if we simply guess 'even' or 'odd' than if we guess at the actual number; and the oracle-monger is more likely to be right if he simply says that a thing will happen than if he says *when* it will happen, and therefore he refuses to add a definite date. All these ambiguities have the same sort of effect, and are to be avoided unless we have some such object as that mentioned. (4) A fourth rule is to observe Protagoras' classification of nouns into male, female, and inanimate; for these distinctions also must be correctly given. 'Upon her arrival she said her say and departed (*ἡ δ' ἐλθοῦσα καὶ διαλεχθεῖσα ᾤχετο*).' (5) A fifth rule is to express plurality, fewness, and unity by the correct wording, e.g. 'Having come, they struck me (*οἱ δ' ἐλθόντες ἔτυπτόν με*).'

[1] Cp. Herodotus, I. 53, 91.

It is a general rule that a written composition should be easy to read and therefore easy to deliver. This cannot be so where there are many connecting words or clauses, or where punctuation is hard, as in the writings of Heracleitus. To punctuate Heracleitus is no easy task, because we often cannot tell whether a particular word belongs to what precedes or what follows it. Thus, at the outset of his treatise he says, 'Though this truth is always men understand it not',[2] where it is not clear with which of the two clauses the word 'always' should be joined by the punctuation. Further, the following fact leads to solecism, viz. that the sentence does not work out properly if you annex to two terms a third which does not suit them both. Thus either 'sound' or 'colour' will fail to work out properly with some verbs: 'perceive' will apply to both, 'see' will not. Obscurity is also caused if, when you intend to insert a number of details, you do not first make your meaning clear; for instance, if you say, 'I meant, after telling him this, that and the other thing, to set out', rather than something of this kind 'I meant to set out after telling him; then this, that, and the other thing occurred.'

6

The following suggestions will help to give your language impressiveness. (1) Describe a thing instead of naming it: do not say 'circle', but 'that surface which extends equally from the middle every way'. To achieve conciseness, do the opposite—put the name instead of the description. When mentioning anything ugly or unseemly, use its name if it is the description that is ugly, and describe it if it is the name that is ugly. (2) Represent things with the help of metaphors and epithets, being careful to avoid poetical effects. (3) Use plural for singular, as in poetry, where one finds

Unto havens Achaean,[3]

though only one haven is meant,
and

Here are my letter's many-leavèd folds.[4]

(4) Do not bracket two words under one article, but put one article with each; e.g. *τῆς γυναικὸς τῆς ἡμετέρας*.[5] The reverse to secure

[2] Heracleitus, fr. 1, Diels. [3] Fr. Adesp. 83, Nauck.
[4] Euripides, *Iphegenia in Tauris*, 727.
[5] 'that wife of ours.'

conciseness; e.g. τῆς ἡμετέρας γυναικός.[1] (5) Use plenty of connecting words; conversely, to secure conciseness, dispense with connectives, while still preserving connexion; e.g. 'having **1408a** gone and spoken', and 'having gone, I spoke', respectively. (6) And the practice of Antimachus, too, is useful—to describe a thing by mentioning attributes it does not possess; as he does in talking of Teumessus—

There is a little wind-swept knoll . . .[2]

A subject can be developed indefinitely along these lines. You may apply this method of treatment by negation either to good or to bad qualities, according to which your subject requires. It is from this source that the poets draw expressions such as the 'stringless' or 'lyreless' melody, thus forming epithets out of negations. This device is popular in proportional metaphors, as when the trumpet's note is called 'a lyreless melody'.

7

Your language will be *appropriate* if it expresses emotion and character, and if it corresponds to its subject. 'Correspondence to subject' means that we must neither speak casually about weighty matters, nor solemnly about trivial ones; nor must we add ornamental epithets to commonplace nouns, or the effect will be comic, as in the works of Cleophon, who can use phrases as absurd as 'O queenly fig-tree'. To express emotion, you will employ the language of anger in speaking of outrage; the language of disgust and discreet reluctance to utter a word when speaking of impiety or foulness; the language of exultation for a tale of glory, and that of humiliation for a tale of pity; and so in all other cases.

This aptness of language is one thing that makes people believe in the truth of your story: their minds draw the false conclusion that you are to be trusted from the fact that others behave as you do when things are as you describe them; and therefore they take your story to be true, whether it is so or not. Besides, an emotional speaker always makes his audience feel with him, even when there is nothing in his arguments; which is why many speakers try to overwhelm their audience by mere noise.

Furthermore, this way of proving your story by displaying these signs of its genuineness expresses your personal character. Each class of men, each type of disposition, will have its own appropriate way of letting the truth appear. Under 'class' I include differences of age, as boy, man, or old man; of sex, as man or woman; of nationality, as Spartan or Thessalian. By 'dispositions' I here mean those dispositions only which determine the character of a man's life, for it is not every disposition that does this. If, then, a speaker uses the very words which are in keeping with a particular disposition, he will reproduce the corresponding character; for a rustic and an educated man will not say the same things nor speak in the same way. Again, some impression is made upon an audience by a device which speech-writers employ to nauseous excess, when they say 'Who does not know this?' or 'It is known to everybody.' The hearer is ashamed of his ignorance, and agrees with the speaker, so as to have a share of the knowledge that everybody else possesses.

1408b All the variations of oratorical style are capable of being used in season or out of season. The best way to counteract any exaggeration is the well-worn device by which the speaker puts in some criticism of himself; for then people feel it must be all right for him to talk thus, since he certainly knows what he is doing. Further, it is better not to have everything always just corresponding to everything else—your hearers will see through you less easily thus. I mean for instance, if your words are harsh, you should not extend this harshness to your voice and your countenance and have everything else in keeping. If you do, the artificial character of each detail becomes apparent; whereas if you adopt one device and not another, you are using art all the same and yet nobody notices it. (To be sure, if mild sentiments are expressed in harsh tones and harsh sentiments in mild tones, you become comparatively unconvincing.) Compound words, fairly plentiful epithets, and strange words best suit an emotional speech. We forgive an angry man for talking about a wrong as 'heaven-high' or 'colossal'; and we excuse such language when the speaker has his hearers already in his hands and has stirred them deeply either by praise or blame or anger or affection, as Isocrates, for instance, does at the end of his *Panegyric*, with his 'name and fame' and 'in that they brooked'. Men do speak in this strain when they are deeply stirred, and so, once the audience is in a like state of feeling, approval of course follows. This is why such language is fitting in poetry, which is an inspired thing. This language, then, should be

[1] 'our wife.' [2] Antimachus, *Thebais*, fr. 2.

used either under stress of emotion, or ironically, after the manner of Gorgias and of the passages in the *Phaedrus*.[1]

8

The form of a prose composition should be neither metrical nor destitute of rhythm. The metrical form destroys the hearer's trust by its artificial appearance, and at the same time it diverts his attention, making him watch for metrical recurrences, just as children catch up the herald's question, 'Whom does the freedman choose as his advocate?', with the answer 'Cleon!' On the other hand, unrhythmical language is too unlimited; we do not want the limitations of metre, but some limitation we must have, or the effect will be vague and unsatisfactory. Now it is number that limits all things; and it is the numerical limitation of the forms of a composition that constitutes rhythm, of which metres are definite sections. Prose, then, is to be rhythmical, but not metrical, or it will become not prose but verse. It should not even have too precise a prose rhythm, and therefore should only be rhythmical to a certain extent.

Of the various rhythms, the heroic has dignity, but lacks the tones of the spoken language. The iambic is the very language of ordinary people, so that in common talk iambic lines occur oftener than any others: but in a speech we need dignity and the power of taking the hearer out of his ordinary self. The trochee is too much akin to wild dancing: we can see this in tetrameter verse, which is one
1409a of the trochaic rhythms.

There remains the paean, which speakers began to use in the time of Thrasymachus, though they had then no name to give it. The paean is a third class of rhythm, closely akin to both the two already mentioned; it has in it the ratio of three to two, whereas the other two kinds have the ratio of one to one, and two to one respectively. Between the two last ratios comes the ratio of one-and-a-half to one, which is that of the paean.

Now the other two kinds of rhythm must be rejected in writing prose, partly for the reasons given, and partly because they are too metrical; and the paean must be adopted, since from this alone of the rhythms mentioned no definite metre arises, and therefore it is the least obtrusive of them. At present the same form of paean is employed at the beginning as at the end of sentences, whereas the end should differ from the beginning. There are two opposite kinds of paean, one of which is suitable to the beginning of a sentence, where it is indeed actually used; this is the kind that begins with a long syllable and ends with three short ones, as

Δᾱλογενὲς | εἴτε Λυκί|αν,[2]

and

Χρυσεοκόμ|α Ἕκατε | παῖ Διός.[3]

The other paean begins, conversely, with three short syllables and ends with a long one, as

μετὰ δὲ γᾶν | ὕδατά τ᾽ ὠκ|εανὸν ἠ|φάνισε νύξ.[4]

This kind of paean makes a real close: a short syllable can give no effect of finality, and therefore makes the rhythm appear truncated. A sentence should break off with the long syllable: the fact that it is over should be indicated not by the scribe, or by his period-mark in the margin, but by the rhythm itself.

We have now seen that our language must be rhythmical and not destitute of rhythm, and what rhythms, in what particular shape, make it so.

9

The language of prose must be either free-running, with its parts united by nothing except the connecting words, like the preludes in dithyrambs; or compact and antithetical, like the strophes of the old poets. The free-running style is the ancient one, e.g. 'Herein is set forth the inquiry of Herodotus the Thurian.'[5] Every one used this method formerly; not many do so now. By 'free-running' style I mean the kind that has no natural stopping-places, and comes to a stop only because there is no more to say of that subject. This style is unsatisfying just because it goes on indefinitely—one always likes to sight a stopping-place in front of one: it is only at the goal that men in a race faint and collapse; while they see the end of the course before them, they can keep on going. Such, then, is the free-running kind of style; the compact is that which is in periods. By a period I mean a portion of speech that has in itself a beginning and an end, being at the same time not

[1] Cf. Plato, *Phaedrus*, 238, 241.

[2] 'O Delos-born, or if perchance Lycia (thou callest thy birthplace).'

[3] 'Golden-haired Archer, Son of Zeus.'

[4] 'After earth and its waters, night shrouded the Ocean from sight.' These three lines are from the *Paeans of* Simonides in Bergk, III, p. 398; Simonides, fr. 26b.

[5] Herodotus, I. 1, beginning.

too big to be taken in at a glance. Language of
1409b this kind is satisfying and easy to follow. It is satisfying, because it is just the reverse of indefinite; and moreover, the hearer always feels that he is grasping something and has reached some definite conclusion; whereas it is unsatisfactory to see nothing in front of you and get nowhere. It is easy to follow, because it can easily be remembered; and this because language when in periodic form can be numbered, and number is the easiest of all things to remember. That is why verse, which is measured, is always more easily remembered than prose, which is not: the measures of verse can be numbered. The period must, further, not be completed until the sense is complete: it must not be capable of breaking off abruptly, as may happen with the following iambic lines of Sophocles—

Calydon's soil is this; of Pelops' land
⟨The smiling plains face us across the strait.⟩[1]

By a wrong division of the words the hearer may take the meaning to be the reverse of what it is: for instance, in the passage quoted, one might imagine that Calydon is in the Peloponnesus.

A Period may be either divided into several members or simple. The period of several members is a portion of speech (1) complete in itself, (2) divided into parts, and (3) easily delivered at a single breath—as a whole, that is; not by fresh breath being taken at the division. A member is one of the two parts of such a period. By a 'simple' period, I mean that which has only one member. The members, and the whole periods, should be neither curt nor long. A member which is too short often makes the listener stumble; he is still expecting the rhythm to go on to the limit his mind has fixed for it; and if meanwhile he is pulled back by the speaker's stopping, the shock is bound to make him, so to speak, stumble. If, on the other hand, you go on too long, you make him feel left behind, just as people who when walking pass beyond the boundary before turning back leave their companions behind. So too if a period is too long you turn it into a speech, or something like a dithyrambic prelude. The result is much like the preludes that Democritus of Chios jeered at Melanippides for writing instead of antistrophic stanzas—

He that sets traps for another man's feet
Is like to fall into them first;
And long-winded preludes do harm to us all,
But the preluder catches it worst.[2]

Which applies likewise to long-membered orators. Periods whose members are altogether too short are not periods at all; and the result is to bring the hearer down with a crash.

The periodic style which is divided into members is of two kinds. It is either simply divided, as in 'I have often wondered at the conveners of national gatherings and the founders of athletic contests';[3] or it is antithetical, where, in each of the two members, one of one pair of opposites is put along with one of another pair, or the same word is used to bracket
1410a two opposites, as 'They aided both parties—not only those who stayed behind but those who accompanied them: for the latter they acquired new territory larger than that at home, and to the former they left territory at home that was large enough'.[4] Here the contrasted words are 'staying behind' and 'accompanying', 'enough' and 'larger'. So in the example, 'Both to those who want to get property and to those who desire to enjoy it',[5] where 'enjoyment' is contrasted with 'getting'. Again, 'it often happens in such enterprises that the wise men fail and the fools succeed';[6] 'they were awarded the prize of valour immediately, and won the command of the sea not long afterwards';[7] 'to sail through the mainland and march through the sea, by bridging the Hellespont and cutting through Athos';[8] 'nature gave them their country and law took it away again';[9] 'some of them perished in misery, others were saved in disgrace';[10] 'Athenian citizens keep foreigners in their houses as servants, while the city of Athens allows her allies by thousands to live as the foreigner's slaves';[11] and 'to possess in life or to bequeath at death'.[12] There is also what some one said about Peitholaus and Lycophron in a law-court, 'These men used to sell you when they were at home, and now they have come to you here and bought you'.[13] All these passages have the structure described above. Such a form of speech is satisfying, because the significance of contrasted ideas is easily felt, especially when they are thus put side by side, and also because it has the effect of a logical argument; it is by putting two op-

[1] Euripides, *Meleager*, Nauck, p. 525.

[2] Democritus, Χῖος μουσικός; Laertius, IX. 49.

[3] Isocrates, *Paneg.*, § 1.

[4] *Ibid.*, §§ 35, 36.

[5] *Ibid.*, § 41. [6] *Ibid.*, § 48. [7] *Ibid.*, § 72.

[8] *Ibid.*, § 89. [9] *Ibid.*, § 105. [10] *Ibid.*, § 149.

[11] *Ibid.*, § 181. [12] *Ibid.*, § 186.

[13] Cf. Baiter-Sauppe, *op. cit.*, p. 346.

posing conclusions side by side that you prove one of them false.

Such, then, is the nature of *antithesis*. *Parisosis* is making the two members of a period equal in length. *Paromoeosis* is making the extreme words of both members like each other. This must happen either at the beginning or at the end of each member. If at the beginning, the resemblance must always be between whole words; at the end, between final syllables or inflexions of the same word or the same word repeated. Thus, at the beginning

ἀγρὸν γὰρ ἔλαβεν ἀργὸν παρ' αὐτοῦ[1]

and

δωρητοί τ' ἐπέλοντο παράρρητοί τ' ἐπέεσσιν.[2]

At the end

οὐκ ᾠήθησαν αὐτὸν παιδίον τετοκέναι,
ἀλλ' αὐτοῦ αἴτιον γεγονέναι,[3]

and

ἐν πλείσταις δὲ φροντίσι καὶ ἐν ἐλαχίσταις ἐλπίσιν.[4]

An example of inflexions of the same word is

ἄξιος δὲ σταθῆναι χαλκοῦς, οὐκ ἄξιος ὢν χαλκοῦ;[5]

Of the same word repeated,

σὺ δ' αὐτὸν καὶ ζῶντα ἔλεγες κακῶς καὶ νῦν γράφεις κακῶς.[6]

Of one syllable,

τί δ' ἂν ἔπαθες δεινόν, εἰ ἄνδρ' εἶδες ἀργόν;[7]

It is possible for the same sentence to have all
1410b these features together—*antithesis, parison,* and *homoeoteleuton*. (The possible beginnings of periods have been pretty fully enumerated in the *Theodectea*.) There are also spurious antitheses, like that of Epicharmus—

There one time I as their guest did stay,
And they were my hosts on another day.[8]

10

We may now consider the above points settled, and pass on to say something about the way to devise lively and taking sayings. Their actual invention can only come through natural talent or long practice; but this treatise may indicate the way it is done. We may deal with them by enumerating the different kinds of them. We will begin by remarking that we all naturally find it agreeable to get hold of new ideas easily: words express ideas, and therefore those words are the most agreeable that enable us to get hold of new ideas. Now strange words simply puzzle us; ordinary words convey only what we know already; it is from metaphor that we can best get hold of something fresh. When the poet calls old age 'a withered stalk',[9] he conveys a new idea, a new fact, to us by means of the general notion of 'lost bloom', which is common to both things. The similes of the poets do the same, and therefore, if they are good similes, give an effect of brilliance. The simile, as has been said before,[10] is a metaphor, differing from it only in the way it is put; and just because it is longer it is less attractive. Besides, it does not say outright that 'this' *is* 'that', and therefore the hearer is less interested in the idea. We see, then, that both speech and reasoning are lively in proportion as they make us seize a new idea promptly. For this reason people are not much taken either by obvious arguments (using the word 'obvious' to mean what is plain to everybody and needs no investigation), nor by those which puzzle us when we hear them stated, but only by those which convey their information to us as soon as we hear them, provided we had not the information already; or which the mind only just fails to keep up with. These two kinds do convey to us a sort of information: but the obvious and the obscure kinds convey nothing, either at once or later on. It is these qualities, then, that, so far as the meaning of what is said is concerned, make an argument acceptable. So far as the style is concerned, it is the antithetical form that appeals to us, e.g. 'judging that the peace common to all the rest was a war upon their own private interests',[11] where there is an antithesis

[1] Aristophanes, fr. 649: "A field he took from him, a fallow field."

[2] *Iliad*, IX. 526: "Yet might they by presents be won, and by pleadings be pacified."

[3] "They didn't imagine that he *had borne* the child, but that he was the cause of its *having been borne*." Anonymous.

[4] "In the midst of plenteous cares and exiguous hopes." Anonymous.

[5] "Is he worthy to have a copper statue, when he is not worth a copper?" Anonymous.

[6] "When he was alive you spoke evil of him, and now you write evil of him." Anonymous.

[7] "Would it have been very shocking to you if you had seen a man idling?" Anonymous.

[8] Epicharmus, fr. 49, in Lorenz's *Leben und Schriften des Koers Epicharmos*, p. 273.

[9] *Odyssey*, XIV. 213.

[10] III, 4, beginning.

[11] Isocrates, *Philippus*, 73.

between war and peace. It is also good to use metaphorical words; but the metaphors must not be far-fetched, or they will be difficult to grasp, nor obvious, or they will have no effect. The words, too, ought to set the scene before our eyes; for events ought to be seen in progress rather than in prospect. So we must aim at these three points: Antithesis, Metaphor, and Actuality.

1411a Of the four kinds of Metaphor the most taking is the proportional kind. Thus Pericles, for instance, said that the vanishing from their country of the young men who had fallen in the war was 'as if the spring were taken out of the year'. Leptines, speaking of the Lacedaemonians, said that he would not have the Athenians let Greece 'lose one of her two eyes'.[1] When Chares was pressing for leave to be examined upon his share in the Olynthiac war, Cephisodotus was indignant, saying that he wanted his examination to take place 'while he had his fingers upon the people's throat'. The same speaker once urged the Athenians to march to Euboea, 'with Miltiades' decree as their rations'.[2] Iphicrates, indignant at the truce made by the Athenians with Epidaurus and the neighbouring sea-board, said that they had stripped themselves of their travelling-money for the journey of war. Peitholaus called the state-galley 'the people's big stick', and Sestos 'the corn-bin of the Peiraeus'.[3] Pericles bade his countrymen remove Aegina, 'that eyesore of the Peiraeus.' And Moerocles said he was no more a rascal than was a certain respectable citizen he named, 'whose rascality was worth over thirty per cent per annum to him, instead of a mere ten like his own'.[4] There is also the iambic line of Anaxandrides about the way his daughters put off marrying—

My daughters' marriage-bonds are overdue.[5]

Polyeuctus said of a paralytic man named Speusippus that he could not keep quiet, 'though fortune had fastened him in the pillory of disease'. Cephisodotus called warships 'painted millstones'.[6] Diogenes the Dog called taverns 'the mess-rooms of Attica'. Aesion said that the Athenians had 'emptied' their town into Sicily: this is a graphic metaphor.[7] 'Till all Hellas shouted aloud' may be regarded as a metaphor, and a graphic one again. Cephisodotus bade the Athenians take care not to hold too many 'parades'.[8] Isocrates used the same word of those who 'parade' at the national festivals.[9] Another example occurs in the Funeral Speech:[10] 'It is fitting that Greece should cut off her hair beside the tomb of those who fell at Salamis, since her freedom and their valour are buried in the same grave.' Even if the speaker here had only said that it was right to weep when valour was being buried in their grave, it would have been a metaphor, and a graphic one; but the coupling of 'their **1411b** valour' and 'her freedom' presents a kind of antithesis as well. 'The course of my words', said Iphicrates, 'lies straight through the middle of Chares' deeds':[11] this is a proportional metaphor, and the phrase 'straight through the middle' makes it graphic. The expression 'to call in one danger to rescue us from another' is a graphic metaphor. Lycoleon said, defending Chabrias, 'They did not respect even that bronze statue of his that intercedes for him yonder'.[12] This was a metaphor for the moment, though it would not always apply; a vivid metaphor, however; Chabrias is in danger, and his statue intercedes for him —that lifeless yet living thing which records his services to his country. 'Practising in every way littleness of mind'[13] is metaphorical, for practising a quality implies increasing it. So is 'God kindled our reason to be a lamp within our souls',[14] for both reason and light reveal things. So is 'we are not putting an end to our wars, but only postponing them',[15] for both literal postponement and the making of such a peace as this apply to future action. So is such a saying as 'This treaty is a far nobler trophy than those we set up on fields of battle; *they* celebrate small gains and single successes; *it* celebrates our triumph in the war as a whole';[16] for both trophy and treaty are signs of victory. So is 'A country pays a heavy reckoning in being condemned by the judgement of mankind',[17] for a reckoning is damage deservedly incurred.

11

It has already been mentioned that liveliness is got by using the proportional type of metaphor

[1] Baiter-Sauppe, *op. cit.*, p. 250; Leptines.
[2] Baiter-Sauppe, p. 220; Cephisodotus.
[3] *Ibid.*, p. 318; Peitholaus.
[4] *Ibid.*, p. 275 (Moerocles).
[5] Anaxandrides; Kock, *Com. Att. Fragm.*, II, p. 162.
[6] Baiter-Sauppe, p. 220; Cephisodotus.
[7] *Ibid.*, p. 318 (Aesion).
[8] *Ibid.*, p. 220; Cephisodotus.
[9] Isocrates, *Philippus*, 12.
[10] *Epitaphius* (by Lysias?), 60.
[11] Baiter-Sauppe, *op. cit.*, p. 191; *under* Lysias.
[12] *Ibid.*, p. 249; Lycoleon.
[13] Isocrates, *Paneg.*, 151.
[14] Anonymous.
[15] Isocrates, *Paneg.*, 172.
[16] *Ibid.*, 180.
[17] Anonymous; cf. Isocrates, *De Pace*, 120.

and by being graphic (i.e. making your hearers *see* things). We have still to explain what we mean by their 'seeing things', and what must be done to effect this. By 'making them see things' I mean using expressions that represent things as in a state of activity. Thus, to say that a good man is 'four-square'[1] is certainly a metaphor; both the good man and the square are perfect; but the metaphor does not suggest activity. On the other hand, in the expression 'with his vigour in full bloom'[2] there is a notion of activity; and so in 'But you must roam as free as a sacred victim';[3] and in

Thereat up sprang the Hellenes to their feet,[4]

where 'up sprang' gives us activity as well as metaphor, for it at once suggests swiftness. So with Homer's common practice of giving metaphorical life to lifeless things: all such passages are distinguished by the effect of activity they convey. Thus,

Downward anon to the valley rebounded the boulder remorseless;[5]

and

The ⟨bitter⟩ arrow flew;[6]

and

Flying on eagerly;[7]

and

1412a *Stuck in the earth, still* panting *to feed on the flesh of the heroes;*[8]

and

And the point of the spear in its fury *drove full through his breastbone.*[9]

In all these examples the things have the effect of being active because they are made into living beings; shameless behaviour and fury and so on are all forms of activity. And the poet has attached these ideas to the things by means of proportional metaphors: as the stone is to Sisyphus, so is the shameless man to his victim. In his famous similes, too, he treats inanimate things in the same way:

Curving and crested with white, host following host without ceasing.[10]

Here he represents everything as moving and living; and activity is movement.

Metaphors must be drawn, as has been said already,[11] from things that are related to the original thing, and yet not obviously so related—just as in philosophy also an acute mind will perceive resemblances even in things far apart. Thus Archytas said that an arbitrator and an altar were the same, since the injured fly to both for refuge. Or you might say that an anchor and an overhead hook were the same, since both are in a way the same, only the one secures things from below and the other from above. And to speak of states as 'levelled'[12] is to identify two widely different things, the equality of a physical surface and the equality of political powers.

Liveliness is specially conveyed by metaphor, and by the further power of surprising the hearer; because the hearer expected something different, his acquisition of the new idea impresses him all the more. His mind seems to say, 'Yes, to be sure; I never thought of that'. The liveliness of epigrammatic remarks is due to the meaning not being just what the words say: as in the saying of Stesichorus that 'the cicalas will chirp to themselves on the ground'.[13] Well-constructed riddles are attractive for the same reason; a new idea is conveyed, and there is metaphorical expression. So with the 'novelties' of Theodorus. In these the thought is startling, and, as Theodorus puts it, does not fit in with the ideas you already have. They are like the burlesque words that one finds in the comic writers. The effect is produced even by jokes depending upon changes of the letters of a word; this too is a surprise. You find this in verse as well as in prose. The word which comes is not what the hearer imagined: thus

Onward he came, and his feet were shod with his—chilblains,[14]

where one imagined the word would be 'sandals'. But the point should be clear the moment the words are uttered. Jokes made by altering the letters of a word consist in meaning, not just what you say, but something that gives a twist to the word used; e.g. the remark of Theodorus about Nicon the harpist *Θρᾷττ' εἶ σύ* ('you Thracian slavey'), where he pretends to mean *θράττεις σύ* ('you harp-player'), and surprises us when we find he
1412b means something else. So you enjoy the point when you see it, though the remark will

[1] Simonides, fr. 5, Bergk.
[2] Isocrates, *Philippus*, 10.
[3] *Ibid.*, 127.
[4] Euripides, *Iphigenia in Aulis*, 80.
[5] *Odyssey*, XI. 598.
[6] *Iliad*, XIII. 587.
[7] *Ibid.*, IV. 126.
[8] *Ibid.*, XI. 574.
[9] *Ibid.*, XV. 542.
[10] *Ibid.*, XIII. 799.
[11] III. 10(1410b 32).
[12] Cf. Isocrates, *Philippus*, 40.
[13] Cf. II. 21, above.
[14] Anonymous.

fall flat unless you are aware that Nicon is Thracian. Or again: *βούλει αὐτὸν πέρσαι*.[1] In both these cases the saying must fit the facts. This is also true of such lively remarks as the one to the effect that to the Athenians their empire (ἀρχή) of the sea was not the beginning (ἀρχή) of their troubles, since they gained by it. Or the opposite one of Isocrates, that their empire (ἀρχή) *was* the beginning (ἀρχή) of their troubles. Either way, the speaker says something unexpected, the soundness of which is thereupon recognized. There would be nothing clever is saying 'empire is empire'. Isocrates means more than that, and uses the word with a new meaning. So too with the former saying, which denies that ἀρχή in one sense was ἀρχή in another sense. In all these jokes, whether a word is used in a second sense or metaphorically, the joke is good if it fits the facts. For instance, *Ἀνάσχετος* (proper name) *οὐκ ἀνασχετός*:[2] where you say that what is so-and-so in one sense is not so-and-so in another; well, if the man is unpleasant, the joke fits the facts. Again, take—

Thou must not be a stranger stranger than Thou should'st.[3]

Do not the words 'thou must not be', &c., amount to saying that the stranger must not always be strange? Here again is the use of one word in different senses. Of the same kind also is the much-praised verse of Anaxandrides:

Death is most fit before you do
Deeds that would make death fit for you.[4]

This amounts to saying 'it is a fit thing to die when you are not fit to die', or 'it is a fit thing to die when death is not fit for you', i.e. when death is not the fit return for what you are doing. The type of language employed is the same in all these examples; but the more briefly and antithetically such sayings can be expressed, the more taking they are, for antithesis impresses the new idea more firmly and brevity more quickly. They should always have either some personal application or some merit of expression, if they are to be true without being commonplace—two requirements not always satisfied simultaneously. Thus 'a man should die having done no wrong' is true but dull: 'the right man should marry the right woman'[5] is also true but dull. No, there must be both good qualities together, as in 'it is fitting to die when you are not fit for death'. The more a saying has these qualities, the livelier it appears: if, for instance, its wording is metaphorical, metaphorical in the right way, antithetical, and balanced, and at the same time it gives an idea of activity.

Successful similes also, as has been said above,[6] are in a sense metaphors, since they always involve two relations like the proportional metaphor. Thus: a shield, we say, is **1413a** the 'drinking-bowl of Ares',[7] and a bow is the "chordless lyre'.[8] This way of putting a metaphor is not 'simple', as it would be if we called the bow a lyre or the shield a drinking-bowl. There are 'simple' similes also: we may say that a flute-player is like a monkey, or that a short-sighted man's eyes are like a lamp-flame with water dropping on it, since both eyes and flame keep winking. A simile succeeds best when it is a converted metaphor, for it is possible to say that a shield *is like* the drinking-bowl of Ares, or that a ruin *is like* a house in rags, and to say that Niceratus *is like* a Philoctetes stung by Pratys—the simile made by Thrasymachus when he saw Niceratus, who had been beaten by Pratys in a recitation competition, still going about unkempt and unwashed. It is in these respects that poets fail worst when they fail, and succeed best when they succeed, i.e. when they give the resemblance pat, as in

Those legs of his curl just like parsley leaves;[9]

and

Just like Philammon struggling with his punchball.[10]

These are all similes; and that similes are metaphors has been stated often already.[11]

Proverbs, again, are metaphors from one species to another.[12] Suppose, for instance, a man to start some undertaking in hope of gain and then to lose by it later on, 'Here we have once more the man of Carpathus and his hare', says he. For both alike went through the said experience.

It has now been explained fairly completely how liveliness is secured and why it has the ef-

[1] "You wish [or, do you wish] to *perse*cute him."
[2] "Baring is past bearing."
[3] Kock, *Com., Fragm.*, III. 209.
[4] Anaxandrides, *ibid.*, II, p. 161.

[5] *Ibid.*, III, p. 447; fr. adesp. 206.
[6] III. 4 and 10.
[7] Timotheus, fr. 16, Bergk. Cf. III. 4, end.
[8] Bergk[4], fr. adesp. 127, vol. III. p. 728.
[9] Kock, *Com. Att. Fragm.*, III. fr. adesp. 207, p. 448.
[10] *Ibid*, III, fr. 208, p. 448.
[11] III. 4, 10, 11.
[12] Cf. *Poetics*, 21.

fect it has. Successful hyperboles are also metaphors, e.g. the one about the man with a black eye, 'you would have thought he was a basket of mulberries'; here the 'black eye' is compared to a mulberry because of its colour, the exaggeration lying in the quantity of mulberries suggested. The phrase '*like* so-and-so' may introduce a hyperbole under the form of a simile. Thus

Just like *Philammon struggling with his punch-ball*

is equivalent to '*you would have thought he was* Philammon struggling with his punch-ball'; and

Those legs of his curl just like *parsley leaves*

is equivalent to 'his legs are so curly that *you would have thought* they were not legs but parsley leaves'. Hyperboles are for young men to use; they show vehemence of character; and this is why angry people use them more than other people.

Not though he gave me as much as the dust or the sands of the sea . . .[1]
But her, the daughter of Atreus' son, I never will marry,
Nay, not though she were fairer than Aphrodite the Golden,
Defter of hand than Athene . . .[2]

1413b (The Attic orators are particularly fond of this method of speech.) Consequently it does not suit an elderly speaker.

12

It should be observed that each kind of rhetoric has its own appropriate style. The style of written prose is not that of spoken oratory, nor are those of political and forensic speaking the same. Both written and spoken have to be known. To know the latter is to know how to speak good Greek. To know the former means that you are not obliged, as otherwise you are, to hold your tongue when you wish to communicate something to the general public.

The written style is the more finished: the spoken better admits of dramatic delivery—alike the kind of oratory that reflects character and the kind that reflects emotion. Hence actors look out for plays written in the latter style, and poets for actors competent to act in such plays. Yet poets whose plays are meant to be read *are* read and circulated: Chaeremon, for instance, who is as finished as a professional speech-writer; and Licymnius among the dithyrambic poets. Compared with those of others, the speeches of professional writers sound thin in actual contests. Those of the orators, on the other hand, are good to hear spoken, but look amateurish enough when they pass into the hands of a reader. This is just because they are so well suited for an actual tussle, and therefore contain many dramatic touches, which, being robbed of all dramatic rendering, fail to do their own proper work, and consequently look silly. Thus strings of unconnected words, and constant repetitions of words and phrases, are very properly condemned in written speeches: but not in spoken speeches—speakers use them freely, for they have a dramatic effect. In this repetition there must be variety of tone, paving the way, as it were, to dramatic effect; e.g. 'This is the villain among you who deceived you, who cheated you, who meant to betray you completely'. This is the sort of thing that Philemon the actor used to do in the *Old Men's Madness* of Anaxandrides, whenever he spoke the words 'Rhadamanthus and Palamedes',[3] and also in the prologue to the *Saints* whenever he pronounced the pronoun 'I'.[4] If one does not deliver such things cleverly, it becomes a case of 'the man who swallowed a poker'. So too with strings of unconnected words, e.g. 'I came to him; I met him; I besought him'. Such passages must be *acted,* not delivered with the same quality and pitch of voice, as though they had only one idea in them. They have the further peculiarity of suggesting that a number of separate statements have been made in the time usually occupied by one. Just as the use of conjunctions makes many statements into a single one, so the omission of conjunctions acts in the reverse way and makes a single one into many. It thus makes everything more important: e.g. 'I came to him; I talked **1414a** to him; I entreated him'—what a lot of facts! the hearer thinks—'he paid no attention to anything I said'. This is the effect which Homer seeks when he writes,

Nireus likewise from Syme ⟨*three well-fashioned ships did bring*⟩,
Nireus, the son of Aglaia ⟨*and Charopus, bright-faced king*⟩,
Nireus, the comeliest man ⟨*of all that to Ilium's strand*⟩.[5]

[1] *Iliad,* IX. 385.
[2] *Ibid.,* IX. 388-90.
[3] Kock, *Com. Att. Fragm.,* II, p. 139; Anaxandrides, Γεροντομανία, fr. 10.
[4] *Ibid.,* II, p. 140; Anaxandrides, Εὐσεβεῖς.
[5] *Iliad,* II. 671-3.

If many things are said about a man, his name must be mentioned many times; and therefore people think that, if his name is mentioned many times, many things have been said about him. So that Homer, by means of this illusion, has made a great deal of Nireus, though he has mentioned him only in this one passage, and has preserved his memory, though he nowhere says a word about him afterwards.

Now the style of oratory addressed to public assemblies is really just like scene-painting. The bigger the throng, the more distant is the point of view: so that, in the one and the other, high finish in detail is superfluous and seems better away. The forensic style is more highly finished; still more so is the style of language addressed to a single judge, with whom there is very little room for rhetorical artifices, since he can take the whole thing in better, and judge of what is to the point and what is not; the struggle is less intense and so the judgement is undisturbed. This is why the same speakers do not distinguish themselves in all these branches at once; high finish is wanted least where dramatic delivery is wanted most, and here the speaker must have a good voice, and above all, a strong one. It is ceremonial oratory that is most literary, for it is meant to be read; and next to it forensic oratory.

To analyse style still further, and add that it must be agreeable or magnificent, is useless; for why should it have these traits any more than 'restraint', 'liberality', or any other moral excellence? Obviously agreeableness will be produced by the qualities already mentioned, if our definition of excellence of style has been correct. For what other reason should style be 'clear', and 'not mean' but 'appropriate'? If it is prolix, it is not clear; nor yet if it is curt. Plainly the middle way suits best. Again, style will be made agreeable by the elements mentioned, namely by a good blending of ordinary and unusual words, by the rhythm, and by the persuasiveness that springs from appropriateness.

This concludes our discussion of style, both in its general aspects and in its special applications to the various branches of rhetoric. We have now to deal with Arrangement.

13

A speech has two parts. You must state your case, and you must prove it. You cannot either state your case and omit to prove it, or prove it without having first stated it; since any proof must be a proof of something, and the only use of a preliminary statement is the proof that follows it. Of these two parts the first part is called the Statement of the case, the second part the Argument, just as we distinguish between Enunciation and Demonstration. The current division is absurd. For 'narration' surely is part of a forensic speech only: how in a political speech or a speech of display can there be 'narration' in the technical **1414b** sense? or a reply to a forensic opponent? or an epilogue in closely-reasoned speeches? Again, introduction, comparison of conflicting arguments, and recapitulation are only found in political speeches when there is a struggle between two policies. They *may* occur then; so may even accusation and defence, often enough; but they form no essential part of a political speech. Even forensic speeches do not always need epilogues; not, for instance, a short speech, nor one in which the facts are easy to remember, the effect of an epilogue being always a reduction in the apparent length. It follows, then, that the only necessary parts of a speech are the Statement and the Argument. These are the essential features of a speech; and it cannot in any case have more than Introduction, Statement, Argument, and Epilogue. 'Refutation of the Opponent' is part of the arguments: so is 'Comparison' of the opponent's case with your own, for that process is a magnifying of your own case and therefore a part of the arguments, since one who does this *proves* something. The Introduction does nothing like this; nor does the Epilogue—it merely reminds us of what has been said already. If we make such distinctions we shall end, like Theodorus and his followers, by distinguishing 'narration' proper from 'post-narration' and 'pre-narration', and 'refutation' from 'final refutation'. But we ought only to bring in a new name if it indicates a real species with distinct specific qualities; otherwise the practice is pointless and silly, like the way Licymnius invented names in his *Art of Rhetoric*—'Secundation', 'Divagation', 'Ramification'.

14

The Introduction is the beginning of a speech, corresponding to the prologue in poetry and the prelude in flute-music; they are all beginnings, paving the way, as it were, for what is to follow. The musical prelude resembles the introduction to speeches of display; as flute-players play first some brilliant passage they know well and then fit it on to the opening notes of the piece itself, so in speeches of display the writer should proceed in the same way; he should begin with what best takes his fancy, and then strike up his theme and lead into it; which is indeed what *is* always done. (Take as an example the introduction to the *Helen* of Isocrates—there is nothing in common between the 'eristics' and Helen.) And here, even if you travel far from your subject, it is fitting, rather than that there should be sameness in the entire speech.

The usual subject for the introductions to speeches of display is some piece of praise or censure. Thus Gorgias writes in his *Olympic Speech,* 'You deserve widespread admiration, men of Greece', praising thus those who started the festival gatherings.[1] Isocrates, on the other hand, censures them for awarding distinctions to fine athletes but giving no prize for intellectual ability. Or one may begin with a piece of advice, thus: 'We ought to honour good men and so I myself am praising Aristeides' or 'We ought to honour those who are unpopular but not bad men, men whose good qualities have never been noticed, like Alexander son
1415a of Priam.' Here the orator gives *advice.* Or we may begin as speakers do in the lawcourts; that is to say, with appeals to the audience to excuse us if our speech is about something paradoxical, difficult, or hackneyed; like Choerilus in the lines—

But now when allotment of all has been made . . .[2]

Introductions to speeches of display, then, may be composed of some piece of praise or censure, of advice to do or not to do something, or of appeals to the audience; and you must choose between making these preliminary passages connected or disconnected with the speech itself.

Introductions to forensic speeches, it must be observed, have the same value as the prologues of dramas and the introductions to epic poems; the dithyrambic prelude resembling the introduction to a speech of display, as

For thee, and thy gifts, and thy battle-spoils . . .[3]

In prologues, and in epic poetry, a foretaste of the theme is given, intended to inform the hearers of it in advance instead of keeping their minds in suspense. Anything vague puzzles them: so give them a grasp of the beginning, and they can hold fast to it and follow the argument. So we find—

Sing, O goddess of song, of the Wrath . . .[4]
Tell me, O Muse, of the hero . . .[5]
Lead me to tell a new tale, how there came great warfare to Europe
Out of the Asian land . . .[6]

The tragic poets, too, let us know the pivot of their play; if not at the outset like Euripides, at least somewhere in the preface to a speech like Sophocles—

Polybus was my father . . .;[7]

and so in Comedy. This, then, is the most essential function and distinctive property of the introduction, to show what the aim of the speech is; and therefore no introduction ought to be employed where the subject is not long or intricate.

The other kinds of introduction employed are remedial in purpose, and may be used in any type of speech. They are concerned with the speaker, the hearer, the subject, or the speaker's opponent. Those concerned with the speaker himself or with his opponent are directed to removing or exciting prejudice. But whereas the defendant will begin by dealing with this sort of thing, the prosecutor will take quite another line and deal with such matters in the closing part of his speech. The reason for this is not far to seek. The defendant, when he is going to bring himself on the stage, must clear away any obstacles, and therefore must begin by removing any prejudice felt against him. But if you are to *excite* prejudice, you must do so at the close, so that the judges may more easily remember what you have said.

The appeal to the hearer aims at securing his goodwill, or at arousing his resentment, or sometimes at gaining his serious attention to the case, or even at distracting it—for gaining it is not always an advantage, and speakers will often for that reason try to make him laugh.

You may use any means you choose to make your hearer receptive; among others, giving him a good impression of your character, which always helps to secure his attention. He
1415b will be ready to attend to anything that touches himself and to anything that is impor-

[1] Baiter-Sauppe, *op. cit.*, p. 129 (Gorgias).
[2] Choerilus of Samos, *Perseis.*
[3] Bergk, III, p. 728, fr. adesp. 124.
[4] *Iliad*, I. 1.
[5] *Odyssey*, I. 1.
[6] Choerilus?; cf. Kinkel, *op. cit.*, p. 267.
[7] Sophocles, *Oedipus the King*, 774.

tant, surprising, or agreeable; and you should accordingly convey to him the impression that what you have to say is of this nature. If you wish to distract his attention, you should imply that the subject does not affect him, or is trivial or disagreeable. But observe, all this has nothing to do with the speech itself. It merely has to do with the weak-minded tendency of the hearer to listen to what is beside the point. Where this tendency is absent, no introduction is wanted beyond a summary statement of your subject, to put a sort of head on the main body of your speech. Moreover, calls for attention, when required, may come equally well in any part of a speech; in fact, the beginning of it is just where there is least slackness of interest; it is therefore ridiculous to put this kind of thing at the beginning, when every one is listening with most attention. Choose therefore any point in the speech where such an appeal is needed, and then say 'Now I beg you to note this point—it concerns you quite as much as myself'; or

I will tell you that whose like you have never yet[1]

heard for terror, or for wonder. This is what Prodicus called 'slipping in a bit of the fifty-drachma show-lecture for the audience whenever they began to nod'. It is plain that such introductions are addressed not to ideal hearers, but to hearers as we find them. The use of introductions to excite prejudice or to dispel misgivings is universal—

My lord, I will not say that eagerly . . .[2]

or

Why all this preface?[3]

Introductions are popular with those whose case is weak, or looks weak; it pays them to dwell on anything rather than the actual facts of it. That is why slaves, instead of answering the questions put to them, make indirect replies with long preambles. The means of exciting in your hearers goodwill and various other feelings of the same kind have already been described.[4] The poet finely says

May I find in Phaeacian hearts, at my coming, goodwill and compassion;[5]

and these are the two things we should aim at. In speeches of display we must make the hearer feel that the eulogy includes either himself or his family or his way of life or something or other of the kind. For it is true, as Socrates says in the *Funeral Speech*,[6] that 'the difficulty is not to praise the Athenians at Athens but at Sparta'.

The introductions of political oratory will be made out of the same materials as those of the forensic kind, though the nature of political oratory makes them very rare. The subject is known already, and therefore the *facts* of the case need no introduction; but you may have to say something on account of yourself or to your opponents; or those present may be inclined to treat the matter either more or less seriously than you wish them to. You may accordingly have to excite or dispel some prejudice, or to make the matter under discussion seem more or less important than before: for either of which purposes you will want an introduction. You may also want one to add elegance to your remarks, feeling that otherwise they will have a casual air, like Gorgias' eulo-
1416a gy of the Eleans, in which, without any preliminary sparring or fencing, he begins straight off with 'Happy city of Elis!'[7]

15

In dealing with prejudice, one class of argument is that whereby you can dispel objectionable suppositions about yourself. It makes no practical difference whether such a supposition has been put into words or not, so that this distinction may be ignored. Another way is to meet any of the issues directly: to deny the alleged fact; or to say that you have done no harm, or none to *him*, or not as much as he says; or that you have done him no injustice, or not much; or that you have done nothing disgraceful, or nothing disgraceful enough to matter: these are the sort of questions on which the dispute hinges. Thus Iphicrates replying to Nausicrates, admitted that he had done the deed alleged, and that he had done Nausicrates harm, but not that he had done him wrong. Or you may admit the wrong, but balance it with other facts, and say that, if the deed harmed him, at any rate it was honourable; or that, if it gave him pain, at least it did him good; or something else like that. Another way is to allege that your action was due to mistake, or bad luck, or necessity—as Sophocles said he was not trembling, as his traducer maintained, in order to make people think him an old man, but because he

[1] Anonymous. [2] Sophocles, *Antigone*, 223.
[3] Cf. Euripides, *Iphigenia in Tauris*, 1162.
[4] II, c. 1 ff. [5] *Odyssey*, VI. 327.

[6] Cf. Plato, *Menexenus*, 235 D.
[7] Baiter-Sauppe, *Or. Att.*, Pt. II. p. 130; Gorgias.

could not help it; he would rather *not* be eighty years old. You may balance your motive against your actual deed; saying, for instance, that you did not mean to injure him but to do so-and-so; that you did not do what you are falsely charged with doing—the damage was accidental—'I should indeed be a detestable person if I had deliberately intended this result.' Another way is open when your calumniator, or any of his connexions, is or has been subject to the same grounds for suspicion. Yet another, when others are subject to the same grounds for suspicion but are admitted to be in fact innocent of the charge: e.g. 'Must I be a profligate because I am well-groomed? Then so-and-so must be one too.' Another, if other people have been calumniated by the same man or some one else, or, without being calumniated, have been suspected, like yourself now, and yet have been proved innocent. Another way is to return calumny for calumny and say, 'It is monstrous to trust the man's statements when you cannot trust the man himself.' Another is when the question has been already decided. So with Euripides' reply to Hygiaenon, who, in the action for an exchange of properties, accused him of impiety in having written a line encouraging perjury—

My tongue hath sworn: no oath is on my soul.[1]

Euripides said that his opponent himself was guilty in bringing into the law-courts cases whose decision belonged to the Dionysiac contests. 'If I have not already answered for my words there, I am ready to do so if you choose to prosecute me there.'[2] Another method is to denounce calumny, showing what an enormity it is, and in particular that it raises false issues, and that it means a lack of confidence in the merits of his case. The argument from evidential circumstances is available for both parties:
1416b thus in the *Teucer* Odysseus says that Teucer is closely bound to Priam, since his mother Hesione was Priam's sister. Teucer replies that Telamon his father was Priam's enemy, and that he himself did not betray the spies to Priam. Another method, suitable for the calumniator, is to praise some trifling merit at great length, and then attack some important failing concisely; or after mentioning a number of good qualities to attack one bad one that really bears on the question. This is the method of thoroughly skilful and unscrupulous prosecutors. By mixing up the man's merits with what is bad, they do their best to make use of them to damage him.

There is another method open to both calumniator and apologist. Since a given action can be done from many motives, the former must try to disparage it by selecting the worse motive of two, the latter to put the better construction on it. Thus one might argue that Diomedes chose Odysseus as his companion because he supposed Odysseus to be the best man for the purpose; and you might reply to this that it was, on the contrary, because he was the only hero so worthless that Diomedes need not fear his rivalry.

16

We may now pass from the subject of calumny to that of Narration.

Narration in ceremonial oratory is not continuous but intermittent. There must, of course, be some survey of the actions that form the subject-matter of the speech. The speech is a composition containing two parts. One of these is not provided by the orator's art, viz. the actions themselves, of which the orator is in no sense author. The other part is provided by his art, namely, the proof (where proof is needed) that the actions were done, the description of their quality or of their extent, or even all these three things together. Now the reason why sometimes it is not desirable to make the whole narrative continuous is that the case thus expounded is hard to keep in mind. Show, therefore, from one set of facts that your hero is, e.g. brave, and from other sets of facts that he is able, just, &c. A speech thus arranged is comparatively simple, instead of being complicated and elaborate. You will have to recall well-known deeds among others; and because they are well-known, the hearer usually needs no narration of them; none, for instance, if your object is the praise of Achilles; we all know the facts of his life—what you have to do is to apply those facts. But if your object is the praise of Critias, you *must* narrate his deeds, which not many people know of . . .

Nowadays it is said, absurdly enough, that the narration should be rapid. Remember what the man said to the baker who asked whether he was to make the cake hard or soft: 'What, can't you make it *right*?' Just so here. We are not to make long narrations, just as we are not to make long introductions or long arguments. Here, again, rightness does not

[1] Euripides, *Hippolytus*, 612.

[2] Baiter-Sauppe, *Or. Att.*, Pt. II, p. 216.

consist either in rapidity or in conciseness, but in the happy mean; that is, in saying just so much as will make the facts plain, or will lead the hearer to believe that the thing **1417a** has happened, or that the man has caused injury or wrong to some one, or that the facts are really as important as you wish them to be thought: or the opposite facts to establish the opposite arguments.

You may also narrate as you go anything that does credit to yourself, e.g. 'I kept telling him to do his duty and not abandon his children'; or discredit to your adversary, e.g. 'But he answered me that, wherever he might find himself, there he would find other children', the answer Herodotus[1] records of the Egyptian mutineers. Slip in anything else that the judges will enjoy.

The defendant will make less of the narration. He has to maintain that the thing has not happened, or did no harm, or was not unjust, or not so bad as is alleged. He must therefore not waste time about what is admitted fact, unless this bears on his own contention; e.g. that the thing was done, but was not wrong. Further, we must speak of events as past and gone, except where they excite pity or indignation by being represented as present. The Story told to Alcinous is an example of a brief chronicle, when it is repeated to Penelope in sixty lines. Another instance is the Epic Cycle as treated by Phayllus, and the prologue to the *Oeneus*.

The narration should depict character; to which end you must know what makes it do so. One such thing is the indication of moral purpose; the quality of purpose indicated determines the quality of character depicted and is itself determined by the end pursued. Thus it is that mathematical discourses depict no character; they have nothing to do with moral purpose, for they represent nobody as pursuing any end. On the other hand, the Socratic dialogues do depict character, being concerned with moral questions. This end will also be gained by describing the manifestations of various types of character, e.g. 'he kept walking along as he talked', which shows the man's recklessness and rough manners. Do not let your words seem inspired so much by intelligence, in the manner now current, as by moral purpose: e.g. 'I willed this; aye, it was my moral purpose; true, I gained nothing by it, still it is better thus.' For the other way shows good sense, but this shows good character; good sense making us go after what is useful, and good character after what is noble. Where any detail may appear incredible, then add the cause of it; of this Sophocles provides an example in the *Antigone*, where Antigone says she had cared more for her brother than for husband or children, since if the latter perished they might be replaced,

But since my father and mother in their graves
Lie dead, no brother can be born to me.[2]

If you have no such cause to suggest, just say that you are aware that no one will believe your words, but the fact remains that such is your nature, however hard the world may find it to believe that a man deliberately does anything except what pays him.

Again, you must make use of the emotions. Relate the familiar manifestations of them, and those that distinguish yourself and your opponent; for instance, 'he went away scowling **1417b** at me'. So Aeschines described Cratylus as 'hissing with fury and shaking his fists'. These details carry conviction: the audience take the truth of what they know as so much evidence for the truth of what they do not. Plenty of such details may be found in Homer:

Thus did she say: but the old woman
buried her face in her hands:[3]

a true touch—people beginning to cry do put their hands over their eyes.

Bring yourself on the stage from the first in the right character, that people may regard you in that light; and the same with your adversary; but do not let them see what you are about. How easily such impressions may be conveyed we can see from the way in which we get some inkling of things we know nothing of by the mere look of the messenger bringing news of them. Have some narrative in many different parts of your speech; and sometimes let there be none at the beginning of it.

In political oratory there is very little opening for narration; nobody can 'narrate' what has not yet happened. If there is narration at all, it will be of past events, the recollection of which is to help the hearers to make better plans for the future. Or it may be employed to attack some one's character, or to eulogize him—only then you will not be doing what the political speaker, as such, has to do.

[1] Cf. Herodotus, II. 30.

[2] Sophocles, *Antigone*, 911, 912.

[3] *Odyssey*, XIX. 361.

If any statement you make is hard to believe, you must guarantee its truth, and at once offer an explanation, and then furnish it with such particulars as will be expected. Thus Carcinus' Jocasta, in his *Oedipus,* keeps guaranteeing the truth of her answers to the inquiries of the man who is seeking her son; and so with Haemon in Sophocles.

17

The duty of the Arguments is to attempt demonstrative proofs. These proofs must bear directly upon the question in dispute, which must fall under one of four heads. (1) If you maintain that the act *was not committed,* your main task in court is to prove this. (2) If you maintain that the act *did no harm,* prove this. If you maintain that (3) the act was *less* than is alleged, or (4) *justified,* prove these facts, just as you would prove the act not to have been committed if you were maintaining that.

It should be noted that only where the question in dispute falls under the first of these heads can it be true that one of the two parties is necessarily a rogue. Here ignorance cannot be pleaded, as it might if the dispute were whether the act was justified or not. This argument must therefore be used in this case only, not in the others.

In ceremonial speeches you will develop your case mainly by arguing that what has been done is, e.g., noble and useful. The facts themselves are to be taken on trust; proof of them is only submitted on those rare occasions when they are not easily credible or when they have been set down to some one else.

In political speeches you may maintain that a proposal is impracticable; or that, though practicable, it is unjust, or will do no good, or is not so important as its proposer thinks. Note any falsehoods about irrelevant matters—they **1418a** will look like proof that his other statements also are false. Argument by 'example' is highly suitable for political oratory, argument by 'enthymeme' better suits forensic. Political oratory deals with future events, of which it can do no more than quote past events as examples. Forensic oratory deals with what is or is not *now* true, which can better be demonstrated, because not contingent—there is no contingency in what has now already happened. Do not use a continuous succession of enthymemes: intersperse them with other matter, or they will spoil one another's effect. There are limits to their number—

Friend, you have spoken as much *as a sensible man would have spoken.*[1]—

'as *much*' says Homer, not 'as *well*'. Nor should you try to make enthymemes on every point; if you do, you will be acting just like some students of philosophy, whose conclusions are more familiar and believable than the premisses from which they draw them. And avoid the enthymeme form when you are trying to rouse feeling; for it will either kill the feeling or will itself fall flat: all simultaneous motions tend to cancel each other either completely or partially. Nor should you go after the enthymeme form in a passage where you are depicting character—the process of demonstration can express neither moral character nor moral purpose. Maxims should be employed in the Arguments—and in the Narration too—since these do express character: 'I have given him this, though I am quite aware that one should "Trust no man".' Or if you are appealing to the emotions: 'I do not regret it, though I have been wronged; if he has the profit on his side, I have justice on mine.'

Political oratory is a more difficult task than forensic; and naturally so, since it deals with the future, whereas the pleader deals with the past, which, as Epimenides of Crete said, even the diviners already know. (Epimenides did not practise divination about the future; only about the obscurities of the past.) Besides, in forensic oratory you have a basis in the law; and once you have a starting-point, you can prove anything with comparative ease. Then again, political oratory affords few chances for those leisurely digressions in which you may attack your adversary, talk about yourself, or work on your hearers' emotions; fewer chances indeed, than any other affords, unless your set purpose is to divert your hearers' attention. Accordingly, if you find yourself in difficulties, follow the lead of the Athenian speakers, and that of Isocrates, who makes regular attacks upon people in the course of a political speech, e.g. upon the Lacedaemonians in the *Panegyricus,* and upon Chares in the speech about the allies. In ceremonial oratory, intersperse your speech with bits of episodic eulogy, like Isocrates, who is always bringing some one forward for this purpose. And this is what Gorgias meant by saying that he always found something to talk about. For if he speaks of Achilles, he praises Peleus, then Aeacus, then Zeus; and in

[1] *Odyssey,* IV. 204.

like manner the virtue of valour, describing its good results, and saying what it is like.

Now if you have proofs to bring forward, bring them forward, and your moral discourse as well; if you have no enthymemes, then fall **1418b** back upon moral discourse: after all, it is more fitting for a good man to display himself as an honest fellow than as a subtle reasoner. Refutative enthymemes are more popular than demonstrative ones: their logical cogency is more striking: the facts about two opposites always stand out clearly when the two are put side by side.

The 'Reply to the Opponent' is not a separate division of the speech; it is part of the Arguments to break down the opponent's case, whether by objection or by counter-syllogism. Both in political speaking and when pleading in court, if you are the first speaker you should put your own arguments forward first, and then meet the arguments on the other side by refuting them and pulling them to pieces beforehand. If, however, the case for the other side contains a great variety of arguments, begin with these, like Callistratus in the Messenian assembly, when he demolished the arguments likely to be used against him before giving his own. If you speak later, you must first, by means of refutation and counter-syllogism, attempt some answer to your opponent's speech, especially if his arguments have been well received. For just as our minds refuse a favourable reception to a *person* against whom they are prejudiced, so they refuse it to a speech when they have been favourably impressed by the speech on the other side. You should, therefore, make room in the minds of the audience for your coming speech; and this will be done by getting your opponent's speech out of the way. So attack that first—either the whole of it, or the most important, successful, or vulnerable points in it, and thus inspire confidence in what you have to say yourself—

First, champion will I be of Goddesses . . .
Never, I ween, would Hera . . .:[1]

where the speaker has attacked the silliest argument first. So much for the Arguments.

With regard to the element of moral character: there are assertions which, if made about yourself, may excite dislike, appear tedious, or expose you to the risk of contradiction; and other things which you cannot say about your opponent without seeming abusive or ill-bred. Put such remarks, therefore, into the mouth of some third person. This is what Isocrates does in the *Philippus* and in the *Antidosis,* and Archilochus in his satires. The latter represents the father himself as attacking his daughter in the lampoon

Think nought impossible at all,
Nor swear that it shall not befall . . .[2]

and puts into the mouth of Charon the carpenter the lampoon which begins

Not for the wealth of Gyes . . .[3]

So too Sophocles makes Haemon appeal to his father on behalf of Antigone as if it were others who were speaking.[4]

Again, sometimes you should restate your enthymemes in the form of maxims; e.g. 'Wise men will come to terms in the hour of success; for they will gain most if they do'.[5] Expressed as an enthymeme, this would run, '*If* we ought to come to terms when doing so will enable us to gain the greatest advantage, *then* we ought to come to terms in the hour of success.'

18

Next as to Interrogation. The best moment to **1419a** employ this is when your opponent has so answered one question that the putting of just one more lands him in absurdity. Thus Pericles questioned Lampon about the way of celebrating the rites of the Saviour Goddess. Lampon declared that no uninitiated person could be told of them. Pericles then asked, 'Do you know them yourself?' 'Yes', answered Lampon. 'Why,' said Pericles, 'how can that be, when you are uninitiated?'

Another good moment is when one premiss of an argument is obviously true, and you can see that your opponent must say 'yes' if you ask him whether the other is true. Having first got this answer about the other, do not go on to ask him about the obviously true one, but just state the conclusion yourself. Thus, when Meletus denied that Socrates believed in the existence of gods but admitted that he talked about a supernatural power, Socrates proceeded to ask whether 'supernatural beings were not either children of the gods or in some way divine?' 'Yes', said Meletus. 'Then', replied Socrates, 'is there any one who believes

[1] Euripides, *Troades*, 969 and 971.

[2] Archilochus, fr. 74, Bergk, II, p. 403.

[3] *Ib.*, fr. 25, Bergk, II, p. 390.

[4] Sophocles, *Antigone*, 688-700.

[5] Cf. Isocrates, *Archidamus*, 50.

in the existence of children of the gods and yet not in the existence of the gods themselves?"[1] Another good occasion is when you expect to show that your opponent is contradicting either his own words or what every one believes. A fourth is when it is impossible for him to meet your question except by an evasive answer. If he answers 'True, and yet not true', or 'Partly true and partly not true', or 'True in one sense but not in another', the audience thinks he is in difficulties, and applauds his discomfiture. In other cases do not attempt interrogation; for if your opponent gets in an objection, you are felt to have been worsted. You cannot ask a series of questions owing to the incapacity of the audience to follow them; and for this reason you should also make your enthymemes as compact as possible.

In replying, you must meet ambiguous questions by drawing reasonable distinctions, not by a curt answer. In meeting questions that seem to involve you in a contradiction, offer the explanation at the outset of your answer, before your opponent asks the next question or draws his conclusion. For it is not difficult to see the drift of his argument in advance. This point, however, as well as the various means of refutation, may be regarded as known to us from the *Topics*.[2]

When your opponent in drawing his conclusion puts it in the form of a question, you must justify your answer. Thus when Sophocles was asked by Peisander whether he had, like the other members of the Board of Safety, voted for setting up the Four Hundred, he said 'Yes.' 'Why, did you not think it wicked?' —'Yes.'—'So *you* committed this wickedness?' —'Yes', said Sophocles, 'for there was nothing better to do.' Again, the Lacedaemonian, when he was being examined on his conduct as ephor, was asked whether he thought that the other ephors had been justly put to death. 'Yes', he said. 'Well then', asked his opponent, 'did not *you* propose the same measures as they?'—'Yes.'—'Well then, would not *you* too be justly put to death?'—'Not at all', said he; '*they* were bribed to do it, and I did it from conviction'. Hence you should not **1419b** ask any further questions after drawing the conclusion, nor put the conclusion itself in the form of a further question, unless there is a large balance of truth on your side.

As to jests. These are supposed to be of some service in controversy. Gorgias said that you should kill your opponents' earnestness with jesting and their jesting with earnestness; in which he was right. Jests have been classified in the *Poetics*. Some are becoming to a gentleman, others are not; see that you choose such as become *you*. Irony better befits a gentleman than buffoonery; the ironical man jokes to amuse himself, the buffoon to amuse other people.

19

The Epilogue has four parts. You must (1) make the audience well-disposed towards yourself and ill-disposed towards your opponent, (2) magnify or minimize the leading facts, (3) excite the required state of emotion in your hearers, and (4) refresh their memories.

(1) Having shown your own truthfulness and the untruthfulness of your opponent, the natural thing is to commend yourself, censure him, and hammer in your points. You must aim at one of two objects—you must make yourself out a good man and him a bad one either in yourselves or in relation to your hearers. How this is to be managed—by what lines of argument you are to represent people as good or bad—this has been already explained.[3]

(2) The facts having been proved, the natural thing to do next is to magnify or minimize their importance. The facts must be admitted before you can discuss how important they are; just as the body cannot grow except from something already present. The proper lines of argument to be used for this purpose of amplification and depreciation have already been set forth.[4]

(3) Next, when the facts and their importance are clearly understood, you must excite your hearers' emotions. These emotions are pity, indignation, anger, hatred, envy, emulation, pugnacity. The lines of argument to be used for these purposes also have been previously mentioned.[5]

(4) Finally you have to review what you have already said. Here you may properly do what some wrongly recommend doing in the introduction—repeat your points frequently so as to make them easily understood. What you *should* do in your introduction is to state your subject, in order that the point to be judged may be quite plain; in the epilogue you should summarize the arguments by which your case has been proved. The first step in this reviewing process is to observe that you have

[1] Cf. Plato, *Apology*, 27. [2] *Topics*, VIII.

[3] I. 9. [4] II. 19. [5] II. 1-11.

done what you undertook to do. You must, then, state what you have said and why you have said it. Your method may be a comparison of your own case with that of your opponent; and you may compare either the ways you have both handled the same point or make your comparison less direct: 'My opponent said so-and-so on this point; I said so-and-so, and this is why I said it'. Or with modest **1420a** irony, e.g. 'He certainly said so-and-so, but I said so-and-so'. Or 'How vain he would have been if he had proved all this instead of *that!*' Or put it in the form of a question. 'What has *not* been proved by me?' or 'What *has* my opponent proved?' You may proceed then, either in this way by setting point against point, or by following the natural order of the arguments as spoken, first giving your own, **1420b** and then separately, if you wish, those of your opponent.

For the conclusion, the disconnected style of language is appropriate, and will mark the difference between the oration and the peroration. 'I have done. You have heard me. The facts are before you. I ask for your judgement.'

ON POETICS

CONTENTS: ON POETICS

ON POETICS

I

1447a Our subject being Poetry, I propose to speak not only of the art in general but also of its species and their respective capacities; of the structure of plot required for a good poem; of the number and nature of the constituent parts of a poem; and likewise of any other matters in the same line of inquiry. Let us follow the natural order and begin with the primary facts.

Epic poetry and Tragedy, as also Comedy, Dithyrambic poetry, and most flute-playing and lyre-playing, are all, viewed as a whole, modes of imitation. But at the same time they differ from one another in three ways, either by a difference of kind in their means, or by differences in the objects, or in the manner of their imitations.

I. Just as colour and form are used as means by some, who (whether by art or constant practice) imitate and portray many things by their aid, and the voice is used by others; so also in the above-mentioned group of arts, the means with them as a whole are rhythm, language, and harmony—used, however, either singly or in certain combinations. A combination of harmony and rhythm alone is the means in flute-playing and lyre-playing, and any other arts there may be of the same description, e.g. imitative piping. Rhythm alone, without harmony, is the means in the dancer's imitations; for even he, by the rhythms of his attitudes, may represent men's characters, as well as what they do and suffer. There is further an art which imitates by language alone, without harmony, in prose or in **1447b** verse, and if in verse, either in some one or in a plurality of metres. This form of imitation is to this day without a name. We have no common name for a mime of Sophron or Xenarchus and a Socratic Conversation; and we should still be without one even if the imitation in the two instances were in trimeters or elegiacs or some other kind of verse—though it is the way with people to tack on 'poet' to the name of a metre, and talk of elegiac-poets and epic-poets, thinking that they call them poets not by reason of the imitative nature of their work, but indiscriminately by reason of the metre they write in. Even if a theory of medicine or physical philosophy be put forth in a metrical form, it is usual to describe the writer in this way; Homer and Empedocles, however, have really nothing in common apart from their metre; so that, if the one is to be called a poet, the other should be termed a physicist rather than a poet. We should be in the same position also, if the imitation in these instances were in all the metres, like the *Centaur* (a rhapsody in a medley of all metres) of Chaeremon; and Chaeremon one has to recognize as a poet. So much, then, as to these arts. There are, lastly, certain other arts, which combine all the means enumerated, rhythm, melody, and verse, e.g. Dithyrambic and Nomic poetry, Tragedy and Comedy; with this difference, however, that the three kinds of means are in some of them all employed together, and in others brought in separately, one after the other. These elements of difference in the above arts I term the means of their imitation.

Note: The bold face numbers and letters are approximate indications of the pages and columns of the standard Berlin Greek text; the bracketed numbers, of the lines in the Greek text; they are here assigned as they are assigned in the Oxford translation.

2

1448a II. The objects the imitator represents are actions, with agents who are necessarily either good men or bad—the diversities of human character being nearly always derivative from this primary distinction, since the line between virtue and vice is one dividing the whole of mankind. It follows, therefore, that the agents represented must be either above our own level of goodness, or beneath it, or just such as we are; in the same way as, with the painters, the personages of Polygnotus are better than we are, those of Pauson worse, and those of Dionysius just like ourselves. It is clear that each of the above-mentioned arts will admit of these differences, and that it will become a separate art by representing objects with this point of difference. Even in dancing, flute-playing, and lyre-playing such diversities are possible; and they are also possible in the nameless art that uses language, prose or verse without harmony, as its means; Homer's personages, for instance, are better than we are; Cleophon's are on our own level; and those of Hegemon of Thasos, the first writer of parodies, and Nicochares, the author of the *Diliad,* are beneath it. The same is true of the Dithyramb and the Nome: the personages may be presented in them with the difference exemplified in the . . . of . . . and Argas, and in the Cyclopses of Timotheus and Philoxenus. This difference it is that distinguishes Tragedy and Comedy also; the one would make its personages worse, and the other better, than the men of the present day.

3

III. A third difference in these arts is in the manner in which each kind of object is represented. Given both the same means and the same kind of object for imitation, one may either (1) speak at one moment in narrative and at another in an assumed character, as Homer does; or (2) one may remain the same throughout, without any such change; or (3) the imitators may represent the whole story dramatically, as though they were actually doing the things described.

As we said at the beginning, therefore, the differences in the imitation of these arts come under three heads, their means, their objects, and their manner.

So that as an imitator Sophocles will be on one side akin to Homer, both portraying good men; and on another to Aristophanes, since both present their personages as acting and doing. This in fact, according to some, is the reason for plays being termed dramas, because in a play the personages act the story. Hence too both Tragedy and Comedy are claimed by the Dorians as their discoveries; Comedy by the Megarians—by those in Greece as having arisen when Megara became a democracy, and by the Sicilian Megarians on the ground that the poet Epicharmus was of their country, and a good deal earlier than Chionides and Magnes; even Tragedy also is claimed by certain of the Peloponnesian Dorians. In support of this claim they point to the words 'comedy' and 'drama'. Their word for the outlying hamlets, they say, is *comae,* whereas Athenians call them *demes*—thus assuming that comedians got the name not from their *comoe* or revels, but from their strolling from hamlet to hamlet, lack of appreciation keeping
1448b them out of the city. Their word also for 'to act', they say, is *dran,* whereas Athenians use *prattein.*

So much, then, as to the number and nature of the points of difference in the imitation of these arts.

4

It is clear that the general origin of poetry was due to two causes, each of them part of human nature. Imitation is natural to man from childhood, one of his advantages over the lower animals being this, that he is the most imitative creature in the world, and learns at first by imitation. And it is also natural for all to delight in works of imitation. The truth of this second point is shown by experience: though the objects themselves may be painful to see, we delight to view the most realistic representations of them in art, the forms for example of the lowest animals and of dead bodies. The explanation is to be found in a further fact: to be learning something is the greatest of pleasures not only to the philosopher but also to the rest of mankind, however small their capacity for it; the reason of the delight in seeing the picture is that one is at the same time learning—gathering the meaning of things, e.g. that the man there is so-and-so; for if one has not seen the thing before, one's pleasure will not be in the picture as an imitation of it, but will be due to the execution or colouring or some similar cause. Imitation, then, being natural to us—as also the sense of harmony and rhythm, the metres being obviously species of rhythms—it was through their original aptitude, and by a series of improvements for the most part gradual on their first efforts, that they created poetry out of their improvisations.

Poetry, however, soon broke up into two kinds according to the differences of character in the individual poets; for the graver among them would represent noble actions, and those of noble personages; and the meaner sort the actions of the ignoble. The latter class produced invectives at first, just as others did hymns and panegyrics. We know of no such poem by any of the pre-Homeric poets, though there were probably many such writers among them; instances, however, may be found from Homer downwards, e.g. his *Margites,* and the similar poems of others. In this poetry of invective its natural fitness brought an iambic metre into use; hence our present term 'iambic', because it was the metre of their 'iambs' or invectives against one another. The result was that the old poets became some of them writers of heroic and others of iambic verse. Homer's position, however, is peculiar: just as he was in the serious style the poet of poets, standing alone not only through the literary excellence, but also through the dramatic character of his imitations, so too he was the first to outline for us the general forms of Comedy by producing not a dramatic invective, but a dramatic picture of the Ridiculous; his *Margites* in fact stands in the same relation **1449a** to our comedies as the *Iliad* and *Odyssey* to our tragedies. As soon, however, as Tragedy and Comedy appeared in the field, those naturally drawn to the one line of poetry became writers of comedies instead of iambs, and those naturally drawn to the other, writers of tragedies instead of epics, because these new modes of art were grander and of more esteem than the old.

If it be asked whether Tragedy is now all that it need be in its formative elements, to consider that, and decide it theoretically and in relation to the theatres, is a matter for another inquiry.

It certainly began in improvisations—as did also Comedy; the one originating with the authors of the Dithyramb, the other with those of the phallic songs, which still survive as institutions in many of our cities. And its advance after that was little by little, through their improving on whatever they had before them at each stage. It was in fact only after a long series of changes that the movement of Tragedy stopped on its attaining to its natural form. (1) The number of actors was first increased to two by Aeschylus, who curtailed the business of the Chorus, and made the dialogue, or spoken portion, take the leading part in the play. (2) A third actor and scenery were due to Sophocles. (3) Tragedy acquired also its magnitude. Discarding short stories and a ludicrous diction, through its passing out of its satyric stage, it assumed, though only at a late point in its progress, a tone of dignity; and its metre changed then from trochaic to iambic. The reason for their original use of the trochaic tetrameter was that their poetry was satyric and more connected with dancing that it now is. As soon, however, as a spoken part came in, nature herself found the appropriate metre. The iambic, we know, is the most speakable of metres, as is shown by the fact that we very often fall into it in conversation, whereas we rarely talk hexameters, and only when we depart from the speaking tone of voice. (4) Another change was a plurality of episodes or acts. As for the remaining matters, the superadded embellishments and the account of their introduction, these must be taken as said, as it would probably be a long piece of work to go through the details.

5

As for Comedy, it is (as has been observed)[1] an imitation of men worse than the average; worse, however, not as regards any and every sort of fault, but only as regards one particular kind, the Ridiculous, which is a species of the Ugly. The Ridiculous may be defined as a mistake or deformity not productive of pain or harm to others; the mask, for instance, that excites laughter, is something ugly and distorted without causing pain.

Though the successive changes in Tragedy and their authors are not unknown, we cannot say the same of Comedy; its early stages passed unnoticed, because it was not as yet **1449b** taken up in a serious way. It was only at a late point in its progress that a chorus of comedians was officially granted by the archon; they used to be mere volunteers. It had also already certain definite forms at the time when the record of those termed comic poets begins. Who it was who supplied it with masks, or prologues, or a plurality of actors and the like, has remained unknown. The invented Fable, or Plot, however, originated in Sicily, with Epicharmus and Phormis; of Athenian poets Crates was the first to drop the Comedy of invective and frame stories of a general and non-personal nature, in other words, Fables or Plots.

Epic poetry, then, has been seen to agree with Tragedy to this extent, that of being an imitation of serious subjects in a grand kind of verse. It differs from it, however, (1) in that it is one kind of verse and in narrative form; and (2) in its length—which is due to its action having no fixed limit of time, whereas Tragedy endeavours to keep as far as possible within a single circuit of the sun, or something near that. This, I say, is another point of difference between them, though at first the practice in this respect was just the same in tragedies as in epic poems. They differ also (3) in their constituents, some being common to both and others peculiar to Tragedy—hence a judge of good and bad in Tragedy is a judge of that in epic poetry also. All the parts of an epic are

1 1448a 17, 1448b 37.

included in Tragedy; but those of Tragedy are not all of them to be found in the Epic.

6

Reserving hexameter poetry and Comedy for consideration hereafter,[1] let us proceed now to the discussion of Tragedy; before doing so, however, we must gather up the definition resulting from what has been said. A tragedy, then, is the imitation of an action that is serious and also, as having magnitude, complete in itself; in language with pleasurable accessories, each kind brought in separately in the parts of the work; in a dramatic, not in a narrative form; with incidents arousing pity and fear, wherewith to accomplish its catharsis of such emotions. Here by 'language with pleasurable accessories' I mean that with rhythm and harmony or song superadded; and by 'the kinds separately' I mean that some portions are worked out with verse only, and others in turn with song.

I. As they act the stories, it follows that in the first place the Spectacle (or stage-appearance of the actors) must be some part of the whole; and in the second Melody and Diction, these two being the means of their imitation. Here by 'Diction' I mean merely this, the composition of the verses; and by 'Melody', what is too completely understood to require explanation. But further: the subject represented also is an action; and the action involves agents, who must necessarily have their distinctive qualities both of character and thought, since it is from these that we ascribe certain **1450a** qualities to their actions. There are in the natural order of things, therefore, two causes, Thought and Character, of their actions, and consequently of their success or failure in their lives. Now the action (that which was done) is represented in the play by the Fable or Plot. The Fable, in our present sense of the term, is simply this, the combination of the incidents, or things done in the story; whereas Character is what makes us ascribe certain moral qualities to the agents; and Thought is shown in all they say when proving a particular point or, it may be, enunciating a general truth. There are six parts consequently of every tragedy, as a whole (that is) of such or such quality, viz. a Fable or Plot, Characters, Diction, Thought, Spectacle, and Melody; two of them arising from the means, one from the manner, and three from the objects of the dramatic imitation; and there is nothing else besides these six. Of these, its formative elements, then, not a few of the dramatists have made due use, as every play, one may say, admits of Spectacle, Character, Fable, Diction, Melody, and Thought.

II. The most important of the six is the combination of the incidents of the story. Tragedy is essentially an imitation not of persons but of action and life, of happiness and misery. All human happiness or misery takes the form of action; the end for which we live is a certain kind of activity, not a quality. Character gives us qualities, but it is in our actions—what we do——that we are happy or the reverse. In a play accordingly they do not act in order to portray the Characters; they include the Characters for the sake of the action. So that it is the action in it, i.e. its Fable or Plot, that is the end and purpose of the tragedy; and the end is everywhere the chief thing. Besides this, a tragedy is impossible without action, but there may be one without Character. The tragedies of most of the moderns are characterless—a defect common among poets of all kinds, and with its counterpart in painting in Zeuxis as compared with Polygnotus; for whereas the latter is strong in character, the work of Zeuxis is devoid of it. And again: one may string together a series of characteristic speeches of the utmost finish as regards Diction and Thought, and yet fail to produce the true tragic effect; but one will have much better success with a tragedy which, however inferior in these respects, has a Plot, a combination of incidents, in it. And again: the most powerful elements of attraction in Tragedy, the Peripeties and Discoveries, are parts of the Plot. A further proof is in the fact that beginners succeed earlier with the Diction and Characters than with the construction of a story; and the same may be said of nearly all the early dramatists. We maintain, therefore, that the first essential, the life and soul, so to speak, of Tragedy is the Plot; and that the Characters come second—compare the **1450b** parallel in painting, where the most beautiful colours laid on without order will not give one the same pleasure as a simple black-and-white sketch of a portrait. We maintain that Tragedy is primarily an imitation of action, and that it is mainly for the sake of the action that it imitates the personal agents. Third comes the element of Thought, i.e. the power of saying whatever can be said, or what is appropriate to the occasion. This is what, in the speeches in Tragedy, falls under

[1] For hexameter poetry cf. chapter 23 f.

the arts of Politics and Rhetoric; for the older poets make their personages discourse like statesmen, and the moderns like rhetoricians. One must not confuse it with Character. Character in a play is that which reveals the moral purpose of the agents, i.e. the sort of thing they seek or avoid, where that is not obvious—hence there is no room for Character in a speech on a purely indifferent subject. Thought, on the other hand, is shown in all they say when proving or disproving some particular point, or enunciating some universal proposition. Fourth among the literary elements is the Diction of the personages, i.e., as before explained,[1] the expression of their thoughts in words, which is practically the same thing with verse as with prose. As for the two remaining parts, the Melody is the greatest of the pleasurable accessories of Tragedy. The Spectacle, though an attraction, is the least artistic of all the parts, and has least to do with the art of poetry. The tragic effect is quite possible without a public performance and actors; and besides, the getting-up of the Spectacle is more a matter for the costumier than the poet.

7

Having thus distinguished the parts, let us now consider the proper construction of the Fable or Plot, as that is at once the first and the most important thing in Tragedy. We have laid it down that a tragedy is an imitation of an action that is complete in itself, as a whole of some magnitude; for a whole may be of no magnitude to speak of. Now a whole is that which has beginning, middle, and end. A beginning is that which is not itself necessarily after anything else, and which has naturally something else after it; an end is that which is naturally after something itself, either as its necessary or usual consequent, and with nothing else after it; and a middle, that which is by nature after one thing and has also another after it. A well-constructed Plot, therefore, cannot either begin or end at any point one likes; beginning and end in it must be of the forms just described. Again: to be beautiful, a living creature, and every whole made up of parts, must not only present a certain order in its arrangement of parts, but also be of a certain definite magnitude. Beauty is a matter of size and order, and therefore impossible either (1) in a very minute creature, since our perception becomes indistinct as it approaches instantaneity; or (2) in a creature of vast size—one, say, 1,000 miles long—as in that

1451a case, instead of the object being seen all at once; the unity and wholeness of it is lost to the beholder. Just in the same way, then, as a beautiful whole made up of parts, or a beautiful living creature, must be of some size, but a size to be taken in by the eye, so a story or Plot must be of some length, but of a length to be taken in by the memory. As for the limit of its length, so far as that is relative to public performances and spectators, it does not fall within the theory of poetry. If they had to perform a hundred tragedies, they would be timed by water-clocks, as they are said to have been at one period. The limit, however, set by the actual nature of the thing is this: the longer the story, consistently with its being comprehensible as a whole, the finer it is by reason of its magnitude. As a rough general formula, 'a length which allows of the hero passing by a series of probable or necessary stages from misfortune to happiness, or from happiness to misfortune', may suffice as a limit for the magnitude of the story.

8

The Unity of a Plot does not consist, as some suppose, in its having one man as its subject. An infinity of things befall that one man, some of which it is impossible to reduce to unity; and in like manner there are many actions of one man which cannot be made to form one action. One sees, therefore, the mistake of all the poets who have written a *Heracleid,* a *Theseid,* or similar poems; they suppose that, because Heracles was one man, the story also of Heracles must be one story. Homer, however, evidently understood this point quite well, whether by art or instinct, just in the same way as he excels the rest in every other respect. In writing an *Odyssey,* he did not make the poem cover all that ever befell his hero—it befell him, for instance, to get wounded on Parnassus and also to feign madness at the time of the call to arms, but the two incidents had no necessary or probable connexion with one another—instead of doing that, he took as the subject of the *Odyssey,* as also of the *Iliad,* an action with a Unity of the kind we are describing. The truth is that, just as in the other imitative arts one imitation is always of one thing, so in poetry the story, as an imitation of action, must represent one action, a complete whole, with its several incidents so closely connected that the trans-

[1] 1449b 34.

posal or withdrawal of any one of them will disjoin and dislocate the whole. For that which makes no perceptible difference by its presence or absence is no real part of the whole.

9

From what we have said it will be seen that the poet's function is to describe, not the thing that has happened, but a kind of thing that might happen, i.e. what is possible as being probable or necessary. The distinction between **1451b** historian and poet is not in the one writing prose and the other verse—you might put the work of Herodotus into verse, and it would still be a species of history; it consists really in this, that the one describes the thing that has been, and the other a kind of thing that might be. Hence poetry is something more philosophic and of graver import than history, since its statements are of the nature rather of universals, whereas those of history are singulars. By a universal statement I mean one as to what such or such a kind of man will probably or necessarily say or do—which is the aim of poetry, though it affixes proper names to the characters; by a singular statement, one as to what, say, Alcibiades did or had done to him. In Comedy this has become clear by this time; it is only when their plot is already made up of probable incidents that they give it a basis of proper names, choosing for the purpose any names that may occur to them, instead of writing like the old iambic poets about particular persons. In Tragedy, however, they still adhere to the historic names; and for this reason: what convinces is the possible; now whereas we are not yet sure as to the possibility of that which has not happened, that which has happened is manifestly possible, else it would not have come to pass. Nevertheless even in Tragedy there are some plays with but one or two known names in them, the rest being inventions; and there are some without a single known name, e.g. Agathon's *Antheus,* in which both incidents and names are of the poet's invention; and it is no less delightful on that account. So that one must not aim at a rigid adherence to the traditional stories on which tragedies are based. It would be absurd, in fact, to do so, as even the known stories are only known to a few, though they are a delight none the less to all.

It is evident from the above that the poet must be more the poet of his stories or Plots than of his verses, inasmuch as he is a poet by virtue of the imitative element in his work, and it is actions that he imitates. And if he should come to take a subject from actual history, he is none the less a poet for that; since some historic occurrences may very well be in the probable and possible order of things; and it is in that aspect of them that he is their poet.

Of simple Plots and actions the episodic are the worst. I call a Plot episodic when there is neither probability nor necessity in the sequence of its episodes. Actions of this sort bad poets construct through their own fault, and good ones on account of the players. His work being for public performance, a good poet often stretches out a Plot beyond its capabilities, and is thus obliged to twist the sequence of incident.

1452a Tragedy, however, is an imitation not only of a complete action, but also of incidents arousing pity and fear. Such incidents have the very greatest effect on the mind when they occur unexpectedly and at the same time in consequence of one another; there is more of the marvellous in them then than if they happened of themselves or by mere chance. Even matters of chance seem most marvellous if there is an appearance of design as it were in them; as for instance the statue of Mitys at Argos killed the author of Mitys' death by falling down on him when a looker-on at a public spectacle; for incidents like that we think to be not without a meaning. A Plot, therefore, of this sort is necessarily finer than others.

10

Plots are either simple or complex, since the actions they represent are naturally of this twofold description. The action, proceeding in the way defined, as one continuous whole, I call simple, when the change in the hero's fortunes takes place without Peripety or Discovery; and complex, when it involves one or the other, or both. These should each of them arise out of the structure of the Plot itself, so as to be the consequence, necessary or probable, of the antecedents. There is a great difference between a thing happening *propter hoc* and *post hoc.*

11

A Peripety is the change of the kind described from one state of things within the play to its opposite, and that too in the way we are saying, in the probable or necessary sequence of events; as it is for instance in *Oedipus*: here the opposite state of things is produced by the Messenger, who, coming to gladden Oedipus and to remove his fears as to his mother, reveals the secret of his birth.[1] And in *Lynceus*: just as he is being led off for execution, with Danaus at his side to put him to death, the incidents preceding this bring it about that he is saved and Danaus put to death. A Discovery is, as the very word implies, a change from ignorance to knowledge, and thus to either love or hate, in the personages marked for good or evil fortune. The finest form of Discovery is one attended by Peripeties, like that which goes with the Discovery in *Oedipus*. There are no doubt other forms of it; what we have said may happen in a way in reference to inanimate things, even things of a very casual kind; and it is also possible to discover whether some one has done or not done something. But the form most directly connected with the Plot and the action of the piece is the **1452b** first-mentioned. This, with a Peripety, will arouse either pity or fear—actions of that nature being what Tragedy is assumed to represent; and it will also serve to bring about the happy or unhappy ending. The Discovery, then, being of persons, it may be that of one party only to the other, the latter being already known; or both the parties may discover themselves. Iphigenia, for instance, was discovered to Orestes by sending the letter;[2] and another Discovery was required to reveal him to Iphigenia.

Two parts of the Plot, then, Peripety and Discovery, are on matters of this sort. A third part is Suffering; which we may define as an action of a destructive or painful nature, such as murders on the stage, tortures, woundings, and the like. The other two have been already explained.

12

The parts of Tragedy to be treated as formative elements in the whole were mentioned in a previous Chapter.[3] From the point of view, however, of its quantity, i.e. the separate sections into which it is divided, a tragedy has the following parts: Prologue, Episode, Exode, and a choral portion, distinguished into Parode and Stasimon; these two are common to all tragedies, whereas songs from the stage and *Commoe* are only found in some. The Prologue is all that precedes the Parode of the chorus; an Episode all that comes in between two whole choral songs; the Exode all that follows after the last choral song. In the choral portion the Parode is the whole first statement of the chorus; a Stasimon, a song of the chorus without anapaests or trochees; a *Commos*, a lamentation sung by chorus and actor in concert. The parts of Tragedy to be used as formative elements in the whole we have already mentioned; the above are its parts from the point of view of its quantity, or the separate sections into which it is divided.

13

The next points after what we have said above will be these: (1) What is the poet to aim at, and what is he to avoid, in constructing his Plots? and (2) What are the conditions on which the tragic effect depends?

We assume that, for the finest form of Tragedy, the Plot must be not simple but complex; and further, that it must imitate actions arousing fear and pity, since that is the distinctive function of this kind of imitation. It follows, therefore, that there are three forms of Plot to be avoided. (1) A good man must not be seen passing from happiness to misery, or (2) a bad man from misery to happiness. The first situation is not fear-inspiring or piteous, but simply odious to us. The second is the most untragic that can be; it has no one of the requisites of Tragedy; it does not appeal either to the human feeling in us, or to our **1453a** pity, or to our fears. Nor, on the other hand, should (3) an extremely bad man be seen falling from happiness into misery. Such a story may arouse the human feeling in us, but it will not move us to either pity or fear; pity is occasioned by undeserved misfortune, and fear by that of one like ourselves; so that there will be nothing either piteous or fear-inspiring in the situation. There remains, then, the intermediate kind of personage, a man not preeminently virtuous and just, whose misfortune, however, is brought upon him not by vice and depravity but by some error of judgement, of the number of those in the enjoyment of great reputation and prosperity; e.g. Oedipus, Thyestes, and the men of note of similar families. The perfect Plot, accordingly, must have a single, and not (as some tell us) a double issue; the change in the hero's fortunes must be not from misery to happiness, but on the contrary from happiness to misery; and the cause of it must lie not in any depravity, but in some great error on his part;

[1] *Oedipus the King*, 911-1085.
[2] *Iphigenia in Tauris*, 727 ff.
[3] Chapter 6.

the man himself being either such as we have described, or better, not worse, than that. Fact also confirms our theory. Though the poets began by accepting any tragic story that came to hand, in these days the finest tragedies are always on the story of some few houses, on that of Alcmeon, Oedipus, Orestes, Meleager, Thyestes, Telephus, or any others that may have been involved, as either agents or sufferers, in some deed of horror. The theoretically best tragedy, then, has a Plot of this description. The critics, therefore, are wrong who blame Euripides for taking this line in his tragedies, and giving many of them an unhappy ending. It is, as we have said, the right line to take. The best proof is this: on the stage, and in the public performances, such plays, properly worked out, are seen to be the most truly tragic; and Euripides, even if his execution be faulty in every other point, is seen to be nevertheless the most tragic certainly of the dramatists. After this comes the construction of Plot which some rank first, one with a double story (like the *Odyssey*) and an opposite issue for the good and the bad personages. It is ranked as first only through the weakness of the audiences; the poets merely follow their public, writing as its wishes dictate. But the pleasure here is not that of Tragedy. It belongs rather to Comedy, where the bitterest enemies in the piece (e.g. Orestes and Aegisthus) walk off good friends at the end, with no slaying of any one by any one.

14

1453b The tragic fear and pity may be aroused by the Spectacle; but they may also be aroused by the very structure and incidents of the play—which is the better way and shows the better poet. The Plot in fact should be so framed that, even without seeing the things take place, he who simply hears the account of them shall be filled with horror and pity at the incidents; which is just the effect that the mere recital of the story in *Oedipus* would have on one. To produce this same effect by means of the Spectacle is less artistic, and requires extraneous aid. Those, however, who make use of the Spectacle to put before us that which is merely monstrous and not productive of fear, are wholly out of touch with Tragedy; not every kind of pleasure should be required of a tragedy, but only its own proper pleasure.

The tragic pleasure is that of pity and fear, and the poet has to produce it by a work of imitation; it is clear, therefore, that the causes should be included in the incidents of his story. Let us see, then, what kinds of incident strike one as horrible, or rather as piteous. In a deed of this description the parties must necessarily be either friends, or enemies, or indifferent to one another. Now when enemy does it on enemy, there is nothing to move us to pity either in his doing or in his meditating the deed, except so far as the actual pain of the sufferer is concerned; and the same is true when the parties are indifferent to one another. Whenever the tragic deed, however, is done within the family—when murder or the like is done or meditated by brother on brother, by son on father, by mother on son, or son on mother—these are the situations the poet should seek after. The traditional stories, accordingly, must be kept as they are, e.g. the murder of Clytaemnestra by Orestes and of Eriphyle by Alcmeon. At the same time even with these there is something left to the poet himself; it is for him to devise the right way of treating them. Let us explain more clearly what we mean by 'the right way'. The deed of horror may be done by the doer knowingly and consciously, as in the old poets, and in Medea's murder of her children in Euripides.[1] Or he may do it, but in ignorance of his relationship, and discover that afterwards, as does the Oedipus in Sophocles. Here the deed is outside the play; but it may be within it, like the act of the Alcmeon in Astydamas, or that of the Telegonus in *Ulysses Wounded*. A third possibility is for one meditating some deadly injury to another, in ignorance of his relationship, to make the discovery in time to draw back. These exhaust the possibilities, since the deed must necessarily be either done or not done, and either knowingly or unknowingly.

The worst situation is when the personage is with full knowledge on the point of doing the deed, and leaves it undone. It is odious and also (through the absence of suffering) untragic; hence it is that no one is made to act **1454a** thus except in some few instances, e.g. Haemon and Creon in *Antigone*.[2] Next after this comes the actual perpetration of the deed meditated. A better situation than that, however, is for the deed to be done in ignorance, and the relationship discovered afterwards, since there is nothing odious in it, and the Discovery will serve to astound us. But the best of all is the last; what we have in

[1] *Medea*, 1236. [2] l. 1231.

Cresphontes,[1] for example, where Merope, on the point of slaying her son, recognizes him in time; in *Iphigenia,* where sister and brother are in a like position; and in *Helle,* where the son recognizes his mother, when on the point of giving her up to her enemy.

This will explain why our tragedies are restricted (as we said just now)[2] to such a small number of families. It was accident rather than art that led the poets in quest of subjects to embody this kind of incident in their Plots. They are still obliged, accordingly, to have recourse to the families in which such horrors have occurred.

On the construction of the Plot, and the kind of Plot required for Tragedy, enough has now been said.

15

In the Characters there are four points to aim at. First and foremost, that they shall be good. There will be an element of character in the play, if (as has been observed)[3] what a personage says or does reveals a certain moral purpose; and a good element of character, if the purpose so revealed is good. Such goodness is possible in every type of personage, even in a woman or a slave, though the one is perhaps an inferior, and the other a wholly worthless being. The second point is to make them appropriate. The Character before us may be, say, manly; but it is not appropriate in a female Character to be manly, or clever. The third is to make them like the reality, which is not the same as their being good and appropriate, in our sense of the term. The fourth is to make them consistent and the same throughout; even if inconsistency be part of the man before one for imitation as presenting that form of character, he should still be consistently inconsistent. We have an instance of baseness of character, not required for the story, in the Menelaus in *Orestes*; of the incongruous and unbefitting in the lamentation of Ulysses in *Scylla,* and in the (clever) speech of Melanippe,[4] and of inconsistency in *Iphigenia at Aulis,*[5] where Iphigenia the suppliant is utterly unlike other later Iphigenia. The right thing, however, is in the Characters just as in the incidents of the play to endeavour always after the necessary or the probable; so that whenever such-and-such a personage says or does such-and-such a thing, it shall be the necessary or probable outcome of his character; and whenever this incident follows on that, it shall be either the necessary or the probable consequence of it. From this one sees (to digress for a moment) that the Dénouement also **1454b** should arise out of the plot itself, and not depend on a stage-artifice, as in *Medea,*[6] or in the story of the (arrested) departure of the Greeks in the *Iliad.*[7] The artifice must be reserved for matters outside the play—for past events beyond human knowledge, or events yet to come, which require to be foretold or announced; since it is the privilege of the Gods to know everything. There should be nothing improbable among the actual incidents. If it be unavoidable, however, it should be outside the tragedy, like the improbability in the *Oedipus* of Sophocles. But to return to the Characters. As Tragedy is an imitation of personages better than the ordinary man, we in our way should follow the example of good portrait-painters, who reproduce the distinctive features of a man, and at the same time, without losing the likeness, make him handsomer than he is. The poet in like manner, in portraying men quick or slow to anger, or with similar infirmities of character, must know how to represent them as such, and at the same time as good men, as Agathon and Homer have represented Achilles.

All these rules one must keep in mind throughout, and, further, those also for such points of stage-effect as directly depend on the art of the poet, since in these too one may often make mistakes. Enough, however, has been said on the subject in one of our published writings.

16

Discovery in general has been explained already.[8] As for the species of Discovery, the first to be noted is (1) the least artistic form of it, of which the poets make most use through mere lack of invention, Discovery by signs or marks. Of these signs some are congenital, like the 'lance-head which the Earth-born have on them', or 'stars', such as Carcinus brings in his *Thyestes*; others acquired after birth—these latter being either marks on the body, e.g. scars, or external tokens, like necklaces, or (to take another sort of instance) the ark in the Discovery in *Tyro.*[9] Even these, however, admit of two uses, a better and a worse; the scar of Ulysses is an instance; the Discovery of him through it is made in one

[1] By Euripides. [2] 1453a 19. [3] 1450b 8. [4] Euripides. [5] ll. 1211 ff., 1368 ff.

[6] l. 1317. [7] ii. 155. [8] 1452a 29. [9] By Euripides.

way by the nurse and in another by the swineherds. A Discovery using signs as a means of assurance is less artistic, as indeed are all such as imply reflection; whereas one bringing them in all of a sudden, as in the *Bath-story,*[1] is of a better order. Next after these are (2) Discoveries made directly by the poet; which sister reveals who she is by the letter,[2] Orestes' Discovery of himself in *Iphigenia*: whereas his sister reveals who she is by the letter,[4] Orestes is made to say himself what the poet rather than the story demands.[3] This, therefore, is not far removed from the first-mentioned fault, since he might have presented certain tokens as well. Another instance is the 'shuttle's voice' in the *Tereus* of Sophocles. (3) A third species is Discovery through memory, **1455a** from a man's consciousness being awakened by something seen. Thus in *The Cyprioe* of Dicaeogenes, the sight of the picture makes the man burst into tears; and in the *Tale of Alcinous,*[4] hearing the harper Ulysses is reminded of the past and weeps; the Discovery of them being the result. (4) A fourth kind is Discovery through reasoning e.g. in *The Choephoroe,*[5] 'One like me is here; there is no one like me but Orestes; he, therefore, must be here.' Or that which Polyidus the Sophist suggested for *Iphigenia*; since it was natural for Orestes to reflect: 'My sister was sacrificed and I am to be sacrificed like her.' Or that in the *Tydeus* of Theodectes: 'I came to find a son, and am to die myself.' Or that in *The Phinidae*: on seeing the place the women inferred their fate, that they were to die there, since they had also been exposed there. (5) There is, too, a composite Discovery arising from bad reasoning on the side of the other party. An instance of it is in *Ulysses the False Messenger:* he said he should know the bow—which he had not seen; but to suppose from that that he would know it again (as though he had once seen it) was bad reasoning. (6) The best of all Discoveries, however, is that arising from the incidents themselves, when the great surprise comes about through a probable incident, like that in the *Oedipus* of Sophocles; and also in *Iphigenia;*[6] for it was not improbable that she should wish to have a letter taken home. These last are the only Discoveries independent of the artifice of signs and necklaces. Next after them come Discoveries through reasoning.

[1] *Odyssey*, XIX. 392. [2] *Iphigenia in Tauris*. 727 ff. [3] *Ibid.*, 800 ff. [4] *Odyssey*, VIII. 521 ff. (cf. VIII. 83 ff.). [5] ll. 168-234. [6] *Iphigenia in Tauris*, 582.

17

At the time when he is constructing his Plots, and engaged on the Diction in which they are worked out, the poet should remember (1) to put the actual scenes as far as possible before his eyes. In this way, seeing everything with the vividness of an eye-witness as it were, he will devise what is appropriate, and be least likely to overlook incongruities. This is shown by what was censured in Carcinus, the return of Amphiaraus from the sanctuary; it would have passed unnoticed, if it had not been actually seen by the audience; but on the stage his play failed, the incongruity of the incident offending the spectators. (2) As far as may be, too, the poet should even act his story with the very gestures of his personages. Given the same natural qualifications, he who feels the emotions to be described will be the most convincing; distress and anger, for instance, are portrayed most truthfully by one who is feeling them at the moment. Hence it is that poetry demands a man with a special gift for it, or else one with a touch of madness in him; the former can easily assume the required mood, and the latter may be actually beside himself with emotion. (3) His story, again, whether already made or of his own making, he should first simplify and reduce to a uni- **1455b** versal form, before proceeding to lengthen it out by the insertion of episodes. The following will show how the universal element in *Iphigenia,* for instance, may be viewed: A certain maiden having been offered in sacrifice, and spirited away from her sacrificers into another land, where the custom was to sacrifice all strangers to the Goddess, she was made there the priestess of this rite. Long after that the brother of the priestess happened to come; the fact, however, of the oracle having for a certain reason bidden him go thither, and his object in going, are outside the Plot of the play. On his coming he was arrested, and about to be sacrificed, when he revealed who he was—either as Euripides puts it, or (as suggested by Polyidus) by the not improbable exclamation, 'So I too am doomed to be sacrificed, as my sister was'; and the disclosure led to his salvation. This done, the next thing, after the proper names have been fixed as a basis for the story, is to work in episodes or accessory incidents. One must mind, however, that the episodes are appropriate, like the fit of madness[7] in Orestes, which led to his arrest,

[7] *Ibid.*, 281 ff.

and the purifying,[1] which brought about his salvation. In plays, then, the episodes are short; in epic poetry they serve to lengthen out the poem. The argument of the *Odyssey* is not a long one. A certain man has been abroad many years; Poseidon is ever on the watch for him, and he is all alone. Matters at home too have come to this, that his substance is being wasted and his son's death plotted by suitors to his wife. Then he arrives there himself after his grievous sufferings; reveals himself, and falls on his enemies; and the end is his salvation and their death. This being all that is proper to the *Odyssey*, everything else in it is episode.

18

(4) There is a further point to be borne in mind. Every tragedy is in part Complication and in part Dénouement; the incidents before the opening scene, and often certain also of those within the play, forming the Complication; and the rest the Dénouement. By Complication I mean all from the beginning of the story to the point just before the change in the hero's fortunes; by Dénouement, all from the beginning of the change to the end. In the *Lynceus* of Theodectes, for instance, the Complication includes, together with the presupposed incidents, the seizure of the child and that in turn of the parents; and the Dé-
1456a7 nouement all from the indictment for the murder to the end. Now it is right, when one speaks of a tragedy as the same or not the same as another, to do so on the ground before all else of their Plot, i.e. as having the same or not the same Complication and Dénouement. Yet there are many dramatists who, after a good Complication, fail in the Dénouement. But it is necessary for both points of con-
1455b32 struction to be always duly mastered. (5) There are four distinct species of Tragedy—that being the number of the constituents also that have been mentioned: first, the complex Tragedy, which is all Peripety and Discovery; second, the Tragedy of suffering, e.g. the *Ajaxes* and *Ixions*; third, the Tragedy of
1456a character, e.g. *The Phthiotides*[2] and *Peleus*. The fourth constituent is that of 'Spectacle', exemplified in *The Phorcides*,[3] in *Prometheus*, and in all plays with the scene laid in the nether world. The poet's aim, then, should be to combine every element of interest, if possible, or else the more important and the major part of them. This is now especially necessary owing to the unfair criticism to which the poet is subjected in these days. Just because there have been poets before him strong in the several species of tragedy, the critics now expect the one man to surpass that which was the strong point of each one of his predecessors. (6) One should also remember what has been said more than once, and not write a tragedy on an epic body of incident (i.e. one with a plurality of stories in it), by attempting to dramatize, for instance, the entire story of the *Iliad*. In the epic owing to its scale every part is treated at proper length; with a drama, however, on the same story the result is very disappointing. This is shown by the fact that all who have dramatized the fall of Ilium in its entirety, and not part by part, like Euripides, or the whole of the Niobe story, instead of a portion, like Aeschylus, either fail utterly or have but ill success on the stage; for that and that alone was enough to ruin even a play by Agathon. Yet in their Peripeties, as also in their simple plots, the poets I mean show wonderful skill in aiming at the kind of effect they desire—a tragic situation that arouses the human feeling in one, like the clever villain (e.g. Sisyphus) deceived, or the brave wrongdoer worsted. This is probable, however, only in Agathon's sense, when he speaks of the probability of even improbabilities coming to pass. (7) The Chorus too should be regarded as one of the actors; it should be an integral part of the whole, and take a share in the action—that which it has in Sophocles, rather than in Euripides. With the later poets, however, the songs in a play of theirs have no more to do with the Plot of that than of any other tragedy. Hence it is that they are now singing intercalary pieces, a practice first introduced by Agathon. And yet what real difference is there between singing such intercalary pieces, and attempting to fit in a speech, or even a whole act, from one play into another?

19

The Plot and Characters having been discussed, it remains to consider the Diction and Thought. As for the Thought, we may assume what is said of it in our Art of Rhetoric,[4] as it belongs more properly to that department of inquiry. The Thought of the personages is shown in everything to be effected

[1] *Ibid.*, 1163 ff.
[2] This does not agree with anything actually said before.
[3] By Aeschylus.
[4] Cf. especially *Rhetoric*, 1356a 1.

by their language—in every effort to prove or disprove, to arouse emotion (pity, fear, anger, **1456b** and the like), or to maximize or minimize things. It is clear, also, that their mental procedure must be on the same lines in their actions likewise, whenever they wish them to arouse pity or horror, or to have a look of importance or probability. The only difference is that with the act the impression has to be made without explanation; whereas with the spoken word it has to be produced by the speaker, and result from his language. What, indeed, would be the good of the speaker, if things appeared in the required light even apart from anything he says?

As regards the Diction, one subject for inquiry under this head is the turns given to the language when spoken; e.g. the difference between command and prayer, simple statement and threat, question and answer, and so forth. The theory of such matters, however, belongs to Elocution and the professors of that art. Whether the poet knows these things or not, his art as a poet is never seriously criticized on that account. What fault can one see in Homer's 'Sing of the wrath, Goddess'?—which Protagoras has criticized as being a command where a prayer was meant, since to bid one do or not do, he tells us, is a command. Let us pass over this, then, as appertaining to another art, and not to that of poetry.

20

The Diction viewed as a whole is made up of the following parts: the Letter (or ultimate element), the Syllable, the Conjunction, the Article, the Noun, the Verb, the Case, and the Speech. (1) The Letter is an indivisible sound of a particular kind, one that may become a factor in an intelligible sound. Indivisible sounds are uttered by the brutes also, but no one of these is a Letter in our sense of the term. These elementary sounds are either vowels, semi-vowels, or mutes. A vowel is a Letter having an audible sound without the addition of another Letter. A semi-vowel, one having an audible sound by the addition of another Letter; e.g. S and R. A mute, one having no sound at all by itself, but becoming audible by an addition, that of one of the Letters which have a sound of some sort of their own; e.g. G and D. The Letters differ in various ways: as produced by different conformations or in different regions of the mouth; as aspirated, not aspirated, or sometimes one and sometimes the other; as long, short, or of variable quantity; and further as having an acute, grave, or intermediate accent. The details of these matters we must leave to the metricians. (2) A Syllable is a non-significant composite sound, made up of a mute and a Letter having a sound (a vowel or semivowel); for GR, without an A, is just as much a Syllable as GRA, with an A. The various forms of the Syllable also belong to the theory of metre. (3)A Conjunction is (*a*) a non-significant sound which, **1457a** when one significant sound is formable out of several, neither hinders nor aids the union, and which, if the Speech thus formed stands by itself (apart from other Speeches), must not be inserted at the beginning of it; e.g. μέν, δή, τοι, δέ. Or (*b*) a non-significant sound capable of combining two or more significant sounds into one; e.g. ἀμφί, περί, &c. (4) An Article is a non-significant sound marking the beginning, end, or dividing-point of a Speech, its natural place being either at the extremities or in the middle. (5) A Noun or name is a composite significant sound not involving the idea of time, with parts which have no significance by themselves in it. It is to be remembered that in a compound we do not think of the parts as having significance also by themselves; in the name 'Theodorus', for instance, the δῶρον means nothing to us. (6) A Verb is a composite significant sound involving the idea of time, with parts which (just as in the Noun) have no significance by themselves in it. Whereas the word 'man' or 'white' does not imply *when*, 'walks' and 'has walked' involve in addition to the idea of walking that of time present or time past. (7) A Case of a Noun or Verb is when the word means 'of' or 'to' a thing, and so forth, or for one or many (e.g. 'man' and 'men'); or it may consist merely in the mode of utterance, e.g. in question, command, &c. 'Walked?' and 'Walk!' are Cases of the verb 'to walk' of this last kind. (8) A Speech is a composite significant sound, some of the parts of which have a certain significance by themselves. It may be observed that a Speech is not always made up of Noun and Verb; it may be without a Verb, like the definition of man; but it will always have some part with a certain significance by itself. In the Speech 'Cleon walks', 'Cleon' is an instance of such a part. A Speech is said to be one in two ways, either as signifying one thing, or as a union of several Speeches made into one by conjunction. Thus the *Iliad* is one Speech by conjunction of several; and the definition of man is one through its signifying one thing.

21

Nouns are of two kinds, either (1) simple, i.e. made up of non-significant parts, like the word γῆ, or (2) double; in the latter case the word may be made up either of a significant and a non-significant part (a distinction which disappears in the compound), or of two significant parts. It is possible also to have triple, quadruple, or higher compounds, like most of our amplified names; e.g. 'Hermocaïcoxanthus' and the like.

1457b Whatever its structure, a Noun must always be either (1) the ordinary word for the thing, or (2) a strange word, or (3) a metaphor, or (4) an ornamental word, or (5) a coined word, or (6) a word lengthened out, or (7) curtailed, or (8) altered in form. By the ordinary word I mean that in general use in a country; and by a strange word, one in use elsewhere. So that the same word may obviously be at once strange and ordinary, though not in reference to the same people; *οἴγυνον*, for instance, is an ordinary word in Cyprus, and a strange word with us. Metaphor consists in giving the thing a name that belongs to something else; the transference being either from genus to species, or from species to genus, or from species to species, or on grounds of analogy. That from genus to species is exemplified in 'Here stands my ship';[1] for lying at anchor is the 'standing' of a particular kind of thing. That from species to genus in 'Truly ten thousand good deeds has Ulysses wrought',[2] where 'ten thousand', which is a particular large number, is put in place of the generic 'a large number'. That from species to species in 'Drawing the life with the bronze',[3] and in 'Severing with the enduring bronze';[3] where the poet uses 'draw' in the sense of 'sever' and 'sever' in that of 'draw', both words meaning to 'take away' something. That from analogy is possible whenever there are four terms so related that the second (B) is to the first (A), as the fourth (D) to the third (C); for one may then metaphorically put D in lieu of B, and B in lieu of D. Now and then, too, they qualify the metaphor by adding on to it that to which the word it supplants is relative. Thus a cup (B) is in relation to Dionysus (A) what a shield (D) is to Ares (C). The cup accordingly will be metaphorically described as the 'shield *of Dionysus*' (D+A), and the shield as the 'cup *of Ares*'[4] (B+C). Or to take another instance: As old age (D) is to life (C), so is evening (B) to day (A). One will accordingly describe evening (B) as the 'old age *of the day*' (D+A)—or by the Empedoclean equivalent; and old age (D) as the 'evening'[5] or 'sunset *of life*'[6] (B+C). It may be that some of the terms thus related have no special name of their own, but for all that they will be metaphorically described in just the same way. Thus to cast forth seed-corn is called 'sowing'; but to cast forth its flame, as said of the sun, has no special name. This nameless act (B), however, stands in just the same relation to its object, sunlight (A), as sowing (D) to the seed-corn (C). Hence the expression in the poet, 'sowing around a god-created *flame*' (D+A). There is also another form of qualified metaphor. Having given the thing the alien name, one may by a negative addition deny of it one of the attributes naturally associated with its new name. An instance of this would be to call the shield not the 'cup *of Ares*', as in the former case, but a 'cup *that holds no wine*'. . . . A coined word is a name which, being quite unknown among a people, is given by the poet himself; e.g. (for there are some words that seem to be of this origin) *ἔρνυγες* for horns, and *ἀρητήρ* for priest.[7] A word **1458a** is said to be lengthened out, when it has a short vowel made long, or an extra syllable inserted; e.g. *πόληος* for *πόλεως*, *Πηληιάδεω* for *Πηλείδου*. It is said to be curtailed, when it has lost a part; e.g. *κρῖ*, *δῶ*, and *ὄψ* in *μία γίνεται ἀμφοτέρων ὄψ*.[8] It is an altered word, when part is left as it was and part is of the poet's making; e.g. *δεξιτερόν* for *δεξιόν*, in *δεξιτερὸν κατὰ μαζόν*.[9]

The Nouns themselves (to whatever class they may belong) are either masculines, feminines, or intermediates (neuter). All ending in N, P, Σ, or in the two compounds of this last Ψ and Ξ, are masculines. All ending in the invariably long vowels, H and Ω, and in A among the vowels that may be long, are feminines. So that there is an equal number of masculine and feminine terminations, as Ψ and Ξ are the same as Σ, and need not be counted. There is no Noun, however, ending in a mute or in either of the two short vowels, E and O. Only three (*μέλι*, *κόμμι*, *πέπερι*)

[1] *Odyssey*, I. 185, XXIV. 308.
[2] *Iliad*., II. 272.
[3] Empedocles, *Καθαρμοί*; cf. fr. 143, Diels.
[4] Timotheus, fr. 22, Wilamowitz.
[5] Alexis, fr. 228, Kock.
[6] Plato, *Laws*, 770.
[7] *Iliad*, I. 11.
[8] Empedocles, fr. 88, Diels.
[9] *Iliad*, V. 393.

end in I, and five in Υ. The intermediates, or neuters, end in the variable vowels or in N, P, Σ.

22

The perfection of Diction is for it to be at once clear and not mean. The clearest indeed is that made up of the ordinary words for things, but it is mean, as is shown by the poetry of Cleophon and Sthenelus. On the other hand the Diction becomes distinguished and non-prosaic by the use of unfamiliar terms, i.e. strange words, metaphors, lengthened forms, and everything that deviates from the ordinary modes of speech.—But a whole statement in such terms will be either a riddle or a barbarism, a riddle, if made up of metaphors, a barbarism, if made up of strange words. The very nature indeed of a riddle is this, to describe a fact in an impossible combination of words (which cannot be done with the real names for things, but can be with their metaphorical substitutes); e.g. 'I saw a man glue brass on another with fire',[1] and the like. The corresponding use of strange words results in a barbarism.—A certain admixture, accordingly, of unfamiliar terms is necessary. These, the strange word, the metaphor, the ornamental equivalent, &c., will save the language from seeming mean and prosaic, while the ordinary words in it will secure the requi- **1458b** site clearness. What helps most, however, to render the Diction at once clear and non-prosaic is the use of the lengthened, curtailed, and altered forms of words. Their deviation from the ordinary words will, by making the language unlike that in general use, give it a non-prosaic appearance; and their having much in common with the words in general use will give it the quality of clearness. It is not right, then, to condemn these modes of speech, and ridicule the poet for using them, as some have done; e.g. the elder Euclid, who said it was easy to make poetry if one were to be allowed to lengthen the words in the statement itself as much as one likes—a procedure he caricatured by reading *Ἐπιχάρην εἶδον Μαραθῶνάδε βαδίζοντα*, and *οὐκ ἄν γ' ἐράμενος τὸν ἐκείνου ἐλλέβορον* as verses. A too apparent use of these licences has certainly a ludicrous effect, but they are not alone in that; the rule of moderation applies to all the constituents of the poetic vocabulary; even with metaphors, strange words, and the rest, the effect will be the same, if one uses them improperly and with a view to provoking laughter. The proper use of them is a very different thing. To realize the difference one should take an epic verse and see how it reads when the normal words are introduced. The same should be done too with the strange word, the metaphor, and the rest; for one has only to put the ordinary words in their place to see the truth of what we are saying. The same iambic, for instance, is found in Aeschylus and Euripides, and as it stands in the former it is a poor line; whereas Euripides, by the change of a single word, the substitution of a strange for what is by usage the ordinary word, has made it seem a fine one. Aeschylus having said in his *Philoctetes*:

φαγέδαινα ἥ μου σάρκαος ἐσθίει ποδός,[2]

Euripides has merely altered the *ἐσθίει* here into *θοινᾶται*.[3] Or suppose

νῦν δέ μ' ἐὼν ὀλίγος τε καὶ οὐτιδανὸς καὶ ἀεικής[4]

to be altered, by the substitution of the ordinary words, into

νῦν δέ μ' ἐὼν μικρός τε καὶ ἀσθενικὸς καὶ ἀειδής.

Or the line

δίφρον ἀεικέλιον καταθεὶς ὀλίγην τε τράπεζαν[5]

into

δίφρον μοχθηρὸν καταθεὶς μικράν τε τράπεζαν.

Or *ἠιόνες βοόωσιν*[6] into *ἠιόνες κράζουσιν*. Add to this that Ariphrades used to ridicule the tragedians for introducing expressions unknown in the language of common life, *δωμάτων ἄπο* (for *ἀπὸ δωμάτων*), *σέθεν*, *ἐγὼ δέ νιν*,[7] *Ἀχιλλέως πέρι* (for *περὶ Ἀχιλλέως*), and the **1459a** like. The mere fact of their not being in ordinary speech gives the Diction a non-prosaic character; but Ariphrades was unaware of that. It is a great thing, indeed, to make a proper use of these poetical forms, as also of compounds and strange words. But the greatest thing by far is to be a master of metaphor. It is the one thing that cannot be learnt from others; and it is also a sign of genius, since a good metaphor implies an intuitive perception of the similarity in dissimilars.

Of the kinds of words we have enumerated

[1] Cleobulina, fr. 1, Bergk.

[2] Nauck, *T. G. F.*, p. 81.
[3] *Ibid.*, p. 618.
[4] *Odyssey*, IX. 515.
[5] *Ibid.*, XX.259.
[6] *Iliad*, XVII. 265.
[6] Sophocles, *Oedipus at Colonus*, 986.

it may be observed that compounds are most in place in the dithyramb, strange words in heroic, and metaphors in iambic poetry. Heroic poetry, indeed, may avail itself of them all. But in iambic verse, which models itself as far as possible on the spoken language, only those kinds of words are in place which are allowable also in an oration, i.e. the ordinary word, the metaphor, and the ornamental equivalent.

Let this, then, suffice as an account of Tragedy, the art imitating by means of action on the stage.

23

As for the poetry which merely narrates, or imitates by means of versified language (without action), it is evident that it has several points in common with Tragedy.

I. The construction of its stories should clearly be like that in a drama; they should be based on a single action, one that is a complete whole in itself, with a beginning, middle, and end, so as to enable the work to produce its own proper pleasure with all the organic unity of a living creature. Nor should one suppose that there is anything like them in our usual histories. A history has to deal not with one action, but with one period and all that happened in that to one or more persons, however disconnected the several events may have been. Just as two events may take place at the same time, e.g. the sea-fight off Salamis and the battle with the Carthaginians in Sicily, without converging to the same end, so too of two consecutive events one may sometimes come after the other with no one end as their common issue. Nevertheless most of our epic poets, one may say, ignore the distinction. Herein, then, to repeat what we have said before,[1] we have a further proof of Homer's marvellous superiority to the rest. He did not attempt to deal even with the Trojan war in its entirety, though it was a whole with a definite beginning and end—through a feeling apparently that it was too long a story to be taken in in one view, or if not that, too complicated from the variety of incident in it. As it is, he has singled out one section of the whole; many of the other incidents, however, he brings in as episodes, using the Catalogue of the Ships, for instance, and other episodes to relieve the uniformity of his narrative. As for the other epic poets, they treat of one man, or one period; or else of an action which, although one, has a multiplicity of parts in it. **1459b** This last is what the authors of the *Cypria* and *Little Iliad* have done. And the result is that, whereas the *Iliad* or *Odyssey* supplies materials for only one, or at most two tragedies, the *Cypria* does that for several and the *Little Iliad* for more than eight: for an *Adjudgment of Arms*, a *Philoctetes*, a *Neoptolemus*, a *Eurypylus*, a *Ulysses as Beggar*, a *Laconian Women*, a *Fall of Ilium*, and a *Departure of the Fleet*; as also a *Sinon*, and a *Women of Troy*.

24

II. Besides this, Epic poetry must divide into the same species as Tragedy; it must be either simple or complex, a story of character or one of suffering. Its parts, too, with the exception of Song and Spectacle, must be the same, as it requires Peripeties, Discoveries, and scenes of suffering just like Tragedy. Lastly, the Thought and Diction in it must be good in their way. All these elements appear in Homer first; and he has made due use of them. His two poems are each examples of construction, the *Iliad* simple and a story of suffering, the *Odyssey* complex (there is Discovery throughout it) and a story of character. And they are more than this, since in Diction and Thought too they surpass all other poems.

There is, however, a difference in the Epic as compared with Tragedy, (1) in its length, and (2) in its metre. (1) As to its length, the limit already suggested[2] will suffice: it must be possible for the beginning and end of the work to be taken in in one view—a condition which will be fulfilled if the poem be shorter than the old epics, and about as long as the series of tragedies offered for one hearing. For the extension of its length epic poetry has a special advantage, of which it makes large use. In a play one cannot represent an action with a number of parts going on simultaneously; one is limited to the part on the stage and connected with the actors. Whereas in epic poetry the narrative form makes it possible for one to describe a number of simultaneous incidents; and these, if germane to the subject, increase the body of the poem. This then is a gain to the Epic, tending to give it grandeur, and also variety of interest and room for episodes of diverse kinds. Uniformity of incident by the satiety it soon creates is apt to ruin tragedies on the stage. (2) As for its metre, the heroic has been as-

[1] 1451a 23 ff.

[2] 1451a 3.

signed it from experience; were any one to attempt a narrative poem in some one, or in several, of the other metres, the incongruity of the thing would be apparent. The heroic in fact is the gravest and weightiest of metres—which is what makes it more tolerant than the rest of strange words and metaphors, that also being a point in which the narrative form of poetry goes beyond all others. The iambic and trochiac, on the other hand, are metres of movement, the one representing that of life and action, the other that of the dance. Still **1460a** more unnatural would it appear, if one were to write an epic in a medley of metres, as Chaeremon did.[1] Hence it is that no one has ever written a long story in any but heroic verse; nature herself, as we have said,[2] teaches us to select the metre appropriate to such a story.

Homer, admirable as he is in every other respect, is especially so in this, that he alone among epic poets is not unaware of the part to be played by the poet himself in the poem. The poet should say very little *in propria persona,* as he is no imitator when doing that. Whereas the other poets are perpetually coming forward in person, and say but little, and that only here and there, as imitators, Homer after a brief preface brings in forthwith a man, a woman, or some other Character—no one of them characterless, but each with distinctive characteristics.

The marvellous is certainly required in Tragedy. The Epic, however, affords more opening for the improbable, the chief factor in the marvellous, because in it the agents are not visibly before one. The scene of the pursuit of Hector would be ridiculous on the stage—the Greeks halting instead of pursuing him, and Achilles shaking his head to stop them;[3] but in the poem the absurdity is overlooked. The marvellous, however, is a cause of pleasure, as is shown by the fact that we all tell a story with additions, in the belief that we are doing our hearers a pleasure.

Homer more than any other has taught the rest of us the art of framing lies in the right way. I mean the use of paralogism. Whenever, if A is or happens, a consequent, B, is or happens, men's notion is that, if the B is, the A also is—but that is a false conclusion. Accordingly, if A is untrue, but there is something else, B, that on the assumption of its truth follows as its consequent, the right thing then is to add on the B. Just because we know the truth of the consequent, we are in our own minds led on to the erroneous inference of the truth of the antecedent. Here is an instance, from the *Bath-story* in the *Odyssey.*[4]

A likely impossibility is always preferable to an unconvincing possibility. The story should never be made up of improbable incidents; there should be nothing of the sort in it. If, however, such incidents are unavoidable, they should be outside the piece, like the hero's ignorance in *Oedipus* of the circumstances of Laius' death; not within it, like the report of the Pythian games in *Electra,*[5] or the man's having come to Mysia from Tegea without uttering a word on the way, in *The Mysians.* So that it is ridiculous to say that one's Plot would have been spoilt without them, since it is fundamentally wrong to make up such Plots. If the poet has taken such a Plot, however, and one sees that he might have put it in a more probable form, he is guilty of absurdity as well as a fault of art. Even in the *Odyssey* the improbabilities in the setting-ashore of Ulysses[6] **1460b** would be clearly intolerable in the hands of an inferior poet. As it is, the poet conceals them, his other excellences veiling their absurdity. Elaborate Diction, however, is required only in places where there is no action, and no Character or Thought to be revealed. Where there is Character or Thought, on the other hand, an over-ornate Diction tends to obscure them.

25

As regards Problems and their Solutions, one may see the number and nature of the assumptions on which they proceed by viewing the matter in the following way. (1) The poet being an imitator just like the painter or other maker of likenesses, he must necessarily in all instances represent things in one or other of three aspects, either as they were or are, or as they are said or thought to be or to have been, or as they ought to be. (2) All this he does in language, with an admixture, it may be, of strange words and metaphors, as also of the various modified forms of words, since the use of these is conceded in poetry. (3) It is to be remembered, too, that there is not the same kind of correctness in poetry as in politics, or indeed any other art. There is, however, within the limits of poetry itself a possibility of two kinds of error, the one di-

[1] *Centaur,* cf. 1447b 21.
[2] 1449a 24.
[3] *Iliad,* XXII. 205.
[4] XIX. 164-260.
[5] Sophocles, *Electra,* 660 ff.
[6] XIII. 116 ff.

rectly, the other only accidentally connected with the art. If the poet meant to describe the thing correctly, and failed through lack of power of expression, his art itself is at fault. But if it was through his having meant to describe it in some incorrect way (e.g. to make the horse in movement have both right legs thrown forward) that the technical error (one in a matter of, say, medicine or some other special science), or impossibilities of whatever kind they may be, have got into his description, his error in that case is not in the essentials of the poetic art. These, therefore, must be the premisses of the Solutions in answer to the criticisms involved in the Problems.

I. As to the criticisms relating to the poet's art itself. Any impossibilities there may be in his descriptions of things are faults. But from another point of view they are justifiable, if they serve the end of poetry itself—if (to assume what we have said of that end)[1] they make the effect of either that very portion of the work or some other portion more astounding. The Pursuit of Hector is an instance in point. If, however, the poetic end might have been as well or better attained without sacrifice of technical correctness in such matters, the impossibility is not to be justified, since the description should be, if it can, entirely free from error. One may ask, too, whether the error is in a matter directly or only accidentally connected with the poetic art; since it is a lesser error in an artist not to know, for instance, that the hind has no horns, than to produce an unrecognizable picture of one.

II. If the poet's description be criticized as not true to fact, one may urge perhaps that the object ought to be as described—an answer like that of Sophocles, who said that he drew men as they ought to be, and Euripides as they were. If the description, however, be neither true nor of the thing as it ought to be, the answer must be then, that it is in accordance with opinion. The tales about Gods, for instance, may be as wrong as Xenophanes thinks, neither true nor the better thing to say; but they are certainly in accordance with opinion. **1461a** Of other statements in poetry one may perhaps say, not that they are better than the truth, but that the fact was so at the time; e.g. the description of the arms: 'their spears stood upright, butt-end upon the ground';[2] for that was the usual way of fixing them then, as it is still with the Illyrians. As for the question whether something said or done in a poem is morally right or not, in dealing with that one should consider not only the intrinsic quality of the actual word or deed, but also the person who says or does it, the person to whom he says or does it, the time, the means, and the motive of the agent—whether he does it to attain a greater good, or to avoid a greater evil.

III. Other criticisms one must meet by considering the language of the poet: (1) by the assumption of a strange word in a passage like *οὐρῆας μὲν πρῶτον*,[3] where by *οὐρῆας* Homer may perhaps mean not mules but sentinels. And in saying of Dolon, *ὅς ῥ' ἤ τοι εἶδος μὲν ἔην κακός*,[4] his meaning may perhaps be, not that Dolon's body was deformed, but that his face was ugly, as *εὐειδής* is the Cretan word for handsome-faced. So, too, *ζωρότερον δὲ κέραιε*[5] may mean not 'mix the wine stronger', as though for topers, but 'mix it quicker'. (2) Other expressions in Homer may be explained as metaphorical; e.g. in *ἄλλοι μέν ῥα θεοί τε καὶ ἀνέρες εὗδον ⟨ἅπαντες⟩ παννύχιοι*,[6] as compared with what he tells us at the same time, *ἤ τοι ὅτ' ἐς πεδίον τὸ Τρωικὸν ἀθρήσειεν, αὐλῶν συρίγγων †τε ὁμαδόν†*,[7] the word *ἅπαντες* 'all', is metaphorically put for 'many', since 'all' is a species of 'many'. So also his *οἴη δ' ἄμμορος*[8] is metaphorical, the best known standing 'alone'. (3) A change, as Hippias of Thasos suggested, in the mode of reading a word will solve the difficulty in *δίδομεν δέ οἱ*,[9] and in *τὸ μὲν οὗ καταπύθεται ὄμβρῳ*.[10] (4) Other difficulties may be solved by another punctuation; e.g. in Empedocles, *αἶψα δὲ θνήτ' ἐφύοντο, τὰ πρὶν μάθον ἀθάνατα ζωρά τε πρὶν κέκρητο*.[11] Or (5) by the assumption of an equivocal term, as in *παρῴχηκεν δὲ πλέω νύξ*,[12] where *πλέω* is equivocal. Or (6) by an appeal to the custom of language. Wine-and-water we call 'wine'; and it is on the same principle that Homer speaks of a *κνημὶς νεοτεύκτου κασσιτέροιο*,[13] a 'greave of new-wrought *tin*'. A worker in iron we call a 'brazier'; and it is on the same principle that Ganymede is described as the '*wine*-server' of Zeus,[14] though the Gods do not drink wine. This latter, however, may be an instance of metaphor. But whenever also a word seems to imply some contradiction, it is necessary to reflect how many ways there

[1] 1452a 4, 1454a 4, 1455a 17, 1460a 11.
[2] *Iliad*, x. 152.

[3] *Ibid.*, I. 50. [4] *Ibid.*, x. 316. [5] *Ibid.* IX. 202.
[6] Cf. *Ibid.*, x. 1, II. 1. [7] *Ibid.*, x. 11–13.
[8] *Ibid.*, XVIII. 489 = *Odyssey*, v. 275.
[9] Cf. *On Sophistical Refutations*, 166b 1; *Iliad*, II. 15.
[10] *Iliad*, XXIII. 327. [11] Fr. 35. 14–15, Diels.
[12] *Iliad*, x. 251. [13] *Ibid.*, XXI. 592.
[14] *Ibid.*, XX. 234.

may be of understanding it in the passage in question; e.g. in Homer's *τῇ ῥ' ἔσχετο χάλκεον ἔγχος*[1] one should consider the possible senses of 'was stopped there'—whether by taking it in this sense or in that one will best avoid the fault of which Glaucon speaks: 'They start **1461b** with some improbable presumption; and having so decreed it themselves, proceed to draw inferences, and censure the poet as though he had actually said whatever they happen to believe, if his statement conflicts with their own notion of things.' This is how Homer's silence about Icarius has been treated. Starting with the notion of his having been a Lacedaemonian, the critics think it strange for Telemachus not to have met him when he went to Lacedaemon. Whereas the fact may have been as the Cephallenians say, that the wife of Ulysses was of a Cephallenian family, and that her father's name was Icadius, not Icarius. So that it is probably a mistake of the critics that has given rise to the Problem.

Speaking generally, one has to justify (1) the Impossible by reference to the requirements of poetry, or to the better, or to opinion. For the purposes of poetry a convincing impossibility is preferable to an unconvincing possibility; and if men such as Zeuxis depicted be impossible, the answer is that it is better they should be like that, as the artist ought to improve on his model. (2) The Improbable one has to justify either by showing it to be in accordance with opinion, or by urging that at times it is not improbable; for there is a probability of things happening also against probability. (3) The contradictions found in the poet's language one should first test as one does an opponent's confutation in a dialectical argument, so as to see whether he means the same thing, in the same relation, and in the same sense, before admitting that he has contradicted either something he has said himself or what a man of sound sense assumes as true. But there is no possible apology for improbability of Plot or depravity of character, when they are not necessary and no use is made of them, like the improbability in the appearance of Aegeus in *Medea*[2] and the baseness of Menelaus in *Orestes*.

The objections, then, of critics start with faults of five kinds: the allegation is always that something is either (1) impossible, (2) improbable, (3) corrupting, (4) contradictory, or (5) against technical correctness. The answers to these objections must be sought under one or other of the above-mentioned heads, which are twelve in number.

[1] *Ibid.*, xx. 267. [2] l. 663.

26

The question may be raised whether the epic or the tragic is the higher form of imitation. It may be argued that, if the less vulgar is the higher, and the less vulgar is always that which addresses the better public, an art addressing any and every one is of a very vulgar order. It is a belief that their public cannot see the meaning, unless they add something themselves, that causes the perpetual movements of the performers—bad flute-players, for instance, rolling about, if quoit-throwing is to be represented, and pulling at the conductor, if Scylla is the subject of the piece. Tragedy, then, is said to be an art of this order—to be in fact just what the later actors were in the eyes of their predecessors; for Mynniscus used to call Callippides 'the ape', because he thought he so overacted his parts; and a similar **1462a** view was taken of Pindarus also. All Tragedy, however, is said to stand to the Epic as the newer to the older school of actors. The one, accordingly, is said to address a cultivated audience, which does not need the accompaniment of gesture; the other, an uncultivated one. If, therefore, Tragedy is a vulgar art, it must clearly be lower than the Epic.

The answer to this is twofold. In the first place, one may urge (1) that the censure does not touch the art of the dramatic poet, but only that of his interpreter; for it is quite possible to overdo the gesturing even in an epic recital, as did Sosistratus, and in a singing contest, as did Mnasitheus of Opus. (2) That one should not condemn all movement, unless one means to condemn even the dance, but only that of ignoble people—which is the point of the criticism passed on Callippides and in the present day on others, that their women are not like gentlewomen. (3) That Tragedy may produce its effect even without movement or action in just the same way as Epic poetry; for from the mere reading of a play its quality may be seen. So that, if it be superior in all other respects, this element of inferiority is no necessary part of it.

In the second place, one must remember (1) that Tragedy has everything that the Epic has (even the epic metre being admissible), together with a not inconsiderable addition in the shape of the music (a very real factor in the pleasure of the drama) and the Spectacle. (2) That its reality of presentation is felt in

the play as read, as well as in the play as acted. (3) That the tragic imitation requires less
1462b space for the attainment of its end; which is a great advantage, since the more concentrated effect is more pleasurable than one with a large admixture of time to dilute it—consider the *Oedipus* of Sophocles, for instance, and the effect of expanding it into the number of lines of the *Iliad*. (4) That there is less unity in the imitation of the epic poets, as is proved by the fact that any one work of theirs supplies matter for several tragedies; the result being that, if they take what is really a single story, it seems curt when briefly told, and thin and waterish when on the scale of length usual with their verse. In saying that there is less unity in an epic, I mean an epic made up of a plurality of actions, in the same way as the *Iliad* and *Odyssey* have many such parts, each one of them in itself of some magnitude; yet the structure of the two Homeric poems is as perfect as can be, and the action in them is as nearly as possible one action. If, then, Tragedy is superior in these respects, and also, besides these, in its poetic effect (since the two forms of poetry should give us, not any or every pleasure, but the very special kind we have mentioned), it is clear that, as attaining the poetic effect better than the Epic, it will be the higher form of art.

So much for Tragedy and Epic poetry—for these two arts in general and their species; the number and nature of their constituent parts; the causes of success and failure in them; the Objections of the critics, and the Solutions in answer to them.

PRINTED IN THE U.S.A.